Automotive Engine Management Systems & Fuel Injection Techbook

Charles White

Systems covered

(3344-336)

Bosch Mono-Motronic
Bosch Motronic First Generation
Bosch Motronic 1.1
Bosch Motronic 1.3
Bosch Motronic 1.5
Bosch Motronic 1.7
Bosch Motronic 2.5
Bosch Motronic 2.7
Bosch Motronic 2.8 and 2.8.1
Bosch Motronic 3.1
Bosch Motronic 3.2
Bosch Motronic ML4.1
Bosch Motronic 5.1 and 5.1.1
Ford EEC IV
GM Multec MPi
GM Multec SPi
Honda / Rover PGM-Fi
Magneti-Marelli G5
Magneti-Marelli G6
Magneti-Marelli 8F
Magneti-Marelli 8P
Mazda EGI
Nissan ECCS
Renix MPi
Renix SPi
Rover MEMS MPi
Rover MEMS SPi
Rover SPi
Toyota TCCS
VW Digifant
Weber-Marelli (IAW)

ABCDE
FGHIJ
KLM

A book in the **Haynes Techbook Series**

ISBN **1 85960 344 0**

British Library Cataloguing in Publication Data
A catalogue record for this book is available from the British Library.

Printed in the USA

Haynes Publishing
Sparkford, Yeovil, Somerset BA22 7JJ, England

Haynes North America, Inc
861 Lawrence Drive, Newbury Park, California 91320, USA

Editions Haynes
4, Rue de l'Abreuvoir
92415 COURBEVOIE CEDEX, France

Haynes Publishing Nordiska AB
Box 1504, 751 45 UPPSALA, Sweden

Contents

GENERAL INFORMATION

SYSTEM SPECIFICS

REFERENCE

This book is devoted to unravelling the mysteries of the Engine Management System (EMS) on the modern automobile. The book first describes the history and function of fuel injection and the EMS and then goes on to give a technical overview on how modern systems work. Other chapters describe general test routines and each system has its own chapter detailing system operation and test procedures. Even if the reader has no intention of actually attempting to investigate faults on his or her own vehicle, the book provides valuable insight into the electronic management of the modern car engine.

On the other hand, if you relish the task of electronic fault diagnosis, then this book will provide you with much of the background knowledge necessary to test the circuits and components on your engine. Generally we describe how to work using simple tools and equipment available from most good auto retailers. We will also mention where the use of specialised equipment is really necessary, and describe some of the common routines used by the professional garage trade.

This book does not go too deeply into electrical or electronic theory, but there are many other excellent publications available for that purpose. See *"Automobile Electrical & Electronic Systems"* by Tony Tranter (publisher Haynes, book number 3049).

Many of our tests and routines may not be as specifically recommended by the Vehicle Manufacturer (VM). One of the reasons is because the VM may describe procedures for use with his own special test equipment that is not readily available to the aftermarket user. Another reason is that all too often the VM places too much reliance upon the ohmmeter as the primary testing tool.

The accepted test method used by all good electronic vehicle specialists is to place more weight on voltage readings, which tend to give more reliable results. We will discuss this issue at greater length in the appropriate sections later on. In almost all instances, our own tests follow well-defined test methods taught in independent training schools and used by many modern vehicle technical specialists.

The routines and test methods that we describe are perfectly safe to carry out on electronic systems, so long as certain simple rules are observed. These rules are actually the observation of good electrical practice. Be aware that damage resulting in the replacement of a very expensive Electronic Control Module (ECM or ECU) may be the result of not following the rules. Please refer to the Warnings section in Reference; these warnings will be repeated in the various chapters where necessary.

We have described the operation and test procedures of most of the modern EMS's fitted to a whole host of popular vehicles. However, you must be aware of the generic nature of our illustrations and wiring diagrams. Each EMS may have many variations according to the specific vehicle in the range to which it is actually fitted. For example, one vehicle may be equipped with an Idle Speed Control Valve (ISCV), another vehicle with the same system may utilise a stepper motor or even an Auxiliary Air Valve (AAV). Some vehicles may be equipped with two separate relays or one double relay, depending on year. In some applications even the position of the ECM pins differs, and particular care must be taken in this instance.

Although we have tried to define most of the variations in components fitted to a particular system, we have only provided an example of the wiring diagrams for any particular system. It is essential that a specific wiring diagram for the vehicle under test is obtained where serious tracing of wiring faults is required.

Throughout Europe, the USA and the Far East the various VM's tend to use their own particular terms to describe a particular component. Of course, all of these terms tend to be different, and the problem is exacerbated by translation from the various languages. This often leads to confusion when several terms are used to describe the same component. There have been attempts to bring all the VM's into line with a common standard for all, and one does now exist (J1930). It seems unlikely, however, that all VM's will adopt this particular standard, and we are unsure that the terms used are that meaningful anyway. So, the terms used in this book will tend to follow terms that are commonly used in the UK. To avoid confusion, we will tend to use similar terms over the whole range of EMS's, and alternatives will be listed in the Glossary.

Acknowledgements

We would like to thank all of those at Sparkford and elsewhere that helped us in the production of this manual. In particular we would like to thank Equiptech for permission to use illustrations from the 'CAPS' fuel injection fault diagnostic database and for providing much of the technical information that was used in authoring this book. We also thank Kate Eyres who compiled the majority of vehicle lists, data lists and Fault Code tables, Martin White who drew many of the illustrations, Jan Norbye for some of the historical information, and Simon Ashby of RA Engineering for additional technical information.

Working on your car can be dangerous. This page shows just some of the potential risks and hazards, with the aim of creating a safety-conscious attitude.

General hazards

Scalding

• Don't remove the radiator or expansion tank cap while the engine is hot.
• Engine oil, automatic transmission fluid or power steering fluid may also be dangerously hot if the engine has recently been running.

Burning

• Beware of burns from the exhaust system and from any part of the engine. Brake discs and drums can also be extremely hot immediately after use.

Crushing

• When working under or near a raised vehicle, always supplement the jack with axle stands, or use drive-on ramps. ***Never venture under a car which is only supported by a jack.***
• Take care if loosening or tightening high-torque nuts when the vehicle is on stands. Initial loosening and final tightening should be done with the wheels on the ground.

Fire

• Fuel is highly flammable; fuel vapour is explosive.
• Don't let fuel spill onto a hot engine.
• Do not smoke or allow naked lights (including pilot lights) anywhere near a vehicle being worked on. Also beware of creating sparks (electrically or by use of tools).
• Fuel vapour is heavier than air, so don't work on the fuel system with the vehicle over an inspection pit.
• Another cause of fire is an electrical overload or short-circuit. Take care when repairing or modifying the vehicle wiring.
• Keep a fire extinguisher handy, of a type suitable for use on fuel and electrical fires.

Electric shock

• Ignition HT voltage can be dangerous, especially to people with heart problems or a pacemaker. Don't work on or near the ignition system with the engine running or the ignition switched on.
• Mains voltage is also dangerous. Make sure that any mains-operated equipment is correctly earthed. Mains power points should be protected by a residual current device (RCD) circuit breaker.

Fume or gas intoxication

• Exhaust fumes are poisonous; they often contain carbon monoxide, which is rapidly fatal if inhaled. Never run the engine in a confined space such as a garage with the doors shut.

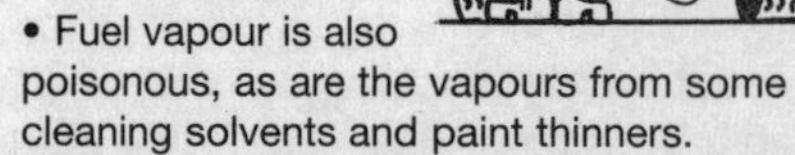

• Fuel vapour is also poisonous, as are the vapours from some cleaning solvents and paint thinners.

Poisonous or irritant substances

• Avoid skin contact with battery acid and with any fuel, fluid or lubricant, especially antifreeze, brake hydraulic fluid and Diesel fuel. Don't syphon them by mouth. If such a substance is swallowed or gets into the eyes, seek medical advice.
• Prolonged contact with used engine oil can cause skin cancer. Wear gloves or use a barrier cream if necessary. Change out of oil-soaked clothes and do not keep oily rags in your pocket.
• Air conditioning refrigerant forms a poisonous gas if exposed to a naked flame (including a cigarette). It can also cause skin burns on contact.

Asbestos

• Asbestos dust can cause cancer if inhaled or swallowed. Asbestos may be found in gaskets and in brake and clutch linings. When dealing with such components it is safest to assume that they contain asbestos.

Special hazards

Hydrofluoric acid

• This extremely corrosive acid is formed when certain types of synthetic rubber, found in some O-rings, oil seals, fuel hoses etc, are exposed to temperatures above 400°C. The rubber changes into a charred or sticky substance containing the acid. *Once formed, the acid remains dangerous for years. If it gets onto the skin, it may be necessary to amputate the limb concerned.*
• When dealing with a vehicle which has suffered a fire, or with components salvaged from such a vehicle, wear protective gloves and discard them after use.

The battery

• Batteries contain sulphuric acid, which attacks clothing, eyes and skin. Take care when topping-up or carrying the battery.
• The hydrogen gas given off by the battery is highly explosive. Never cause a spark or allow a naked light nearby. Be careful when connecting and disconnecting battery chargers or jump leads.

Air bags

• Air bags can cause injury if they go off accidentally. Take care when removing the steering wheel and/or facia. Special storage instructions may apply.

Diesel injection equipment

• Diesel injection pumps supply fuel at very high pressure. Take care when working on the fuel injectors and fuel pipes.

Warning: Never expose the hands, face or any other part of the body to injector spray; the fuel can penetrate the skin with potentially fatal results.

Remember...

DO

• Do use eye protection when using power tools, and when working under the vehicle.

• Do wear gloves or use barrier cream to protect your hands when necessary.

• Do get someone to check periodically that all is well when working alone on the vehicle.

• Do keep loose clothing and long hair well out of the way of moving mechanical parts.

• Do remove rings, wristwatch etc, before working on the vehicle – especially the electrical system.

• Do ensure that any lifting or jacking equipment has a safe working load rating adequate for the job.

DON'T

• Don't attempt to lift a heavy component which may be beyond your capability – get assistance.

• Don't rush to finish a job, or take unverified short cuts.

• Don't use ill-fitting tools which may slip and cause injury.

• Don't leave tools or parts lying around where someone can trip over them. Mop up oil and fuel spills at once.

• Don't allow children or pets to play in or near a vehicle being worked on.

Model	Engine code	Year	System
Alfa Romeo			
1.7iE 4x4 cat 80kW	307.37	1993 to 1995	Motronic 3.1
Sportwagon 4x4 cat 80kW	307.37	1993 to 1995	Motronic 3.1
33 4x4 cat 80kW	307.37	1993 to 1995	Motronic 3.1
33 16V & 4x4 & cat DOHC 16V 98kW	307.46	1990 to 1995	Motronic 4.1
75 Twin Spark DOHC 107kW	017.13	1987 to 1992	Motronic ML 1.1
75 3.0i V6 cat	061.20	1987 to 1993	Motronic 4.1
145 1.6ie SOHC 76kW	AR33201	1994 to 1996	Motronic 3.1
146 1.6ie SOHC 76kW	AR33201	1994 to 1996	Motronic 3.1
155 T-Spark cat DOHC	AR671.03	1992 to 1992	Motronic
155 1.8 T-Spark cat DOHC 93kW	AR671.02	1992 to 1996	Motronic 1.7
155 2.0 T-Spark cat DOHC 93kW	AR671.02	1992 to 1996	Motronic 1.7
155 2.5 V6 cat SOHC 121kW	AR673.01/03	1992 to 1996	Motronic 1.7
164 2.0 T-Spark cat DOHC 107kW	064.16	1990 to 1993	Motronic 4.1
164 2.0 T-Spark DOHC 107kW	064.20	1990 to 1993	Motronic 4.1
164 2.0 T-Spark DOHC 16V 109kW	AR64.103	1993 to 1996	Motronic 1.7
164 V6	064.10	1988 to 1993	Motronic 4.1
164 V6 & cat	064.12	1988 to 1993	Motronic 4.1
164 V6 Cloverleaf cat SOHC 145kW	064.301	1990 to 1993	Motronic 4.1
164 V6 24V 157kW	066.301	1993 to 1995	Motronic 1.7
164 V6 24V 157kW	AR66.302	1995 to 1997	Motronic 1.7
164 V6 24V Cloverleaf	064.304	1994 to 1997	Motronic 1.7
164 V6 24V Cloverleaf	AR64.308	1995 to 1997	Motronic 1.7
Boxer 16V 4x4 cat DOHC 16V 98kW	307.46	1990 to 1995	Motronic 4.1
Spider cat DOHC 90kW	015.88	1990 to 1994	Motronic 4.1
Audi			
Audi 80 1.8i cat	PM	1990 to 1991	Mono-Motronic
Audi 80 2.0i Quattro cat	ABT	1991 to 1995	Mono-Motronic
Audi 100 2.0 cat	AAE	1991 to 1994	Mono-Motronic
BMW			
316i (E30) & cat	M40/B16 164E1	1988 to 1993	Motronic 1.3
316i (E36) cat	M40/B16 164E1	1990 to 1993	Motronic 1.7
316i (E36) cat & Compact	M43/B16	1993 to 1996	Motronic 1.7
318i (E30) Touring & cat	M40/B18 184E11	1988 to 1993	Motronic 1.3
318i (E30) & Touring	M40/B18	1989 to 1992	Motronic 1.7
318i (E36) & cat	M40/B18 184E2	1991 to 1993	Motronic 1.7
318i (E36)	M43/B18	1993 to 1996	Motronic 1.7
318iS (E30) 16V Touring & cat	M42/B18 184S1	1990 to 1991	Motronic 1.7
318iS (E36) & Compact	M42/B18 184S1	1992 to 1996	Motronic 1.7
320i (E30)	M20/B20 206EE	1986 to 1988	Motronic 1.1
320i (E30) & Touring & cat	M20/B20 206EE	1988 to 1993	Motronic 1.3
320i (E36) 24V cat	M50/B20 206S1	1991 to 1993	Motronic 3.1
320i (E36) 24V cat	M50 2.0 Vanos	1993 to 1996	Motronic 3.1
325i (E30)	M20/B25	1985 to 1986	Motronic (First gen.)
325i (E30) & 4x4	M20/B25 6K1	1985 to 1987	Motronic 1.1
325i & Touring (E30)	M20/B25 6K1	1988 to 1993	Motronic 1.3
325iX (E30-4)	M20/B25 6E2	1985 to 1987	Motronic 1.1
325iX & Touring	M20/B25 6E2	1988 to 1993	Motronic 1.3
325i (E36) 24V cat	M50/B25 256S1	1991 to 1993	Motronic 3.1
325i (E36) 24V	M50 2.5 Vanos	1993 to 1996	Motronic 3.1
325e (E30) & cat	M20/B27	1986 to 1991	Motronic 1.1
325e (E30 cat	M20/B27	1985 to 1987	Motronic (First gen.)
518i (E34)	M40/B18	1988 to 1993	Motronic 1.3
518i (E34) cat	M43/B18	1993 to 1996	Motronic 1.7
520i (E34) & cat	M20/B20M 206KA	1988 to 1991	Motronic 1.3
520i (E34) 24V & Touring cat	M50/B20 206S1	1990 to 1993	Motronic 3.1
520i (E34) 24V & Touring cat	M50 2.0 Vanos	1993 to 1996	Motronic 3.1
525i (E34) & cat	M20/B25M 256K1	1988 to 1991	Motronic 1.3
525i (E34) 24V cat	M50/B25 256S1	1990 to 1993	Motronic 3.1
525i (E34) 24V	M50 2.5 Vanos	1993 to 1996	Motronic 3.1
525e (E28)	M20/B27	1983 to 1988	Motronic (First gen.)
525e (E28) cat	M20/B27	1983 to 1988	Motronic (First gen.)
530i (E34) & cat	M30/B30M 306KA	1988 to 1992	Motronic 1.3
535i (E28)	M30/B34	1982 to 1986	Motronic (First gen.)

Model	Engine code	Year	System
BMW (continued)			
535i (E34) & cat	M30/B35M 346KB	1988 to 1993	Motronic 1.3
M535i (E28)	M30/B34	1982 to 1986	Motronic (First gen.)
633 CSi (E24)	M30/B32	1982 to 1989	Motronic (First gen.)
635 CSi (E24)	M30/B34	1982 to 1986	Motronic (First gen.)
635 CSi (E24)	M30/B34	1986 to 1987	Motronic 1.1
635 CSi (E24) & cat	M30/B35M 346EC	1988 to 1990	Motronic 1.3
M635i CSi (E24)	M88/3	1982 to 1989	Motronic (First gen.)
M635i CSi (E24) cat	S38z	1986 to 1989	Motronic (First gen.)
M635i CSi (E24)	S38/B35 356EY	1986 to 1990	Motronic (First gen.)
M635 CSi (E24)	M88/3	1987 to 1989	Motronic 1.3
730i (E32) & cat	M30/B30M2 306KA	1986 to 1987	Motronic 1.1
730i (E32) & cat	M30/B30M2 306KA	1988 to 1994	Motronic 1.3
732i (E23)	M30/B32	1982 to 1987	Motronic (First gen.)
735i (E32) & cat	M30/B35M2	1986 to 1987	Motronic 1.1
735i (E32) & cat	M30/B35M2 346EC	1987 to 1992	Motronic 1.3
735i (E23)	M30/B34	1982 to 1985	Motronic (First gen.)
745i Turbo (E23)	M30/B34	1982 to 1987	Motronic (First gen.)
750i & cat	M70/B50 5012A	1992 to 1994	Motronic 1.7
750iL	M70/B50 5012A	1992 to 1994	Motronic 1.7
750i	M70/B54	1994 to 1996	Motronic
850i	M70/B50 5012A	1989 to 1994	Motronic 1.7
M3 (E36)	S50/B30	1993 to 1996	Motronic
M5 (E34)	S38/B38 386S1	1992 to 1996	Motronic
M5 (E28)	M30/B34	1985 to 1987	Motronic (First gen.)
M5 (E28) cat	M88-3/S38Z	1984 to 1988	Motronic (First gen.)
Z1 (325)	M20/B25	1985 to 1988	Motronic (First gen.)
Z1 M20/B25	1988 to 1992	Motronic 1.3	
Citroën			
AX 1.0i cat	TU9M/L.Z (CDY)	1992 to 1996	Mono-Motronic MA3.0
AX 1.0i cat	TU9M/L.Z (CDZ)	1992 to 1996	Mono-Motronic MA3.0
AX 1.1i cat	TU1M/L.Z (HDY)	1992 to 1994	Magneti Marelli G6-11
AX 1.1i cat	TU1M/L.Z (HDZ)	1992 to 1994	Magneti Marelli G6-11
AX 1.4i cat	TU3FM/L.Z (KDX)	1992 to 1996	Mono-Motronic MA3.0
AX 1.4 GTi	TU3J2/K (K6B)	1991 to 1992	Motronic MP3.1
AX 1.4 GTi cat	TU3J2/L.Z (KFZ)	1991 to 1996	Motronic MP3.1
BX16i cat	XU5M3Z (BDY)	1991 to 1994	Magneti Marelli G6-10
BX19 1.9 GTi 16V	XU9J4 (D6C)	1987 to 1991	Motronic ML4.1
BX19 TZi 8V cat	XU9JAZ (DKZ)	1990 to 1993	Motronic 1.3
BX19 16V DOHC cat	XU9J4Z (DFW)	1990 to 1992	Motronic 1.3
BX19 16V DOHC	XU9J4K (D6C)	1991 to 1992	Motronic 1.3
BX19i GTi & 4X4	XU9J2 (D6D)	1990 to 1992	Motronic MP3.1
XM 2.0i	XU10J2 (R6A)	1990 to 1992	Magneti Marelli BA G5 MPi
XM 2.0i cat LHD	XU10M (RDZ)	1990 to 1993	Magneti Marelli G5
XM 2.0i cat	XU10J2/Z (RFZ)	1990 to 1992	Motronic MP3.1
XM 2.0i cat	XU10J2/Z (RFZ)	1992 to 1994	Motronic MP5.1
XM 2.0i 16V cat	XU10J4R/L/Z (RFV)	1994 to 1996	Motronic MP5.1
XM 2.0i turbo cat	XU10J2TE/Z (RGY)	1993 to 1994	Motronic MP3.2
ZX 1.1i cat	TU1M/Z (HDY)	1994 to 1996	Mono-Motronic MA3.0
ZX 1.1i cat	TU1M/Z (HDZ)	1994 to 1996	Mono-Motronic MA3.0
ZX 1.4i & Break cat	TU3M (KDX)	1992 to 1996	Mono-Motronic MA3.0
ZX 1.4i & Break cat	TU3M (KDX)	1994 to 1996	Magneti Marelli G6-14
ZX 1.6i	XU5M.2K (B4A)	1991 to 1992	Magneti Marelli G5 S2
ZX 1.6i	XU5M.3K (B4A)	1991 to 1993	Magneti Marelli G6 12
ZX 1.6i cat	XU5M.3Z (BDY)	1992 to 1993	Magneti Marelli G6.10
ZX 1.6i & Break cat	XU5JPL/Z (BFZ)	1994 to 1995	Magneti Marelli 8P-13 MPi
ZX 1.8i & Break cat	XU7JPL/Z (LFZ)	1992 to 1994	Motronic MP5.1
ZX 1.8i & Break cat	XU7JPL/Z (LFZ)	1995 to 1996	Magneti Marelli 8P-10 MPi
ZX 1.9 8V	XU9JAZ (DKZ)	1992 to 1994	Motronic 1.3
ZX 1.9i	XU9JA/K (D6E)	1991 to 1992	Motronic MP3.1
ZX 2.0i cat	XUJ10J2/C/L/Z (RFX)	1992 to 1996	Magneti Marelli 8P-20
ZX 2.0i 16V cat	XUJ10J4/D/L/Z (RFY)	1992 to 1995	Motronic MP3.2
ZX 2.0i 16V	XUJ10J4/D/L/Z (RFT)	1994 to 1996	Motronic MP3.2
Evasion 2.0i cat	XU10J2CZ/L (RFU)	1994 to 1996	Magneti Marelli 8P22 MPi
Evasion 2.0i turbo cat	XU10J2CTEZ/L (RGX)	1994 to 1996	Motronic MP3.2

Model	Engine code	Year	System
Citroën (continued)			
Jumper 2.0i cat	XU10J2U (RFW)	1994 to 1996	Magneti Marelli DCM8P-11
Jumpy 1.6i	220 A2.000	1995 to 1996	Mono-Motronic MA1.7
Relay 2.0i cat	XU10J2U (RFW)	1994 to 1996	Magneti Marelli DCM8P-11
Synergie 2.0i cat	XU10J2CZ/L (RFU)	1994 to 1996	Magneti Marelli 8P22 MPi
Synergie 2.0i turbo cat	XU10J2CTEZ/L (RGX)	1994 to 1996	Motronic MP3.2
Xantia 1.6i cat	XU5JP/Z (BFX)	1993 to 1996	Magneti Marelli DCM8P13
Xantia 1.8i 16V	XU7JP4/L3 (LFY)	1995 to 1996	Motronic MP5.1.1
Xantia 1.8i & Break	XU7JP/Z (LFZ)	1993 to 1996	Motronic MP5.1
Xantia 2.0i & Break	XU10J2C/Z (RFX)	1993 to 1996	Magneti Marelli DCM8P20
Xantia 2.0i 16V cat	XU10J4D/Z (RFY)	1993 to 1995	Motronic MP3.2
Xantia 2.0i 16V & Break	XU10J4R/Z/L3 (RFV)	1995 to 1996	Motronic MP5.1.1
Xantia Activa 2.0i	XU10J4D/Z (RFT)	1994 to 1996	Motronic MP3.2
Xantia Turbo 2.0i CT	XU10J2CTE/L3 (RGX)	1995 to 1996	Motronic MP3.2
Fiat			
Coupe 16V	836 A3.000	1994 to 1996	Weber-Marelli IAW MPi
Coupe 16V Turbo	175 A1.000	1994 to 1996	Weber-Marelli IAW MPi
Croma 2000ie	834 B.000	1986 to 1989	Weber-Marelli IAW MPi
Croma 2000ie DOHC 8V	154 C.000	1989 to 1991	Weber-Marelli IAW MPi
Croma 2.0ie DOHC	154 C3.000	1990 to 1992	Weber-Marelli IAW MPi
Croma 2.0ie DOHC cat static	154 C3.046	1991 to 1994	Weber-Marelli IAW MPi
Croma 2.0ie 16V cat	154 E1.000	1993 to 1995	Motronic M1.7
Punto 75	176 A8.000	1994 to 1995	Weber-Marelli IAW MPi
Tempra 1.6ie cat SOHC	159 A3.046	1993 to 1994	Mono-Motronic MA1.7
Tempra 1.8ie DOHC 8V	159 A4.000	1990 to 1992	Weber-Marelli IAW MPi
Tempra 1.8ie DOHC 8V cat	159 A4.046	1992 to 1994	Weber-Marelli IAW MPi
Tempra 1.8 DOHC 76kW	835 C2.000	1993 to 1996	Weber-Marelli IAW MPi
Tempra 2.0ie & 4x4 DOHC 8V	159 A6.046	1991 to 1996	Weber-Marelli IAW MPi
Tipo 1.6ie SOHC 55kW	835 C1.000	1994 to 1996	Mono-Motronic MA1.7
Tipo 1.6ie SOHC cat	159 A3.046	1993 to 1995	Mono-Motronic MA1.7
Tipo 1.8ie DOHC 8V	159 A4.000	1990 to 1992	Weber-Marelli IAW MPi
Tipo 1.8ie DOHC 8V	159 A4.000	1992 to 1995	Weber-Marelli IAW MPi
Tipo 1.8i DOHC 16V	160 A5.000	1990 to 1991	Weber-Marelli IAW MPi
Tipo 1.8i cat	159 A4.046	1992 to 1994	Weber-Marelli IAW MPi
Tipo 2.0ie DOHC 8V cat	159 A4.046	1992 to 1994	Weber-Marelli IAW MPi
Tipo 2.0ie DOHC 8V cat	159 A5.046	1990 to 1992	Weber-Marelli IAW MPi
Tipo 2.0ie DOHC 8V cat	159 A6.046	1992 to 1995	Weber-Marelli IAW MPi
Tipo 2.0ie DOHC 16V cat	160 A8.046	1991 to 1992	Weber-Marelli IAW MPi
Ulysse 2.0 SOHC 89kW	ZFA220000	1995 to 1996	Weber-Marelli IAW MPi
Ford			
Escort 1.3 cat	HCS	1991 to 1992	EEC IV
Escort 1.3 cat	J6A	1991 to 1995	EEC IV
Escort 1.4 CFi cat	F6D	1989 to 1990	EEC IV
Escort 1.4 CFi cat	F6D	1989 to 1990	EEC IV
Escort 1.4 CFi cat	F6F	1990 to 1992	EEC IV
Escort 1.4 CFi cat	F6F	1990 to 1995	EEC IV
Escort 1.4 CFi cat	F6G	1990 to 1995	EEC IV
Escort 1.4i pte	F4	1994 to 1996	EEC IV
Escort 1.6iXR3i	LJA	1989 to 1992	EEC IV
Escort 1.6iXR3i cat	LJB	1989 to 1992	EEC IV
Escort 1.6 DOHC 16V cat	L1E	1992 to 1996	EEC IV
Escort 1.6i	LJA	1989 to 1990	EEC IV
Escort 1.6i	LJE	1990 to 1992	EEC IV
Escort XR3i 1.6 & cat	LJA-LJD	1989 to 1992	EEC IV
Escort XR3i 1.6 DOHC 16V cat	LJE-LJF	1992 to 1997	EEC IV
Escort RS2000 DOHC 16V cat	N7A	1991 to 1992	EEC IV
Escort RS Cosworth DOHC 16V turbo cat	N5F	1992 to 1995	Weber IAW
Escort RS2000 DOHC 16V 4x4 cat	N7A	1991 to 1995	EEC IV
Escort 1.8i 16V DOHC cat	RDA	1992 to 1995	EEC IV
Escort 1.8i 16V DOHC cat	RQB	1992 to 1995	EEC IV
Escort 1.6i cat	ZETEC	1992 to 1996	EEC IV
Escort 2.0i 7 4x4 cat	N7A	1991 to 1996	EEC IV
Fiesta 1.1 & Van cat	G6A	1989 to 1996	EEC IV
Fiesta 1.3 Van courier cat	HCS	1991 to 1994	EEC IV

Model	Engine code	Year	System
Ford (continued)			
Fiesta 1.3 Van courier cat	J6B	1991 to 1995	EEC IV
Fiesta 1.4i & Van cat	F6E	1989 to 1990	EEC IV
Fiesta 1.4i & Van cat	F6E	1990 to 1995	EEC IV
Fiesta XR2i1.6 cat	LJD	1989 to 1993	EEC IV
Fiesta RS turbo 1.6	LHA	1990 to 1992	EEC IV
Fiesta 1.6i & cat	LUC	1989 to 1992	EEC IV
Fiesta XR2i1.6	LJC	1989 to 1993	EEC IV
Fiesta 1.6i 16V	LIG	1994 to 1995	EEC IV
Fiesta XR2i 1.8i 16V DOHC cat	RDB	1992 to 1995	EEC IV
Fiesta 1.8i 16V DOHC cat	RQC	1992 to 1995	EEC IV
Granada 2.0 EFi & 4wd DOHC 8V	N9B	1989 to 1995	EEC IV
Granada 2.0 EFi 4wd DOHC 8V cat	N9D	1989 to 1992	EEC IV
Granada 2.4 V6	ARC	1987 to 1993	EEC IV
Granada 2.4 V6 cat	ARD	1987 to 1991	EEC IV
Granada 2.9 V6 & 4x4	BRC	1987 to 1992	EEC IV
Granada 2.9 V6 cat	BRD	1987 to 1994	EEC IV
Granada 2.9 V6 cat	BRE	1987 to 1992	EEC IV
Granada 2.9 V6 24V DOHC cat	BOA	1991 to 1995	EEC IV
Mondeo 1.6 DOHC 16V cat	L1F	1993 to 1996	EEC IV
Mondeo 1.8i 16V DOHC & 4x4 cat	RKA	1993 to 1996	EEC IV
Mondeo 2.0i 16V DOHC & 4x4 cat	NGA	1993 to 1996	EEC IV
Mondeo 2.5 V6 24V DOHC cat	SEA	1994 to 1996	EEC IV
Orion 1.3 cat	HCS	1991 to 1992	EEC IV
Orion 1.3 cat	J6A	1991 to 1995	EEC IV
Orion 1.4 CFi cat	F6D	1989 to 1990	EEC IV
Orion 1.4 CFi cat	F6F	1990 to 1992	EEC IV
Orion 1.4 CFi cat	F6F	1990 to 1995	EEC IV
Orion 1.4 CFi cat	F6G	1990 to 1995	EEC IV
Orion 1.6i	LJE	1990 to 1993	EEC IV
Orion 1.6i cat	LJF	1990 to 1994	EEC IV
Orion 1.6i	LJA	1989 to 1990	EEC IV
Orion 1.6 DOHC 16V cat	L1E	1992 to 1996	EEC IV
Orion 1.8i 16V DOHC cat	RDA	1992 to 1995	EEC IV
Orion 1.8i 16V DOHC cat	RQB	1992 to 1995	EEC IV
Sapphire 1.6 CVH cat	L6B	1990 to 1993	EEC IV
Sapphire 1.8 CVH cat	R6A	1992 to 1993	EEC IV
Sapphire 2.0 EFi DOHC 8V	N9A	1989 to 1992	EEC IV
Sapphire 2.0 EFi DOHC 8V cat	N9C	1989 to 1992	EEC IV
Scorpio 2.9 V6 & 4x4	BRC	1987 to 1992	EEC IV
Scorpio 2.9 V6 cat	BRD	1987 to 1995	EEC IV
Scorpio 2.9 V6 cat	BRE	1987 to 1995	EEC IV
Scorpio 2.9 V6 24V DOHC cat	BOA	1991 to 1995	EEC IV
Scorpio 2.9i V6	BRG	1994 to 1996	EEC IV
Scorpio 2.9i V6 24V	BOB	1994 to 1996	EEC IV
Scorpio 2.0i	NSD	1994 to 1996	EEC IV
Scorpio 2.0i 16V	N3A	1994 to 1996	EEC IV
Sierra 1.6 CVH cat	L68	1990 to 1992	EEC IV
Sierra 1.6 CVH cat	L6B	1990 to 1993	EEC IV
Sierra 1.8 CVH cat	R6A	1992 to 1993	EEC IV
Sierra 2.0 EFi DOHC 8V	N9A	1989 to 1992	EEC IV
Sierra 2.0 EFi DOHC 8V cat	N9C	1989 to 1992	EEC IV
Sierra 2.9 XR 4x4 V6	B4A	1989 to 1991	EEC IV
Sierra 2.9 XR 4x4 V6 cat	B4B	1989 to 1993	EEC IV
Transit Van 2.0 CFi cat	N6T	1990 to 1991	EEC IV
Transit Van 2.0 CFi cat		1991 to 1992	EEC IV
Transit 2.9 V6 EFi	BRT	1991 to 1994	EEC IV
Transit 2.9 EFi	B4T	1989 to 1991	EEC IV
Honda			
Accord EFi A4 SOHC	A20	1985 to 1989	PGM-Fi
Accord 2.0i-16 A2 DOHC 16V	B20	1987 to 1989	PGM-Fi
Accord 2.0i & cat SOHC16V 101kW	F20A4	1989 to 1992	PGM-Fi
Accord 2.0i & cat SOHC 16V	F20A5	1992 to 1996	PGM-Fi
Accord 2.0i Coupe cat SOHC 16V	F20A7	1992 to 1996	PGM-Fi
Accord 2.2i cat SOHC 16V 112kW	F22A3/A7/A8	1989 to 1996	PGM-Fi

Model	Engine code	Year	System
Honda (continued)			
Accord 2.3i cat DOHC 16V 118kW	H23A2	1993 to 1996	PGM-Fi
Aerodeck EFi A4 SOHC	A20	1985 to 1989	PGM-Fi
Aerodeck 2.2i cat SOHC 16V	F22A3/A7/A8	1989 to 1996	PGM-Fi
Ballade EXi SOHC 3W	EW3	1986 to 1989	PGM-Fi
Civic 1.4i SOHC 16V 66kW	D14A2	1995 to 1996	PGM-Fi
Civic CRX	EW3	1984 to 1987	PGM-Fi
Civic GT	EW3	1984 to 1987	PGM-Fi
Civic 1.5 VEi cat SOHC 16V	D15Z1	1991 to 1995	PGM-Fi
Civic 1.5 LSi SOHC 16V 67kW	D15B2	1991 to 1995	PGM-Fi
Civic Coupe cat SOHC 16V 67kW	D15B2	1991 to 1995	PGM-Fi
Civic 1.5i VTEC-E SOHC 16V 66kW	D15Z3	1995 to 1996	PGM-Fi
Civic 1.6i-16 DOHC 16V	D16A9	1987 to 1992	PGM-Fi
CRX 1.6i-16 DOHC 16V	D16A9	1987 to 1992	PGM-Fi
Civic 1.6 VT cat DOHC 16V	B16A1	1990 to 1991	PGM-Fi
CRX 1.6 VT cat DOHC 16V VTEC	B16A1	1990 to 1991	PGM-Fi
Civic 1.6 ESi cat SOHC 16V VTEC	D16Z6	1991 to 1996	PGM-Fi
CRX 1.6 ESi cat SOHC16V VTEC	D16Z6	1991 to 1996	PGM-Fi
Civic 1.6 VTi cat DOHC 16V VTEC	B16A2	1991 to 1995	PGM-Fi
CRX 1.6 VTi cat DOHC 16V VTEC	B16A2	1991 to 1995	PGM-Fi
Civic 1.6i SOHC 16V 83kW	D16Y3	1995 to 1996	PGM-Fi
Civic 1.6i VTEC SOHC 16V 93kW	D16Y2	1995 to 1996	PGM-Fi
Civic CRX DOHC 16V	ZC1	1987 to 1987	PGM-Fi
Concerto 1.5i cat SOHC 16V 67kW	D15B2	1991 to 1995	PGM-Fi
Concerto 1.6 DOHC 16V	D16A9	1989 to 1991	PGM-Fi
Concerto 1.6i SOHC 16V cat	D16Z2	1992 to 1995	PGM-Fi
Concerto 1.6i DOHC 16V cat	D16A8	1992 to 1995	PGM-Fi
Integra EX 16 A2 DOHC 16V	D16	1986 to 1990	PGM-Fi
Legend	C25A2	1986 to 1988	PGM-Fi
Legend 2.7 & Coupe SOHC	C27A2	1988 to 1991	PGM-Fi
Legend 2.7 cat SOHC	C27A1	1990 to 1991	PGM-Fi
Legend 3.2 cat SOHC 24V 152kW	C32A2	1992 to 1996	PGM-Fi
NSX cat DOHC 24V V-TEC 201kW	C30A	1991 to 1996	PGM-Fi
Prelude Fi	B20A1	1985 to 1987	PGM-Fi
Prelude 4WS 2.0i-16 DOHC 16V	B20A7	1987 to 1992	PGM-Fi
Prelude 4WS 2.0i-16 cat DOHC	B20A9	1987 to 1992	PGM-Fi
Prelude 2.0i 16V cat SOHC 16V	F20A4	1992 to 1996	PGM-Fi
Prelude 2.2i VTECDOHC 16V	H22A2	1994 to 1996	PGM-Fi
Prelude 2.3i 16V cat DOHC 16V	H23A2	1992 to 1996	PGM-Fi
Shuttle 1.6i 4WD SOHC 16V	D16A7	1988 to 1990	PGM-Fi
Lancia			
Dedra 1.8ie DOHC	835 A2.000	1990 to 1993	Weber-Marelli IAW MPi
Dedra 1.8ie DOHC cat	835 A2.046	1990 to 1994	Weber-Marelli IAW MPi
Dedra 2.0ie DOHC	835 A5.000	1990 to 1992	Weber-Marelli IAW MPi
Dedra 2.0ie DOHC cat	835 A5.045	1990 to 1994	Weber-Marelli IAW MPi
Dedra 2.0ie DOHC cat	835 A5.046	1990 to 1994	Weber-Marelli IAW MPi
Dedra 2.0ie DOHC Turbo & cat	835 A8.000	1991 to 1996	Weber-Marelli IAW MPi
Dedra 2.0ie Integrale Turbo & cat	835 A7.000	1991 to 1996	Weber-Marelli IAW MPi
Delta 1600ie DOHC	831 B7.000	1986 to 1989	Weber-Marelli IAW MPi
Delta 1600ie DOHC	831 B7.000	1989 to 1990	Weber-Marelli IAW MPi
Delta 1600ie DOHC static	831 B7.000	1991 to 1992	Weber-Marelli IAW MPi
Delta HF Turbo & Martini	831 B3.000	1986 to 1992	Weber-Marelli IAW MPi
Delta HF Turbo DOHC cat	831 B7.046	1991 to 1993	Weber-Marelli IAW MPi
Delta HF Integrale Turbo DOHC	831 B5.000	1988 to 1989	Weber-Marelli IAW MPi
Delta HF Integrale Turbo DOHC	831 C5.000	1988 to 1989	Weber-Marelli IAW MPi
Delta HF Integrale Turbo DOHC	831 D5.000	1989 to 1992	Weber-Marelli IAW MPi
Delta HF Integrale Turbo 16V & cat	831 E5.000	1991 to 1994	Weber-Marelli IAW MPi
Prisma 1600ie DOHC	831 B7.000	1986 to 1989	Weber-Marelli IAW MPi
Prisma 1600ie DOHC	831 B7.000	1989 to 1990	Weber-Marelli IAW MPi
Prisma 1600ie DOHC static	831 B7.000	1991 to 1992	Weber-Marelli IAW MPi
Tempra 1.8	835 C2.000	1993 to 1996	Weber-Marelli IAW MPi
Thema FL 2000ie 16V DOHC cat	834 F1.000	1992 to 1994	Motronic M1.7
Thema FL 3000 V6 SOHC cat	834 F.000	1992 to 1994	Motronic M1.7
Y10 1108ie & 4x4 cat	156 C.046	1992 to 1995	Motronic M1.7

Model	Engine code	Year	System
Mazda			
323 1.3i cat SOHC 16V 55kW	B3	1991 to 1995	EGI MPi
323 1.6i cat SOHC 16V 66kW	B6	1991 to 1994	EGI MPi
323 1.6i Estate cat SOHC 8V 42kW	B6E	1991 to 1994	EGI MPi
323 1.6i SOHC 16V 66kW	B6	1991 to 1996	EGI MPi
323 1.8 GTi DOHC 16V	BP	1989 to 1991	EGI MPi
323 1.8i cat DOHC 16V 101kW	BP	1991 to 1994	EGI MPi
323 SOHC 16V 55kW	B3	1991 to 1995	EGI MPi
323 1.5i	B6	1985 to 1987	EGI MPi
323 1600i	B6	1985 to 1987	EGI MPi
323 Turbo 4x4 DOHC turbo	B6	1986 to 1989	EGI MPi
323 cat SOHC 16V 66kW	B6	1991 to 1994	EGI MPi
323 Estate cat SOHC 8V 42kW	B6E	1991 to 1994	EGI MPi
323 GTi DOHC 16V	BP	1989 to 1991	EGI MPi
323 cat DOHC 16V 101kW	BP	1991 to 1994	EGI MPi
626 1.8i cat DOHC 16V 77kW	FP	1992 to 1996	EGI MPi
626 2.0i cat DOHC 16V 85kW	FS	1992 to 1996	EGI MPi
626 cat DOHC 16V 77kW	FP	1992 to 1996	EGI MPi
626 cat DOHC 16V 85kW	FS	1992 to 1996	EGI MPi
626 2.5i V6 cat DOHC 24V 121kW	KL	1992 to 1996	EGI MPi
MX-31.8i V6 DOHC 24V 100kW	K8	1991 to 1996	EGI MPi
MX-3 SOHC 16V 66kW	B6	1991 to 1996	EGI MPi
MX-3 DOHC 24V 100kW	K8	1991 to 1996	EGI MPi
MX-6 2.5i V6 cat	KL	1992 to 1996	EGI MPi
RX7 Rotary	RE13B	1986 to 1990	EGI MPi
Xedos 6 1.6i DOHC 16V 78kW	B6	1994 to 1996	EGI MPi
Xedos 6 2.0 DOHC 24V 107kW	KF	1992 to 1996	EGI MPi VRIS
Xedos 9 2.0i DOHC 24V V6 105kW	KF	1994 to 1995	EGI MPi
Xedos 9 2.5i DOHC 24V V6 125kW	KL	1994 to 1996	EGI MPi
Nissan			
4WD pick-up 2.4i cat	Z24I	1990 to 1994	ECCS SPi
4WD Wagon 3.0i cat	VG30E	1990 to 1994	ECCS MPi
100NX 2.0 cat SOHC 16V 105 kW	SR20DE	1991 to 1994	ECCS MPi
200 SX cat DOHC 16V Turbo	CA18DET	1989 to 1994	ECCS MPi
200 SX DOHC 16V Turbo	SR20DET	1994 to 1996	ECCS MPi
300 CX	VG30E	1984 to 1991	ECCS MPi
300 ZX	VG30E	1984 to 1990	ECCS MPi
300 ZX Turbo	VG30ET	1984 to 1990	ECCS MPi
300 ZX Turbo cat DOHC 2x turbo	VG30DETT	1990 to 1995	ECCS MPi
Bluebird ZX Turbo SOHC	CA 18T	1986 to 1990	ECCS MPi
Bluebird 2.0i SOHC	CA 20E	1988 to 1990	ECCS
Micra 1.0i cat DOHC 16V 40kW	CG10DE	1993 to 1996	ECCS MPi
Micra 1.3i cat DOHC 16V 55kW	CG13DE	1993 to 1996	ECCS MPi
Maxima	VG30E	1989 to 1994	ECCS MPi
Maxima cat	VG30E	1989 to 1994	ECCS MPi
Prairie 2.0i cat SOHC	CA20E	1989 to 1991	ECCS
Primera 1.6i	GA16DE	1994 to 1996	ECCS
Primera 2.0 SPi	SR20Di	1991 to 1995	ECCS
Primera 2.0 cat DOHC 16V	SR20Di	1990 to 1995	ECCS SPi with Hot wire
Primera Estate 2.0 cat DOHC 16V	SR20Di	1990 to 1996	ECCS SPi with Hot wire
Primera 2.0e ZX DOHC 16V	SR20DE	1991 to 1995	ECCS MPi with Hot wire
Primera 2.0e GT	SR20DE	1991 to 1995	ECCS MPi with Hot wire
Primera 2.0e cat	SR20DE	1991 to 1995	ECCS MPi with Hot wire
Primera 2.0i DOHC 16V	SR20DE	1994 to 1996	ECCS SPi
Primera 2.0i GT DOHC 16V	SR20DE	1994 to 1996	ECCS SPi
QX 2.0 DOHC 24V V6	VQ20DE	1994 to 1996	ECCS MPi
QX 3.0 DOHC 24V V6	VQ30DE	1994 to 1996	ECCS MPi
Serena 1.6i DOHC 16V 71kW	GA16DE	1993 to 1996	ECCS MPi
Serena 2.0i DOHC 16V 93kW	SR20DE	1993 to 1996	ECCS MPi
Silvia Turbo ZX	CA18ET	1984 to 1990	ECCS MPi
Sunny 1.6i cat SOHC 12V	GA16I	1989 to 1991	ECCS SPi
Sunny ZX Coupe DOHC 16V	CA16DE	1987 to 1989	ECCS SPi
Sunny 1.8 ZX cat DOHC 16V	CA18DE	1989 to 1991	ECCS SPi
Sunny GTi-R DOHC 16V 164kW	SR20DET	1991 to 1994	ECCS MPi
Sunny 2.0 GTi cat DOHC 16V 105kW	SR20DE	1991 to 1994	ECCS MPi

Model	Engine code	Year	System
Nissan (continued)			
Sunny 2.0 DOHC 16V Turbo	SR20DET	1994 to 1996	ECCS MPi
Patrol 4.2i OHV 128kW	TB42E	1992 to 1996	ECCS MPi
Urvan 2.4i cat	Z24I	1989 to 1994	ECCS SPi
Vanette 2.4i cat OHV 52 kW	Z24I	1987 to 1994	ECCS SPi
Opel			
Corsa 1.2i cat	C12NZ	1990 to 1994	GM-Multec CFi
Corsa 1.4i cat	C14NZ	1990 to 1993	GM-Multec CFi
Corsa 1.6i cat	C16NZ	1990 to 1992	GM-Multec CFi
Corsa 1.4i cat	C14SE	1992 to 1993	GM-Multec MPi
Corsa 1.6i cat	C16SE	1992 to 1993	GM-Multec MPi
Corsa 1.2i cat	X12SZ	1993 to 1996	GM-Multec CFi
Corsa 1.4i cat	C14SE	1993 to 1994	GM-Multec MPi
Corsa 1.6i cat	C16SE	1993 to 1994	GM-Multec MPi
Kadett-E 1.4i cat	C14NZ	1990 to 1993	GM-Multec CFi
Kadett-E 1.6 cat	C16NZ	1990 to 1993	GM-Multec CFi
Kadett-E 1.8i cat	C18NZ	1990 to 1991	GM-Multec CFi
Kadett 2.0i	20NE	1987 to 1990	Motronic ML4.1
Kadett 2.0i	20SEH	1987 to 1990	Motronic ML4.1
Kadett GSi 8V 2.0i SOHC	20SEH	1990 to 1993	Motronic 1.5
Kadett 2.0i Cat SOHC	C20NE	1990 to 1993	Motronic 1.5
Kadett 2.0i 16V DOHC	C20XEJ	1990 to 1991	Motronic 2.5
Kadett 2.0i 16V DOHC Cat	C20XE	1990 to 1992	Motronic 2.5
Peugeot			
106 1.0 cat	TU9ML/Z (CDY)	1993 to 1996	Mono-Motronic MA3.0
106 1.0 cat	TU9ML/Z (CDZ)	1993 to 1996	Mono-Motronic MA3.0
106 1.1i cat	TU1ML/Z (HDY)	1993 to 1996	Magneti Marelli FDG6
106 1.1i cat	TU1ML/Z (HDZ)	1993 to 1996	Magneti Marelli FDG6
106 1.4i 8V SOHC Rallye cat	TU2J2L/Z (MFZ)	1993 to 1996	Magneti Marelli 8P
106 1.4i	TU3J2K (K6B)	1991 to 1992	Motronic MP3.1
106 1.4i cat	TU3J2L/Z (KFZ)	1991 to 1996	Motronic MP3.1
106 1.4i cat	TU3MCL/Z (KDX)	1993 to 1996	Mono-Motronic MA3.0
106 1.6	TU5JPL/Z (NFZ)	1994 to 1996	MP5.1
106 1.6 MPi	TU5J2L/Z/K (NFY)	1994 to 1996	Magneti Marelli 8P
205 1.1i cat	TU1ML/Z (HDZ)	1992 to 1996	Magneti Marelli FDG6
205 1.4i	TU3FM/L (KDY2)	1994 to 1996	Mono-Motronic MA3.0
205 1.6i cat	XU5M2L/Z (BDY)	1990 to 1991	Magneti Marelli BAG5
205 1.6i & AT cat	XU5M3L/Z (BDY)	1992 to 1996	Magneti Marelli FDG6
205 GTi 1.9 8V cat	XU9JAZ (DKZ)	1989 to 1993	Motronic 1.3
306 1.1i	TU1ML/Z (HDY)	1993 to 1996	Magneti Marelli FDG6
306 1.1i	TU1ML/Z (HDZ)	1993 to 1996	Magneti Marelli FDG6
306 1.1i	TU1ML/Z (HDY)	1993 to 1996	Mono-Motronic MA3.0
306 1.1i	TU1ML/Z (HDZ)	1993 to 1996	Mono-Motronic MA3.0
306 1.4i cat	TU3MCL/Z (KDX)	1993 to 1995	Mono-Motronic MA3.0
306 1.4i cat	TU3MCL/Z (KDX)	1994 to 1996	Magneti Marelli FDG6
306 1.6i cat	TU5JPL/Z (NFZ)	1993 to 1996	Motronic MP5.1
306 1.8i cabrio & cat	XU7JPL/Z (LFZ)	1993 to 1996	Magneti Marelli 8P
306 2.0i cabrio & cat	XU10J2CL/Z (RFX)	1994 to 1996	Magneti Marelli 8P
306 2.0i 16V cat	XU10J4L/Z (RFY)	1994 to 1996	Motronic MP3.2
309 1.6i cat	XU5MZ (BDZ)	1989 to 1991	Magneti Marelli BAG5
309 1.6i cat	XU5M2L/Z (BDY)	1991 to 1992	Magneti Marelli G5
309 1.6i cat	XU5M3L/Z (BDY)	1992 to 1994	Magneti Marelli FDG6
309 1.9 8V	XU9JA/Z (DKZ)	1988 to 1992	Motronic 1.3
309 1.9 16V DOHC	XU9J4K (D6C)	1990 to 1991	Motronic 4.1
309 1.9 16V DOHC	XU9J4K (D6C)	1991 to 1992	Motronic 1.3
309 1.9 16V cat	XU9J4L/Z (DFW)	1990 to 1992	Motronic 1.3
405 1.4i cat	TU3MCL/Z (KDX)	1992 to 1994	Mono Motronic MA3.0
405 1.6i cat	XU5MZ (BDZ)	1989 to 1991	Magneti Marelli BAG5
405 1.6i cat	XU5M2L/Z (BDY)	1989 to 1991	Magneti Marelli FDG5
405 1.6i cat	XU5M3Z (BDY)	1991 to 1992	Magneti Marelli FDG6
405 1.6i cat	XU5M3L/Z (BDY)	1992 to 1993	Magneti Marelli FDG6
405 1.6i cat	XU5JPL/Z (BFZ)	1993 to 1995	Magneti Marelli DCM8P13
405 1.6i cat	XU5JPL/Z (BFZ)	1989 to 1992	Motronic 1.3
405 1.9 Mi16 & Mi16x4 16V	XU9J4K (D6C)	1988 to 1991	Motronic ML4.1

Model	Engine code	Year	System
Peugeot (continued)			
405 1.9 Mi16 & Mi16x4 16V	XU9J4K (D6C)	1990 to 1992	Motronic 1.3
405 1.9 Mi16 cat	XU9J4/Z (DFW)	1990 to 1992	Motronic 1.3
405 1.9i W/ distributor	XU9J2K (D6D)	1990 to 1991	Motronic MP3.1
405 1.9i DIS	XU9J2K (D6D)	1991 to 1992	Motronic MP3.1
405 2.0i & 4x4 8V cat	XU10J2CL/Z (RFX)	1992 to 1996	Magneti Marelli 8P MPi
405 2.0i 16V cat	XU10J4/Z (RFY)	1992 to 1995	Motronic MP3.2
405 2.0i 16V turbo cat	XU10J4TEL/Z (RGZ)	1993 to 1995	Magneti Marelli 8P MPi
406 1.8 16V	XU7JP4L	1995 to 1996	Motronic MP5.1.1
406 2.0 16V	XU10J4RL	1995 to 1996	Motronic MP5.1.1
605 2.0i cat	XU10ML/Z (RDZ)	1989 to 1994	Magneti Marelli G5
605 2.0i cat	XU10J2L/Z (RFZ)	1990 to 1995	Motronic MP3.1
605 2.0i 16V	XU10J4RL/Z/L3 (RFV)	1995 to 1996	Motronic MP5.1.1
605 2.0i turbo cat	XU10J2TEL/Z (RGY)	1993 to 1994	Motronic MP3.2
605 2.0i turbo	XU10J2CTEL/Z (RGX)	1995 to 1996	Motronic MP3.2
806 2.0	XU10J2CL/Z (RFU)	1995 to 1996	Magneti Marelli 8P-22
806 2.0 Turbo	XU10J2CTEL/Z (RGX)	1995 to 1996	Motronic MP3.2
Boxer 2.0	XU10J2U (RFW)	1994 to 1996	Magneti Marelli 8P11
Renault			
5 1.4 cat	C3J700 (B/C/F407)	1986 to 1990	Renix SPi
5 1.4 cat	C3J760 (B/C/F407)	1990 to 1996	Renix SPi
5 1.7i cat	F3NG716 (B/C408)	1987 to 1991	Renix SPi
5 1.7i cat	F3NG717 (B/C409)	1987 to 1991	Renix SPi
5 1.7 cat	F3N702 (C409)	1989 to 1992	Renix MPi
9 1.7 cat	F3N718 (L42F/BC37F)	1986 to 1989	Renix SPi
9 1.7 cat	F3N708 (L42E/C37E)	1986 to 1989	Renix MPi
11 1.7 cat	F3N718 (L42F/BC37F)	1986 to 1989	Renix SPi
11 1.7 cat	F3N708 (L42E/C37E)	1986 to 1989	Renix MPi
19 1.4i cat	C3J710 (B/C/L532)	1990 to 1992	Renix SPi
19 1.4i cat	C3J700	1991 to 1992	Renix SPi
19 1.4 cat	E7J700 (B/C/L53A)	1991 to 1995	Bosch SPi
19 1.7i cat	F3N740 B/C/L53B	1990 to 1992	Renix SPi
19 1.7i AT cat	F3N741 (B/C/L53B)	1990 to 1992	Renix SPi
19 1.7 DOHC 16V	F7P700 (B/C/L/D53D)	1991 to 1993	Renix MPi
19 1.7 DOHC 16V cat	F7P704 (B/C/L/D53D)	1991 to 1995	Renix MPi
19 1.7 DOHC 16V cat	F7P704 (X53D)	1991 to 1995	Renix MPi
19 1.7i cat	F3N746 (B/C/L53F)	1992 to 1993	Renix MPi
19 1.7i cat	F3N742 (B/C/L/X53C)	1990 to 1992	Renix MPi
19 1.7i AT cat	F3N743 (X53C)	1990 to 1992	Renix MPi
19 1.8 cat	F3P700 (X538)	1992 to 1996	Renix MPi
21 1.7i cat	F3N723 (X48F)	1991 to 1995	Renix SPi
21 1.7i cat	F3N722 (B/K/L/48E)	1991 to 1995	Renix MPi
21 1721 cat	F3N 726 (L42F/BC37F)	1986 to 1989	Renix SPi
21 2.0 12V & 4x4 cat	J7R740 (B/L/X48R)	1991 to 1995	Renix MPi
21 2.0 cat	J7R746 (B/K/L48C)	1991 to 1995	Renix MPi
21 2.0 AT cat	J7R747 (B/K/L48C)	1991 to 1995	Renix MPi
21 2.0 & 4x4	J7R750 (B/L/K483)	1986 to 1993	Renix MPi
21 2.0 & AT 4x4	J7R751 (K483)	1986 to 1993	Renix MPi
21 2.0 TXi 12 valve	J7RG754(X48Q/Y/R)	1989 to 1994	Renix MPi
21 2.0 turbo & 4x4 cat	J7R756 (L48L)	1991 to 1994	Renix MPi
21 2.0 turbo	J7R752 (L485)	1988 to 1992	Renix MPi
21 2.0 turbo 4x4	J7R752 (L485)	1991 to 1992	Renix MPi
21 2.2 cat	J7T754 (B/K/L48K)	1992 to 1995	Renix MPi
21 2.2 AT cat	J7T755 (B/K/L48K)	1992 to 1995	Renix MPi
25 2.0	J7R722 (B29H)	1986 to 1992	Renix MPi
25 2.0 AT	J7R723 (B29H)	1986 to 1992	Renix MPi
25 2.0 TXi 12V	J7RG720 (B292)	1989 to 1992	Renix MPi
25 2.0 TXi AT 12V	J7RG721 (B292)	1989 to 1993	Renix MPi
25 2.0 TXi 12V cat	J7R726 (B294)	1991 to 1993	Renix MPi
25 2.2	J7TE706 (B29E)	1984 to 1987	Renix MPi
25 2.2 AT	J7TG707 (B29E)	1984 to 1987	Renix MPi
25 2.2	J7TJ730 (B29E)	1987 to 1990	Renix MPi
25 2.2 AT	J7TK731 (B29E)	1987 to 1990	Renix MPi
25 2.2 cat	J7T732 (B29B)	1990 to 1991	Renix MPi
25 2.2 AT cat	J7T733 (B29B)	1990 to 1991	Renix MPi

Model	Engine code	Year	System
Renault (continued)			
25 2.5 V6 turbo	Z7UA702 (B295)	1985 to 1990	Renix MPi
25 2.5 V6 turbo cat	Z7U700 (B29G)	1991 to 1993	Renix MPi
25 V6 2.9i	Z7WA700 (B293)	1989 to 1993	Renix MPi
25 V6 2.9i AT	Z7W701 (B293)	1989 to 1992	Renix MPi
25 V6 2.9i AT	Z7W709 (B293)	1992 to 1993	Renix MPi
25 V6 2.9i cat	Z7W706 (B29F)	1991 to 1992	Renix MPi
25 V6 2.9i AT cat	Z7W707 (B29F)	1991 to 1992	Renix MPi
Alpine 2.5 GTA V6 turbo	Z7UC730 (D501)	1986 to 1992	Renix MPi
Alpine 2.5 GTA V6 turbo cat	Z7U734 (D502)	1990 to 1992	Renix MPi
Alpine 2.5 V6 turbo cat	Z7X744 (D503)	1992 to 1995	Renix MPi
Chamade 1.4i cat	(B/C/L532)C31710	1990 to 1992	Renix SPi
Chamade 1.4i cat	C3J700	1991 to 1992	Renix SPi
Chamade 1.7i cat	F3N742 (X53C)	1990 to 1992	Renix MPi
Chamade 1.7i AT cat	F3N743 (X53C)	1990 to 1992	Renix MPi
Chamade 19 1.7i cat	F3N740	1990 to 1992	Renix SPi
Chamade 19 1.7i AT cat	F3N741 (B/C/L53B)	1990 to 1992	Renix SPi
Chamade 1.8 cat	F3P700	1992 to 1994	Renix MPi
Clio 1.8 cat	F3P712 (C579)	1993 to 1996	Renix MPi
Clio 1.8 16V DOHC	F7P720 (C575)	1991 to 1992	Renix MPi
Clio 1.8 16V DOHC cat	F7P722 (C57D)	1991 to 1996	Renix MPi
Clio Williams 2.0 cat	F7P	1993 to 1995	Renix MPi
Espace 2.0i TXE & 4x4	J7RE760 (J116)	1988 to 1991	Renix MPi
Espace 2.0i cat	J7R768 (J636)	1991 to 1996	Renix MPi
Espace 2.2i TXE&4x4 cat	J7T770 (J117)	1991 to 1992	Renix MPi
Espace 2.2i & 4x4 cat	J7T772 (J/S637)	1991 to 1995	Renix MPi
Espace 2.9i V6 & 4X4 cat	Z7W712 (J638)	1991 to 1995	Renix MPi
Espace 2.9i V6 & 4X4 cat	Z7W713 (J638)	1991 to 1995	Renix MPi
Extra 1.4 cat	C3J760 (B/C/F407)	1990 to 1995	Renix SPi
Extra 1.4 cat	C3J762 (F407)	1992 to 1995	Renix SPi
Express 1.4 cat	C3J762 (F407)	1992 to 1995	Renix SPi
Laguna 2.0i	F3R722	1994 to 1995	Renix MPi
Master 2.2i cat	J7T782 (RxxA)	1991 to 1993	Renix MPi
Safrane 2.0i cat	J7R732 (B540)	1993 to 1996	Renix MPi
Safrane 2.0i AT cat	J7R733 (B540)	1993 to 1995	Renix MPi
Safrane 2.0i 12V cat	J7R734 (B542)	1993 to 1994	Renix MPi
Safrane 2.0i 12V cat	J7R735 (B542)	1993 to 1994	Renix MPi
Safrane 2.2i 12V cat	J7T760 (B543)	1993 to 1995	Renix MPi
Safrane 2.2i 12V AT cat	J7T761 (B543)	1993 to 1995	Renix MPi
Safrane 3.0i V6 cat	Z7X722 (B544)	1993 to 1995	Renix MPi
Safrane 3.0i V6 AT cat	Z7X723 (B544)	1993 to 1995	Renix MPi
Safrane Quadra 3.0i V6 cat	Z7X722 (B544)	1992 to 1994	Renix MPi
Savanna 1.7i cat	F3N722 (X48E)	1991 to 1995	Renix MPi
Savanna 1.7i cat	F3N723 (X48F)	1991 to 1995	Renix SPi
Savanna 2.0 & 4x4	J7R750 (K483)	1986 to 1993	Renix MPi
Savanna 2.0 & 4x4 AT	J7R751 (K483)	1986 to 1993	Renix MPi
Trafic 2.2i & 4x4 cat	J7T 780 (T/VxxA)	1991 to 1993	Renix MPi
Rover			
111 1.1 SOHC	K8	1995 to 1996	Rover MEMS SPi
114 1.4 SOHC	K8	1995 to 1996	Rover MEMS SPi
114 1.4 GTi cat	K8	1991 to 1994	Rover MEMS MPi
214 1.4 DOHC 16V	K16	1989 to 1992	Rover MEMS SPi
214 1.4 DOHC 16V cat	K16	1990 to 1993	Rover MEMS SPi
214 1.4 DOHC 16V cat	K16	1992 to 1996	Rover MEMS MPi
216 SOHC 16V	D16A7	1989 to 1996	Honda PGM-Fi
216 SOHC 16V cat	D16A6	1989 to 1996	Honda PGM-Fi
216 SOHC 16V AT cat	D16Z2	1989 to 1996	Honda PGM-Fi
216 DOHC 16V	D16A9	1990 to 1994	Honda PGM-Fi
216 DOHC 16V AT	D16Z4	1990 to 1994	Honda PGM-Fi
216 DOHC 16V cat	D16A8	1990 to 1994	Honda PGM-Fi
220 2.0 DOHC 16V cat	20M4 M16	1991 to 1994	Rover MEMS MPi
220 2.0 DOHC 16V turbo cat	20T4 T16	1992 to 1996	Rover MEMS MPi
220 2.0 DOHC 16V cat	20T4 T16	1992 to 1996	Rover MEMS MPi
414 1.4 DOHC 16V	K16	1990 to 1993	Rover MEMS SPi
414 1.4 DOHC 16V cat	K16	1990 to 1993	Rover MEMS SPi

Model	Engine code	Year	System
Rover (continued)			
414 1.4 DOHC 16V cat	K16	1992 to 1996	Rover MEMS MPi
414 1.4 DOHC 16V	K16	1995 to 1996	Rover MEMS MPi
416 SOHC 16V	D16A7	1989 to 1996	Honda PGM-Fi
416 SOHC 16V cat	D16A6	1989 to 1996	Honda PGM-Fi
416 SOHC 16V AT cat	D16Z2	1989 to 1996	Honda PGM-Fi
416 DOHC 16V	D16A9	1990 to 1994	Honda PGM-Fi
416 DOHC 16V AT	D16Z4	1990 to 1994	Honda PGM-Fi
416 DOHC 16V cat	D16A8	1990 to 1994	Honda PGM-Fi
416i 1.6 auto SOHC 16V	D16	1995 to 1996	Honda PGM-Fi
416 1.6 DOHC 16V	K16	1995 to 1996	Rover MEMS MPi
420 2.0 DOHC 16V cat	20M4 M16	1991 to 1994	Rover MEMS MPi
420 2.0 DOHC 16V turbo cat	20T4 T16	1992 to 1996	Rover MEMS MPi
420 2.0 DOHC 16V cat	20T4 T16	1992 to 1996	Rover MEMS MPi
618 SOHC 16V	F18A3	1995 to 1996	Honda PGM-Fi
620i SOHC 16V	F20Z2	1993 to 1996	Honda PGM-Fi
620i S SOHC 16V	F20Z1	1993 to 1996	Honda PGM-Fi
620 2.0 DOHC 16V turbo	20T4 T16	1994 to 1996	Rover MEMS MPi
623i DOHC 16V	H23A3	1993 to 1996	Honda PGM-Fi
820E SPi DOHC	20HD/M16e	1986 to 1990	Rover SPi
820SE SPi DOHC	20HD/M16e	1986 to 1990	Rover SPi
820i 2.0 DOHC 16V cat	20T4	1991 to 1996	Rover MEMS MPi
820 2.0 DOHC 16V turbo cat	20T4	1992 to 1996	Rover MEMS MPi
825i V6 SOHC 24V	V6 2.5	1986 to 1988	Honda PGM-Fi
827i V6 SOHC 24V	V6 2.7	1988 to 1991	Honda PGM-Fi
827i V6 SOHC 24V cat	V6 2.7	1988 to 1991	Honda PGM-Fi
827i V6 SOHC 24V cat	V6 2.7	1991 to 1996	Honda PGM-Fi
Metro 1.1i SOHC cat	K8	1991 to 1994	Rover MEMS SPi
Metro 1.4i SOHC	K8	1991 to 1992	Rover MEMS SPi
Metro 1.4i SOHC cat	K8	1991 to 1994	Rover MEMS SPi
Metro 1.4i GTi DOHC 16V cat	K16	1991 to 1992	Rover MEMS SPi
Metro 1.4 GTi DOHC 16V	K16	1990 to 1992	Rover MEMS SPi
Metro 1.4 GTi DOHC 16V cat	K16	1991 to 1994	Rover MEMS MPi
MGF 1.8 DOHC 16V	K16	1995 to 1996	Rover MEMS 1.9 MPi
MGF 1.8 VVC DOHC 16V	K16	1995 to 1996	Rover MEMS 2J SFi
Mini Cooper 1.3i	12A2DF75	1991 to 1996	Rover MEMS SPi
Mini Cooper 1.3i AT	12A2DF76	1991 to 1996	Rover MEMS SPi
Mini Cooper 1.3i cabriolet	12A2EF77	1993 to 1994	Rover MEMS SPi
Montego 2.0 EFi	20HE36	1989 to 1992	Rover MEMS MPi
Montego 2.0 EFi AT	20HE37	1989 to 1992	Rover MEMS MPi
Sterling V6 SOHC 24V	V6 2.5	1986 to 1988	Honda PGM-Fi
Toyota			
Camry cat 5S-FE (SXV10)	5S-FE	1992 to 1997	TCCS
Camry 2.0i OHC	3S-FE	1987 to 1991	TCCS
Camry 2.0i OHC 4WD	3S-FE	1988 to 1989	TCCS
Camry 2.0i OHC	3S-FE	1987 to 1991	TCCS
Camry 2.0i OHC 4WD	3S-FE	1988 to 1989	TCCS
Camry 2.2i 16V DOHC cat	5S-FE	1991 to 1996	TCCS
Camry 2.5i V6 OHC cat	2VZ-FE	1989 to 1991	TCCS
Camry 3.0i V6 24V DOHC cat	3VZ-FE	1991 to 1995	TCCS
Carina E 1.6i 16V DOHC	4A-FE	1992 to 1996	TCCS
Carina E 1.6i 16V DOHC cat	4A-FE	1992 to 1996	TCCS
Carina II 2.0i OHC	3S-FE	1988 to 1992	TCCS
Carina II 2.0i OHC cat	3S-FE	1988 to 1992	TCCS
Carina E 2.0i DOHC cat	3S-FE	1992 to 1995	TCCS
Carina E 2.0 16V DOHC cat	3S-GE	1992 to 1995	TCCS
Celica 2.0 16V DOHC	3S-GE	1990 to 1994	TCCS
Celica 2.0 16V DOHC cat	3S-GE	1990 to 1994	TCCS
Celica 2.0 16V DOHC	3S-GEL	1985 to 1990	TCCS
Celica 2.0 GT-4 turbo 16V DOHC cat	3S-GTE	1988 to 1990	TCCS
Celica 2.0 GT-4 turbo 16V DOHC cat	3S-GTE	1990 to 1993	TCCS
Celica 2.2i 16V DOHC cat	5S-FE	1991 to 1994	TCCS
Corolla /Starlet 1.3i OHC cat	2E-E	1990 to 1992	TCCS
Corolla 1.3i 16V DOHC cat	4E-FE	1992 to 1995	TCCS
Corolla 1.6 GT OHC	4A-GEL	1985 to 1987	TCCS

Model	Engine code	Year	System
Toyota (continued)			
Corolla 1.6 GT coupe OHC	4A-GE	1984 to 1987	TCCS
Corolla 1.6 GTi OHC	4A-GE	1987 to 1989	TCCS
Corolla 1.6 GTi OHC cat	4A-GE	1989 to 1992	TCCS
Corolla 1.6 GTi OHC cat	4A-GE	1987 to 1989	TCCS
Corolla 1.6 GTi OHC cat	4A-GE	1989 to 1992	TCCS
Corolla 1.6i & 4x4 OHC cat	4A-FE	1989 to 1992	TCCS
Corolla 1.6i 16V DOHC cat	4A-FE	1992 to 1996	TCCS
Corolla 1.6 GTi OHC	4A-GE	1987 to 1989	TCCS
Corolla 1.6 GTi OHC	4A-GE	1989 to 1992	TCCS
Corolla 1.6 GTi OHC cat	4A-GE	1987 to 1989	TCCS
Corolla 1.6 GTi OHC cat	4A-GE	1989 to 1992	TCCS
Corolla 1.6i & 4x4 OHC cat	4A-FE	1989 to 1992	TCCS
Corolla 1.8i 16V DOHC cat	7A-FE	1993 to 1995	TCCS
Hi-Ace 2.4i OHC	2RZ-E	1989 to 1994	TCCS
Hi-Ace 2.4i 4x4 OHC	2RZ-E	1989 to 1994	TCCS
MR2 1.6 OHC	4A-GEL	1984 to 1990	TCCS
MR2 2.0 16V DOHC GT cat	3S-GE	1990 to 1995	TCCS
MR2 2.0 16V DOHC cat	3S-FE	1990 to 1994	TCCS
Previa 2.4i 16V DOHC cat	2TZ-FE	1990 to 1996	TCCS
Supra 3.0i 24V DOHC	7M-GE	1986 to 1993	TCCS
Supra 3.0i 24V DOHC cat	7M-GE	1986 to 1993	TCCS
Supra 3.0i turbo DOHC DIS cat	7M-GTE	1989 to 1993	TCCS
Tarago 2.4i 16V DOHC cat	2TZ-FE	1990 to 1995	TCCS
4 Runner 3.0i 4wd V6 SOHC cat	3VZ-E	1991 to 1995	TCCS
Vauxhall			
Astra-F 1.4i	X14NZ	1997	GM-Multec CFi
Astra-F 1.4i	X14XE	1996 to 1997	GM-Multec CFi
Astra-F 1.4i cat	C14NZ	1990 to 1996	GM-Multec CFi
Astra-F 1.6 cat	C16NZ	1990 to 1995	GM-Multec CFi
Astra-F 1.8i cat	C18NZ	1991 to 1994	GM-Multec CFi
Astra Van 1.6i cat	C16NZ	1991 to 1994	GM-Multec CFi
Astra-F 1.4i cat	C14SE	1991 to 1996	GM-Multec MPi
Astra-F 1.6i cat	C16SE	1992 to 1995	GM-Multec MPi
Astra-F 1.4i cat	C14SE	1993 to 1994	GM-Multec MPi
Astra-F 1.6i	X16SZ	1993 to 1996	GM-Multec CFi
Astra-F 1.6i cat	C16SE	1993 to 1994	GM-Multec MPi
Astra-F 1.6i	X16SZR	1996 to 1997	GM-Multec CFi
Astra 1.6i cat	C16SE	1991 to 1992	Motronic 1.5
Astra 1.8i	18SE	1987 to 1991	Bosch L3 and EZ61
Astra GTE 2.0	20NE	1987 to 1990	Motronic ML4.1
Astra GTE 2.0	20SEH	1987 to 1990	Motronic ML4.1
Astra 2.0i	20SEH	1990 to 1993	Motronic 1.5
Astra 2.0i Cat	C20NE	1991 to 1995	Motronic 1.5
Astra 2.0i 16V DOHC	20XEJ	1988 to 1991	Motronic 2.5
Astra-F 2.0i 16V DOHC		1993 to 1996	Motronic 2.5
Astra-F 2.0i cat SOHC 85kW	C20NE	1991 to 1995	Motronic 1.5.2
Belmont 1.4i cat	C14NZ	1990 to 1993	GM-Multec CFi
Belmont 1.6i	C16NZ	1987 to 1993	GM-Multec CFi
Belmont 1.8i cat	C18NZ	1990 to 1992	GM-Multec CFi
Brava cat 2.3	4ZD1	1995 to 1996	GM-Multec MPi
Calibra 2.0i SOHC & 4x4 Cat	C20NE	1990 to 1996	Motronic 1.5.4
Calibra 2.0i 16V 4x4 DOHC Cat	C20XE	1990 to 1993	Motronic 2.5
Calibra 2.0 16V & 4x4 DOHC cat	C20XE	1993 to 1996	Motronic 2.8
Calibra Turbo 4x4 16V 150kW	C20LET	1992 to 1996	Motronic 2.7
Calibra 2.5i 24V	C25XE	1993 to 1996	Motronic 2.8
Calibra 2.5i 24V	X25XE	1997 to 1997	Motronic 2.8
Carlton 2.0i	20SE	1987 to 1990	Motronic ML4.1
Carlton 2.0i SOHC	20SE	1990 to 1994	Motronic 1.5
Carlton 2.0i Cat SOHC	C20NEJ	1990 to 1993	Motronic 1.5
Carlton 2.4i Cat CIH	C24NE	1990 to 1993	Motronic 1.5
Carlton 2.6i Cat CIH	C26NE	1990 to 1994	Motronic 1.5
Carlton 3.0i Cat CIH	C30NE	1990 to 1994	Motronic 1.5
Carlton 24V Cat DOHC 24V	C30SE	1989 to 1994	Motronic 1.5
Carlton 24V Cat Estate DOHC 24V	C30SEJ	1990 to 1994	Motronic 1.5

Model	Engine code	Year	System
Vauxhall (continued)			
Campo 2.3 cat	4ZD1	1995 to 1996	GM-Multec MPi
Cavalier 2.0	20NE	1987 to 1990	Motronic ML4.1
Cavalier 2.0	20SEH	1987 to 1990	Motronic ML4.1
Cavalier SRi 130	20SEH	1987 to 1988	Motronic ML4.1
Cavalier 2.0i SOHC	20NE	1990 to 1993	Motronic 1.5
Cavalier 2.0i 4x4 SOHC	20SEH	1990 to 1993	Motronic 1.5
Cavalier 1.6i	C16NZ/NZ2	1995 to 1996	GM-Multec CFi
Cavalier 2.0i Cat SOHC	C20NE	1990 to 1993	Motronic 1.5
Cavalier 2.0i 16V DOHC	20XEJ	1989 to 1991	Motronic 2.5
Cavalier 2.0 16V	C20XE	1989 to 1995	Motronic 2.5
Cavalier 1.6i cat	C16NZ	1990 to 1993	GM-Multec CFi
Cavalier 1.6i cat	C16NZ2	1993 to 1994	GM-Multec CFi
Cavalier 1.6	X16SZ	1993 to 1995	GM-Multec CFi
Cavalier 1.6i	C16NZ/NZ2	1995 to 1987	GM-Multec CFi
Cavalier 1.8i cat	C18NZ	1990 to 1995	GM-Multec CFi
Corsa-B & Combo 1.2i	C12NZ	1993 to 1996	GM-Multec CFi
Corsa-B & Combo 1.4i	X14SZ	1996 to 1997	GM-Multec CFi
Corsa-B 1.4i & Van	C14NZ	1993 to 1996	GM-Multec CFi
Corsa-B 1.6 Gsi	C16XE	1993 to 1995	GM-Multec MPi
Frontera 2.0i Cat SOHC	C20NE	1991 to 1995	Motronic 1.5
Frontera 2.4i Cat CIH	C24NE	1991 to 1995	Motronic 1.5
Frontera 2.0i	X20XE	1995 to 1996	Motronic 1.5
Frontera 2.0i 8V 85kW	X20SE	1995 to 1997	Motronic 1.5.4
Frontera 2.2i	X22XE	1995 to 1996	Motronic 1.5.4
Nova 1.2i cat	C12NZ	1990 to 1994	GM-Multec CFi
Nova 1.4i cat	C14NZ	1990 to 1993	GM-Multec CFi
Nova 1.6i cat	C16NZ	1990 to 1992	GM-Multec CFi
Nova 1.4i cat	C14SE	1992 to 1993	GM-Multec MPi
Nova 1.6i cat	C16SE	1992 to 1993	GM-Multec MPi
Nova 1.6i cat	C16SE	1993 to 1994	GM-Multec MPi
Nova 1.6 MPI cat	C16SEI	1990 to 1992	Motronic 1.5
Omega 2.0i	20SE	1987 to 1990	Motronic ML4.1
Omega 2.0i SOHC	20SE	1990 to 1993	Motronic 1.5
Omega 2.0i SOHC Cat	C20NE	1990 to 1993	Motronic 1.5
Omega 2.0i SOHC Cat	C20NEJ	1990 to 1993	Motronic 1.5
Omega-B 2.0i 8V 85kW	X20SE	1994 to 1997	Motronic 1.5.4
Omega 2.4i CIH Cat	C24NE	1990 to 1993	Motronic 1.5
Omega 2.5i	X25XE	1994 to 1996	Motronic 2.8
Omega-B 2.5i 24V 125kW	X25XE	1994 to 1997	Motronic 2.8.1
Omega 2.6i CIH Cat	C26NE	1990 to 1993	Motronic 1.5
Omega 3.0i	X30XE	1994 to 1996	Motronic 2.8.1
Omega 3.0i CIH Cat	C30NE	1990 to 1994	Motronic 1.5
Omega 24V DOHC Cat	C30SE	1989 to 1994	Motronic 1.5
Omega 24V DOHC Estate Cat	C30SEJ	1990 to 1994	Motronic 1.5
Senator 2.6i CIH Cat	C26NE	1990 to 1993	Motronic 1.5
Senator 3.0i CIH Cat	C30NE	1990 to 1994	Motronic 1.5
Senator 24V DOHC Cat	C30SE	1989 to 1994	Motronic 1.5
Senator 24V Estate DOHC Cat	C30SEJ	1990 to 1992	Motronic 1.5
Tigra 1.4i 16V	X14XE	1994 to 1996	GM-Multec MPi
Tigra 1.6i	X16XE	1994 to 1997	GM-Multec MPi
Vectra 1.6i cat	C16NZ	1990 to 1993	GM-Multec CFi
Vectra 1.6i cat	C16NZ2	1993 to 1994	GM-Multec CFi
Vectra-A 1.6i	C16NZ/NZ2	1993 to 1995	GM-Multec CFi
Vectra-A 1.6i	X16SZ	1993 to 1995	GM-Multec CFi
Vectra 1.8i cat	C18NZ	1990 to 1994	GM-Multec CFi
Vectra 2.0i	20SEH	1987 to 1990	Motronic ML4.1
Vectra 2.0i Cat	C20NE	1991 to 1992	Motronic 1.5
Vectra 2.0 SOHC	20NE	1990 to 1993	Motronic 1.5
Vectra 2.0i & 4x4 SOHC	20SEH	1990 to 1993	Motronic 1.5
Vectra 2.0i SOHC Cat	C20NE	1990 to 1993	Motronic 1.5
Vectra GSi 2000	16V DOHC	1989 to 1991	Motronic 2.5
Vectra 2.0 16V 4x4 DOHC cat	C20XE	1989 to 1992	Motronic 2.5
Vectra-B 2.5i V6 24V	X25XE	1995 to 1997	Motronic 2.8.3

Model	Engine code	Year	System
Volkswagon			
Caravelle 2.0i & cat	AAC	1990 to 1996	VW Digifant 38 pin
Caravelle 2.0i cat	AAC	1994 to 1995	VW Digifant 45 pin
Caravelle 2.5i cat	AAF	1991 to 1995	VW Digifant 38 pin
Corrado 1.8i G60 supercharger cat	PG	1988 to 1992	Digifant 25 pin
Corrado 1.8i G60 supercharger cat	PG	1992 to 1993	Digifant 38 pin
Corrado 2.0i cat	2E	1993 to 1995	Digifant 45 pin
Corrado VR6 SOHC 12V 140kW	ABV	1992 to 1996	Motronic 2.9
Golf 1.3i cat	AAV	1991 to 1992	Mono-Motronic
Golf 1.4i cat	ABD	1991 to 1995	Mono-Motronic 1.2.3
Golf 1.4i	AEX	1995 to 1996	Mono-Motronic
Golf 1.6i cat	ABU	1992 to 1995	Mono-Motronic 1.2.3
Golf 1.6i cat	AEA	1994 to 1995	Mono-Motronic 1.3
Golf 1.6i	AEK	1994 to 1996	Mono-Motronic
Golf 1.8i cat	AAM	1992 to 1996	Mono-Motronic 1.2.3
Golf 1.8i cat	ABS	1992 to 1994	Mono-Motronic
Golf 1.8i & 4x4	ADZ	1994 to 1996	Mono-Motronic
Golf 1.8i	PB	1987 to 1992	Digifant 25 pin
Golf 1.8i cat	PB	1989 to 1992	Digifant 25 pin
Golf 1.8i cat	1P	1988 to 1989	Digifant 25 pin
Golf 1.8i cat	1P	1989 to 1992	Digifant 25 pin
Golf 1.8i cat	PF	1987 to 1992	Digifant 25 pin
Golf 1.8i cat	PF	1989 to 1992	Digifant 25 pin
Golf 1.8i Cabrio cat	2H	1990 to 1993	Digifant 25 pin
Golf 2.0i cat	2E	1991 to 1995	Digifant 45 pin
Golf 2.0i 16V cat	ABF	1992 to 1996	Digifant 68 pin
Golf GTi G60 supercharger cat	PG	1990 to 1992	Digifant 25 pin
Golf Rallye G60 supercharger cat	1H	1989 to 1992	Digifant 25 pin
Golf Syncro 2.9 140kW	ABV	1994 to 1997	Motronic 2.9
Golf VR6	AAA	1992 to 1996	Motronic 2.7/2.9
Jetta 1.8i	PB	1987 to 1992	Digifant 25 pin
Jetta 1.8i cat	PB	1989 to 1992	Digifant 25 pin
Jetta 1.8i cat	1P	1988 to 1989	Digifant 25 pin
Jetta 1.8i cat	1P	1988 to 1992	Digifant 25 pin
Jetta 1.8i cat	1P	1989 to 1992	Digifant 25 pin
Jetta 1.8i cat	PF	1987 to 1992	Digifant 25 pin
Jetta 1.8i cat	PF	1989 to 1990	Digifant 25 pin
Jetta 1.8i cat	PF	1990 to 1992	Digifant 25 pin
LT Van 2.4i cat	1E	1988 to 1996	Digifant 25 pin
Passat 1.6i SOHC 8V	AEK	1994 to 1996	Motronic 2.9
Passat 1.8i	RP	1990 to 1991	Mono-Motronic 1.2.1
Passat 1.8i & cat	RP	1990 to 1991	Mono-Motronic 1.2.1
Passat 1.8i cat	AAM	1990 to 1995	Mono-Motronic 1.2.1
Passat 1.8i	ABS	1991 to 1994	Mono-Motronic 1.2.1
Passat 1.8i cat	ABS	1992 to 1995	Mono-Motronic 1.2.3
Passat 1.8i GT	PB	1988 to 1990	Digifant 25 pin
Passat 1.8i cat	PF	1988 to 1992	Digifant 25 pin
Passat 1.8i cat	ADZ	1994 to 1995	Mono-Motronic MA1.7
Passat 1.8i G60 supercharger cat	PG	1988 to 1993	Digifant 25 pin
Passat 2.0i & 4x4 cat	2E	1990 to 1994	Digifant 38 pin
Passat 2.0i cat	ABF	1994 to 1995	Digifant 68 pin
Passat VR6	AAA	1991 to 1993	Motronic 2.7/ 2.9
Passat 2.8 VR6	AAA	1993 to 1996	Motronic 2.7/ 2.9
Passat 2.9 Syncro VR6 128kW	ABV	1994 to 1996	Motronic 2.9
Polo 1.0i cat	AEV	1994 to 1996	Mono-Motronic 1.2.3
Polo 1.05i cat	AAU	1990 to 1994	Mono-Motronic 1.2.1
Polo 1.3i cat	AAV	1993 to 1994	Mono-Motronic 1.2.3
Polo 1.3i cat	ADX	1994 to 1995	Mono-Motronic 1.3
Polo 1.6i cat	AEA	1994 to 1996	Mono-Motronic 1.3
Polo 1.3 GT cat	3F	1990 to 1994	Digifant 25 pin
Polo 1.3 GT cat	3F	1993 to 1994	Digifant 25 pin
Polo 1.3 G40 & cat		1987 to 1990	Digifant 25 pin
Polo 1.3 G40 & cat	PY	1991 to 1994	Digifant 25 pin
Sharan 2.0	ADY	1995 to 1996	Mono-Motronic MA1.7
Transporter 2.0i & cat	AAC	1990 to 1996	Digifant 38 pin
Transporter 2.0i cat	AAC	1994 to 1995	Digifant 45 pin

Model	Engine code	Year	System
Volkswagen (continued)			
Transporter 2.1i cat	MV	1987 to 1992	Digifant 25 pin
Transporter 2.1i cat	SR	1987 to 1991	Digifant 25 pin
Transporter 2.1i cat	SS	1989 to 1991	Digifant 25 pin
Transporter 2.5i cat	AAF	1991 to 1995	Digifant 38 pin
Transporter 2.5i cat	ACU	1994 to 1996	Digifant 45 pin
Vento 1.4i cat	ABD	1991 to 1995	Mono-Motronic 1.2.3
Vento 1.4i	AEX	1995 to 1996	Mono-Motronic MA1.7
Vento 1.6i cat	ABU	1992 to 1995	Mono-Motronic 1.2.3
Vento 1.6i cat	AEA	1994 to 1995	Mono-Motronic 1.3
Vento 1.8i cat	AAM	1992 to 1997	Mono-Motronic1.2.3
Vento 1.8i cat	ABS	1992 to 1994	Mono-Motronic MA1.7
Vento 1.8i & 4x4	ADZ	1994 to 1996	Mono-Motronic MA1.7
Vento 2.0i cat	2E	1991 to 1995	Digifant 45 pin
Vento 2.0i 16V cat	ABF	1992 to 1995	Digifant 68 pin
Volvo			
740 turbo	B230ET	1985 to 1989	Motronic (First gen.)
760 turbo	B230ET	1985 to 1989	Motronic (First gen.)

Chapter 1
A brief history of Fuel Injection and the Engine Management System

Mechanical fuel injection

Fuel injection is almost as old as the oldest motor car. As long ago as 1881, when most of the pioneer automotive engineers were engaged in carburettor design, a Frenchman named Eteve was issued with a patent for a compressed air metering device. A German patent was issued to J. Spiel in 1883 for devising a method of injecting fuel into a flame-filled chamber linked to the engine cylinders. About the same time in Kent, England, Edward Butler devised an engine equipped with an injection system that forced fuel under pressure through a hollow-stem inlet valve.

The first production engine equipped with fuel injection was manufactured by the Charter Gas Engine Company of Sterling, Illinois, USA in 1887 **(see ilustration 1.1)**. This engine was actually a stationary engine, and fuel was gravity-fed from a tank into the injector body via the throttle valve. Deutz in Europe developed its own stationary engine with low-pressure-fed kerosene into the inlet port. Three hundred models of the single-cylinder engine were built between 1898 and 1901.

Orville Wright was not blind to the attractions of fuel injection, and his 1903 Flier was equipped with fuel injection **(see ilustration 1.2)**. Fuel-injected aircraft suffered less from carburettor icing and carburettor fires, and this meant less chance of them falling out of the sky. For this reason, fuel injection evolved more quickly in aircraft engines, although progress was still painfully slow. A high-pressure plunger pump and the calibrated injector principle was introduced by Leon Levavassuer in 1906, while 1912 saw the first involvement of Bosch, who adapted a two-stroke outboard engine utilising a lubrication pump as the injector pressure pump.

The First World War and the years leading up to 1920 saw considerable evolution of the carburettor, and reliability was achieved in aircraft engines to the extent that fuel injection was placed on the back burner, where it was to languish for a good number of years. During the 1930's, the German DVL (Deutsche Versuchsanstalt für Luftfahrt - otherwise known as the German Aviation Test Centre), Bosch, BMW and Mercedes-Benz all began development programmes of aviation-based high-pressure fuel injection systems. When Mercedes-Benz introduced the 1200 HP DB-601 V-12 engine to the world in 1937, fuel injection became the premier fuel system in aircraft engines. However, the design was inevitably akin to the diesel system, with direct injection into the combustion chamber. SU carburettors of Birmingham, England developed a fuel injection system for Rolls-Royce Merlin aircraft engines during the latter

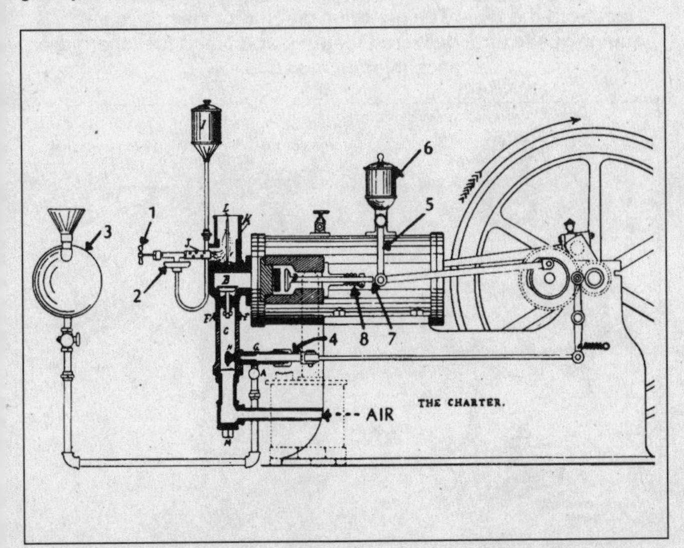

1.1 As early as 1887, the Charter engine combined the basic elements needed for low-pressure port-type fuel injection

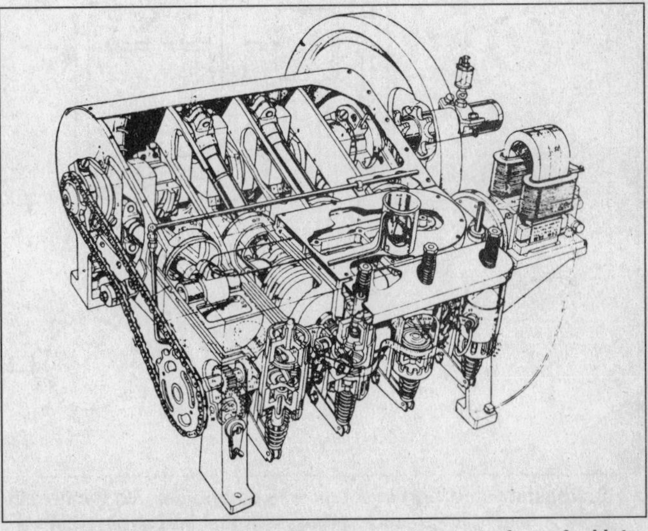

1.2 The Wright brothers used a gear-type pump to force fuel into the intake manifold of their 28 hp four-cylinder engine in 1903

stages of World War II. This system was later used on the American Patton tank during the Korean war of 1950 to 1953.

Fuel injection in automobiles between the 1930's and 50's mainly appeared on racing engines; one early pioneer was Ed Winfield, who obtained a patent for a port-type injection system **(see ilustration 1.3)**. A similar system appeared on the splendid Indy Offenhausers of the 1950's. The fuel system fitted to the Offenhauser engines was designed by Stuart Hilborn, and this system was also based on the low-pressure port principle. Fuel was continuously injected at constant pressure through a throttle body at each inlet port, via a spray nozzle inside the port area. The Hilborn system was used into the late 1960's, and European racing car manufacturers soon began to follow suit.

Lucas developed a system for the 1956 D-Type Jaguar, which then won the Le-Mans 24 hour race **(see ilustration 1.4)**. The production version that followed was a commercial disaster, however, due to the very high cost. The only manufacturer ever to fit it in production was Maserati, who fitted it to the 3500 Gti in 1961. Further development of the Lucas system saw it introduced to Formula one racing engines, where it was used alongside Kugelfischer fuel injection in the 1960's and 1970's. A production version was fitted to some Triumph sports cars, where it gained a reputation for unreliability.

Meanwhile, Mercedes-Benz used their vast experience in fuel-injected aircraft engines to develop a fuel-injected version of the 300SL sports car that went into production in 1954 **(see ilustration 1.5)**. This system was further refined when fitted to the W-196 Formula one racing car and racing versions of the 300SL. However, these direct injection systems owed much to diesel technology, and were considered too noisy in operation for the sophisticated Mercedes-Benz saloons. A more refined indirect intermittent injection system was put into production in 1957, and this evolved into an even better system that was fitted to the 220SE in 1958. Various refinements were made over the next ten years which improved system operation and horsepower.

Chevrolet experimented with a Rochester fuel injection system, overtly based on the Hilborn system, during 1957, and it was offered as an optional extra on the Corvette model. Pontiac used a revised version on the 1957 Bonneville models. However, it was found to be expensive, and reliability problems saw both manufacturers discard the system in 1959.

In the late 1960's Bendix developed a system that was soon challenging the domination of the Hilborn system for Indy racing cars. The Bendix system was adopted by 32 out of the 33 runners for the 1971 Indy 500, and was unchallenged during the remainder of the decade.

A number of fuel injection systems manufactured by smaller companies appeared and disappeared over the period from 1950 to about 1986. In modern times, fuel injection has become the province of the bigger players, and there is now no place in the market for the smaller operation.

Kugelfischer were undoubtedly the most successful of the smaller companies, and

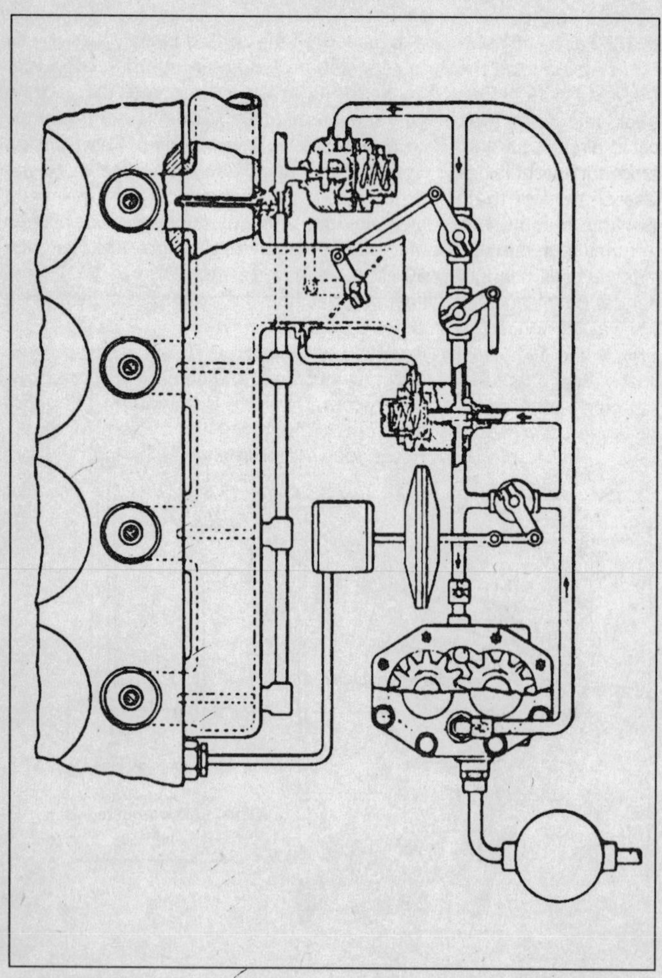

1.3 Constant-flow port injection was patented by Ed Winfield in 1934. A gear-type pressure pump sent fuel into a rail, where a pressure regulator controlled fuel flow in accordance with throttle position and manifold vacuum

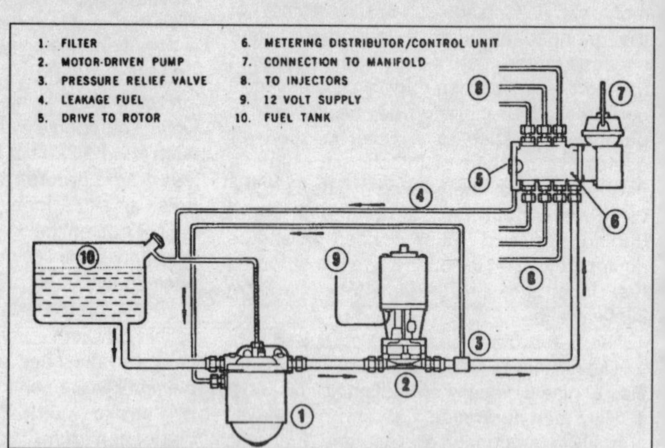

1.4 Lucas fuel injection used a motor-driven fuel pump to draw fuel from the tank. The metering distributor was driven at half engine speed, and delivered metered and timed fuel charges to each injector in sequence

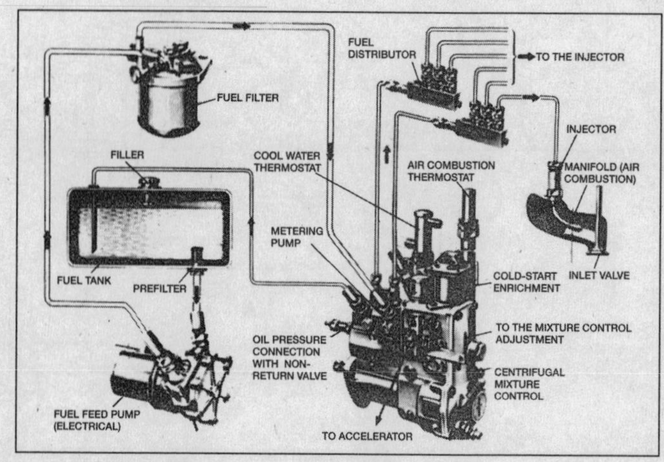

1.5 Schematic of the intermittent port injection system introduced on the Mercedes 220 SE in 1958

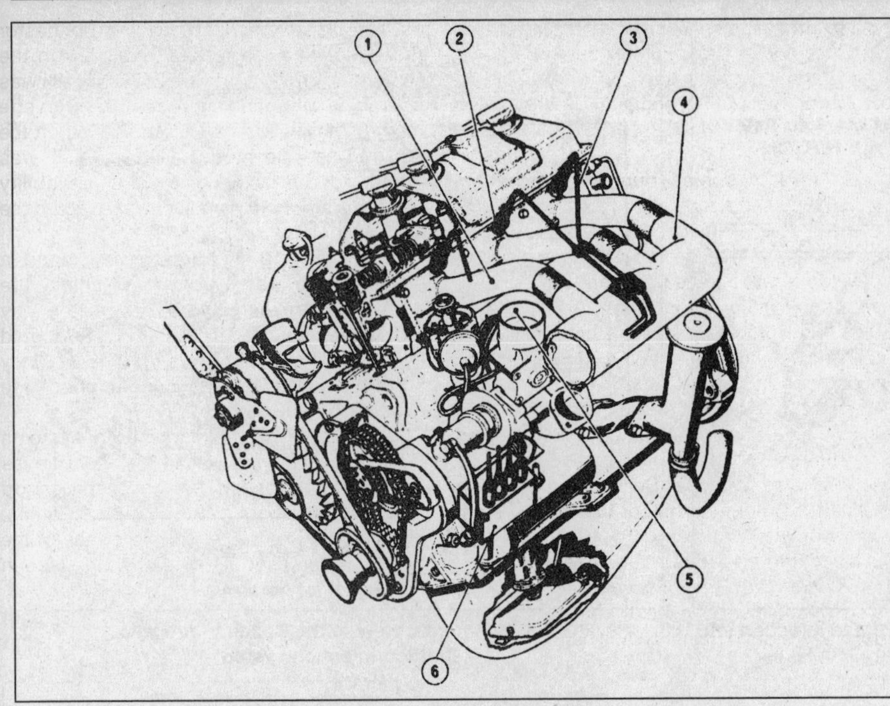

1.6 Kugelfischer system on a Peugeot 404

1 Intake runner
2 Injector
3 High-pressure fuel line
4 Manifold
5 Throttle body
6 Injection pump

their injection systems were fitted to a number of production European vehicles during the 1960's until the company was absorbed by Bosch in 1974 **(see ilustration 1.6)**.

In 1973 Bosch introduced the K-Jetronic mechanical injection system **(see ilustration 1.7)**. The 'K' system was destined to become the most successful mechanical injection system ever, due to its reliable effective operation and low emissions. With the introduction of electronic controls in 1984, the 'KE' Jetronic was born, with improved starting and pollution control. This hybrid part mechanical and part-electronic system is still in service well into the 1990's. But times they were a-changing and from slow beginnings, Electronic Fuel Injection systems gradually evolved until all mechanical systems, other than K-Jetronic, have now given way to the onward march of electronics.

Electronic fuel injection

Many features of the modern automobile were actually tried and discarded by pioneers many years before the technology became available that made their employment possible. The use of automotive electronic controls is a prime example; although attempts were made in the 1930's and the 1950's, a viable electronic system was not put into production until 1966.

The very first recorded use of an electronic valve to spray fuel occurred in 1932, when an engineer named Kennedy - an employee of the Atlas Imperial Diesel Engine Company - adapted a six-cylinder, spark-ignition, oil-burning marine engine. The system was devoid of transistors (the transistor was not invented for another 16 years) and any of the components that make up the modern system. In 1934, Kennedy installed a six-cylinder engine equipped with the same system into a truck, He then successfully drove the truck from Los Angeles to New York

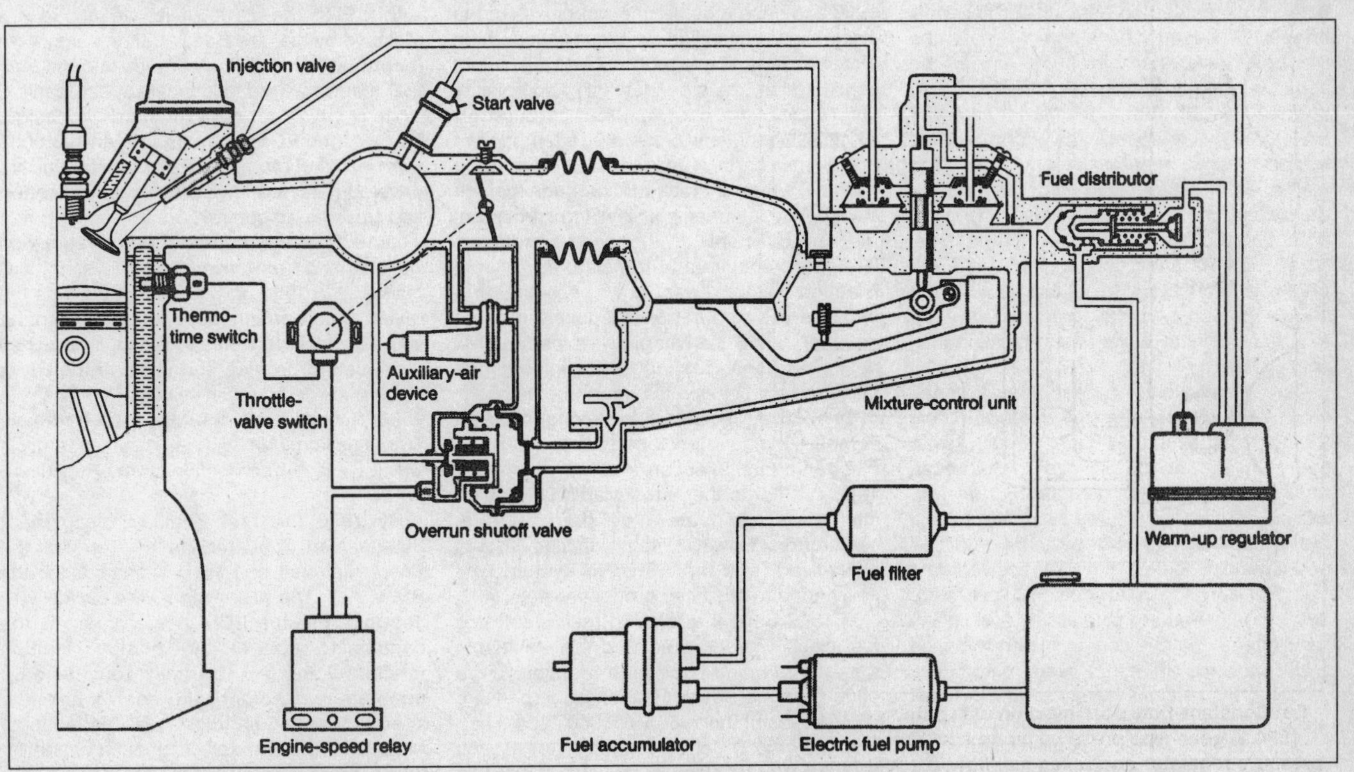

1.7 The Bosch K-Jetronic system, with fuel cut-off on the overrun, permitted fuel savings as well as a cleaner exhaust

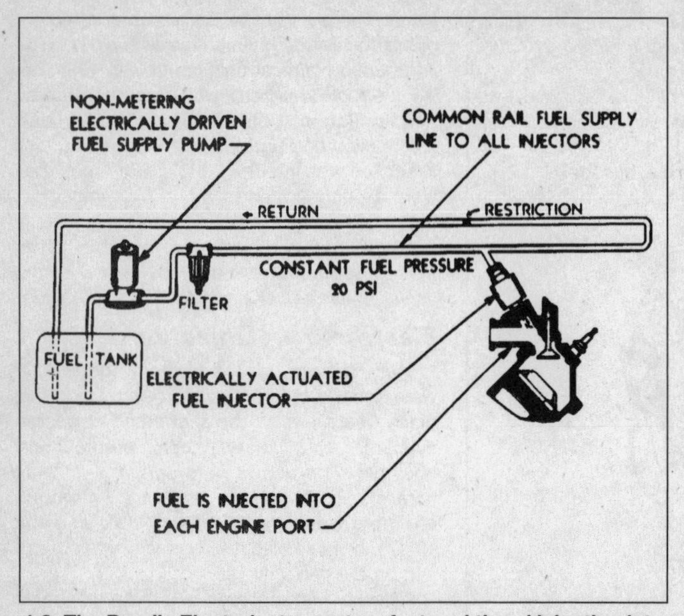

1.8 The Bendix Electrojector system featured timed injection into the intake ports, with a 20 psi common-rail fuel line

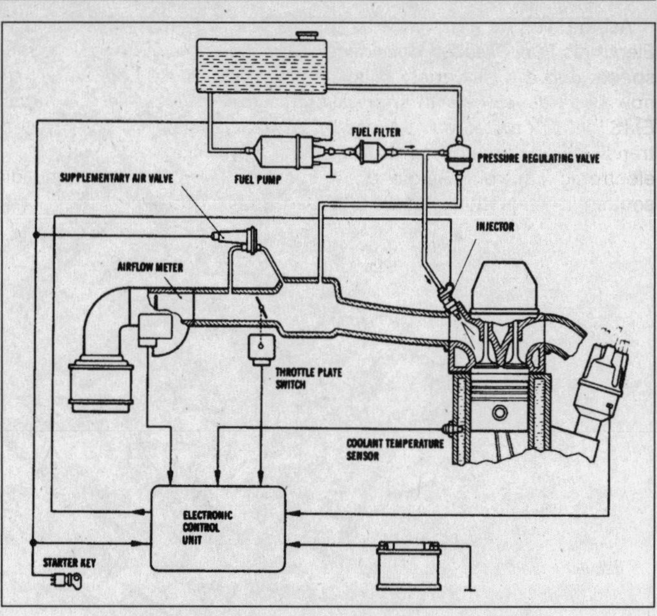

1.9 Schematic view of the Bosch L-Jetronic ignition/injection system

and back. When Atlas Imperial went bust, the Kennedy system disappeared into obscurity.

On February 4, 1957, the Bendix Corporation filed for a patent on automotive Electronic Fuel Injection systems. Thirty-nine claims were cited, and this foresight gave Bendix effective world-wide patent rights to all forms of Electronic Fuel Injection. The patent was granted on April 18, 1961. Bendix originally began development of the Electrojector system in 1952, under the supervision of Robert W. Sutton **(see ilustration 1.8)**. Although many years and $1,000,000 were spent in development, the system never reached production. The Electrojector system was made, tested and developed into a working system with great potential; but the high cost of components, harsh underbonnet environment, and the primitive technology available during the 1950's proved a bridge too far. However, much of the initial work was to prove fruitful some years later.

During early development, whenever the vehicle was driven under power cables during a road test, the induced current would trigger the modulator, and the injectors would open to fill the cylinders with neat fuel! Fortunately, this problem was eventually overcome.

The basic Electrojector system comprised an Electronic Control Unit that received data from sensors on inlet manifold pressure, ambient temperature, air pressure and engine rpm. After a computation according to speed and load, the injectors were electrically actuated by solenoid valves, so that a timed fuel pulse was injected into the inlet port. Fuel pressure in the fuel rail was maintained at 20 psi by use of an electrical fuel pump. The injection signal was triggered by a set of contact breakers mounted in the ignition distributor, and actuated by the same cam as the ignition contact breakers.

In 1966, Bendix granted Bosch a licence to manufacture electronic fuel injection systems in Germany and Brazil, and rights to market the systems world-wide.

A number of factors emerged in the late 1960's to bring together the last pieces of the electronic injection jigsaw. These included the looming issue of pollution control and petrol consumption, the ever-increasing complexity and increasing cost of the carburettor, driveability problems created by attempting to make the carburettor cope with a lean mixture, the increased ruggedness of electronic components and wiring harnesses, the improvement of the semi-conductor, integrated circuits and transistors. A viable injection system was now possible, and because the carburettor was failing to meet pollution and driveabilty expectations, designers began turning to fuel injection as the long-term solution to current problems.

By 1966, Associated Engineering (a British company) had developed the AE-Brico Electronic Fuel Injection system, which was fitted in 1969 to the Aston Martin DB6 as an alternative to the standard Weber carburettors. However, its production life was short-lived, and the AE-Brico system was never fitted to any other production vehicle.

In 1967 Bendix re-started their electronic fuel injection programme, and this resulted in the system being fitted in production to the 1976 Cadillac Seville. Bosch equipped the USA version of the 1968 VW 1600 Type 3 flat-four with the D-Jetronic, first of the Bosch Electronic Fuel Injection systems. Once the system had been proven, D-Jetronic was fitted to many other production vehicles, including models from the Citroen, Lancia , Mercedes-Benz, Opel, Renault, SAAB and Volvo ranges. Roots of the modern Electronic Fuel Injection system were laid with the D system, and modern systems have many similarities with the system that was first manufactured back in 1967.

In 1973 the D-Jetronic began to be replaced by the new Bosch L-Jetronic system **(see ilustration 1.9)**. Many of the systems that followed were influenced by the basic L system, which set new standards in design. Many of the ECM components and circuits were packed into integrated circuits. Further development saw EGR, Lambda operation and closed-loop control.

In 1978 Bendix formed a partnership with Renault, and the Renix injection system, first marketed in 1984 on the Renault 25, was the result. But Renault subsequently sold its share in Renix to Bendix-France, which then continued to develop and improve the Renix Electronic Fuel Injection system. Previously, in 1966, Renault itself developed an Automatic Transmission unit with electronic controls which went into production on the Renault 16 in 1969.

By 1978 the first Engine Management System had appeared, in the form of the Bosch Motronic, and this was first fitted to the BMW 732i. The fuel system was basically L-Jetronic, but the ECM now contained the circuits to control the primary ignition function. Later on, Motronic would also be adapted to automatically control the idle speed, and handle self-diagnostics. Meantime, the first self-diagnostic capability was produced on a Cadillac equipped with a Bendix digital system in 1981.

As the 1980's gave way to the 1990's, Electronic Fuel Injection development gained speed, and a wide variety of systems have now been developed. In some systems the EMS was connected to the automatic transmission, traction control and/or other electronic controls. Single point injection, sequential injection, and distributorless ignition are just some of the later developments. Self-diagnostics have also moved on, and where the early systems were limited in the number of fault codes, later systems are capable of logging perhaps one hundred or more.

The preceding diatribe has been a brief potted history of early fuel injection developments. For the student of automotive history, a far more comprehensive account of the history of fuels, the carburettor and fuel injection is described *in "Automotive Fuel Injection systems"* by Jan P. Norbye (available from Haynes Publishing).

Chapter 2
Technical overview of Fuel Injection and the Engine Management System

Contents

1 Definition of the engine management system

An engine management system (EMS) is essentially an electronic control system whereby the engine ignition, fuelling and idle speed functions are controlled by an electronic control module (ECM). The distributor, when used, is provided purely to distribute the HT spark to the correct cylinder in firing order. It is important to understand that the EMS does not control these functions separately. During the different engine control operations, the ECM synchronises timing and injection so that the various inputs and outputs work hand in hand, and not as separate entities **(see illustration 2.1)**.

The modern EMS employs digital technology and has a high degree of self-diagnostic capability. In addition, an EMS may also control other vehicle functions such as the air conditioning and communicate with other vehicle ECMs such as those controlling the ABS, automatic transmission or traction control when fitted.

However, in early systems the ECM did not always control the idle speed and the self-diagnostic function was often of limited performance. We will describe the components of a specific system under the various Chapter headings, but first we will look at the technology and the component parts that make-up a typical system.

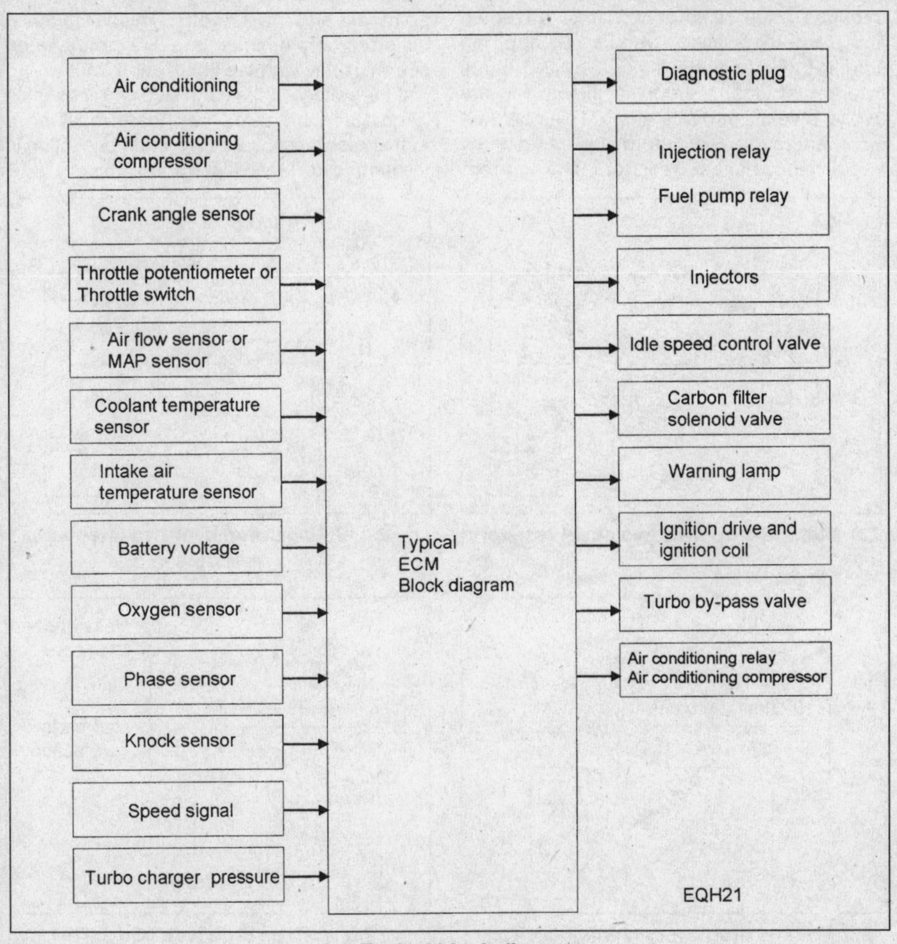

2.1 Typical block diagram

2 Analogue and digital signals

An analogue signal is any continuous signal that can change by an infinitely small amount. Typically, an analogue signal is measured by an instrument that uses a needle to progressively sweep across a fixed scale. Any change in the signal will cause the needle to move by a similar amount. One example would be the throttle potentiometer. As the throttle is opened and closed, the voltage output signal from the throttle pot increases and decreases and an analogue signal is passed to the ECM.

On the other hand, a digital signal is represented by a code that has two states, on and off. In simple terms, the signal consists of a series of digital pulses where the pulse width or frequency (number of pulses) is used to indicate a specific value **(see illustration 2.2)**.

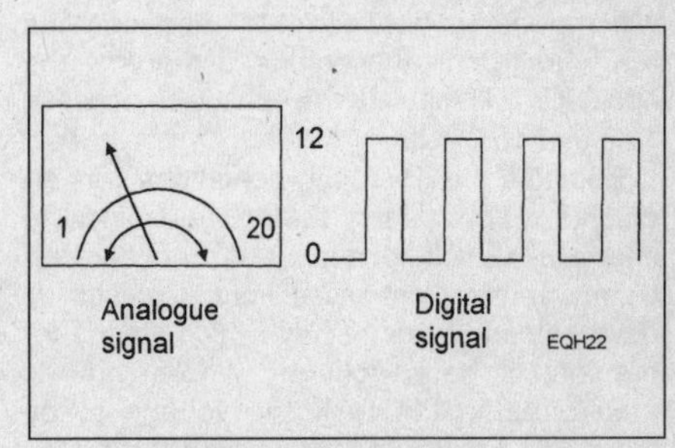

2.2 Analogue and digital signal

Many of the signals passed to the ECM from the engine sensors are analogue signals. Because the ECM works in a digital fashion, all analogue signals must pass through an analogue to digital converter (ADC) when the signal will be stored by the ECM in digital format. If the sensor is able to output data in digital form, so much the better. A digital signal from a digital sensor does not need converting, and processing by the ECM is therefore much faster. Very few sensors at this time are capable of digital output. One notable exception is the Ford MAP sensor which returns a digital signal based on frequency. All other MAP sensors return an analogue voltage signal.

3 Basic electrical facts

General

The reader needs to be conversant with a basic understanding of electrical measurements and terms if he is to obtain the most benefit from this section. If you do not understand the meaning of voltage, voltage drop, resistance, amperes, and series and parallel circuits, then you will need to study a basic automotive electrical textbook before you go any further. One such textbook is *"Automobile Electrical & Electronic Systems"* by Tony Tranter (available from Haynes Publishing).

Moving on, in order to gain a better comprehension of the EMS it is important to grasp the following principles. We will start off by looking at Ohm's Law.

Ohm's Law

Ohm's Law: I = V/R when V = Volts, R = Resistance (ohms) and I = current (amps).

The Law can be expressed as V + IR or R + V/I, but the expression I = V/R is the one we shall use most in the following descriptions.

Nominal battery voltage (nbv)

In any automotive circuit, the voltage will vary at any moment according to the vehicle operating conditions. With the engine stopped, voltage at the battery will be somewhere between 12.0 and 12.6 volts. During engine start-up when the engine is cranked upon the starter motor, the voltage will reduce to between 11.0 and perhaps 9.5 volts. Once the engine is running, the alternator will regulate the voltage to between 13.5 and 15.0 volts.

Because the operating conditions vary so much it is obvious that asking the engineer to check for 12 volts during a test procedure will be incorrect in most cases. For this reason we have coined the term 'nbv' which stands for nominal battery voltage. Where nbv is mentioned in the text, the voltage to be measured will depend on whether the engine is at rest, cranking or running.

Note: *nbv will vary in any particular vehicle and manufacturers specifications should be obtained for accuracy of testing. However, the following figures are a good 'rule of thumb' guide.*

Engine at rest:	12.0 to 12.6 volts
Engine cranking:	9.5 to 11.0 volts
Engine running:	13.5 to 15.0 volts*

**Voltage may be slightly lower at idle*

We will continue to use 12.0 volts during the examples set in this Chapter, since this value is a known constant and it also makes the calculations easier. In a real-life situation you would use the exact voltage value.

Circuit fundamentals

In the first example, a 12-volt circuit consists of a wire connecting two resistors of equal value to a voltage supply and earth. We will use two resistors of (say) 1.5 ohms.

A voltmeter may be used to measure the voltage at the various points in the circuit. 12 volts is measured in the supply to the first resistor, and zero volts is measured in the earth part of the circuit. The voltage drop measured over the whole of any circuit must equal 12 volts. The voltage measured between the two resistors is 6 volts. This is because each resistor will take an equal amount of the available voltage. By applying Ohm's Law (12 volts divided by 3.0 ohms total resistance) the current flowing in the circuit is calculated at 4 amps. This could be represented in a real automotive situation by a coil and ballast resistor. The current flowing in the circuit will vary according to changes in voltage and/or resistance **(see illustration 2.3)**.

For example: 15.0 volts divided by 3.0 ohms total resistance gives a current flow of 5 amps.

For the purist, Ohm's Law may be used to calculate the voltage drop in the circuit so: V = IR or 4 (amps) x 1.5 (ohms) = 6 volts. Since this value is the voltage drop, we need to deduct the voltage drop as follows. 12.0 - 6.0 = 6.0. 6.0 volts is therefore the voltage value measured between the resistors in the circuit.

If the two resistors are now substituted for unequal values ie. 2 ohms and 1 ohms respectively, then the equation changes. The total resistance is 3 ohms and the first resistor is 2 ohms which is two-thirds of the total amount. The first resistor therefore takes two-thirds of the voltage (8 volts) and the second takes 4 volts. The voltages measured at the three points of the circuit will now be 12, 4, and 0 **(see illustration 2.4)**.

Note: *It is not the actual resistor values that are important but the comparative values.*

If the supply wire to the first resistor is disconnected, the voltage measured at this point will be 12 volts. Similarly, on disconnecting the cable between the two resistors; then the voltage measured at this point will also be 12 volts. This is because resistors only function in a live circuit when current is flowing **(see illustration 2.5)**.

If the voltage at the earth side of a resistance is greater than zero, then there must be a further resistance, such as a bad connection in the earth circuit **(see illustration 2.6)**.

2.3 Voltage drop over two equal resistors

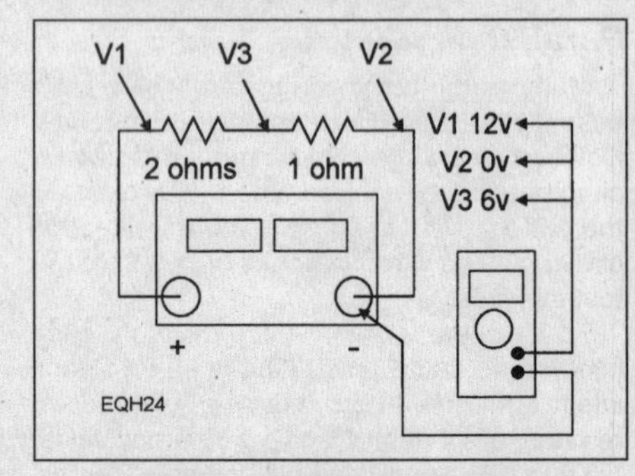

2.4 Voltage drop over two unequal resistors

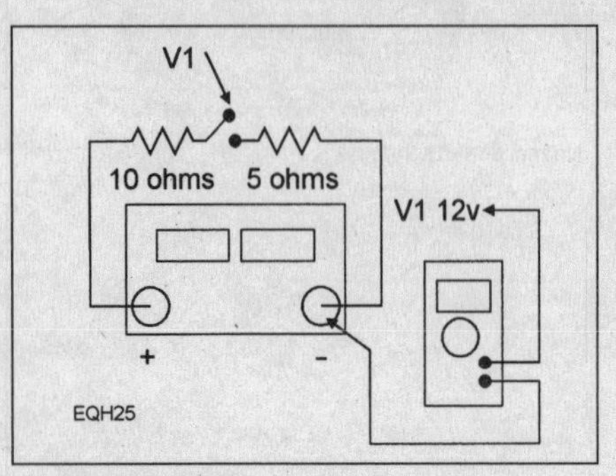

2.5 Voltage drop over an unequal circuit

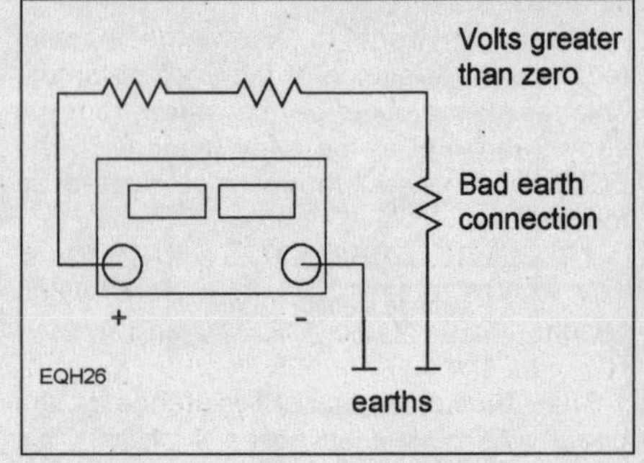

2.6 Voltage drop with bad earth connection

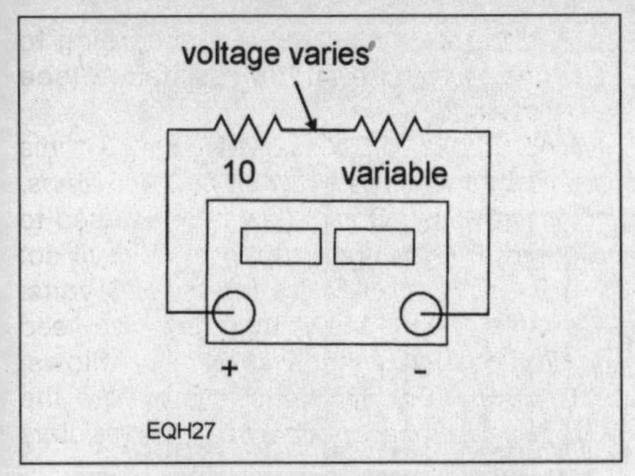

2.7 Variable voltage when resistance varies

If the resistor at B is made to vary, then the voltage between the resistors will also vary. This is the principle by which a variable analogue signal is sent from a sensor to the ECM. For example, as the CTS thermistor varies in resistance according to temperature, a variable voltage signal from is sent to the ECM for evaluation. The ATS, AFS, CTS, TPS and many other sensors operate on the same principle. In practice, we do not know the value of the first resistor located in the ECM. However, we do know the value of the variable resistor under various conditions, and we can then ascertain whether the sensor is functioning within its operating parameters. When the resistance varies, so does the voltage and although the voltages measured in this circuit will remain constant irrespective of resistance, measuring the voltage signal is much more useful than measuring the resistance **(see illustration 2.7)**.

Parallel circuits

Many automotive wiring circuits can be essentially identified as series circuits. However, there are also a number of parallel circuits and the most common form exists in the fuel injection wiring circuit. The injection circuit may be wired in banks of two, three or four injectors.

To find the current flow through each injector we could apply Ohm's Law to each injector branch. In our example, the injector resistance is 4 ohms - again a common value.

Thus: 12 volts divided by 4 ohms = 3 amps. The current flow through the whole injector circuit would be 3 amps x 4 cylinders = 12 amps.

We might want to know the parallel (equivalent) resistance of the injector circuit. This resistance could be measured from the supply terminal at the relay (typical) to the ECM pin. The resistance is calculated as follows.

1/R = 1/R1 + 1/R2 + 1/R3 + 1/R4. Thus, 1/R = 1/16 + 1/16 + 1/16 + 1/16 which becomes 1/R = 4/16 or 1/R = 1/4 and inverted R/1 = 4/1 ohms.

Thus the total parallel resistance of the circuit will be measured as 4 ohms. This assumes of course that the circuit is fault-free. Let us take a look at what could happen to a circuit with one or more faults that will increase the circuit resistance. Let us say that one injector circuit has a high resistance of 160,000 ohms. If we use the above formula the values are as follows:-

1/R = 1/16 + 1/16 + 1/16 + 1/16000, which becomes 1/R = 30001/160000 or R = 5.33 ohms.

Such a small difference in resistance between a good and a bad value is very easy to overlook and great care must therefore be taken when evaluating the injector circuit by measuring the resistance of the parallel circuit.

Assuming that the resistance of a single injector is 16 ohms, the values that are likely to be obtained with various configurations of the injector circuit are as follows:

Four injectors in bank

Res. value (ohms)	Condition
4 to 5	*all injectors ok*
5 to 6	*one injector suspect*
8 to 9	*two injectors suspect*
16 to 17	*three injectors suspect*

Three injectors in bank

Res. value (ohms)	Condition
5 to 6	*all injectors ok*
8 to 9	*one injector suspect*
16 to 17	*two injectors suspect*

Two injectors in bank

Res. value (ohms)	Condition
8 to 9	*all injectors ok*
16 to 17	*one injector suspect*

Note: *When the injector resistance is other than 16 ohms, the values will be different to those in the above table.*

Dwell and duty cycle

Traditionally, a dwell angle is defined as being the number of degrees through which a distributor rotates when the CB points are closed. However, in modern times we should consider the wider context of the meaning of 'dwell'. A good definition of a dwell angle would be the rotational angle during which a device is active or switched 'on' **(see illustration 2.8)**.

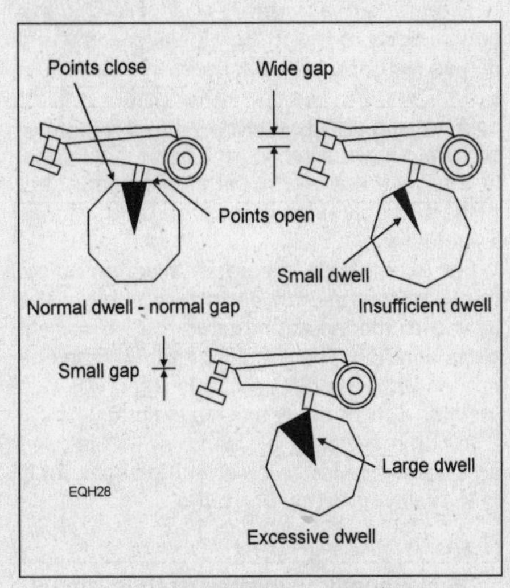

2.8 Conventional dwell angle

A more meaningful term might be 'duty cycle', and we could expand duty cycle to include any switchable device. Such devices need not be confined to the rotating type. Duty cycle could thus be measured in terms of degrees of rotation, percentage (%) of time 'on' - (or even off), or time on or off in milliseconds (ms). All we need is the appropriate meter. Usually, dwell is measured in degrees, but if we use either (%) or (ms), it is more appropriate to refer to duty cycle.

Devices capable of providing a dwell or duty cycle are usually actuators connected to the ECM or some other type of electronic module, and are normally switched quite rapidly. Examples would include the ignition coil, Hall-effect pulse generator, fuel injector, ISCV, VSS, CFSV etc - note that this list is by no means exhaustive.

The modern automotive multimeter usually contains functions to measure both dwell angle and duty cycle %. Some can even measure duty cycle in ms. By connecting the meter between the pulse terminal and earth on actuators such as the coil, ignition module, hall-effect switch, injector, ISCV or in fact any other device that is rapidly switched, a duty cycle may be obtained. By comparing this value with known operating parameters, correct operation of the device can be determined.

To convert dwell degrees to dwell percent and vice versa, use the following formulae:

Dwell° x cyls/360 x 100/1 =
Dwell% ie 45° x 4/360 x 100/1 = 50%
Dwell% / 100 x 360/cyls =
Dwell° ie 50 / 100 x 360 / 6 = 30°

Most automotive actuated devices are switched to earth, although the occasional device that is switched to live may be discovered. For example, if battery voltage is provided to an actuator such as an ISCV and the ECM switches the ISCV 'on'. A voltmeter would measure the voltage at a level of zero - ie earth. As the ISCV is switched off, the voltage returns to battery voltage level. This occurs many time a second and a digital voltmeter could also be used to measure the average switching voltage, which for an ISCV would usually be 6 to 7 volts **(see illustration 2.9)**.

In addition, the frequency meter facility provided on many digital multi-meters could also measure the frequency of pulse, and thus we have several methods of measuring the

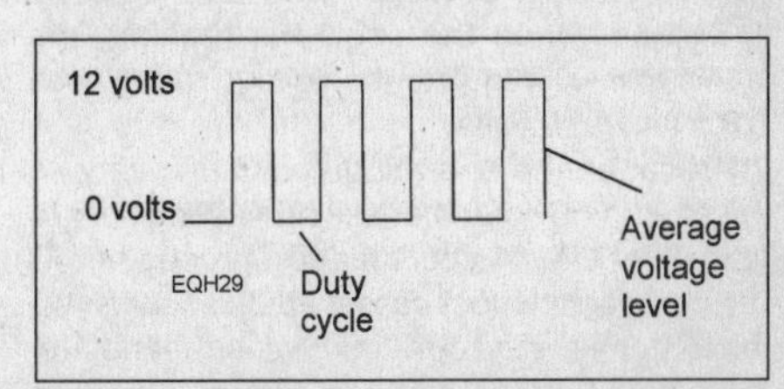

2.9 Typical ISCV waveform (graphical example of voltage switching at the ISCV as seen on an oscilloscope)

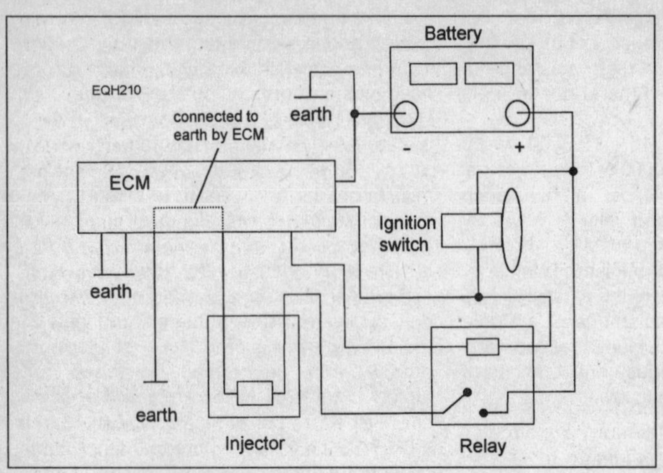

2.10 Typical ECM earth and voltage supplies

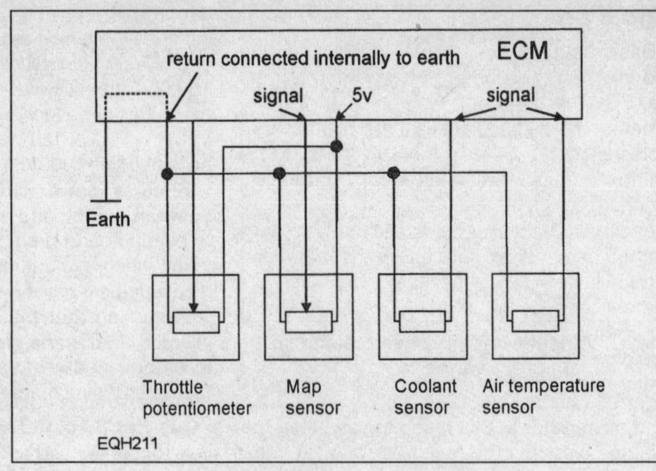

2.11 Typical sensor wiring

pulsing of a device. Since the pulse wire is the earth wire, measurement must always be made at the earth connection. All the devices mentioned above can be measured in a similar fashion.

4 Engine management systems (EMS)

Basic electronic control module (ECM) operation

This section describes the operation of a typical EMS. Although the components of each specific system may vary, the principles involved are fairly constant and this description is relevant to many of the modern systems. You will need to refer to a specific system for a more detailed description of how that particular system works.

Sensors and actuators

A sensor is an input device that provides variable information on an engine function. Examples include the airflow sensor (AFS), crank angle sensor (CAS), coolant temperature sensor (CTS), throttle potentiometer sensor (TPS) etc, and these provide data on load, rpm, temperature, throttle opening etc. This data is signalled to the ECM, which then analyses the results and computes an output signal. The output signal is used to actuate an output device. An actuator is a device that is switched or actuated by the ECM for a period of time depending on the input signal. Examples include the fuel injector, idle speed control valve (ISCV), carbon filter solenoid valve (CFSV), relay driver etc.

Put in simple computer terms, the process is summed up as input, compute, and output. Input is determined by the signals from the engine sensors, the ECM computes the actuator values required, and an appropriate signal is output to switch actuator components such as the injector, coil negative terminal, idle system, emission system, air conditioning etc. This process is repeated many times per second.

ECM power supplies and earths

A permanent voltage supply is usually applied from the vehicle battery to one of the ECM pins. This allows the self-diagnostic function to retain data of an intermittent nature. Once the ignition is switched on, a voltage supply is made to the ECM, ignition coil(s), injectors, ISCV and other devices. The voltage supplies may be made direct from the ignition or come from the system relay. The ignition 'on' supply to the ECM effectively powers up the ECM so that it is ready to go about its business.

When the engine is cranked or run, a speed signal from the ignition (often the CAS) causes the ECM to earth the fuel pump relay so that the fuel pump will run. Ignition and injection functions are also activated. Actuators such as the injectors and ISCV are supplied with nbv from the main relay or ignition switch and the ECM completes the circuit by pulsing the relevant actuator wire to earth **(see illustration 2.10)**.

There are normally several earth connections to the ECM. However, only one or two will normally be used as the actual ECM system earth. The other earth connections are provided to allow the ECM to complete various sensor and actuator circuits. In effect, these earth paths are secondary paths and only used when the ECM switches an actuator.

For example, to create an injection pulse, the ECM will use an earth to complete the circuit for the instant required to give correct pulse duration. The circuit to earth will then be broken until the next pulse is required. This practice occurs many times a second.

In some systems, an inertia switch is used as a safety device to break the power supply to the relay or to the fuel pump.

Reference voltage

During normal engine operation, battery voltage could vary between 9.5 (cranking) and 14.5 (running). To minimise the effect on engine sensors (for which the ECM would need to compensate), the voltage supplies from the ECM to the engine sensors are made at a constant voltage (known as a reference voltage) of 5.0 volts **(see illustration 2.11)**.

Once the ECM has powered up then, the majority of sensors (other than those that generate a voltage such the CAS and OS), are supplied with the 5.0 volt reference.

In most instances the engine sensors are not directly connected to earth. Rather, the sensor earth path is connected to one or two common earth return connections that connect directly to the ECM. This ECM pin is not usually connected directly to earth. The ECM internally connects that pin to earth via one of the ECM pins that are directly connected to earth.

Signal shielding

To reduce radio frequency interference or RFI, some signals are protected with a shielded cable. The shielded cable is often connected to the main ECM earth pin, so that interference is reduced to a minimum **(see illustration 2.12)**.

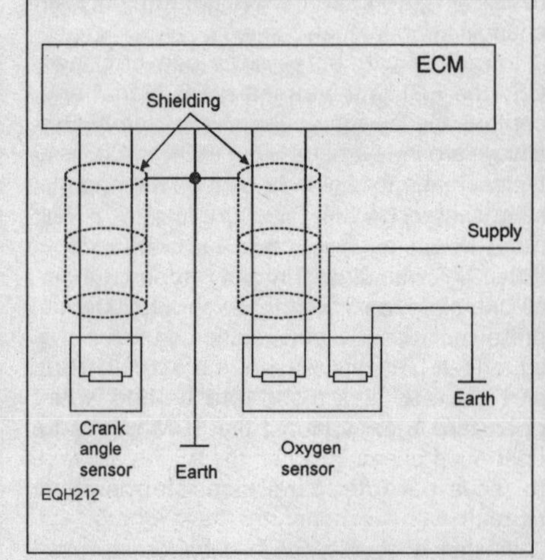

2.12 Sensor shielding to reduce RFI

Signal processing

Basic data on dwell angle, ignition timing and injection duration are stored internally in the ECM in a number of two- or three-dimensional maps. These maps or look-up tables allow the ECM to look-up the correct ignition timing and injection duration according to speed and load.

Accessing data from a table is a far quicker method of selecting data than by computing it. If the system is well designed, the map will contain settings for almost every possible engine load and speed. Even so, the map would be enormous if every single rpm or load setting was listed, and rpm may be mapped every 5 rpm and the load logged in a similar fashion. The ECM will interpolate in-between values so that most operating conditions are extensively covered. Some early systems were not always well mapped, and this created a 'black hole' for some operating conditions with consequent deterioration of performance.

In addition, the ignition point and injection duration are jointly processed by the ECM so that the best moment for ignition and fuelling are determined for every operating condition.

The main engine load sensor is either the AFS or MAP sensor and engine speed is determined from the ignition signal - usually the CAS. Correction factors are then applied for starting, idle, deceleration and part and full-load operation. The main correction factor is engine temperature from the CTS. Minor correction to timing and air-fuel ratio (AFR) are made with reference to the battery voltage, ATS and TPS signals.

In models with an ISCV or a stepper motor, the ECM accesses a different map for idle running conditions, and this map is implemented whenever the engine speed is at idle. Idle speed during warm-up and normal hot running conditions are maintained automatically by the idle control function. However, in most systems the ECM makes small adjustments to the idle speed by advancing or retarding the timing, and this results in an ignition timing that is forever changing during engine idle.

In models with an catalytic converter and OS, the ECM monitors the OS signal and controls the injection pulse so that the AFR is always around Lambda = 1.0 (0.97 to 1.03 is a typical range for Lambda control). Lambda is represented by the Greek symbol 'λ'. This mode of operation is known as 'closed-loop'. If the AFR was placed into closed-loop under all operating conditions, the vehicle would be pretty much undriveable during certain driving situations. For this reason, during cold start and warm-up, sharp acceleration and wide-open throttle conditions, the ECM slips into open-loop operation when the AFR is allowed to move outside of the Lambda operating range.

If the engine speed exceeds a pre-designated engine rpm, the ECM cuts off injector operation as a safety precaution. Fuel is also cut during deceleration to maintain smooth running and as an economy measure. Fuel is re-introduced when the deceleration speed falls below a certain rpm. After a period of closed throttle running; when the throttle is opened again, the ECM re-introduces fuel injection in a controlled manner to prevent a loss of smoothness.

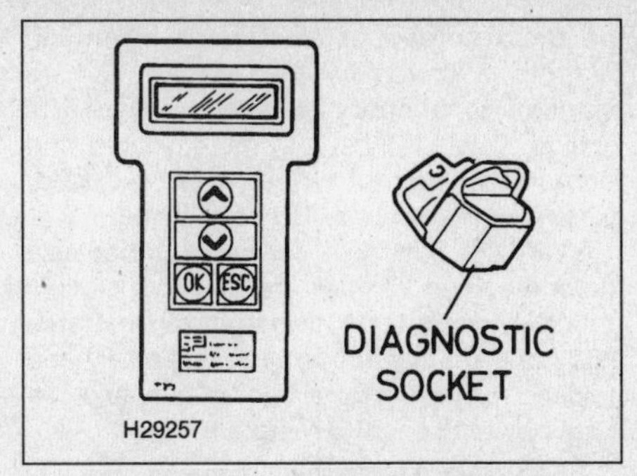

2.13 FCR and typical serial port

Self-diagnostic function

The modern engine management system has a self-test capability that regularly examines the signals from the engine sensors and in some instances the actuators. In the event of a fault being present the ECM internally logs a code. This code can be extracted from an output terminal, known as a serial port, by a suitable fault code reader **(see illustration 2.13)**.

To a large degree, the format and type of data to be output is determined by the vehicle manufacturer (VM). The function of the fault code reader (FCR) is to initiate the VM's program and to make the best of what is actually available. In other words, if the VM does not make certain information available, then it is not possible to access such information through the serial port. For example, apart from reading fault codes and clearing fault codes, it may be possible to obtain datastream information on the signal output from the sensors, or make adjustments to CO or timing, or fire the injector, ISCV, relays and other actuators or log sensor data during a road test. But these functions will only be available if the VM has made them available. However, it is usually still possible to obtain such information in other more traditional ways, and we will explore these methods in Chapter 3.

Some vehicles are provided with a dash-mounted warning lamp. When the ECM detects that a major fault is present, it earths a dedicated ECM pin and the warning lamp on the dash will light whilst the engine is running. The lamp remain lit until the fault is no longer present. If the fault clears, the code will remain logged until wiped clean with a suitable FCR, or when the battery is disconnected. However, not all vehicles utilise a warning lamp; those without one will require interrogation by a FCR to determine whether a fault is logged or not. Some ECMs retain codes for faults of an intermittent nature, and this is a valuable aid to fault diagnosis.

Codes emitted by an ECM may be designated as 'slow codes' or 'fast codes'. Slow codes (sometimes termed flash codes) are fault codes emitted by an EMS that are slow enough to be displayed on an LED lamp or on a dash-mounted warning lamp. Fast codes are digital fault codes emitted by an EMS that are too fast to be displayed on an LED lamp or on a dash-mounted warning lamp. A digital FCR instrument is required for capturing fast codes.

Limited operating strategy (LOS)

In addition to the self-test capability, the modern EMS normally contains a 'limp-home' facility that is usually termed LOS or Limited Operating Strategy. This means that in the event of a serious fault in one or more of the sensor circuits, and the system perceives that a sensor is operating outside of its design parameters, the EMS will substitute a fixed default value in place of the defective sensor. A fault that puts the circuit outside of its design parameters would normally be a short circuit or when the circuit is virtually open. Other sensor faults may not necessarily cause a code to be logged.

The LOS is a safety system which allows the engine to operate at a reduced efficiency level. and allows the vehicle to be driven to a service area. Some LOS systems are so smart that the driver may be unaware that a fault has occurred during most of the vehicle's operating conditions.

However, since the substituted values are usually those of a hot (sometimes warm) engine, cold starting and running during the warm-up period may be less than satisfactory. Also, failure of a major sensor, ie the AFS or the MAP sensor, will tend to make driving conditions less easy.

The instrument panel warning light (where fitted) is switched on to indicate that a fault has occurred. Some systems (for example Ford) may also lock the timing to a set figure (with no timing advance) and allow the fuel pump to run continuously.

Adaptive systems

The ECM is adaptive to changing engine operating characteristics, and constantly monitors the data from the various sensors (ie AFS or MAP, ATS, CTS. TPS etc). As the engine or its components wear, the ECM reacts to new circumstances by adopting the changed values as a correction to the basic map.

When the adaptive map is used in conjunction with the oxygen sensor (OS), the ECM is able to respond much more quickly and retain tighter control over the changing gases in the exhaust system. During closed-loop operation, the basic injection value is determined by the values stored in the map for a specific rpm and load. If the basic injection value causes exhaust emissions outside of the Lambda value (ie 0.97 to 1.03 AFR) the mixture would be too rich or too lean and the OS would signal the ECM, which in turn will correct the mixture. However, this response takes a little time and so the ECM learns a correction value and adds this 'adaptive' values to the basic map. From now on, under most operating conditions, the emissions will be very close to Lambda and so, after reference to the OS signal, the ECM will only need to make small corrections to keep it that way.

Adaptation and correction of the map occurs during the following engine operations.

a) CFSV operation
b) ISCV operation
c) Idle speed and mixture adjustment
d) Part-load mixture adjustment

Operation of the CFSV introduces a combustible mixture to the engine that is compensated for by the fuel evaporation adaptive correction values after detection by the OS.

At idle speed the system will settle down to idle at the best speed for each individual application. Most adaptive systems will lose their settings if the battery is disconnected. Once the battery is reconnected and the engine is restarted, the system will need to go through a relearning curve. This usually occurs fairly quickly, although idle quality may be poor until the adaptive process is completed.

Not all systems are affected by battery disconnection, and the Rover MEMS is an example of a system that uses non-volatile memory to retain adaptive settings when the battery is disconnected.

When one or more system components have been renewed, the ECM will need to relearn the new values, and this can sometimes create operating problems until the ECM has completed the process.

Rogue adaptive function

The danger with an adaptive function is that sometimes an erroneous signal may be adopted as a valid measurement, and this may create an operating problem. If the erroneous signal is not serious enough to generate a fault code, the fault may remain undetected.

In some instances the ECM can become confused, and the adaptive values could become corrupted. This may cause operational problems and a system check will reveal 'no fault found'. Disconnecting the vehicle battery may effect a cure, since the re-calibration will reset the ECM default base values.

5 Electronic ignition

General description

Reduced exhaust emissions figures highly in automotive design these days, and much of the rapid spread of electronics in engine controls is driven by the need to reduce pollution to acceptable levels. Where the ignition system is inherently more reliable, and the need for regular tune-ups are reduced, exhaust emissions will also be reduced.

A very rich mixture is easy to burn because the molecules of fuel are packed closely together. Once fired, the spark propagates easily and the flame front spreads easily and quickly. As the mixture becomes weaker, a more powerful spark is required.

But actually a powerful spark is of little use in burning a lean mixture. What is more important is the energy to prolong the spark. Mainly this is because there are less molecules of fuel in the mixture, and the spark will easily 'blow out'. Thus, the spark must be prolonged for about 1.3 to 1.5 ms, and adequate energy is required in the primary circuit to accomplish this task.

In a standard CB points ignition system with a 12 volt battery, the primary resistance of the coil is approximately 3 ohms. By applying Ohm's Law : I = V/R, it is apparent that about 4 amps of current is running in the primary circuit. The same is also true for a circuit with a ballast resistor, because the value of the resistor is (typically) 1.5 ohms and is used with a coil of 1.5 ohms primary resistance. Total current in a ballasted circuit is also about 4 amps.

Because the level of secondary HT voltage depends upon the level of primary current, it is obvious that for an increase in secondary output, there must be first an increase in primary current.

In older technology systems the maximum current that a set of CB points will handle is about 4 to 5 amps and this limits the amount of energy developed by the ignition coil. Furthermore, as the CB wears it causes misfires, retarded timing, higher emissions and a need for regular 'tune-ups'. In addition, because the dwell angle is fixed, coil performance is unsatisfactory at both low and high engine speeds. We will examine the reasons for this in the next paragraph. The modern electronic ignition system is capable of high output at all engine speeds, and has now become the definitive ignition system so replacing the once-ubiquitous CB.

Constant-energy ignition

Electronic ignition, used with a coil of lower primary resistance, produces increased primary current resulting in increased coil output. Coupled with higher coil energy, this will produce an arc of longer duration at the spark plug, and enable a weaker mixture to be ignited with a corresponding improvement in economy and exhaust emissions. Improved reliability, better control of timing and longer periods between 'tune-ups' are other benefits over the conventional CB system.

Virtually all modern types of electronic ignition use the variable-dwell current-limiting constant-energy system.

If Ohm's Law: I = V/R is applied to a 12-volt system with a coil of 0.75 ohms primary resistance, it is apparent that the potential current will be about 16 amps. Because this current flow would be far too high for most conditions, the electronic ignition module utilises an in-built current limiter device that limits the energy to a pre-determined figure of about 8 amps to avoid circuit overload and coil overheating.

As rpm and voltage rise and dwell increases with a equivalent rise in current flow, current limitation occurs earlier. As rpm, voltage and dwell levels decrease, with an equivalent drop in current flow, current limitation occurs later. Current is thus always limited to around 8 amps, irrespective of engine operating conditions. The advantage of having a high current reserve ensures a rapid build-up of coil energy. This results in a faster spark rise time, and sufficient energy is always available to maintain current flow across the spark plug gap for the required spark duration of about 1.3 to 1.5 ms.

Dependence by the ignition system on the battery voltage, temperature and engine speed is therefore much reduced.

At slow engine speeds, when the ignition cycle is relatively long, the dwell angle remains small. Also, because the current flows for shorter periods of time, the coil remains cool. As the engine speed increases, the dwell angle progressively increases to provide the necessary high speed coil saturation.

Let us now look at how this works in real terms. First a four-cylinder engine with a CB system. Refer to chart 'A'.

Chart A - CB points system

RPM	Dwell °	Dwell (time)
800	45° (50%)	16 ms
1600	45°	8 ms
3200	45°	4 ms
6400	45°	2 ms

A dwell of between 3 and 6 ms is required for good coil saturation. Referring to the CB chart, it is apparent that as rpm rises the points cannot 'dwell' closed for a long enough period to ensure a good spark. Good coil saturation is essential if the spark is to be adequate. It is obvious that this system will run out of spark at high engine rpm. The quality of the spark varies considerably, and due to the (comparatively) prolonged duration of points closure at low speeds, the primary circuit becomes overheated thus reducing the longevity of the CB and coil.

Let us now apply the same logic to an electronic system on a four-cylinder engine. Refer to chart 'B'.

Chart B - Electronic system

RPM	Dwell	Dwell (time)
800	10°	6 ms
1600	20°	6 ms
3200	40°	6 ms
6400	80°	6 ms

The variable factor is now the dwell angle. Please note that not all vehicle manufacturers use a module 'on' time of 6 ms, but most will fall within the range of 3-6 ms. It is apparent that if the dwell time remains constant (ie constant energy) the spark would also be generally constant over most of the engine operating range. A degradation of spark would, however, be inevitable at high engine rpm because the dwell angle for our four-cylinder example could not exceed 90°. This concept then, is the basis for all modern electric ignition systems, irrespective of whether they are part of an EMS or a simple stand-alone electronic ignition. The short dwell time at low speeds has the further advantage of allowing the coil to remain cool under these conditions.

Early electronic ignition systems used a fixed dwell with some of the limitations of the conventional system, ie secondary output was restricted at higher engine speeds. In addition, these systems normally used a ballast resistor and by-pass to regulate current and voltage in a similar fashion to breaker points operation.

In the early days of electronic ignition, some manufacturers turned to capacitor discharge systems to provide a powerful spark. However, this spark only burned for about 0.1 ms, and has proved inadequate to the task (with one notable exception - the SAAB multiple spark system).

Ignition

Data on load (AFS or MAP), engine speed (CAS), engine temperature (CTS) and throttle position (TPS) are collected by the ECM, which then refers to the digital map stored within its microprocessor. This map contains an advance angle for each operating condition, and thus the best ignition advance angle for a particular operating condition can be determined. The ECM looks-up the correct dwell duration and timing point, and signals the amplifier - which in turn switches the coil negative terminal to achieve correctly-timed ignition **(see illustration 2.14)**.

Air and coolant temperatures are also monitored by the ECM, and the timing is automatically retarded by a knock sensor (where so equipped) if engine knock occurs.

Ignition amplifier operation

In a conventional ignition, the CB switches the negative side of the coil on and off to produce a spark. The electronic system is very similar in operation but uses (typically) a pulse generator and amplifier to achieve the same result.

A pulse generator provides correctly-timed electrical pulses for the amplifier to trigger the ignition by switching off the coil negative (-) terminal. The pulse generator can be an inductive magnet located inside the distributor or adjacent to the flywheel. Or it may use a Hall-effect generator to produce the pulse **(see illustration 2.15)**.

The voltage of the generated pulse is too weak to operate the switching transistor and must be amplified. The amplifier senses the trigger pulse, and amplifies the voltage to the correct level to operate the switching transistor. The coil is thus switched on by the amplifier circuitry to build the magnetic field, and switched off by the switching transistor to collapse the magnetic field and induce the secondary spark.

A safety circuit is used to prevent coil overheating. The primary current is switched off after (typically) one second if the ignition is switched on and the engine not started. The amplifier also contains the constant energy limiting circuitry.

EMS ignition operation

The EMS works very much along the principles of the above systems, and is usually triggered by a CAS or Hall-effect switch. The amplifier may be an integral part of the ECM, or may be a separate amplifier that is switched by the ECM. One advantage of a separate amplifier, is that if the amplifier fails, it is less costly to renew than a new ECM.

A typical sequence of events is as follows. The CAS or Hall-effect switch signals the ECM which 'looks up' the correct ignition dwell time and timing advance from data received from its sensors. The ECM then sends a signal to the amplifier (internal or external) which in turn switches the coil negative terminal. Where the ignition amplifier is combined with the ECM, the current-limiting function is often controlled by the ECM.

Distributor

The early distributor used in an EI system functioned much the same as its CB counterpart with mechanical and vacuum advance units. As the ECM developed, the mechanical and vacuum advance functions were removed from the distributor, and are now embodied in the ECM map. The modern distributor (where fitted) contains secondary HT components (distributor cap, rotor and HT leads) and serves to distribute the HT current from the coil secondary terminal to each spark plug in firing order.

DIS (direct ignition system - sometimes termed 'distributorless')

Two reasons for discarding the distributor:

1) *An ignition coil should be capable of producing enough voltage to bridge the rotor gap and spark plug electrodes, with enough in reserve to provide a fairly good spark burn time. Even so, as much as 10 kV (10,000 volts) can be required to bridge the rotor gap. If the energy required to produce this voltage can be saved, the energy could be used more productively to prolong the burn time* ***(see illustration 2.16)****.*
2) *The distributor cap and rotor account for a high proportion of electrical breakdowns and ignition problems on cars with EI. Further, RFI from a defective ignition system can disrupt ECM operation.*

By discarding the distributor and firing both spark plugs together, the coil energy saved can be used to maintain the burn time across the plug gap. About 3 kV is still required to fire the 'wasted spark' plug, but this is far less than that required to bridge the rotor gap.

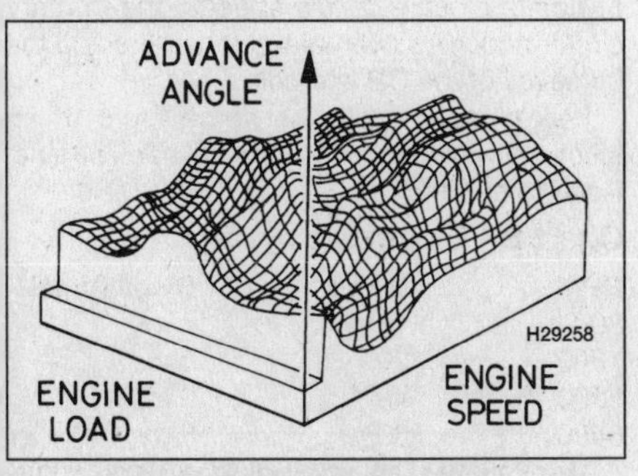

2.14 Typical timing map

2.15 Typical ignition with Hall-effect trigger

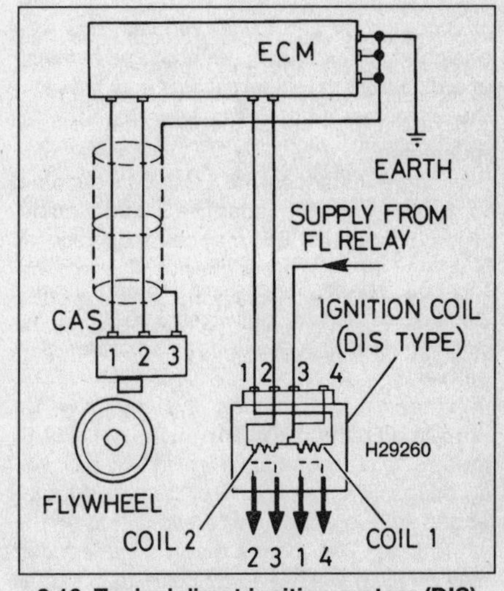

2.16 Typical direct ignition system (DIS) with CAS trigger

2

Wasted spark DIS operation

To understand what is actually happening, we first need to look at some scientific theory. Whatever the polarity of the engine earth, the plug body and earth electrode will always have a positive polarity. Also, the spark plug central electrode will always be negative polarity. Polarity in this context has nothing to do with whether the vehicle is positive- or negative-earth.

The negative-earth EI system provides a spark of negative polarity from the ignition coil, and the spark will jump from the central electrode to the side (earth) electrode. The negative spark is provided by the coil high tension output when the coil negative terminal is connected to earth through a CB or other switching circuit.

In a positive-earth system, the spark will jump from the earth electrode (still positive polarity) to the central electrode (still negative polarity). Thus the system provides a positive spark. Electrons move more readily from negative to positive, and more readily from a hot object (plug central electrode) to a cold object (plug earth electrode).

Therefore, less HT voltage is required to fire the plug when a negative-polarity spark is used. This means that with conventional ignition, there is less wear in a negative spark system, and until recently that was the norm. When the coil low tension terminals are incorrectly connected to give reverse polarity, 20 to 40% more voltage is required to bridge the spark plug gap.

However, in our distributorless system the spark travels through the central electrode of one plug to earth (negative spark). The spark then travels through earth and the earth electrode to the central electrode of the companion cylinder (positive spark) and back to the coil. The circuit is thus completed. In our four-cylinder engine, we therefore have two negative and two positive sparks.

This principle was used with some success in Citroën 2CV and Dyane models, and was designed for simplicity without the expense of a distributor. Coil output was very low, and the Citroën would tend to foul plugs on the positive spark plug. Many owners swapped the plugs every 3000 miles to even up wear.

In the modern DIS system, an EMS is used in conjunction with a low primary resistance coil, CAS and other engine sensors to control the coil, spark energy and ignition timing. Because of the very high level of coil energy, a positive spark is no longer considered a problem.

Although the ignition system may be termed DIS, the basic operation is similar to models with conventional ignition. In a DIS or so called 'wasted spark' system, a double-ended coil is used to fire two plugs at the same time. This means that the system can only be used where two cylinders rise and fall together. Two pairs of coils will therefore be required for a four-cylinder engine, and three pairs of coils for a six-cylinder engine.

One cylinder will fire on the compression stroke and the companion cylinder will fire on the exhaust stroke where the spark is 'wasted'. Each ignition coil receives a voltage supply from the ignition switch, and a separate dwell connection to the amplifier (or ECM). In addition, separate connections for each coil are made between the ECM and the amplifier. In effect, the ECM and amplifier contains two separate circuits so that each coil can be switched individually and alternately.

A CAS is used to trigger the timing moment for cylinders 1 and 4, and the engine ECM calculates the correct timing for cylinders 2 and 3.

Ignition timing adjustment

Few modern systems allow adjustments to the ignition timing, irrespective of whether the model is equipped with DIS ignition or a distributor. Where adjustment is possible, some systems utilise an octane adjuster to enable small adjustments to be made. Alternatively, the ECM may be placed into a base timing mode with the aid of a handheld FCR, and the base timing may then be adjusted by turning the distributor.

Octane coding

An octane coding connector or a jumper cable may be provided, to enable the ECM to adopt certain timing characteristics that suit the various octane grades of fuel. In some instances, when the ECM recognises the installation of a certain octane coding connector, the ECM may modify both the basic timing and fuel injection maps **(see illustration 2.17)**.

The ECM provides a 5.0 volt reference feed to the octane connector multi-plug. When this cable is connected to earth, via a resistor (octane plug), a voltage of lower value than 5.0 volt will be returned to the ECM. Once the ECM sees the lower voltage value, appropriate adjustments are made to its internal program.

Knock sensor

The optimal ignition timing (at engine speeds greater than idle) for a given high-compression engine is quite close to the point where engine knock occurs. However, running so close to the point of knock occurrence, means that knock will certainly occur on one or more cylinders at certain times during the engine operating cycle.

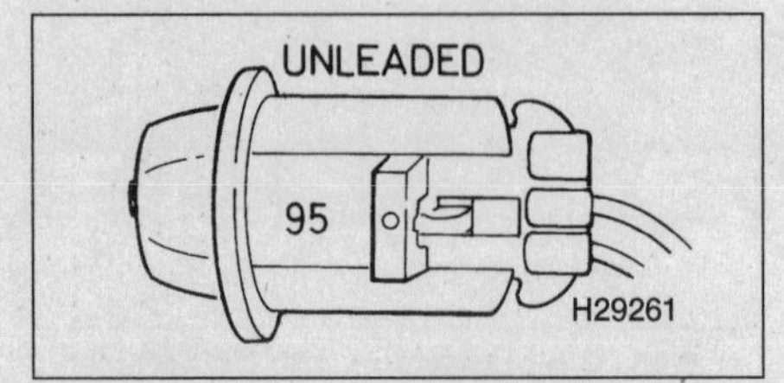

2.17 Typical octane coding plug

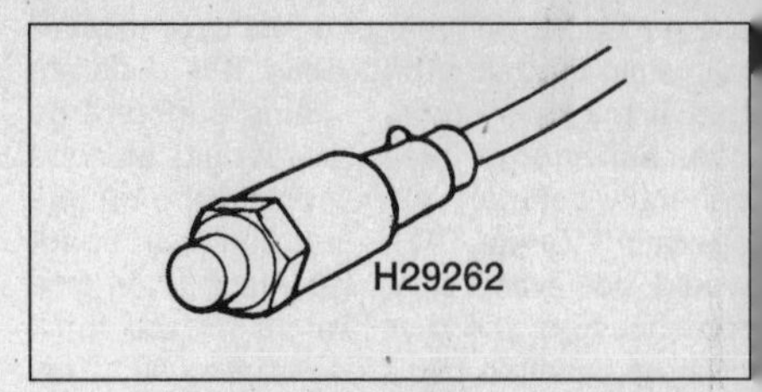

2.18 Typical knock sensor (KS)

Since knock may occur at a different moment in each individual cylinder, the ECM employs a knock control processor to pinpoint the actual cylinder or cylinders that are knocking. The knock sensor is mounted on the engine block, and consists of a piezo-ceramic measuring element that responds to engine noise oscillations. This signal is converted to a voltage signal that is proportional to the level of knock, and returned to the ECM for evaluation and action **(see illustration 2.18)**.

The knocking usual frequency is in the 6 to 15kHz frequency band.

The ECM will analyse the noise from each individual cylinder and set a reference noise level for that cylinder based upon the average of the noise over a pre-determined period. If the noise level exceeds the reference level by a certain amount, the ECM identifies the presence of engine knock.

Initially, timing will occur at its optimal ignition point. Once knock is identified, the knock control microprocessor retards the ignition timing for that cylinder or cylinders by degrees. After knocking ceases, the timing is advanced until the reference timing value is achieved or knock occurs once more when the timing is once more retarded. This process continually occurs so that all cylinders will consistently run at their optimum timing.

Inductive magnet signal generator

The inductive trigger is mounted in the distributor, and is essentially a permanent magnet and pole piece attached to a stator. The two most common types in current service are the pick-up limb or the annular coil **(see illustration 2.19)**.

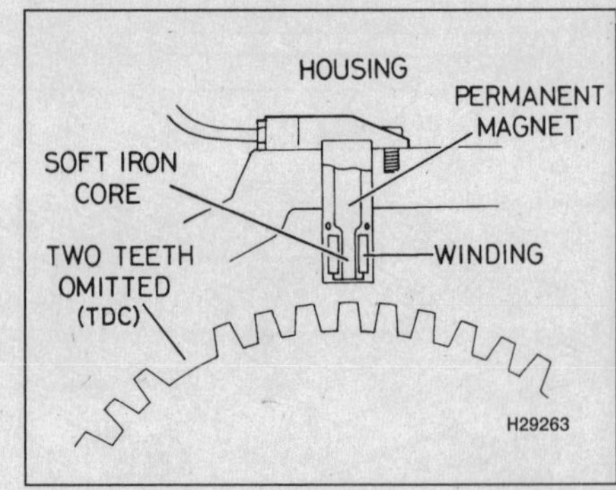

2.19 Bosch distributor with inductive trigger

If a reluctor containing one arm for every cylinder is connected to the distributor cam and rotated within the magnetic field, an AC voltage will be generated.

The AC voltage will fluctuate between positive and negative, and when the arm on the reluctor and stator are directly opposite, the voltage will change from positive to negative. This is the moment of trigger. Two wires connect the trigger unit to the module, and the module will amplify this signal to switch off the coil negative terminal. Without amplification, the signal would be too weak to accomplish this aim.

From the switch-off point, the module can determine the switch-on point and therefore calculate the correct dwell duration.

Crank angle sensor (CAS)

The CAS works on the same principle as the inductive signal generator. A number of steel pegs or pins are set at regular intervals around the circumference of the flywheel or crankshaft. Typically, a pin may be set at every 10° - thirty-six in all - but the number does vary between different VM's. The flywheel thus becomes a reluctor.

A permanent magnet inductive signal generator is mounted in close proximity to the flywheel, where it radiates a magnetic field. As the flywheel spins and the pins are rotated in the magnetic field, an alternating (AC) waveform is delivered to the ECM to indicate speed of rotation.

If a pin is intentionally omitted at two points on the flywheel, or by contrast a double pin is used, the signal will vary at these points, and a reference to TDC will be returned to the ECM. The location of the positional signal is not at TDC, but may be at 90° BTDC or some other point fixed by the VM.

In addition, as the flywheel spins, the missing pins or double pins cause a variance of the signal which is returned to the ECM as reference to the TDC position.

Although most modern systems utilise a single CAS, some of the older systems use two CAS - one for RPM and one for position. The waveform produced by each type of CAS will be slightly different.

The peak-to-peak voltage of the speed signal varies according to engine speed, and can vary from 5 volts at idle to over 100 volts at 6000 rpm. Because computers prefer their data as on/off signals, an analogue-to-digital converter (ADC) transforms the AC pulse into a digital signal **(see illustration 2.20)**.

When used, the CAS provides the primary signal to initiate both ignition and fuelling.

Hall-effect trigger operation

Hall-effect ignition is usually fitted to vehicles equipped with a distributor, and this is where the Hall switch is located. The module supplies a voltage slightly under nbv to the Hall-effect switch in the distributor. An earth return wire completes the circuit back to the module. Opposite the Hall switch is a magnet whose field causes the switch to return a small voltage back to the module. Attached to the distributor shaft is a rotor with the same number of cut-outs as cylinders. Passing the rotor between the switch and the magnet will cause the switch to be turned off and on. As the cut-out space proceeds past the switch, a voltage is returned to the amplifier via a third wire termed the output wire. When the solid portion comes between the switch and magnet, the voltage is turned off as the magnetic field is diverted. The number of voltages returned per four-stroke engine cycle will equal the number of cut-outs. Essentially then, the voltage signal returned is either voltage or no voltage, and the waveform produced is that of a square wave.

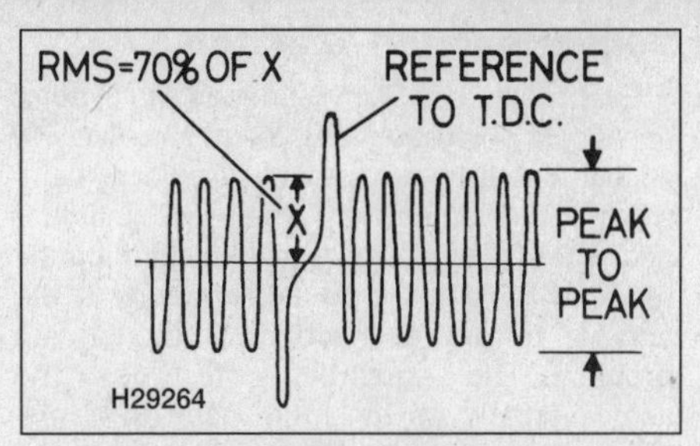

2.20 AC voltage waveform from inductive trigger

The main advantage of the Hall-effect signal is that output is in digital form, and this means faster processing by the ECM. However, Hall-effect ignition is usually fitted to vehicles equipped with a distributor, and since the modern trend is to remove the distributor, Hall-effect ignition is tending to be less used in modern vehicles.

When used, the Hall-effect sensor provides the primary signal to initiate both ignition and fuelling.

6 Electronic fuel injection systems

General

The AFR in carburettor systems varies according to intake air temperature and density. This makes accurate control of the correct mixture strength virtually impossible. In contrast, the electronic fuel injection system uses a number of sensors to monitor all conditions that will affect the AFR, and responds very quickly to the changing operating conditions. This means that very accurate control of the mixture is possible.

The ECM is programmed to calculate a basic fuel injection duration. This is the time that the ECM will actually hold the injector open, and is usually measured in milliseconds (ms). Data from the engine sensors, which include the AFS or MAP sensor, the TPS or throttle pot, and the CTS and ATS is collected and used by the ECM to modify this figure so that the quantity of injected fuel is computed exactly for all conditions of temperature, speed and load. The ECM will also actuate the ISCV to automatically control idle speed depending on coolant temperature and engine load at idle.

There are several different kinds of injection system in current use, but the three main types are:

Simultaneous multi-point fuel injection (MPi)
Single point injection (SPi)
Sequential fuel injection

Simultaneous multi-point injection (MPi)

This is the most common type of injection system in current use. A number of injectors are looped together in a parallel 'bank', with a single connection to the ECM. Where an engine has more than one bank, each bank has its own ECM connection.

In a 4-cylinder engine, one bank connects all of the injectors. In a 6-cylinder engine, the injectors are placed in two groups of three, and an 8-cylinder engine has two groups of four; V6 and V8 engine injector groups are termed left or right 'bank'. In 12-cylinder engines, the injectors are placed into four groups of three cylinders. Two power resistors control two groups each.

The injectors are triggered from a reference signal, which may originate from the ignition system or from a timing pulse at the CAS. Normally, the injectors operate twice per complete engine cycle. Half of the fuel required is injected onto the back of a closed inlet valve, waiting for it to open, and the other half is injected as the valve opens for the intake stroke. Once the valve has opened, the fuel enters the cylinder in the normal way **(see illustration 2.21)**.

This system is fairly effective and usually works quite well. It is also cheaper to develop than a full-blown sequential system, which makes it very popular amongst vehicle manufacturers.

However, a particular type of fault can sometimes afflict vehicles with a high mileage (or sometimes even a low mileage). What happens is that a build-up of carbon on the back of the inlet valve allows the injected fuel to 'soak' into the carbon whilst awaiting its

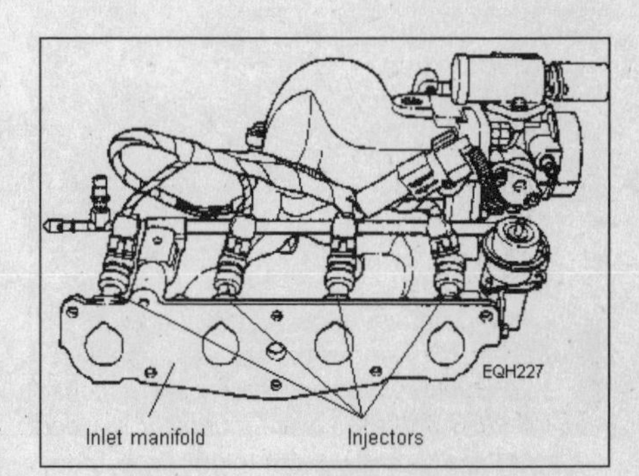

2.21 Multi-point injection system

2

turn to be injected into the cylinder. This can cause a slight hesitation on acceleration, as the air fuel ratio becomes too lean. A decoke is the only real cure.

Single point injection (SPi)

Sometimes known as 'throttle body injection', the SPi system has gained much popularity over recent years. Essentially less costly, SPi uses the same sensors as the MPi systems. A single injector (normally of the current-controlled type) injects fuel into a distributing manifold in much the same fashion as a carburettor.

Although the injection of fuel is much more precise, the problems of manifold heating becomes critical and the warm-up period must be carefully controlled if driveability is not to be impaired. Furthermore, the manifold is said to be of the 'wet' type. This term means that fuel is present in the manifold. In contrast, a multi-point injection system is said to be of the 'dry' type because fuel is injected into the inlet stub to the valve, and thus only air is present in the manifold.

Due to emission considerations, SPi may now be used less in future vehicles because noxious exhaust emissions tend to be greater than with other types of injection **(see illustration 2.22)**.

Current-controlled/pulse-modulated, and peak-and-hold injector

Some systems rely on the principle that more current is required to open the injector than to actually keep it open. The injector solenoid circuit is also earthed - but for only about one millisecond (ms: one thousandth of a second) - which is just long enough to open the injector. The opening circuit is then switched off, and another circuit rapidly closed and opened, to apply a small holding current to the injector so that it remains open for the correct time duration. The pulsing is so blindingly fast that the injector does not have time to close, and current flow is therefore much reduced. This type of system is known as 'current-controlled' or 'pulse-modulated'. A variation of this method is termed 'peak-and-hold'. After the initial pulse, the second circuit holds the injector open without the rapid pulse modulation.

2.22 Nissan single point injection system and hot film AFS

Sequential fuel injection

Eventually, both simultaneous multi-point and single point injection systems are likely to succumb to the sequential multi-point system, where the injectors open in cylinder sequence. Emissions can be significantly reduced with this type - particularly if the engine suffers a mechanical or ignition problem. The sequential system uses the same sensors as the multi-point systems. However, an additional sensor pinpoints the correct cylinder for the sequential system. The most common form of sensor used to indicate a specific cylinder is one that generates an AC signal similar to the signal generated by the CAS. This sensor is often attached to the camshaft. A Hall-effect device located in the distributor is another sensor sometimes employed.

7 Fuel injection system engine sensors

The electronic fuel system comprises a number of components. The components can be divided into two groups - sensors and actuators. Sensors send data to the ECM so that it can actuate the injector and idle control correctly. The electronic fuel injection system therefore consists of the following components.

All engine sensors have a resistance that responds to either temperature or load. As the temperature or load varies, the resistance value of the sensor also varies. In turn, a resistance variation will cause a variation in the voltage being returned to the ECM. By measuring this voltage, according to certain parameters, we can ascertain correct operation of any particular sensor at a range of engine temperatures or loads.

Injection system sensors can generally be divided into several groups. The first and second group contain sensors that are termed variable signal output types. We could define the sensors in these groups as being either a two-wire or a three-wire type. The third group may have a combination of two- and three-wire sensors incorporated into its body. An example of this type is the AFS fitted to many Bosch systems. This AFS combines the AFS, ATS and CO pot into the AFS unit - all with a common earth. The final group contains sensors that are basically switches (ie Lambda and TPS).

The two-wire sensors utilise an earth wire and a 5-volt supply wire in a circuit that begins and ends at the ECM. The supply wire also doubles as the output wire in the following manner. Once the supply and earth wires are connected to the sensor, the resistance value of the sensor causes the voltage value of the supply to vary. Thus, if we take an example of a two-wire CTS, the supply value of 5 volts will reduce (typically) to between two and three volts if the engine is cold (20°C), and to between 0.6 and 0.8 volts once the engine has become warm (80°C). Examples would include the ATS, CTS and CO pot.

The three-wire sensor has a voltage supply of 5 volts, an earth connection (often made through the ECM) and an output (signal) wire. The output wire returns a variable voltage signal to the ECM. The two most common forms of output are by resistance track and wiper arm, or via a transducer. Examples would include the AFS and TP (wiper arm) and MAP (transducer).

Load sensor

The sensor which detects the load placed upon the engine may be the AFS, MAP sensor or even the TPS. The ECM will detect the load from the signal that is returned from whichever of the three components is used. The AFS signals the volume of air that passes into the engine, the MAP sensor signals the absolute pressure from the depression in the inlet manifold with respect to atmospheric pressure, and the TPS signals the throttle position. However, the first two are more commonly used to signal the main load, and although the TPS is sometimes used to signal load without aid of another sensor, in practice the signal from the TPS is more usually used to trim the signal that is returned from one of the other two sensors.

Vane-type airflow sensor (AFS)

The AFS is normally located between the air filter and the throttle body. As air flows through the sensor, it deflects a vane (flap). The greater the volume of air, the more will the flap be deflected. The vane is connected to a wiper arm which wipes a potentiometer resistance track and so varies the resistance of the track. This allows a variable voltage signal to be returned to the ECM **(see illustration 2.23)**.

Three wires are used by the circuitry of this sensor, and it is often referred to as a three-wire sensor. A 5-volt reference voltage is applied to the resistance track with the other end connected to the sensor earth return. The third wire is connected to the wiper arm.

From the voltage returned, the ECM is able to calculate the volume of air (load) entering the engine and this is used to calculate the main fuel injection duration. To smooth out

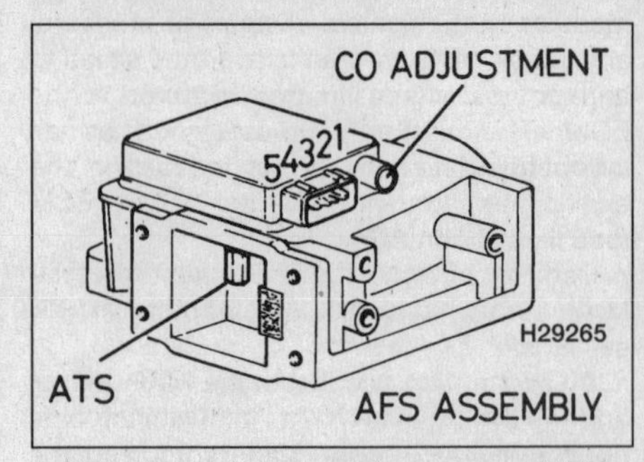

2.23 Motronic type airflow sensor (AFS)

inlet pulses, a damper is connected to the AFS vane. The AFS exerts a major influence on the volume of fuel injected.

Hot-wire airflow sensor (AFS) - often termed 'mass airflow meter'

Because the volume, temperature and density of air, at all altitudes is accurately measured - the hot-wire or hot-film AFS is becoming increasingly popular as a technically superior alternative to the vane and MAP sensor types (refer to illustration 2.22).

The AFS may be mounted in the airflow trunking between the air filter and the engine, or on the throttle body. A voltage of either 5 or 12 volts, according to system, is applied to the AFS unit.

Air passes through the AFS body into the engine. A small quantity of air is drawn into a by-pass channel containing two wires. These wires are known as the sensing wire and the compensating wire.

A small current is applied to the compensating wire, which remains unheated. As air passes over the wire, its resistance and current change and the AFS is able to determine the temperature of the incoming air. The sensing wire is heated to a temperature of 100°C above that of the compensating wire. Air passing over the sensing wire causes it to become cooler, and its current and resistance values change. More current is passed through the sensing wire so that it remains 100°C above that of the compensating wire. An output voltage, proportional to the current applied to the sensing wire, is returned to the ECM.

The value of this voltage is directly related to the volume, temperature and density of air introduced into the engine. The beauty of the hot-wire system allows automatic compensation for altitudes from sea-level to mountain top, and the ECM will correctly calculate the AFR under virtually all conditions.

Manifold absolute pressure (MAP) sensor

The MAP sensor is often used as an inexpensive alternative to the airflow meter. It is less accurate than the various forms of AFS but is often chosen on grounds of cost rather than its technical attributes. The MAP sensor measures the manifold vacuum or pressure, and uses a transducer to convert the signal to an electrical signal which is returned to the ECM. The unit may be designed as an independent sensor that is located in the engine compartment or integral with the ECM **(see illustration 2.24)**.

Used in both MPi and SPi systems, the MAP sensor is particularly popular in SPi systems.

A vacuum hose connects the MAP sensor and the inlet manifold. Manifold vacuum acts upon the MAP sensor diaphragm, and the ECM internally converts the pressure into an electrical signal. MAP is calculated from the formula: Atmospheric Pressure less Manifold Pressure = Manifold Absolute Pressure.

2.24 Manifold absolute pressure (MAP) sensor assembly

1 *MAP sensor*
2 *Mounting screws (some units are simply clipped into a bracket*
3 *MAP sensor vacuum line (goes to intake manifold vacuum)*
4 *MAP sensor electrical connector (usually goes to main harness)*

Using the speed/density method, the ECM calculates the AFR from the MAP signal and the speed of the engine. The speed/density method is based on the theory that the engine will draw in a fixed volume of air per revolution. This method can never be as accurate as using an AFS to accurately measure airflow and then calculating the AFR from the volume or mass of air that is entering the engine.

When manifold vacuum is high (ie idle condition), MAP is moderately low and the ECM provides less fuel. When manifold vacuum is low (ie wide-open throttle), MAP is high and the ECM provides more fuel.

MAP sensors may take one of two forms. The most common form is the analogue sensor where the voltage output is proportional to the load. The other form is that of a digital sensor which is mainly used by the Ford EEC IV system.

A digital MAP sensor sends a square waveform in the form of a frequency. As the load increases, the frequency also increases and the time in ms between pulses becomes shorter. An ECM will respond much faster to a digital signal, because an analogue-to-digital converter is no longer necessary.

Where the manifold is of the 'wet' type (ie SPi), the changing pressures in the manifold will cause fuel to enter the vacuum hose, where it may eventually reach the MAP sensor. Installation of a fuel trap and careful routing of the vacuum hose may slow down the ingress of fuel. However, once fuel reaches the MAP sensor, its diaphragm may be adversely affected. If the MAP sensor is an independent unit, renewal is comparatively inexpensive. A new ECM may be necessary for the integral types.

The inlet manifold on MPi models is a 'dry' manifold. Since fuel does not enter the manifold - due to injection onto the back of the inlet valve - there is no risk of fuel being drawn into the MAP sensor to contaminate the diaphragm, and a fuel trap is not used.

Cylinder identification sensor (sequential injection engines only)

In non-sequential systems, the ECM does not recognise number one cylinder, or indeed even the firing order. This is because it is deemed unnecessary. When the crankshaft or distributor provides a timing signal, the correct cylinder is identified by the mechanical position of the crankshaft, camshaft, valves and ignition rotor.

On models fitted with sequential injection, the ECM must determine which cylinder is on its firing stroke, and the CID sensor provides the appropriate signal. The CID sensor operates on the inductive principle, and is a permanent magnet device mounted adjacent to the camshaft. The operation of this sensor differs according to VM, and a more detailed description will be described in the appropriate Chapter.

Air and coolant temperature sensors

These sensors are thermistors that usually work on the NTC principle. A number of vehicles fitted with the Renix system may use sensors that work on the PTC principle. As the temperature changes, the thermistor resistance changes, and thus the ECM is able to calculate the air and engine coolant temperature from the level of voltage (or current) that is registered on the sensor signal wire **(see illustration 2.25)**.

NTC & PTC (negative & positive temperature co-efficient)

An NTC resistor decreases (negatively) in resistance as the temperature rise, and a PTC type increases (positively) on temperature rise. Both types are example of the two-wire resistor, but in one case the voltage increases and in the other case the voltage decreases.

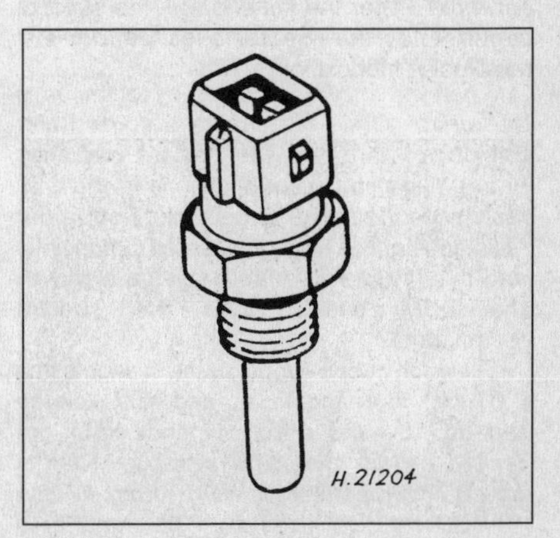

2.25 Typical air or coolant temperature sensor (ATS or CTS)

Air temperature sensor (ATS)

The ATS is a two-wire thermistor that measures the air temperature in the manifold. Because the density of air varies in inverse proportion to the temperature, the ATS signal allows more accurate assessment of the volume of air entering the engine.

The open circuit supply to the sensor is applied at 5.0 volt reference level, and the earth path is usually made through the sensor return. A variable voltage signal is returned to the ECM based upon the air temperature.

The ATS may be mounted in various locations according to the design features of a particular vehicle or model. Locations may include the inlet manifold, air filter or AFS intake. The location has an important bearing on the air temperature range that is sensed in any particular engine.

The range of the air temperature signal will vary considerably between a cold and a hot engine according to the location of the ATS. For example, when the ATS is located in the air filter inlet or in the AFS intake, the air temperature will vary according to engine compartment heat, and the range is likely to be in the range of 20°C to 40°C. However, when the ATS is mounted in the inlet manifold or in the throttle body (some SPi systems), the temperature range will be much greater because the air temperature may reach 70°C when the engine is hot.

Some vehicles may utilise two sensors, one to measure ambient air temperature in the engine compartment, and the other to measure the intake air temperature. This may be particularly important in turbocharged applications.

Although the majority of vehicles are equipped with an ATS that conforms to the NTC principle, a number of vehicles that are fitted with the Renix system may use sensors that work on the PTC principle.

Coolant temperature sensor (CTS)

The CTS is a two-wire thermistor that measures the coolant temperature. The CTS is immersed in the engine coolant, and contains a variable resistor that usually operates on the NTC principle.

When the engine is cold, the resistance is quite high. Once the engine is started and begins to warm-up, the coolant becomes hotter, and this causes a change in the CTS resistance. As the CTS becomes hotter, the resistance of the CTS reduces (NTC principle) and this returns a variable voltage signal to the ECM based upon the coolant temperature.

The open circuit supply to the sensor is at a 5.0 volt reference level, and this voltage reduces to a value that depends upon the resistance of the CTS resistor. Normal operating temperature is usually from 80°C to 100°C. The ECM uses the CTS signal as a main correction factor when calculating ignition timing and injection duration.

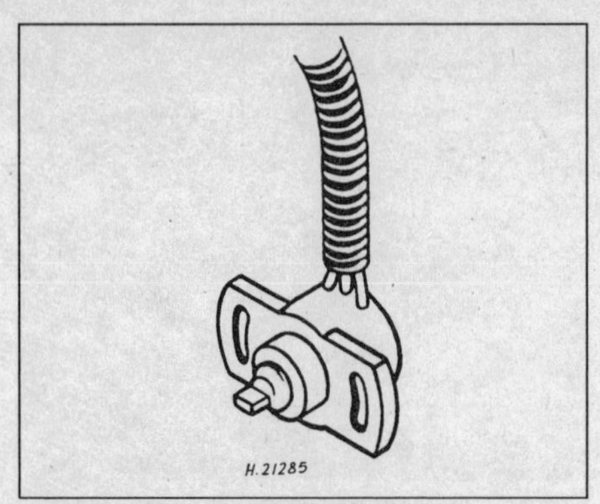

2.26 Typical throttle potentiometer sensor (TPS)

A number of vehicles fitted with the Renix system may use sensors that work on the PTC principle. In this case, the resistance and voltage will rise as the temperature rises.

Throttle signals

Throttle position may be signalled by a simple switch (TS), a potentiometer (TPS), or even a combination switch that contains both a TS and TPS. Sometimes, both switches are present in a system as separate components.

Throttle potentiometer sensor (TPS)

A TPS is provided to inform the ECM of idle position, deceleration, rate of acceleration and wide-open throttle (WOT) conditions. The TPS is a potentiometer with three wires. A 5-volt reference voltage is supplied to a resistance track with the other end connected to the sensor earth return. The third wire is connected to an arm which wipes along the resistance track and so varies the resistance and voltage of the signal returned to the ECM **(see illustration 2.26)**.

From the voltage returned, the ECM is able to calculate idle position (usually less than 0.7 volts), full-load (approximately 4.5 volts) and also how quickly the throttle is opened. During full-load operation, the ECM provides additional enrichment. During closed throttle operation above a certain rpm (deceleration), the ECM will cut off fuel injection. Injection will be reintroduced once the rpm returns to idle or the throttle is opened. It is adjustable on some models.

Throttle switch (TS)

The throttle switch informs the ECM when the engine is in idle mode. An additional contact is also usually provided to indicate wide-open throttle (WOT). Additional enrichment is often provided at idle and during full-throttle running. Each TS contact has two conditions - that of closed or open and the ECM is therefore able to recognise three different engine situations:

1) *Throttle closed (idle contact closed).*
2) *Throttle open (idle contact open and WOT contact open).*
3) *Throttle wide open (idle contact open and WOT contact closed).*

The TS is adjustable on some models.

Mixture adjustment

Catalyst-equipped vehicles often have no form of CO adjustment. Where adjustment is possible, turning the screw only effects small changes in CO - and then only at the idle position. Once the throttle is opened from its idle stop, the volume of fuel injected depends entirely upon the pulse duration. There are two different types of CO adjustment in current use:

1) *An air screw that varies air volume through an idle passage. As the screw position is varied, airflow acting upon the metering flap varies, causing the flap to change its idle position. The changed position results in an altered signal to the ECM, and the idle mixture will either increase or decrease. Usually fitted to older type vehicles.*
2) *A potentiometer ('pot') that varies the voltage signal being returned to the ECM. This sensor may be mounted upon the ECM, on the airflow meter, or even upon the inner engine compartment wing. It may be of the two- or three-wire type.*

CO pot (non-cat models only)

The CO pot mixture adjuster is a potentiometer that allows small changes to be made to the idle CO. The CO pot may be mounted directly on the ECM, or may be a separate three-wire sensor that is mounted in the engine compartment or on the AFS. In the case of the three-wire sensor, a 5.0 volt reference voltage is applied to the sensor and connected to the sensor earth return circuit. The third wire is the variable CO pot signal **(see illustration 2.27)**.

As the CO pot adjustment screw is turned, the change in resistance returns a voltage signal to the ECM that will result in a change in CO.

8 Fuel injection system actuators

Fuel injector

The injector is a solenoid-operated valve that delivers an exact amount of fuel according to an opening duration signal from the ECM. Voltage to the injector is applied from the main relay or ignition switch, and the

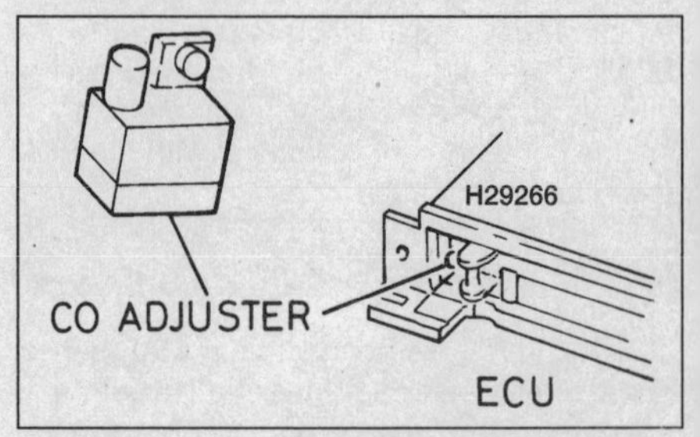

2.27 CO pot, external and ECM-located

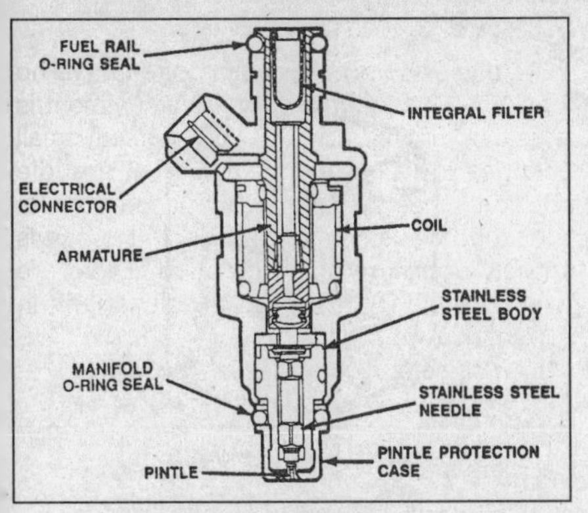

2.28 Fuel injector

earth path is completed by the ECM for a period of time (called pulse duration) of between 1.5 and 10 milliseconds. The pulse duration is very much dependent upon engine temperature, load, speed and operating conditions. When the magnetic solenoid closes, a back EMF voltage of up to 60 volts is induced **(see illustration 2.28)**.

Essentially, the injector is simply earthed by the ECM for a calculated period of time, During this time, the injector solenoid operates and fuel is injected.

A fine filter is used to prevent debris damaging the precision action. However, gums and lacquers can build-up on this filter and on the injection pintle, eventually reducing fuel flow. Injection fouling is a serious problem on many injection systems.

The fuel injectors are mounted in the inlet stubs to the engine inlet valves, so that a finely-atomised fuel spray is directed onto the back of each valve. When injectors are pulsed simultaneously, fuel will briefly rest upon the back of a valve before being drawn into a cylinder.

Idle speed control

Most modern vehicles have fully-automatic idle control, with no means of manual adjustment. Where adjustment is possible, this is usually effected by placing the idle system outside of the ECM's jurisdiction, and setting a base idle speed with a by-pass idle speed air screw.

Most modern systems utilise an ECM-controlled ISCV or stepper motor to maintain idle speed under engine load. This prevents poor idle and stalling with heavy electrical loads and a lean mixture; the automatic idle system is also used to provide a higher idle during engine warm-up.

A small volume of air is allowed to by-pass the throttle plate. This air may pass through a hose, or through a port in the inlet manifold. The ISCV is mounted *in situ*, thus allowing the by-pass air to pass through the body of the valve. If the amount of air in the by-pass is varied, the idle speed can also be varied.

ISCV (Bosch 3-wire)

Early Bosch systems use an ISCV attached to an DC electric motor that can be rotated

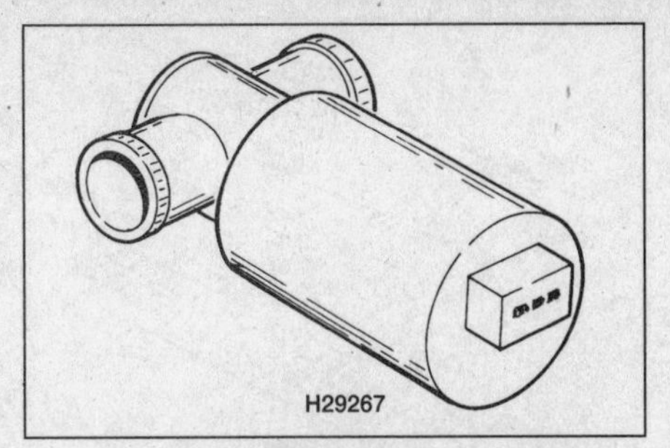

2.29 Idle speed control valve (ISCV), three-wire

clockwise or anti-clockwise by virtue of two opposing circuits **(see illustration 2.29)**. The motor is supplied with a voltage supply and two earth paths that are made through the ECM. When one path is earthed, the motor will attempt to rotate in one direction, and vice-versa. This prevents the valve from being fully opened or closed in one particular direction. The valve will thus take up an average position that reflects circuit bias to be open or closed. Normally, this bias would be towards the open position. By varying the time that each circuit is energised, the ECM will place the ISCV in the exact position required. A duty cycle can be measured on each earth circuit to determine the opening or closing time period as a percentage of the total time available.

ISCV (Bosch 2-wire)

Later Bosch systems use a solenoid that is opposed by a strong spring. The solenoid is supplied with a voltage supply and one earth path, made through the ECM **(see illustration 2.30)**. When the ISCV is earthed by the ECM, the solenoid will overcome the spring force and open the ISCV. If the solenoid fails, it will normally fail-safe closed. However, even when closed, a small amount of air will travel through the valve to give a basic (but low) idle speed.

The longer time that the ECM energises (holds open) the ISCV, the further open it will become. However, this process occurs many times a second (the frequency is about 110 Hz), and by varying the time that the

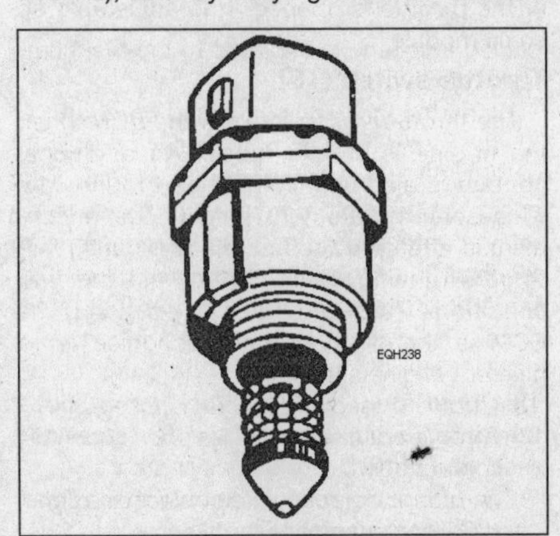

2.31 Idle control, stepper motor

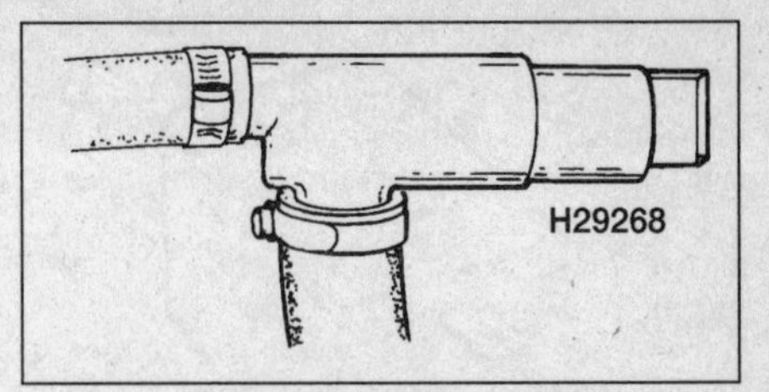

2.30 Idle speed control valve (ISCV), two-wire

circuit is energised, the ECM will place the ISCV in the exact position required. A duty cycle for the time energised can be obtained on the ISCV earth terminal, or at the corresponding ECM pin.

Ford ISCV

Ford use an ISCV which is very similar in operation to the later Bosch two-wire type. However, due to the use of a diode, the ISCV waveform is distorted to that of a sawtooth.

Stepper motor

The stepper motor may take several forms, and here are described the two most common systems:

1) *A motor is used to drive a valve which opens or closes an air by-pass passage in the inlet manifold* ***(see illustration 2.31)****.*
2) *A motor is used to increment the throttle plate by so many steps, thereby allowing more or less air through the opening.*

Usually the motor is fed with a battery voltage supply connected to four earth paths. By pulsing the motor using a combination of the earth paths, the motor can be stepped to the correct position.

Auxiliary air valve (AAV)

The AAV is a control valve that is used to increase the idle speed during cold engine operation. It is mainly used in fairly early systems, and is not controlled by the ECM. The AAV is mounted in a hose that by-passes the throttle plate. A circular gate valve responds to temperature and allows extra air to by-pass the throttle when the engine is cold. During cold engine operation, the valve is open and so engine idle speed is increased. As the engine warms-up, the gate valve gradually closes until it is fully closed at normal operating temperature. In fact, the AAV is usually fully closed within 2 to 4 minutes of the engine starting from cold **(see illustration 2.32)**.

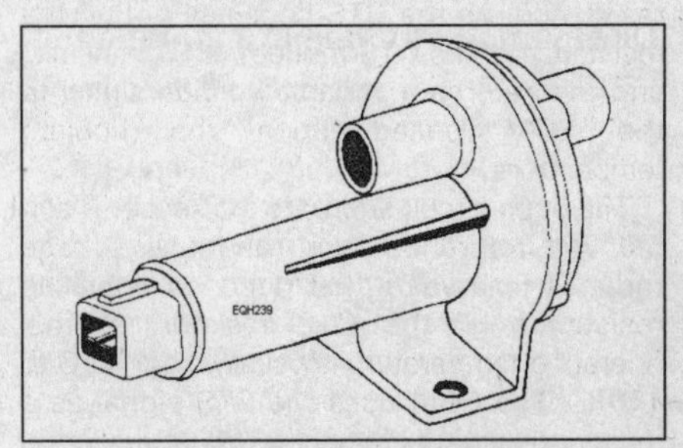

2.32 Auxiliary air valve (AAV)

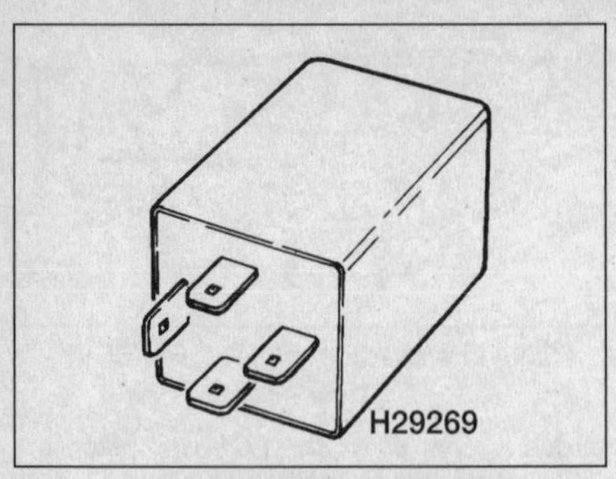

2.33 Standard four-pin relay

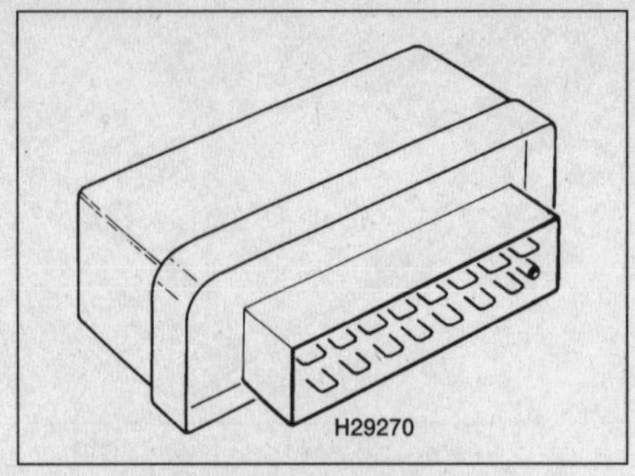

2.34 Fifteen-pin relay

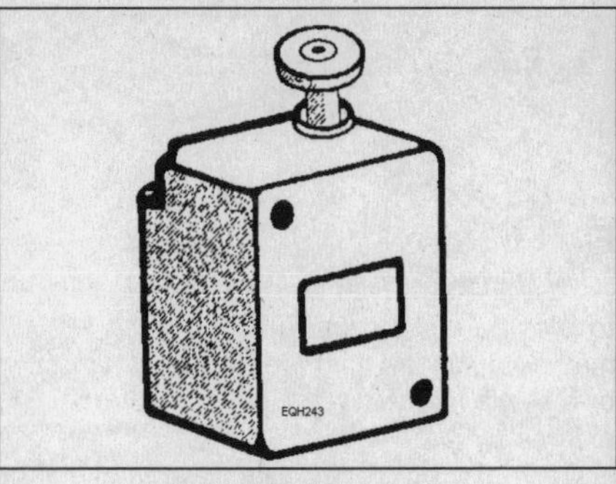

2.35 Inertia switch

The AAV is usually connected to the fuel pump relay output terminal, so that it will only operate during the time that the engine is actually running. Radiated heat from the engine will affect valve operation, and allow the valve to remain closed when the engine is hot and is not being operated.

Vehicle speed sensor (VSS)

The VSS is used to advise the ECM of vehicle speed. Typically. The VSS operates upon the Hall-effect principle, and is often mounted on the gearbox or speedometer.

A voltage of approximately 12 volts is applied to the VSS from the ignition switch. As the speedometer cable turns, the Hall switch is alternately turned on and off, to return a square wave signal to the ECM. The signal frequency usually denotes the vehicle speed.

Fuel injection system relays

Due to the variations between the different systems, it is impossible to mention all the various relay combinations. The following is generally correct, although there are a number of systems that may use other methods.

One system relay may be used to control the whole fuel injection system. In that instance, the relay will have double contacts. Alternatively, two relays may be used to control the system. In that instance, the output from the main system relay will be used to supply the energising voltage to the second (fuel pump) relay.

In this book, the relay terminal numbers are usually annotated to the DIN standard, to which most (but not all) European VM's subscribe. In some instances, however, the VM will use his own method of terminal marking **(see illustrations 2.33 and 2.34)**.

DIN method of terminal annotation

30 *Supply voltage direct from the battery positive terminal.*

31 *Earth return direct to the battery (little used in modern systems, may be found in older fuel injection systems).*

85 *Relay earth for energising system. May be connected direct to earth, or connected to earth through the ECM.*

85b *Relay earth for output. May be connected direct to earth, or connected to earth through the ECM.*

86 *Energising system supply. May be applied from the battery positive or through the ignition switch.*

87 *Output from the first relay or first relay winding. This terminal will often provide power to the second relay terminal 86 and provide voltage to the ECM, injectors, ISCV etc.*

87b *Output from the second relay or second relay winding. Often provides power to the fuel pump and OS etc.*

Note: *In some relays, the terminals 30 & 87/87b and /or terminal 85 & 86 may be reversed. This is so that the internal relay diode protection path is reversed, and prevents voltage spikes during relay actuation from reversing and creating a short circuit.*

Main and fuel pump relays (separate relays)

Where this set-up is used, the engine electrical system is controlled by a main fuel injection relay and a fuel pump relay. A permanent voltage supply is made to the main relay terminal 30 and fuel pump relay terminal 30 from the battery positive terminal. When the ignition is switched on, a voltage supply is made to fuel injection terminal 86, and this energises the relay winding which is connected to earth. This causes the relay contacts to close and terminal 30 is connected to the output circuit at terminal 87 or 87b. A voltage supply is thus output at this terminal, which normally supplies voltage to the injectors, the ECM and the ISCV. In addition, voltage is supplied to the fuel pump relay terminal 86.

When the ignition is switched on, the ECM briefly earths the fuel pump relay contact 87 or 87b at the appropriate ECM pin. This energises the relay winding, which closes the relay contact and connects voltage from terminal 30 to the output terminal 87 or 87b, thereby providing voltage to the fuel pump circuit. After approximately one second, the ECM opens the circuit and the pump stops. This brief running of the fuel pump allows pressure to build within the fuel pressure lines, and provides for an easier start.

The fuel pump relay circuit will then remain open until the engine is cranked or run. Once the ECM receives a speed signal, the relay winding will again be energised by the ECM, and the fuel pump will run until the engine is stopped.

Main and fuel pump relays (single 'dual' relay)

Where this set-up is used, the electrical system is protected by a single relay with dual contacts. There are a number of different kinds of dual relay, and each will be described more specifically under the appropriate Chapter heading. Some relays (eg GM dual type) use the DIN annotation method, other types (eg Magneti Marelli dual type) use other methods of annotation. However, the following statements are generally true.

A permanent voltage supply is made to the relay terminals from the battery positive terminal. When the ignition is switched on, a voltage supply is connected to earth which energises the first relay winding. When the relay winding is energised, this causes the relay contacts to close and a voltage supply is output to the appropriate ECM pin and to the injectors, ISCV and a further terminal of the relay.

When the ignition is switched on. the ECM briefly earths the fuel pump driver at the appropriate ECM pin. This energises the second relay winding, which closes the second relay contact and connects voltage to the fuel pump circuit. After approximately one second, the ECM opens the circuit and the pump stops. This brief running of the fuel pump allows pressure to build within the fuel pressure lines, and provides for an easier start.

The second circuit will then remain open until the engine is cranked or run. Once the ECM receives a speed signal from the CAS, the second winding will again be energised by the ECM, and the fuel pump, ignition and injection will run until the engine is stopped.

Inertia switch

The inertia switch is a safety cut-out switch used to isolate the fuel pump in the event of a very sharp deceleration - ie a collision. Once the switch has been activated, the electrical supply to the fuel pump remain open circuit until the inertia switch has been reset **(see illustration 2.35)**.

9 Fuel pressure system

Fuel pump

The VM uses a number of different methods to provide fuel to the Injection rail. A system may be designed with a single external pump or a single internal pump, or both internal and external.

Generally, both internal and external pumps are of the 'wet' variety, in that fuel actually flows through the pump and the electric motor. There is no actual fire risk, because the fuel drawn through the pump is not in a combustible condition. The system for MPi and SPi are fairly similar, although the SPi operates at a much lower pressure.

The fuel pump normally provides much more fuel than is required, and surplus fuel is thus returned to the fuel tank via a return pipe. In fact, a maximum fuel pressure in excess of 5 bar is possible in MPi systems. To prevent pressure loss in the supply system, a non-return valve is provided in the fuel pump outlet. When the ignition is switched off, and the fuel pump ceases operation, pressure is thus maintained for some time. A fuel pulsation damper may also be fitted in the fuel line - close to the fuel filter - to reduce noise from the injectors.

External fuel pump

A roller-type fuel pump, driven by a permanent magnet electric motor mounted close to the fuel tank, draws fuel from the tank and pumps it to the fuel rail via a fuel filter **(see illustration 2.36)**.

Mounted on the armature shaft is an eccentric rotor, holding a number of pockets arranged around the circumference - each pocket containing a metal roller. As the pump is actuated, the rollers are flung outward by centrifugal force to act as seals. The fuel between the rollers is forced to the pump pressure outlet. A fuel pressure damper is mounted before the fuel rail, to reduce the pulsating effects of pump operation. The appearance of the damper is similar to the pressure regulator, but without a vacuum pipe.

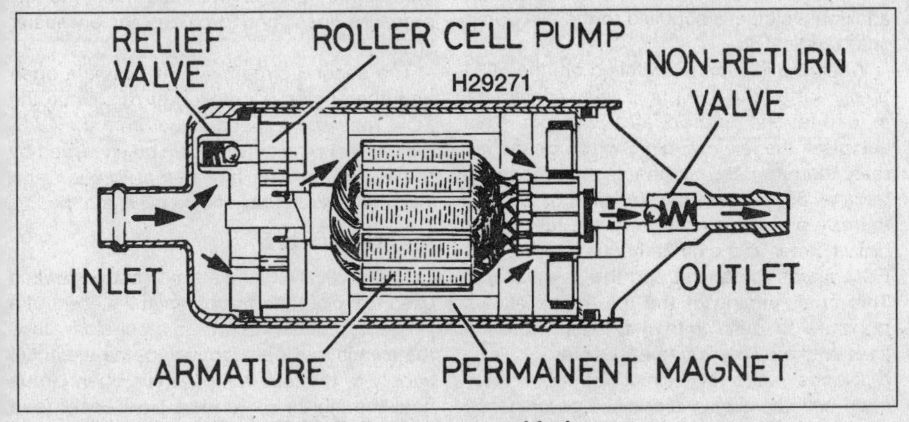

2.36 Roller-type external fuel pump

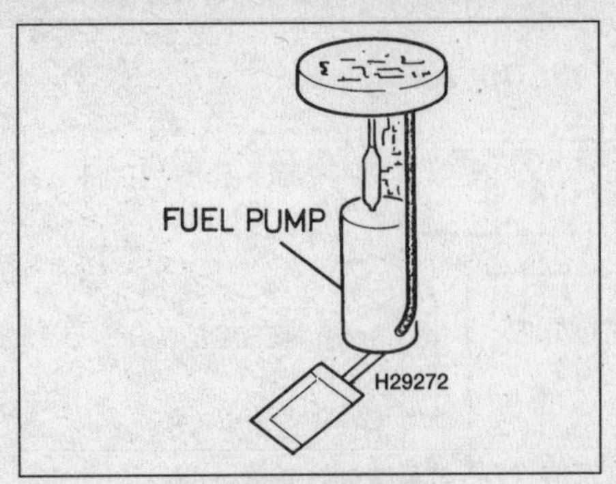

2.37 Internal fuel pump

Internal fuel pump

The fuel pump is mounted vertically in the fuel tank, and comprises an outer and inner gear assembly, termed a 'gerotor'. Once the pump motor becomes energised, the gerotor rotates, and as the fuel passes through the individual teeth of the gerotor, a pressure differential is created. Fuel is drawn through the pump inlet, to be pressurised between the rotating gerotor teeth and discharged from the pump outlet into the fuel supply line **(see illustration 2.37)**.

Fuel pressure regulator

The fuel pump supplies fuel to the fuel rail at a pressure that exceeds the required system pressure. The function of the fuel pressure regulator is to maintain a constant pressure, and allow excess fuel to flow back to the tank via a fuel return line **(see illustration 2.38)**.

The pressure regulator is fitted on the outlet side of the fuel rail, and consists of two chambers separated by a diaphragm. The upper chamber contains a spring which exerts pressure upon the lower chamber and closes off the outlet diaphragm. Pressurised fuel flows into the lower chamber, and this exerts pressure upon the diaphragm. Once pressure exceeds a pre-designated value, the outlet diaphragm opens, and excess fuel flows back to the fuel tank via the fuel return line.

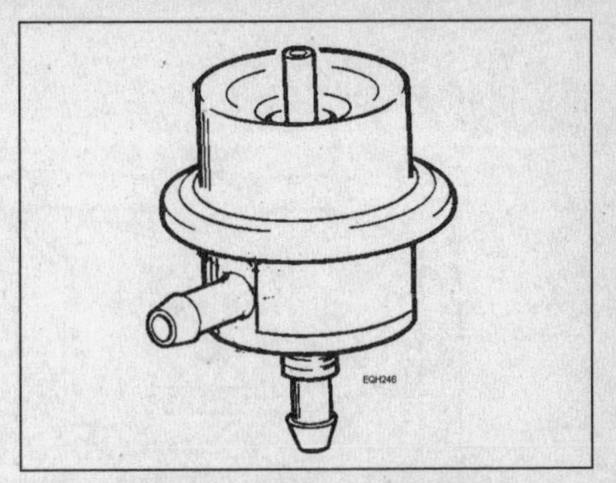

2.38 Fuel pressure regulator

It is important that fuel pressure in the fuel rail is maintained at a constant pre-set pressure. This is usually about 2.5 to 3.0 bar in MPi systems, and 1.0 bar in SPi systems. When constant pressure is achieved, the opening time of the fuel injector will be the prime factor that influences the quantity of injected fuel delivered to the engine, as determined by the ECM, and not on a variable fuel pressure. If the fuel pressure were to vary, so too would the volume of fuel delivered through the injector for any given period of injection open time.

In MPi systems, there is another factor that creates a variation in fuel pressure, and this is the negative pressure in the inlet manifold. As the depression in the inlet manifold varies according to throttle opening, so too will the depression acting upon the injector needle. This will affect the volume of fuel that is injected. By connecting the pressure regulator to the inlet manifold via a short length of vacuum hose, the fuel pressure will increase on acceleration to give a richer mixture and reduce during cruising to give a leaner mixture. However, whatever the throttle opening, the pressure drop across the injector is held at a constant pressure above the pressure in the inlet manifold.

At idle speed with the vacuum hose disconnected, or with the engine stopped and the pump running, or at full-throttle, the system fuel pressure for a typical MPi system will be approximately 3.0 bar. At idle speed (vacuum hose connected), the fuel pressure will be approximately 0.5 bar under the system pressure.

10 Turbocharger

General

The power output for any given engine is limited by the volume of air that the engine can 'inhale'. Simply put, the more air that an engine can cram into a cylinder, the greater is the volumetric efficiency, and the more power will be produced. Obviously, as the air intake is increased, so too must the fuel intake so that the AFR is maintained.

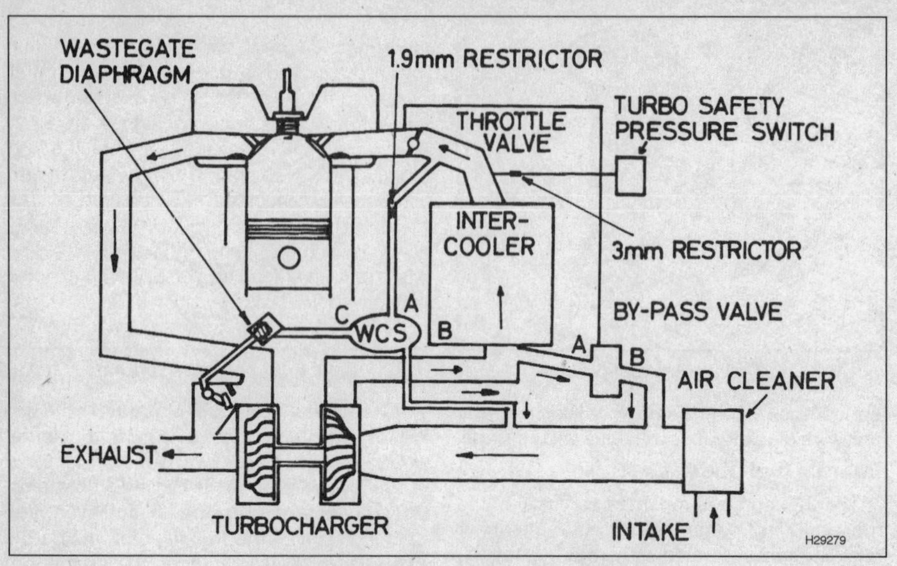

2.39 Typical turbocharged circuits

Turbocharging is a method of compressing the inlet air so that the maximum charge can be forced into a cylinder under high pressure or boost.

Exhaust gases are used to drive a turbine and impeller to compress the intake air. The turbine is mounted in the exhaust system, fairly close to the exhaust manifold. Compressing the air generates heat, so the air tends to expand and lose some of its efficiency. A method of overcoming this problem is to use an intercooler, which is a kind of 'air radiator', so that the air is cooled on its way to the inlet manifold, ensuring maximum compression of the air charge **(see illustration 2.39)**.

Boost control

As the volume of exhaust gases increase, the turbine is driven ever faster; at high engine speeds, there is a danger of excessive turbine speeds and over-pressurisation causing engine damage. This is overcome by using a wastegate control valve to actuate a wastegate flap in the exhaust system - upstream of the turbo **(see illustration 2.40)**.

When the boost control valve receives a signal from the ECM, a solenoid valve is actuated to open a channel. This channel allows compressed air to flow from a point before the throttle plate, through the boost valve to the wastegate actuator. The compressed air acts upon the wastegate diaphragm, which mechanically opens a flap inside the exhaust pipe. Some of the exhaust gases flow through the flap and by-pass the turbine so that the boost pressure is reduced.

A hose connects the turbo compressor to the diaphragm of the wastegate actuating valve. As pressure rises to a pre-determined level, the compressed air acts upon the wastegate diaphragm which mechanically actuates a flap inside the exhaust pipe. Some of the exhaust gases flow through the flap and by-pass the turbine so that the boost pressure is reduced.

In its simplest form, this provides adequate protection from over-pressurisation. However, by utilising a wastegate control solenoid (WCS) under control of the ECM, maximum turbo boost can be varied to improve power under acceleration and at different engine speeds. The WCS is located in the hose from the turbo to the wastegate, and acts to allow all or part of the boost to be applied to the wastegate. When the valve is open, air is vented back to the low-pressure side of the induction system.

At low engine speeds (typically less than 2500 rpm), boost is negligible and the valve is not actuated until rpm rises above that level. The ECM tends to pulse the valve with a fixed frequency, and the duration of the pulse is varied so that the valve is open for longer or shorter time periods as desired.

Air by-pass

A phenomenon known as 'turbo-lag' can cause hesitation during initial acceleration as the turbo takes a moment to come to speed. This can be very noticeable on acceleration after a period of deceleration when the turbine has been slowed by back pressure in the turbocharger housing. Turbo-lag can be reduced by use of an air by-pass valve **(see illustration 2.41)**.

A sensing pipe connects the by-pass valve with the inlet manifold. When the turbine supplies compressed air to the manifold, the compressed air pushes upon the air by-pass valve and it remains shut. During deceleration or light load when the turbo is inactive, the manifold contains depressed air (a vacuum) and the depression will open the air by-pass valve. Air pressure from the impeller wheel is circulated throughout the turbocharger housing, and prevents a back pressure forming. The turbine slows very little, and turbo-lag is much reduced when the accelerator is re-applied.

11 Catalytic converter and emission control

General

All new vehicles sold in the UK from January 1st 1993 onwards are equipped with a catalytic converter, and implement a closed-loop control system so that exhaust emissions may be reduced.

Catalytic converter

A catalyst is something which promotes a chemical reaction, but itself remains unaffected by the reaction. The catalytic converter consists of a stainless steel housing containing a ceramic monolith element with a honeycomb of passages called cells. There are 400 cells per square inch, giving an internal surface area of 3.55 metres. The element is coated with a rough-surfaced aluminium oxide washcoat and fired in a kiln to give a surface area of 1-2 football pitches (depending on catalyst size). The washcoat is coated with a microscopically-thin layer containing 2-3 grams of the precious metals platinum and rhodium **(see illustration 2.42)**.

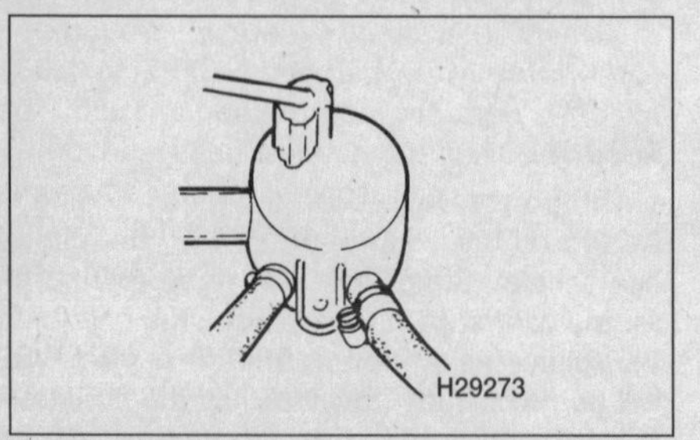

2.40 Wastegate control solenoid (WCS)

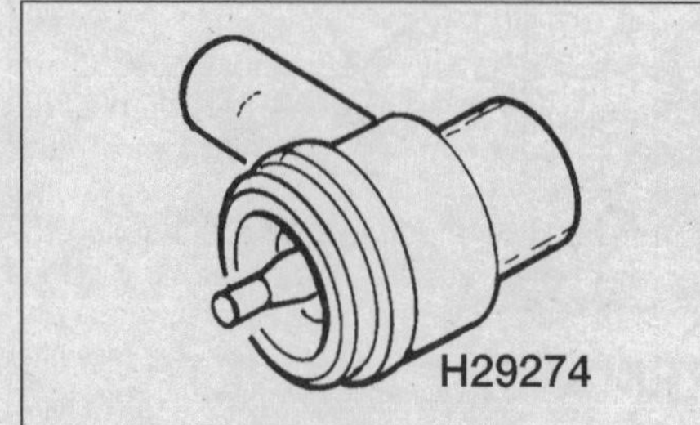

2.41 Turbo by-pass valve

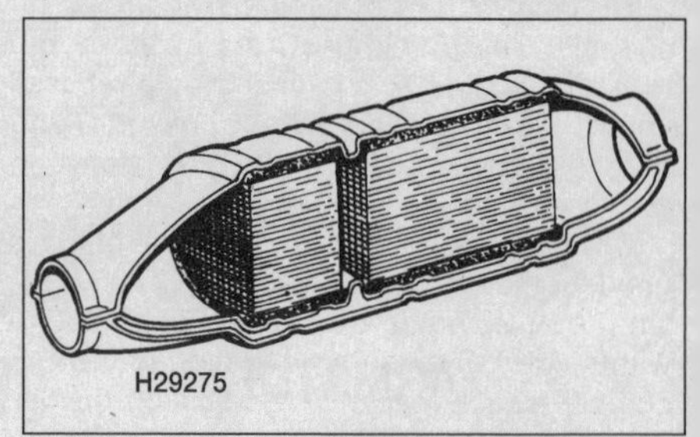

2.42 Catalytic converter

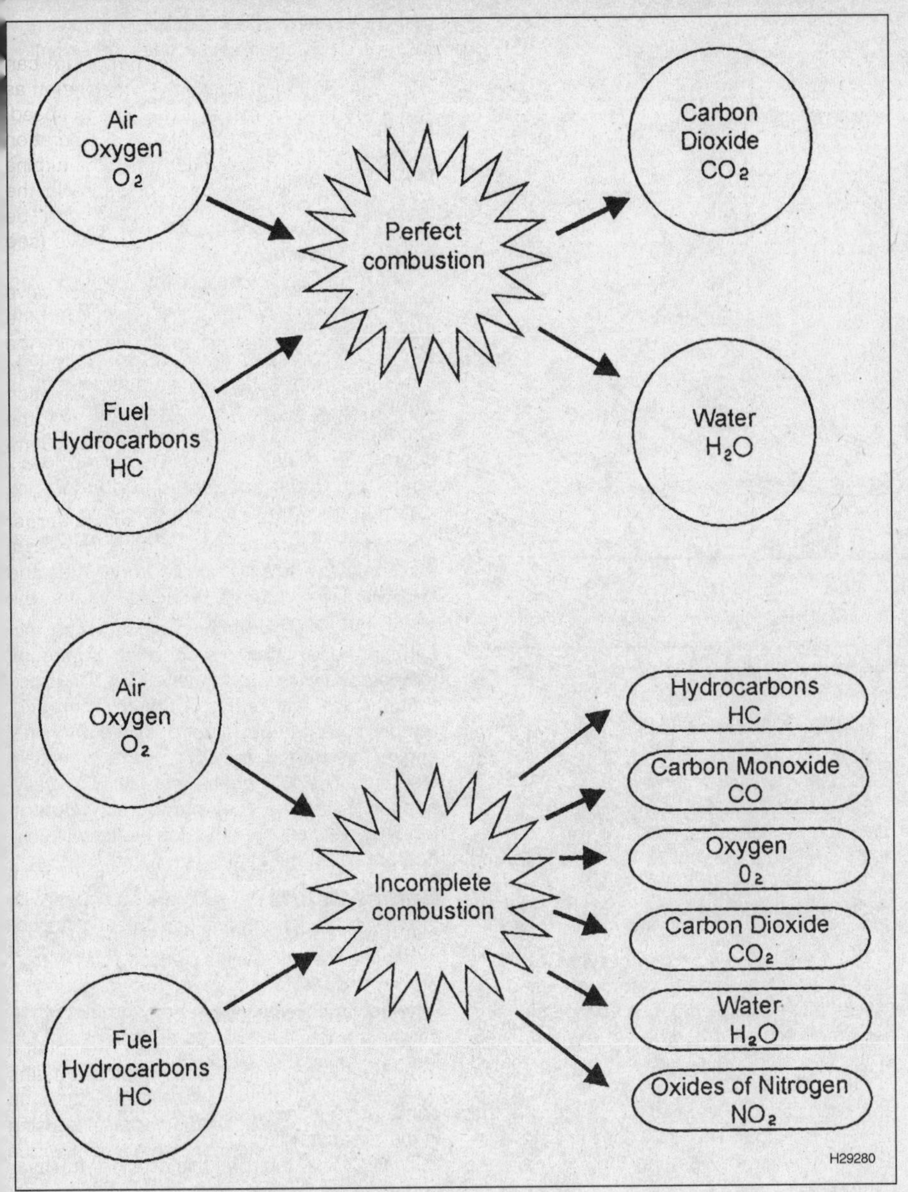

2.43 Combustion chart

A steel mesh blanket is used to protect the monolith from heat and road vibrations. Some form of heat shielding is placed between the vehicle underbody and exhaust, and thus the passenger compartment is heat-insulated from the high operating temperature of the converter.

The catalyst is like a secondary combustion chamber, and CO and HC are oxidised into H_2O and CO_2. NOx is oxidised by a process known as reduction, where oxygen and nitrogen are forced apart. The oxygen combines with CO to produce CO_2 and N_2.

A weak mixture with a high level of O_2 is good for the efficient oxidation of CO and HC. On the other hand, a relatively rich mixture with some CO aids the reduction of NOx. A compromise is reached by adjusting the air-fuel ratio of the catalyst-equipped engine to the stoichiometric ratio of 14:1. This means that the engine is perhaps adjusted slightly richer than desirable, and will therefore use more fuel **(see illustration 2.43)**.

A catalyst needs to reach a minimum temperature of 300°C before it begins to work efficiently, and a working temperature of 400-800°C is more desirable. As the temperature rises over 800-1000°C, the precious metals will begin to break down. Above 1000°C, the catalyst will melt. Excess fuel or misfires causes overheating. Leaded petrol and excessive oil residue also destroys the catalyst. Here the lead compounds clog the pores of the washcoat, and coat the precious metals, thus reducing the conversion rate and eventually rendering it useless. The fuel filler pipe in a catalyst-equipped vehicle is restricted to prevent the use of anything other than unleaded petrol.

When new, the catalyst may emit H_2S (hydrogen sulphide) gas. This smells like rotten eggs, and is caused by the sulphur contained in petrol. Under deceleration when the AFR is lean, sulphur trioxide is stored in the catalyst. After deceleration, when the AFR enriches, this sulphur trioxide reacts with hydrogen in the exhaust to be emitted as H_2S. Although H_2S is toxic, the emission is considered to be quite safe. Generally, the smell becomes less pronounced after a few thousand miles.

An engine with a catalytic converter, but without an ECM and an oxygen/Lambda sensor and therefore operating in 'open-loop' control, will convert approximately 50% of emissions. However, in an engine with a catalytic converter, and with an ECM and oxygen/Lambda sensor ('closed-loop' control), the emission conversion rate is likely to be more than 90%.

Precautions

DO NOT

a) *Turn the engine off at engine speeds above idle rpm.*
b) *Start the vehicle by towing.*
c) *Use fuel or oil additives.*
d) *Drive when the engine burns oil.*
e) *Park over dry leaves or long grass.*

It is essential that an engine with a catalyst is operating correctly at all times. Any engine problem or misfire that results in unburnt fuel passing into the catalyst will destroy it in very quick order. The unburnt fuel causes the catalyst to overheat. Once temperatures over 900°C are attained, the catalyst substrate will melt. This will destroy the catalyst, and a blocked exhaust is also highly likely. The blocked exhaust will cause lack of power and starting problems, and this will almost certainly become a common occurrence.

'Closed-loop' control

'Closed-loop' systems are equipped with an oxygen sensor which monitors the exhaust gas for oxygen content. A low oxygen level in the exhaust signifies a rich mixture. A high oxygen level in the exhaust signifies a weak mixture.

When the engine is operating in closed-loop control, the OS signal causes the ECM to modify the injector pulse so that the AFR is maintained close to the stoichiometric ratio. By controlling the injection pulse, during most operating conditions, so that the air/ fuel ratio is always in a small 'window' around the Lambda point (ie Lambda = 0.97 to 1.03), almost perfect combustion could be achieved. Thus the catalyst has less work to do, and it will last longer with fewer emissions at the tail pipe **(see illustration 2.44)**.

The closed-loop control is implemented during engine operation at coolant temperatures near normal operating temperature. When the coolant temperature is low, or the engine is at full-load or on the overrun, the ECM will operate in 'open-loop'.

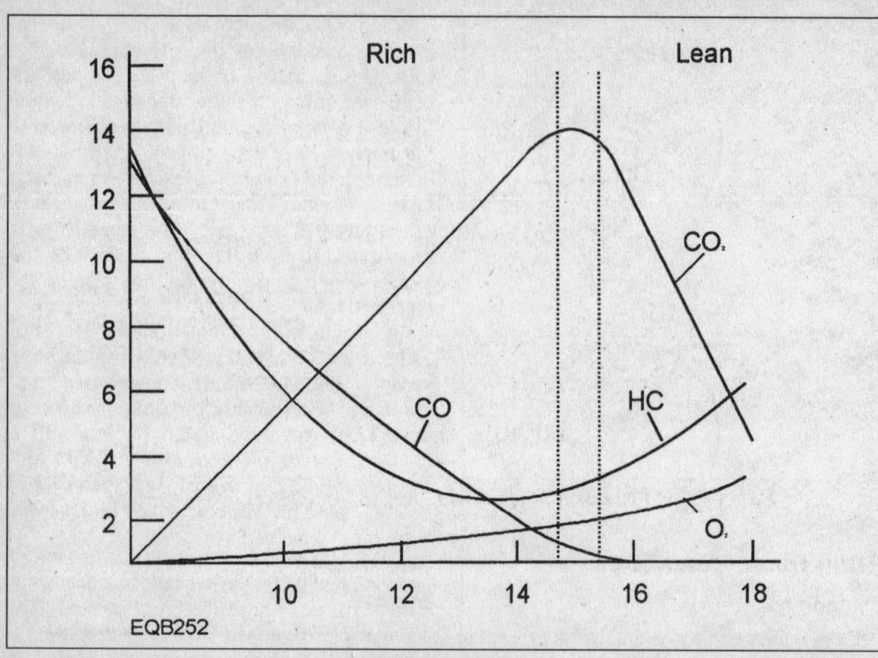

2.44 AFR chart

When operating in open-loop, the ECM allows a richer or leaner AFR than the stoichiometric ratio. This prevents engine hesitation, for example, during acceleration with a wide-open throttle.

Oxygen sensor (OS)

An oxygen sensor is a ceramic device placed in the exhaust manifold on the engine side of the catalytic converter. Various names have been given to this sensor, and it could equally be called a Lambda sensor, oxygen sensor or even an exhaust gas oxygen sensor (EGOS) **(see illustration 2.45)**.

The quantity of oxygen remaining after combustion is an excellent indicator of a deficit or surplus of air (rich or weak mixture). The oxygen sensor returns a signal to the ECM, which can almost instantaneously (within 50 ms) adjust the injection duration. By controlling the engine electronically so that the AFR is always at the Lambda point, no matter the load or speed, almost perfect combustion could be achieved.

Essentially, the OS contains two porous platinum electrodes. The outer surface electrode is exposed to exhaust air and coated in porous ceramic. The inner surface electrode is exposed to ambient atmospheric air.

There are now two different types of OS in use. The first and most commonly used OS utilises a zirconia element. A voltage signal is generated by the difference in oxygen levels at the two electrodes, and this is transmitted to the ECM. This voltage is inversely proportional to the level of oxygen in the exhaust manifold. The ECM uses this signal to adjust the injector opening time to maintain Lambda = 1.0 ± 0.02.

The OS closed-loop voltage is quite low, and switches between 100 millivolts (weak) to 1.0 volt (rich). The signal actually takes the form of a switch, and switches very quickly from weak to rich.

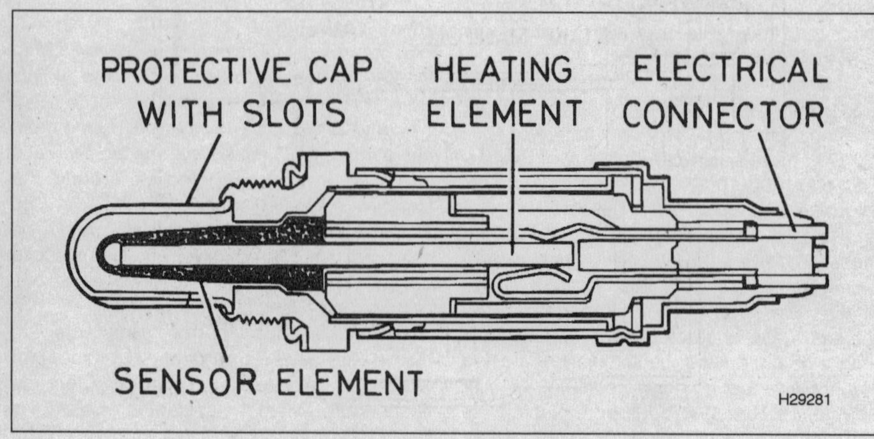

2.45 Oxygen sensor (OS)

The second type of OS is made from titania, and functions by a change in resistance which alters a digital signal that originates from the ECM. Response of the titania OS is much faster than those made from zirconia, and the signal is much more stable over a range of exhaust temperatures.

Unfortunately, driveability would be impaired if the engine was set at Lambda for its entire driving cycle. Controlling the engine to the Lambda ideal would cause hesitation, flat spots and a lack of smoothness that would make a car pretty near undriveable. Therefore, when the engine is under Lambda control (ie cruising) it is in 'closed-loop' operation. Under acceleration or during the warm-up period, the system goes into 'open-loop' operation, and a richer mixture is allowed to prevent hesitation.

Heated OS

The OS only produces a signal when the exhaust gas, has reached a minimum temperature of approximately 300°C. In order that the OS will reach optimum operating temperature as quickly as possible after the engine has started, the OS contains a heating element. The OS heater supply is usually applied from the fuel pump relay output terminal. This ensures that the heater will only operate whilst the engine is running.

Engine faults

Although the oxygen sensor method of regulating the AFR works perfectly well with a properly operating engine, things go awry once faults develop. Almost any problem that affects combustion will see an increase of O_2 in the exhaust. For example, a misfire due to an ignition or mechanical problem means that combustion is incomplete, and the level of O_2 in the exhaust will rise.

The ECM will interpret this as a lean mixture and increase the fuel injection duration. When the fuel injection method is Multi-point simultaneous injection or single point injection, all cylinders will be enriched. This is the main reason why use of the sequential injection method will almost certainly increase. With sequential injection, only the afflicted cylinder will receive more fuel.

Evaporation control (activated carbon filter and control valve)

An activated carbon canister is employed in catalyst equipped vehicles to aid evaporative emission control. The carbon canister stores fuel vapours and a control valve (CFSV) or (CFCV) is used to control the vapours stored in the canister. Depending upon the system, the control valve may be actuated by the ECM, or mechanically actuated according to temperature. Once the control valve is actuated, fuel vapours are drawn into the inlet manifold to be burnt by the engine during

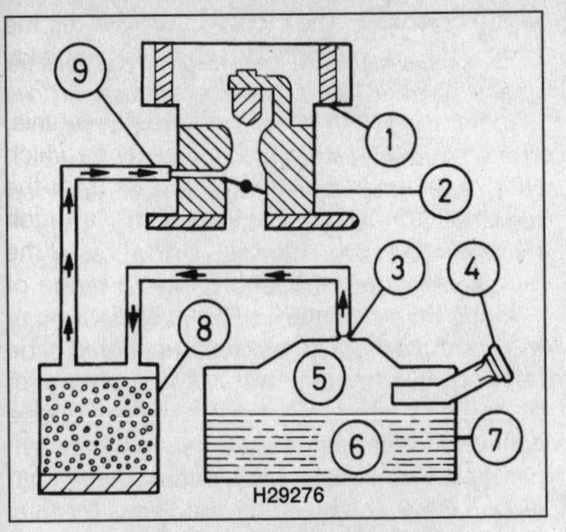

2.46 Mechanically-controlled evaporation circuit

1 Air filter
2 Throttle body
3 Restrictor
4 Sealed fuel cap
5 Fuel vapour
6 Fuel
7 Fuel tank
8 Charcoal canister
9 Purge hose

normal combustion. Alternatively, a very simple evaporative purge system may simply be operated by the position of the throttle **(see illustration 2.46)**.

ECM-actuated

When the engine is stopped, the carbon filter solenoid valve (CFSV) is open. As soon as the ignition is switched 'on' the CFSV closes. So that engine performance will not be affected, the CFSV remains closed during cold engine operation and also during engine idle. Once the engine coolant temperature reaches normal operating temperature and the throttle is partially open (normal cruise conditions with a hot engine) the CFSV will be modulated (pulsed) on and off by the ECM. Once the CFSV is actuated by the ECM, fuel vapours are drawn into the inlet manifold to be burnt by the engine during normal combustion **(see illustration 2.47)**.

Mechanically-actuated

Vacuum is usually applied to the carbon filter control valve (CFCV) through a thermistor. The CFCV remains closed during cold engine operation, so that engine performance will not be affected, and the vacuum supply is arranged so that vacuum to the CFCV is not available during engine idle. Once the engine coolant temperature reaches normal operating temperature and the throttle is partially open (normal cruise conditions with a hot engine) vacuum is applied to the CFCV so that fuel vapours are drawn into the inlet manifold to be burnt by the engine during normal combustion **(see illustration 2.48)**.

Throttle-actuated

When the throttle is closed, the purge line to the canister is closed. After the engine is started and the throttle is opened, vacuum acts upon the canister to draw the vapours into the inlet manifold, to be burnt by the engine during normal combustion.

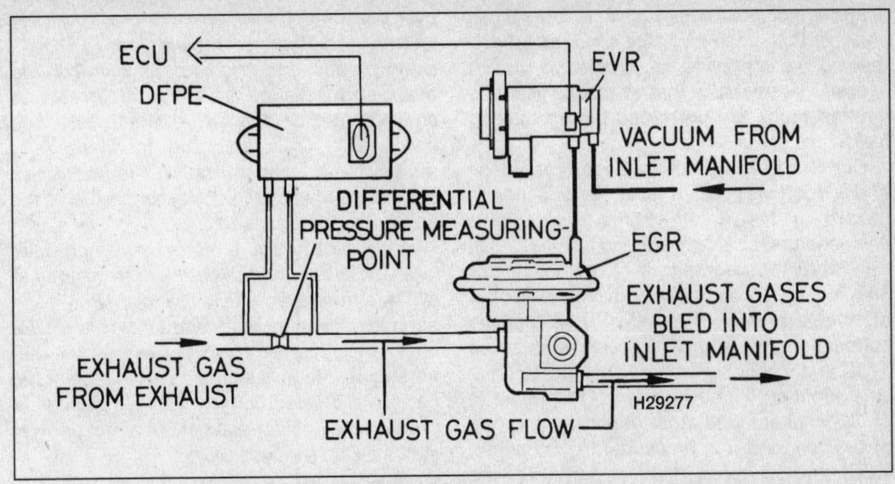

2.47 Typical ECM-actuated exhaust gas re-circulation (EGR) system

Analysis of exhaust gases

Oxygen (O_2)

Oxygen is a harmless gas that is present in about 21% of air, and is necessary for proper combustion. O_2 consists of two oxygen atoms and is measured in % volume. A small proportion of oxygen (1 - 2%) will be left after proper combustion. Too much or too little would indicate an incorrect air/fuel ratio, ignition or mechanical problems, or an exhaust leak. The amount of O_2 that is expelled into the exhaust is that which is left over after combustion, and is a good indicator of the AFR - so long as the engine is operating correctly.

Carbon monoxide (CO)

Carbon monoxide is formed by the partial burning of the fuel due to a lack of oxygen. A low proportion of CO in the exhaust indicates how well the air/fuel ratio is maintained. A high proportion of CO in the exhaust indicates a rich fuel mixture, choked air filter, choked PCV valve or low idle speed. Low CO would indicate a lean fuel mixture or a vacuum leak, or even an exhaust leak. CO (and HC) emissions decrease as load (heat and temperature) rises to give a more efficient engine.

The CO content in the exhaust is an indicator of the AFR, but only when the engine is functioning normally. Any engine condition that causes a misfire will reduce the amount of CO that is burnt. CO is produced from the partial burning of fuel, and if you don't burn the fuel you won't produce the CO.

It is therefore obvious that an engine with a burnt valve or a dead spark plug would produce less CO. In this instance, any attempt to adjust the fuel mixture would result in an over-rich mixture, even though the gas

2

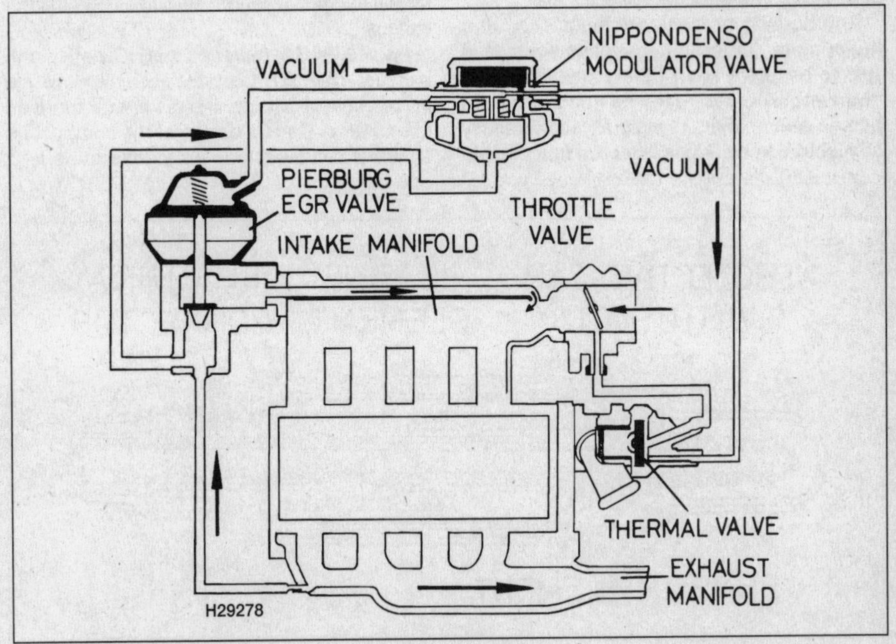

2.48 Typical mechanically-actuated exhaust gas re-circulation (EGR) system

analyser indicated a lean mixture. Only a gas analyser that could calculate a 'corrected' CO reading would provide the complete picture. It is essential therefore that all mechanical and ignition faults are corrected before making fuel adjustments.

CO is a poisonous, tasteless, colourless and odourless gas. It is a serious health hazard in dense city traffic or in semi-enclosed areas. A concentration of 0.3% can be fatal if breathed in continually for 30 minutes. CO combines with red blood cells at the expense of oxygen, and causes suffocation. By weight, CO accounts for about 47% of air pollution, but is thought to have little effect on the environment. One molecule of CO contains one atom of carbon and one of oxygen, and it is measured in % volume. CO is inversely proportional to the AFR - the less fuel, the lower the CO.

Carbon dioxide (CO_2)

CO_2 is the product of an efficient engine. With low CO and HC levels, the percentage of CO_2 in the exhaust is likely to be 13 to 15%. Less than 8% CO_2 indicates an incorrect AFR, or a misfire or leaky exhaust. CO_2 is directly proportional to the AFR, but inversely proportional to CO. The less fuel, the higher the CO_2. At speeds over 2000 rpm, the level will be 1-2% higher than at idle, due to an increase in engine efficiency.

One molecule of CO_2 contains one atom of carbon and two of oxygen. CO_2 is chemically stable, and does not easily react with other substances. Not poisonous, it is produced by all breathing animals, including fish. Oxygen is inhaled and CO_2 exhaled at a concentration of about 5%. CO_2 is absorbed by all green plants by a process called 'photo-synthesis', which only happens in daylight, and which also releases O_2 into the atmosphere.

Any burning process produces CO_2, and the contribution from automotive sources is said to be less than half that of industrial and domestic sources. The contribution from people and animals is insignificant. A heavy concentration of CO_2 is like placing a blanket over the atmosphere, and this prevents heat loss by radiation. At present, more CO_2 is being produced than is being consumed, and the disappearance of the rain forests is another significant factor. As the forests fade away, less CO_2 is absorbed; the increase in atmospheric concentration is said to contribute towards 'global warming' and the so-called 'greenhouse effect'.

In the automobile, the only way to produce less CO_2 is to burn less petrol, or even none at all. This means an efficient engine with good economy (a lean-burn engine), or a diesel engine with high economy, or even a car with no engine - ie an electric motor. But electric cars need electricity, and electricity is produced by power stations, and most power stations also produce CO_2.

Hydrocarbons (HC)

Composed of 15% hydrogen and 85% carbon, petrol is almost pure hydrocarbons. HC is a generic term, and refers to unburnt and partially-burnt hydrocarbon fuel. It is measured in PPM - parts per million. There are many different kinds of HC in the exhaust and HC is generally capable of serious damage to eyes, nose and lungs. When mixed with NOx and in the presence of bright sunshine, photochemical smog is formed. HC is also said to be a reason for the death of the forests.

During combustion, the hydrogen atoms combine with the O_2 atoms to produce H_20. The carbon atoms combine with O_2 atoms to produce CO_2. High levels of HC in the exhaust signifies ignition problems such as defective plugs or HT leads, incorrect timing, vacuum leaks, incorrect air/fuel ratio or engine mechanical faults. In fact, anything that causes inefficient engine operation will increase the level of unburnt HC in the exhaust.

As the AFR weakens, the HC emissions increase due to a lean misfire. This is why a black exhaust is often the result of a too-lean idle mixture. Careful design of the combustion chamber can overcome this problem.

Oxides of nitrogen (NOx)

NOx is a term for a group of poisonous gases formed due to high temperatures (exceeding 1300°C). and high compression. There are many different kinds of NOx (ie NO, NO_2, NO_3 etc) and they are all lumped together under the term NOx, the N representing one nitrogen atom and Ox representing any number of oxygen atoms.

The nitrogen content of air passes through the combustion process unchanged until high temperature (more than 1370°C) and high pressures are reached. Under these conditions, nitrogen and oxygen react to form nitrogen monoxide - sometimes called Nitric oxide - (NO). The breeding conditions for NOx are wide-open throttle, acceleration and high-speed cruising. When NO is produced in the presence of strong sunshine, NO_2 (nitrogen dioxide), ozone (O_3) and NO_3 (nitrogen nitrate) are the result. NO_2 is a light brown gas commonly called 'smog'. Unfortunately, NOx emissions reach their peak at Lambda = 1, the so-called perfect combustion point.

Exhaust gas re-circulation (EGR)

Modern engines that run at a high temperature with high compression tend to produce an excessive level of NOx. NOx production can be reduced by recycling a small amount of exhaust gas into the combustion chamber. This procedure effectively lowers the combustion temperature, and reduces the incidence of NOx. So long as the recycling of the exhaust gas is properly controlled, engine operation will be little affected.

EGR operation in modern engines is controlled by the ECM, as distinct from earlier vehicles which used mechanical means. EGR control only occurs after the engine has attained normal operating temperature and the engine is operating under part-load conditions. The ECM monitors the voltage returned from the EGR sensor, and adjusts the signal to actuate the EGR vacuum control. The vacuum control device opens the EGR valve, which allows a finely-metered supply of exhaust gas to be introduced into the inlet manifold.

Chapter 3
Test equipment, training and technical data

Contents

1 Introduction

Testing the modern automobile engine is a serious business. To be good at it, you need to seriously invest in three areas. We can liken the three areas to the good old three-legged stool. In our automotive stool, the legs are equipment, training and information. Kick one leg away, and the others are left a little shaky. Those with serious diagnostic intentions will make appropriate investments in all three areas.

That is not to say that those without the best equipment, or the necessary know-how, or the information, are completely stuck. It will just require a little more time and patience, that's all.

However, we do have to say at the outset that although quite a lot can be accomplished with a digital multi-meter (DMM), a number of tests and checks do require specialist equipment. For the sake of completeness, we will detail test procedures that do require the use of sophisticated equipment.

Fault diagnosis then, and your method of diagnosis, will largely depend upon the equipment available. and your expertise. There is a definite trade-off in time against cost. The greater the level of investment in equipment and training, the speedier the diagnosis. The less investment, the longer it will take. Obvious, really!

2 Equipment

Within the motor trade, there are several different approaches to testing vehicles and diagnosing faults. Let us take a look at the various options.

Multi-meter

This is the equipment required for the most basic approach. These days, the meter will probably be digital, and must be designed for use with electronic circuits. An analogue meter or even a test lamp may be used, so long as it meets the same requirements as the digital meter. Depending on the sophistication of the meter, the DMM can be used to test for basic voltage (AC and DC), resistance, frequency, rpm, duty cycle, temperature etc. A selection of thin probes and banana plugs for connecting to a break-out box (BOB) will also be useful. Use a splitpin or hairgrip for probing into square or oblong multi-plugs. The round DMM probes can 'spread' the connection and turn a good connection into a bad one **(see illustrations 3.1 to 3.3)**.

If the fault is a straightforward electrical fault, the meter will often be adequate. However, the drawback is that it cannot analyse the complex electrical waveforms produced by many electronic sensors and actuators, and test results can sometimes be misleading.

Programmed test equipment

This kind of proprietary equipment will interface between the ECM and the ECM multi-plug. This equipment checks the input and output signals moving between the ECM and its sensors and actuators. If one or more of the signals are outside of pre-programmed parameters, the equipment will display the erroneous signals as faults. Once again, other test equipment may be required to pinpoint the actual fault.

Oscilloscope (with or without DMM and engine analyser)

An oscilloscope is essentially a graphic voltmeter. Voltage is rarely still, and tends to rise and fall over a period of time. The oscilloscope (or 'scope) measures voltage against time, and displays it in the form of a waveform. Even when the voltage change is very rapid, the scope can usually capture the changes. Circuit faults can often be spotted

3.1 Two typical high-impedance DMM's with similar performance but different sets of leads and probes. The left unit is equipped with alligator clips, and the right unit with spiked probes. Using the alligator clips frees your hands for other tasks, whilst the probes are useful for backprobing multi-plug connectors

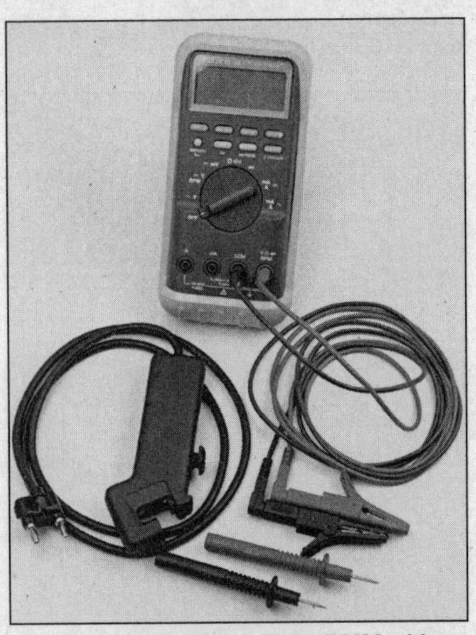

3.2 Top-of-the-range Fluke DMM with a multitude of features and attachments

3.3 A cooking thermometer like this can be useful as a last resort. Most good DMM's incorporate a thermometer function and a selection of probes that may be more effective

much faster than when using other types of test instrument. Traditionally, the 'scope has been used for many years to diagnose faults in the primary and secondary ignition systems of conventional non-electronic vehicles. With the advent of electronics, the 'scope has become even more important, and when a labscope function is available, analysis of complex waveforms is possible. This equipment is often used in conjunction with other equipment, for speedy diagnosis of a wide range of problems. The large engine analyser and 'scope is now giving way to a plethora of smaller handheld 'scopes that pack great diagnostic power into portable form.

Exhaust gas analyser

These days the state-of-the-art gas analyser comes with the ability to measure four of the gases present in the exhaust pipe, and it also calculates the Lambda ratio. The gases are oxygen, carbon dioxide, carbon monoxide and hydrocarbons. Less-expensive gas analysers are available that will measure one, two or three gases. However, the better the gas analyser, the easier it gets. The gas analyser is now a recognised diagnostic tool. Faults in ignition, fuelling and various mechanical engine problems can be diagnosed from the state of the various gases present in the exhaust.

Battery saver

Actually, 'battery saver' is a misnomer, since the function of this device is to hold power to permanently live circuits whilst the battery is removed or changed. The live circuits may provide power to the radio security and station memory, and to the ECM adaptive memory, etc.

Jump leads with surge protection

It is possible to destroy an ECM if unprotected jump leads are used to provide emergency power to the battery. Rather than use jump leads, it is far safer to charge the battery before attempting to start the vehicle. A poor engine or chassis earth, flat battery or tired starter motor, and unprotected jump leads are a recipe for total disaster.

Flight recorder

Useful for capturing a 'snapshot' of the signals produced by an EMS during a road test or some other operating condition for later analysis in the workshop. The recorder is usually set to record signals just before and after a particular incident. Particularly useful for diagnosis of intermittent faults, the flight recorder function may be built into the FCR or other portable equipment.

ECM testing equipment

Usually the province of those companies that specialise in the repair of the ECM, and not available for purchase by the garage or workshop. One company (ATP) offer an ECM test via a modem over the telephone network if the ECM is taken to one of their agents. Other ECM testing companies require that the ECM is sent to them by post for evaluation.

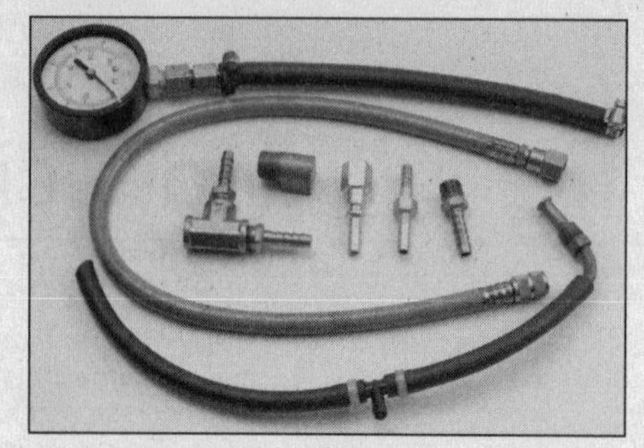

3.4 Fuel pressure gauge and adapter kit

Fuel pressure test kit

Fuel pressure is vitally important to the well-being of the fuel-injected engine and a proper test gauge that will measure fuel pressures up to 7.0 bar is essential. The pressure gauge is normally supplied with a kit of adapters to connect it to a wide range of disparate fuel systems **(see illustration 3.4)**.

Vacuum gauge

As useful as it always was. The vacuum gauge takes the pulse of the engine from a connection to the inlet manifold, and is useful for diagnosing a wide range of timing and mechanical faults, including a blocked exhaust system or vacuum leak **(see illustration 3.5)**.

Vacuum pump

The vacuum pump can be used to check the multitude of vacuum-operated devices that are fitted to many modern vehicles **(see illustration 3.6)**. A crude vacuum pump can be constructed from a bicycle pump. Reverse the washer in the pump, and the pump will then 'suck' instead of 'blow'.

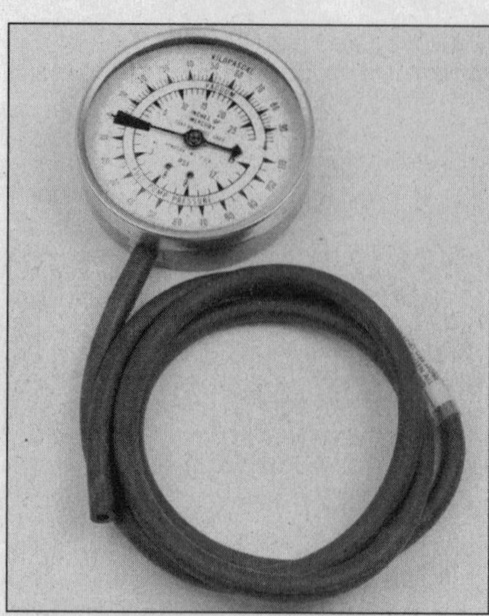

3.5 Vacuum gauge

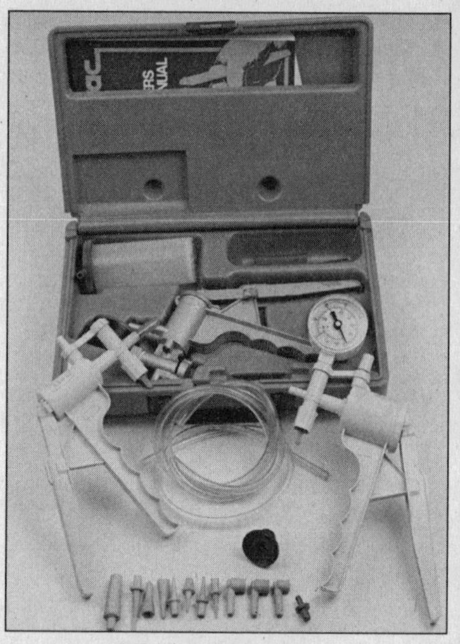

3.6 Vacuum pump kit

Spark jumper

Useful for attaching to an HT lead to check for a spark. If you hold the lead from a modern high-output ignition system whilst cranking the engine, you may get quite a shock when testing for spark. Apart from curling your hair, the ignition system may also be damaged.

Feeler gauges

Still useful for measuring the various clearances at the CAS, TS, spark plug, valve clearances etc.

Hairdryer and cold spray

Useful for gently heating and cooling components during a test where heat may be contributing to failure.

HT lead puller

Ideal for safely breaking the HT lead-to-spark plug seal and then safely disconnecting the lead **(see illustration 3.7)**. How many times have you pulled at a lead to have it disintegrate into your hand?

Exhaust back-pressure tester

Useful for checking for exhaust back-pressure. Screws into the OS hole. The presence of back-pressure indicates an exhaust blockage.

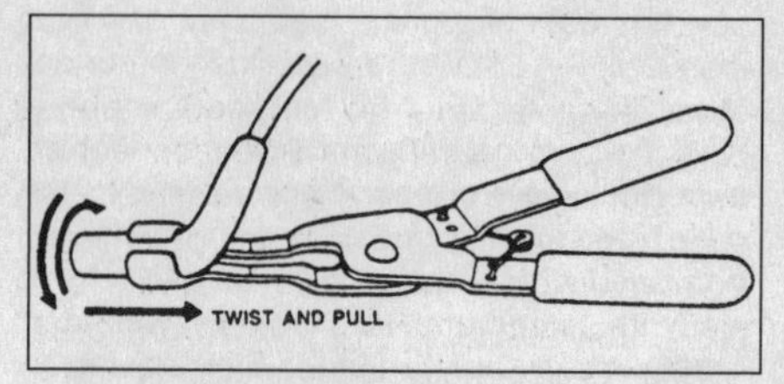

3.7 Ignition HT lead removal tool. Makes safe removal of HT leads a doddle

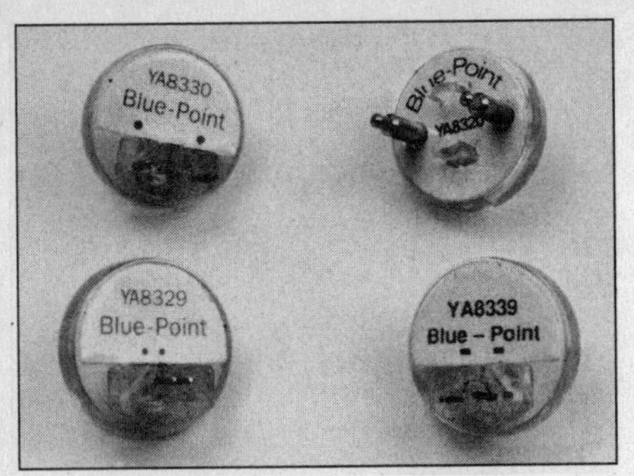

3.8 Injector noid light

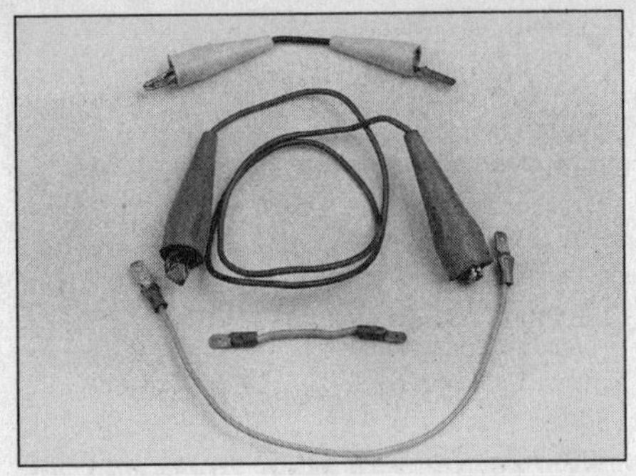

3.9 A selection of temporary jumper wires

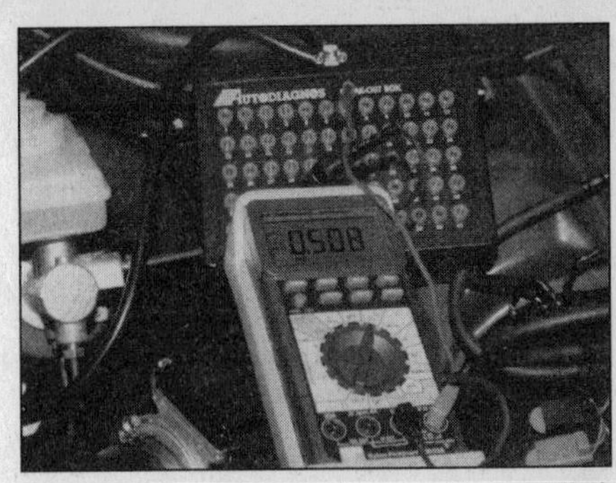

3.10 Using a BOB to obtain voltage at the ECM pins

Variable potentiometer

Because of the widespread use of 'limp home' or LOS in the modern EMS, disconnecting a sensor such as the CTS may have little effect on the running of the engine. The ECM will assume a fault, and place a fixed value as replacement for that sensor. However, it is useful to be able to vary the resistance sent to the ECM and note the effect. One answer is to use a potentiometer with a variable resistance. If this is connected in place of the CTS resistor, then ECM response, injection duration and CO may be checked at the various resistance values that relate to certain temperature.

Noid light

A noid light is a small inexpensive light with inbuilt terminals for checking the signal to the injector. The injector harness is detached at the injector, and the noid light plugged into the injector harness. If the engine is then cranked, the light will flash if the injector is being pulsed by the ECM **(see illustration 3.8)**.

Jumper wires

Useful for checking out circuits, and bridging or 'by-passing' the relay **(see illustration 3.9)**.

Break-out box (BOB)

The BOB is a box containing a number of connectors that allows easy access to the ECM input and output signals, without directly probing the ECM pins. The BOB loom terminates in a universal connector. A multi-plug harness of similar construction to the ECM harness is interfaced between the ECM and its multi-plug, and the other end is connected to the BOB loom. The BOB will now intercept all signals that go to and from the ECM. If a DMM or an oscilloscope or any other suitable kind of test equipment is connected to the relevant BOB connectors, the ECM signals can be easily measured. The main drawback is the number of different ECM multi-plug connectors required for a good coverage of electronic systems. Small BOB's are also available for measuring values at components where it is difficult to connect the test equipment **(see illustration 3.10)**.

There are three main reasons why use of a BOB is desirable in order to access the signals:

1) *Ideally, the connection point for measuring data values from sensors and actuators is at the ECM multi-plug (with the ECM multi-plug connected). The ECM multi-plug is the point through which all incoming and outgoing signals will pass, and dynamically testing at this point is considered to give more accurate results.*
2) *In modern vehicles, the multi-plug is becoming more heavily insulated, and removing the insulation or dismantling the ECM multi-plug so that back-probing is possible, is becoming more difficult, and in some instances, almost impossible. To a certain extent, the same is true of components, with certain components becoming increasingly difficult to backprobe or even probe at all.*
3) *ECM multi-plug terminals (pins) are at best fragile, and frequent probing or backprobing can cause damage. Some pins are gold-plated, and will lose their conductivity if the plating is scraped off. Using a BOB protects the pins from such damage.*

Fault code reader (FCR) - sometimes called a 'scanner'

A number of manufacturers market test equipment for connecting to the EMS serial port. These general-purpose FCR's allow data on a wide range of vehicles and systems to be obtained. The FCR could be used to obtain and clear fault codes, display datastream information on the state of the various sensors and actuators, and also "fire" the system actuators. The FCR is very useful for pointing the engineer in the direction of a specific fault. However, other test equipment may be required to pinpoint the actual fault, and the faults detected may be limited by the self-diagnostics designed into the vehicle ECM **(see illustration 3.11)**.

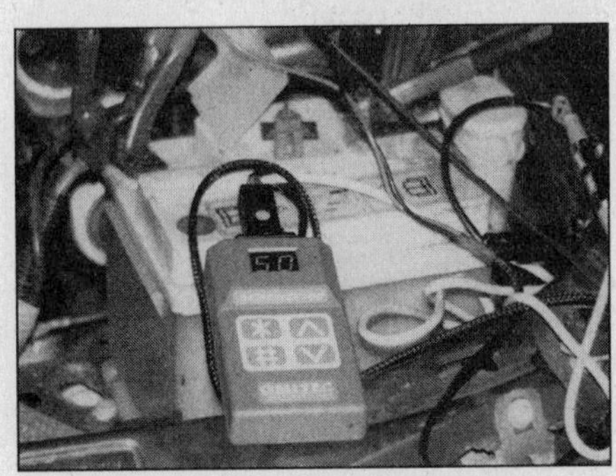

3.11 A typical FCR or 'scanner'

Franchised vehicle dealer

Will often use dedicated test equipment that relies on programmed test methods. The equipment will interface with the ECM, usually through the serial port, and lead the engineer through a programmed test procedure. Depending on its sophistication, the test equipment may be able to test most circuits, or may refer the engineer to test procedures using additional equipment. This equipment is dedicated to one vehicle manufacturer, and may not be available to other workshops outside of the franchised network **(see illustration 3.12)**.

3.12 The Rover TESTBOOK - a laptop computer-based piece of test equipment that contains a very sophisticated and interactive test programme

3 Major suppliers of diagnostic equipment

Note: *The details below are correct at the time of writing (Summer 1997).*

ASNU (UK) Ltd
27 Bournehall Avenue
Bushey, Herts
WD2 3AU
Tel : 0181 420 4494

ATP Electronic Developments Ltd
Victoria St
Hednesford,
Staffordshire
WS12 5BU
Tel : 05438 79788

AutoDiagnos (UK) Ltd
Preston Technology Centre
Marsh Lane
Preston,
Lancashire
PR1 8UD
Tel : 01772 887774

Crypton Ltd
Bristol Road
Bridgwater,
Somerset
TA6 4BX
Tel : 01278 436210

Fluke (UK) Ltd
Colonial Way
Watford,
Herts
WD2 4WD
Tel : 01923 240511

Gunson Ltd
Pudding Mill Lane
London
E15 2PJ
Tel : 0181 555 7421

Intermotor
Occupational Road
Hucknall, Nottingham
NG15 6DZ
Tel: 0602 528000

Lucas Test
International Training Centre
Unit 7, Mica Close
Tamworth, Staffs
B77 4QH
Tel: 0827 63503

Omitech Instrumentation Ltd
Hopton Industrial Estate
London Road
Devizes, Wiltshire
SN10 2EU
Tel : 01380 729256

OTC Europe Ltd
VL Churchill Ltd
PO Box 3, London Road
Daventry, Northants
NN11 4NF
Tel : 01327 704461

Robert Bosch Ltd
PO Box 98
Broadwater Park
Denham, Uxbridge
Middx
UB9 5HJ
Tel : 01895 838353

Sun Electric (UK) Ltd
Oldmedow Road
Kings Lynn, Norfolk
PE30 4JW
Tel : 01553 692422

Sykes-Pickavant Ltd
Kilnhouse Lane
Lytham St. Annes, Lancs.
FY8 3DU
Tel : 01253 784800

4 Training courses

There are a number of companies that specialise in training for the motor industry. The same training courses are usually available to the general public. Please contact the various bodies listed in Section 5 if you wish to learn more about training for the automotive industry.

Note: *The details below are correct at the time of writing (Summer 1997).*

AA External Training Courses
Widmerpool Hall
Keyworth, Notts
NG12 5QB
Tel: 021 501 7357/7389

Crypton Ltd
Bristol Road
Bridgwater, Somerset
TA6 4BX
Tel : 01278 436210

Fuel Injection Services
Unit 7
Salter Street
Preston
PR1 1NT
Tel: 01772 201597

Lucas Test
International Training Centre
Unit 7, Mica Close
Tamworth, Staffs
B77 4QH
Tel: 0827 63503

MasterTech
Freepost RM1109
Wickford, Essex
SS11 8BR
Tel: 01268 570100

OTC Europe Ltd
VL Churchill Ltd
PO Box 3, London Road
Daventry,
Northants
NN11 4NF
Tel : 01327 704461

Sun Electric (UK) Ltd
Oldmedow Road
Kings Lynn,
Norfolk
PE30 4JW
Tel : 01553 692422

Sykes-Pickavant Ltd
Kilnhouse Lane
Lytham St. Annes
Lancs.
FY8 3DU
Tel : 01253 784800

5 Technical information

Specific information on the various systems is essential if effective diagnosis and repairs are to be completed. Companies that specialise in automotive technical information are listed below.

Note: *The details below are correct at the time of writing (Summer 1997).*

Autologic Data Systems Ltd
Arnewood Bridge Road, Sway
Lymington, Hants
S041 6DA
Tel: 01590 683868

Equiptech
Yawl House
Main Road
Marchwood, Southampton
SO40 4UZ
Tel: 01703 862240

Glass's Information Services Ltd
Elgin House
St George's Avenue
Weybridge, Surrey
KT13 OBX
Tel: 01932 823823

Haynes Publishing
Sparkford, Nr Yeovil
Somerset
BA22 7JJ
Tel: 01963 440635

Chapter 4
General test procedures

Contents

General tests

1 Introduction

Generally speaking, test results obtained using a voltmeter or oscilloscope (particularly recommended) are more reliable and may reveal more faults than the ohmmeter. Voltage tests are much more dynamic and are obtained with voltage applied to the circuit, which is far more likely to reveal a problem than if the circuit is broken and the component measured for resistance. In some instances, disconnecting a multi-plug may break the actual connection that is at fault, and the circuit test may then reveal 'no fault found'.

In addition, the oscilloscope may reveal some faults that the voltmeter fails to find; the 'scope is particularly useful for analysing and displaying the complex signals and waveforms from some sensors and actuators. With the proliferation of small, portable handheld oscilloscopes at a cost of less than £2500, the 'scope is not quite in the province of the home mechanic, but every workshop that is serious about fault diagnosis should certainly have one.

For the purposes of this book, we will generally test the majority of components with reference to the voltmeter. Resistance or continuity tests using an ohmmeter will be mentioned where appropriate.

Ideally, the connection point for measuring data values from sensors and actuators is at the ECM multi-plug (with the ECM multi-plug connected). The ECM multi-plug is the point through which all incoming and outgoing signals will pass, and dynamically testing at this point is considered to give more accurate results. However, for a variety of reasons it is not always possible to test at the ECM multi-plug, and other points of testing may also give satisfactory results.

2 Voltage tests

Connecting equipment probes

1 Connect the voltmeter negative probe to an engine earth.

2 Use the positive probe to backprobe for voltage at the actual terminals of the component under test **(see illustration 4.1)**. **Note:** *This procedure will give acceptable results in most instances, and is the one we would recommend to non-professionals.*

3 Alternatively, if possible, peel back the insulated boot to the ECM multi-plug, and backprobe the terminals using the equipment probes **(see illustration 4.2)**.

4 If the ECM terminals are not accessible, then ideally connect a BOB between the ECM and its multi-plug. This is the preferred method, and will avoid any possibility of damage to the ECM terminals. **Note:** *Refer to Warning No 3 (in Reference) before disconnecting the ECM multi-plug.*

5 Otherwise, the ECM multi-plug could be disconnected and the ECM multi-plug terminals probed for voltages. **Note:** *This procedure is mainly used for checking voltage supplies to the ECM and integrity of the earth connections.*

4.1 The art of backprobing for DC voltage. Circuit multi-plugs connected and the ignition switched 'on': Attach the negative probe to earth and push the positive probe past the boot until it makes contact with the terminal connection. This is a dynamic test of a live circuit and makes for accurate diagnosis of voltage faults

4.2 Backprobing at the ECM multi-plug

6 Unless otherwise stated, attach the voltmeter negative test lead to an earth on the engine, and probe or backprobe the component terminal under test with the voltmeter positive test lead. **Note:** *DO NOT push round tester probes into square or oblong terminal connectors. This leads to terminal deformation and poor connections. A splitpin is the correct shape for inserting into square or oblong terminals.*

7 In this book, the multi-plug diagram usually shows the terminals of the harness connector. When back-probing the multi-plug (or viewing the sensor connector terminals), the terminal positions will be reversed.

Probing for supply or reference voltage

8 Ignition key on, component multi-plug connected or disconnected as stated in the appropriate test. Probe or backprobe for nominal battery voltage or the reference voltage 5.0 volt supply.

Probing for signal voltage

9 Ignition key on, component multi-plug connected. Backprobe for nominal battery voltage or the reference voltage 5.0 volt supply.

Earth or return

10 Method one: Ignition key on, component multi-plug connected. Backprobe for 0.25 volts max.

11 Method two: Component multi-plug connected or disconnected: Voltmeter positive test lead attached to the supply or reference terminal, and the voltmeter negative test lead attached to the earth or return terminal. The voltmeter should indicate supply voltage if the earth is satisfactory.

3 Resistance tests

1 Ensure that the ignition key is off, and that the circuit or component under test is isolated from a voltage supply.

2 DO NOT push round tester probes into square terminal connectors. This leads to deformation of the terminal and poor connections.

3 Circuits that begin and end at the ECM are best tested for resistance (and continuity) at the ECM multi-plug (after it has been disconnected) **(see illustration 4.3)**. **Note:** *Refer to Warning No 3 (in Reference) before disconnecting the ECM multi-plug.*

4 The use of a BOB is also recommended for resistance tests, but the BOB must be connected to the ECM multi-plug, and NOT to the ECM itself.

5 If the resistance test for a sensor circuit is made at the ECM multi-plug pins, and the sensor has a common connection to the ECM

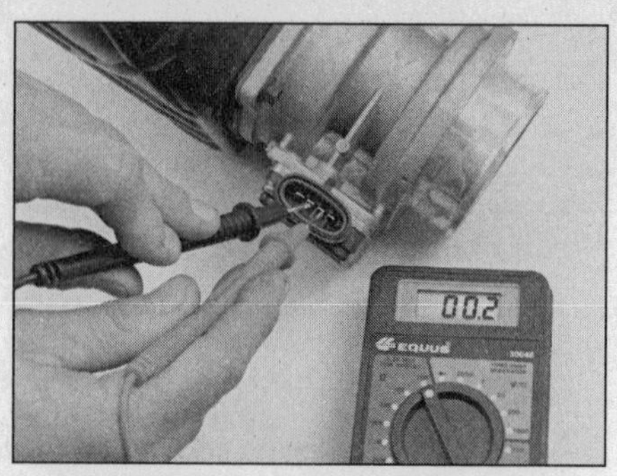

4.3 Measuring resistance: Detach the circuit multi-plug, select the appropriate resistance range and then touch the probes to the two terminal under test

(either through a 5.0 volt reference supply and/or a sensor earth return), the multi-plug connectors for the remaining components must be disconnected. If this procedure is not followed, the results may be inaccurate.

6 When checking continuity of a circuit or continuity to earth, the maximum resistance should be less than 1.0 ohm.

7 When checking the resistance of a component against specifications, care should be taken in evaluating the condition of that component as the result of a good or bad test result **(see illustration 4.4)**. A component with a resistance outside of its operating parameters may not necessarily be faulty. Conversely, a circuit that measures within its operating parameters may still be faulty. However, an open-circuit or a very high resistance will almost certainly be indicative of a fault. The ohmmeter is more useful for checking circuit continuity than it is for indicating faulty components.

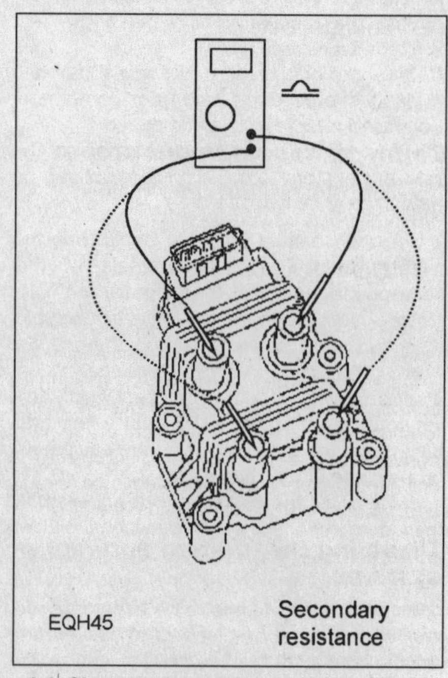

4.4 Checking secondary resistance on a typical DIS coil

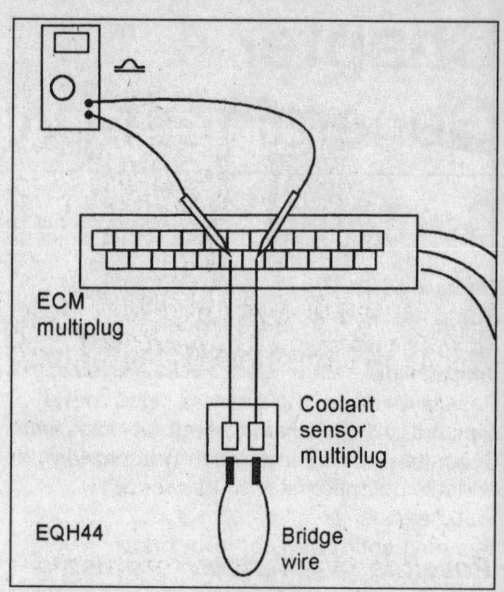

4.5 Check continuity of circuit between the ECM and the component multi-plug

Checking for continuity of circuit

Note: *These tests can be used to quickly check for continuity of a circuit between most components (sensors and actuators) and the ECM.*

8 Disconnect the ECM multi-plug. Refer to Warning No 3 in Reference.

9 Disconnect the component multi-plug.

10 Connect a temporary bridge wire between terminals 1 and 2 at the component multi-plug.

11 Identify the two ECM pins which are connected to the component under test.

12 Connect an ohmmeter between the two pins at the ECM multi-plug. The meter should display continuity of the circuit.

13 If no continuity, check for a break in the wiring or a bad connection between the ECM pin and its corresponding terminal at the multi-plug **(see illustration 4.5)**.

14 Move one of the ohmmeter probes and touch to earth. The ohmmeter should display an open-circuit.

15 If the component is connected to the ECM by more than two wires, repeat the test using a combination of two wires at one time.

4 Duty cycle tests

Connecting equipment probes

1 Connect the negative dwell meter probe to an engine earth.

2 Use the positive probe to backprobe the signal terminal of the component under test.

3 Make the duty cycle tests at various engine temperatures, with the engine cranking or running and at different engine speeds **(see illustration 4.6)**.

4.6 Connect the positive dwell meter probe to coil negative terminal No 1, and measure the duty cycle under varying engine operating speeds

Possible dwell meter problems

Use of dwell meter during primary cranking tests

4 Although meaningful readings can generally be obtained with most modern DMM's, it is true that some may not be totally accurate during a cranking test on the primary ignition. This occurs when the meter's own preset trigger level may not be suitable for capturing the true voltage level of the component being tested.

Use of dwell meter during injector tests

5 Where the injector is either the current-controlled type or the peak-and-hold kind, very few dwell meters may be capable of registering the rapid pulsing to earth or the current holding that occurs during the second stage of the pulse duration. The meter may only register the switch-on circuit of approximately 1.0 or 2.0%. This means that the injector duty cycle reading will be inaccurate, and not representative of the total pulse width seen in the circuit.

5 Variable potentiometer

It can be very useful to make certain tests on an engine at various operating temperatures. If the engineer has to wait for the engine to become cold, or reach its normal operating temperature, or indeed reach any other important temperature, the task of testing can be irksome and prolonged **(see illustration 4.7)**. Most fuel injection ECM's (and some ignition ECM's) recognise the engine temperature by monitoring the voltage signal returned from the CTS. **Note:** *In a very few instances, this signal may be returned from the oil temperature sensor (OTS) in addition to, or instead of, the CTS.*

If a variable resistor (or potentiometer) is connected between the CTS or OTS terminals, the engine temperature may be simulated over the entire engine operating temperature range. Obtain a variable resistor or potentiometer ('pot'). A simple pot can be obtained from an electrical/electronic component store. Although the simple pot type is adequate for most tests, we recommend the use of the best quality pot that you can obtain. A good quality pot will give more 'feel' and better control of the engine. The pot range should be from 1 ohm to 100 000 ohms.

4.7 Using a variable potentiometer to vary the CTS resistance. Voltage change can be measured and the engine can be fooled into thinking it is cold or hot. This means that simulated cold running tests can be accomplished with the engine hot and without waiting for it to cool

Variable potentiometer (test methods)

1 The following procedures should be followed when using the pot with either the OTS or CTS.
2 Disconnect the CTS multi-plug.
3 Connect the pot between the two multi-plug terminals.
4 Set the pot to the correct resistance for the temperature that you wish to simulate.
5 Vary the resistance and make the test procedures as required.
6 On some engines you will set fault codes during test procedures, and these codes must be erased after testing is completed.
7 Refer to the Fault Code section in the relevant system Chapter for instructions on how to clear fault codes.

6 Compression test

Care must be taken when making a compression test on an engine with electronic ignition, fuel injection and/or a catalytic converter. As a general rule, disconnect the coil negative terminal, fuel system fuse or relay and, where the VM recommends, the ECM.

Disabling the ignition and fuel systems

If the cranking test is to be accomplished, the ignition must be disabled to prevent the engine from starting. In an injection engine, the fuel system must also be disabled. Reference should be made to the manufacturer's recommended method of disabling the engine. However, the following methods may be suitable in some instances.

a) Use a spark gap jumper to connect the coil to distributor HT lead (king lead) to engine earth. Injection (where fitted) will still occur, and this method is unsuitable for wasted-spark ignition.
b) Disconnect the wire from the coil (-) terminal. Many injection systems are pulsed from the coil (-) terminal, and disabling the primary ignition will also disable the injection system.
c) An engine with an EMS (one combined ECM to control both fuel and ignition) may still inject, even with the coil (-) terminal disconnected. Disconnecting the CAS will therefore disable both ignition and fuel. The coil (-) terminal should also be disconnected.
d) Disconnect the fuel pump, or the main relay, or the electrical connection to the injectors.

7 Secondary (HT) ignition system testing - vehicles with distributor

Secondary circuit tuning

A 'scope is invaluable for analysis of the ignition secondary circuit. However, much of the secondary circuit can be easily tested with inexpensive equipment and a careful visual inspection.

Overview of secondary 'tuning'

The ignition system should provide sufficient voltage to bridge the rotor and spark plug gaps, with an adequate coil voltage in reserve. If the coil reserve is lower than the voltage required by the ignition system, a misfire will be the result.

Tuning, in the modern sense, is building an adequate coil reserve so that the engine will run powerfully and economically. Over a period of time (not necessarily mileage), it is possible for faults to develop and components to wear or become dirty so that the reserve of coil voltage becomes too low for reliable running. The engine may then become difficult to start, or develop a misfire or a hesitation, and engine operation will become less than smooth and uneconomical. A high percentage of engine faults can be attributed to a low coil reserve, and faults resulting in excessive HT could lead to disruptive ECM operation or premature ECM failures.

Pre-testing

1 Ensure that the battery, starter motor and alternator are operating properly. Faults in these areas can cause problems in other areas. For example, a defective alternator diode can cause RFI which can disrupt ECM operation and cause it to erratically switch the ignition and fuelling systems.

2 The engine should also be mechanically sound, with fresh engine oil of the correct grade.

3 Many engine running problems are caused by dirty or faulty secondary HT components. A careful check of the ignition secondary, and a renewal of all worn or faulty components, will reap dividends and help to build a healthy voltage reserve.

4 Where possible, the vehicle manufacturer's original equipment parts should be fitted as replacements in the HT circuit. Pattern parts rarely perform as well, or for as long, as the originals, and premature failure is often the norm.

Coil tower

5 Carefully check the coil, and in particular the coil tower, for a skeletal etching that denotes tracking.

6 Clean and polish the coil tower. A polished tower will reduce tracking in damp conditions. Any leakage from the coil will reduce the coil voltage reserve.

Coil secondary resistance

7 Disconnect the coil LT wires, and connect the ohmmeter probes between the coil tower (usually terminal 4) and one of the two LT terminals. Compare the measured value to the specification in the system Chapter. In most instances, the value will be within the range 5000 ohms to 15 000 ohms. If the probe is moved from one LT terminal to the other, the measured value should be very similar to the first reading obtained.

HT leads

8 Carefully remove the HT leads from the spark plugs. If you are less than careful, it is possible to damage the HT lead connection ends, resulting in an increase in HT lead resistance.

9 Check the HT leads for damage, poor insulation, pinhole leaks in the insulation, or poor connections at either end.

10 Measure the HT lead resistance with an ohmmeter.

11 Similarly check all HT suppression caps that may be fitted.

12 Remove and discard suppression devices that are not fitted as original equipment.

13 Do not use unsuppressed HT leads in any engine that has electronic components - a disrupted ECM is usually the result.

14 In some engines, unsuppressed HT leads are used along with suppressed HT caps (eg BMW). If fitted as original equipment, then this type of lead is acceptable.

15 Renew all HT leads that are excessively oily or dirty.

16 Check that the HT leads are correctly installed in the proper firing order.

17 Ensure that the HT lead connection ends are making proper contact with the coil and distributor cap towers.

Distributor cap

18 Remove the distributor cap for inspection, even if this is a difficult task.

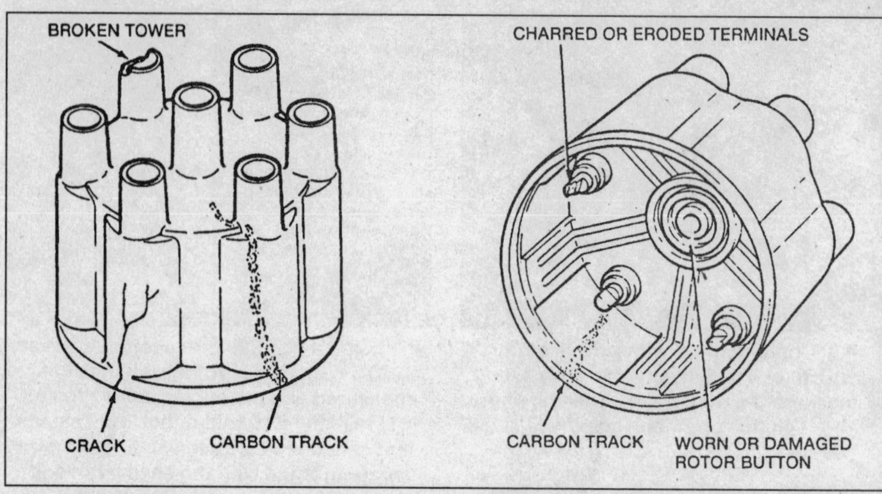

4.8 Carefully inspect the distributor cap for defects and renew it, along with the rotor arm, if there is any doubt about the condition

19 Inspect the cap insulation for scratches, cracks and tracking - both internally and externally.

20 Check for oil or moisture on the internal surfaces. Signs of oil seepage could suggest a defective distributor seal; oil will reduce the quality of the spark by bleeding the HT current to earth. Water may be present in the engine oil (oil change overdue, head gasket fault, etc), and find its way into the cap along with the oil mist through a faulty distributor seal.

21 Inspect the HT towers for corrosion, and the internal terminals for pitting and erosion.

22 Clean off all the old dirt, grease, cold start, electrical spray etc from the outside of the distributor cap, and polish the surface. A polished cap will reduce tracking in damp conditions.

23 If there is any doubt about the condition of the distributor cap, it should be renewed along with the rotor arm **(see illustration 4.8)**.

Rotor arm

24 Check the rotor arm for tracking.

25 If the rotor arm contains a resistor, use an ohmmeter to check the resistance value, and compare with the specified value. If no figure is quoted, the value will normally be approximately 1000 to 5000 ohms. Excessive rotor resistance will dramatically increase secondary output, which results in a reduced coil voltage reserve.

26 DO NOT polish the rotor tip, as this will increase the rotor air gap and result in a reduced coil voltage reserve.

Spark plugs

27 The spark plugs should generally be renewed according to the VM recommendation.

28 Where operating conditions are known to be 'severe service' including low-mileage and short-journey operation, plugs should be renewed more frequently.

29 Remove the spark-plugs and inspect them carefully. Spark plug condition provides many clues to the observant and it is possible to detect engine condition, mixture strength and many other faults from 'reading' the plugs **(see illustration 4.9)**.

30 Renew spark plugs with eroded electrodes, a cracked insulator (internal and external), heavy carbonisation or glazing.

31 A new set of plugs will often work wonders; remember to re-gap new plugs to the specified gap.

Spark plug removal

32 Before removing a plug, check that it has not been cross threaded by observation of the angle of installation. Cross threading usually occurs due to sloppy installation and aluminium cylinder heads are particularly at risk.

33 Extreme care must be observed during the offering up and entry of the plug into the spark plug aperture.

34 Removal is best done from a cold engine, particularly where the cylinder head is made from aluminium. Several VM's warn against removing plugs from a hot engine, in any case.

35 Slacken the plug two or three turns, and then use an air line to blast away debris and dirt from the plug wells, as it may enter the cylinders on removing a plug.

36 If the plug is overtight, squirt penetrating oil into the well, and gently move the plug backwards and forwards until it loosens.

37 A badly-worn or wrong-size spanner will round the plug hexagons, making removal difficult.

Spark plug type

38 The plug must be the correct size and heat range. Sizes differ in length from 3/8" to 3/4", and in diameter from 10 mm to 18 mm. Within these sizes, the seats may be tapered or use a sealing washer.

39 It is quite possible to fit a plug with an incorrect seat, length or heat range with sometimes disastrous results.

CARBON DEPOSITS
Symptoms: Dry sooty deposits indicate a rich mixture or weak ignition. Causes misfiring, hard starting and hesitation.
Recommendation: Check for a clogged air cleaner, high float level, sticky choke and worn ignition points. Use a spark plug with a longer core nose for greater anti-fouling protection.

OIL DEPOSITS
Symptoms: Oily coating caused by poor oil control. Oil is leaking past worn valve guides or piston rings into the combustion chamber. Causes hard starting, misfiring and hesition.
Recommendation: Correct the mechanical condition with necessary repairs and install new plugs.

TOO HOT
Symptoms: Blistered, white insulator, eroded electrode and absence of deposits. Results in shortened plug life.
Recommendation: Check for the correct plug heat range, over-advanced ignition timing, lean fuel mixture, intake manifold vacuum leaks and sticking valves. Check the coolant level and make sure the radiator is not clogged.

PREIGNITION
Symptoms: Melted electrodes. Insulators are white, but may be dirty due to misfiring or flying debris in the combustion chamber. Can lead to engine damage.
Recommendation: Check for the correct plug heat range, over-advanced ignition timing, lean fuel mixture, clogged cooling system and lack of lubrication.

HIGH SPEED GLAZING
Symptoms: Insulator has yellowish, glazed appearance. Indicates that combustion chamber temperatures have risen suddenly during hard acceleration. Normal deposits melt to form a conductive coating. Causes misfiring at high speeds.
Recommendation: Install new plugs. Consider using a colder plug if driving habits warrant.

GAP BRIDGING
Symptoms: Combustion deposits lodge between the electrodes. Heavy deposits accumulate and bridge the electrode gap. The plug ceases to fire, resulting in a dead cylinder.
Recommendation: Locate the faulty plug and remove the deposits from between the electrodes.

NORMAL
Symptoms: Brown to grayish-tan color and slight electrode wear. Correct heat range for engine and operating conditions.
Recommendation: When new spark plugs are installed, replace with plugs of the same heat range.

ASH DEPOSITS
Symptoms: Light brown deposits encrusted on the side or center electrodes or both. Derived from oil and/or fuel additives. Excessive amounts may mask the spark, causing misfiring and hesitation during acceleration.
Recommendation: If excessive deposits accumulate over a short time or low mileage, install new valve guide seals to prevent seepage of oil into the combustion chambers. Also try changing gasoline brands.

WORN
Symptoms: Rounded electrodes with a small amount of deposits on the firing end. Normal color. Causes hard starting in damp or cold weather and poor fuel economy.
Recommendation: Replace with new plugs of the same heat range.

DETONATION
Symptoms: Insulators may be cracked or chipped. Improper gap setting techniques can also result in a fractured insulator tip. Can lead to piston damage.
Recommendation: Make sure the fuel anti-knock values meet engine requirements. Use care when setting the gaps on new plugs. Avoid lugging the engine.

SPLASHED DEPOSITS
Symptoms: After long periods of misfiring, deposits can loosen when normal combustion temperature is restored by an overdue tune-up. At high speeds, deposits flake off the piston and are thrown against the hot insulator, causing misfiring.
Recommendation: Replace the plugs with new ones or clean and reinstall the originals.

MECHANICAL DAMAGE
Symptoms: May be caused by a foreign object in the combustion chamber or the piston striking an incorrect reach (too long) plug. Causes a dead cylinder and could result in piston damage.
Recommendation: Remove the foreign object from the engine and/or install the correct reach plug.

4.9 Spark plug condition chart

40 If a longer plug than standard is fitted (eg 3/4" instead of 1/2"), there would be a danger of the piston fouling the spark plug tip. Also, the threads projecting into the combustion chamber will carbon up, making removal very difficult.

41 When a shorter plug than standard is fitted (eg 1/2" instead of 3/4"), the first few threads of the spark plug hole will also tend to carbon up, making the later fitting of the correct plug a very difficult task without re-cutting the thread. Incomplete combustion will also result from the shrouded spark.

42 A spark plug with the wrong heat range can be a very expensive mistake. A hotter-than-standard spark plug can cause overheating, pre-ignition and piston failure. A colder plug is usually safer, but will tend to foul around town, as it does not get hot enough to burn off the low-speed deposits that form on the insulator.

43 When an engine is worn and tends to regularly oil foul one or more plugs, a temporary cure may be to fit a plug with a hotter heat range. The hotter plug will burn the oily deposits more readily and be less prone to fouling.

Warning: Fitting a hotter spark plug than standard is not recommended because of the danger of engine failure if the engine is driven at medium to high engine or vehicle speeds, or under heavy load. When high speeds are attempted with hotter plugs than normal, there is a strong danger that the hotter plug will cause pre-ignition and piston failure with very little warning.

Spark plug servicing

44 Spark plug cleaning with a wire brush is not recommended as this can cause plug damage and tracking.

45 Oiled plugs are caused by defective piston rings or valve guides. A compression test should identify the fault, which must be remedied if efficient engine operation is to be maintained. A dirty insulator can also lead to tracking of the spark to earth.

Spark plug gap

46 Always check the gap when inspecting or renewing spark plugs. A gap that is too narrow or too wide will cause poor starting, poor performance and poor economy.

Spark plug installation

47 Where the thread in the cylinder head is dirty, use a spark plug thread restorer, with plenty of grease, to clean up the threads before installation.

48 Be very careful that debris does NOT enter a cylinder.

49 Install the spark plug by hand until the faces are felt to make contact, then tighten (using a plug tool) by a further 1/4 turn (flat seat plugs) or by a further 1/16 turn (taper seat plugs). DO NOT overtighten the plugs - you'll risk stripping the threads out of the cylinder head!

50 If using a torque wrench, the correct figure for taper-seat plugs is 8 to 15 lbf ft. If the spark plug is overtightened, subsequent removal can be extremely difficult.

51 Taper-seat plugs are easily overtightened on installation due to the wedging effect of the taper. The plug may break at the boss during a subsequent attempt at removal. In this instance, the plug may need to be extracted with a special tool. In extreme cases, the head will need to be removed to facilitate plug removal.

52 Taper seat plugs installed in certain engines may fit less tightly into the threads of the spark plug hole than is desirable. In the first few hundred miles, combustion fumes may escape via the loose-fitting plug, giving a very slight compression loss. Eventually, carbon will seal this leak, but this may make subsequent removal more difficult. Where this is noticed (the spark plug boss will be carbon-contaminated) the manufacturer's original-equipment spark plug recommendation should be used.

Checking for secondary HT voltage (non-runner test)

53 Check for an HT spark to the plugs. Use one of the following methods whilst cranking the engine on the starter, referring to Warning No 2 in Reference. A powerful spark should consistently bridge the gap:

a) Use a set of insulated pliers to hold one of the HT leads 6 mm from an engine earth.
b) Connect a spark jumper between the HT lead and cylinder head ***(see illustration 4.10).***
c) An alternative method can be used with some diagnostic equipment, when the equipment can detect rpm from an HT lead via an inductive probe. Connect the equipment's inductive trigger probe to an HT lead. Crank the engine. If the equipment registers rpm, the ignition system must be providing a spark. Having tested one lead, test the other three in a similar fashion.

54 No spark: Check for primary ignition switching. If no switching, check the primary ignition system. Refer to the specific Chapters for the system under test.

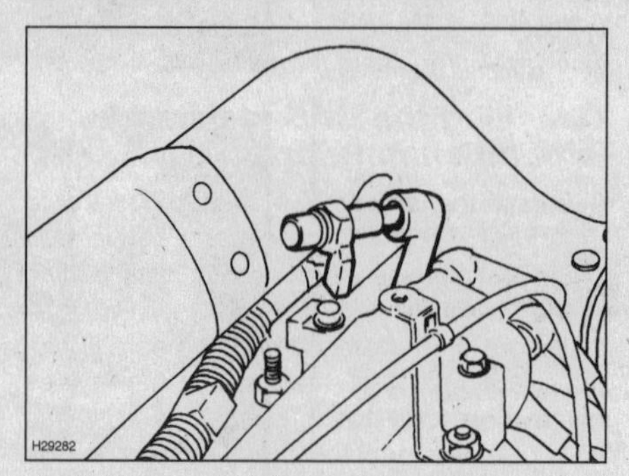

4.10 Use a spark jumper to test for an HT spark from the coil 'king' lead

55 Check for an HT spark from the coil tower. Use one of the three methods listed above whilst cranking the engine on the starter. Refer to Warning No 2 in Reference. A powerful spark should consistently bridge the gap.

56 No spark from the coil tower: If the coil primary is switching, yet no secondary output, the coil is suspect.

57 Before renewing the coil, check the main HT lead for a high resistance (greater than 30000 ohms) and that it is making a good contact with the inner coil tower.

58 Check the coil secondary resistance. Attach an ohmmeter between the coil tower and each primary coil terminal in turn. Compare with the specification in the system Chapter.

59 If there is output from the coil secondary, but no spark at the plugs, check the following components:

a) HT leads. Mark each HT lead so that it may be removed and returned to its correct location.
b) Ensure that the HT leads are pressed firmly into full contact with the coil and distributor cap towers. Loose or poorly fitting HT leads are a common HT fault.
c) Remove the leads (one by one) and measure the resistance with an ohmmeter. Maximum HT lead resistance should be no more than 30 000 ohms.
d) Visually inspect each lead. Replace a lead where the insulation is cracked or chafed or insulating boots & connectors are loose.
e) Check that the HT leads are connected to the correct coil tower in the correct firing order.
f) Remove the distributor cap and check the cap and rotor for defects.
g) Check for wet or damp HT components.
h) Check the spark plugs for condition, gap and correct type. Many faults in poor running electronic engines can actually be traced to worn out spark plugs, renew them if at all in doubt.

Engine running tests

60 Some of the above faults that might prevent the engine from starting may also be present when the engine is running badly:

a) Check the HT leads.
b) Check the coil secondary resistance.
c) Check the spark plugs for condition, gap and for correct type.

Secondary insulation

61 An insulation failure occurs when the spark is allowed to track to earth.

62 Secondary insulation can be tested as follows:

a) Run the engine at idle. A dark garage or workshop will help the result, by making any 'stray' HT voltage easier to spot.
b) Use an insulated probe with one end connected to earth.
c) Slowly pass the probe over the HT leads, distributor cap and ignition coil.

4.11 Pass an insulated probe over the HT leads, cap and coil. If an insulation leak is present, a spark will jump to earth through the tip of the probe

d) The probe should be held no more than 6 mm above the secondary component under test.
e) If a spark jumps from an HT lead or coil to earth through the tip of the probe, the component has inadequate insulation, and should be renewed **(see illustration 4.11)**.

Faulty secondary HT circuit

63 The following list of faults are common reasons for HT failure:

a) Fouled spark plugs.
b) Spark plugs with eroded electrodes or wide gaps.
c) Reversed coil polarity.
d) High resistance HT leads.
e) Incorrect HT leads.
f) Corroded coil towers.
g) Poor primary connections.
h) Over suppression.
i) Faulty HT can cause either electronic component failure or a spurious RFI signal. RFI can disrupt ECM operation.

8 Secondary (HT) ignition system testing - vehicles without distributor (DIS)

Testing the DIS secondary circuit

1 Testing the DIS secondary HT circuit is similar in many respects to testing the secondary with a distributor. Check the following points, and also refer to the secondary tests with distributor.

2 Visually inspect and check the HT leads. The maximum resistance of a lead of any length should not exceed 30 000 ohms.

3 Visually inspect and check the spark plugs.

4 Check the spark plugs for condition, gap and correct type. Many faults in poor-running electronic engines can actually be traced to worn-out spark plugs; renew them if at all in doubt.

5 Because two plugs fire together in a wasted-spark DIS ignition system, a faulty HT lead will affect both cylinders.

6 Check that the HT leads are connected to the correct coil tower, in the correct firing order.

7 The coil towers are normally marked with the appropriate cylinder numbers. Connection of HT leads to the wrong coil tower can cause engine damage.

8 Visually inspect and check the DIS coil unit and towers.

9 Check the coil secondary resistance as follows:

a) Detach the HT leads from the coil unit.
b) Mark the leads so that they can be replaced in the correct position.
c) Measure the resistance between each pair of matched HT terminals and compare to the specifications in the system Chapter (refer to illustration 4.4).

Analysis

10 A spark at only one plug of a set (ie 1 and 4 or 2 and 3) indicates an HT lead or plug fault.

11 Failure of both plugs to spark would indicate a coil secondary or primary fault.

12 Failure of all plugs to spark would indicate a coil secondary or primary fault, or possibly a primary trigger (ie CAS) fault.

System sensor and actuator tests

Important: The following test procedures are general in nature, and should be followed with reference to the Chapter which covers the system under test, and to the system wiring diagram.

9 Primary trigger - crank angle sensor (CAS)

1 Inspect the CAS multi-plug for corrosion and damage.

2 Check that the terminal pins in the CAS multi-plug are fully pushed home and making good contact with the CAS.

3 Remove the CAS from the engine block. Inspect the end surface for corrosion and damage.

4 Measure the CAS resistance, and compare to the specifications in the system Chapter. Refer also to the resistance tests at the end of this section.

5 A fault in any of the above areas are common reasons for a poor or inaccurate signal from the CAS. **Note:** *These tests are also applicable to RPM and TDC sensors, and distributor-located inductive triggers.*

Checking the CAS output with an AC voltmeter (engine cranking)

Note: *This test is more likely to be made if the engine is a non-runner.*

6 Detach the CAS or ECM multi-plug *(refer to Warning No 3 in Reference)* and connect an AC voltmeter between the two terminals leading to the CAS. If a third wire is present, it will be a shield wire.

7 Crank the engine. A minimum AC RMS voltage of about 0.7 should be obtained, although most good sensors will provide an output of more than 1.4 AC RMS voltage **(see illustration 4.12)**. **Note:** *The AC voltmeter at least proves that a signal is being generated by the CAS. However, the AC voltage is an average voltage, and would not clearly indicate damage to the CAS lobes or that the sinewave is regular in formation.*

Checking the CAS resistance with an ohmmeter

8 Detach the CAS or ECM multi-plug *(refer to Warning No 3 in Reference)* and connect an ohmmeter between the two terminals leading to the sensor.

9 Record the resistance and compare it with the specified value in the system Chapter **(see illustration 4.13)**. **Note:** *Even if the resistance is within the quoted specifications in the system Chapter, this does not prove that the CAS can generate an acceptable signal.*

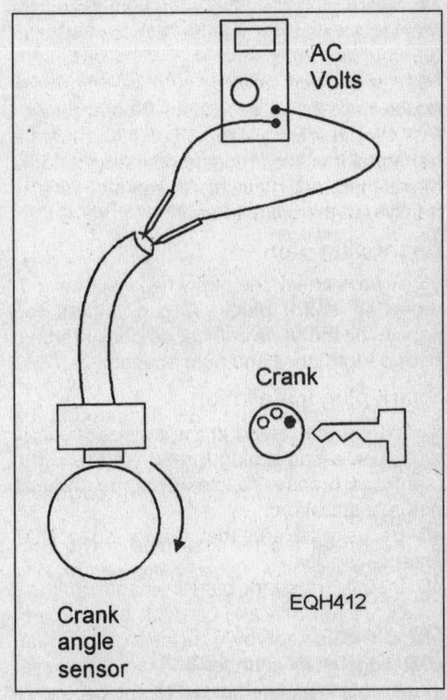

4.12 Check the CAS output with an AC voltmeter

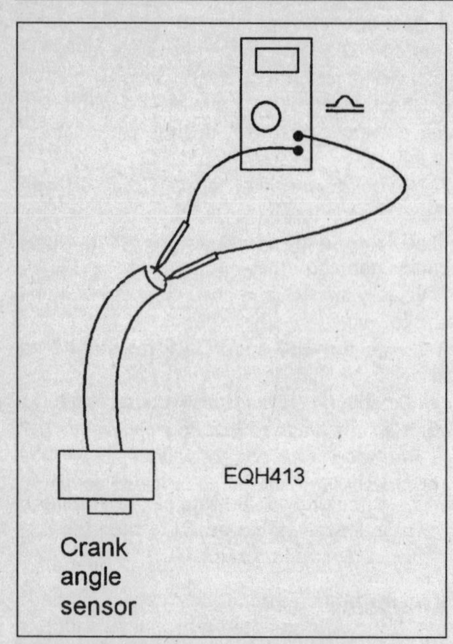

4.13 Measure the CAS resistance

Checking the CAS shield connection

10 The CAS may have a shield wire (not in all cases). Locate the wiring multi-plug connector or disconnect the ECM multi-plug *(refer to Warning No 3 in Reference).*

11 Attach an ohmmeter probe to one of the sensor terminals (1 or 2).

12 Attach the other ohmmeter probe to the shield wire terminal. A reading of infinity should be obtained.

13 Move the ohmmeter probe from the shield wire terminal, and connect it to earth. A reading of infinity should also be obtained. **Note:** *The shield wire on the CAS in some systems is connected to the CAS earth return wire. In such a case, continuity will be registered on the ohmmeter and this is normal for that vehicle. Refer to the wiring diagrams for the system under test to determine how the CAS is wired.*

10 Primary trigger - Hall-effect sensor (HES)

1 In most systems the HES is located in the distributor. A flywheel-mounted HES is found in some VAG systems.

2 Inspect the HES multi-plug for corrosion and damage.

3 Check that the terminal pins in the HES multi-plug are fully pushed home and making good contact with the HES.

Quick test (non-runner, no spark)

4 Remove the main HT lead from the distributor cap centre tower, and connect it to the cylinder head via a spark jumper.

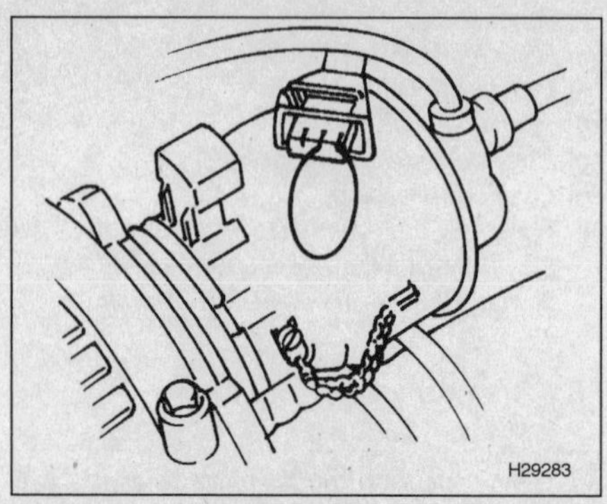

4.14 Very briefly flash the 'O' and (-) terminals at the HES multi-plug to check for a spark

5 Detach the HES multi-plug at the distributor.

6 Identify the supply, signal and earth terminals.

7 Briefly flash a small jumper lead between the (O) and (-) terminals on the HES harness multi-plug **(see illustration 4.14).**

8 If a spark jumps across the spark jumper terminals to the cylinder head, the coil and amplifier are capable of producing a spark, and the Hall switch in the distributor is suspect.

HES test procedures

9 Roll back the rubber protection boot to the HES multi-plug.

10 Connect the voltmeter negative or dwell meter probe to an engine earth.

11 Identify the supply, signal and earth terminals.

12 Connect the voltmeter positive or dwell meter probe to the wire attached to the HES signal terminal.

13 Allow the engine to idle.

14 An average voltage of approximately 7 to 8 volts, or a duty cycle of approximately 35% should be obtained.

Signal voltage or duty cycle signal not available

15 Stop the engine.

16 Remove the distributor cap.

17 HES multi-plug connected, ignition on, voltmeter positive probe connected to the signal terminal **(see illustration 4.15).**

18 Turn the engine over slowly. As the trigger vane cut-out space moves in and out of the air gap, the voltage should alternate between 10.0 to 12.0 volts and zero volts.

Signal voltage not available

19 Disconnect the HES multi-plug at the distributor.

20 Probe output terminal 2 (O) of the harness multi-plug with the voltmeter positive probe. A voltage of between 10 and 12 volts should be obtained.

21 No voltage from the ECM to terminal 2: Check for continuity of the signal wiring between the HES and the ECM. Recheck for voltage at the ECM terminal.

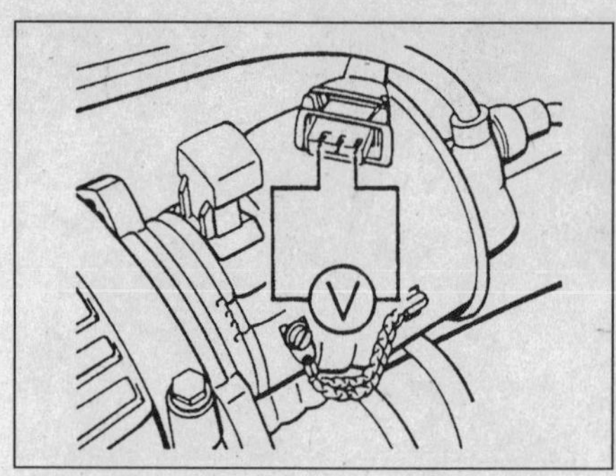

4.15 Connect the voltmeter between the HES (+) and (-) terminals. A voltage of between 10 and 12 volts should be obtained

22 No voltage available at the ECM: Check all voltage supplies and earth connections to the ECM. If the voltage supplies and earth connections are satisfactory, the ECM is suspect.

23 Check the voltage supply (10 to 12 volts) at HES terminal number 1 (+). If the supply is unsatisfactory, check for continuity of the wiring between the HES and the ECM.

24 Check the earth connection at HES terminal number 3 (-).

25 If the voltage supply and earth are ok, the HES in the distributor is suspect.

11 Primary ignition

1 Check the coil terminals for good clean connections.

2 Clean away accumulations of dirt, and the residue from a maintenance spray. The residue will attract dirt, and often leads to bleeding of the HT current to earth.

3 Inspect the ignition coil for signs of tracking, particularly around the coil tower area.

4 Although the following tests are accomplished with the aid of a basic dwell meter, an oscilloscope is a more suitable instrument for analysing the signals generated by the primary ignition.

Engine non-runner test procedures

5 Connect the negative dwell meter probe to an engine earth.

6 Connect the positive dwell meter probe to the coil negative (-) terminal (usually marked 1 in Bosch systems).

7 Crank the engine on the starter.

8 A duty cycle reading of approximately 5 to 20% should be obtained. If the instrument can measure the value in milliseconds, then this is even more useful.

9 Good primary signal: The primary ignition (including the CAS or HES) are providing an acceptable signal.

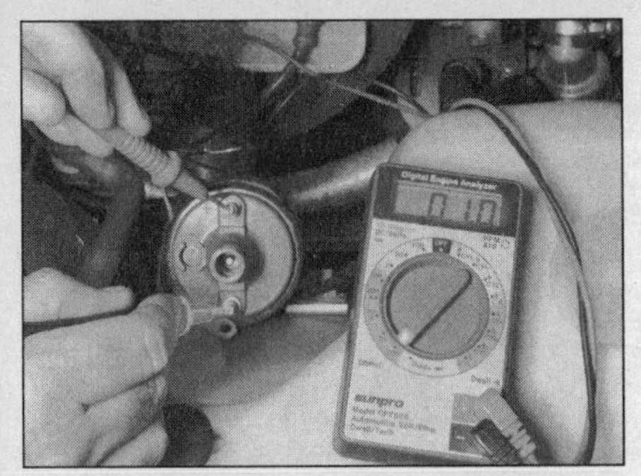

4.16 Check the primary resistance. Disconnect the low tension wires and connect the ohmmeter between the positive and negative terminals

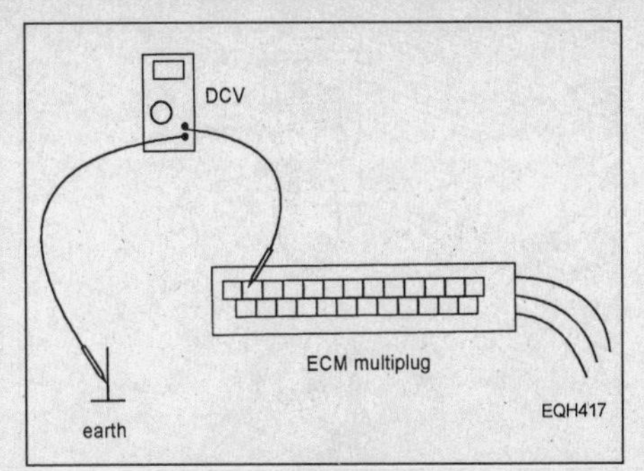

4.17 Detach the ECM multi-plug and check for nbv at the ECM primary ignition terminal

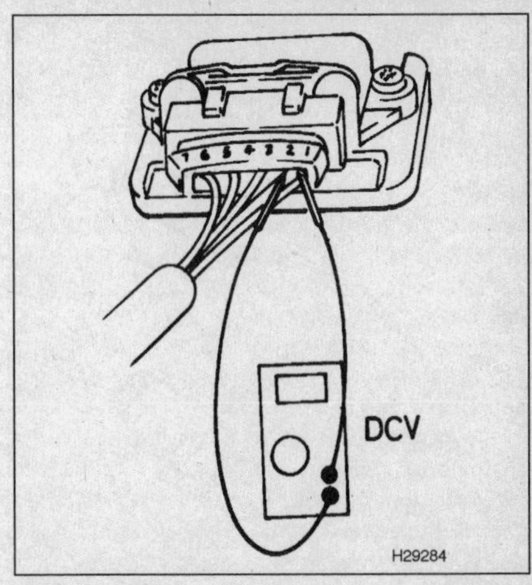

4.18 Checking for voltage at the amplifier terminal that is connected to the ignition coil terminal No 1

Primary signal not available (amplifier inside the ECM)

10 Check the primary trigger for a good signal (refer to CAS or HES test).
11 Switch the ignition on.
12 Check for a voltage supply to the coil positive (+) terminal (15). If there is no voltage, check the wiring back to the supply (usually the ignition switch, but could be one of the relays).
13 Check for voltage to the coil negative (-) terminal (1). If there is no voltage, remove the wire to the coil (-) terminal and recheck. If there is still no voltage, check the coil primary resistance **(see illustration 4.16)**. Refer to the specifications in the system Chapter.
14 With voltage at nbv level, check for a short to earth between the coil No 1 terminal and the appropriate ECM pin.
15 Detach the ECM multi-plug (refer to Warning No 3 in Reference) and check for nbv at the appropriate ECM pin **(see illustration 4.17)**. If there is no voltage, check for continuity between the coil No 1 terminal and the appropriate ECM pin.
16 If the wiring is satisfactory, check all ECM voltage supplies and earth connections. If tests find no faults, the ECM is suspect. However, a substitute ignition coil should be tried before renewing the ECM.
17 If the ignition system is DIS, repeat the tests for the second coil. The ECM connection varies according to system.

Primary signal not available (separate external amplifier)

18 Check the primary trigger for a good signal (Refer to CAS or HES test).
19 Switch the ignition on.
20 Check for a voltage supply to the coil positive (+) terminal (15). If there is no voltage, check the wiring back to the supply (usually the ignition switch, or one of the system relays).
21 Check for voltage to the coil negative (-) terminal (1).

a) *No voltage: Remove the wire to the coil (-) terminal and recheck.*
b) *Still no voltage: Check the coil primary resistance, the coil is suspect.*
c) *Voltage at nbv level: Check for a short to earth between the coil No 1 terminal and the amplifier. If the wiring is ok, the amplifier is suspect.*

22 Disconnect the amplifier multi-plug *(refer to Warning No 3 in Reference)*. Check for voltage at the amplifier terminal that is connected to the ignition coil terminal 1 **(see illustration 4.18)**. If there is no voltage, check for continuity of wiring between the amplifier and ignition coil terminal No 1.
23 Check for voltage to the amplifier from the ignition switch.
24 Check the amplifier earth connection.
25 Crank the engine and check for a control signal from the ECM to the amplifier. **Note:** *Although it is possible to use a dwell meter to check for a duty cycle signal from the ECM to the amplifier, the integrity of the signal may be difficult to establish. Once again, an oscilloscope is more likely to make sense of this signal. If there is no control signal, check continuity of the wiring between the amplifier and the ECM terminal.*
26 If the control signal is ok, no output from the amplifier suggests a faulty amplifier.
27 If the wiring is satisfactory, check all ECM voltage supplies and earth connections. If tests find no faults, the ECM is suspect. However, a substitute ignition coil and/or amplifier should be tried before renewing the ECM.
28 If the ignition system is DIS, repeat the tests for the second coil. The ECM connection varies according to system.

Engine running test procedures

29 Connect the negative dwell meter probe to an engine earth.
30 Connect the positive dwell meter probe to the coil negative (-) terminal (usually marked 1 in Bosch systems).
31 Run the engine at idle and various speeds. Record the duty cycle values - approximate values are as follows:

Idle speed: 5 to 20%
2000 rpm: 15 to 35%
3000 rpm: 25 to 45%

32 It is important that the duty cycle in % increases in value as the engine rpm is raised. If your DMM can measure the duty cycle in ms, the reading should not change much in value as the engine rpm is raised.
33 Check the amplifier earth.
34 Check that devices such as a radio suppresser or a burglar alarm have not been connected to the coil primary (-) terminal. *All other tests and any detailed primary analysis really requires an oscilloscope.*

12 Knock sensor (KS)

1 Inspect the KS multi-plug for corrosion and damage.
2 Check that the terminal pins in the KS multi-plug are fully pushed home and making good contact with the KS.
3 Attach the probe of an inductive timing light to the HT lead of No 1 cylinder.
4 Allow the engine to idle.
5 Gently tap the engine block close to No 1 cylinder.
6 The timing should be seen to retard.

13 Fuel injector operation (MPi)

General fuel injector test procedures

1 Inspect the injector multi-plugs for corrosion and damage.
2 Check that the terminal pins in the injector multi-plugs are fully pushed home and making good contact with the injector.
3 Check for corrosion in the connection plugs between the relay and the injector, and the ECM and the injector. Corrosion in connection plugs is a common reason for poor injector performance.

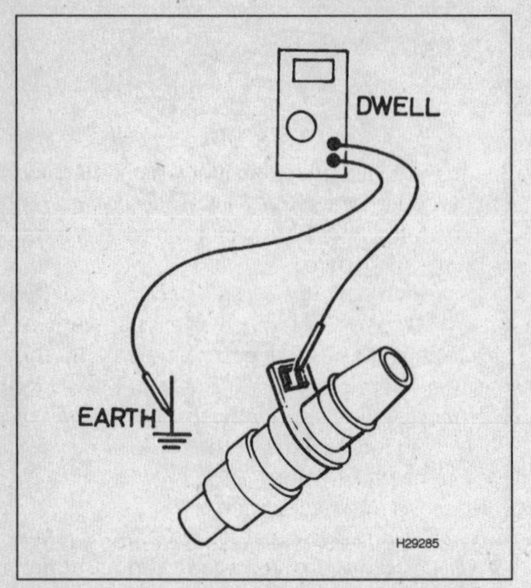

4.19 Checking the fuel injection pulse

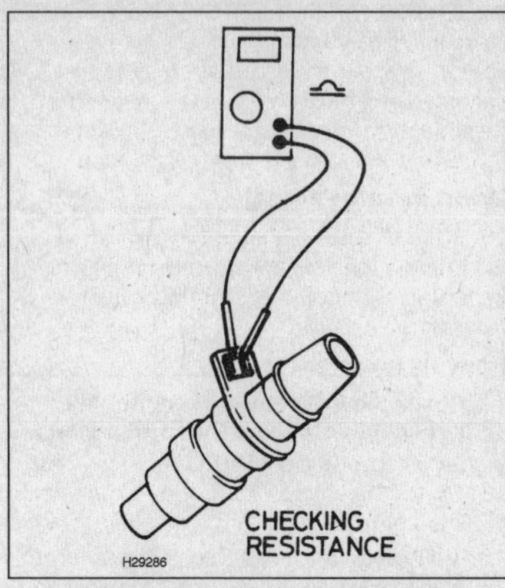

4.20 Checking the injector resistance

4 Roll back the rubber protection boot to the injector multi-plug **(see illustration 4.19)**.
5 Connect the negative dwell meter probe to an engine earth.
6 Identify the supply and signal terminals. **Note:** *An injector dwell reading will only be obtained upon the signal terminal, which is the wire connecting the injector to the ECM. If you cannot obtain a reading, reconnect the probe to the other terminal and retry.*
7 Connect the positive dwell meter probe to the wire attached to the Injector signal terminal.
8 Although the following tests are accomplished with the aid of a basic dwell meter, an oscilloscope is a more suitable instrument for analysing the signals generated by the electronic fuel injector circuits.
9 Initially, the probe can be connected to the signal terminal of any one of the injectors.

Current-controlled or peak-and-hold injection circuits (dwell meter testing)

10 If the injector is of the current-controlled kind, very few dwell meters are capable of registering the second stage of the pulse duration. The meter may only register the switch-on circuit of approximately 1.0 or 2.0%. This means that the injector duty cycle reading will be inaccurate, and not representative of the total pulse width seen in the circuit. A small number of DMM's are available that can actually measure this circuit satisfactorily.

Engine non-runner test procedures

11 Crank the engine.
12 A duty cycle reading (injector duty cycle) of approximately 5 to 10% should be obtained. If the dwell meter can measure the value in milliseconds, this could be even more useful.

Good injector signal

a) Check for an injector pulse on the other injectors.
b) If the injector signal is satisfactory and if the primary ignition signal is also providing an acceptable signal, the fault is unlikely to be related to the ECM.

Poor or no injector signal on one or more injectors

Note: *In some Motronic systems, the frequency of injection increases for several seconds during initial cranking.*
13 Check the fuel pressure and fuel flow.
14 Check the CAS or HES for a good signal.
15 Check the voltage at the signal terminal of the injector multi-plug. Battery voltage should be obtained.
16 No voltage: Check the injector resistance and the injector voltage supply **(see illustration 4.20)**.
17 Disconnect the ECM multi-plug (see Warning No 3 in Reference).
18 Switch on the ignition.
19 Use a jumper lead to very briefly touch each one of the injector actuator pins in the ECM multi-plug to earth **(see illustration 4.21)**.
20 If the injector actuates, check the ECM main voltage supplies and earths. If the tests reveal no fault, the ECM is suspect.
21 If the injector does not actuate, check for nbv at the ECM pin.

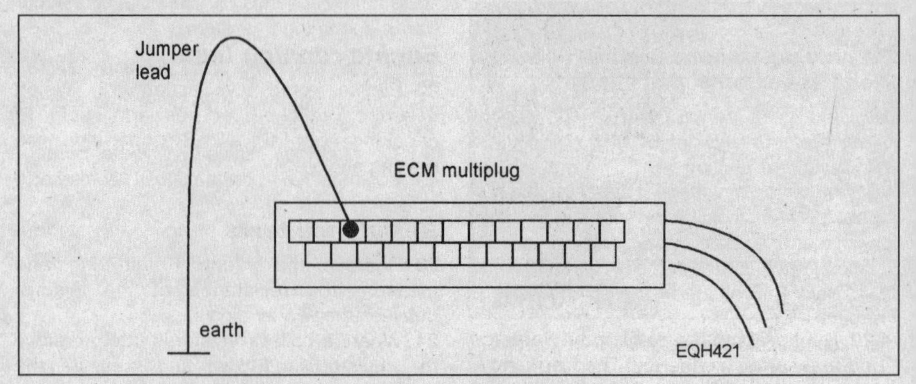

4.21 Use a jumper lead to very briefly touch an injector actuator pin in the ECM multi-plug to earth

a) Voltage present: the injector is suspect.
b) No voltage present: Check for continuity of wiring between the injector multi-plugs and the ECM multi-plug.

22 If the injector circuit is banked or sequential, individually check each connection to the ECM.

Duty cycle too long or too short

23 Check the CTS.
24 Check the AFS or MAP sensor. **Note:** *If the ECM has entered LOS due to a fault in one of the sensors, the engine may generally behave quite well whilst the engine is hot, but may be difficult to start when cold.*

Engine running tests

25 Run the engine at various speeds. Record the duty cycle and compare to the approximate values in the following table. When the engine is cold, the values will slightly increase.

Engine speed	Duty cycle
Idle speed	*3 to 6%*
2000 rpm	*7 to 14%*
3000 rpm	*11 to 16%*
Slow throttle increase	*11 to 16%*
Rapid throttle increase	*20+ %*
Deceleration	*Zero (release throttle at 3000 rpm)*

26 Evaluate as follows:
a) The duty cycle in % should increase in value as the engine rpm is raised.
b) Under rapid acceleration, the duty cycle should show a great increase in value.
c) Under deceleration, when the engine is hot, the duty cycle should drop to zero (digital meter) and reappear as the engine speed sinks below approximately 1200 rpm.
d) Where the meter does not drop to zero, check the throttle valve for correct adjustment and the TPS or TS for correct operation.
e) Noise from the injectors should also temporarily disappear as the cut-off operates.
f) Please note that a slow-responding digital meter may not show the drop to zero and this should also be considered.

Duty cycle that is too long or too short

27 Check the CTS.
28 Check the AFS or MAP sensor.

Injector resistance tests

29 Remove each injector multi-plug, and measure the resistance of the injector between the two terminals.

a) Current-controlled injectors: 4 ohms.
b) Most other systems: 16 ohms.

30 Parallel injector circuits: Refer to Chapter 2 for a description of the merits of parallel circuit measurement.

14 Fuel injector operation (SPi)

1 Inspect the injector multi-plug for corrosion and damage.
2 Check that the terminal pins in the multi-plug are fully pushed home and making good contact with the injector.
3 Check for corrosion in the connection plug between the relay and the injector, and the ECM and the injector. Corrosion in connection plugs is a common reason for poor injector performance.
4 Roll back the rubber protection boot to the injector multi-plug.
5 Connect the negative dwell meter probe to an engine earth.
6 Identify the supply and signal terminals.
7 Connect the positive dwell meter probe to the wire attached to the injector signal terminal **(see illustration 4.22)**. **Note:** *The majority of SPi systems utilise current control, and the average dwell meter will not accurately measure this kind of injection signal. An oscilloscope is therefore recommended for signal tests on the majority of SPi systems.*

Engine non-runner test procedures

8 Crank the engine.
9 A duty cycle reading (injector duty cycle) of some description should be obtained. If the dwell meter can measure the full pulse width value in milliseconds, this could be even more useful. If a signal is obtained, this at least indicates that the ECM is capable of switching the injection circuit. However, it does not prove that the signal is totally satisfactory.

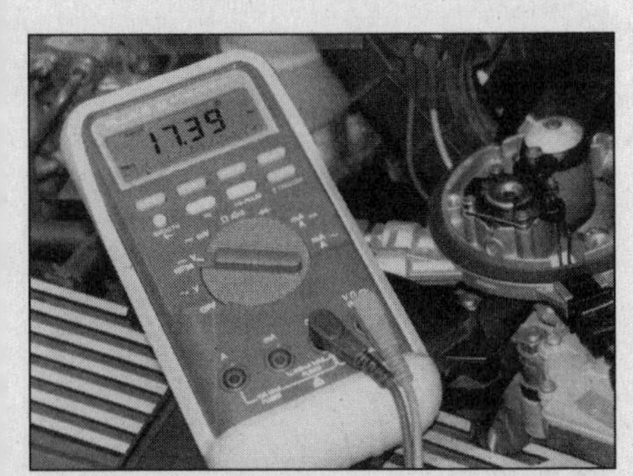

4.22 Backprobing the single point injector and measuring frequency. The frequency of injection may change during a cold start or during acceleration

Good injector signal

10 If the injector signal is satisfactory and if the primary ignition signal is also providing an acceptable signal, the fault is unlikely to be related to the ECM.

Poor or no injector signal

11 Check the fuel pressure and fuel flow.
12 Check the CAS, HES or other primary trigger for a good signal.
13 Check the voltage at the signal terminal of the injector multi-plug. Battery voltage should be obtained.
14 No voltage:

a) Check the injector resistance.
b) Check the ballast resistor resistance (where fitted).
c) Check for continuity of wiring between the injector multi-plug and the ECM multi-plug.
d) Check the voltage supply to the injector.

15 Disconnect the ECM multi-plug (see Warning No 3 in Reference).
16 Switch on the ignition.
17 Use a jumper lead to very briefly touch the injector actuator pin in the ECM multi-plug to earth.
18 If the injector actuates, check the ECM main voltage supplies and earths. If the tests reveal no fault, the ECM is suspect.
19 If the injector does not actuate: check for nbv at the ECM pin:

a) Voltage present: The injector is suspect.
b) No voltage present: Check for continuity of wiring between the injector multi-plug and the ECM multi-plug.

Incorrect pulse width (if an accurate measurement can be made)

20 Check the CTS.
21 Check the MAP sensor. **Note:** *If the ECM has entered LOS due to a fault in one of the sensors, the engine may generally behave quite well whilst the engine is hot, but may be difficult to start when cold.*

Engine running tests

22 Please refer to Section 13, which describes test procedures applicable to checking both MPi and SPi operation in a running engine.

Resistance tests

23 Remove the injector multi-plug and measure the resistance of the injector between the two terminals.
24 Where a ballast resistor is fitted, remove the resistor multi-plug and measure the resistance of the ballast resistor between the two terminals.

15 Inductive phase sensor (CID)

1 The inductive phase sensor which identifies the cylinders for sequential injection operation may be fitted inside the distributor or mounted upon the camshaft.
2 The timing of the phase sensor and the primary trigger is particularly important in sequential fuel injected vehicles. If the phasing is out of synchronisation, at best the engine may sink into LOS mode, with loss of power and increased emissions. At worst, the engine may fail to start.
3 Reasons for phasing errors:

a) Incorrectly-adjusted distributor (only if the distributor is adjustable).
b) Slack timing belt (very common fault).
c) Misaligned timing belt.

4 Inspect the CAS multi-plug for corrosion, and damage.
5 Inspect the CID multi-plug for corrosion, and damage.
6 Check that the connector terminal pins are fully pushed home and making good contact with the CID multi-plug.
7 Measure the CID resistance and compare it with the specified value in the system Chapter.

CID output

8 Detach the CID or ECM multi-plug (refer to Warning No 3 in Reference)
9 Connect an AC voltmeter between the two terminals at the CID or at the corresponding multi-plug terminals at the ECM. **Note:** *Better results are usually obtained by probing the + terminal, although the signal can often be obtained on the CID earth return.*
10 Crank the engine. A minimum AC RMS voltage of about 0.40 volts should be obtained.
11 Reconnect the CID or ECM multi-plug.
12 Backprobe the CID signal and earth terminals.
13 Start the engine and allow it to idle. A minimum AC RMS voltage of about 0.75 volts should be obtained.
14 No signal, or a very weak or intermittent signal:

a) Measure the CID resistance.
b) Check the sensor for damage, dirt or oil contamination.
c) Check the camshaft or distributor for damage

CID resistance

15 Detach the CID or ECM multi-plug, and connect an ohmmeter between the two terminals leading to the sensor.
16 Record the resistance and compare it with the specified values in the system Chapter.

16 Hall-effect phase sensor (CID)

1 The sensor is located in the distributor
2 Inspect the multi-plug for corrosion and damage.
3 Check that the terminal pins in the multi-plug are fully pushed home and making good contact with the sensor.
4 Roll back the rubber protection boot to the sensor multi-plug.
5 Connect the voltmeter negative or dwell meter probe to an engine earth.
6 Identify the supply, signal and earth terminals.
7 Connect the voltmeter positive or dwell meter probe to the wire attached to the sensor signal terminal.
8 Allow the engine to idle.
9 An average voltage of around 2.5 volts, or an approximate duty cycle of 50% should be obtained.

Signal voltage or duty cycle signal not available

10 Stop the engine.
11 Remove the distributor cap.
12 Sensor multi-plug connected, ignition on, voltmeter positive probe connected to the signal terminal.
13 Turn the engine slowly by hand. As the trigger vane cut-out space moves in and out of the air gap, the voltage should alternate between 5.0 volts and zero volts.

Signal voltage not available

14 Disconnect the sensor multi-plug at the distributor.
15 Probe output terminal 2 (O) of the harness multi-plug with the voltmeter positive probe:

a) *No voltage from the ECM to terminal 2: Check for continuity of the signal wiring between the sensor and the ECM.*
b) *Recheck for voltage at the ECM terminal.*
c) *If no voltage is available at the ECM, check all voltage supplies and earth connections to the ECM. If the voltage supplies and earth connections are satisfactory, the ECM is suspect.*

16 Check the voltage supply (5.0 volts) at sensor terminal number 1 (+). If the supply is unsatisfactory, check for continuity of the wiring between the sensor and the ECM.
17 Check the earth connection at sensor terminal number 3 (-).
18 If the voltage supply and earth are ok, the sensor in the distributor is suspect.

17 Airflow sensor (AFS)

1 Inspect the air trunking from the AFS and check for splits, poor fitting or damage. A large vacuum leak at this point will cause the engine to fire but fail to continue running, and a small vacuum leak will adversely affect the AFR.

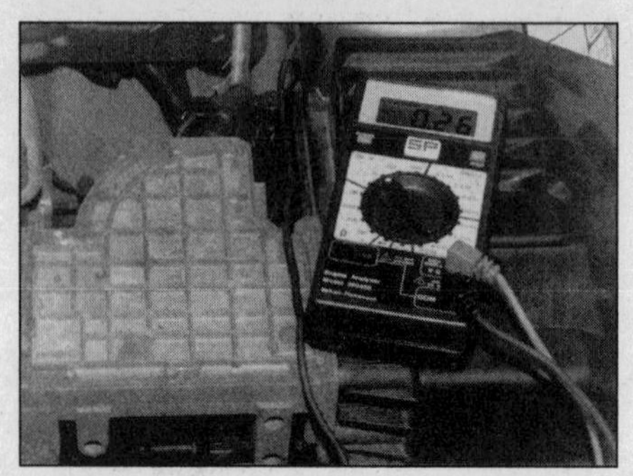

4.23 Backprobing the AFS for voltage

2 Inspect the AFS multi-plug for corrosion, and damage.
3 Check that the terminal pins in the AFS multi-plug are fully pushed home and making good contact with the AFS.
4 The AFS may be of the vane, hot-wire or hot-film type, depending on system.

Vane-type AFS voltage tests

5 Roll back the rubber protection boot to the AFS multi-plug.
6 Connect the voltmeter negative probe to an engine earth.
7 Identify the supply, signal and earth terminals.
8 Connect the voltmeter positive probe to the wire attached to the AFS signal terminal **(see illustration 4.23)**.
9 Remove the air trunking.
10 Remove the air filter box so that the AFS flap can be easily opened and closed.
11 Open and close the AFS flap several times and check for smooth operation. Also check that the flap does not stick **(see illustration 4.24)**.
12 Switch on the ignition, engine stopped. A voltage of approximately 0.20 to 0.30 volts should be obtained.
13 Open and close the flap several times, and check for a smooth voltage increase to a maximum of 4.0 to 4.5 volts. **Note:** *If a digital voltmeter is used, then it is useful for it to have a bar graph facility. The smoothness of the voltage increase can then be more easily seen.*

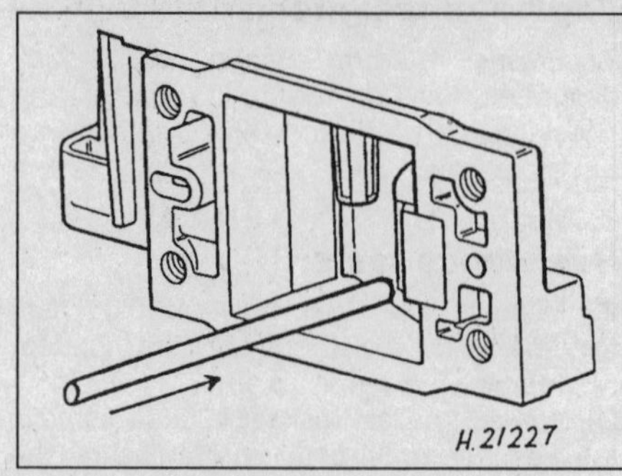

4.24 Check the vane AFS flap for a smooth opening and closing action

14 Start the engine and allow it to idle. A voltage of approximately 0.5 to 1.5 volts should be obtained.
15 Open the throttle to no more than 3000 rpm. A voltage of approximately 2.0 to 2.5 volts should be obtained.
16 Snap open the throttle. A voltage greater than 3.0 volts should be obtained.

Erratic signal output

17 An erratic output occurs when the voltage output is stepped, or drops to zero or becomes open circuit.
18 When the AFS signal output is erratic, this usually suggests a faulty signal track or sticking flap. In this instance, a new or reconditioned AFS may be the only cure. If the carbon signal track is thought to be dirty, remove the AFS top cover and try cleaning the track carefully - do not use strong solvents, however.
19 Sometimes the wiper arm becomes disengaged from the signal track at certain points during its traverse. This can also give an erratic output.

a) *Remove the AFS top cover, and check that the wiper arm touches the track during its swing from the open to the closed position.*
b) *Carefully bending the arm so that it touches the signal track can cure this fault.*

Signal voltage not available

20 Check for the 5.0-volt reference voltage supply at the AFS supply terminal.
21 Check the earth return connection at the AFS earth terminal.
22 If the supply and earth are satisfactory, check for continuity of the signal wiring between the AFS and the ECM.
23 If the supply and/or earth are unsatisfactory, check for continuity of the wiring between the AFS and the ECM.
24 If the AFS wiring is satisfactory, check all voltage supplies and earth connections to the ECM. If the voltage supplies and earth connections are satisfactory, the ECM is suspect.

Signal or supply voltage at nbv level

25 Check for a short to a wire connected to the battery positive (+) terminal or a switched supply voltage.

Vane-type AFS resistance tests

26 Connect an ohmmeter between the AFS signal terminal and supply terminal, or between the AFS signal terminal and earth terminal.
27 Open and close the AFS flap several times, and check for a smooth resistance change. As the AFS flap is moved slowly from the closed to the fully-open position, the AFS resistance may increase and decrease in a series of steps. This is normal. If the AFS resistance becomes open- or short-circuit, a fault is revealed.

28 We are not providing resistance specifications for the AFS in this book. It is less important that the resistance of the AFS remains within arbitrary values, than the operation is correct.
29 Connect an ohmmeter between the AFS earth terminal and supply terminal. A stable resistance should be obtained.
30 Renew the AFS if the resistance is open-circuit or shorted to earth.
31 Refer to the comments on resistance readings in Section 3.

Hot-wire/hot-film type AFS tests

Note: *The voltage measurements are based on the Vauxhall 16-valve engines with Motronic 2.5. The readings from other vehicles should be similar.*
32 Switch on the ignition. A voltage of approximately 1.4 volts should be obtained.
33 Start the engine and allow it to idle. A voltage of approximately 1.9 to 2.3 volts should be obtained.
34 Snap open the throttle several times. The voltage will not increase significantly over the idle value during this off-load test. **Note:** *If a digital voltmeter is used, then it is useful for it to have a bar graph facility. The smoothness of the voltage increase can then be more easily seen.*
35 It is less easy to test the AFS Hot Wire signal output, because It is impossible to simulate full-load conditions in the workshop without putting the vehicle on a chassis dynamometer (rolling road). However, the following test procedure will usually prove if the signal output is consistent.
36 Disconnect the air trunking so that the hot wire is exposed.
37 Switch on the ignition.
38 Use a length of plastic tubing to blow air over the hot wire.
39 It should be possible to plot a voltage curve, although the curve will be much steeper than that obtained with the engine running.

Erratic signal output

40 An erratic output occurs when the voltage output is stepped, or drops to zero or becomes open-circuit.
41 Check the AFS resistance by connecting an ohmmeter between AFS terminals 2 and 3. A resistance of approximately 2.5 to 3.1 ohms should be obtained.
42 When the AFS signal output is erratic, and all supply and earth voltages are satisfactory, this suggests a faulty AFS. In this case, a new or reconditioned AFS may be the only cure.

Signal voltage not available

43 Check for the battery voltage supply to AFS terminal No 5.
44 Check the earth return connection at AFS terminal No 2.
45 Check the earth connection at AFS terminal No 1.
46 If the supply and earths are satisfactory, check for continuity of the signal wiring between the AFS and the ECM.

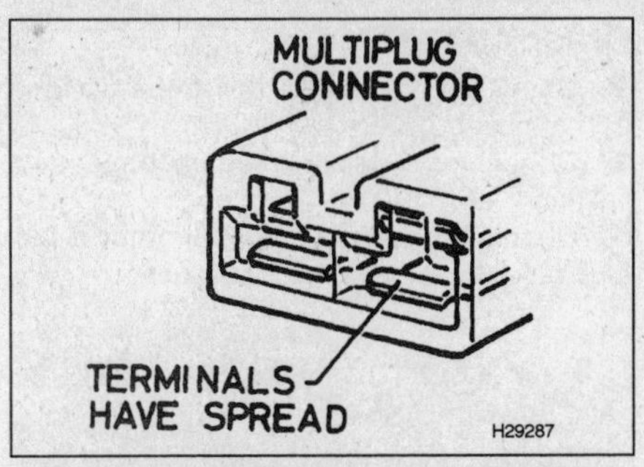

4.25 Check that the terminal pins in the multi-plug are fully pushed home and making good contact with the MAP sensor

47 If the supply and/or earths are unsatisfactory, check for continuity of the supply and / or earth wiring between the AFS and the ECM.
48 If the AFS wiring is satisfactory, check all voltage supplies and earth connections to the ECM. If the voltage supplies and earths are satisfactory, the ECM is suspect.

18 MAP sensor (analogue and digital types)

1 Inspect the MAP sensor multi-plug for corrosion and damage.
2 Check that the terminal pins in the MAP sensor multi-plug are fully pushed home and making good contact with the MAP sensor **(see illustration 4.25)**.
3 Where the MAP sensor is located internally in the ECM, voltage tests are not possible.

MAP sensor test procedures (Analogue: external and internal MAP sensor)

4 Use a 'T' connector to connect a vacuum gauge between the inlet manifold and the MAP sensor **(see illustration 4.26)**.
5 Allow the engine to idle. If the engine vacuum is low (less than 425 to 525 mm Hg), check for the following faults:

a) A vacuum leak.
b) A damaged or perished vacuum pipe.
c) A restricted vacuum connection.

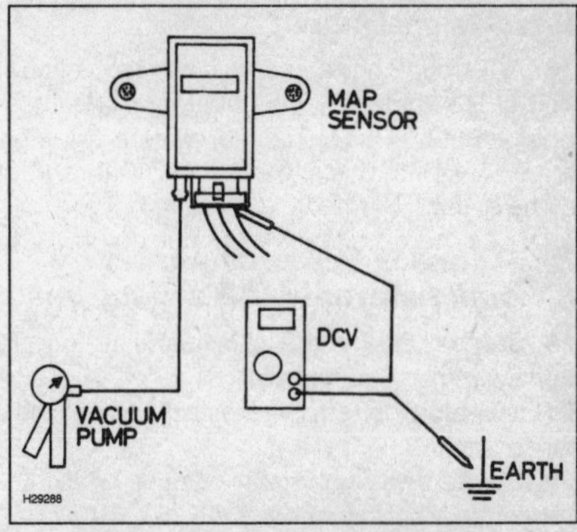

4.26 Using a vacuum gauge and a voltmeter to check the MAP sensor signal

d) An engine problem - eg a misaligned cambelt.
e) A leaky MAP diaphragm (inside the ECM if the MAP sensor is internal).

6 Disconnect the vacuum gauge, and connect a vacuum pump in its place.
7 Use the pump to apply vacuum to the MAP sensor until approximately 560 mm Hg is reached.
8 Cease pumping, and the MAP sensor diaphragm should hold pressure for a minimum of 30 seconds at this vacuum setting.

MAP sensor test procedures (Analogue: external MAP sensor)

9 Roll back the rubber protection boot to the MAP sensor multi-plug.
10 Connect the voltmeter negative probe to an engine earth.
11 Identify the supply, signal and earth terminals.
12 Connect the voltmeter positive probe to the wire attached to the MAP sensor signal terminal.
13 Disconnect the vacuum pipe from the MAP sensor.
14 Connect a vacuum pump to the sensor.
15 Switch the ignition on.
16 Compare the ignition-on voltage to that specified in the system Chapter.
17 Apply vacuum as shown in the table, and check for a smooth voltage change.

MAP voltage table (Analogue: signal terminal, engine stopped)

Vacuum	Volts	MAP applied (bar)
Zero	4.3 to 4.9	1.0 ± 0.1
200 mbar	3.2	0.8
400 mbar	2.2	0.6
500 mbar	1.2 to 2.0	0.5
600 mbar	1.0	0.4

Condition	Volts	MAP (bar)	Vacuum (bar)
Full-throttle	4.35	1.0 ± 0.1	Zero
Ignition on	4.35	1.0 ± 0.1	Zero
Idle speed	1.5	0.28 to 0.55	0.72 to 0.45
Deceleration	1.0	0.20 to 0.25	0.80 to 0.75

Erratic signal output

18 An erratic output occurs when the voltage output is stepped, drops to zero, or becomes open-circuit. This usually suggests a faulty MAP sensor. In this instance, a new sensor is the only cure.

MAP sensor test procedures (Digital: external MAP sensor only)

19 Set the DMM to the volts scale.
20 Switch on the ignition.
21 Identify the supply, signal and earth terminals.
22 Connect the voltmeter positive probe to the wire attached to the MAP sensor signal terminal. An average voltage of approximately 2.5 volts should be obtained. If not, refer to the 'Signal voltage not available' tests below.
23 Set the meter to the tachometer 4-cylinder scale (all engines).
24 Disconnect the vacuum hose to the MAP sensor.
25 Connect the positive DMM probe to the signal terminal, and connect the negative probe to the earth terminal.
26 An rpm reading of 4500 to 4900 should be obtained.
27 Attach a vacuum pump to the MAP sensor hose connection. During the following tests, the vacuum should hold steady at all of the pressure settings:

- *a) Apply 200 mb, the rpm should drop by 525 ± 120 rpm.*
- *b) Apply 400 mb, the rpm should drop by 1008 ± 120 rpm.*
- *c) Apply 600 mb, the rpm should drop by 1460 ± 120 rpm.*
- *d) Apply 800 mb, the rpm should drop by 1880 ± 120 rpm.*

28 Release the pressure when the measured value should return to the original setting of 4500 to 4900.
29 Renew the MAP sensor if it fails to behave as described.

Signal voltage not available (both Analogue and Digital external types)

30 Check the reference voltage supply (5.0 volts).
31 Check the earth return.
32 If the supply and earth are satisfactory, check for continuity of the signal wiring between the MAP sensor and the ECM.
33 If the supply and/or earth are unsatisfactory, check for continuity of the wiring between the MAP sensor and the ECM.
34 If the MAP sensor wiring is satisfactory, check all voltage supplies and earth connections to the ECM. If the voltage supplies and earth connections are satisfactory, the ECM is suspect.

Signal or supply voltage at nbv level

35 Check for a short to a wire connected to the battery positive (+) terminal or a switched supply voltage.

Other checks

36 Check for excessive fuel in the vacuum trap or hose.
37 Check for a faulty vacuum hose or a vacuum leak.
38 Check for mechanical, ignition or a fuel fault resulting in low engine vacuum.

19 Air temperature sensor (ATS)

1 The ATS has only a minor effect on engine operation. However, if the ATS is suspect, the following tests could be made.
2 The ATS may be located in the inlet tract of the AFS, or in the inlet manifold:

- *a) If located in the AFS, the ATS shares a common earth return.*
- *b) Both types of ATS are examples of two-wire sensors, and test procedures are similar.*

3 Inspect the ATS multi-plug for corrosion, and damage.
4 Check that the terminal pins in the ATS or AFS multi-plug are fully pushed home and making good contact with the ATS.

ATS test procedures

5 Roll back the rubber protection boot to the ATS (or AFS multi-plug if the ATS is located in the AFS).
6 Connect the voltmeter negative probe to an engine earth.
7 Identify the signal and earth terminals.
8 Connect the voltmeter positive probe to the wire attached to the ATS signal terminal **(see illustration 4.27)**.
9 With the engine off, and ignition on, a voltage of approximately 2.0 to 3.0 volts, depending upon air temperature, is likely to be obtained. Refer to the ATS chart for typical voltages at various temperatures.
10 The signal voltage will vary according to the temperature of the air in the AFS inlet tract or inlet manifold. As the engine compartment or inlet manifold air rises in temperature, the voltage signal passed to the ECM will reduce. When the engine is cold, the air temperature will match the ambient temperature. After the engine is started, the temperature of the air in the engine compartment and the inlet manifold will rise. The temperature of the air in the inlet manifold will rise to approximately 70 or 80°C. which is a much higher temperature than that of the air in the engine compartment.

4.27 Backprobing for an ATS signal (ATS located in air filter box)

11 When undergoing tests at various temperatures, the ATS can be warmed with a hairdryer or cooled with something like 'Freezit', which is an ice-cold aerosol spray, sold in electronic component shops. As the ATS is heated or cooled, the temperature will change and so too will the resistance and voltage.

ATS voltage and resistance table (typical)

Temp (°C)	Resistance	Volts
0	*4800 - 6600*	*4.00 - 4.50*
10	*4000*	*3.75 - 4.00*
20	*2200 - 2800*	*3.00 - 3.50*
30	*1300*	*3.25*
40	*1000 - 1200*	*2.50 - 3.00*
50	*1000*	*2.50*
60	*800*	*2.00 - 2.50*
80	*270 - 380*	*1.00 - 1.30*
110		*0.50*
Open-circuit	*5.0 ± 0.1*	
Short to earth	*Zero*	

12 Check that the ATS voltage corresponds to the temperature of the ATS. A temperature gauge is required here.
13 Start the engine and allow it to warm-up to normal operating temperature. As the engine warms up, the voltage should reduce in accordance with the ATS chart.
14 Make the following tests and checks if the ATS signal voltage is zero (supply is open-circuit or shorted to earth) or at 5.0 volt level (ATS is open-circuit).

Zero volts at the ATS signal terminal

15 Check that the ATS signal terminal is not shorted to earth.
16 Check for continuity of the signal wiring between the ATS and the ECM.
17 If the ATS wiring is satisfactory, yet no voltage is output from the ECM, check all voltage supplies and earth connections to the ECM. If the voltage supplies and earth connections are satisfactory, the ECM is suspect.

5.0 volts at the ATS signal terminal

18 This is the open circuit voltage, and will be obtained in the event of one or more of the following conditions:

- *a) The signal terminal in the ATS (or AFS) multi-plug is not making contact with the ATS.*
- *b) The ATS is open circuit.*
- *c) The ATS earth connection is open-circuit.*

Signal or supply voltage at nbv level

19 Check for a short to a wire connected to the battery positive (+) terminal or a switched supply voltage.

Resistance tests

20 A resistance test may be made at various temperatures, and a comparison made with the temperature/resistance chart. Refer to paragraph 11 for a method of heating/cooling the ATS.

21 When the ATS resistance is within the stated parameters for a cold engine (20°C) the coolant temperature should also be within ± 5°C of that figure.

20 CO potentiometer ('pot')

1 The CO pot may be located in the AFS, or may be a separate sensor, located in the engine compartment or directly attached to the ECM.

a) If located in the AFS, the CO pot shares a common earth return.

b) Both the AFS located CO pot and the separate CO pot in the engine compartment are examples of three-wire sensors, and test procedures follow similar paths.

c) The CO pot attached to the ECM cannot be tested separately; a new ECM is required if the CO pot fails.

2 Inspect the CO pot or AFS multi-plug for corrosion and damage.

3 Check that the terminal pins in the multi-plug are fully pushed home and making good contact with the CO pot or AFS.

CO pot test procedures

4 Roll back the rubber protection boot to the CO pot multi-plug (or AFS multi-plug if located in the AFS).

5 Connect the voltmeter negative probe to an engine earth.

6 Identify the supply, signal and earth terminals.

7 Connect the voltmeter positive probe to the wire attached to the CO pot signal terminal.

8 A voltage of approximately 2.5 volts should be obtained in most systems.

9 Record the exact voltage so that the voltage can be reset to the exact value after tests are complete.

10 Remove the tamperproof cap from the adjustment screw.

11 Turn the adjustment screw one way and then the other. The voltage should vary smoothly.

CO pot voltage does not alter during adjustment

12 Check for the 5.0 volt reference voltage supply to the sensor.

13 Check the earth return connection to the sensor.

14 If the supply and earth are satisfactory, check for continuity of the signal wiring between the CO pot and the ECM.

15 If the supply and/or earth are unsatisfactory, check for continuity of the supply and/or earth wiring between the CO pot or AFS (as appropriate) and the ECM.

16 If the AFS wiring is satisfactory, check all voltage supplies and earth connections to the ECM. If the voltage supplies and earths are satisfactory, the ECM is suspect.

21 Coolant temperature sensor (CTS)

1 Inspect the CTS multi-plug for corrosion and damage.

2 Check that the terminal pins in the CTS multi-plug are fully pushed home and making good contact with the CTS. **Note:** *Poor contact and corrosion are common reasons for an inaccurate signal from the CTS.*

3 Roll back the rubber protection boot to the CTS multi-plug.

4 Connect the voltmeter negative probe to an engine earth.

5 Identify the signal and earth terminals.

6 Connect the voltmeter positive probe to the wire attached to the CTS signal terminal.

7 Allow the engine to become cold. With the engine off, and ignition on, a voltage of approximately 2.0 to 3.0 volts, depending upon temperature, is likely to be obtained. Refer to the CTS chart for typical voltages at various temperatures.

CTS voltage and resistance table (typical)

Temp (°C)	Resistance	Volts
0	*4800 - 6600*	*4.00 - 4.50*
10	*4000*	*3.75 - 4.00*
20	*2200 - 2800*	*3.00 - 3.50*
30	*1300*	*3.25*
40	*1000 - 1200*	*2.50 - 3.00*
50	*1000*	*2.50*
60	*800*	*2.00 - 2.50*
80	*270 - 380*	*1.00 - 1.30*
110		*0.50*
Open-circuit	*5.0 ± 0.1*	
Short to earth	*Zero*	

8 Check that the CTS voltage corresponds to the temperature of the CTS.

9 Start the engine, and allow it to warm up to normal operating temperature. As the engine warms up, the voltage should reduce in accordance with the CTS chart.

10 A common problem may occur where the CTS varies in resistance (and voltage) outside of its normal range. If, for example, the CTS voltage is normally 3 volts cold/0.5 volts hot, a faulty CTS may give a voltage of 1.5 volts cold/1.25 volts hot, resulting in the engine being difficult to start when cold and running richer than normal when hot. This will NOT result in the generation of a fault code, because the CTS is still operating within its design parameters. Renew the CTS if this fault occurs.

11 Make the following tests and checks if the CTS signal voltage is zero (supply is open-circuit or shorted to earth) or at 5.0 volt level (CTS is open-circuit).

Zero volts obtained at the CTS signal terminal

a) Check that the CTS signal terminal is not shorted to earth.

b) Check for continuity of the signal wiring between the CTS and the ECM.

c) If the CTS wiring is satisfactory, yet no voltage is output from the ECM, check all voltage supplies and earth connections to the ECM. If the voltage supplies and earth connections are satisfactory, the ECM is suspect.

5.0 volts obtained at the CTS signal terminal

12 This is the open-circuit voltage, and will be obtained in the event of one or more of the following conditions:

a) The signal terminal in the CTS multi-plug is not making contact with the CTS.

b) The CTS is open-circuit.

c) The CTS earth connection is open-circuit.

Signal or supply voltage at nbv level

13 Check for a short to a wire connected to the battery positive (+) terminal or a switched supply voltage.

Resistance tests

CTS on vehicle

14 A resistance test may be made at various temperatures and a comparison made with the temperature/resistance chart **(see illustration 4.28)**. When the resistance is within the stated parameters for a cold engine (20°C) the coolant temperature should be within ± 5°C of that figure.

15 An allowance should be made for a temperature obtained by probing the outside of the CTS or coolant passage. This is because the actual temperature of the coolant may be hotter than the surface temperature of the CTS.

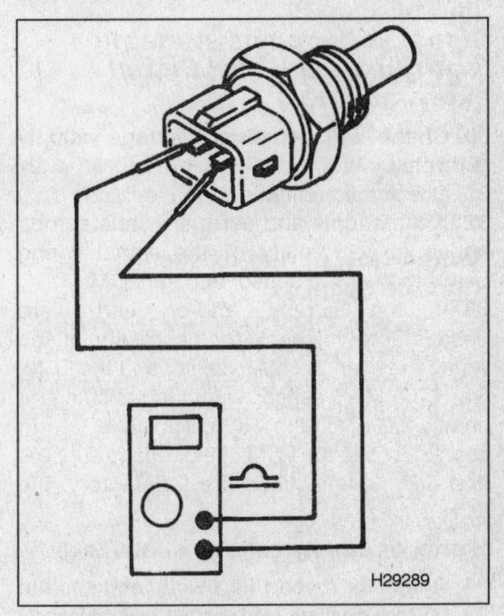

4.28 Checking the CTS resistance

CTS off vehicle

16 The recommended method is described as follows.
17 Remove the CTS from the vehicle.
18 Place the CTS in a suitable container of water and measure the temperature of the water.
19 Measure the resistance of the CTS, and check the resistance against the temperature chart.
20 Heat the water, periodically measuring the water temperature and the CTS resistance, and comparing the resistance with the temperature chart.

22 Throttle switch (TS)

1 Inspect the TS multi-plug for corrosion and damage.
2 Check that the terminal pins in the TS multi-plug are fully pushed home and making good contact with the TS.
Poor contact and corrosion are common reasons for an inaccurate signal from the TS.
3 The three wires to the TS multi-plug connector are earth, idle signal and WOT signal.
4 Roll back the rubber protection boot to the TS multi-plug.
5 Connect the voltmeter negative probe to an engine earth.
6 Identify the idle signal, WOT signal and earth terminals.
7 Engine stopped, ignition on.
8 Connect the voltmeter positive probe to the wire attached to the TS idle signal terminal.
9 Zero volts should be obtained. If the meter indicates 5.0 volts, loosen the screws and adjust the TS so that zero volts is obtained.

Zero volts cannot be obtained (throttle closed)

a) Check the throttle valve position.
b) Check the TS earth connection.
c) Make the TS resistance tests (below).

10 If the voltage is satisfactory with the throttle closed, crack open the throttle; the switch should 'click' and the voltage rise to 5.0 volts.

Voltage low or non-existent (throttle open)

a) Check that the TS idle terminal is not shorted to earth.
b) Disconnect the TS multi-plug and check for 5.0 volts at the multi-plug idle terminal. If no voltage, make the following checks.
c) Check for continuity of the idle signal wiring between the TS and the ECM.
d) If the TS wiring is satisfactory, check all voltage supplies and earth connections to the ECM. If the voltage supplies and earth connections are satisfactory, the ECM is suspect.

Voltage satisfactory (throttle open)

11 Reconnect the voltmeter probe to the wire attached to the TS full-load signal terminal.
12 With the throttle in either the idle or just open positions, the meter should indicate 5.0 volts.

Voltage low or non-existent (throttle closed or just open)

a) Check the earth connection.
b) Check that the TS full-load terminal is not shorted to earth.
c) Disconnect the TS multi-plug and check for 5.0 volts at the full-load multi-plug terminal. If no voltage, make the following checks.
d) Check for continuity of the full-load signal wiring between the TS and the ECM.
e) If the TS wiring is satisfactory, check all voltage supplies and earth connections to the ECM. If the voltage supplies and earth connections are satisfactory, the ECM is suspect.

Voltage satisfactory (throttle closed or just open)

13 Fully open the throttle. As the throttle angle becomes greater than 72°, the voltage should drop to zero volts. If the voltage does not drop, the TS is suspect.

Resistance tests

14 Disconnect the TS multi-plug.
15 Connect an ohmmeter between the TS earth terminal (sometimes marked 18) and terminal 2 (idle contact).
16 With the TS closed, the ohmmeter should indicate very close to zero ohms.
17 Slowly open the throttle; as the TS cracks open, it should click and the resistance should become open-circuit and remain so - even as the throttle is opened fully.
18 Reconnect the ohmmeter between the earth terminal (sometimes marked 18) and terminal 3 (full-load contact). With the TS closed, the ohmmeter should indicate an open circuit.
19 Slowly open the throttle, as the TS cracks open, it should click and the resistance should remain open circuit until the throttle angle becomes greater than 72°, when the resistance should change to continuity of approximately zero ohms.
20 If the TS does not behave as described, and it is not prevented from opening or closing fully by the binding of the throttle linkage, the TS is suspect.

23 Throttle potentiometer sensor (TPS)

1 Inspect the TPS multi-plug for corrosion, and damage.
2 Check that the terminal pins in the TPS multi-plug are fully pushed home and making good contact with the TPS. **Note:** *Poor contact and corrosion are common reasons for an inaccurate signal from the TPS.*
3 Roll back the rubber protection boot to the TPS multi-plug.
4 Connect the voltmeter negative probe to an engine earth.
5 Identify the supply, signal and earth terminals.
6 Connect the voltmeter positive probe to the wire attached to the TPS signal terminal.
7 Switch on the ignition, engine stopped. In most systems, a voltage less than 0.70 volts should be obtained.
8 Open and close the throttle several times and check for a smooth voltage increase to a maximum of 4.0 to 4.50 volts. **Note:** *If a digital voltmeter is used, then it is useful for it to have a bar graph facility. The smoothness of the voltage increase can then be more easily seen.*

Erratic signal output

9 An erratic output occurs when the voltage output is stepped, or drops to zero or becomes open-circuit.
10 When the TPS signal output is erratic, this usually suggests a faulty potentiometer. In this instance, a new or reconditioned TPS is the only cure.

Signal voltage not available

11 Check for the 5.0 volt reference voltage supply at the TPS supply terminal.
12 Check the earth return connection at the TPS earth terminal.
13 If the supply and earth are satisfactory, check for continuity of the signal wiring between the TPS and the ECM.
14 If the supply and/or earth are unsatisfactory, check for continuity of the wiring between the TPS and the ECM.
15 If the TPS wiring is satisfactory, check all voltage supplies and earth connections to the ECM. If the voltage supplies and earths are satisfactory, the ECM is suspect.

Signal or supply voltage at nbv level

16 Check for a short to a wire connected to the battery positive (+) terminal or a switched supply voltage.

Resistance tests

17 Connect an ohmmeter between the TPS signal terminal and supply terminal or the TPS signal terminal and earth terminal.
18 Open and close the throttle several times and check for a smooth resistance change. If the TPS resistance becomes open- or short-circuit, a fault is revealed.
19 We are not providing resistance specifications for the TPS's described in this book. For one thing, many vehicle manufacturers do not publish test values. Also, it is less important that the resistance of the TPS remains within arbitrary values, than the operation is correct.
20 Connect an ohmmeter between the TPS earth terminal and supply terminal. A stable resistance should be obtained.

21 Renew the TPS if the resistance is open-circuit or shorted to earth.
22 Refer to the comments on resistance readings in Section 3.

24 Vehicle speed sensor (VSS)

Note: *These test procedures describe testing of the most common type of VSS which operates upon the Hall-effect principle.*
1 The VSS is usually located on the gearbox.
2 Inspect the VSS multi-plug for corrosion, and damage.
3 Check that the terminal pins in the VSS multi-plug are fully pushed home and making good contact with the VSS.
4 Roll back the rubber protection boot to the VSS multi-plug.
5 Connect the voltmeter negative or dwell meter probe to an engine earth.
6 Identify the supply, signal and earth terminals.
7 Connect a voltmeter positive or dwell meter probe to the wire attached to the VSS signal terminal.

Checking for a VSS signal

8 The drive wheels must rotate for a signal to be generated. This may be accomplished by using one of the two following methods:
- *a) Push the vehicle forward.*
- *b) Place the vehicle upon a ramp, or jack up the vehicle so that the drive wheels can freely turn.*

9 Rotate the wheels by hand so that a duty cycle or voltage can be obtained.

No signal or an erratic duty cycle or voltage

10 VSS multi-plug disconnected, ignition on.
11 Check the voltage at the signal terminal. A voltage between 8.5 and 10.0 volts should be obtained.
12 Check the voltage supply at the VSS supply terminal. A voltage slightly less than nbv should be obtained.
13 Check the VSS earth connection.

Supply and earth voltages ok

14 The VSS is suspect or the VSS is not being rotated by the speedometer drive (ie broken cable or gearbox fault).

No signal voltage

15 Check the voltage at the ECM multi-plug terminal.
- *a) If voltage is satisfactory at the ECM, check the diode in the wire between the ECM and VSS and continuity of the signal wiring.*
- *b) If no voltage is available at the ECM, check all voltage supplies and earth connections to the ECM. If the voltage supplies and earth connections are satisfactory, the ECM is suspect.*

25 Idle speed control valve (ISCV)

1 Inspect the ISCV multi-plug for corrosion, and damage.
2 Check that the connector terminal pins are fully pushed home and making good contact with the ISCV multi-plug.
3 Allow the engine to idle.
4 Check that the idle speed is within its operating limits.
5 Load the system by switching on the headlamps, rear screen heater and heater motor onto high. The idle speed should barely change.
6 If possible, squeeze one of the air hoses. The idle speed should surge and then return to normal **(see illustration 4.29)**.
7 If the idle condition meets the above criteria, it is unlikely to be at fault.
8 The following faults will adversely affect idle integrity, and these components should be checked before attempting diagnosis of the ISCV.
- *a) Engine mechanical fault.*
- *b) Incorrect ignition timing.*
- *c) An induction vacuum leak.*
- *d) Incorrect CO level.*
- *e) Clogged air filter.*
- *f) An incorrectly adjusted throttle valve.*
- *g) Carbon-fouled throttle plate.*
- *h) An incorrectly-adjusted TS or TPS.*

Test procedures (two-wire)

9 Detach the ISCV multi-plug.
10 Identify the supply and signal terminals.
11 Measure the ISCV resistance. See below.
12 Use a jump lead to connect a battery voltage supply to the ISCV supply terminal.
13 Use a second jump lead to connect the ISCV earth terminal to earth. **Note:** *The connection should be made only briefly.*
14 The ISCV should actuate.
15 Roll back the rubber protection boot to the ISCV multi-plug.
16 Connect the negative instrument probe to an engine earth.
17 Connect the voltmeter positive or dwell meter probe to the wire attached to the ISCV signal terminal.

4.29 Squeeze an idle air hose to check ISCV response

18 Start the engine and allow it to idle.
19 Hot engine: A varying voltage of average 7.0 to 9.0 volts or a duty cycle of 40 to 44% will be obtained. A frequency of 110 can also be measured.
20 When the engine is cold or placed under load, the voltage will decrease and the duty cycle will increase. **Note:** *The reading on a digital voltmeter will indicate the average voltage.*
21 Load the engine by switching on the headlamps, rear screen heater and heater motor onto high. The average voltage will decrease and the duty cycle will increase. The frequency of pulse should remain constant.
22 If an air leak or another fault is present resulting in more air by-passing the throttle, the ISCV duty cycle will be lower than normal as the ECM pulses the ISCV less open.
23 When more load is placed upon the engine, the ECM pulses the ISCV more open (larger duty cycle) to increase the idle speed.
24 In addition, if the engine is mechanically unsound or the throttle valve is dirty, the ECM may pulse the ISCV more open to increase the idle speed. This may result in an uneven idle, and a larger-than-normal duty cycle.

ISCV signal not available

25 Check the ISCV resistance. See below.
26 Ignition on. Check for nbv at the supply terminal.
27 No voltage, trace the wiring back to the main relay or ignition switch as appropriate.
28 Disconnect the ECM multi-plug (see Warning No 3 in Reference).
29 Switch on the ignition.
30 Use a jumper lead to very briefly touch the actuator pin in the ECM multi-plug to earth.
- *a) If the ISCV actuates, check the ECM main voltage supplies and earths. If tests reveal no fault, the ECM is suspect.*
- *b) If the ISCV does not actuate: check for continuity of of wiring between the ISCV multi-plug and the ECM.*

Resistance checks

31 Remove the ISCV multi-plug.
32 Connect an ohmmeter between the two terminals. A resistance of 8 to 16 ohms should be obtained.

Test procedures (three-wire)

33 Detach the ISCV multi-plug.
34 Check the ISCV resistance. See below
35 Identify the supply and signal terminals. The three wires to the ISCV multi-plug are supply and two signal wires.
36 Use a jump lead to connect a battery voltage supply to the ISCV middle terminal.
37 Use a second jump lead to connect one of the outer ISCV terminals to earth. The ISCV should actuate.
38 Remove the second jump lead and use it to connect the other outer ISCV terminals to earth. The ISCV should actuate in the reverse direction.
39 If the ISCV does not actuate, or operation is poor the ISCV is suspect.

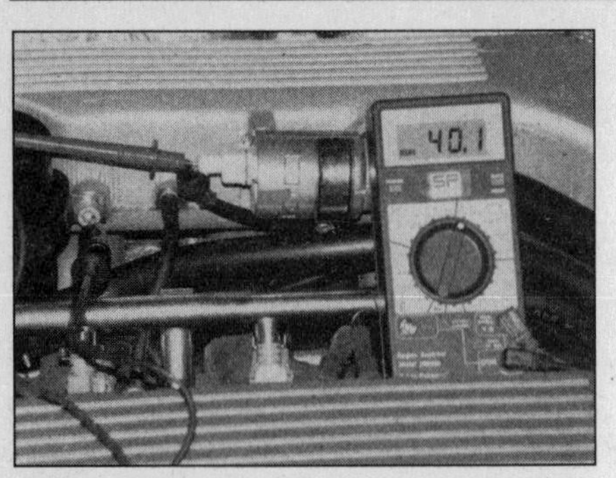

4.30 Backprobing for a typical dwell at the ISCV, engine at idle speed

40 Roll back the rubber protection boot to the ISCV multi-plug.
41 Connect the voltmeter negative or dwell meter probe to an engine earth.
42 Connect the voltmeter positive or dwell meter probe to the wire attached to one of the two ISCV signal terminals.
43 Start the engine and allow it to idle.
44 Hot engine: A varying voltage or a duty cycle of either approximately 31% or 69% will be obtained **(see illustration 4.30)**. The duty cycle obtained will depend upon which terminal the instrument is connected.
45 When the engine is cold or placed under load, the voltage will decrease and the duty cycle will increase. **Note:** *The reading on a digital voltmeter will indicate the average voltage.*
46 Load the engine by switching on the headlamps, rear screen heater and heater motor onto high. The average voltage will decrease and the duty cycle will increase.
47 If an air leak or another fault is present resulting in more air by-passing the throttle, the ISCV duty cycle will be lower than normal as the ECM pulses the ISCV less open.
48 When more load is placed upon the engine, the ECM pulses the ISCV more open (larger duty cycle) to increase the idle speed.
49 In addition, if the engine is mechanically unsound or the throttle valve is dirty, the ECM may pulse the ISCV more open to increase the idle speed. This may result in an uneven idle and a larger than normal duty cycle.
50 Switch the voltmeter positive or dwell meter probe to the wire attached to the other one of the two ISCV signal terminals.
51 Hot engine: A varying voltage or a duty cycle of either approximately 31% or 69% will be obtained. The duty cycle obtained will depend upon which terminal the instrument is connected.

ISCV signal not available

52 Check the ISCV resistance
53 Ignition on. Check for nbv at the supply terminal.
54 No voltage: Trace the wiring back to the main relay or ignition switch as appropriate.
55 Disconnect the ECM multi-plug see Warning No 3 in Reference.
56 Switch on the ignition.
57 Use a jumper lead to very briefly touch one of the two actuator pins in the ECM multi-plug to earth.

- a) *If the ISCV actuates, check the ECM main voltage supplies and earths. If the tests reveal no fault, the ECM is suspect.*
- b) *If the ISCV does not actuate, check for continuity of of wiring between the ISCV multi-plug and the ECM.*

58 Switch the jumper lead to very briefly touch the other ISCV actuator pin in the ECM multi-plug to earth. Evaluate the results as in paragraph 57.

Resistance checks

59 Remove the ISCV multi-plug.
60 Connect an ohmmeter between the centre terminal and one of the outer terminals. A resistance of 20 ohms should be obtained.
61 Reconnect the ohmmeter between the centre terminal and the other outer ISCV terminal. A resistance of 20 ohms should be obtained.
62 Reconnect the ohmmeter between the two outer ISCV terminals. A resistance of 20 ohms should be obtained.

26 Throttle body and manifold heater (TBH)

Quick check

1 Start the engine when cold and feel the area around the throttle body or inlet manifold (as appropriate), if the heater is working, this area should become hot quite quickly. Take care not to burn your fingers!

Throttle body heater tests

2 Allow the engine to idle.
3 Attach the voltmeter negative probe to an earth.
4 Attach the voltmeter positive probe to the heater supply connector. Battery voltage (nbv) should be obtained.

No voltage supply

- a) *Check the TBH supply.*
- b) *Check continuity of the wiring between the relay and the heater.*

Nbv present, but heater does not operate

- a) *Check the heater resistance.*
- b) *Check the heater earth.*

27 ECM voltage supplies and earths

Note: *Refer to the relevant Warnings in the Reference section at the end of this book before starting work.*

1 Inspect the ECM multi-plug for corrosion and damage.
2 Check that the terminals in the ECM multi-plug are fully pushed home and making good contact with the ECM pins. **Note:** *Poor contact and corrosion are common reasons for inaccurate signals from the ECM.*
3 Voltage supplies and earths are best measured at the ECM multi-plug. Use one of these test methods.

- a) *Peel back the ECM multi-plug insulation (not always possible) and backprobe the ECM multi-plug pins.*
- b) *Attach a BOB between the ECM and its multi-plug, and probe the box for voltages.*
- c) *Detach the ECM from its multi-plug, and probe for voltages at the multi-plug pins.*

4 Attach the voltmeter negative probe to an engine earth for the ECM connected tests.
5 Identify the various types of connection and the relevant ECM pins from a wiring diagram for the vehicle in question.

ECM test procedures

Note: *Not all of the following connections will be available in any particular system.*

ECM battery supply pin

6 This pin is directly connected to the battery (+) terminal and a constant voltage should be available at all times, even with the ignition key turned Off.
7 ECM multi-plug connected: Backprobe the relevant ECM pin - nominal battery voltage (nbv) should be obtained.
8 ECM multi-plug disconnected:

- a) *Attach the voltmeter negative probe to an ECM earth pin.*
- b) *Attach the voltmeter positive probe to the relevant ECM pin: Nominal battery voltage (nbv) should be obtained.*

9 No voltage: Check the supply back to the battery.

ECM cranking supply pin

10 This pin is connected to the ignition switch starter terminal, and a battery voltage will only be available during engine cranking.
11 ECM multi-plug connected:

- a) *Backprobe the relevant ECM pin.*
- b) *Crank the engine on the starter: Voltage should only be obtained during cranking.*

12 ECM multi-plug disconnected:

- a) *Attach the voltmeter negative probe to an ECM earth pin.*
- b) *Attach the voltmeter positive probe to the relevant ECM pin*
- c) *Crank the engine on the starter: Voltage should only be obtained during cranking.*

13 No voltage: Check the supply back to the ignition switch starter terminal.

ECM supply from the ignition switch

14 This pin is connected to the ignition switch, and voltage should be available at all times whilst the ignition is on
or the engine is running.
15 ECM multi-plug connected:

- a) *Backprobe the relevant ECM pin.*
- b) *Switch on the ignition: nbv should be obtained.*

16 ECM multi-plug disconnected:

a) *Attach the voltmeter negative probe to an ECM earth pin.*
b) *Attach the voltmeter positive probe to the relevant ECM pin.*
c) *Switch on the ignition: nbv should be obtained.*

17 No voltage: Check the supply back to the ignition switch.

ECM supply from the main system relay

18 This pin is connected to the main relay, and voltage should be available at all times whilst the ignition is on or the engine is running. Supply may be made to more than one ECM pin.

19 ECM multi-plug connected:

a) *Backprobe the relevant ECM pin.*
b) *Switch on the ignition: nbv should be obtained.*

20 ECM multi-plug disconnected:

a) *Attach the voltmeter negative probe to an ECM earth pin.*
b) *Attach the voltmeter positive probe to the relevant ECM pin.*
c) *Switch on the ignition: nbv should be obtained.*

21 No voltage: check the supply back to the main system relay and make the relay checks.

ECM earth connections

22 ECM multi-plug connected, ignition on:

a) *Attach the voltmeter negative probe to an engine earth*
b) *Attach the voltmeter positive probe to the earth terminal under test: The voltmeter should indicate 0.25 volts maximum.*

23 ECM multi-plug disconnected, ignition on or off:

a) *Attach the voltmeter negative probe to the earth terminal under test.*
b) *Attach the voltmeter positive probe to the ECM battery supply or directly to the battery positive terminal: The voltmeter should indicate nbv if the earth is satisfactory.*

ECM coding earth pins

Note: *The coding pins are used to code the ECM for certain vehicle configurations (some systems only).*

24 ECM multi-plug connected, ignition on:

a) *Attach the voltmeter negative probe to an engine earth.*
b) *Attach the voltmeter positive probe to the coding earth pin under test: The voltmeter should indicate 0.25 volt maximum if the coding earth is connected. 5.0 volts if the coding earth is not connected.*

ECM relay driver pins (relays and ECM connected)

Note: *Depending on system, the ECM may drive the main, fuel pump or OS relay winding to earth.*

Main relay driver

25 Identify the ECM relay driver pins.

26 With the ignition off, backprobe the ECM main relay driver pin with the voltmeter positive probe: nbv should be obtained. If not, check the relay and the relay wiring.

27 Switch on the ignition: The voltage should drop to near zero.

a) *If not, disconnect the ECM multi-plug (see Warning No 3 in Reference), and connect a temporary jumper lead from the driver pin to earth.*
b) *Relay operates: Check all voltage supplies and earth connections to the ECM. If the wiring is satisfactory, the ECM is suspect.*
c) *Relay does not operate: Check the relay and the relay wiring.*

Note: *In some systems, the main relay winding is connected directly to earth.*

Pump relay driver

28 The main relay driver operation (previous test) must be satisfactory before commencing this test, including when the main relay winding is directly connected to earth.

29 With the ignition on, backprobe the pump relay driver with the voltmeter positive probe: nbv should be obtained. If not, check the relay and the relay wiring.

30 Crank or run the engine: The voltage should drop to near zero.

a) *If not, disconnect the ECM multi-plug (see Warning No 3 in Reference), and connect a temporary jumper lead from pin 3 to earth.*
b) *Relay operates: Check all voltage supplies and earth connections to the ECM. If the wiring is satisfactory, the ECM is suspect.*
c) *Relay does not operate: Check the relay and the relay wiring.*

31 Essentially, the tests for any additional relay drivers are similar to the pump driver tests.

28 Inertia switch

1 The inertia switch is a safety device, designed to isolate the fuel pump or cut the engine electrical system in the event of a crash. It can sometimes be affected by heavy deceleration or a thump close to its location.

2 Reset the inertia switch by pressing down the reset button.

3 If voltage is still not available at the fuel pump, continue with the tests.

4 Inspect the inertia switch terminal connections for corrosion and damage.

5 Check that the terminal connections are making good contact with the switch.

6 Study a specific wiring diagram to identify the circuit which the inertia switch protects. Typical circuits are:

a) *Relay output to the fuel pump.*
b) *Relay supply.*
c) *Relay driver circuit to the ECM.*

7 Check the supply voltage and earth connections to the inertia switch.

4.31 Test the relay, probe for voltages

29 System relays

Quick relay tests

1 If the engine does not run, or a relay fed component does not function, the following method is a quick way of determining whether the relay is defective:

a) *Check for a supply voltage at the component(s) supplied by the relay.*
b) *If voltage is not available, by-pass the relay (see below) and retest the component for voltage or attempt to run the engine.*
c) *If the engine runs or voltage is now available, test the relay (see below) or renew the relay.*
d) *If voltage is not available, check for supply, earth and output voltages at the relay terminals **(see illustration 4.31)**. Trace supply faults back to the source. Check for a blown fuse or fusible link in the supply line.*

Common relay terminal connections (standard relays)

2 Dual relays operate in a similar fashion, but may use different numbers. Some Citroën, Peugeot, Renault and Far Eastern systems (including Japanese manufacturers) may use a numbering system based on the numbers one to five or six.

Main relay terminal 30: Supply from the battery positive terminal. Constant voltage available.

Main relay terminal 86: Supply from the battery positive terminal or the ignition switch. Either constant or switched voltage available.

Main relay terminal 85: Relay winding, connected to earth or ECM driver terminal. Voltage almost zero when ignition switched on.

Main relay terminal 87: Output terminal supplies voltage to ECM, ISCV, injectors etc. Battery voltage available when ignition switched on.

Pump relay terminal 30: Supply from the battery positive terminal. Constant voltage available.

Pump relay terminal 86: Supply from the main relay terminal 87 or the ignition switch. Either constant or switched voltage available.
Pump relay terminal 85: Relay winding, ECM driver terminal. Voltage less than 1.25 volts when engine cranking or running
Pump relay terminal 87: Output terminal supplies voltage to fuel pump and sometimes OS heater. Battery voltage available when engine cranking or running
Terminal 85a and 85b similar to terminal 85 depending on use.
Terminal 87a and 87b similar to terminal 87 depending on use.

Citroën, Peugeot and Fiat 15-pin relay terminals (typical)

1 *Relay output terminal: Usually connected to fuel pump circuit.*
2 *Battery supply to relay: Supply from the battery positive terminal. Constant voltage available.*
3 *Battery supply to relay: Supply from the battery positive terminal. Constant voltage available.*
4 *Relay output terminal: Components supplied vary depending on system.*
5 *Relay output terminal: Components supplied vary depending on system.*
6 *Relay output terminal: Components supplied vary depending on system.*
7 *Relay earth or driver terminal*
8 *Battery supply to relay: Supply from the battery positive terminal. Constant voltage available.*
9 *Relay output terminal: Usually connected to fuel pump circuit.*
10 *Relay earth or driver terminal.*
11 *Battery supply to relay: Supply from the battery positive terminal. Constant voltage available.*
12 *Unused*
13 *Relay output terminal: Components supplied vary depending on system.*
14 *Supply from the ignition switch: Switched voltage available.*
15 *Battery supply to relay: Supply from the battery positive terminal. Constant voltage available.*

Note: *Although the function of the above terminal numbers are generally as stated, there are wide differences in how the relay is wired in any particular application.*

By-passing the relay

3 Remove the relay from the relay multi-plug.
4 Connect a fused (15 amp) jumper lead between the battery supply terminal (usually terminal 30) and the output terminal (usually terminal 87) on the terminal block where power to the fuel pump or other fuel injection components is required.
5 Do not run the fuel pump continually under this condition; disconnect the by-pass whenever a particular test is completed.

Testing the relay

6 Remove the relay from the terminal block.
7 Connect an ohmmeter across terminals 30 and 87.
8 Attach a wire between terminal 86 and a 12 volt supply.
9 Attach a wire between terminal 85 and earth.
10 The ohmmeter should indicate continuity.

30 Fuel pump and circuit

1 Locate the fuel pump. Typical fuel pump locations are:

a) *Bolted to the chassis outside of the fuel tank.*
b) *Located inside the fuel tank. Access to the in-tank pump is often gained by burrowing under the rear passenger seat.*

2 Connect the voltmeter negative probe to an earth.
3 Identify the supply and earth terminals.
4 Connect the voltmeter positive probe to the wire attached to the fuel pump supply terminal.
5 Crank the engine or by-pass the fuel pump relay: nbv should be obtained.

Voltage supply not available

a) *Check the fuel pump fuse (where fitted).*
b) *Check the fuel pump relay.*
c) *Check the inertia switch (where fitted).*
d) *Check continuity of the wiring.*

6 Attach the voltmeter positive probe to the fuel pump earth terminal.
7 Crank the engine or by-pass the relay. A voltage of 0.25 maximum should be obtained **(see illustration 4.32)**.

31 Fuel pressure system (MPi and SPi)

Note: *The fuel pressure system operates at high pressure. Refer to Warning No 12 in Reference, and take all possible* care.
1 The fuel system should be de-pressurised before the fuel filter is changed or work is carried out upon the fuel lines.

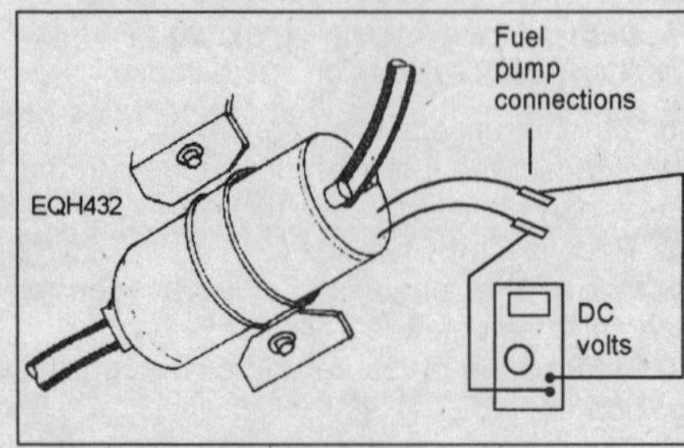

4.32 Check the voltage to the fuel pump

De-pressurise the fuel system (single 'dual' relay)

2 Remove the fuel pump fuse, or disconnect the earth wire on the fuel pump.
3 Crank or briefly run the engine until it stops.
Note: *System pressure cannot be relieved by removing a single fuel system relay. The single relay also supplies power to the injectors, which would be disabled by removal of the relay.*

De-pressurise the fuel system (separate fuel pump relay)

4 Remove the fuel pump relay.
5 Crank or briefly run the engine until it stops.

Check the fuel system volume

Note: *Fuel system volume is a good indicator of system integrity. If the pressure is satisfactory, yet the volume is low, the reason for low volume should definitely be investigated.*
6 Disconnect the fuel return line at a point after the pressure regulator, and place into a suitable graduated container **(see illustration 4.33)**.
7 Operate the fuel pump by allowing the engine to idle, or by-pass the relay.
8 Measure the volume of fuel flow.

a) *A good MPi system will provide in excess of 2.0 litres per minute.*
b) *A good SPi system will provide in excess of 1.0 litres per minute.*

9 If the fuel volume is low, check for the following faults:

a) *Clogged fuel filter.*
b) *crushed or blocked fuel lines.*
c) *Blocked fuel tank outlet.*

Check the fuel pressure (engine stopped)

Note: *A high-pressure fuel gauge and adapters for the fuel system under test is required for these tests.*
10 De-pressurise the fuel system. See above.

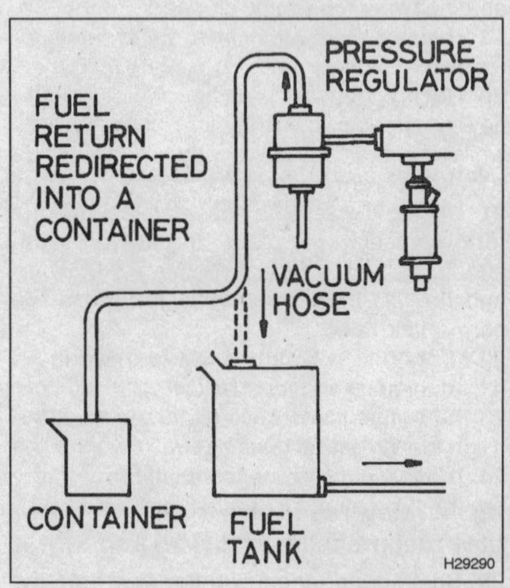

4.33 Fuel flow volume test. Disconnect the fuel return at a point after the pressure regulator, and direct the flow of fuel into a suitable container

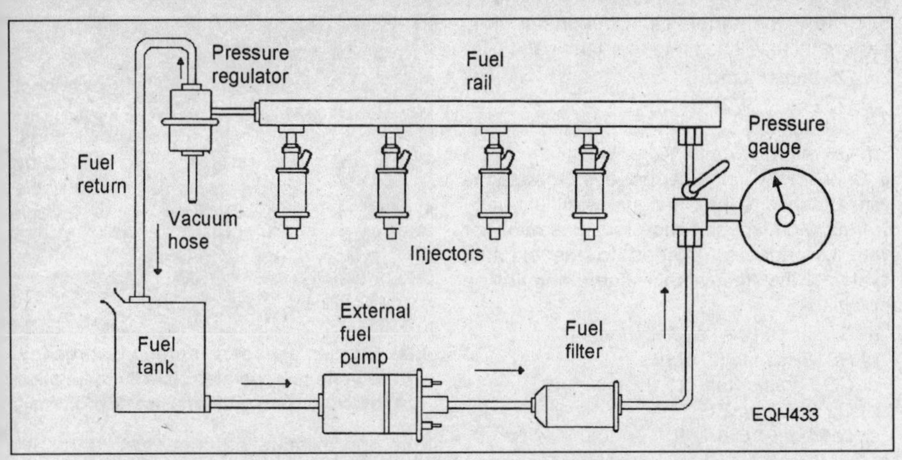

4.34 Connect a pressure gauge and check the fuel pressure in the fuel rail

11 Connect the fuel pressure gauge into the fuel supply pipe **(see illustration 4.34)**:

a) MPi: before the fuel rail.
b) SPi: before the injector on the throttle body.

12 Reconnect the fuel lines.

13 By-pass the relay. An alternative method of pressurising the fuel system is to switch the ignition on and off several times.

14 Record the fuel pressure, and compare with the specified values in the system Chapter.

a) In most MPi systems, the system pressure will be either 2.5 or 3.0 bar.
b) In most SPi systems, the system pressure will be approximately 1.0 bar.

Check the fuel pressure (engine running, MPi only)

15 Reconnect the fuel pump relay.

16 Start the engine and allow it to idle.

17 Connect a gas analyser (optional).and record the CO value.

18 Record the fuel pressure which should be approximately 0.5 bar under the pressure obtained with the engine stopped.

19 Remove the vacuum hose to the pressure regulator, and plug it.

20 Record the fuel pressure which should now be comparable to the pressure obtained whilst the engine was stopped. The CO value should be slightly richer than before.

21 Unplug the vacuum hose and reconnect it to the pressure regulator. The fuel pressure should decrease by approximately 0.5 bar, and the CO level should also return to the normal idle value.

22 If the fuel pressure is low, carry out the 'Low fuel pressure' tests below.

23 If the fuel pressure is high, carry out the 'High fuel pressure' tests below.

24 If the fuel pressure is satisfactory, carry out the 'Maximum fuel system pressure' test.

Low fuel pressure test (MPi and SPi)

25 Briefly clamp the fuel return line from the pressure regulator back to the fuel tank **(see illustration 4.35)**.

26 If the pressure now rises, the pressure regulator is faulty.

27 A low pressure coupled with a much slower pressure rise could be due to a severe supply line or filter blockage. This would normally be discovered in a fuel volume test.

28 Check the injectors for leakage.

29 If the pressure is still low, and there are no other fuel leaks, suspect a faulty fuel pump.

High fuel pressure test (MPi and SPi)

30 Disconnect the fuel return line from the pressure regulator.

31 Attach a temporary pipe from the pressure regulator to a container, and run the engine.

32 If the fuel pressure remains high, renew the pressure regulator.

33 If the fuel pressure is now satisfactory, check the return line for a blockage.

Maximum fuel system pressure test

Warning: If the fuel line connections or rubber joining hoses are weak, a hose may fracture during this test. The test must be accomplished as quickly as possible and if the pressure seems likely to exceed the gauge capability, the test must be instantly curtailed.

34 By-pass the relay and briefly clamp the fuel return pipe. The system pressure should now reach its peak pressure. A failure to reach peak pressure would indicate a faulty fuel pump.

a) MPi: between 4 and 6 bar.
b) SPi: approximately 3.0 bar.

35 A brake clamp hose could be used to clamp the return hose during this procedure on the majority of fuel pressure systems.

Residual pressure drop test (MPi and SPi)

36 De-pressurise the fuel system.

37 Connect the fuel pressure gauge into the fuel supply pipe (before the fuel rail).

38 Reconnect the fuel lines.

39 Allow the engine to idle at normal operating temperature.

40 Record the pressure and switch off the ignition.

41 The pressure should not drop more than 0.5 bar in 60 seconds.

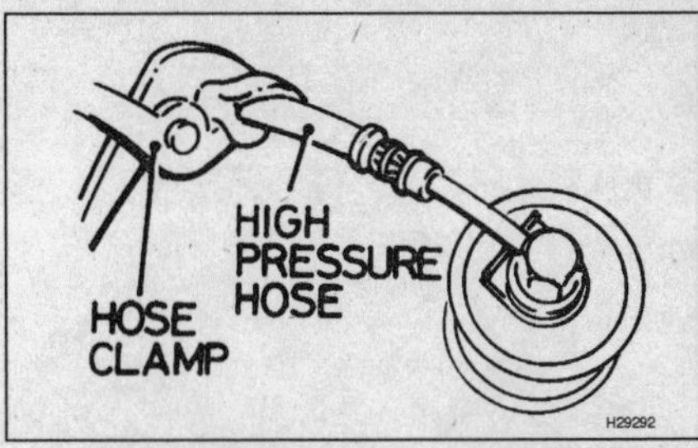

4.35 Clamping the fuel supply hose to check for a pressure drop through the fuel pump check valve

Note: *A drop in residual pressure will not usually affect running but may cause difficult starting, particularly when the engine is hot.*

High residual pressure drop (MPi and SPi)

42 Switch off the ignition and at the same moment clamp the fuel return pipe.

43 If the pressure drop is still higher than specified:

a) Test the fuel pump check valve.
b) Test the injectors.

44 If the pressure drop is now acceptable, the pressure regulator is suspect.

Fuel pump check valve test (MPi and SPi)

45 Switch off the ignition whilst clamping the fuel supply line before the fuel rail. The pressure should remain high to confirm that the fuel pump check valve is faulty. Check valves are sometimes supplied separately to the pump. Otherwise, renew the pump.

Checking the injectors for flow (MPi and SPi)

46 Remove the injectors from the cylinder head, and use a dedicated fuel injection test rig to test for injector flow. This is the more satisfactory method of injector testing. Fuel Injection specialists who can carry out the work are available in most areas.

47 An alternative method (MPi only):

a) Remove the injectors from the cylinder head and place into separate graduated containers. The injectors must remain connected to the fuel rail and pressure regulator.
b) By-pass the relay ***(see illustration 4.36)***.

4.36 By-pass the relay. Connect a jumper lead between terminal 30 and 87 when power will be supplied to the relay output

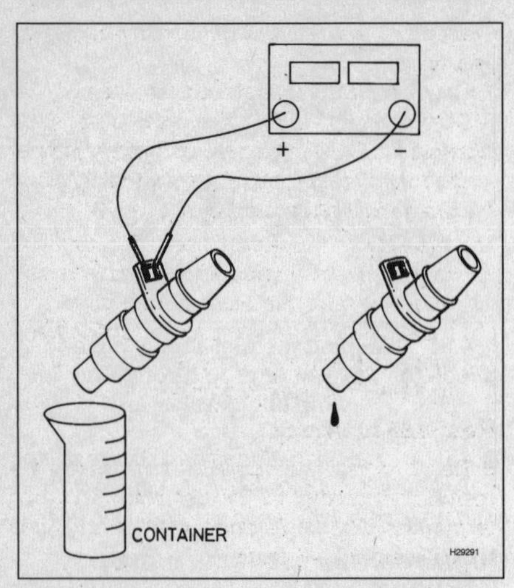

4.37 Injector volume and spray test. See checking the injectors for flow

- c) *Remove the electrical connections from all of the injectors.*
- d) *Use a jumper lead to connect the injector supply terminal to a 12-volt supply.*
- e) *Use a second jumper lead to connect the injector earth terminal to an earth.*
- f) *Apply power for 15 seconds exactly.*
- g) *Similarly test each of the injectors in turn.*
- h) *The difference in quantity sprayed from each injector should be within 5cc.*
- i) *Each injector should emit a fine conical spray* **(see illustration 4.37)**.
- j) *Repeat the test to ensure consistent results.*
- k) *On removal of the jumper leads, the injector should leak no more than one drop in 60 seconds.*

Visual flow test (SPi)

48 Remove the air filter.
49 Allow the engine to idle and then stop the engine.
50 Visually check for leaking fuel from the injector. If the injector is leaking, it will need to be renewed or serviced.
51 Remove the injector from the throttle body, and use a dedicated fuel injection test rig to test for spray pattern and injector flow.
52 If a test rig is not available in-house, take the injector to a specialist who can carry out the work.

32 Oxygen sensor (OS)

1 Inspect the OS multi-plug for corrosion and damage.
2 Check that the terminal pins in the OS multi-plug are fully pushed home and making good contact with the OS.
3 Roll back the rubber protection boot to the OS multi-plug.
4 Connect the voltmeter negative probe to an engine earth.
5 Identify the terminals. Depending upon system there will be up to four terminals:

- a) *OS heater earth.*
- b) *OS heater supply.*
- c) *OS signal.*
- d) *OS return or earth.*

6 Connect the voltmeter positive probe to the wire attached to the OS signal terminal.
7 If an MOT-specification four-gas analyser with Lambda is attached to the exhaust system, the following values should be obtained.

- a) *CO: as vehicle specification.*
- b) *HC: less than 50 ppm*
- c) *CO_2: greater than 15.0*
- d) *O_2: less than 2.0*
- e) *Lambda: 1.0 ± 0.03*

8 Run the engine to operating temperature.
9 Raise the engine speed to 3000 rpm for 30 seconds. This will raise the temperature of the OS so that switching should occur.
10 Hold the engine speed at a steady 2500 rpm. If the engine is allowed to idle for prolonged periods, the OS will become cool and switching may stop.
11 Check for OS switching. See below for full details and analysis.

OS heater tests

12 Check for nbv at the OS heater supply terminal.

- a) *No voltage: Trace the supply wiring back to the relay or ignition switch as appropriate.*
- b) *Check the OS heater earth connection*

OS signal output

Condition	Voltage
Engine running (hot, at 2500 rpm)	*0.2 to 1.0 volts*
Throttle fully-open	*1.0 volt constant*
Fuel cut-off	*0 volt constant*
Switching frequency	*1 sec intervals (approx)*

33 Oxygen sensor (OS)

Check for switching

1 All closed-loop catalyst vehicles monitor the presence of oxygen in the exhaust system and adjust the injector output to keep the AFR within Lambda 1.0 ± 0.03. The switching of the OS is fundamental to the proper operation of the injection system. Checking that OS switching is correctly occurring is a vitally-important test routine.
2 Attach a suitable oscilloscope or voltmeter to the OS switching wire.
3 Increase the engine speed to between 2500 and 3000 rpm for a period of 3 minutes in order to heat the OS and light the catalyst.
4 Allow the engine to fast idle and check for OS switching.
5 The OS voltage should switch high and low

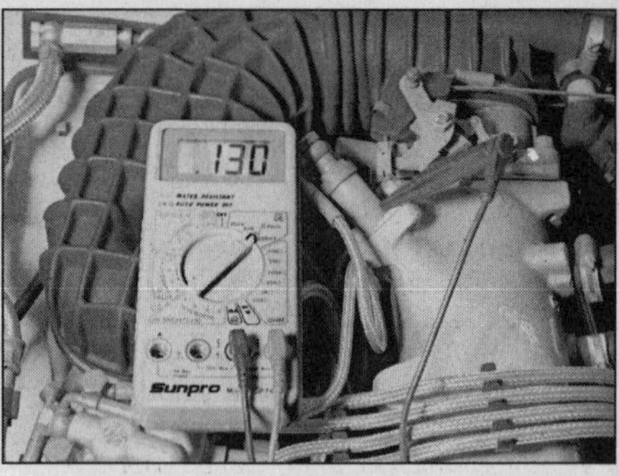

4.38 Oxygen sensor switching voltage low. 0.130 volts is equivalent to 130 millivolts. A low voltage signifies a weak mixture

from approximately 200 mv to 800 mv at a frequency of 8 to 10 times every 10 seconds (1 Hz) **(see illustration 4.38)**. **Note:** *A digital voltmeter will indicate an average voltage of approximately 450 mv. A sluggish OS may appear to be switching correctly, and may not reveal that the voltage is slightly high. An oscilloscope is the more accurate form of test equipment, and will reveal most faults. However, if the voltmeter has a max. and min. function, the range of average switching will be more easily spotted.*

No OS switching

- a) *Check the self-diagnostic system for fault codes. If the OS has failed, the ECM will either go into open-loop, or use a fixed voltage of approximately 0.45 to establish Lambda = 1.0.*
- b) *Check the OS heater circuit (heated OS only, 2, 3 or 4 wire types). Refer to the 'Oxygen sensor' tests in the system specific Chapter.*
- c) *If the OS heater circuit has failed, the OS may never (or only occasionally) reach operating temperature.*
- d) *Snap-accelerate the engine: As the AFR goes rich, the OS should give a high voltage.*
- e) *If the exhaust is equipped with a CO inspection port before the catalyst, measure the CO vol % and HC at the port. If the cat is operating efficiently, the following tests may not be so productive when the CO is measured at the tailpipe.*
- f) *Increase the engine speed to between 2500 and 3000 rpm for 3 minutes to heat the OS and light the catalyst.*
- g) *Allow the engine to fast idle.*
- h) *Place the system in open-loop by disconnecting the multi-plug to the OS.*
- i) *MPi engines: Remove the vacuum hose from the fuel pressure regulator, and seal the hose end.*
- j) *SPi engines: Briefly clamp the fuel return line from the pressure regulator back to the fuel tank.*
- k) *The CO should increase, and the OS voltage should switch high.*
- l) *Return the system to closed-loop operation by reconnecting the multi-plug to the OS.*

m) The CO should return to normal as the engine responds to the rich mixture. This proves that the OS and ECM can handle a rich mixture.

n) MPi engines: Refit the hose to the pressure regulator.

o) Place the system in open-loop by disconnecting the multi-plug to the OS.

p) Pull the dipstick halfway out or detach a vacuum hose to introduce a vacuum leak.

q) The CO should decrease, and the OS voltage should switch low.

r) Return the system to closed-loop operation by reconnecting the multi-plug to the OS.

s) The CO should return to normal as the engine responds to the lean mixture. This proves that the OS and ECM can handle a weak mixture.

34 Carbon filter solenoid valve (CFSV)

1 Inspect the CFSV multi-plug for corrosion and damage.

2 Check that the connector terminal pins are fully pushed home and making good contact with the CFSV multi-plug.

CFSV test procedures

3 Roll back the rubber protection boot (where possible) to the CFSV multi-plug.

4 Identify the supply and signal terminals.

5 Switch the ignition on.

6 Check for nbv at the CFSV supply terminal. If there is no voltage, trace the wiring back to the battery, ignition switch or relay output as appropriate.

7 Check the CFSV resistance (see below).

8 Disconnect the ECM multi-plug *(see Warning No 3 in Reference)* and use a jumper lead to very briefly touch the switching pin in the ECM multi-plug to earth.

a) If the CFSV actuates: Check the ECM main voltage supplies and earths. If tests reveal no fault, the ECM is suspect.

b) If the CFSV does not actuate: Check for continuity of wiring between the CFSV and the ECM switching pin.

Resistance check

9 Remove the multi-plug and measure the resistance of the CFSV between the two terminals. The resistance of the CFSV is typically around 40 ohms.

Chapter 5
Fault diagnosis

The modern 'tune-up'

Due to improved reliability and developments in electronic engine and fuel management systems, tuning as a regular process is gradually changing to diagnostics - the science of fault diagnosis. Although the reason for a tune-up may be receding, with fewer engine adjustments being possible, regular diagnostic checks are desirable to identify possible problem areas and pinpoint faults. Quick and accurate diagnosis is particularly important where a catalyst is fitted, because certain catalyst destruction will follow when more than a small amount of unburnt fuel is allowed to pass through the exhaust system.

Radiated RFI can also be a problem, and this can emanate from items such as the secondary HT circuits or the alternator. Excess RFI can disrupt ECM operation, and can affect EMS operation - particularly where both ignition and fuelling functions are located in the same ECM.

The modern tune-up is concerned with ensuring that the engine is running at maximum efficiency, and this can be accomplished with the minimum of tools or equipment. Refer to Chapter 3 for details on the various kinds of equipment required.

Diagnosis of automotive faults is sometimes a time-consuming process. Unless you are very lucky and stumble across the fault immediately, the best and ultimately quickest method is to follow a logical test pattern that checks, tests and evaluates all possibilities.

1) *Interrogate the customer (even if you are the customer)*
Use an Incident check list to log details of the incident and record under what conditions the problem occurs. This is an important pre-requisite to determining test procedures, and also prevents misunderstandings between workshop and customer.

2) *Basic inspection*
Faults in engines with electronic systems are often similar to problems found in engines with non-electronic controls. Make a basic inspection, and follow a sequence of visual checks & adjustments and the problem area can often be quickly diagnosed.

3) *Evaluation of the general engine functions using diagnostic equipment*
Connect appropriate diagnostic equipment, and run through a series of mechanical and electrical checks. These checks are recommended for a basic analysis of the general engine and electrical system condition. Many of the checks can be completed using basic test meters.

4) *Fault code reader (FCR) diagnosis - also refer to the appropriate Chapter for the system under test*
If possible, connect a FCR to the serial port and interrogate the self-diagnostic function for fault codes. If a FCR is not available, flash codes can sometimes be obtained by following the procedures detailed for the particular system under test. If a fault code is present, test the relevant circuit by following the system sensor and actuator tests.

5) *Symptom-related fault diagnosis - also refer to the appropriate Chapter for the system under test*
If a fault code is not available, follow the symptom-related fault diagnosis charts, and systematically test the circuits and components that might be responsible for the fault condition.

1 Incident check list

Customer name: ______________________ Date: ______________________

Vehicle make: ______________________ Model and year : ______________________

Speedometer mileage reading: ______________________ Registration number: ______________________

VIN: ______________________ Engine number: ______________________

Starting ability

	no start O	cold O	hot O	
	difficult to start O	cold O	hot O	after brief stop O
Starting affected by throttle position:	easier O	harder O		

Idle speed

Fast idle when cold or during warm-up:	yes O	no O	
Stalls when cold or during warm-up:	yes O	no O	
Hot idle:	unstable idle O	high idle O	low idle O
	engine stalls O	occasionally O	frequently O

Driving concerns

hesitation O	from low speed O	from high speed O
inlet backfire O	cold O	hot O
exhaust backfire	cold O	hot O
surge O	detonation O	lack of power O

Time of incident

	morning (first thing) O	during day O	night O
Frequency:	occasionally O	all of the time O	certain conditions (please state) O

Weather conditions

	not affected O	fine O	wet/damp O	snowing O	other O
Temperature:	hot O	cold O	cool O	humid O	

Engine conditions

	cold O	warm-up O	hot O
	2.000 rpm O	4.000 rpm O	6000 + rpm O
	idle O	acceleration O	overrun O
Check Engine warning light:	illuminated O	not illuminated O	

Road conditions

in town O	in suburbs O	motorway O	off-road O

Driving conditions

	not affected O	starting O	idling O	at high speeds O	
	accelerating O	cruising O	decelerating O	turning (RH/LH) O	
Vehicle speed (mph):	0-30 O	30-50 O	50-70 O	70-90 O	90+ O

Other comments

____

____

____

2 Basic inspection

No matter what is the problem, the following checks are an essential pre-requisite to the use of diagnostic equipment. In many instances, the fault will be revealed during these procedures. Make a careful visual inspection of the following items. Not all checks will be appropriate for all engines. This basic inspection can save a great deal of valuable diagnostic time. Worn but electrically-sound components do not always fail tests.

- Check the engine oil level, oil condition and positive crankcase ventilation (PCV) circuit condition. Maintenance of the lubrication system is particularly important for good engine operation. In catalyst-equipped vehicles, contaminated oil, a poorly-maintained PCV system or an oil-burning engine will contaminate the catalyst in a very short period of time.
- Check the coolant level and coolant system condition. Maintenance of the cooling system is particularly important for good engine operation. An engine that is overcooled or running too hot will cause an incorrect CTS signal to be passed to the EMS, which may result in incorrect output signals. This will affect timing and fuelling actuation.
- Check the automatic transmission fluid level and condition.
- Check the battery condition.
- Check the battery for security.
- Check the battery electrolyte level.
- Check the battery cables and connections.
- Check the drivebelt(s) condition and tension.
- Remove the spark plugs and check the condition. Renew if necessary.
- Check that the spark plug electrode gap is correct.
- Check that the spark plug type is the correct type for the vehicle.
- Remove the distributor cap and check the condition, both external and internal. Look for cracks or signs of tracking.
- Look for oil or water that may have seeped into the cap through a defective seal.
- Check the rotor condition and measure the resistance where appropriate.
- Check the coil tower condition. Look for cracks or signs of tracking.
- Check for poor or corroded electrical connections
- Check for freedom from vacuum leaks from the vacuum hoses, inlet manifold, AFS trunking, oil dipstick seal and rocker cover seal.
- Check the breathing system condition. Clean away accumulated sludge, and ensure that the hoses are clear.
- Check the air filter condition. Renew if it is even slightly dirty.
- Check the exhaust system condition.
- Check the fuel system condition. Check for fuel leaks, and for worn or broken components. If available, the probe from a gas analyser with HC meter can be passed over the fuel and evaporation pipes and hoses. If the HC meter registers a measurement, that component may be leaking fuel or vapour.
- Visually inspect all connections, multi-plugs and terminals. Check for corrosion and loose or displaced terminals.
- Check the throttle body for a carbon build-up - usually as a result of fumes from the breathing system. The carbon can cause a sticking or jacked-open throttle, which can cause idle, cruising and other running problems. Carburettor cleaning fluid usually cleans away the carbon nicely.

3 Evaluate main engine functions using diagnostic equipment

Generally, an engine analyser or various pieces of hand-held diagnostic equipment should be used to locate and diagnose faults in the following areas:

a) Mechanical condition of engine.
b) Vacuum.
c) Compression.
d) Battery.
e) Charging system.
f) Ignition secondary circuit.
g) Fuel system.
h) Exhaust system.

The list below is based on a professional check list, and enables analysis of the basic mechanical and electrical condition of the engine. Many of the checks require only a DMM or other low-cost gauges. However, some tests may require specialist equipment.

Customer name: ____________________ Date: ____________________

Vehicle make: ____________________ Model and year : ____________________

Speedometer mileage reading: ____________________ Registration number: ____________________

Fault reported: ____________________

Tests		***Results***
1	Battery volts *(12.4+, nominal battery volts)*	______
2	Cranking volts *(9.6+, disable the engine and crank it for 15 seconds)*	______
3	Battery recover volts *(12.0+, battery voltage 15 seconds after cranking ceases)*	______
4	Cranking amps *(current drawn during cranking)*	______
5	Charging amps after cranking *(immediately after cranking, start engine and raise engine speed to 3000 rpm, the current drawn should be within 10% of maximum alternator output)*	______
6	Charging volts, off load *(engine speed 3000 rpm, all electrical loads switched off, voltage should be less than rated maximum charging voltage).*	______
7	Charging volts, on load *(engine speed 3000 rpm, heated rear window and heater blower switched on, voltage should be 12.0 to 13.0 volts)*	______
8	Volts at coil + *(11.0+, ignition on)*	______
9	Cranking volts at coil + *(9.0+, during engine cranking)*	______
10	Primary ignition dwell in % or ms at idle	______
11	Primary ignition dwell in % or ms at 2000 rpm	______
12	Check that the coil polarity is correct	______
13	Check for good secondary insulation	______
14	Check the basic Ignition timing and adjust (where possible)	______
15	Check ignition timing advance	______
16	Check the CAS adjustment (where possible).	______
17	Check the throttle valve position adjustment (where possible).	______
18	Check the throttle pot or switch adjustment (where possible).	______
19	Check the CO and base idle speed values and adjust (where possible).	______
20	Check the engine vacuum at idle speed *(580 to 750 mbar)*	______
21	Check the engine vacuum at 2500 rpm	______
22	Idle speed	______
23	Lambda switching *(rich/weak/OK)*	______
24	Gas analysis:	

	Idle	***2000 rpm***	***3000 rpm***	***Acceleration***
O_2				
CO				
CO_2				
HC				

4 Fault code reader (FCR) diagnosis

Serial data testing - introduction

1 As a general rule, it is usually more beneficial to work through the checks listed in "Basic inspection" and "Engine evaluation" before connecting the FCR. The reason for this is clear - electrical and HT faults may adversely affect ECM operation, giving incorrect or spurious results, and causing much confusion. Only after electrical and HT problems have been resolved should the operation of the ECM and its sensors be evaluated.

Testing self-diagnostic systems

2 Is the warning lamp (if fitted) illuminated while the engine is running?. If so, this is indicative of a system fault. **Note:** *Be aware that some lamps do not illuminate for faults that are designated as minor faults.*

3 Connect a FCR to the serial port connector, and interrogate the ECM for fault codes, or trigger the flash codes if this is possible.

4 If faults are logged, use the appropriate system test procedures to check out the relevant circuits.

5 If fault codes are not logged, use the FCR to view the datastream (live data on system sensors and actuators, and not available for all systems) or follow the symptom-driven fault diagnosis charts.

Limitations of self-diagnostic systems

6 Some may see the FCR as a panacea for solving all electronic problems with the car, but reading the fault code is only the beginning. To a large degree, the information decoded by the FCR is provided by the software designed into the vehicle ECM. The FCR makes the most of this information, but if certain facilities or data are not designed to be output at the serial port, these facilities will not be available to the FCR.

7 In many instances, the FCR can provide the answer to a puzzling fault very quickly. However, it will not provide all the answers, because some faults (including actual ECM faults), may not even generate a fault code.

8 There are a number of distinct limitations to self-diagnostic systems:

a) *The basic data extracted from the EMS by the FCR is laid down by the vehicle manufacturer, and the self-diagnostic system and FCR must work within those limitations.*

b) *A code will not be logged if the ECM is not programmed to recognise that a particular component is faulty.*

c) *Spurious codes can be triggered by electrical or secondary HT faults.*

d) *One or more spurious codes can be triggered by a faulty component that may or may not trigger a code by itself.*

e) *The fault code indicates a faulty circuit, and not necessarily a component. For example, a code indicating a CTS fault may be caused by a faulty sensor, wiring fault, or corroded connector. Always check the wiring and connectors, and apply proper tests to the component before judging it to be faulty.*

f) *Limited range or out of range sensors. If the sensor remains within its design parameter, even if the parameters are incorrect for certain operating conditions, a fault code will not be logged. For example, a faulty CTS will generate a fault code if it is open-circuit or shorted to earth. However, if the CTS is stuck at either the hot or cold resistance, a code may not be generated, although the engine will indeed run badly at some temperatures.*

g) *Some vehicle systems are capable of logging faults that occur intermittently, and others are not.*

h) *In some instances, a fault code may be lost the moment that the ignition is switched off, and due allowance should be made for this kind of system.*

i) *Older vehicles with basic electronic fuel injection systems may not support self-diagnosis.*

Using a FCR

9 The FCR can be used for the following tasks. Some more sophisticated FCR's may interact with the ECM and allow a diagnostic trail to be followed.

a) *Reading fault codes.*

b) *Clearing fault codes.*

c) *Datastream testing (not all systems, for example Ford EEC IV cannot provide datastream).*

d) *Actuator testing.*

Dynamic test procedures

10 Use the FCR to interrogate the ECM via the serial port.

11 Once the FCR has diagnosed one or more faults, further tests are usually required, and the technician may use the FCR (where possible), or it may be necessary to use a DMM or an oscilloscope to complete diagnosis. Refer to the Sensor and Actuator tests in the specific Chapter for the system under test.

12 Once the FCR has logged a fault, a datastream enquiry (some systems only) is a quick method of determining where the fault might lie. This data may take various forms, but is essentially electrical data on voltage, frequency, dwell or pulse duration, temperature etc, provided by the various sensors and actuators. Unfortunately, such data is not available in all vehicle systems, and datastream is not an option if you are working with flash codes. Since the data is in real time, various tests can be made, and the response of the sensor or actuator evaluated.

13 Driving or actuating the system actuators such as the idle control valve, relays and injectors through the ECM is an excellent method of testing effectiveness of the actuator and associated wiring circuit. If the actuator operates when driven in this fashion, you have proved that there is little wrong with the circuit or component. This procedure is not possible for engine sensors.

14 Use an oscilloscope or DMM to check voltages at the faulty component. Compare with the vehicle specifications in the relevant system Chapter.

15 Use an ohmmeter to check the faulty circuit for continuity of the wiring and component resistance. Compare with the specifications in the relevant system Chapter.

16 A faulty circuit should be tested and any faults that are discovered should be repaired. The FCR should then be used to clear the errors and the ECM interrogated once again to see if other fault codes are still present.

17 An important point to bear in mind is that the ECM will only log faults in the electronic circuits; mechanical, ignition secondary or fuel problems will still require to be diagnosed using time-honoured methods.

18 Check that the faults remain cleared and do not return.

Intermittent faults

19 Wiggle the component wiring, apply heat from a hairdryer, or freeze with a cold spray.

20 Intermittent faults can be extremely difficult to find, and on-road testing is often desirable, with codes or datastream information being generated as the fault occurs. Take the vehicle for a road test with the FCR attached.

5 Fault diagnosis

1 Emission test failure - non-catalyst/open-loop catalyst vehicles

Requirements for the (UK) MOT test

Vehicle registered	Registration letter	CO limit (% vol.)
01/08/1975 to 31/07/1986	'P' suffix to 'C' prefix	4.50
01/08/1986 onwards	'D' prefix onwards	3.50

Maximum HC limit for all vehicles: 1200 ppm. The test is manual in operation, and normally carried out at idle speed.

Emission test

1 Run the engine to normal operating temperature. Connect a gas analyser to the exhaust tailpipe. If an MOT emission test is being executed, the gas analyser must meet relevant legislation.
2 CO test at normal idle speed. Measure the CO vol. % and HC level.
3 If either the CO vol. %, or the HC level or both values are greater than the statutory specifications, the vehicle has failed the emission test. *Diagnosis is more straightforward with non-catalyst equipped vehicles because there is no OS to alter the mixture. The measurements are therefore more open to interpretation.*

Fault analysis

Note: *Because the vehicle's own CO limit will usually be lower than the statutory limit, the vehicle's CO value should always be used when attempting to diagnose faults as a result of the CO measurement. Similarly, because the statutory HC limit is set so high, an HC value of 300 ppm would be a more realistic ceiling when attempting to diagnose faults as a result of the HC measurement. An HC measurement serious enough to allow failure of the UK MOT test is indicative of a fairly serious fault or faults.*
4 The following analysis is made with comparison to the vehicle's normal CO level and an HC limit of 300 ppm.

High CO and higher-than-normal HC

- Rich mixture

Low CO and high HC

- Fouled spark plug
- Misfire
- Weak mixture

Low CO and low or normal HC

- Fouled injector
- Exhaust system leak

2 Emission test failure - catalyst-equipped vehicles

Requirements for the (UK) MOT test

Vehicle registered	Registration letter	CO limit (% vol.)
01/08/1992 onwards	from 'K' prefix	VM specification

Fast idle speed: CO, HC and Lambda test
Idle speed: Idle speed band, CO test

The test is automatic, and values are compared to VM's values. Where VM values are not available, the following default values are used.

Fast idle speed	CO	HC	Lambda
2500 to 3000 rpm	0.3%	200 ppm	1.0 ± 0.03
Idle speed	**CO**		
500 to 1100 rpm	0.3%		

Emission test

1 Run the engine to normal operating temperature. Connect a gas analyser to the exhaust tailpipe. If an MOT emission test is being executed, the gas analyser must meet current legislation.
2 Increase the engine speed to between 2500 and 3000 rpm for a period of 3 minutes to heat the OS and light the catalyst.
3 CO test at either normal idle speed or fast idle. Measure the CO %.
4 If the CO vol. % is either greater than the VM specifications or higher than 0.3%, the vehicle has failed.
5 Increase the engine speed to between 2500 and 3000 rpm for a period of 3 minutes to heat the OS and light the catalyst.
6 Retest the engine (recheck the CO value).
7 If the CO vol. % is either greater than the VM specifications or higher than 0.3%, the vehicle has failed the CO vol % emission test. Refer to "Fault analysis".
8 HC test at fast idle speed. Measure the HC level.
9 If the HC level is either greater than the VM specifications or higher than 200 ppm, the vehicle has failed the HC emission test. Refer to "Fault analysis".
10 Lambda test at fast idle speed. Measure the Lambda ratio.
11 If the Lambda ratio is either outside of the VM specifications or higher than 1.03, the vehicle has failed the Lambda emission test. Refer to "Fault analysis".

Fault analysis

12 Diagnosis is less straightforward with closed-loop catalyst and OS-equipped vehicles as compared to non-catalyst vehicles, because of the tendency of the OS to alter the mixture. If the engine is operating properly without faults, the situation is quite clear. However, when a combination of fuel or sensor faults, exhaust and vacuum leaks and ignition or mechanical faults are present, the OS will attempt to compensate and the effect on the various gases may lead to some initial confusion.

Important note: *Exhaust leaks, and any mechanical/ignition faults, must be put right before attempts are made to correct the AFR.*

13 If the catalyst requires replacement:

a) *Ensure that faults are not present in the mechanical, ignition or fuel systems that might lead to premature failure of the replacement cat.*

b) Ensure that the engine is not being run on leaded fuel. All cat-equipped engines must run on unleaded fuel. Although the cat-equipped vehicle utilises a small filler cap to prevent filling with leaded fuel at the petrol filling station, the determined person may still manage to find a way to introduce leaded fuel to the petrol tank.

14 The reasons for an emission failure are many and diverse. The following reasons for failure are based on the data obtained during the test procedure. In addition, attach a suitable DMM or oscilloscope to the OS, and increase the engine speed to between 2500 and 3000 rpm for a period of 3 minutes to heat the OS and light the catalyst. Allow the engine to fast idle, and record the following data.

a) Lambda ratio
b) OS switching at the correct frequency
c) CO vol. %
d) HC value
e) O_2 content
f) CO_2 content

15 A faulty catalyst is indicated if the following were found:

a) The CO vol. % is either greater than the VM specifications, or higher than 0.3%,
b) The HC level is either greater than the VM specifications, or higher than 200 ppm,
c) The Lambda ratio is higher than the VM minimum specification, or greater than 0.97.
d) The O_2 content is between 0.5 and 1.5 %
e) The OS is switching high and low at the correct frequency.

16 If the catalytic converter was definitely lit during the test, the symptoms suggest that the cat is faulty. Confirm diagnosis in one of the following ways:

a) If the exhaust is equipped with an CO inspection port before the cat, measure the CO vol % and HC at the port. The readings at the tailpipe should be lower than the readings obtained at the inspection port. Similar readings indicate that the cat is inefficient and is not 'catalysing' the CO or HC gases.
b) Allow the cat to cool. Measure the CO vol % and HC at the exhaust tailpipe. The readings should be slightly higher than the readings obtained when the cat is lit. Similar readings indicate that the cat is inefficient and is not 'catalysing' the CO or HC gases.
c) Measure the exhaust temperature both before and after the cat, if the cat is operating efficiently, the temperature after the cat will be approximately 55°C higher than the temperature before. If the two temperatures are approximately equal, the cat is probably not functioning.

Rich mixture and exhaust leak

- The CO vol. % is either greater than the VM specifications or higher than 0.3%,
- The HC level is either greater than the VM specifications or higher than 200 ppm.
- The Lambda ratio is higher than the VM minimum specification or greater than 0.97.
- The O_2 content is between 0.5 and 1.5 %
- The OS is not switching and reading high.

17 The symptoms suggest that the mixture is probably rich together with a small hole in the exhaust which is deceiving the gas analyser into calculating an incorrect Lambda ratio.

18 Check the self-diagnostic system for fault codes.

19 Make the rich mixture checks Refer to 'Fault diagnosis', Section 7.

Faulty OS and exhaust leak

- The CO vol. % is either greater than the VM specifications or higher than 0.3%,
- The HC level is either greater than the VM specifications or higher than 200 ppm,
- The Lambda ratio is higher than the VM minimum specification or greater than 0.97.
- The O_2 is between 0.5 and 1.5 %
- The OS is not switching and reading low.

20 The symptoms suggest that the OS is probably faulty together with a small hole in the exhaust which is deceiving the gas analyser into calculating an incorrect Lambda ratio.

21 Check the self-diagnostic system for fault codes.

Rich mixture

- The CO vol. % is either greater than the VM specifications or higher than 0.3%
- The Lambda ratio is higher than the VM minimum specification or greater than 0.97.
- The O_2 content is lower than 0.5 %.
- The OS is not switching and reading high.

22 The symptoms suggest that the mixture is too rich.

23 Check the self-diagnostic system for fault codes.

24 Make the rich mixture checks Refer to 'Fault diagnosis', Section 7.

Slightly rich mixture, with or without a faulty catalytic converter, and a hole in the exhaust system

- The CO vol. % is either greater than the VM specifications, or higher than 0.3%.
- The Lambda ratio is higher than the VM minimum specification, or greater than 0.97.
- The O_2 content is higher than 1.5 %.
- The CO_2 content is also likely to be low.
- The HC value is less than 250 ppm.

25 The symptoms suggest a slightly rich mixture, with or without a faulty catalytic converter, and a hole in the exhaust system.

26 A hole in the exhaust pipe, upstream of the OS, will cause the OS to return a lean signal to the EMS, which is deceived into forcing the mixture rich.

27 Check the self-diagnostic system for fault codes.

28 Make the rich mixture checks. Refer to 'Fault diagnosis', Section 7.

Engine misfire

- The CO vol. % is either greater than the VM specifications, or higher than 0.3%.
- The Lambda ratio is higher than the VM minimum specification, or greater than 0.97.
- The O_2 content is higher than 1.5 %.
- The HC is higher than 200 ppm (emission test HC failure).

29 The symptoms suggest a misfire. A high CO level is not usually associated with a misfire. However, the closed-loop catalyst vehicle may produce extra CO at the exhaust pipe due to one or more of the following reasons:

a) The misfire is caused by a very rich mixture and the high 0_2 in the exhaust is deceiving the gas analyser into calculating an incorrect Lambda ratio.
b) The vehicle has been driven for some time with a misfire present and the efficiency of the catalytic converter has been so greatly impaired that a higher than normal CO level can be measured at the exhaust tailpipe. The Lambda ratio is correct.
c) The misfire has caused a high level of O_2 content to be exhausted. The OS returns a lean signal to the EMS which is deceived into forcing the mixture rich. The same high 0_2 in the exhaust is deceiving the gas analyser into calculating an incorrect Lambda ratio.

30 Check the self-diagnostic system for fault codes.

31 Make the rich mixture checks. Refer to 'Fault diagnosis', Section 7.

32 Make the misfire checks. Refer to 'Fault diagnosis', Section 6.

Rich mixture and engine misfire

- The CO vol. % is either greater than the VM specifications, or higher than 0.3%,
- The Lambda ratio is lower than the VM minimum specification, or lower than 0.97.
- If the O_2 content is higher than 0.5 %, the symptoms suggest a rich mixture with a misfire.

33 Check the self-diagnostic system for fault codes.

34 Make the rich mixture checks. Refer to 'Fault diagnosis', Section 7.

35 Make the misfire checks. Refer to 'Fault diagnosis', Section 6.

3 Essential pre-fault diagnosis routines

1 Firstly, no matter what is the fault, always make a basic inspection.
2 Next, use an engine analyser or DMM to make diagnostic checks.
3 Then use a FCR to check the self-diagnostic system for fault codes.

a) *If one or more codes are present, a serious fault may have occurred in the circuit that has raised the code. In that case, the system may have entered LOS and this will turn the dash-mounted warning lamp on (some systems).*

b) *When the EMS enters LOS, it will usually substitute a fixed value for the faulty circuit and the engine may behave fairly normally. The EMS should operate in 'open-loop' control and may substitute a fixed value for the OS output of 0.45.*

c) *Check the relevant circuits as described under the system specific test routines, put right any faults and clear the fault codes. Refer to the general self-diagnostic routines.*

4 Now continue with the following test procedures, with reference to the specific Chapter for the system under test.

4 Non-starter, cold engine

1 Check for a broken cambelt

- Engines with distributor: Remove the distributor cap. Carefully turn the engine over and check that the rotor also turns.
- DIS engines: Remove the rocker cover. Carefully turn the engine over and check that the valve gear also turns.
- Even if the cambelt (or timing chain) is not broken, check for misalignment.

2 Sluggish rotation of the engine whilst the starter motor is engaged

- Check that the battery and starter motor are not defective.
- Incorrect ignition timing can give symptoms not unlike a defective battery or starter motor.
- Check that the engine is being lubricated by the correct grade of oil. An incorrect grade of oil, or oil that has seriously deteriorated, can cause sluggish rotation of the engine.
- If the engine has been recently rebuilt, engine tolerances that are on the tight side can lead to very sluggish rotation of the engine.

3 Check the fuel supply

- If a gas analyser with HC facility is available, crank the engine (do not disable the ignition); an HC reading of more than 4000 ppm should be displayed.
- An HC meter that cannot display measurements of 4000 ppm or more will give an indication of fuel passing through the engine up to the meter's maximum HC potential, which should be of some help.
- Low HC: Insufficient fuel is being supplied to the cylinders. Check for an engine compression or injection system failure.
- HC measurement greater than 4000 ppm: Check for ignition or mechanical faults. It is also possible that too much fuel is being injected.
- Check the condition of the air filter. A clogged air filter could cause a mixture that is too rich for good starting.
- Test for a cranking injection signal. Record whether the signal is too long or too short. Refer to the non-runner tests under 'Injection' tests in the appropriate system Chapter.
- If no injection signal is obtained during cranking, this indicates an electrical supply fault or a major component failure.

4 Check the ignition for a spark

- *Refer to the 'Secondary ignition' non-runner tests in Chapter 4 for methods on how to check for a spark.*
- If no spark, refer to the 'Secondary' non-runner test procedures in Chapter 4.
- If no ignition secondary signal, check the HT leads, distributor cap, rotor, coil tower and coil secondary resistance. Faulty HT can cause either electronic component failure or a spurious signal. The spurious signal can disrupt ECU operation (particularly in an EMS).
- If no ignition primary signal, make the 'primary trigger' and 'primary ignition' tests. Refer to the appropriate system Chapter.
- The fuel injection in many EFI engines is triggered from the ignition primary circuit. If there is no ignition, there will be no injection. The foregoing is not always true where an EMS controls both ignition and fuel from the same ECU.
- If the system contains a CID (phasing) signal (often used in sequential injection engines), check that the two signals are in phase. In some systems, out-of-phase signals can result in a non-start or poor running situation.
- Remove the spark plugs and check for engine compression. Before commencing the test, disable the engine to prevent it from starting
- Check the spark plugs.

5 No ignition or injection signal

- **Note:** *If primary ignition and injection are established, then the fault lies in the secondary HT, air intake or fuel pressure system, or is a mechanical or timing fault.*
- If the primary trigger is an CAS or Hall-effect trigger, check for proper operation of these devices. Refer to the non-runner tests under the 'CAS' or 'HES' tests in the appropriate system Chapter.

6 Primary trigger satisfactory, yet no output from ECM

- Check the inertia switch (if fitted).
- Check the voltage supplies and earth connections to the ECM.
- Check the fuel system pressure.
- Check the voltage supply to the fuel pump.

7 Check the CTS operation

- Refer to the 'CTS' tests in the system specific Chapter.
- Check for a voltage signal according to temperature.
- Check for a poor connection at the CTS. A slightly higher than normal resistance at the connection will add to the CTS resistance, and cause an over-rich mixture during cranking.
- A very high CTS resistance could place the EMS in LOS. The fixed value used by the EMS in LOS is normally that of a warm engine. Ease of cold starting will therefore deteriorate.
- Engine without LOS will fail to start if the CTS circuit is shorted or open-circuit. The ECM will recognise a very high or a very low resistance as a very cold or a very hot engine, and will apply the injection duration accordingly.

8 Check the AFS operation (if fitted)

- Refer to the 'AFS' tests in the system specific Chapter.
- Check for a voltage output signal.
- Check for poor or sticky mechanical operation.

9 Check the MAP sensor operation (if fitted)

- Refer to the 'MAP sensor' tests in the system specific Chapter.
- Check for a voltage output signal.
- Check for a vacuum leak or displaced hose, manifold to MAP sensor.

10 Check for a major inductive vacuum leak, displaced or incorrectly-routed vacuum hose

4 Non-starter, cold engine (continued)

11 Check the evaporation system (if fitted)

- Refer to the 'CFSV' tests in the system specific Chapter.
- Check the carbon filter canister.
- Check the CFSV circuit. A fault could result in a vacuum leak.

12 Check the EGR system (if fitted)

- Refer to the 'EGR' tests in the system specific Chapter.
- A fault could result in a vacuum leak or permanent leakage of exhaust into the inductive system.

13 Check for failure of the ATS, TS or TPS

- A failure of one or more of these minor components may not be serious enough to cause total system failure. However, starting may become harder than normal. Refer to the system specific routines in the relevant Chapter under 'component' tests.

14 Check the idle control system

- The engine may fire but not run if the ISCV or circuit is faulty. Refer to the 'ISCV, stepper motor or AAV' tests in the system specific Chapter.

15 Check the CSV and TTS (only on some vehicles - prior to 1992)

- A failure of one or more of these two components may not be serious enough to cause total system failure. However, starting may become harder than normal. Refer to the system specific routines under 'CSV' and 'TTS' tests.

16 Check for injector mechanical faults

- If the vehicle has been laid up for some time, the injector(s) may be stuck (open or closed). In this case, either too much fuel will be injected or too little.
- Fouling of the injector pintle(s) may cause too little fuel or an inefficient spray pattern that may affect starting.

17 Check for a blocked catalyst

- Remove one of the spark plugs. Crank the engine. If the cat is blocked, the exhaust gases will escape to atmosphere through the open plug hole and the engine will probably start-up.

18 ECM suspect

- If all signals and voltages are present at the ECM multi-plug, yet an injection signal is not available, the ECM is suspect and could be tested by substitution.

5 Non-starter, hot engine

1 Cambelt (or timing chain) misalignment

2 Crank the engine and check for an ignition spark or secondary signal

3 Check the spark plugs

- Refer to spark plug tests under 'Secondary' ignition tests in Chapter 4.

4 Mixture too rich

- Check the CO % value. If the mixture is adjustable, set to VM specifications

5 Mixture too weak

- Check the CO % value. If the mixture is adjustable, set to VM specifications

6 Check the condition of the air filter

- A clogged air filter could cause a mixture that is too rich for good starting.

7 Check the fuel system pressure

- Refer to the 'fuel pressure' tests in the system specific Chapter.
- In particular, check for a high pressure loss after engine shutdown.

8 Check for fuel vaporisation

- Refer to the relevant component tests in the system specific Chapter.
- If a fuel rail temperature sensor or switch is fitted, check its operation.

9 Test for a cranking injection signal

- Refer to the 'Injection' tests in the system specific Chapter.
- Record whether the signal is too long or too short.

10 Check the CTS

- Refer to the 'CTS' tests in the system specific Chapter.
- Check for a voltage signal according to temperature.

11 Check for injector mechanical faults

- Fouling of the injector pintle(s) may cause too little fuel or an inefficient spray pattern that could affect starting.
- One or more leaking injectors may cause an over rich mixture that could affect starting.

12 Check the MAP sensor operation (if fitted)

- Refer to the 'MAP sensor' tests in the system specific Chapter.
- Check for a voltage output signal.
- Check for a vacuum leak or displaced hose, manifold to MAP sensor. A vacuum leak could cause an over rich mixture.

13 Check the evaporation system (if fitted)

- Refer to the 'CFSV' tests in the system specific Chapter.
- Check the carbon filter canister.
- Check the CFSV circuit. A fault could result in a vacuum leak.

14 Check the EGR system (if fitted)

- Refer to the 'EGR' tests in the system specific Chapter.
- A fault could result in a vacuum leak or permanent leakage of exhaust into the inductive system.

15 Check for failure of the ATS, TS or TPS

- A failure of one or more of these minor components may not be serious enough to cause total system failure. However, starting may become harder than normal. Refer to the component tests in the system specific Chapter.

16 Check the CSV and TTS (only on some vehicles - prior to 1992)

- A failure of one or more of these two components could cause fuel to be injected or dribbled when the engine is warm. Refer to the system specific routines under 'CSV' and 'TTS' tests.

6 Misfire

1 Check the primary ignition system

- Refer to the running tests under the system 'primary' tests. Pay particular attention to the following primary components:
- Dwell angle at idle, 2000 and 3000 rpm.

2 Check the secondary ignition system

- Refer to the running tests under the system 'secondary' tests. Pay particular attention to the following secondary components: Spark plugs, HT leads, coil secondary, distributor cap & rotor arm (if fitted).

3 Check the ignition timing

- If timing marks are fitted and specifications are available, compare to specs at idle, 2000 rpm and 3000 rpm.
- If timing marks are not fitted or specifications are not available, make your own marks on the pulley and timing case. Start the engine and check that timing at idle is around 0 to 15° BTDC. If the timing is under ECM control, the marks will be unsteady as the ECM alters the timing to control the idle speed. As the throttle is opened the timing should smoothly advance.

4 Check for a mixture that is too rich

5 Check for a mixture that is too lean

6 Check the AFS operation (if fitted)

- Refer to 'AFS' tests in the system specific Chapter.
- Pay particular attention to the smoothness of the voltage output as the engine rpm increases.

7 Check the TPS or TS operation

- Some engines may utilise a TS or even a combined TPS/ TS. Refer to the 'TPS' or 'TS' tests in the system specific Chapter.
- TPS operation (if fitted). Pay particular attention to the smoothness of the voltage output as the throttle is opened.
- TS operation (if fitted). Pay particular attention to the TS adjustment at idle and full-throttle (where appropriate).

8 Check for cambelt (or timing chain) misalignment

9 CID signal out of phase

- If the system contains a CID (phasing) signal (often used in sequential injection engines), check that the two signals are in phase. An out-of-phase signal can result in poor performance.
- Check that the distributor has not been moved from its datum position (where appropriate). A tiny movement out of position can result in an out-of-phase signal.
- An misaligned cambelt or even a stretched belt can result in an out-of-phase signal.

10 Poor connections

- Check for poor or corroded connections in the electrical harness, and at the sensor and actuator multi-plug connectors.

11 Check the compression pressures

- Remove the spark plugs.
- Before commencing the compression test, disable the engine to prevent it from starting.

7 Mixture too rich

1 Check the condition of the air filter

- A clogged air filter could result in a mixture that is too rich for good emissions or performance.

2 Check the condition of the engine oil and PCV system

- Contaminated oil and excessive fumes can result in high CO and HC levels.

3 Check the CO vol % at idle, 2000 and 3000 rpm

- Adjust the mixture (if possible), otherwise check for EMS or fuel injection system faults. *Be aware that attempting to adjust the CO value when system faults are present will result in an incorrect setting.*

4 A lean mixture setting at idle can result in excessive HC emissions

5 A high fuel pressure could result in a rich mixture

- Refer to the system specific routines under 'fuel pressure' tests.
- Check the fuel system pressure
- Check for a faulty pressure regulator
- Check for a clogged fuel return line.

6 Check for injector mechanical faults

- Fouling of the injector pintle(s) may cause too little fuel or an inefficient spray pattern that may affect emissions and engine performance.
- One or more leaking injectors may result in an over-rich mixture that may affect emissions or engine performance.

7 OS (where fitted)

- Check the OS for switching. Refer to the system specific routines under 'oxygen sensor' tests.
- A hole in the exhaust system, upstream of the OS, will cause the OS to return a lean signal to the EMS which is deceived into forcing the mixture rich.

8 Coolant temperature sensor (CTS)

- Check for a voltage signal according to temperature. Refer to the 'CTS' tests in the system specific Chapter.
- A high voltage or resistance or an out-of-range sensor could result in a rich mixture.

9 Check the MAP sensor operation (if fitted)

- Refer to the 'MAP sensor' tests in the system specific Chapter.
- Check for a voltage output signal.
- Check for a vacuum leak or displaced hose, manifold to MAP sensor. A vacuum leak could result in an over-rich mixture.

10 AFS operation (if fitted)

- Refer to the 'AFS' tests in the system specific Chapter.

11 Check the injection signal, and record the pulse duration

- Refer to the 'injection' tests in the system specific Chapter. Check the CTS, AFS or MAP sensor and other fuel system sensors.
- A pulse duration that is too long could result in a rich mixture.

12 Check the evaporation system (if fitted)

- Refer to the 'CFSV' tests in the system specific Chapter.
- Check the carbon filter canister.

7 Mixture too rich (continued)

- Check the CFSV circuit. A fault could result in a leakage of fuel vapours into the inductive system.
- In most systems, the evaporation purge system should not operate whilst the engine is cold or during the warm-up period or whilst the engine is idling.

13 Check the EGR system (if fitted)

- Refer to the 'EGR' tests in the system specific Chapter.
- A fault could result in a permanent leakage of exhaust fumes into the inductive system.
- In most systems, the EGR system should not operate when the engine is cold, during warm-up, nor when the engine is idling.

8 Mixture too lean

1 Check the CO vol % at idle, 2000 and 3000 rpm

- Adjust the mixture (if possible), otherwise check for EMS or fuel injection system faults. *Be aware that attempting to adjust the CO value when system faults are present will result in an incorrect setting.*

2 Lean misfire

- A lean mixture setting at idle can result in a lean misfire that will result in excessive HC emissions.

3 Low fuel pressure

- A low fuel pressure could result in a lean mixture. Refer to the system specific routines under 'fuel pressure' tests.
- Check the fuel system pressure.
- Check for a faulty pressure regulator.
- Check for a faulty fuel pump.

4 Check the injection signal and record the pulse duration

- Refer to the 'injection' tests in the system specific Chapter. Check the CTS, AFS or MAP sensor and other fuel system sensors.
- A pulse duration that is too short could result in a lean mixture.

5 Coolant temperature sensor (CTS)

- Refer to the 'CTS' tests in the system specific Chapter.
- Check for a voltage signal according to temperature.
- A low voltage or resistance or an out-of-range sensor could result in a lean mixture.

6 Check for injector mechanical faults

- Fouling of the injector pintle(s) may cause too little fuel or an inefficient spray pattern that may affect emissions and engine performance.

7 Check for an induction vacuum leak

- Manifold induction leak.
- Displaced or incorrectly routed vacuum hose.
- Other possible sources of vacuum leaks are at the rocker or cam box seal, or at the dipstick seal.

8 Check the evaporation system (if fitted)

- Refer to the 'CFSV' tests in the system specific Chapter.
- Check the carbon filter canister.
- Check the CFSV circuit. A fault could result in a vacuum leak into the inductive system.
- In most systems, the evaporation purge system should not operate whilst the engine is cold, during the warm-up period, or whilst the engine is idling.

9 Check the EGR system (if fitted)

- Refer to the 'EGR' tests in the system specific Chapter.
- A fault could result in a vacuum leak into the inductive system.
- In most systems, the EGR system should not operate when the engine is cold, during warm-up, or when the engine is idling.

10 Check the pulse air system (if fitted)

- Refer to the system specific routines under 'pulse air' tests.
- A fault could result in a vacuum leak into the exhaust system.
- In most systems, the pulse air system should only operate when the engine is cold, and then only for a few minutes after start-up.

9 Lack of power

1 Check the primary ignition system

- Refer to the running tests under the system 'primary' test.
- Check the dwell angle at idle, 2000 and 3000 rpm.

2 Check the secondary ignition system

- Refer to the running tests under the system 'secondary' tests. Pay particular attention to the following secondary components: Spark plugs, HT leads, coil secondary, distributor cap & rotor arm (if fitted)

3 Check the ignition timing

- If timing marks are fitted and specifications are available, compare to specifications at idle, 2000 rpm and 3000 rpm.
- If timing marks are not fitted or specifications are not available, make your own marks on the pulley and timing case. Start the engine and check that timing at idle is approximately 0 to 15° BTDC. If the timing is under ECM control, the marks will be unsteady as the ECM alters the timing to control the idle speed. As the throttle is opened, the timing should smoothly advance.

4 Check for a mixture that is too rich

5 Check for a mixture that is too lean

6 Check the condition of the air filter

- A clogged air filter could cause a mixture that is too rich for good performance.

7 Check for a blocked fuel filter

8 Check the AFS operation (if fitted)

- Refer to the 'AFS' tests in the system specific Chapter.
- Pay particular attention to the smoothness of the voltage output as the engine rpm increases.

9 Check the TPS or TS operation

- Some engines may utilise a TS or even a combined TPS/ TS. Refer to the 'TPS' or 'TS' tests in the system specific Chapter.
- TPS operation (if fitted). Pay particular attention to the smoothness of the voltage output as the throttle is opened.
- TS operation (if fitted). Pay particular attention to the TS adjustment at idle and full-throttle (where appropriate).
- Check that full throttle is achieved when the accelerator pedal (in the car) is fully open.

9 Lack of power (continued)

10 Check for cambelt (or timing chain) misalignment

11 CID signal out of phase

- If the system contains a CID (phasing) signal (often used in sequential injection engines), check that the two signals are in phase. An out-of-phase signal can result in poor performance.
- Check that the distributor has not been moved from its datum position (where appropriate). A tiny movement out of position can result in an out-of-phase signal.
- An misaligned cambelt or even a stretched belt can result in an out-of-phase signal.

12 Coolant temperature sensor (CTS)

- Check for a voltage signal according to temperature. Refer to the 'CTS' tests in the system specific Chapter.
- A high voltage or resistance, or an out-of-range sensor, could result in a rich mixture.

13 Check the injection signal, and record the pulse duration

- Refer to the 'injection' tests in the system specific Chapter. Check the CTS, AFS or MAP sensor and other fuel system sensors.
- A pulse duration that is incorrect could result in lack of power.

14 Check for injector mechanical faults

- Fouling of the injector pintle(s) may cause too little fuel or an inefficient spray pattern that could affect starting.
- One or more leaking injectors may cause an over-rich mixture that may affect engine performance.

15 Check the CO vol % at idle, 2000 and 3000 rpm

- Adjust the mixture (if possible), otherwise check for EMS or fuel injection system faults. *Note that attempting to adjust the CO when system faults are present will result in an incorrect setting.*
- A lean mixture setting at idle can result in a lean misfire that will result in excessive HC emissions.

16 Low fuel pressure

- A low fuel pressure could result in a lean mixture. Refer to the 'fuel pressure' tests in the system specific Chapter.
- Check the fuel system pressure.
- Check for a faulty pressure regulator.
- Check for a faulty fuel pump.

17 Check the MAP sensor operation (if fitted)

- Refer to the 'MAP sensor' tests in the system specific Chapter.
- Check for a voltage output signal.
- Check for a vacuum leak or displaced hose, manifold to MAP sensor. A vacuum leak could result in an over-rich mixture.

18 Check for an induction vacuum leak

- Manifold induction leak.
- Displaced or incorrectly-routed vacuum hose.
- Other possible sources of vacuum leaks are at the rocker or cam box seal, or at the dipstick seal.

19 Poor connections

- Check for poor or corroded connections in the electrical harness, and at the sensor and actuator multi-plug connectors.

20 Check the engine oil grade

- An incorrect grade of oil, or oil that has seriously deteriorated, can cause hydraulic tappets (where fitted) to jack open, thereby affecting the valve timing to restrict engine speed.

21 Check that the engine is not running in LOS

22 Check for a blocked catalytic converter

- Normally, the cat should last 50 000 miles. Premature failure is almost always due to adverse operating conditions.
- In some cars, a blocked cat may be revealed by the distinctive sound of a 'hissing,' noise.
- Grounding the catalyst against speed humps or curbs can lead to damage that may lead to an exhaust blockage.
- An engine misfire or rich mixture will raise the cat temperature so high that the substrate will melt. The cat will be destroyed in a very short time and this often leads to a blocked exhaust.
- When a faulty cat is diagnosed, the reason for failure must be ascertained if the replacement is not to meet the same fate.

23 Check the compression pressures

- Remove the spark plugs and check the compression pressures. Before commencing the compression test, disable the engine to prevent it from starting.

10 Hesitation or uneven running

1 Check the primary ignition system

- Refer to the running tests under the system 'primary' tests.
- Check the dwell angle at idle, 2000 and 3000 rpm.

2 Check the secondary ignition system

- Refer to the running tests under the system 'secondary' tests. Pay particular attention to the following secondary components: Spark plugs, HT leads, coil secondary, distributor cap & rotor arm (if fitted).

3 Check the ignition timing

- If timing marks are fitted and specifications are available, compare to specifications at idle, 2000 rpm and 3000 rpm.
- If timing marks are not fitted or specifications are not available, make your own marks on the pulley and timing case. Start the engine and check that timing at idle is approximately 0 to 15° BTDC. If the timing is under ECM control, the marks will be unsteady as the ECM alters the timing to control the idle speed. As the throttle is opened the timing should smoothly advance.

4 Check for a mixture that is too rich

5 Check for a mixture that is too lean

6 Check the condition of the air filter

- A clogged air filter could cause a mixture that is too rich for good performance.

7 Check for a blocked fuel filter

8 Check the CO vol % at idle, 2000 and 3000 rpm

- Adjust the mixture (if possible), otherwise check for EMS or fuel injection system faults. *Note that attempting to adjust the CO when system faults are present will result in an incorrect setting.*
- A lean mixture setting at idle can result in a lean misfire that will result in excessive HC emissions.

10 Hesitation or uneven running (continued)

9 Check the injection signal, and record the pulse duration

- Refer to the 'injection' tests in the system specific Chapter. Check the CTS, AFS or MAP sensor and other fuel system sensors.
- A pulse duration that is incorrect could result in lack of power.

10 Low fuel pressure

- A low fuel pressure could result in a lean mixture. Refer to the 'Fuel pressure' tests in the system specific Chapter.
- Check the fuel system pressure.
- Check for a faulty pressure regulator.
- Check for a faulty fuel pump.

11 Coolant temperature sensor (CTS)

- Check for a voltage signal according to temperature. Refer to the 'CTS' tests in the system specific Chapter.
- A high voltage or resistance, or an out-of-range sensor, could result in a rich mixture.

12 Check for injector mechanical faults

- Fouling of the injector pintle(s) may cause too little fuel or an inefficient spray pattern that could affect starting.
- One or more leaking injectors may cause an over-rich mixture that may affect engine performance.

13 Check the MAP sensor operation (if fitted)

- Refer to the 'MAP sensor' tests in the system specific Chapter.
- Check for a voltage output signal.
- Check for a vacuum leak or displaced hose, manifold to MAP sensor. A vacuum leak could result in an over-rich mixture.

14 Check the AFS operation (if fitted)

- Refer to the 'AFS' tests in the system specific Chapter.
- Pay particular attention to the smoothness of the voltage output as the engine rpm increases.

15 Check the TPS or TS operation

- Some engines may utilise a TS or even a combined TPS/ TS. Refer to the 'TPS' or 'TS' tests in the system specific Chapter.
- TPS operation (if fitted). Pay particular attention to the smoothness of the voltage output as the throttle is opened.
- TS operation (if fitted). Pay particular attention to the TS adjustment at idle and full-throttle (where appropriate).
- Check that full throttle is achieved when the accelerator pedal (in the cab) is fully open.

16 Check for an induction vacuum leak

- Manifold induction leak.
- Displaced or incorrectly routed vacuum hose.
- Other possible sources of vacuum leaks are at the rocker or cam box seal, or at the dipstick seal.

17 Check the evaporation system (if fitted)

- Refer to the 'CFSV' tests in the system specific Chapter.
- Check the carbon filter canister.
- Check the CFSV circuit. A fault could result in a vacuum leak into the inductive system.
- In most systems, the evaporation purge system should not operate whilst the engine is cold, during the warm-up period, nor whilst the engine is idling.
- If fuel vapours are introduced into the inlet system at the wrong moment, the engine will hesitate. Disconnect and plug the vapour hose to the throttle body. Road test the engine. If the engine runs satisfactorily, test the CFSV circuits.

18 Check for cambelt (or timing chain) misalignment

19 CID signal out of phase

- If the system contains a CID (phasing) signal (often used in sequential injection engines), check that the two signals are in phase. An out-of-phase signal can result in poor performance.
- Check that the distributor has not been moved from its datum position (where appropriate). A tiny movement out of position can result in an out-of-phase signal.
- An misaligned cambelt or even a stretched belt can result in an out-of-phase signal.

20 Poor connections

- Check for poor or corroded connections in the electrical harness, and at the sensor and actuator multi-plug connectors.

21 Carbon build-up

- A build-up of carbon on the back of the inlet valves can result in the injected fuel 'soaking' into the carbon.
- This causes a lean mixture and a 'flat spot' that may be worse when the engine is cold. Excessive deposits are usually caused by seriously-deteriorated engine oil and fumes being drawn through the breather system into the throttle body.

22 Lean-mixture hesitation

- The modern engine is designed to give good economy and low emissions. Mapped EMS settings tend to be on the lean side and, depending on engine tolerances, this means that some engines will run too lean with a hesitation or flat spot at certain engine speeds.
- A number of 'tweaks' have been employed over the years to combat flat spots in injection engines. These 'tweaks' can actually make the situation worse if they are used in an attempt to overcome a system fault. The 'tweaks' should only be used as a last resort on non-catalyst engines. The catalyst engine with closed-loop control will always attempt to control the AFR within the Lambda window.
- Soldering a resistor into the CTS supply wire. The resistor size is determined as follows. Attach a pot to the CTS circuit, and enrich the mixture by dialling in a slightly higher resistance than usual at normal operating temperature. If the engine responds more positively during a road test, a resistor value of the difference between the higher value and the normal resistance should be soldered into the supply wire to the CTS.
- Fitting injectors with slightly better flow rates or enlarged nozzles.
- Drilling a tiny hole in the MAP sensor vacuum hose, the slightly lower vacuum signal will cause the ECM to enrich the mixture.
- Varying the vane AFS spring tension so that less force is required to move the AFS to any particular open position. Less air will flow and the AFR is enriched.
- Catalyst engines: Placing a small air bleed in the exhaust system. Weld a boss to the exhaust pipe above the OS. Attach a small carburettor jet to the boss, so that a small air leak bleeds air into the exhaust pipe. The OS will pass a slightly lean signal to the ECM, which will increase the injection duration to enrich the mixture. The jet will clog with carbon during engine operation, and will need to be regularly checked and cleaned.

Caution: This procedure will almost certainly result in a statutory emission test failure.

11 Engine stalling or cutting out at idle speed (also poor running on warm-up)

Note: *One or more of the following faults are likely to be present when the engine is prone to stalling. Only faults likely to affect the idle condition have been listed. The engine may also display other symptoms, in which case other fault charts may need to be consulted.*

1 Check the primary ignition system

- Refer to the running tests under the system 'primary' tests.
- Check the dwell angle at idle, 2000 and 3000 rpm.

2 Check the secondary ignition system

- Refer to the running tests under the system 'secondary' tests. Pay particular attention to the following secondary components: Spark plugs, HT leads, coil secondary, distributor cap & rotor arm (if fitted).

3 Check the ignition timing

- If timing marks are fitted and specifications are available, compare to specs at idle, 2000 rpm and 3000 rpm.
- If timing marks are not fitted or specifications are not available, make your own marks on the pulley and timing case. Start the engine, and check that timing at idle is around 0 to 15° BTDC. If the timing is under ECM control, the marks will be unsteady as the ECM alters the timing to control the idle speed. As the throttle is opened the timing should smoothly advance.

4 Check for a mixture that is too rich

5 Check for a mixture that is too lean

6 Check the condition of the air filter

- A clogged air filter could cause a mixture that is too rich for good performance.

7 Low base idle speed

- Refer to the 'adjustments' in the system specific Chapter.
- Adjust the base idle speed (if possible).

8 Check the CO vol % at idle

- Adjust the mixture (if possible), otherwise check for EMS or fuel injection system faults. *Note that attempting to adjust the CO when system faults are present will result in an incorrect setting.*
- A lean mixture setting at idle can result in a lean misfire that will result in excessive HC emissions.

9 Check the engine is not in LOS

- If in LOS, the idle speed may be too low during hot engine operation, and too high during cold engine operation.

10 Coolant temperature sensor (CTS)

- Check for a voltage signal according to temperature. Refer to the 'CTS' tests in the system specific Chapter.
- A high voltage or resistance, or an out-of-range sensor, could result in a rich mixture

11 Check for injector mechanical faults

- Fouling of the injector pintle(s) may cause too little fuel or an inefficient spray pattern that could affect starting.
- One or more leaking injectors may cause an over rich mixture that may affect engine performance.

12 Check for a vacuum leak at the injector seals

13 Check the throttle body for a carbon build-up

- This is usually as a result of fumes from the breathing system. The carbon can cause a sticking or jacked-open throttle, which can cause idle, cruising and other running problems.

14 Check the throttle body for wear, particularly around the spindle area

15 Check the TPS or TS operation

- Some engines may utilise a TS or even a combined TPS/TS. Refer to the 'TPS' or 'TS' tests in the system specific Chapter.
- TPS operation (if fitted). Pay particular attention to the smoothness of the voltage output as the throttle is opened.
- TS operation (if fitted). Pay particular attention to the TS adjustment at idle and full-throttle (where appropriate).
- Check that full-throttle is achieved when the accelerator pedal (in the cab) is fully open.

16 Check for an induction vacuum leak

- Manifold induction leak.
- Displaced or incorrectly-routed vacuum hose.
- Other possible sources of vacuum leaks are at the rocker or cam box seal, or at the dipstick seal.

17 Check the evaporation system (if fitted)

- Refer to the 'CFSV' tests in the system specific Chapter.
- Check the carbon filter canister.
- Check the CFSV circuit. A fault could result in a vacuum leak or permanent leakage of fuel vapours into the inductive system.
- In most systems, the evaporation purge system should not operate whilst the engine is cold, during the warm-up period, nor whilst the engine is idling.
- If fuel vapours are introduced into the inlet system at the wrong moment, the engine will hesitate. Disconnect and plug the vapour hose to the throttle body. Road test the engine. If the engine runs satisfactorily, test the CFSV circuits.

18 Check the EGR system (if fitted)

- Refer to the 'EGR' tests in the system specific Chapter.
- A fault could result in a vacuum leak into the inductive system.
- In most systems, the EGR system should not operate whilst the engine is cold, during the warm-up period, nor whilst the engine is idling.

19 Check the ISCV/stepper motor or AAV as appropriate (idle control system)

- Refer to the relevant 'component' tests in the system specific Chapter.

20 If the ECM permanent voltage supply lost or disrupted

- In this event, the adaptive function of the ECM will lose its idle values, and stalling will often occur.
- Check the in-line fuse (if fitted) or supply from the battery (+).
- Systems with non-volatile memory will retain idle values, even after battery disconnection.

21 Check the TBH (where fitted) operation

- Refer to the 'TBH' tests in the system specific Chapter.
- If the TBH is faulty, stalling may occur in low temperatures, or during damp humid conditions, due to the icing phenomenon.
- If the throttle body is coolant-heated, check that the throttle body is heated sufficiently after the engine has reached normal operating temperature. If throttle body heating is insufficient, stalling may occur in low temperatures, or during damp humid conditions, due to the icing phenomenon.

22 Check the valve clearances

- Tight valve clearances, in particular, may contribute to stalling.

11 Engine stalling or cutting out at idle speed (also poor running on warm-up) - continued

23 Check the oxygen sensor (OS) operation

- A defective OS may cause poor idle and 'hunting'. Disconnect the OS multi-plug. If the idle quality improves, the OS is suspect. Refer to the 'oxygen sensor' tests in the system specific Chapter.

24 Stalling after engine deceleration

- Check the throttle valve position and the TS or TPS adjustment. The ECM must receive a throttle-closed signal to activate the engine deceleration fuel injection cut-off routine.

12 Poor running during the warm-up period

The faults that will affect the engine during the warm-up period are generally those that will also affect the engine idle quality. Refer to Section 11. In addition, most running faults are accentuated during periods of cold running.

13 Engine knock

- Spark plugs worn or wrong heat range. Refer to spark plug test routines under the 'secondary ignition' tests in Chapter 4.
- Defective knock sensor. Refer to the 'knock sensor' tests in the system specific Chapter.
- Build-up of carbon deposits in cylinders.
- Cooling fault.
- Over-advanced ignition timing (generally in distributors with mechanical advance). Refer to 'adjustments' in the system specific Chapter.
- Fuel of low octane.

14 Engine backfires through the inlet valve

1 Check the primary ignition system

- Refer to the running tests under the system 'Primary' tests.
- Check the dwell angle at idle, 2000 and 3000 rpm.

2 Check the secondary ignition system

- Refer to the running tests under the system 'secondary' tests. Pay particular attention to the following secondary components: Spark plugs, HT leads, coil secondary, distributor cap & rotor arm (if fitted).

3 Check the ignition timing

- If timing marks are fitted and specifications are available, compare to specs at idle, 2000 rpm and 3000 rpm.
- If timing marks are not fitted or specifications are not available, make your own marks on the pulley and timing case. Start the engine, and check that timing at idle is approximately 0 to 15° BTDC. If the timing is under ECM control, the marks will be unsteady, as the ECM alters the timing to control the idle speed. As the throttle is opened, the timing should smoothly advance.

4 Check for a mixture that is too lean

5 Check for an induction vacuum leak

- Manifold induction leak.
- Displaced or incorrectly routed vacuum hose.
- Other possible sources of vacuum leaks are at the rocker or cam box seal, or at the dipstick seal.

6 Carbon build-up

- A build-up of carbon on the back of the inlet valves can result in the injected fuel 'soaking' into the carbon.
- This causes a lean mixture, and could cause a backfire that may be worse when the engine is cold. Excessive deposits are usually caused by seriously-deteriorated engine oil and fumes being drawn through the breather system into the throttle body.

7 Check for a leaking or burnt inlet valve

- Remove the spark plugs and check the engine compression pressures.
- Before commencing the test, disable the engine to prevent it from starting.

15 Engine backfires through the exhaust valve

1 Coolant temperature sensor (CTS)

- Check for a voltage signal according to temperature. Refer to the 'CTS' tests in the system specific Chapter.
- The ECM may be operating under LOS, or the CTS resistance may be too low when the engine is hot.

2 Check for injector mechanical faults

- Fouling of the injector pintle(s) may cause too little fuel or an inefficient spray pattern that could affect starting.
- One or more leaking injectors may cause an over-rich mixture that may affect engine performance.

3 Check for a leaking or burnt exhaust valve

- Remove the spark plugs and check the engine compression pressures.
- Before commencing the test, disable the engine to prevent it from starting

16 Intermittent faults

1 Intermittent faults are by far the most difficult to deal with, and we can offer only a sketchy guide at best on how to deal with this kind of problem.
2 Carefully follow the procedures described in Section 3. Although you may not necessarily find the problem in those system specific routines, you will have a pretty good idea of what it is not.
3 Most intermittent faults are caused by loose, corroded or poor wiring or connectors.
4 Check for wiring that is tight, as it may pull at the connector as the engine vibrates. The connection may be momentarily broken and then remade.
5 Check for wiring with poor or broken insulation that is shorted, or chafed wires that may occasionally touch to earth.
6 Drive the vehicle and attempt to reproduce the fault under the conditions in which it usually occurs.
7 If the tachometer needle drops to zero during the incident, the fault may be in the primary ignition.
8 If the instrument display switches off, the fault may be in the voltage supply or ignition switch.
9 Connect a dwell meter or voltmeter to suspect circuits, and run the engine or drive the system. Some meters display maximum and minimum values, and this could help to pinpoint a poor supply or earth.
10 Some kinds of test equipment have a 'flight recorder' facility that could attach to either the serial port or interfaces between the ECM and its multi-plug. The flight recorder records the data from virtually all of the sensors, actuators and control functions over a period of time. The engine may then be driven until the fault occurs. Pressing a button will cause approximately 30 seconds of data before and after the incident to be saved to the test equipment memory for later evaluation in the workshop.
11 Run the engine, wiggle wiring connections and gently tap relays and components. If the engine cuts out, the fault may have been revealed.
12 Use a FCR to interrogate the ECM for fault codes. If a code is present, clear the code and drive the vehicle to see if the code returns. One or two occurrences of a fault in a particular circuit may be enough to set a code.
13 If you cannot find an electrical fault, consider the possibility of poor lubrication or the wrong grade of oil. These problems can cause jacking of hydraulic tappets and loss of power (where applicable).
14 Check the valve clearances. Tight clearances can cause loss of power as the clearance closes when the engine becomes hot.

Chapter 6
Bosch Motronic MPi (35, 55 & 88-pin types)

Contents

Specifications

Vehicle	Year	Idle speed	CO%
BMW, Motronic First Generation			
325i non-cat	1985 to 1986	760 ± 40	0.7 ± 0.5
325e cat	1985 to 1991	700 ± 50	0.5 max
525e non-cat	1983 to 1985	700 ± 50	1.0 ± 0.5
525e cat	1986 to 1987	720 ± 40	0.5 max
525e non-cat	1986 to 1987	720 ± 40	1.0 ± 0.5
535i/M535i non-cat	1982 to 1986	800 ± 50	1.0 ± 0.5
M5 DOHC non-cat	1985 to 1987	850 ± 50	1.5 max
BMW, Motronic 1.3			
316/318/518i non cat	1988 to 1991	800 ± 40	0.7 ± 0.5
316/318/518i cat	1988 to 1991	800 ± 40	0.5 max
320/325i non cat	1986 to 1991	760 ± 40	0.7 ± 0.5
320/325i cat	1986 to 1991	760 ± 40	0.5 max
520/525i non cat	1988 to 1991	760 ± 40	0.7 ± 0.5
520/525i cat	1988 to 1991	760 ± 40	0.5 max
530/535i non cat	1988 to 1991	800 ± 50	0.7 ± 0.5
530/535i cat	1988 to 1991	800 ± 50	0.5 max
BMW, Motronic 1.7			
316i cat	1991 to 1993	800 ± 40	0.7 ± 0.5
316i & Compact	1993 to 1996	800 ± 40	0.7 ± 0.5
318is 16V cat	1990 to 1991	850 ± 40	0.7 ± 0.5
318i cat	1991 to 1993	800 ± 40	0.7 ± 0.5
318is & Compact	1992 to 1996	850 ± 40	0.7 ± 0.5
318i	1993 to 1996	800 ± 40	0.7 ± 0.5
518i	1993 to 1996	800 ± 40	0.7 ± 0.5
750i & L & cat	1987 to 1994	700 ± 50	0.7 ± 0.5
850i	1991 to 1994	700 ± 50	0.7 ± 0.5

Vehicle	Year	Idle speed	CO%
BMW, Motronic 3.1			
320i 24V cat	1991 to 1993	700 ± 40	0.7 ± 0.5
320i 24V	1993 to 1996	700 ± 40	0.7 ± 0.5
325i 24V cat	1991 to 1993	700 ± 40	0.7 ± 0.5
325i 24V	1993 to 1996	700 ± 40	0.7 ± 0.5
520i & Touring 24V	1990 to 1993	800 ± 40	0.7 ± 0.5
520i & Touring 24V	1993 to 1996	700 ± 40	0.7 ± 0.5
525i & Touring 24V	1990 to 1993	800 ± 40	0.7 ± 0.5
525i & Touring 24V	1993 to 1996	700 ± 40	0.7 ± 0.5
BMW, Motronic 3.3			
530i & Touring V8	1993 to 1996	600 ± 50	0.7 ± 0.5
540i V8	1993 to 1996	600 ± 50	0.7 ± 0.5
M5	1986 to 1988	850 ± 50	0.3 to 1.5
730i V8 cat	1992 to 1994	600 ± 50	0.7 ± 0.5
730i	1994 to 1996	600 ± 50	0.7 ± 0.5
740i iL V8	1992 to 1994	600 ± 50	0.7 ± 0.5
740i	1994 to 1996	600 ± 50	0.7 ± 0.5
840 Ci	1993 to 1996	600 ± 50	0.7 ± 0.5
Citroën/Peugeot, Motronic 1.3			
Citroën BX19, ZX19 (8V), BX19 (16V) (MT)	-	850 to 950	0.8 to 2.0 (non-cat) / 0.5 (cat)
Citroën BX19, ZX19 (8V), BX19 (16V) (AT)	-	800 to 850	0.8 to 2.0 (non-cat) / 0.5 (cat)
Peugeot 205/309/405 1.9 (8V) (MT)	-	850 to 950	0.8 to 2.0 (non-cat) / 0.5 (cat)
Peugeot 205/309/405 1.9 (8V) (AT)	-	800 to 850	0.8 to 2.0 (non-cat) / 0.5 (cat)
Peugeot 309/405 (16V) (MT)	-	850 to 950	0.8 to 2.0 (non-cat) / 0.5 (cat)
Citroën/Peugeot, Motronic 3.1			
AX 1.4i K6B (TU3J2/K)	1990 to 1991	880	1.0 ± 0.5
AX 1.4i cat KFZ (TU3J2/L.Z)	1991 to 1996	900 ± 50	0.5 max
BX 1.9i XU9J2 (D6D)	1990 to 1992	850 ± 50	1.5 ± 0.5
ZX 1.9i XU9JA/K (D6E)	1991 to 1992	850 ± 50	1.5 ± 0.5
XM 2.0i XU10J2Z (RFZ) cat	1990 to 1992	875 ± 25	0.5 max
106 1.4i TU3FJ2 (K6B)	1991 to 1992	920 ± 50	1.0 ± 0.5
106 1.4i cat TU3FJ2 (KFZ)	1991 to 1996	920 ± 50	
405 1.9i (XU9J2) D6D	1990 to 1992	850 to 900	1.5 ± 0.5
605 2.0i (XU10J2Z) RFZ cat	1990 to 1995	800 ± 20	0.5 max
Citroën/Peugeot, Motronic 3.2			
Xantia 2.0i 16V cat RFY (XU10J4D/Z)	1993 to 1995	880 ± 50	0.4 max
ZX 2.0i 16V cat RFY/RFT (XU10J4D/Z)	1993 to 1995	880 ± 50	0.4 max
306 2.0i16V cat XU10J4/Z (RFY)	1994 to 1996	850 ± 50	0.5 max
405 2.0i 16V cat XU10J4/Z (RFY)	1992 to 1995	880 ± 50	0.5 max
Citroën/Peugeot, Motronic 4.1			
Citroën BX19	-	850	0.8 to 1.5
Peugeot 405	-	830 to 930	1.5 to 2.0
Citroën/Peugeot, Motronic 5.1			
Xantia LX/SX & Break 1.8i 8V cat	1993 to 1996	850 ± 50	0.4 max
Xantia 2.0i 16V & Break XU10J4RL/Z/L3 (RFV)	1995 to 1996	800 ± 50	0.4 max
XM 2.0i 16V cat	1994 to 1996	800 ± 50	0.4 max
ZX 1.8i Advantage, Aura, Furio cat	1993 to 1996	850 ± 50	0.4 max
306 1.6i XL/XR/XS/XT, 1.8i cat XU7JP/Z (LFZ)	1993 to 1996	850 ± 50	0.4 max
405 2.0 XU7JPL/Z (LFZ)	1992 to 1996	850 ± 50	0.4 max
605 SLi 2.0i 16V			
Vauxhall/Opel, Motronic 1.5			
C16SEI, MT	-	820 to 980	1.0
20SEH MT 4x4	-	890 to 990	1.0
C20NE MT 4x4	-	890 to 990	1.0
C24NE, MT	-	820 to 880	1.0
C24NE, AT	-	720 to 780	1.0
C26NE	-	670 to 830	1.0
C30NE	-	670 to 830	1.0
C30SE, SEJ	-	570 to 730	1.0
All other models not listed above	-	720 to 780	1.0

Vehicle	Year	Idle speed	CO%
Vauxhall/Opel, Motronic 2.5			
All non-cat models	-	860 to 1020	0.7 to 1.2 max
All cat models	-	860 to 1020	0.4 max
Vauxhall/Opel, Motronic 2.7			
Cavalier Turbo cat C20LET	1993 to 1995	860 to 1020	0.3 max
Vectra-A Turbo cat C20LET	1993 to 1995	860 to 1020	0.3 max
Calibra Turbo 4x4 C20LET	1992 to 1996	860 to 1020	0.5 max
Vauxhall/Opel, Motronic 2.8			
Cavalier 2.5i 24V C25XE	1993 to 1995	620 to 780	0.3 max
Vectra-A 2.5i 24V C25XE	1993 to 1995	620 to 780	0.3 max
Calibra 2.0 16V & 4x4 C20XE	1993 on	860 to 1020	0.3 max
Calibra 2.5i 24V C25XE	1993 to 1996	620 to 780	0.5 max
Calibra 2.5i 24V X25XE	1997	620 to 780	0.5 max
Vauxhall/Opel, Motronic 2.8.1			
Omega-B 2.5i X25XE	1994 to 1997	570 to 730	0.5 max
Omega-B 3.0i X30XE	1994 to 1997	570 to 730	0.5 max
Vauxhall/Opel, Motronic 2.8.3			
Vectra-B 2.5i V6 24V X25XE	1995 to 1997	570 to 730	0.3 max
Vauxhall/Opel, Motronic 4.1			
All vehicles	-	720 to 780	1.0
Volvo, Motronic			
740 and 760 Turbo	1985 to 1989	800 to 850	0.5 to 2.0

Overview of system operation

1 Introduction

Please read this overview of Motronic operation in conjunction with Chapter 2, which describes some of the functions in more detail.

The name 'Motronic' describes a family of EMS's that first saw light of day in the early 1980's. Motronic was one of the very first true EMS's, and evolved from the well-tried 'L' and 'LE' Jetronic fuel injection systems which first emerged in the mid 1970's. Motronic has evolved considerably over the years, and is now fitted to a wide range of European vehicles.

When fitted to BMW vehicles, Motronic is sometimes labelled 'DME' (Digital Motor Electronics). Interestingly, the term DME is generically applied to most versions of the Motronic family fitted to BMW cars, and does not label any particular Motronic system. Currently there exists a variety of different Motronic versions; First Generation, 1.5, 1.7, 1.8, 2.5, 2.7, 2.8, 2.8.1, 2.8.3, 3.1, MP3.1, 3.2, 4.1, 5.1, 5.1.1, etc **(see illustration 6.1)**.

We can basically divide Motronic descriptions into Motronic 'First Generation' and Motronic MPi. Differences will be detailed under these headings where descriptions differ.

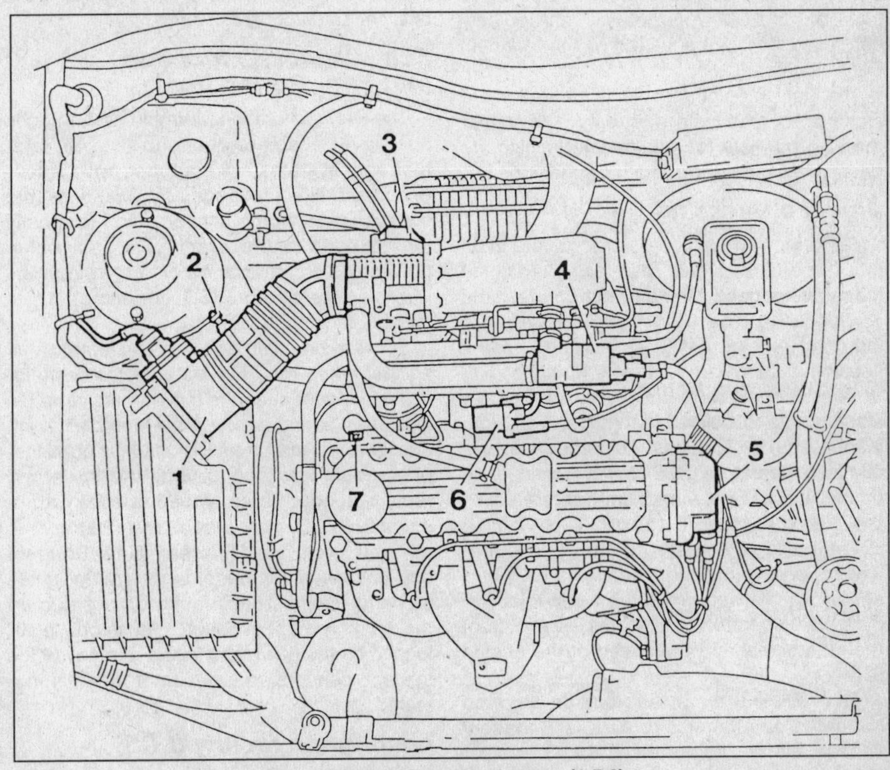

6.1 Typical Motronic system (1.5.2)

1 AFS (air mass type) *2 ATS* *3 TPS* *4 ISCV* *5 Distributor* *6 CFSV* *7 CTS*

6

Motronic 'First Generation'

A 35-pin connector and multi-plug connects the First Generation Motronic ECM to the battery, sensors and actuators. First Generation systems were mainly fitted from 1985 to 1987, and are characterised by separate RPM and TDC sensors. All later models utilise a single CAS.

Motronic MPi

A 35-pin, 55-pin or 88-pin connector and multi-plug connects the Motronic ECM to the battery, sensors and actuators. Motronic 4.1 utilises a 35-pin multi-plug. Motronic 1.7 and MP3.1 utilises a 88-pin multi-plug and the ignition is DIS in operation. All the others, including 3.1, utilise a 55-pin multi-plug.

2 Control functions

General

Motronic normally controls primary ignition, fuelling and idle speed in the vehicles to which it is fitted. An automatic ISCV is directly actuated by the Motronic ECM to maintain a stable idle speed under all conditions of idle load. This is true of all late versions.

However, in some early First Generation systems, the ISCV is actuated by a separate Idle control ECM. Alternatively, an coolant-controlled AAV, not actuated by the Motronic ECM, is utilised.

The ignition point and injection duration are jointly processed by the Motronic ECM so that the best moment for ignition and fuelling are determined for every operating condition.

Signal processing

Basic ignition timing is stored by the ECM in a three-dimensional map, and the engine load and speed signals determines the ignition timing. The main engine load sensor is either an AFS or a MAP sensor, and engine speed is determined from the CAS signal.

Correction factors are then applied for starting, idle, deceleration, and part- and full-load operation. The main correction factor is engine temperature (CTS). Minor correction to timing and AFR are made with reference to the ATS and TPS or TS signals.

The basic AFR is also stored in a three-dimensional map, and the engine load and speed signals determine the basic injection pulse value. Motronic calculates the AFR from the load signal and the speed of the engine (CAS).

The AFR and the pulse duration are then corrected on reference to ATS, CTS, battery voltage and position of the TPS or TS. Other controlling factors are determined by operating conditions such as cold start and warm-up, idle condition, acceleration and deceleration.

Motronic accesses a different map for idle running conditions, and this map is implemented whenever the engine speed is at idle. Idle speed during warm-up and normal hot running conditions is maintained by the idle control (not First Generation). Motronic also makes small adjustments to the idle speed by advancing or retarding the timing, and this results in an ignition timing value that is forever changing during engine idle.

Basic ECM operation (typical)

A permanent voltage supply is made from the vehicle battery to the ECM (not First Generation models). This allows the self-diagnostic function to retain data of an intermittent nature. Once the ignition is switched on, a voltage supply to the ignition coil and to the ECM is made from the ignition switch. This causes the ECM to earth the main fuel injection relay. A relay-switched voltage supply is thus made to the ECM from the main fuel injection relay.

The majority of sensors (other than those that generate a voltage such the CAS, KS and OS), are now provided with a 5.0-volt reference supply from a relevant pin on the ECM. When the engine is cranked or run, a speed signal from the CAS causes the ECM to earth a pin so that the fuel pump will run. Ignition and injection functions are also activated. All actuators (injectors, ISCV etc), are supplied with nbv from the main relay, and the ECM completes the circuit by pulsing the relevant actuator wire to earth.

Self-diagnostic function (not First Generation)

The First Generation Motronic system does not have a self-test capability. All later Motronic systems are equipped with a self-test capability that regularly examines the signals from engine sensors, and internally logs a code in the event of a fault being present. This code can be extracted from the Motronic serial port (SD connector) by a suitable fault code reader.

Some systems utilise a warning lamp circuit so that when the ECM detects that a major fault is present, it earths the warning lamp pin and the warning lamp on the dash will light. The lamp will stay lit until the fault is no longer present. If the fault clears, the code will remain logged until wiped clean with a suitable FCR, or when the battery is disconnected. In Citroën and Peugeot applications, a number of faults are designate as minor faults. These faults do not turn on the warning lamp, although a fault code is still logged by the ECM. The failure of many of the system sensors are designated as minor faults.

Limp-home facility (LOS)

Motronic has a limp-home facility LOS). In the event of a serious fault in one or more of the sensors, the EMS will substitute a fixed default value in place of the defective sensor.

This means that the engine may actually run quite well with failure of one or more minor sensors. However, since the substituted values are those of a hot engine, cold starting and running during the warm-up period may be less than satisfactory. Also, failure of a major sensor, ie the AFS, will tend to make driving conditions less easy.

Adaptive systems

Motronic is adaptive to changing engine operating characteristics, and constantly monitors the data from the various sensors (ie AFS or MAP, ATS, CTS. TPS etc). As the engine or its components wear, the ECM reacts to new circumstances by adopting the changed values as a correction to the basic map.

Reference voltage

Voltage supply from the ECM to many of the engine sensors is at a 5.0 volt reference level. This ensures a stable working voltage, unaffected by variations in system voltage.

The earth return connection for most engine sensors is made through an ECM pin that is not directly connected to earth. The ECM internally connects that pin to earth via one of the ECM pins that are directly connected to earth.

Signal shielding

To reduce RFI, a number of sensors (ie CAS, HES, KS, amplifier and OS) use a shielded cable. The shielded cable is connected to the main ECM earth wire at terminal 19 to reduce interference to a minimum.

Vehicle speed sensor (VSS)

The VSS is used to advise the ECM of vehicle speed. It usually operates upon the Hall-effect principle, and is mounted directly upon the gearbox or on the back of the speedometer drive.

A voltage is applied to the VSS from the system relay or ignition switch. As the speedometer cable turns, the Hall switch is alternately turned on and off to return a square wave signal to the ECM. The frequency of the signal is geared to so many pulses per revolution of the speedometer cable, and is in direct proportion to the vehicle speed.

3 Primary trigger

CAS (not First Generation)

The primary signal to initiate both ignition and fuelling emanates from a CAS mounted in proximity to the flywheel. The CAS consists of an inductive magnet that radiates a magnetic field. A number of steel teeth are set into the periphery of the flywheel at equidistant

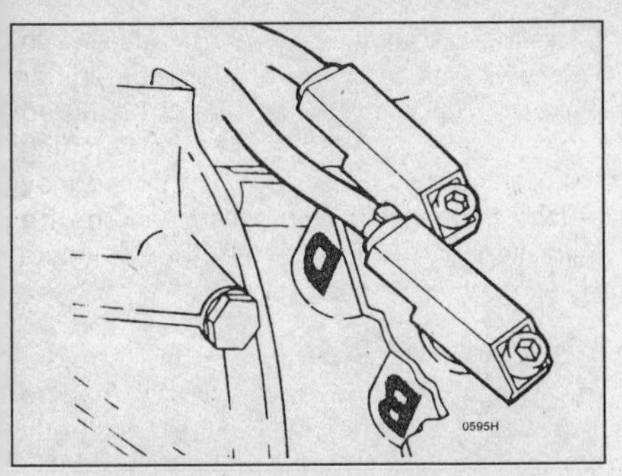

6.2 TDC (B) and RPM (D) sensors (First Generation Motronic). Reversing the multi-plug connections to these sensors will prevent the engine from starting

intervals. As the flywheel spins, and the teeth are rotated in the magnetic field, an AC voltage signal is delivered to the ECM to indicate speed of rotation. In addition, two of the teeth are omitted as a reference mark to TDC. As the flywheel spins, the two missing teeth cause a variance of the signal which is returned to the ECM as reference to the TDC position.

The peak-to-peak voltage of the speed signal can vary from 5 volts at idle to over 100 volts at 6000 rpm. In the ECM, an analogue to digital converter (ADC) transforms the AC pulse into a digital signal.

TDC and RPM sensors (First Generation only)

The primary signal to initiate both ignition and fuelling emanates from two sensors mounted in proximity to the flywheel. The sensors are used to indicate the position of TDC and the engine RPM **(see illustration 6.2)**.

The TDC sensor consists of an inductive magnet that radiates a magnetic field. A reference mark to TDC (raised pin) is mounted upon the flywheel to indicate crankshaft position as the flywheel spins.

The RPM sensor also consists of an inductive magnet that radiates a magnetic field. A number of steel pins are set into the periphery of the flywheel at regular intervals. As the flywheel spins, and the pins are rotated in the magnetic field, an AC voltage signal is delivered to the ECM to indicate speed of rotation.

The peak-to-peak voltage of the signals are fairly similar and can vary from 5 volts at idle to over 100 volts at 6000 rpm. In the ECM, an analogue to digital converter (ADC) transforms the AC pulse into a digital signal.

4 Primary and secondary ignition

General

Data on load (AFS or MAP), engine speed (CAS), engine temperature (CTS) and throttle position (TPS or TS) are collected by the ECM,

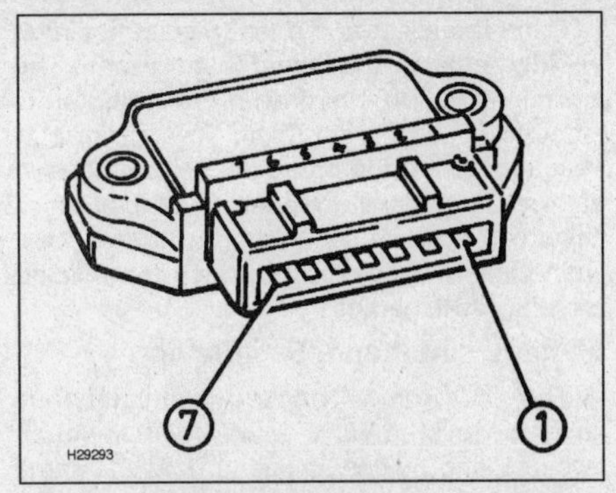

6.3 External amplifier used in some Motronic systems
Pin numbers shown

which then refers to a three-dimensional digital map stored within its microprocessor. This map contains an advance angle for each operating condition, and thus the best ignition advance angle for a particular operating condition can be determined.

Amplifier

The Motronic amplifier contains the circuitry for switching the coil negative terminal at the correct moment to instigate ignition. The signal received by the amplifier from the trigger is of an insufficient level to complete the necessary coil switching. The signal is thus amplified to a level capable of switching the coil negative terminal.

Mainly, the amplifier is contained within the ECM, although some models utilise a separate amplifier mounted on a heat sink plate adjacent to the coil. The ECM thus calculates the correct ignition dwell time and timing advance from data received from its sensors, and sends a signal to the amplifier which then switches the coil negative terminal **(see illustration 6.3)**.

Dwell operation in Motronic is based upon the principle of the 'constant-energy current-limiting' system. This means that the dwell period remains constant at around 4.0 to 5.0 ms, at virtually all engine running speeds. However, the dwell duty cycle, when measured in percent or degrees, will vary as the engine speed varies.

Ignition coil

The ignition coil utilises low primary resistance in order to increase primary current and primary energy. The amplifier limits the primary current to around 8 amps, and this permits a reserve of energy to maintain the required spark burn time (duration) **(see illustration 6.4)**.

Ignition system

Either a distributor or an DIS is employed for ignition purposes. Refer to Chapter 2 for more details on the DIS.

Distributor

Where fitted, the distributor only contains secondary HT components (distributor cap and rotor), and serves to distribute the HT current from the coil secondary terminal to each spark plug in firing order. Ignition timing is not adjustable.

Knock sensor (some models only)

Many Motronic-equipped vehicles employ a knock sensor. The knock sensor is mounted on the engine block, and consists of a piezoceramic measuring element that responds to engine noise oscillations. This signal is converted to a voltage signal by the knock sensor, and returned to the ECM for evaluation and action.

The following description fits the knock control processor (KCP) found on GM 16-valve engines. Knock control in other engines will function in a similar fashion. The KCP analyses the noise from each individual cylinder, and sets a reference noise level for that cylinder based upon the average of the last 16 phases. If the noise level exceeds the reference level by a certain amount, knock control identifies the presence of engine knock.

Initially, timing will occur at its optimal ignition point. Once knock is identified, knock control retards the ignition timing for that cylinder or cylinders by a set number of degrees. Approximately 2 seconds after knocking ceases (20 to 120 knock-free combustion cycles), the timing is advanced in 0.75° increments until the reference timing value is achieved or knock occurs once more. This procedure continually occurs so that all cylinders will consistently run at their optimum timing.

If a fault exists in the knock control processor, knock control sensor or wiring, an appropriate code will be logged in the self-diagnostic unit, and the ignition timing retarded by 10.5° by the LOS program.

Octane coding

It is not possible to adjust the ignition timing on Motronic systems. However, in some

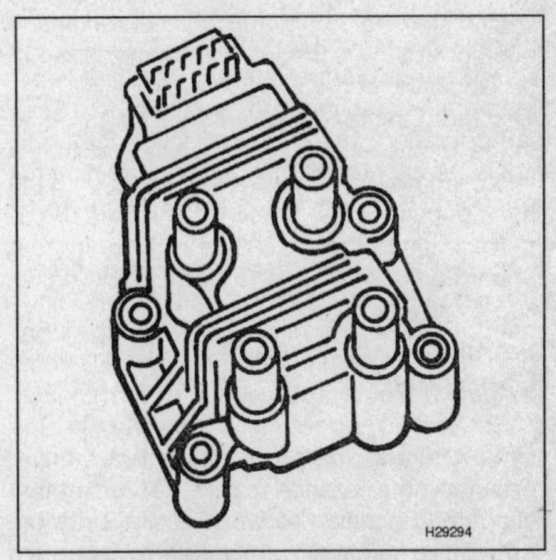

6.4 Ignition coil used in Citroën and Peugeot DIS systems (eg Motronic 5.1 and 3.1)

Vauxhall & Opel applications, an octane coding plug is provided to enable the ECM to adopt different characteristics to suit various operating conditions.

5 Fuel injection (MPi)

General

The Motronic ECM contains a fuel map with an injector opening time for basic conditions of speed and load. Information is then gathered from engine sensors such as the AFS or MAP sensor, CAS, CTS, and TPS or TS. As a result of this information, the ECM will look up the correct injector pulse duration right across the engine rpm, load and temperature range.

Fuel injectors

The fuel injector is a magnetically-operated solenoid valve that is actuated by the ECM. Voltage to the injectors is applied from the main relay, and the earth path is completed by the ECM for a period of time (called pulse duration) of between 1.5 and 10 milliseconds. The pulse duration is very much dependent upon engine temperature, load, speed and operating conditions. When the magnetic solenoid closes, a back-EMF voltage of up to 60 volts is initiated.

Depending on model, there are several different methods of firing the injectors. The methods are, simultaneous injection, banked simultaneous injection, and sequential injection.

Simultaneous injection

The Motronic simultaneous injection system is a Multi-point injection system, and pulses all injectors at the same time - ie simultaneously and twice per engine cycle. Half of the required fuel per engine cycle is injected at each engine revolution. During engine start from cold, the pulse duration and number of pulses (frequency) are increased to provide a richer air/fuel mixture.

The fuel injectors are mounted in the inlet stubs to the engine inlet valves, so that a finely-atomised fuel spray is directed onto the back of each valve. Since the injectors are all pulsed simultaneously, fuel will briefly rest upon the back of a valve before being drawn into a cylinder.

Simultaneous injection (First Generation)

The basic operation is similar to the simultaneous injection described above. However, the injector is switched using two circuits. Operation depends on the principle that more current is required to open an injector than to keep it open. This kind of system is often termed 'current-controlled injection'.

Once the injector is open, a second circuit rapidly pulses the injector to earth. The switching is so rapid that the injector is effectively held open, and less current is required during the operation. Advantages of this arrangement include a reduction in injector operating temperature, and immediate injector closure once the holding circuit is switched off.

Banked simultaneous injection

The Motronic banked simultaneous injection system is a Multi-point injection system, and pulses all injectors at the same time - ie simultaneously and once per engine revolution. This means that half of the fuel for the next power stroke is injected at each opening of the injector and fuel lies briefly on the back of an inlet valve until that valve opens. The injector thus opens twice for every engine cycle. During engine start from cold, the pulse duration is increased to provide a richer air/fuel mixture. During engine cranking (hot or cold), the number of pulses (frequency) is increased from once per revolution to twice per revolution. After 20 seconds of cranking, the pulse reverts to one pulse per revolution.

Although all four injectors are pulsed simultaneously, the injectors are arranged in two banks, with injectors 1 and 2 comprising one bank, and injectors 3 and 4 making up the other bank. Each bank is connected to the ECM via a separate ECM pin).

Sequential injection

The Motronic sequential injection system is a Multi-point system that pulses the injectors sequentially - ie in firing order and once per engine cycle. Each injector is connected to the ECM via a separate ECM pin). During engine start from cold, the pulse duration and number of pulses (frequency) are increased to provide a richer air/fuel mixture.

Cylinder identification (sequential injection only)

In earlier Motronic systems, the ECM does not recognise No 1 cylinder, or indeed even the firing order. This is because it is actually unnecessary. When the crankshaft or distributor provides a timing signal, the correct cylinder is identified by the mechanical position of the crankshaft, camshaft, valves and ignition rotor. In systems where the injectors fire simultaneously, then the fuel will sit upon the back of an inlet valve until the valve opens.

Since fuel injection occurs on an individual cylinder basis in sequential systems, the ECM must be informed which stroke a cylinder is actually on. On GM 16-valve engines, this is achieved by a cylinder identification sensor attached to the distributor, which works on the Hall-effect principle. The sensor identifies No 1 cylinder, and returns a signal to the ECM from which the identification of all the other cylinders can be calculated. The distributor is attached to the exhaust camshaft (the engine is DOHC in configuration) **(see illustration 6.5)**. Other engines (eg BMW) utilise an inductive device that serves the same purpose but identifies No 1 cylinder by generating an inductive pulse.

6.5 Motronic distributor (GM, 2.5). The Hall-effect phase sensor (CID) multi-plug has been disconnected

Load sensors

The ECM requires a load sensor to detect the flow of air into an engine. Once the volume of air is known, the correct amount of fuel can be looked up in the map. Several methods are used by the various Motronic systems to measure load. The vane-type AFS, the hot-wire air mass meter and the MAP sensor are the three types most usually found.

Vane-type AFS

The AFS is located between the air filter and the throttle body. As air flows through the sensor it deflects a vane (flap). The greater the volume of air, the more will the flap be deflected **(see illustration 6.6)**. The vane is connected to a wiper arm, which wipes a potentiometer resistance track and so varies the resistance of the track. This allows a variable voltage signal to be returned to the ECM.

Three wires are used by the circuitry of this sensor, and it is often referred to as a three-wire sensor. A 5-volt reference voltage is applied to the resistance track, with the other end connected to the AFS earth return. The third wire is connected to the wiper arm.

From the voltage returned, the ECM is able to calculate the volume of air (load) entering the engine, and this is used to calculate the main fuel injection duration. To smooth out

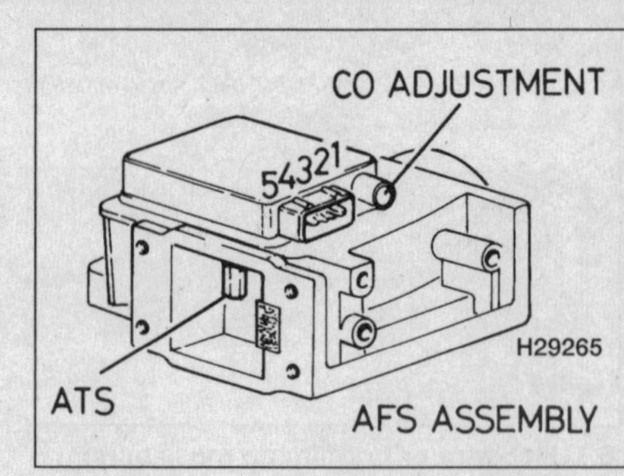

6.6 Motronic type airflow sensor (AFS)

inlet pulses, a damper is connected to the AFS vane. The AFS exerts a major influence on the amount of fuel injected.

Hot-wire or hot-film air mass meter (AFS)

The hot-wire air mass meter has replaced the vane-type AFS fitted to earlier vehicles. The hot-wire air mass meter measures the mass of air entering engine, which allows an accurate fuel injection pulse to be calculated. Hot-wire is a very accurate method of calculating the engine load (air input) and often excludes the need for additional sensors to measure air temperature and air pressure. Automatic compensation for altitude is thus provided. The absence of moving parts improves reliability and lessens maintenance requirements **(see illustration 6.7)**.

Essentially, the hot-wire is so called because a heated wire is placed in the air intake. As air passes over the wire, it has a cooling effect in proportion to the mass of air. As air mass increases or decreases according to engine load, the ECM adjusts the current flow to maintain the wire at its original resistance and temperature. By measuring the change in current flow, the ECM is able to determine the mass of airflow into the engine. As the current varies on the signal wire, so does the voltage, and an indication of load can be assessed by measuring the variable voltage signal. Voltage is applied to the sensor from the system relay. Operation of the hot-film AFS is very similar to hot-wire.

If a fault exists in the hot-wire AFS or wiring, an appropriate code will be logged in the self-diagnostic unit, and a substitute value provided by the LOS program.

Hot-wire burn-off

Over a period of time, deposits tend to build up upon the hot-wire, and this can lead to contamination of the hot-wire. This is avoided with a 'burn-off' function, controlled by the ECM during engine shutdown. Approximately four seconds after the engine has been switched off, the ECM rapidly pulses the hot-wire terminal 4 of the AFS for 1.5 seconds.

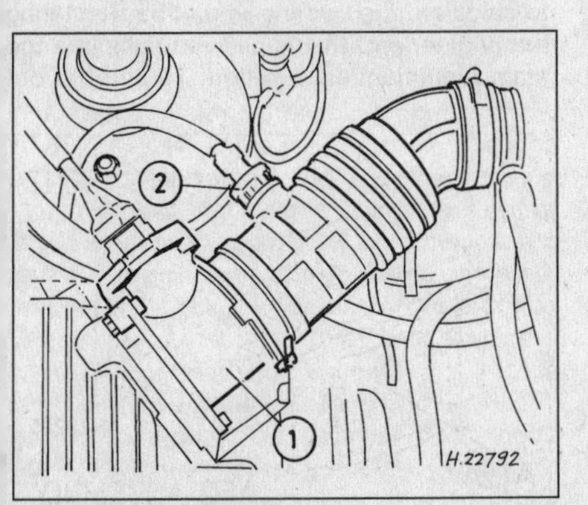

6.7 Hot-wire or hot-film air mass meter (1) and ATS (2) in Motronic 1.5.2

Burn-off will not occur if the engine speed has not exceeded 1000 rpm and the coolant temperature is under approximately 30°C.

MAP sensor

A vacuum hose connects the MAP sensor and the inlet manifold. Manifold vacuum acts upon the MAP sensor diaphragm, and the ECM internally converts the pressure into an electrical signal. MAP is calculated from the formula: Atmospheric Pressure less Manifold Pressure = Manifold Absolute Pressure.

Using the speed/density method, Motronic calculates the AFR from the MAP signal and the speed of the engine (CAS). This method relies on the theory that the engine will draw in a fixed volume of air per revolution.

When manifold vacuum is high (ie idle condition), MAP is moderately low, and the ECM provides less fuel. When manifold vacuum is low (ie wide-open throttle), MAP is high and the ECM provides more fuel.

The inlet manifold on MPi models is a 'dry' manifold. Since fuel does not enter the manifold - due to injection being made onto the back of the inlet valve - there is no risk of fuel being drawn into the MAP sensor to contaminate the diaphragm, and a fuel trap is not used.

The MAP sensor may be located internally in the ECM (no connecting wires) or located internally in the ECM. When located externally, a 5-volt reference voltage is supplied to the sensor, with the other end connected to earth. The third wire is connected to a transducer which converts the manifold pressure signal into a voltage. As the pressure in the manifold varies, so too does the signal voltage returned to the ECM.

Air temperature sensor (ATS)

The ATS is mounted in the AFS inlet tract, and measures the air temperature before it enters AFS. Because the density of air varies in inverse proportion to the temperature, the ATS signal allows more accurate assessment of the volume of air being introduced to the engine.

The open-circuit supply to the sensor is at a 5.0-volt reference level, and the earth path is through the AFS earth return. The ATS operates on the NTC principle. A variable voltage signal is returned to the ECM based upon the air temperature. This signal is approximately 2.0 to 3.0 volts at an ambient temperature of 20°C, and reduces to about 1.5 volt as the temperature rises to around 40°C.

CO potentiometer ('pot')

The CO pot mixture adjuster is located in the AFS, and is a three-wire potentiometer that allows small changes to be made to the idle CO. A 5.0-volt reference voltage is applied to the sensor, and earth is via the AFS earth return circuit. The third wire is the CO pot signal.

As the CO pot adjustment screw is turned, the change in resistance returns a voltage signal to the ECM that will result in a change in CO. The CO pot adjustment only affects idle CO. On catalyst-equipped models, the CO pot has no effect and the CO is thus non-adjustable.

CO adjustment (First Generation only)

The vane type of AFS fitted to early systems utilises an air bleed screw located in the AFS to trim the CO value. An air channel allows a small volume of air to by-pass the air flowing through the vane. As the by-pass is moved, the air volume acting upon the vane is altered, and the vane moves its position. The changed position results in an altered signal to the ECM and a change in fuel volume injected.

Coolant temperature sensor (CTS)

The CTS is immersed in the coolant system, and contains a variable resistance that operates on the NTC principle. When the engine is cold, the resistance is quite high. Once the engine is started and begins to warm-up, the coolant becomes hotter, and this causes a change in the CTS resistance. As the CTS becomes hotter, the resistance of the CTS reduces (NTC principle) and this returns a variable voltage signal to the ECM based upon the coolant temperature

The open-circuit supply to the sensor is at a 5.0-volt reference level, and this voltage reduces to a value that depends upon the resistance of the CTS resistance. The signal is approximately 2.0 to 3.0 volts at an ambient temperature of 20°C, and reduces to between 0.5 to 1.0 volt at a normal operating temperature of 80 to 100°C. The ECM uses the CTS signal as a main correction factor when calculating ignition timing and injection duration.

Throttle potentiometer sensor (TPS)

A TPS is provided to inform the ECM of idle position, deceleration, rate of acceleration and full-load (WOT) conditions. The TPS is a potentiometer with three wires. A 5-volt reference voltage is supplied to a resistance track, with the other end connected to earth. The third wire is connected to an arm which wipes along the resistance track, and so varies the resistance and voltage of the signal returned to the ECM.

From the voltage returned, the ECM is able to calculate idle position (approximately 0.6 volts), full-load (approximately 4.5 volts) and also how quickly the throttle is opened. During full-load operation, the ECM provides additional enrichment. During closed throttle operation above a certain rpm (deceleration), the ECM will cut off fuel injection. Injection will be reintroduced once the rpm returns to idle or the throttle is opened.

Throttle switch (alternative to TPS)

A throttle switch with dual contacts is provided to inform the ECM of idle position, deceleration, cruising and full-load (WOT) conditions. When the engine is at idle, the idle contact is closed and the full-load contact is open. As the throttle is moved to the fully open position, the full-load contact closes and the idle contact becomes open. Under cruising conditions with a part-open throttle, both contacts are open. During full-load operation, the ECM provides additional enrichment. During closed throttle operation above a certain rpm (deceleration), the ECM will cut off fuel injection. Injection will be reintroduced once the rpm returns to idle or the throttle is opened.

Idle speed control

Motronic uses various methods to control the idle speed during engine start-up, the warm-up period and normal hot idle.

When an electrical load, such as headlights or heater fan etc are switched on, the idle speed would tend to drop. The ECM will sense the load and actuate the ISCV to increase the airflow through the valve and thus increase the idle speed. When the load is removed, the ECM will pulse the valve so that the airflow is reduced. Normal idle speed should be maintained under all cold and hot operating conditions. If the ISCV fails, it will fail-safe, with the aperture almost closed. This will provide a basic idle speed.

ISCV (2-wire solenoid valve type)

The ISCV is a solenoid-controlled actuator that the ECM uses to automatically control idle speed during normal idle and during engine warm-up **(see illustration 6.8)**. The ISCV is located in a hose that connects the inlet manifold to the air filter side of the throttle plate. A voltage supply is applied to the ISCV from the battery, and the earth for the motor is made through a connection to the ECM.

A duty cycle can be measured on the earth circuit to determine the opening or closing time period as a percentage of the total time available.

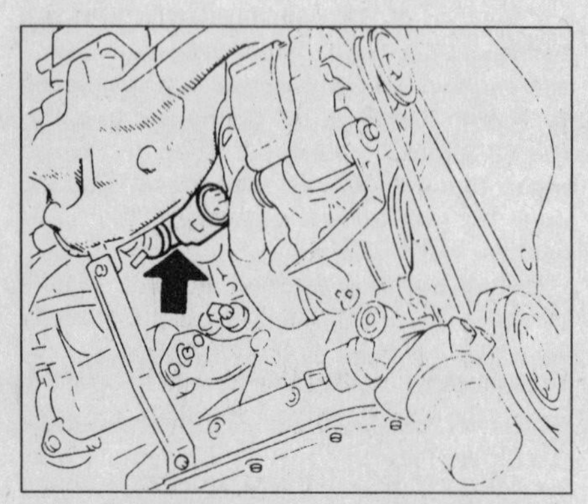

6.8 Idle speed control valve (arrowed), seen from underneath vehicle - two-wire Motronic 2.5 (GM)

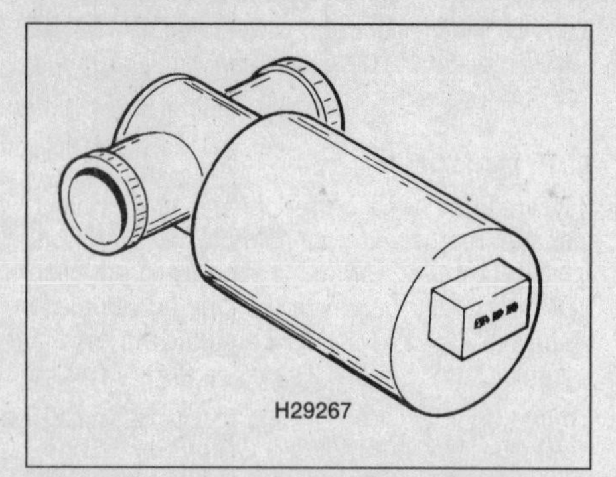

6.9 Idle speed control valve, three-wire

ISCV (3-wire rotary type)

The ISCV is a rotary actuator that the Motronic ECM uses to automatically control idle speed during normal idle and during engine warm-up. The ISCV is located in a hose that connects the inlet manifold to the air filter inside of the throttle plate.

The rotary ISCV is a DC motor that the ECM can rotate either clockwise or anti-clockwise. Rotating in one direction will open the valve; rotating in the opposite direction will cause it to close. A voltage supply is applied to the ISCV from the battery, and the earth for the motor is made through two connections to the ECM **(see illustration 6.9)**.

Rotation of the motor in the appropriate direction is accomplished by actuating the motor through one or the other of the earth circuits. In reality, the two circuits are opposed. This prevents the valve from being fully opened of closed in one particular direction. The valve will thus take up an average position that reflects circuit bias to be open or closed. Normally, this bias would be towards the open position.

A duty cycle can be measured on each earth circuit to determine the opening or closing time period as a percentage of the total time available.

Auxiliary air valve (mainly First Generation)

The AAV is found in vehicles that do not have any form of idle speed regulation. An electrically operated gate control valve is used to increase the idle speed during cold engine operation. The AAV is mounted in a hose that by-passes the throttle plate. The valve responds to temperature and allows extra air to by-pass the throttle when the engine is cold. Extra air entering the inlet manifold causes the idle speed to increase which prevents low idle speed and stalling with a cold or semi-cold engine.

During cold engine operation, the valve is open and so engine idle speed is increased. As the engine warms-up, the valve gradually closes until it is fully closed at normal operating temperature.

The AAV resistance is connected to the relay output terminal. Once the engine has been started voltage is applied to the AAV resistance. The resistance is heated by voltage and the gate valve slowly closes so that it is totally closed once the engine attains normal operating temperature. Radiated heat from the engine will affect valve operation, and allow the valve to remain closed when the engine is hot and is not being operated.

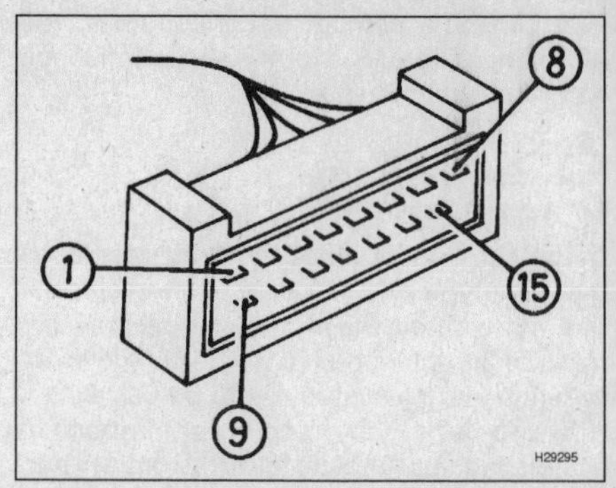

6.10 The multi-plug for the 15-pin relay
Pin numbers shown

Relays (typical operation)

Depending on system, the Motronic electrical system is controlled by either a single system relay with dual contacts, or two separate relays (main system relay and fuel pump relay). Whatever, the general mode of operation is similar for all types. Although the following method of operation is fairly typical of a two relay operation, there are many variations on the theme. The relay terminal numbers are those used in the European Din specification **(see illustration 6.10)**.

A permanent voltage supply is made to main relay terminals 30 and 86 and fuel pump relay terminal 30 from the battery positive terminal. When the ignition is switched on, the ECM earths terminal 85 through an ECM pin which energises the first relay winding. This causes the main relay contacts to close, and the supply through relay terminal 30 is connected to the output circuit at terminal 87. A voltage supply is thus output at main terminal 87. Terminal 87 supplies voltage to the injectors, ECM, ISCV and the CFSV (when fitted). In addition, voltage is applied to the fuel pump relay contact terminal 86.

When the ignition is switched on. the ECM briefly earths pump relay contact 85 at an ECM pin. This energises the pump relay winding, which closes the relay contact and connects voltage from supply terminal 30 to output terminal 87, thereby providing voltage to the fuel pump circuit. After approximately one second, the ECM opens the circuit and the pump stops. This brief running of the fuel pump allows pressure to build within the fuel pressure lines, and provides for an easier start.

The pump relay circuit will then remain open until the engine is cranked or run. Once the ECM receives a speed signal from the CAS, the pump relay winding will again be energised by the ECM, and the fuel pump will run until the engine is stopped. In addition, the

OS heater circuits is usually wired to the pump circuit so that the OS heater will only operate whilst the engine is running.

Fuel pressure system

The fuel pressure systems in Motronic-equipped vehicles all function in a similar fashion. The main difference concerns the location of the fuel pump which may be mounted externally, or internally in the fuel tank. The types are described as follows.

External pump

The roller type fuel pump, mounted close to the fuel tank, draws fuel from the tank and pumps it to the fuel rail via a fuel filter.

Internal pump

The fuel pump is mounted vertically in the fuel tank, and is of the gerotor type. Fuel is drawn through the pump inlet, to be pressurised between the rotating gerotor teeth and discharged from the pump outlet into the fuel supply line.

Fuel transfer pump

In some models, a secondary in-tank fuel transfer pump aids the external pump. The internal fuel pump assembly operates on the gerotor principle described above.

Fuel pump (all)

The fuel pump normally provides much more fuel than is required, and surplus fuel is thus returned to the fuel tank via a return pipe. In fact, a maximum fuel pressure in excess of 5 bar is usually possible. To prevent the possibility of pressure loss in the supply system, a non-return valve is provided in the fuel pump outlet. When the ignition is switched off, and the fuel pump ceases operation, pressure is thus maintained for some time.

Fuel pressure regulator

Fuel pressure in the fuel rail is maintained at a constant 2.5 or 3.0 bar (depending upon vehicle) by a fuel pressure regulator. The pressure regulator is fitted on the outlet side of the fuel rail, and maintains an even pressure of 2.5 or 3.0 bar in the fuel rail.

A vacuum hose connects the upper chamber to the inlet manifold, so that variations in inlet manifold pressure will not affect the amount of fuel injected. This means that the pressure in the rail is always at a constant pressure above the pressure in the inlet manifold. The quantity of injected fuel thus depends solely on injector opening time, as determined by the ECM, and not on a variable fuel pressure.

At idle speed with the vacuum pipe disconnected, or with the engine stopped and the pump running, or at full-throttle, the system fuel pressure will be approximately 2.5 bar or 3.0 bar. At idle speed (vacuum pipe connected), the fuel pressure will be approximately 0.5 bar under the system pressure.

6 Catalytic converter and emission control

Catalytic converter

Versions with a catalytic converter will also be fitted with an oxygen sensor so that closed-loop control of emissions can be implemented. The OS is heated so that it will reach optimum operating temperature as quickly as possible after the engine is started. The OS heater supply is usually made from the fuel pump relay. This ensures that the heater will only operate whilst the engine is running.

Carbon filter solenoid valve (CFSV)

An CFSV and activated carbon canister are also be employed to aid evaporative emission control. The carbon canister stores fuel vapours until the CFSV is opened by the EMS under certain operating conditions. Once the CFSV is actuated by the EMS, fuel vapours are drawn into the inlet manifold to be burnt by the engine during normal combustion.

Adjustments

7 Adjustment pre-conditions

1 Ensure that all of these conditions are met before attempting to make adjustments

a) Engine at operating temperature. Engine oil at a minimum temperature of 80°C; a journey of at least 4 miles is recommended (particularly so if equipped with AT).
b) Ancillary equipment (all engine loads and accessories) switched off.
c) AT vehicles: Transmission in N or P.
d) Engine mechanically sound.
e) Engine breather hoses and breather system in satisfactory condition.
f) Induction system free from vacuum leaks.
g) Ignition system in satisfactory condition.
h) Air filter in satisfactory condition.
i) Exhaust system free from leaks.
j) Throttle cable correctly adjusted.
k) No fault codes logged by the ECM.
l) OS operating satisfactorily (catalyst vehicles with closed-loop control).

2 In addition, before checking the idle speed and CO values, stabilise the engine as follows:

a) Stabilise the engine. Raise the engine speed to 3000 rpm for a minimum of 30 seconds, and then let the engine idle.
b) If the cooling fan operates during adjustment, wait until it stops, re-stabilise the engine and then restart the adjustment procedure.
c) Allow the CO and idle speed to settle.
d) Make all checks and adjustments within 30 seconds. If this time is exceeded, re-stabilise the engine and recheck.

8 Throttle adjustments

Throttle valve position

1 Clean the throttle valve and surrounding areas with carburettor cleaner. Blow-by from the breather system often causes sticking problems here **(see illustration 6.11)**.

2 The throttle valve is critical and should not normally be disturbed. A common fault is maladjustment of the idle speed by use of the throttle stop screw.

3 Where adjustment IS required:

a) Disconnect the throttle cable, and remove the tamperproof cap from the throttle stop screw.
b) Loosen the TPS or TS adjustment/retaining screws, rotate the TPS or TS fully anti-clockwise and re-tighten the screws.
c) Unscrew the throttle stop screw until there is a gap between the stop and screw.
d) Gently turn in the screw until it just touches the stop.
e) Turn-in the screw one further half turn when there should be an air gap of between 0.05 to 0.15 mm (0.002 to 0.006") between the throttle casing and the throttle plate.
f) Adjust the TPS or TS.
g) Refit and readjust the throttle cable and fit a new tamperproof cap to the throttle stop screw.

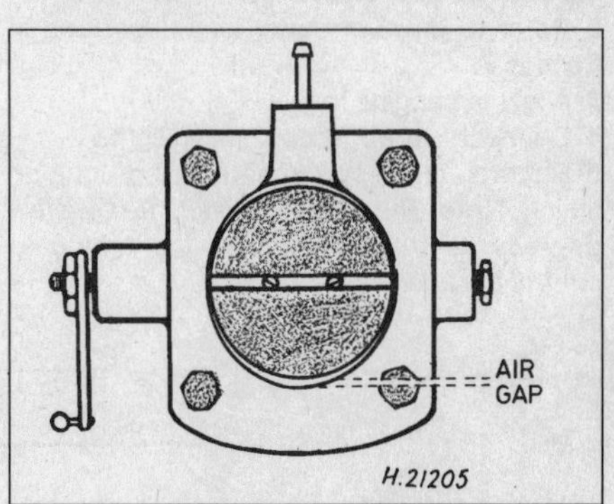

6.11 Throttle valve adjustment

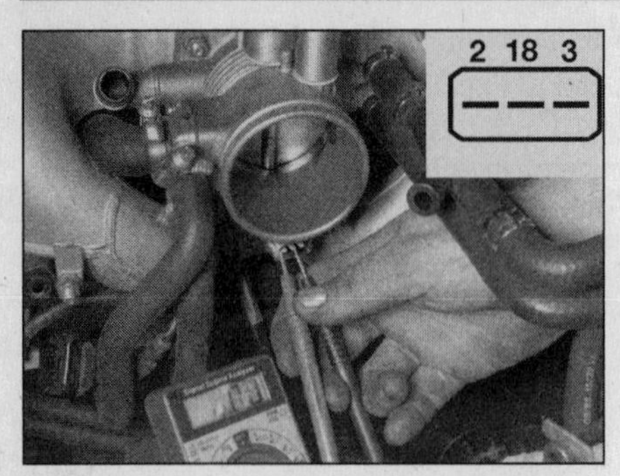

6.12 Adjust the TS with the aid of an ohmmeter. With the ohmmeter connected between terminals 2 and 18 and the throttle closed, the ohmmeter should indicate zero (continuity)

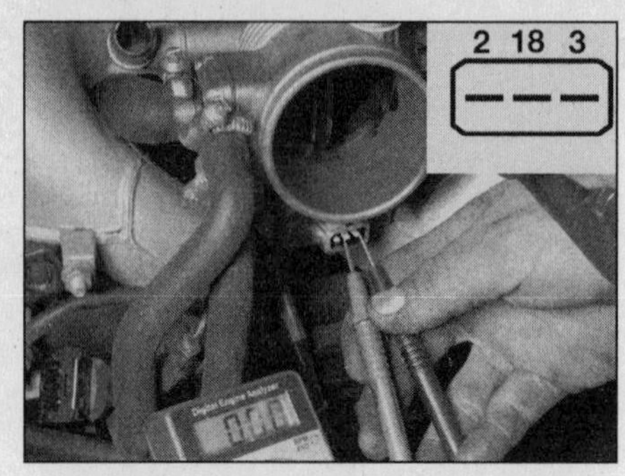

6.13 With the ohmmeter connected between terminals 3 and 18 and the throttle fully open, the ohmmeter should indicate zero (continuity)

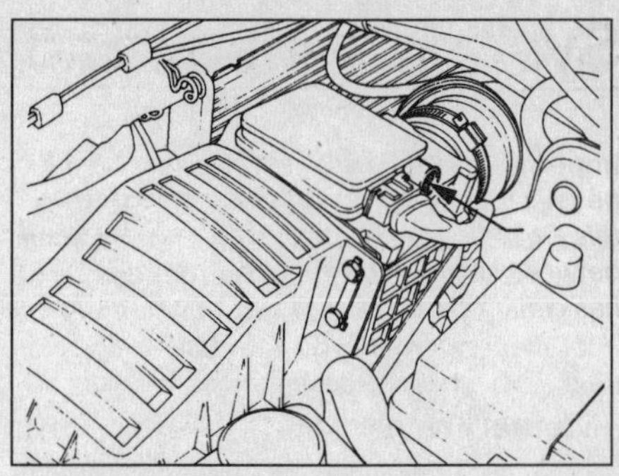

6.14 Adjustment of the idle CO pot located in the vane-type AFS

Throttle switch

Conditions: *engine stopped, throttle closed, TS disconnected.*

4 Attach an ohmmeter between TS terminals 2 and 18. The ohmmeter should indicate zero (continuity) **(see illustration 6.12)**.

5 Open the throttle. The ohmmeter should indicate an open-circuit (infinity) **(also see illustration 6.13)**.

6 As soon as the throttle moves off its stop. An audible 'click' should be heard.

Adjust the TPS

Conditions: *Engine stopped, throttle closed, ignition 'on'.*

7 Attach a voltmeter between the signal terminal and earth and measure the voltage.

8 The switch is requires adjustment if the voltage is greater than 0.60.

9 Loosen the two securing screws and adjust the switch until the voltmeter indicates less than 0.60 volts.

9 Ignition timing checks

1 The ignition timing is not adjustable, and marks are not always provided. However, it is useful to make the following checks. *If no marks are available, make your own marks on the front damper and pulley.*

2 Refer to the test conditions described in Section 7.

3 Allow the engine to idle.

4 Connect a stroboscopic timing light.

5 Record the approximate base ignition timing. **Note:** *The marks will fluctuate by a few degrees as the ECM varies the timing to control the idle speed.*

6 Increase the engine speed. The timing marks should smoothly advance. Expect approximately 25 to 35° of timing advance at 3000 rpm.

7 If the timing is not being controlled properly by the ECM, suspect one of the following faults:

a) The engine is in LOS, due to one or more serious sensor failures.
b) The ECM is faulty.

10 Idle adjustments

Idle adjustment overview

1 Refer to the test conditions described in Section 7.

2 Check the that the throttle valve setting is correct as described above.

3 Check the TS or TPS adjustment as described above.

4 Stabilise the engine. Raise the engine speed to 3000 rpm for a minimum of 20 seconds, and then allow the engine to idle. Make all checks and adjustments within 30 seconds. If this time is exceeded, re-stabilise the engine and recheck. *If the cooling fan operates during adjustment, wait until it stops, re-stabilise the engine and then restart the adjustment procedure.*

5 Allow the idle speed to settle, and check that the regulated idle speed is correct.

6 If the idle speed is outside of the specified parameters, check the system sensors for faults.

7 Connect a gas analyser to the exhaust system.

8 Stabilise the engine as above.

9 Allow the CO value to settle, and check the idle CO value.

CO adjustment (non-cat models only)

Air bleed screw (First Generation Motronic)

10 Where adjustment is necessary, remove the tamperproof plug covering the CO adjustment screw in the AFS.

11 Stabilise the engine as above.

12 Turn the adjustment screw until the CO stabilises at the specified figure). *Turn the screw clockwise to increase the CO level, anti-clockwise to decrease the CO level.*

13 If the CO level remains at a low level and does not respond to adjustment, check for an induction vacuum leak. The slightest leak will adversely affect the idle mixture.

CO pot in AFS (vane-type AFS)

14 Slide back the rubber boot, and connect a voltmeter between the signal wire and earth. A voltage of approximately 2 to 3 volts should be obtained **(see illustration 6.14)**.

15 If the voltage is outside of the stated parameters when the CO is correct, check the system for:

a) Vacuum leak.
b) Incorrect AFS or MAP signal.
c) Incorrect CTS signal.
d) Fouled or leaking injectors.
e) Incorrect fuel pressure.

16 Stabilise the engine as above.

17 Remove the tamperproof cap and turn the CO adjustment screw. *Turn the screw clockwise to increase CO level and raise voltage, anti-clockwise to reduce CO level and lower voltage.*

18 Refer to the CO pot test if the voltage does not vary or no voltage can be obtained.

System sensor and actuator tests

Important note: *Please refer to Chapter 4, which describes common test procedures applicable to this system. The routines in Chapter 4 should be read in conjunction with the component notes and wiring diagrams presented in this Chapter. The wiring diagrams and other data presented in this Chapter are necessarily representative of the system depicted. Because of the variations in wiring and other data that often occurs, even between similar vehicles in any particular VM's range, the reader should take great care in identification of ECM pins, and satisfy himself that he has gathered the correct data before failing a particular component.*

11 Crank angle sensor (CAS)

General

1 Refer to the note at the start of this Section, and refer to the relevant Section of Chapter 4.
2 CAS resistance measurements (ohms):

a) *BMW, Motronic First Generation: 960 ± 96*
b) *BMW, Motronic 1.3, 1.7, 3.1: 550 ± 50*
c) *Citroën/Peugeot, Motronic 4.1: 600 to 1600*
d) *Citroën/Peugeot, Motronic 1.3, 3.1, 3.2, 5.1: 300 to 600*
e) *Opel and Vauxhall, Motronic 1.5, 2.5, 4.1: 500 to 800*
f) *Volvo, Motronic First Generation: 1000*

12 Primary ignition

1 Refer to the note at the start of Section 11, and refer to the relevant Section of Chapter 4. Many different combinations of primary ignition layouts may be found in Motronic systems, and so select the test procedure for the closest one to the system under test.
2 ECM pin No 1 is connected to coil terminal 1 in all versions of Motronic with internal amplifier that we checked.
3 ECM and amplifier terminals numbers may vary depending upon Motronic system.
4 The majority of Motronic systems utilise a CAS as the primary trigger.
5 For the ignition coil resistance specifications, refer to the table below.

Coil resistance measurements (ohms) - Section 12

	Primary	Secondary
BMW, Motronic First Generation	0.60 to 1.00	8250
BMW, Motronic 1.3, 1.7, 3.1	0.30 to 0.80	5000 to 7000
Citroen/Peugeot, Motronic 4.1	0.80	6500
Citroen/Peugeot, Motronic 1.3, 3.1, 3.2, 5.1 (Valeo)	0.60 to 0.80	8600 to 9500
Opel and Vauxhall, Motronic 1.5, 2.5, 4.1	0.60 to 0.76	6400 to 11000
Volvo, Motronic First Generation	0.45 to 0.55	5400 to 6600

13 Knock sensor (KS)

1 Refer to the note at the start of Section 11, and refer to the relevant Section of Chapter 4.

14 Fuel injector operation

1 Refer to the note at the start of Section 11, and refer to the relevant Section of Chapter 4.
2 The ECM may pulse the injectors fully open or according to the current control principle (First Generation Motronic).
3 Where injection is of the current-controlled kind, very few dwell meters may be capable of registering the rapid pulsing to earth that occurs during the second stage of the pulse duration. The meter may only register the switch-on circuit of approximately 1.0 or 2.0%. This means that the injector duty cycle reading will be inaccurate, and not representative of the total pulse width seen in the circuit.
4 In some Motronic systems the frequency of injection increases for several seconds during initial cranking.

Injector resistance tests

5 Remove each injector multi-plug and measure the resistance of the injector between the two terminals.

a) *First Generation Motronic: 4 ohms.*
b) *All other Motronic systems: 16 ohms.*

15 Hall-effect phase sensor (CID, GM 16-valve engines)

1 Refer to the note at the start of Section 11, and refer to the relevant Section of Chapter 4.
2 The HES is located in the distributor.
3 An average signal voltage of approximately 2.5 volts or an approximate duty cycle of 50% should be obtained.

16 Airflow sensor (AFS)

1 Refer to the note at the start of Section 11, and refer to the relevant Section of Chapter 4. The AFS may be of the vane, hot-wire or hot-film type, depending on system.

17 MAP sensor

1 Refer to the note at the start of Section 11, and refer to the relevant Section of Chapter 4.
2 The MAP sensor may be a separate sensor located in the engine compartment, or might be located internally in the ECM depending on system.

18 Air temperature sensor (ATS)

1 Refer to the note at the start of Section 11, and refer to the relevant Section of Chapter 4.
2 The ATS may be located in the inlet tract of the AFS or in the inlet manifold, depending on system.

19 CO potentiometer ('pot')

1 Refer to the note at the start of Section 11, and refer to the relevant Section of Chapter 4.
2 The CO pot will either be located in the AFS, or might be a separate sensor located in the engine compartment, depending on system.

20 Coolant temperature sensor (CTS)

1 Refer to the note at the start of Section 11, and refer to the relevant Section of Chapter 4.

21 Throttle switch (TS)

1 Refer to the note at the start of Section 11, and refer to the relevant Section of Chapter 4.

22 Throttle potentiometer sensor (TPS)

1 Refer to the note at the start of Section 11, and refer to the relevant Section of Chapter 4.

23 Idle speed control valve (ISCV)

1 Refer to the note at the start of Section 11, and refer to the relevant Section of Chapter 4.
2 ISCV resistances:
a) 2-wire ISCV: 8 to 10 ohms
b) 3-wire ISCV: 40 ohms from middle terminal to either of the outer terminals, 80 ohms between the two outer terminals.

24 ECM voltage supplies and earths

1 Refer to the note at the start of Section 11, and refer to the relevant Section of Chapter 4.

25 System relays

1 Refer to the note at the start of Section 11, and refer to the relevant Section of Chapter 4.
2 The majority of Opel and Vauxhall vehicles utilise a single 6-pin relay with dual contacts. Pin numbering is along the DIN lines.
3 Many Citroën and Peugeot vehicles utilise a single 15-pin relay with dual contacts. Numbering is from one to 15 (see wiring diagram).
4 Testing of multi- pin relays follows similar lines to that described in Chapter 4, and the relay supplies, earths and outputs should be checked for voltage. The relay can be bypassed as before with a jumper wire connecting the battery supply terminal to an appropriate output terminal.

26 Fuel pressure

1 Refer to the note at the start of Section 11, and refer to the relevant Section of Chapter 4.

27 Oxygen sensor (OS)

1 Refer to the note at the start of Section 11, and refer to the relevant Section of Chapter 4.
2 The OS found in the majority of Motronic systems is a four-wire sensor.

28 Carbon filter solenoid valve (CFSV)

1 Refer to the note at the start of Section 11, and refer to the relevant Section of Chapter 4.

Pin table - typical 35-pin (First Generation Motronic, BMW)

Note: *Refer to* ***illustrations 6.15 to 6.19***

1 Coil negative
2 TS idle contact
3 TS full-load contact
4 Starter motor
5 Earth
6 AFS return
7 AFS output
8 RPM sensor signal
9 AFS supply
10 Earth (auto only)
11 Fuel consumption gauge
12 Simplified CO testing
13 CTS supply /output
14 Injectors 1 to 3 (pulse)
15 Injectors 4 to 6 (pulse)
16 Earth
17 Earth
18 Battery
19 Earth
20 FP relay driver
21 Tachometer
22 ATS: (AFS)
23 RPM sensor shield
24 OS signal
25 TDC sensor return
26 TDC sensor signal
27 Rpm sensor return
28 A/C
29 A/C
30 -
31 OS relay driver
32 -
33 ISCV pulse
34 ISCV pulse
35 Supply from main relay

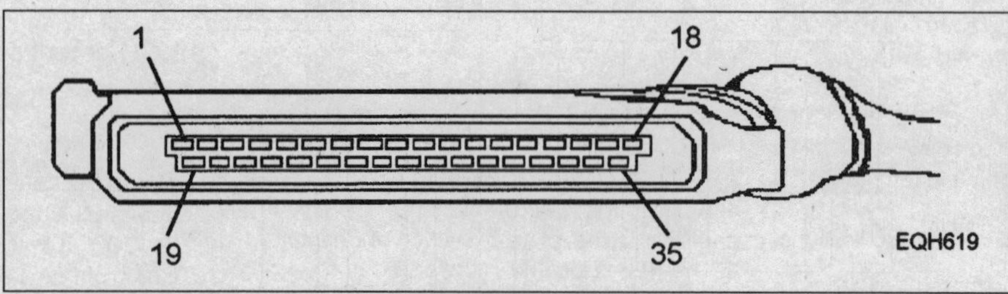

6.15 Typical 35-pin multi-plug
Pin numbers shown

Pin table - typical 35-pin (Motronic 3.1, Citroën/Peugeot)

Note: *Refer to **illustrations 6.15 to 6.19***

1 *Ignition output to amplifier, coil one*
2 *Ignition output to amplifier, coil two*
3 *TPS signal contact*
4 *Diagnostic socket*
5 *Earth*
6 *Sensor return ATS, CTS, CO pot, TPS*
7 *-*
8 *-*
9 *Sensor supply CO pot, TPS*
10 *-*
11 *-*
12 *Diagnostic socket*
13 *CTS supply /output*
14 *Injectors (pulse)*
15 *-*
16 *Earth*
17 *Diagnostic socket*
18 *Battery supply*
19 *-*
20 *FP relay driver*
21 *Tachometer*
22 *ATS supply/output*
23 *CAS return*
24 *CO pot signal*
25 *CAS supply/signal*
26 *-*
27 *Earth*
28 *P/N switch (AT only)*
29 *A/C switch*
30 *-*
31 *-*
32 *A/C compressor supply relay*
33 *-*
34 *-*
35 *Nbv supply from main relay*

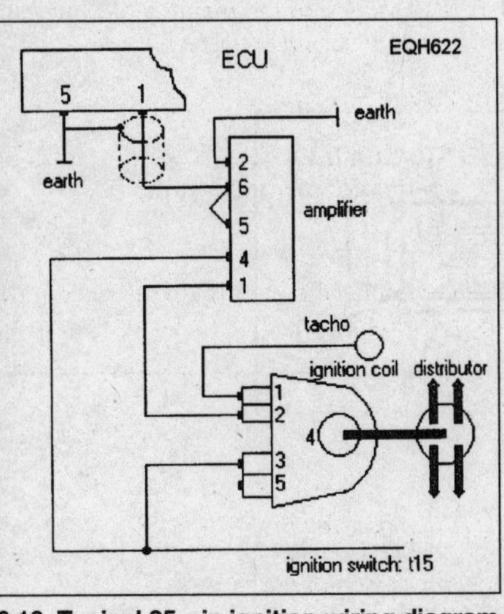

6.16 Typical 35-pin ignition wiring diagram

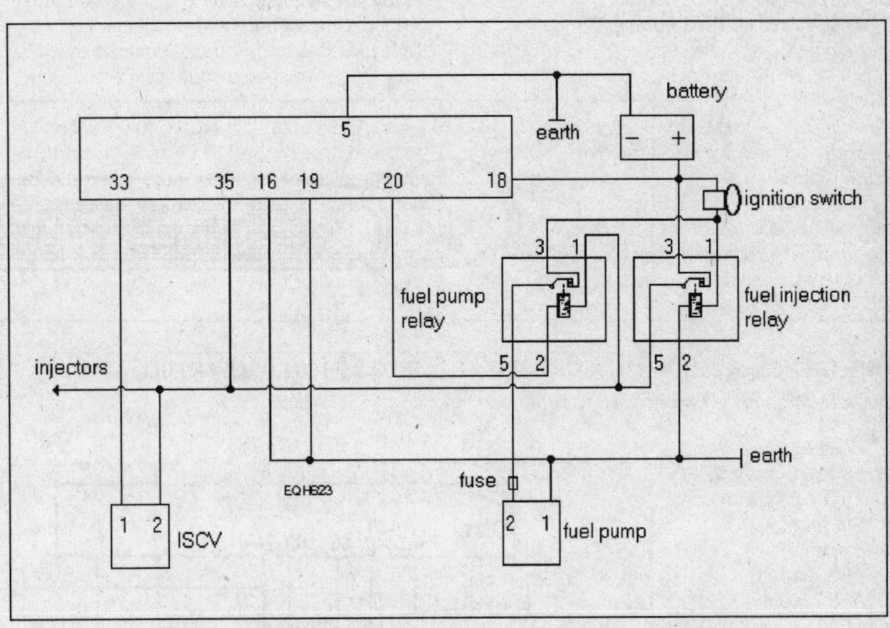

6.17 Typical 35-pin relays and components wiring diagram

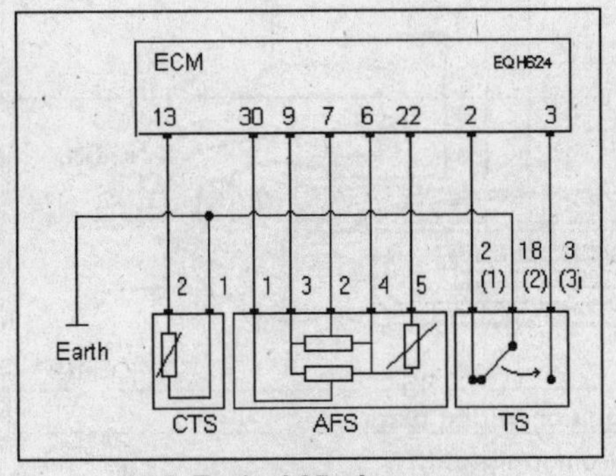

6.18 Typical 35-pin sensors wiring diagram

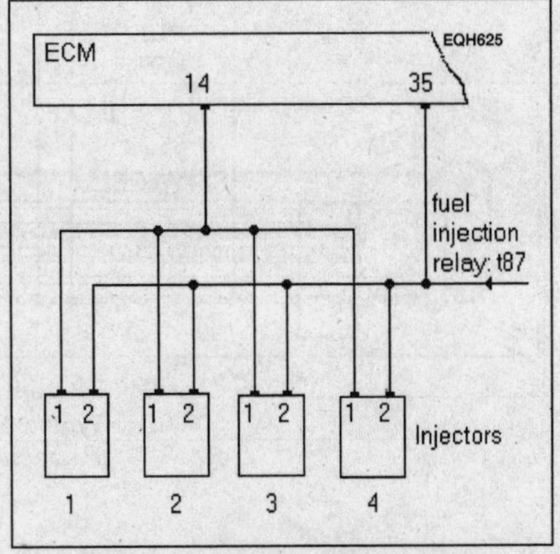

6.19 Typical 35-pin injectors wiring diagram

Pin table - typical 55-pin (Motronic 1.5, Vauxhall)

Note: *Refer to* ***illustrations 6.20 to 6.25***

1 Coil negative
2 Earth
3 Relay earth
4 ISCV
5 CFSV
6 4 WD unit, AT control unit
7 AFS signal
9 Road speed sensor
10 OS return
12 AFS supply
12 TPS supply
13 Diagnostic socket
14 Earth
16 Injector pulse, bank number 1
17 Injector pulse, bank number 2
18 Battery positive
19 Earth (main ECM)
20 Coding earth (non-cat)
21 Coding earth (cat)
22 Warning lamp
24 Earth
25 Sensor return: AFS, ATS, CO
26 Sensor return: CTS, TPS, OA
27 Ignition switch
28 Oxygen sensor
32 On board computer
34 AT control unit
36 Relay earth
37 Nbv supply from relay
40 AC cut-off switch
41 AC pressure switch
42 Ignition switch
42 Coding earth (MT)
43 CO - non-cat (AFS)
44 ATS (AFS)
45 CTS supply/signal
46 Octane adjuster
47 Earth (4x4)
48 CAS return
49 CAS output
51 AT control unit
53 Throttle pot signal
55 Diagnostic socket

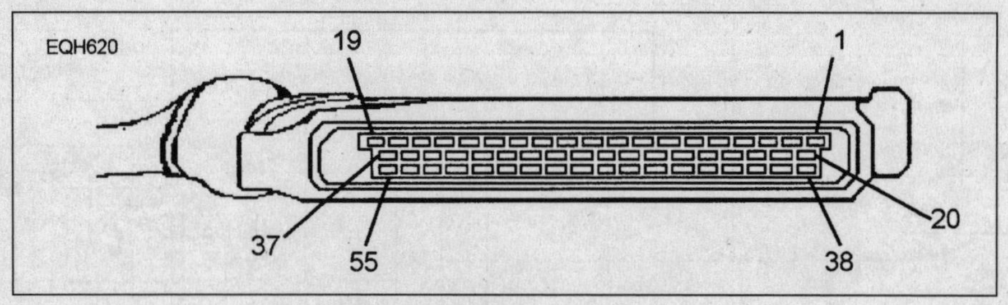

6.20 Typical 55-pin multi-plug

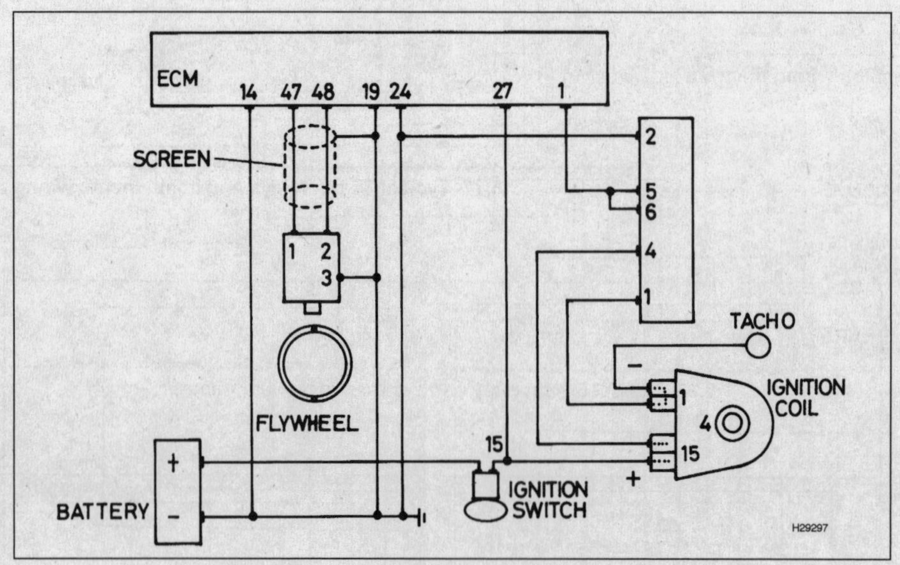

6.21 Typical 55-pin ignition wiring diagram

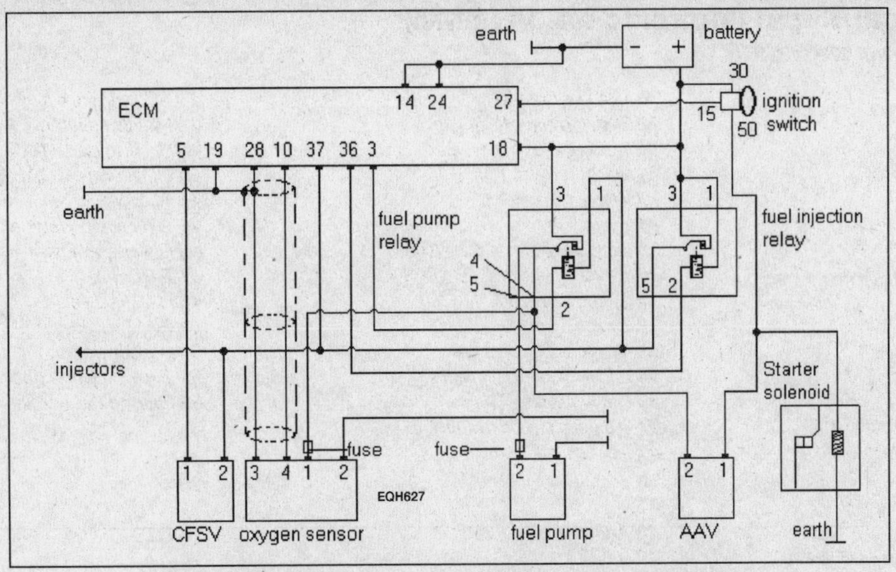

6.22 Typical 55-pin relays and components wiring diagram

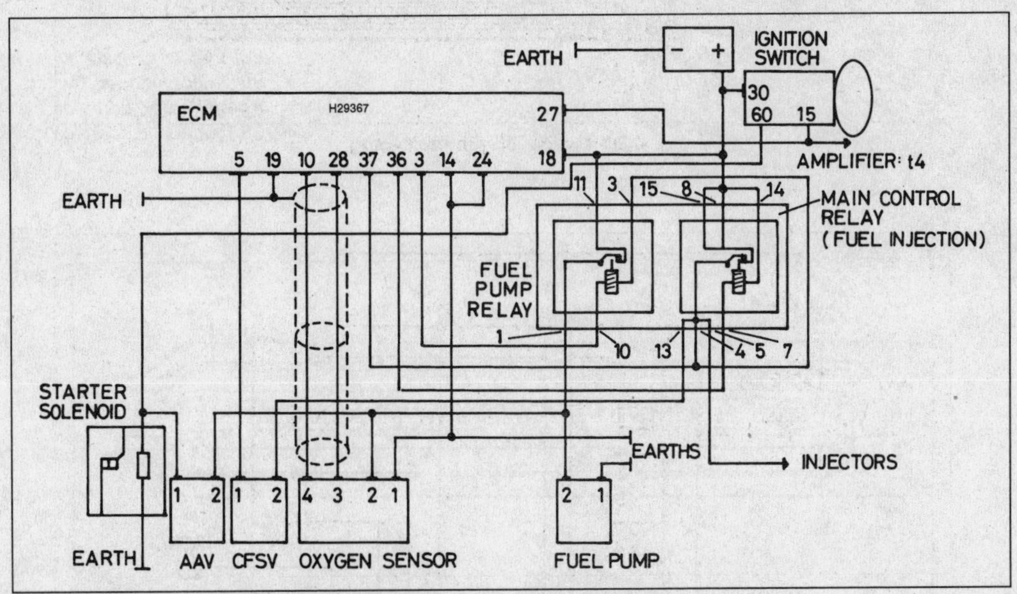

6.23 Typical 55-pin relay and components wiring diagram

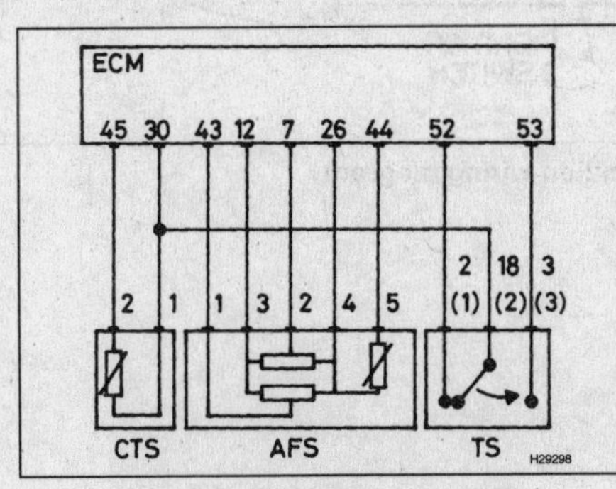

6.24 Typical 55-pin sensors wiring diagram

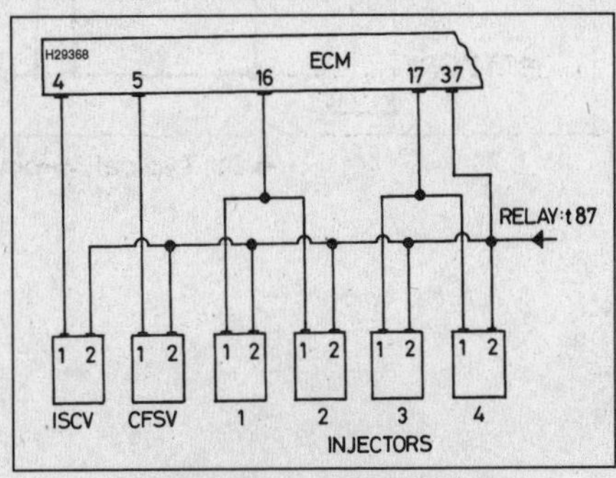

6.25 Typical 55-pin injectors wiring diagram

Pin table - typical 88-pin (Motronic MP3.1, BMW)

Note: *Refer to **illustrations 6.26 and 6.27***

1 Fuel pump relay driver
2 ISCV
3 Injector valve cyl. 1
4 Injector valve cyl. 3
5 Injector valve cyl. 2
6 Earth
7 -
8 Fascia warning lamp (some models)
9 -
10 -
11 -
12 TPS
13 Burn clear
14 Airflow Sensor
15 -
16 CID sensor
17 Ti measurement signal
18 -
19 -
20 -
21 -
22 -
23 Ignition coil cyl. 2
24 Ignition coil cyl. 3
25 Ignition coil cyl. 1
26 Main relay terminal 30
27 Main relay
28 Earth
29 ISCV
30 -
31 Injector valve cyl. 5
32 Injector valve cyl. 6
33 Injector valve cyl. 4
34 Earth
35 -
36 CFSV
37 OS relay
38 -
39 -
40 -
41 Airflow sensor
42 -
43 Earth
44 CID sensor
45 -
46 -
47 -
48 A/C cut-off switch
49 -
50 Ignition coil cyl. 4
51 Ignition coil cyl. 6
52 Ignition coil cyl. 5
53 -
54 Main relay
55 Earth
56 Ignition
57 -
58 -
59 TPS
60 Diagnostic connector
61 -
62 -
63 -
64 Electronic transmission control
65 Drive range P/N
66 -
67 CAS
68 CAS
69 -
70 OS signal
71 OS earth
72 -
73 VSS
74 -
75 -
76 -
77 ATS
78 CTS
79 -
80 -
81 Anti-theft system
82 -
83 -
84 -
85 A/C compressor switch
86 Air conditioning switch
87 Diagnostic connector
88 Diagnostic connector

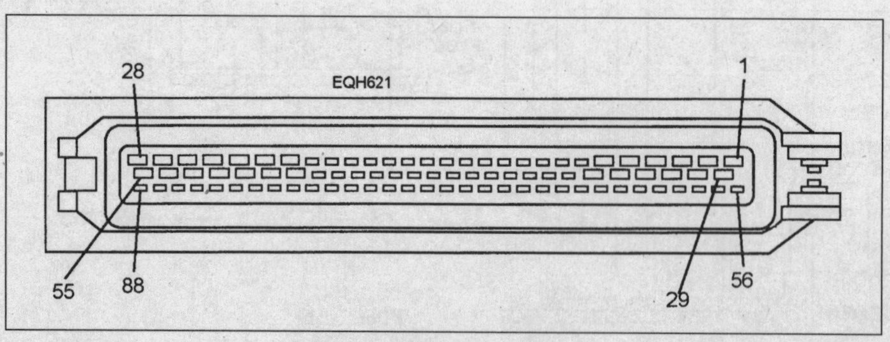

6.26 Typical 88-pin multi-plug

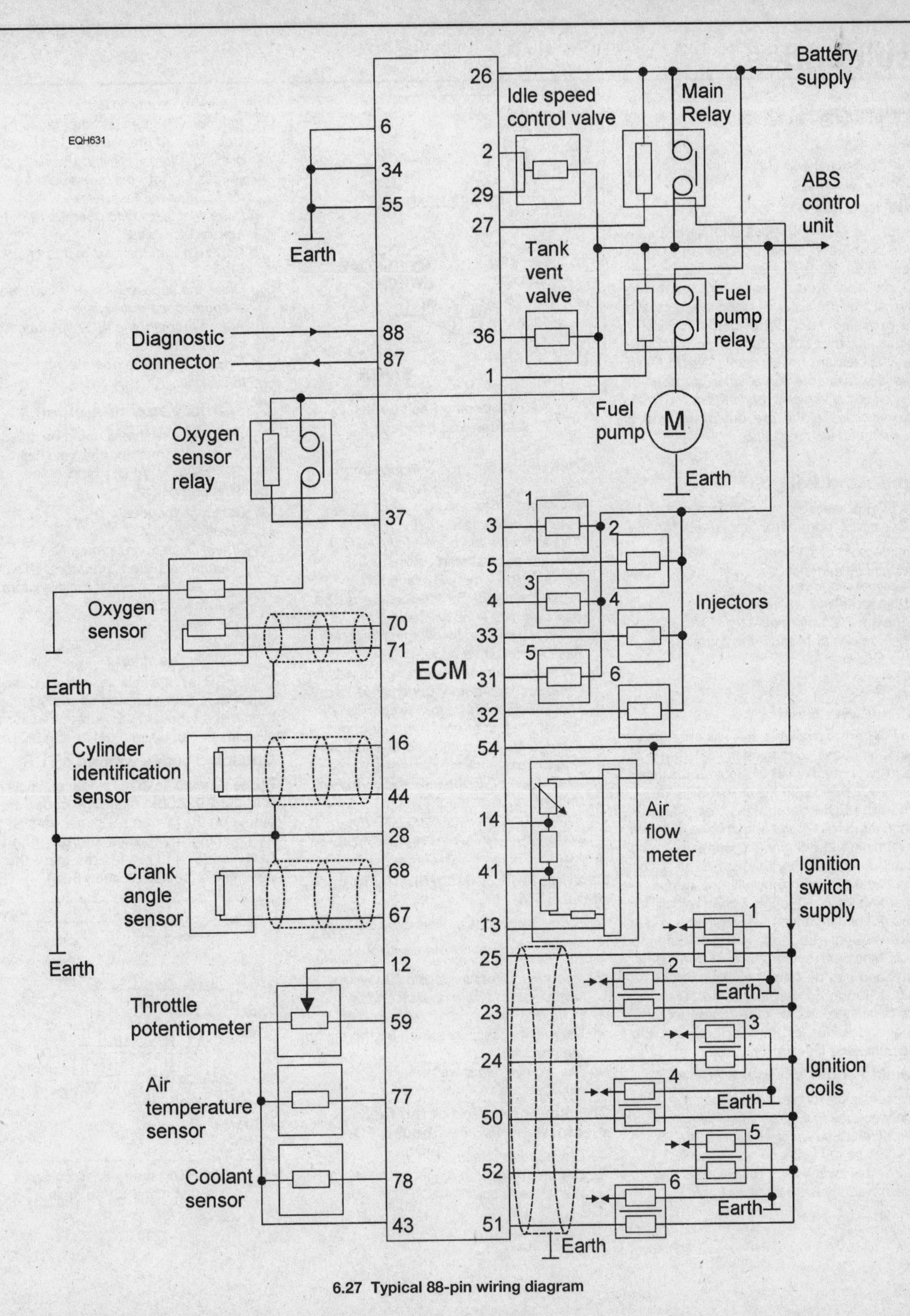

6.27 Typical 88-pin wiring diagram

Fault codes

29 Obtaining fault codes

BMW and Volvo

1 All of the Motronic EMS's fitted to these vehicles ranges require a dedicated FCR to access fault codes. Flash codes are not available for output from any of these systems. For the sake of completeness, we have provided fault code charts for BMW vehicles. At this time, code charts for the other vehicles are not available. **Note:** *Flash codes are available for a small number of codes on BMW vehicles marketed in the USA. These vehicles alone are equipped with a dash-mounted warning lamp.*

Citroën and Peugeot

2 If a FCR is available, it could be attached to the SD serial connector and used for the following purposes:

a) Obtain fault codes.
b) Clear fault codes.
c) Obtain Datastream information.
d) Actuate the system actuators: This may include one or more of the actuators on the following list:
Fuel injectors
ISCV
CFSV (where fitted)

3 If a FCR is not available, it is still possible to obtain fault codes so long as the SD plug is of the two-pin type. A FCR is required for those systems equipped with the 16-pin SD plug.

4 When the ECM determines that a fault is present, it internally logs a fault code, and will also illuminate the diagnostic warning lamp if the fault is regarded by the system as major. Faults regarded as minor will not illuminate the warning lamp, although a code will still be logged. All of the various two-digit fault codes in Citroën and Peugeot vehicles equipped with a Motronic system are of the 'slow' variety, and can be output as flash codes on the dash-mounted warning lamp. The first series of flashes indicates the number of tens, the second series of flashes indicates the single units **(see illustration 6.28)**.

Obtaining codes without a FCR

a) Attach an on /off accessory switch between the FCR green multi-plug terminal 2 (see Diagram) and earth.
b) Switch on the ignition.
c) Close the switch for three seconds (the dash warning lamp will remain off).

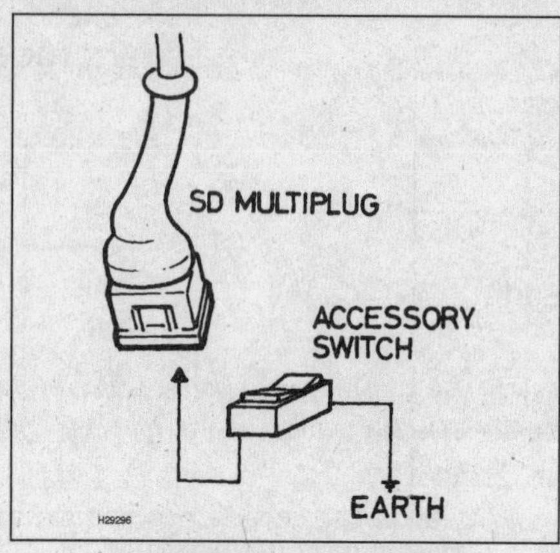

6.28 Obtaining flash codes: Citroën and Peugeot

d) Open the switch, the warning lamp will :-
Flash once (indicating 10).
Pause for 1.5 seconds.
Flash twice (indicating 2).
This indicates the code of twelve (12) which is the test start code.
e) The warning lamp will extinguish.
f) Close the switch for three seconds (the dash warning lamp will remain off).
g) Open the switch, the warning lamp will flash to indicate a code.
h) Once the lamp has extinguished, wait for three seconds before continuing.
i) Close the switch for three seconds & repeat the test to obtain further codes. When code 11 is obtained, this indicates End of Test.
j) After code 11 is obtained the complete test may be repeated.
k) If code 11 is the first code obtained after code 12, no faults are logged by the ECM.

Clearing fault codes from the memory of the ECM

a) Repair all circuits indicated by the fault codes.
b) Switch on the ignition.
c) Perform the test as detailed above to reveal code 11 with no fault codes (optional).
d) Close the accessory switch for more than ten seconds.
e) The warning lamp will remain extinguished.

Checking operation of the fuel injectors and ISCV without a FCR

a) Close the accessory switch
b) Switch the ignition on.
c) Wait 3 seconds.
d) After a moment the fuel injectors will function. This can be determined by vibration and the sound of the injectors clicking. Warning: Avoid the injection of excess fuel into the cylinders by completing the test quickly.
e) If the injectors fail to operate, refer to the fuel injector tests.
f) Continue with the next test to check the ISCV.
g) Close the accessory switch for three seconds once more.
h) After a moment the ISCV will function and vibrate to the touch.
i) If the ISCV fails to operate, refer to the ISCV tests.

Opel and Vauxhall vehicles

5 If a FCR is available, it could be attached to the SD serial connector (the Vauxhall term for the SD plug is ALDL) and used for the following purposes:

a) Obtain fault codes.
b) Clear fault codes.
c) Obtain Datastream information.
d) Actuate the system actuators: This may include one or more of the actuators on the following list:
Fuel injectors
ISCV
CFSV (where fitted)

6 If a FCR is not available, it is still possible to obtain fault codes so long as the SD plug is of the 10-pin type. A FCR is required for those systems equipped with the 16-pin SD plug.

Obtaining codes without a FCR

7 Use a jumper lead to bridge terminals A and B in the SD (ALDL) plug. The codes are then output on the instrument panel warning lamp. By counting the flashes and referring to the fault code table, faults can thus be determined **(see illustration 6.29)**.

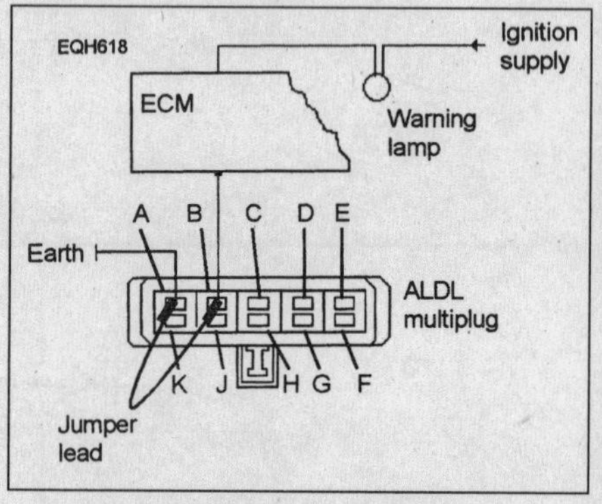

6.29 Obtaining flash codes: GM (Opel & Vauxhall)

Fault code table - BMW Motronic 1.1, 1.3

Flash codes (US)

Note: *US vehicles only: These codes are available via the flashing of the dash-mounted 'Check Engine' warning lamp. Other codes are only available when accessed by the Bosch KTS300 FCR or a BMW FCR.*

Code	Item
1	AFS
2	Oxygen sensor
3	CTS
4	TS

Fault codes

Note: *These codes are only available when accessed by the Bosch KTS300 FCR or a BMW FCR.*
Note: *Most of the fault code numbers correspond to the ECM pin number. e.g. fault code 4 corresponds to ECM pin number 4.*

Code	Item	Fault
1	ECM	Clear the fault code memory and read the codes again, if the code persists, replace ECM
3	Fuel pump relay	Open-circuit or short to earth
4	ISCV	Open-circuit or short to earth
5	CFSV	Short to earth
7	AFS	AFS signal less than 0.04 volts or greater than 0.95 volts
10	OS	Exhaust emissions too rich or too lean
15	Warning lamp (US only)	Short to earth
16	Injectors (cyl 1+3)	Open-circuit or short to earth
17	Injectors (cyl 2+4)	Open-circuit or short to earth
23	OS heater relay	Short to earth, or short between ECM pin 23 and the OS relay
28	OS	Open-circuit or short to earth
29	VSS	No signal
33	Solenoid valve kick down prevent	Open-circuit or short to earth (AT models)
37	ECM	Supply exceeds 16 volts
43	CO pot (non cat models)	Open-circuit or short to earth
44	ATS	Open-circuit or short to earth
45	CTS	Open-circuit or short to earth
51	Ignition timing intervention	Short to earth (models with EGS only)
52	TS	Idle contact short to earth
53	TS	Full load contact short to earth
54	Torque converter clutch	Models with EGS only: This code is stored when the ECM detects a closed torque converter clutch or short to earth when the gear lever is in P or N
100	Output stage (Motronic 1.3 only)	Loose contact
101	Engine operation not possible	Check the following: ECM supply voltages, CAS signal, AFS signals, fuel pump relay activation, injection output signal, injector valves, fuel pressure test

Fault code table - BMW Motronic 1.7, 3.1

Code	Item	Fault
0	Undefined fault	
1	Fuel pump relay/engine speed/CAS signal	
2	Idle air control actuator	
3	Injector Nos, 1 and 3	
4	Injector No. 3	
5	Injector No.2	
6	Injectors	
12	TPS	
16	Camshaft position sensor	
18	Amplifier to ECM terminal 18	Short-circuit
19	ECM	Defective signal
23	Ignition amplifier No.2 cylinder	
24	Ignition amplifier No 3 cylinder	
25	Ignition amplifier No.1 cylinder	
26	ECM supply	
29	Idle air control actuator	
31	Injector No.5	
32	Injector Nos. 2, 4, or 6	
33	Injector No.4	
36	EVAP canister purge valve	
37	Oxygen sensor	Heating
41	AFS	Volume/mass
46	ECM	Defective signal
48	AC compressor	Cut-out
50	Ignition amplifier cylinder No.4	
51	Ignition amplifier cylinder No.6	
54	ECM	Supply
55	Ignition amplifier	
62	Electronic throttle control	
64	Ignition timing (electronic AT)	Interruption
67	Engine speed/crankshaft position sensor	
70	Oxygen sensor	
73	Vehicle speed sensor	
76	CO potentiometer (non-cat)	
77	Intake air temperature sensor	
78	Engine coolant temperature sensor	
81	Alarm system signal	
82	Traction control	Interrupted
83	Suspension control	Interrupted
85	AC compressor	
100	ECM	Defective signal
200	ECM	
201	Oxygen sensor control	
202	ECM	
203	Ignition primary circuit	
204	Electronic throttle control signal	
300	Engine	Cannot be started

Fault code table - Citroën/Peugeot Motronic

Code	Item	Fault
11	End of diagnosis	No faults present
12	Initiation of diagnosis	
13x	ATS	
14x	CTS	
15	Fuel pump relay	Supply fault
21x	TPS/TS	Idle contact
22	ISCV	Supply fault
25	ACAV	
31	Idle switch fault	Motronic 5.1.1
31	OS	Mixture regulation (check OS signal voltage) (Motronic 3.1, 3.2)
31	Mixture regulation (cat models only)	Exhaust/inlet leak(s) or fuel pressure/type (Motronic 1.3)
32	Mixture regulation (cat models only)	Exhaust/inlet leak(s) or fuel pressure/type
33	CFSV	Circuit fault (Motronic 5.1.1)
33x	AFS/MAP	Circuit fault (Motronic 4.1, 3.2)
34	CFSV	
35	TS	Full-load contact
41	CAS	
42	Injectors	
43x	KS (Knock regulation)	Knock sensor/engine temp/plugs etc
44x	KS (Knock detection)	Knock sensor
51x	OS	Circuit fault (cat models only)
52	Mixture control	Supply voltage/air/exhaust leak
53x	Battery voltage	Charging/battery tests
54	ECM	ECM/ECM supply/injection relay
55	CO pot	Circuit fault
56	Immobiliser system	
65	CID	
71	No 1 injector control	
72	No 2 injector control	
73	No 3 injector control	
74	No 4 injector control	

'x' Faults that typically will cause the ECM to enter LOS, and use a default value in place of the sensor

Some faults are designated as major faults, and will illuminate the warning lamp. However, major faults that will illuminate the warning lamp vary from system to system, and it is best to interrogate the ECM for codes if a fault is suspected.

Actuator selection code

82 Injector
83 ISCV
84 CFSV

Fault code table - GM Motronic

Code	Item	Fault
12	Initiation of diagnosis	
13	Oxygen sensor	No change in voltage/open-circuit
14	CTS	Low voltage
15	CTS	High voltage
16	Knock sensor	No change in voltage
17	Knock sensor two	No change in voltage
18	Knock control unit	No signal: ECM fault
19	RPM signal	Interrupted signal
21	Throttle pot	High voltage
22	Throttle pot	Low voltage
23	Knock control module	
24	Vehicle speed sensor	
25	Injector number one	High voltage
26	Injector number two	High voltage
27	Injector number three	High voltage
28	Injector number four	High voltage
29	Injector number five	High voltage
31	Engine RPM signal	No signal
32	Injector number six	Voltage high
33	Inlet manifold pressure sensor	Voltage too high
34	EGR valve	Voltage high
35	ISCV	Poor or no idle speed control
37	Engine self-diagnosis	Low voltage
38	Oxygen sensor	Voltage low (1990 model year on)
39	Oxygen sensor	Voltage high (1990 model year on)
41	Vehicle speed sensor	Low voltage
42	Vehicle speed sensor	High voltage
44	Oxygen sensor	Air/fuel mixture too lean
45	Oxygen sensor	Air/fuel mixture too rich
47	Air pump relay	Low voltage
48	Battery voltage	Low voltage
49	Battery voltage	High voltage
51	Programmable memory	PROM error
52	Engine check light: final stage	High voltage
53	Fuel pump relay	Low voltage
54	Fuel pump relay	High voltage
55	ECM fault	Renew ECM
56	ISCV	Short to earth
57	ISCV	Interruption
59	Inlet manifold valve	Low voltage
61	FTVV	Low voltage
62	FTVV	High voltage
63	Inlet manifold valve	High voltage
65	CO potentiometer	Low voltage
66	CO potentiometer	High voltage
67	TS - idle contact	Idle switch not opening
69	ATS	Low voltage
71	ATS	High voltage
72	TS - full load contact	Full load switch not opening
73	AFS	Low voltage
74	AFS	High voltage
75	Transmission switch	Low voltage
76	AT torque control	Engaged long
79	Traction control unit	Incorrect ignition/injector cut-off
81	Injector number one	Low voltage
82	Injector number two	Low voltage
83	Injector number three	Low voltage
84	Injector number four	Low voltage
85	Injector number five	Low voltage
86	Injector number six	Low voltage
87	AC cut-off relay	Low voltage
88	AC cut-off relay	High voltage
89	Oxygen sensor	Low voltage
91	Oxygen sensor	High voltage
93	HES	Low voltage
94	HES	High voltage
95	Hot start valve	Low voltage
96	Hot start valve	High voltage
97	Traction control unit	Incorrect signal
98	Oxygen sensor	Wiring break
99	Code unknown	
113	Turbo boost control	Boost pressure high
114	Idle boost pressure	Above upper limit
115	Full boost pressure	Below lower limit
116	Boost pressure	Above upper limit
117	Wastegate valve	Low voltage
118	Wastegate valve	High voltage
121	Oxygen sensor 2	Lean exhaust
122	Oxygen sensor 2	Rich exhaust
123	Inlet manifold valve 1	Blocked
124	Inlet manifold valve 2	Blocked
132	EGR valve	Incorrect signal
133	Inlet manifold valve 2	High voltage
133	Inlet manifold valve 2	Low voltage
134	EGR valve 2	Low voltage
134	Inlet manifold valve 2	High voltage
135	'CHECK ENGINE' lamp	Low voltage
136	ECM	
137	ECM box	High temperature

Chapter 7
Ford EEC IV MPi/CFi

Contents

Specifications

Vehicle/engine	Year	Idle speed	CO%
Ford 2.0 SOHC			
Sierra/Sapphire/Granada 2.0 MT	1985 to 1989	875 ± 50	0.6 to 1%
Sierra/Sapphire 2.0 AT	1985 to 1989	875 ± 50	0.6 to 1%
Granada 2.0 AT	1985 to 1986	800 ± 50	0.6 to 1%
Ford 2.0 EFi DOHC 8-valve			
Sierra/Sapphire/Granada/Scorpio 2.0	1989 to 1993	875 ± 50	1.25 ± 0.25%
Sierra/Sapphire 2.0 cat	1989 to 1993	875 ± 50	0.50 max
Granada/Scorpio 2.0 cat	1989 to 1994	875 ± 50	0.50 max
Ford CFi			
Fiesta, Escort, Orion	1989 to 1990	900 ± 50	0.50 max
Ford EDIS			
Fiesta XR2i 1.6 LJC	1989 to 1993	900 ± 50	1.0 ± 0.25
Fiesta XR2i 1.6 cat LJD	1989 to 1993	900 ± 50	0.5
Fiesta RS turbo 1.6 LHA	1990 to 1992	900 ± 50	1.5 ± 0.25
Escort 1.6i XR3i LJA	1989 to 1992	900 ± 50	0.8 ± 0.25
Escort 1.6i XR3i cat LJB	1989 to 1992	900 ± 50	0.5
Escort 1.6i LJE	1990 to 1993	900 ± 50	0.8 ± 0.25
Escort 1.6i cat LJF	1990 to 1994	900 ± 50	0.50 max
Orion 1.6i LJA	1989 to 1990	900 ± 50	0.8 ± 0.25
Orion 1.6i LJE	1990 to 1993	900 ± 50	0.8 ± 0.25
Orion 1.6i cat LJF	1990 to 1994	900 ± 50	0.5
Ford Zetec 1.6, 1.8, 2.0			
Fiesta XR2i 1.8i RDB	1992 to 1995	875 ± 50	0.50 max
Fiesta 1.8i RQC	1992 to 1995	875 ± 50	0.50 max
Escort 1.6i L1E/1.8i RDA/1.8i RQB	1992 to 1995	875 ± 50	0.50 max
Orion 1.6i L1E/1.8i RDA/1.8i RQB	1992 to 1995	875 ± 50	0.50 max
Mondeo 1.6i L1F/1.8i RKA/2.0i NGA	1993 to 1995	880 ± 50	0.50 max

Vehicle/engine	Year	Idle speed	CO%
Ford V6			
Granada 2.4	-	875	0.75 ± 0.20%
Granada/Scorpio 2.8	1985 to 1987	850	0.6 to 1%
Granada/Scorpio/Sierra 2.9	-	825 ± 25	0.80 ± 0.20%
Ford V6 cat			
Granada ARD	-	825 rpm	0.50 max
Granada BRD	-	900 rpm	0.50 max
Granada BRE	-	875 rpm	0.50 max
Sierra B4B/B4C	-	900 rpm	0.50 max

Overview of system operation

1 Introduction

Please read this overview of Ford EEIC IV operation in conjunction with Chapter 2, which describes some of the functions in more detail.

Ford EEC IV is a generic engine management system fitted to all Ford electronically-controlled fuel-injected engines (except the Sierra and Escort Cosworth) from 1985 to 1995. It was first fitted to the Ford SOHC ('Pinto') engines, and is a fully-integrated system that controls primary ignition, fuelling and idle speed from within the same ECM **(see illustration 7.1)**.

Although an ECM of similar appearance is used in all vehicles, there are a number of vital internal differences between applications. In addition, the types of sensors used to provide base information also differ. This is true for both four- and six-cylinder engines. As the EEC IV system has evolved, it has taken on more and more responsibility, and the Zetec version also controls the various emission control systems, the air conditioning and even the radiator fans. This Chapter attempts to deal with the majority of variations between the different years and vehicles.

Zeta and Zetec

Originally, Ford used the code name 'Zeta' to describe the 1.6, 1.8 and 2.0 litre 16-valve engine type, but it was never planned to use this name in production. However, the name was adopted by many - even before production started - and so fell into common use. But the Zeta name was apparently licensed to Fiat, and Ford have therefore renamed the engine series 'Zetec'.

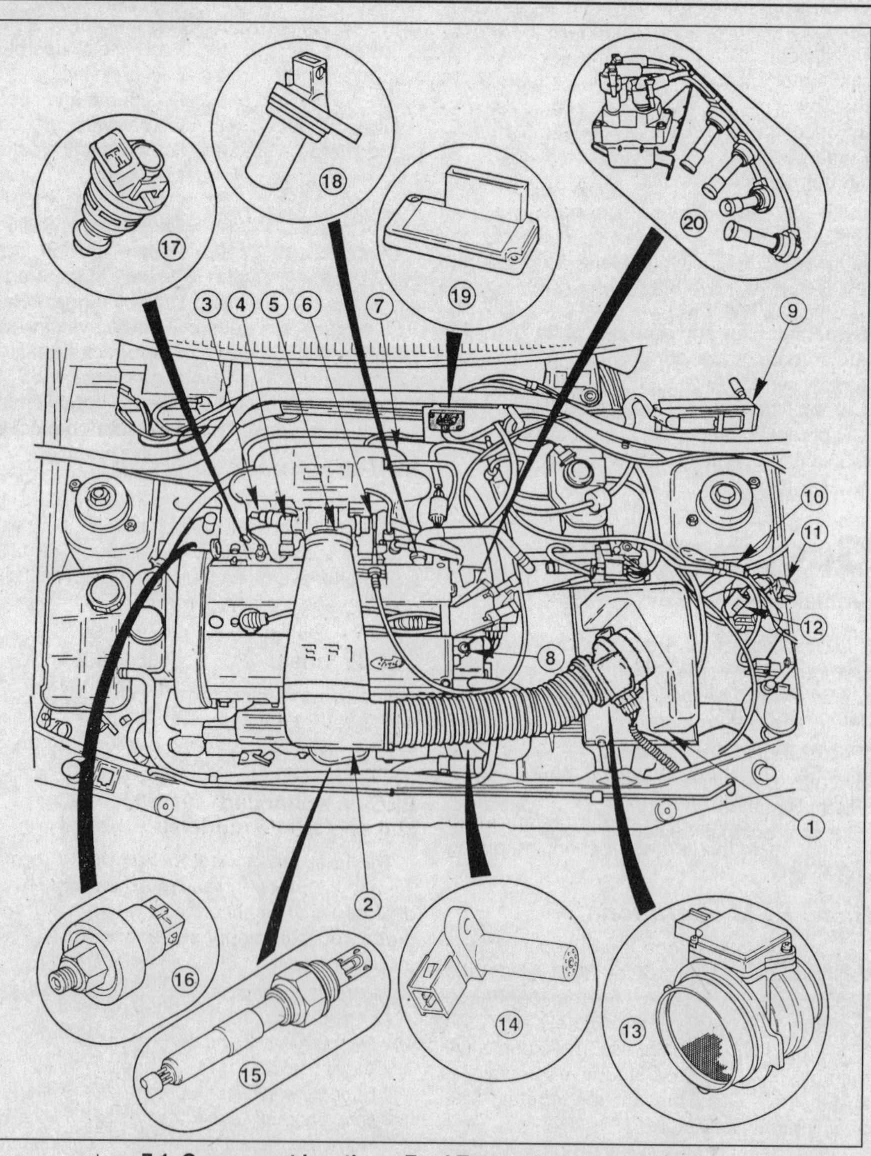

7.1 Component locations: Ford Zetec 16-valve 1.8 DOHC

1 Air filter
2 Air trunking
3 ISCV
4 TPS
5 Throttle body
6 Throttle control
7 Air plenum chamber
8 CTS
9 ABS module
10 Service connector for octane adjustment
11 SD connector
12 SD connector for FDS 2000
13 AFS (hot-wire type)
14 CAS
15 Oxygen sensor
16 PSPS
17 Fuel injectors
18 CID
19 EDIS module
20 DIS coil unit

2 Control functions

Signal processing

The EEC IV ignition point and injection duration are jointly processed by the ECM, so that the best moment for ignition and fuelling are determined for every operating condition. Primary ignition is instigated by either a distributor-mounted Hall-effect sensor or a flywheel-mounted CAS. The multi-point injection function of the EEC IV system was originally based upon the well-tried Bosch 'L' Jetronic system, with a vane-type AFS. However, the Zetec engine utilises a hot-wire AFS, the V6 catalyst engine utilises a MAP sensor, and the CFi engine also utilises a MAP sensor with its single-point injector. A 60-pin connector and multi-plug connects the ECM to the battery, sensors and actuators.

Basic ignition timing is stored by the ECM in a three-dimensional map, and the engine load and speed signals determines the ignition timing during the various operating conditions. The main engine load sensor is either an AFS or a MAP sensor, and engine speed is determined from either the CAS signal or the HES signal.

Correction factors are then applied for starting, idle, deceleration, and part- and full-load operation. The main correction factor is engine temperature (CTS). Minor correction to timing and AFR are made with reference to the ATS and TPS signals.

The basic AFR is also stored in a three-dimensional map, and the engine load and speed signals determine the basic injection pulse value. EEC IV calculates the AFR from the load signal and the engine speed.

The AFR and the pulse duration are then corrected on reference to ATS, CTS, battery voltage, and position of the TPS. Other controlling factors are determined by operating conditions such as cold start and warm-up, idle condition, acceleration and deceleration.

EEC IV accesses a different map for idle running conditions, and this map is implemented whenever the engine is at idle. Idle speed during warm-up and normal hot running conditions are maintained by the EMS idle control. EEC IV also makes small adjustments to the idle speed by advancing or retarding the timing, and this results in an ignition timing that is forever changing during engine idle.

Basic ECM operation

A permanent voltage is applied from the vehicle battery to pin 1 of the ECM (not for the basic EEC IV system, or the enhanced systems used before approximately 1987), via a 3-amp fuse. This allows the keep-alive memory (KAM) to store adaptive idle values, and the self-diagnostic function to retain data of an intermittent nature.

Once the ignition is switched on, a voltage supply from the ignition switch is applied to the ignition coil(s), the TFI module (amplifier) and to the main relay terminal 86. Relay terminal 85 is directly connected to earth and the relay winding is energised to connect terminals 30 and 87. Voltage output from terminal 87 is applied to ECM terminals 37 and 57, the fuel injectors, the majority of

7.2 EEC IV ECM (2.0 SOHC model). The multi-plug arrangement makes backprobing quite easy

actuators and terminal 86 of the fuel pump relay.

The majority of sensors (other than those that generate a voltage such as the VSS, OS and the CAS or Hall-effect sensor), are now provided with a 5.0 volt reference supply from a relevant pin on the ECM. When the engine is cranked or run, a speed signal from the primary ignition causes the ECM to earth pin 22 so that the fuel pump will run. Ignition and injection functions are also activated. All actuators (Injectors, ISCV, etc), are supplied with nbv from the main relay, and the ECM completes the circuit by pulsing the relevant actuator wire to earth **(see illustration 7.2)**.

Self-diagnostic function

The EEC IV system has a self-test capability that regularly examines the signals from engine sensors and internally logs a two-digit code in the event of a fault being present. This code can be extracted from the EEC IV serial port by a suitable fault code reader (FCR).

EEC IV 'basic'

The system used on the early 2.0 SOHC and 2.8 V6 engine was labelled the 'basic' system, and could only produce a small number of codes.

EEC IV 'enhanced' system (2.4 and 2.9 V6 models)

The later 'enhanced' system fitted to the 2.4 and 2.9 models produces many more two-digit codes. The enhanced system has three modes of fault diagnosis, and a service-set mode. The fault diagnosis modes are:

a) *Ignition on, engine off: A static test of the engine sensors.*
b) *Engine running and service-set mode: A dynamic test of the engine sensors. During the service-set mode, the Ignition timing and idle speed can be set. It is no longer possible to make these adjustments other than in service-set mode.*
c) *Continuous running: A test of the engine sensors during normal engine operation, including idle operation or during a road test.*

Note: *Fault codes produced by the basic system and also the enhanced system for these applications are only available whilst the fault is present and when the ignition is switched on. If the fault is permanent (present all the time), then an appropriate code will be logged each time the ignition is switched on. However, if the fault is intermittent and the ignition is switched off, the fault code will be lost.*

EEC IV 'enhanced' system (most Ford vehicles from 1987 to 1995)

The Ford enhanced system fitted to the 1.4 CFi and 2.0 DOHC models contains many more two-digit codes than the original basic and enhanced systems, and has the capability to retain intermittent codes in KAM. If the fault clears, the code will remain logged until wiped clean with a suitable FCR, or until the engine has been started for more than 20 times when the fault code is self-initialising. The enhanced system has three modes of fault diagnosis, and a service-set mode. The three fault diagnosis modes are:

a) *Ignition on, engine off: A static test of the engine sensors.*
b) *Engine running and service-set mode: A dynamic test of the engine sensors. During the service-set mode, the idle speed can be set. It is no longer possible to make this adjustment other than in service-set mode.*
c) *Continuous running: A test of the engine sensors during normal engine operation, including idle operation or during a road test.*

EEC IV 'enhanced' system (2.4 and 2.9 V6 catalyst models)

Very similar to the version fitted to the 2.0 DOHC vehicles above. However, this version of the enhanced system has two modes of fault diagnosis, and a service-set mode denoted by code 60. The two fault diagnosis modes are:

a) *Ignition on, engine off. A static test of the engine sensors.*
b) *Engine running and service-set mode. A dynamic test of the engine sensors. During the service-set mode, the Ignition timing can be set. It is no longer possible to make this adjustments other than in service-set mode.*

EEC IV 'enhanced' system (all Zetec and other Ford DIS engines with sequential injection)

Very similar to the version fitted to the 2.4 and 2.9 V6 catalyst models above. However, this version of the enhanced system now produces three-digit codes, but retains the two modes of fault diagnosis and a service-set mode. A flashing cursor is used to indicate the passing from one routine to another, and code 60 is replaced by this cursor. It is now possible to drive certain actuators through the FCR. The two fault diagnosis modes are:

a) *Ignition on, engine off. A static test of the engine sensors.*
b) *Engine running and service-set mode. A dynamic test of the engine sensors. During the service-set mode, the Ignition*

7

timing can be set. It is no longer possible to make this adjustments other than in service-set mode.

KAM (keep-alive memory)

KAM is a memory unit designed to store self-diagnostic data of an intermittent nature, and also any adaptive idle values 'learned' by the ECM. This means that if a fault occurs on a particular circuit (or circuits), a code will be logged and this code will remain logged - even if the ignition key is switched off; a very useful aid to fault-finding.

KAM is not available in vehicles manufactured prior to 1987, and this includes all SOHC and V6 non-catalyst engines. Those vehicles without KAM are also without an adaptive idle facility. KAM is able to retain data because a permanent voltage is applied from the vehicle battery to pin 1 of the ECM.

There are three ways in which fault codes can be cleared. One way is to use a proprietary FCR for instant clearance. The second way is to remove the battery earth cable for several minutes (however, there is a danger of losing radio codes when using this method). Finally, codes are erased naturally by the ECM after 20 cold engine drive cycles, if the fault does not recur during this time.

Definition of engine drive cycle

A vehicle that is started with a coolant temperature below 49°C, and continues running until the coolant temperature exceeds 65°C.

Adaptive idle

The ECM pulses the ISCV so that it maintains a correct idle speed under all variations of temperature and idle load. The Ford adaptive system compensates for normal wear, and adapts its program according to driving methods. Over a period of time, the ECM will learn the best idle position for a particular engine - irrespective of age, engine condition and load, so that the correct idle speed is always maintained.

Adaptive settings are retained in KAM, and if the battery is disconnected, the settings will be lost. Once battery power is lost to the ECM, the engine operation at idle and low speed may become erratic or stall for a short while, until KAM relearns new idle settings.

LOS (limited operating strategy or limp-home)

In the event of a serious system fault, EEC IV can call upon two levels of LOS or limp-home strategy.

Strategy one: Major system fault

EEC IV deals with a major ECM fault in the following manner:

a) *All sensor signals are ignored, and sensors are allocated fixed values so that the engine will run (usually not that well).*
b) *The timing is fixed to the PIP output value at all engine speeds.*
c) *A basic injection fuel setting is used to provide a constant volume of fuel over the limited load & speed range still available.*
d) *The fuel pump is pulsed to run continuously all the time that the ignition is switched to the ignition key on position.*

Note: *A method of determining whether the engine is in LOS is to listen to the fuel pump. Under normal circumstances, when the ignition key is switched on, the ECM will pulse the fuel pump for a time period not exceeding one second, and the pump will then be switched off to await a cranking or running signal.*

Strategy two: Sensor fault

When a sensor fault occurs, the EEC IV EMS deals with this minor fault in the following manner. The faulty sensor(s) are allocated fixed values corresponding to a warm engine, so that the engine will run satisfactorily at normal operating temperature. However, cold starting and running during the warm-up period are likely to be adversely affected.

Octane coding and service connectors

A service connector is provided, to enable the ECM to adopt a different timing programme (so that the engine will run on a lower octane fuel) or adopt different idle speed characteristics to suit various operating conditions. When one or more of the cables are connected to earth, the ECM will alter either the timing advance map or the idle speed (depending upon the cable used). This removes the need to make arbitrary adjustments to the ignition timing (ie by moving the distributor or by moving the throttle valve). Although adjustments are still possible under the control of the ECM and through the medium of a FCR, it is strongly recommended that the basic timing is only set to the datum position and all adjustments are made by using the service cables. In addition, it is not possible to alter the idle speed on some vehicles other than by using the service cable.

The EEC IV ECM provides a 5.0-volt reference feed to each of the service cables. When this cable is connected to earth, the voltage drops to zero. Once the ECM sees zero volts upon a particular cable, appropriate adjustments are made to its internal program.

Mondeo only

The EEC IV ECM provides a 5.0-volt reference feed to the octane connector multi-plug. When this cable is connected to earth via a resistance (octane plug), a voltage of lower value than 5.0 volts will be returned to the ECM. Once the ECM sees the lower voltage value, appropriate adjustments are made to its internal program.

Ignition timing adjustment

Distributor systems

a) *The 2.0 SOHC model has a fully-adjustable ignition timing function.*
b) *On other models with a distributor: Ignition timing is only adjustable during code 60 operation under ECM control. A dedicated FCR is required to place the ECM into code 60.*
c) *It is not possible to adjust the ignition timing on the 8-valve 2.0 DOHC engine.*
d) *2.4 and 2.9 catalyst models): Ignition timing is only adjustable during code 11 operation under ECM control. A dedicated FCR is required to place the ECM into code 11.*

Distributorless (DIS) systems

a) *It is not possible to physically adjust the ignition timing on any of the DIS models.*
b) *An octane connector (Mondeo) or a jumper cable (Escort, Fiesta, Orion) is provided to enable the ECM to adopt the timing characteristics to suit 95 octane fuel. If the coding plug or jumper cable is removed, the ECM will retard the timing by 'no fixed value'.*

Reference voltage

Voltage supply from the ECM to many of the engine sensors is at a 5.0 volt reference level. This ensures a stable working voltage, unaffected by variations in system voltage. The supply is made from ECM pin number 26.

Earth return

The earth return connection for most engine sensors is made through ECM pin number 46 and this pin is not directly connected to earth. The ECM internally connects pin number 46 to earth via one of the ECM pins that are directly connected to earth.

Signal shielding

To reduce RFI, a number of sensors (ie CAS, PIP & SAW or SPOUT and OS) use a shielded cable. The shielded cable is connected to the main ECM earth wire at terminal 20 to reduce interference to a minimum.

VSS

The VSS is utilised to advise the ECM of vehicle speed. It operates upon the Hall-effect principle, and will be mounted directly upon the gearbox or behind the dash.

A voltage of approximately 10 volts is applied to the VSS from the ignition switch when it is in the on position. As the speedometer cable turns, the Hall switch is alternately turned on and off to return a square wave signal to the ECM. The frequency of the signal denotes the vehicle speed.

3 Primary trigger

The primary trigger on EEC IV systems is either a distributor-mounted Hall-effect sensor, or a flywheel-mounted CAS. The operation of both types is described below.

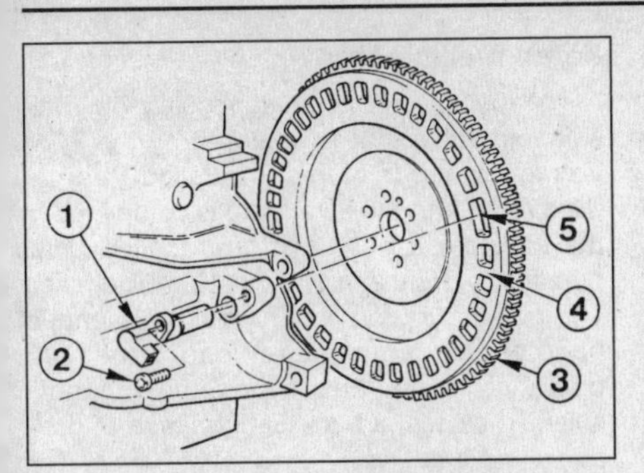

7.3 Flywheel and CAS layout

1 CAS
2 Fixing bolt
3 Flywheel
4 Teeth (36 less one)
5 Missing tooth (90° BTDC)

CAS

A CAS is used in the 8-valve 2.0 DOHC engines, and all of the vehicles with DIS. The primary trigger to initiate both ignition and fuelling emanates from a CAS mounted in close proximity to the flywheel. The CAS consists of an inductive magnet that radiates a magnetic field. Thirty-six teeth are set into the side of the flywheel at 10° intervals. At a position 90° BTDC with respect to No 1 cylinder, one tooth is removed as a reference mark to TDC. Thirty-five teeth thus remain set on the side of the flywheel **(see illustration 7.3)**.

As the flywheel spins, and the teeth are rotated in the magnetic field, an AC voltage signal is delivered to the ECM. The signal generated by the 35 teeth indicate speed of rotation, and the blip in the signal created by the missing tooth denotes crank position.

The AC peak-to-peak voltage of the speed signal can vary from 5 volts at idle to over 100 volts at 6000 rpm. The ECM uses an analogue-to-digital converter (ADC) to transform the AC pulse into a digital signal. The EEC IV variation fitted to the 2.0 DOHC engine does not provide a PIP signal.

Hall-effect sensor

A HES is used in the 2.0 SOHC & DOHC engines, CFi models with distributor, 2.4, 2.8 and 2.9 V6 engines, and all vehicles without DIS.

A voltage is applied to the Hall sensor from the TFI module. The Hall sensor is either directly earthed or the earth connection is made through the ECM. In addition, a signal wire from the TFI, at a voltage potential slightly lower than the Hall supply, is connected to the Hall switch **(see illustration 7.4)**.

Opposite the Hall sensor is a permanent magnet, whose field causes a small voltage to be generated. This small voltage completes the signal circuit. A trigger vane is attached to the distributor shaft, with a number of cut-outs equal to the number of cylinders.

As the distributor shaft rotates, the solid portion of the vane and the cut-out will in turn pass between the magnet and the Hall switch so that the signal voltage is diverted or allowed. The signal voltage will then switch

7.4 Combined HES and TFi (early non-cat V6 models). The arrows show the TFi fixing screws

from high voltage to low voltage (ie within 300 millivolts of earth) and this square waveform signal is returned to the TFI unit as a PIP (base timing) signal.

4 Distributor ignition

Ignition and TFI unit (HES primary trigger)

A PIP signal is produced by the Hall-effect sensor in the distributor, and returned to the TFI unit. The PIP signal is the basic timing signal, and allows the TFI unit to switch the coil to produce a spark. Because there is no advance mechanism in the distributor, and also no advance map in the TFI, initially the TFI will only switch the coil at whatever is the basic timing value. Base ignition timing is usually adjustable for these engines.

The PIP signal is also sent to the ECM via pin 56. The ECM uses the basic PIP signal to calculate the ignition dwell angle and timing advance according to rpm, and returns this modified signal to the TFI as a SPOUT signal. The TFI superimposes the PIP and SPOUT signals, and now has a new timing reference to switch the coil at the correct dwell and ignition advance angle.

Ignition and TFI unit (CAS primary trigger)

In the 2.0 DOHC 8 valve engine, the ECM receives a primary trigger signal directly from the CAS which is converted to a square waveform by an ADC. The ECM then computes ignition dwell and timing advance and returns the computed signal to the TFI as a SPOUT signal. The TFI uses the SPOUT signal to switch the coil at the correct dwell and ignition advance angle. Base ignition timing is non-adjustable for this engine.

Ignition dwell

Dwell operation in EEC IV is based upon the principle of the 'constant-energy current-limiting' system. This means that the dwell period remains constant at around 4.0 to 5.0 ms, at virtually all engine running speeds. However, the dwell duty cycle, when measured in percent or degrees, will vary as the engine speed varies.

Ignition coil

The ignition coil utilises low primary resistance in order to increase primary current and primary energy. The amplifier limits the primary current to around 8 amps, and this permits a reserve of energy to maintain the required spark burn time (duration).

Distributor

In the EEC IV system, the distributor contains the Hall-effect sensor and secondary HT components. The HT components are used to distribute the HT current from the coil secondary terminal to each spark plug in firing order.

5 DIS ignition

DIS ignition (EDIS-4)

The majority of EEC IV-equipped DIS vehicles utilise a separate ignition module termed EDIS-4. EDIS-4 contains additional circuitry for switching the ignition coils. In the Mondeo MT models, the EDIS-4 circuitry is contained in the main EEC IV control unit.

Although the ignition system is DIS, the basic operation is much the same as on models with conventional ignition. In a DIS or so-called 'wasted-spark' system, a double-ended coil is used to fire two plugs at the same time. This means that the system can only be used where two cylinders rise and fall together.

One cylinder will be on compression, and the companion cylinder on the exhaust stroke where the spark is 'wasted'. Two double-ended coils will therefore be required for a four-cylinder engine. About 3 kV is still needed to fire the 'wasted spark' plug, but this is far less than that required to bridge the rotor gap. Each ignition coil requires a voltage supply from the ignition switch, and a separate dwell connection to the ECM (or EDIS-4), so that the ECM can switch each coil individually.

The CAS position signal produces an analogue signal which is converted to a square waveform by an ADC. EDIS-4 sends the square waveform (PIP) signal to the EEC IV ECM. The ECM then computes the ignition dwell and timing advance for cylinders 1 and 4 according to engine speed, and returns the computed signal to the EDIS-4 as a SAW signal. The SAW signal for cylinders 2 and 3 is computed from the signal generated by cylinders 1 and 4.

The SAW signal is an advance warning of an ignition instruction, and is returned to the EDIS-4 module in a window covering a crankshaft angle of 10° ATDC to 170° BTDC. This window is outside of the normal advance angle, and ensures that the signal is not corrupted by secondary HT pulses. EDIS-4 superimposes the PIP and SAW signals, and has now a new timing reference to switch the ignition coils at the correct dwell and ignition advance angle. In effect, the SAW signal controls the ignition spark advance. For systems with an integral EDIS-4 module, the whole process is completed internally.

EDIS is self-monitoring, and in the event of one of a number of different faults, will return a coded EDM signal to the EEC IV ECM. Detectable faults include:

a) *DIS coil failure.*
b) *Failure to synchronise with the CAS signal.*
c) *EDIS microprocessor failure.*
d) *A missing or interrupted SAW signal from the EEC IV ECM.*

In addition, if one SAW signal is received outside of the 10° ATDC to 170° BTDC window, the EDIS module will use the width of the previous pulse. If five consecutive SAW signals are received outside of the window, or outside of the normal ignition spark range (10° ATDC to 57° BTDC), the EDIS module will fire the plugs at 10° BTDC. Some very early models may not return an EDM signal as described.

Base ignition timing is non-adjustable for all DIS engines. During engine cranking, low speed running and when operating in LOS, EDIS fires the spark plugs at 10° BTDC.

Ignition dwell

Dwell operation in EEC IV is based upon the principle of the 'constant-energy current-limiting' system. This means that the dwell period remains constant at around 4.0 to 5.0 ms, at virtually all engine running speeds. However, the dwell duty cycle, when measured in percent or degrees, will vary as the engine speed varies. A current-limiting hump is not visible when viewing an oscilloscope waveform.

Ignition coils

The ignition coils (A and B) utilise low primary resistance in order to increase primary current and primary energy. The amplifier limits the primary current to around 8 amps, and this permits a reserve of energy to maintain the required spark burn time (duration). Coil A is connected to cylinders 1 and 4; Coil B is connected to cylinders 2 and 3.

6 Fuel injection

Multi-point fuel injection

The EEC IV injection system operates as a multi-point (MPi) system in the SOHC, DOHC (8-valve) and V6 engines.

In the MPi system fitted to four-cylinder engines, the injectors are connected in two banks of two, and the ECM pulses all injectors (both banks) at the same time - ie simultaneously and once per engine revolution.

However, the MPi version fitted to V6 engines operates somewhat differently. The injectors are connected in two banks of three, but the ECM pulses each bank in sequence, first one bank and then the other.

Data on load (AFS or MAP sensor), engine speed (CAS or HES), engine temperature (CTS) and throttle position (TPS) are collected by the ECM, which then refers to a digital map stored within its microprocessor. This map contains an injection duration for each operating condition, and thus the best pulse duration angle for a particular operating condition can be determined. During engine start from cold, the pulse duration is increased to provide a richer air/fuel mixture.

Fuel injectors

The fuel injector is a magnetically-operated solenoid valve that is actuated by the ECM. Voltage to the injectors is applied from the main relay, and the earth path is completed by the ECM for a period of time (called pulse duration) of between 1.5 and 10 milliseconds. The pulse duration is very much dependent upon engine temperature, load, speed and operating conditions. When the magnetic solenoid closes, a back-EMF voltage of up to 60 volts is induced.

Fuel supply to the injector is made under pressure, and the amount of fuel injected is governed solely by the time that the injector is held open by the ECM. The fuel injectors are mounted in the inlet stubs to the engine inlet valves, so that a finely-atomised fuel spray is directed onto the back of each valve. Since the injectors are pulsed simultaneously, fuel will briefly rest upon the back of a valve before being drawn into a cylinder.

Sequential multi-point fuel injection

The EEC IV injection system as fitted to the Zetec engine is a multi-point system, and pulses the injectors sequentially - ie in firing order and once per engine cycle. Each injector is connected to the ECM via a separate ECM pin). The Zetec system reverts to simultaneous operation if the engine speed falls below 600 rpm.

Data on engine load (AFS), engine speed (CAS), engine temperature (CTS) and throttle position (TPS) are collected by the ECM, which then refers to a digital map stored within its microprocessor. This map contains an injection duration for each operating condition, and thus the best pulse duration angle for a particular operating condition can be determined.

During engine start from cold, the pulse duration is increased to provide a richer air/fuel mixture.

Zetec fuel injector

The fuel injector is a magnetically-operated solenoid valve that is actuated by the ECM. Voltage to the injectors is applied from the main relay, and the earth path is completed by the ECM for a period of time (called pulse duration) of between 1.5 and 10 milliseconds. The pulse duration is very much dependent upon engine temperature, load, speed and operating conditions. When the magnetic solenoid closes, a back-EMF voltage of up to 60 volts is induced.

Each fuel injector is mounted in the fuel rail, and sealed by means of an 'O' ring. Fuel supply to each injector is made under pressure. Unlike most injection systems where the injector is supplied from the top, fuel supply to the Zetec injectors is made laterally, with the injector immersed in a fuel-filled pocket. The advantage of this arrangement is that the fuel cools the injector, and this minimises the risk of fuel vaporisation and poor hot starting. When the ignition is switched on, fresh fuel is flushed through the injector to reduce the temperature.

The complete fuel rail is plugged into the plastic (Mondeo) or cast (other models) inlet manifold and sealed by means of an 'O' ring. The injector is thus positioned so that when the inlet valve opens, a finely-atomised fuel spray is directed into the cylinder.

Single-point fuel injection (Ford term 'CFi', or 'central fuel injection').

In the single-point injection system, fuel is injected into the inlet manifold to be drawn into a cylinder by the action of a descending piston. During idle conditions, the injector is actuated once per engine revolution. At all other engine speeds above idle, the injector is actuated during the inlet valve opening cycle for each cylinder. The frequency of injection thus becomes twice per engine revolution.

Data on load (MAP), engine speed (CAS or Hall -effect), engine temperature (CTS) and throttle position (TPS) are collected by the ECM, which then refers to a digital map stored within its microprocessor. This map contains an injection duration for each operating condition, and thus the best pulse duration angle for a particular operating condition can be determined.

The injector is switched using two circuits. Operation depends on the principle that more current is required to open an injector than to keep it open. A peak current of 2.75 amps is applied to open the injector valve. Once the injector is open, a second circuit (made through a ballast resistor) applies a reduced current of 1.32 amps to hold the injector open. Advantages of this arrangement include a reduction in injector operating temperature, and immediate injector closure once the holding circuit is switched off.

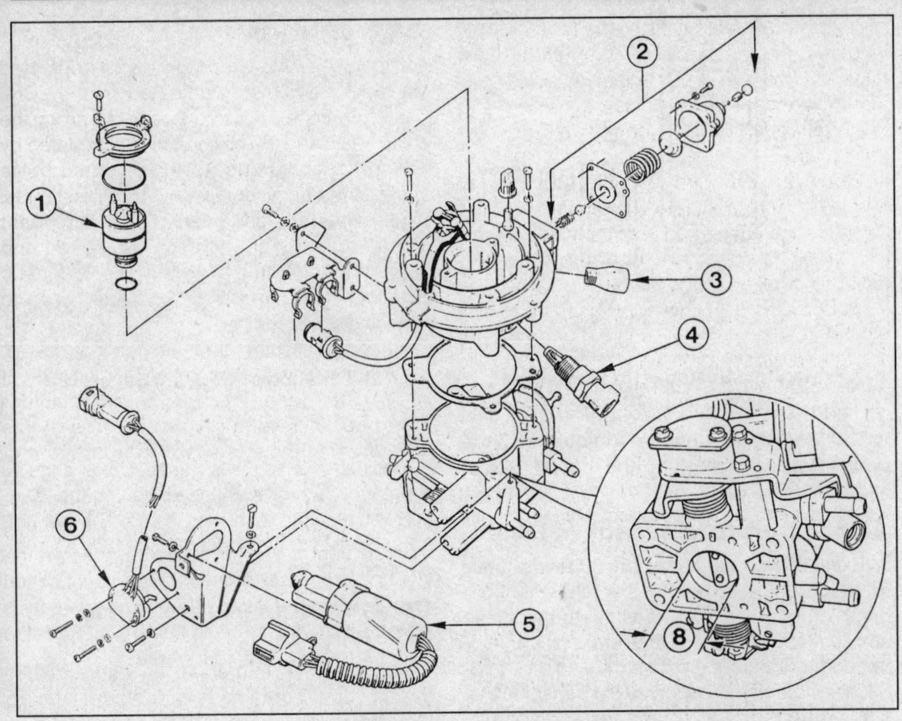

7.5 Ford single-point injection throttle body

1 *Fuel injector*
2 *Fuel pressure regulator*
3 *Fuel inlet connector*
4 *ATS*
5 *Stepper motor*
6 *TPS*
8 *Throttle valve diameter varies according to engine size*

Single-point fuel injector

The fuel injector is a magnetically-operated solenoid valve that is actuated by the ECM **(see illustration 7.5)**. Voltage to the injector is applied from the main relay, and the earth path is completed by the ECM for a period of time (called pulse duration) of between 1.5 and 10 milliseconds. The pulse duration is very much dependent upon engine temperature, load, speed and operating conditions. When the magnetic solenoid closes, a back-EMF voltage of up to 60 volts is induced.

Fuel supply to the injector is made under pressure, and the amount of fuel injected is governed solely by the time that the injector is held open by the ECM.

Cylinder identification sensor (CID)

Because the Zetec engine utilises sequential injection, the system requires knowledge of which cylinder is No 1. The CID sensor operates in a similar fashion to the CAS. A single raised lobe is positioned on the inlet camshaft, adjacent to the permanent magnet sensor mounted in the cylinder head opposite to No 4 cylinder.

As the camshaft rotates and the lobe is positioned opposite the CID sensor, an AC signal is returned to the ECM which exactly identifies the position of No 1 cylinder. In fact, the signal occurs when No 1 cylinder is 46° ATDC.

Once No 1 cylinder is identified, the ECM examines the CAS position signal, and injects fuel into No 1 cylinder as the inlet valve opens. Injection for all other cylinders occurs as the inlet valves open in firing-order sequence. When the engine is first started and until 600 rpm is achieved, the ECM ignores the CID signal, and uses the PIP signal to instigate simultaneous injection. Above 600 rpm, the ECM employs the CID sensor to time the injectors sequentially. Simultaneous injection will occur if the engine speed ever drops below 600 rpm whilst it is running. The signal from the CID sensor is only examined by the ECM during engine start-up. After the engine is running, the signal from the CID sensor is ignored until the engine is next started.

Air intake system

Air is drawn through an air filter and into the inlet manifold via a throttle body.

Mondeo only

In Mondeo models, the air intake trunking comprises several air resonators that are used to reduce induction roar. Noise is reduced when the air pulses are slowed during the movement of air in the intake system resonators. Each resonator is designed to reduce induction noise over a certain engine rpm range. The resonator pipe diameter and volume is the determining factor for the amount of noise reduction and the rpm range covered.

The throttle body is of the single venturi type, and is located in the centre of the inlet manifold. For Mondeo models, an inlet manifold constructed from plastic is used. A by-pass screw is used to set the basic idle speed during production. The screw is then sealed, and it is usually unnecessary to reset this screw in normal service. In fact, the ECM will usually make any adjustments to the idle speed as part of the adaptive process (see adaptive idle under self-diagnostics).

Load sensors

The ECM requires a load sensor to detect the flow of air into an engine. Once the volume of air is known, the correct amount of fuel can be looked up in the map. Several methods are used by the various EEC IV systems to measure load. The vane-type AFS, the hot-wire air mass meter and the MAP sensor are the three types most usually found.

AFS (vane-type)

The AFS is located between the air filter and the throttle body. As air flows through the sensor it deflects a vane (flap). The greater the volume of air, the more will the flap be deflected. The vane is connected to a wiper arm which wipes a potentiometer resistance track and so varies the resistance of the track. This allows a variable voltage signal to be returned to the ECM.

Three wires are used by the circuitry of this sensor, and it is often referred to as a 'three-wire' sensor. A 5-volt reference voltage is applied to the resistance track, with the other end connected to the sensor earth return. The third wire is connected to the wiper arm.

From the voltage returned, the ECM is able to calculate the volume of air (load) entering the engine, and this is used to calculate the main fuel injection duration. To smooth out inlet pulses, a damper is connected to the AFS vane. The AFS exerts a major influence on the volume of fuel injected. In non-cat V6 applications, two AFS's are used.

Hot-wire air mass meter (AFS)

The Zetec engine uses a hot-wire air mass meter to measure the mass of air entering the engine **(see illustration 7.6)**. The hot-wire air mass meter has replaced the vane-type AFS fitted to earlier vehicles. The air mass meter measures the mass of air entering the engine, which allows an accurate fuel injection pulse

7.6 Hot-wire airflow sensor (AFS), 1.8 Escort

to be calculated. Hot-wire is a very accurate method of calculating the engine load (air input), and often excludes the need for additional sensors to measure air temperature and air pressure. Automatic compensation for altitude is thus provided. The absence of moving parts improves reliability and lessens maintenance requirements.

Essentially, the hot-wire is so called because a hot-wire sensor and an air temperature sensor are placed in a by-pass to the main air intake. Both sensors are constructed from platinum, and directly connected to a hybrid integrated circuit (IC) module mounted on the body of the AFS.

The AFS module receives a voltage supply from the system main relay, and applies a constant voltage to the hot-wire air temperature sensor. The hot-wire ATS measures the temperature of air passing through the AFS, and passes the signal to the AFS module, which then heats the hot-wire sensor to 200°C hotter than the hot-wire ATS. As air passes over the hot wire, it has a cooling effect. As air mass increases or decreases according to engine load, the AFS module adjusts the current flow to maintain the wire at its original resistance and temperature. The change in heating current is measured as a voltage drop over a precision resistor, and amplified by the AFS module as a measured value. This measured value is then returned to the EEC IV ECM for evaluation as a load signal.

By measuring the change in current flow, the ECM is able to determine the mass of air flow into the engine. As the current varies on the signal wire, so does the voltage, and an indication of load can be assessed by measuring the variable voltage signal.

MAP sensor

The MAP sensor is used to determine engine load. This sensor is a digital frequency device, and the frequency of the signal determines the load **(see illustration 7.7)**.

Using the speed/density method, the ECM calculates ignition timing and the AFR from the MAP signal and the speed of the engine. This method relies on the theory that the engine will draw in a fixed volume of air per revolution.

A vacuum hose connects the MAP sensor (usually located upon the bulkhead) and the inlet manifold. Manifold vacuum acts upon the MAP sensor diaphragm and the ECM converts the pressure into an electrical signal. MAP is calculated from the formula: Atmospheric Pressure less Manifold Pressure = Manifold Absolute Pressure.

A 5.0-volt reference voltage is applied to the sensor and connected to the EEC IV sensor return circuit. MAP sensor output on the signal wire is returned to the ECM as a frequency that will vary from 100 to 110 Hz at idle speed, and from 150 to 160 Hz with the ignition on or under full load operating conditions.

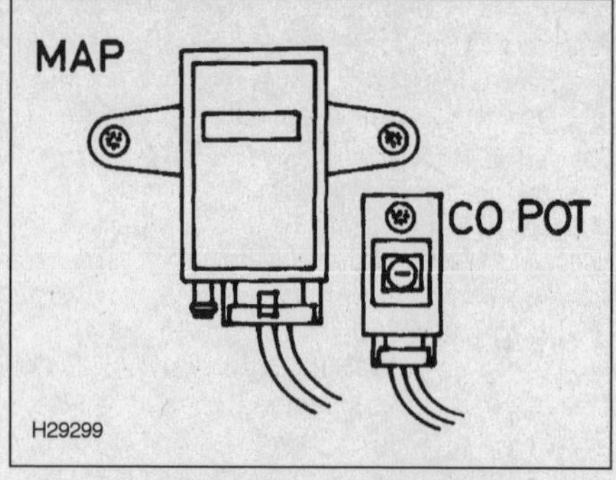

7.7 Manifold absolute pressure (MAP) sensor and CO pot

7.8 Location of CTS, 1.8 Escort DIS

The MAP sensor exerts a major influence on the ignition timing and the volume of fuel injected.

Air temperature sensor (ATS)

The ATS is mounted in the AFS inlet tract (models with AFS) or in the inlet manifold (most other models) or underneath the intake air resonator (Mondeo) and measures the air temperature before it enters the engine.

The open-circuit supply to the sensor is at a 5.0-volt reference level, and the earth path is through the sensor return. The ATS operates on the NTC principle. A variable voltage signal is returned to the ECM based upon the air temperature. This signal is approximately 2.0 to 3.0 volts at an ambient temperature of 20°C, and reduces to about 1.5 volts as the temperature rises to around 40°C.

Because the density of air varies in inverse proportion to the temperature, the ATS signal allows more accurate assessment of the volume of air entering the engine. However, the ATS has only a minor correcting effect on ECM output.

Where two AFS's are used in V6 applications, the ATS is only fitted to the rear sensor.

CO adjustment

Two different types of CO adjustment are utilised in non cat models. Catalyst equipped vehicles are not fitted with a CO pot and the CO is thus non-adjustable.

CO adjustment (vane-type AFS)

The mechanical type of AFS utilises an air bleed screw to trim the CO value. An air channel allows a small volume of air to by-pass the air flowing through the vane. As the by-pass is moved, the air volume acting upon the vane is altered, and the vane moves its position. The changed position results in an altered signal to the ECM and a change in fuel volume injected.

CO pot (all other non-cat vehicles: not fitted to cat models)

The CO pot mixture adjuster is a three-wire potentiometer that allows small changes to be made to the idle CO. A 5.0-volt reference voltage is applied to the sensor and connected to the EEC IV sensor return circuit. The third wire is the CO pot signal. As the CO pot adjustment screw is turned, the change in resistance returns a voltage signal to the ECM that will result in a change in CO. The CO pot adjustment only affects idle CO. Datum position is usually 2.50 volts.

Coolant temperature sensor (CTS)

The CTS is immersed in the coolant system, and contains a variable resistance that operates on the NTC principle **(see illustration 7.8)**. When the engine is cold, the resistance is quite high. Once the engine is started and begins to warm-up, the coolant becomes hotter and this causes a change in the CTS resistance. As the CTS becomes hotter, the resistance of the CTS reduces (NTC principle), and this returns a variable voltage signal to the ECM based upon the coolant temperature.

The open-circuit supply to the sensor is at a 5.0-volt reference level, and this voltage reduces to a value that depends upon the resistance of the CTS resistance. Normal operating temperature is usually from 80 to 100°C. The ECM uses the CTS signal as a main correction factor when calculating ignition timing and injection duration.

Throttle potentiometer sensor (TPS)

A TPS is provided to inform the ECM of idle position, deceleration, rate of acceleration and full-load (WOT) conditions. The TPS is a potentiometer with three wires. A 5.0-volt reference voltage is supplied to a resistance track, with the other end connected to the sensor earth return. The third wire is connected to an arm which wipes along the resistance track and so varies the resistance and voltage of the signal returned to the ECM.

From the voltage returned, the ECM is able to calculate idle position (usually less than 0.7 volts), full-load (approximately 4.5 volts) and also how quickly the throttle is opened. During full-load operation, the ECM provides additional enrichment. During closed throttle operation above a certain rpm (deceleration), the ECM will cut-off fuel injection. Injection will be reintroduced once the rpm returns to idle or the throttle is opened.

Fuel temperature sensor (FTS)

The FTS is used to overcome the problem of vaporisation in the fuel lines. When the engine is switched off at normal operating temperature, the flow of coolant through the radiator and engine block also stops. In addition, with the bonnet down, the engine compartment turns into an oven. For some little while after the engine has been stopped, the engine compartment temperature rises, and the heat generated causes the fuel in the fuel lines to turn to vapour. When the fuel temperature is under 68°C, the FTS is open, and the ECM implements a normal program. When the fuel temperature rises over 87°C, the FTS is closed and the ECM adjusts the air/fuel mixture.

Idle speed control

Multi-point and single-point injection engines utilise a different method of controlling the idle speed. The multi-point injection engines utilise a solenoid-controlled ISCV, whilst the single-point injection engines utilise a stepper motor. A description of both types follows.

Idle speed control valve (ISCV)

The ISCV is a solenoid-controlled actuator that the ECM uses to automatically control idle speed during normal idle and during engine warm-up. The ISCV is located in a by-pass channel to the inlet manifold.

When an electrical load, such as headlights, heater fan etc, are switched on, the idle speed would tend to drop. The ECM will sense the load, and move the ISCV against spring tension to increase the air flow through the valve, and thus increase the idle speed. When the load is removed, the ECM will pulse the valve so that the air flow is reduced. Normal idle speed should be maintained under all cold and hot operating conditions. If the ISCV fails, it will fail-safe, with the aperture almost closed. This will provide a basic idle speed.

Additional signals are applied to dedicated pins at the ECM from automatic transmission and air conditioning components (when fitted). These signals allow the idle speed to be altered to cater for the additional loads presented by the use of these devices.

Stepper motor

The stepper motor is a solenoid-controlled actuator that the ECM uses to automatically control idle speed during normal idle and during engine warm-up. The stepper motor is mainly used in single-point applications, and is located by the side of the single-point injector unit where it acts upon the throttle plate.

Two control circuits are employed. The first circuit is basically a set of contacts known as the idle tracking switch. Only when the switch is closed will idle control be implemented. The second circuit is actuated by the ECM (when the idle tracking switch is closed) so that a constant idle speed can be maintained during all cold and hot operating conditions.

When the engine is cold, a slightly faster idle speed is implemented to cater for the inefficiencies of a cold engine. During deceleration, when the throttle is closed, the ECM monitors the TPS and MAP sensor load conditions so that the motor can impose a damped throttle plate return. The allows the motor to slowly return the throttle plate to the idle position, and hydrocarbon emissions during deceleration are thus much reduced.

When an electrical load, such as headlights, heater fan etc, are switched on, the idle speed would tend to drop. The ECM will sense the load and actuate the stepper motor to move the throttle plate to a more open position and thus increase the idle speed. When the load is removed, the ECM will pulse the motor so that the throttle plate moves to a more closed position. Normal idle speed should therefore be maintained irrespective of engine load.

Additional signals are applied to dedicated pins at the ECM from automatic transmission and air conditioning components (when used). These signals allow the idle speed to be altered to cater for the additional loads presented by the use of these devices.

Power steering pressure switch (PSPS) - Zetec engines

This switch is operated by a change in pressure when the power steering operates during movement of the front wheels. The PSPS is located in the engine compartment, in the delivery pipe to the steering gear. The PSPS is closed when the steering gear fluid pressure is low (ie when the steering is straight). The switch opens when the steering is turned (ie when the oil pressure rises above a pre-determined value).

A voltage slightly less than nbv is applied to the PSPS. When the steering is straight and the PSPS is closed, the voltage drops to near zero. When the steering is turned and the steering gear pressure reaches its pre-determined value, the PSPS opens, and the voltage on the PSPS pin rises to almost nbv. The ECM then increases the idle rpm to maintain the idle speed due to the increased load caused by the power steering coming into play. **Note:** *The PSPS fitted to Ford vehicles other than those with the Zetec engine operates in the exact opposite manner to that described above. In other vehicles, the PSPS switch is open when the steering is straight, and is closed when the steering is turned.*

Relays

The EEC IV electrical system is controlled by a main fuel injection relay and a fuel pump relay. A permanent voltage supply is made to the main relay terminal 30 and fuel pump relay terminal 30 from the battery positive terminal.

Once the ignition is switched on, a voltage supply from the ignition switch is applied to main relay terminal 86. Main relay terminal 85 is directly connected to earth, and the relay winding is energised to connect terminals 30 and 87. Voltage output from terminal 87 is thus applied to ECM terminals 37 and 57, the fuel injectors, various other actuators, and terminal 86 of the fuel pump relay.

When the ignition is switched on, the ECM briefly earths fuel pump relay contact 85 (most models) or contact 86 (Mondeo) at ECM terminal 22. This energises the pump relay winding, which closes the relay contact and connects voltage from terminal 30 to terminal 87, thereby providing voltage to the fuel pump circuit. After approximately one second, the ECM opens the circuit and the pump stops. This brief running of the fuel pump allows pressure to build within the fuel pressure lines, and provides for an easier start.

The fuel pump relay circuit will then remain open until the engine is cranked or run. Once the ECM receives an engine speed signal, the relay winding will again be energised by the ECM, and the fuel pump will run until the engine is stopped.

Inertia switch

The inertia switch is a safety cut-out switch used to isolate the fuel pump in the event of a very sharp deceleration - eg a collision **(see illustration 7.9)**. Once the switch has been activated, the electrical supply to the fuel pump remain open-circuit until the inertia switch has been reset by raising the button.

Fuel pressure system (external pump)

Prior to the middle of 1990, a roller-type fuel pump is used, driven by a permanent magnet electric motor. Mounted close to the fuel tank, it draws fuel from the tank and pumps it to the fuel rail via a fuel filter. The pump is of the 'wet' variety, in that fuel actually flows through the pump and the electric motor. There is no actual fire risk, because the fuel drawn through the pump is not in a combustible condition.

Mounted upon the armature shaft is an eccentric rotor holding a number of pockets arranged around the circumference - each pocket containing a metal roller. As the pump is actuated, the rollers are flung outwards by centrifugal force to act as seals. The fuel between the rollers is forced to the pump pressure outlet.

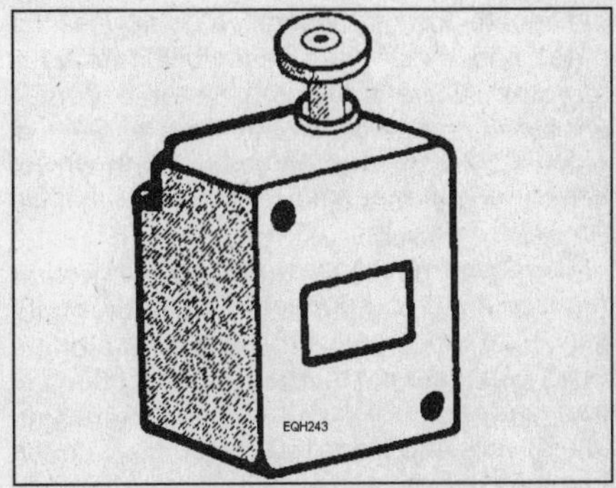

7.9 Inertia switch

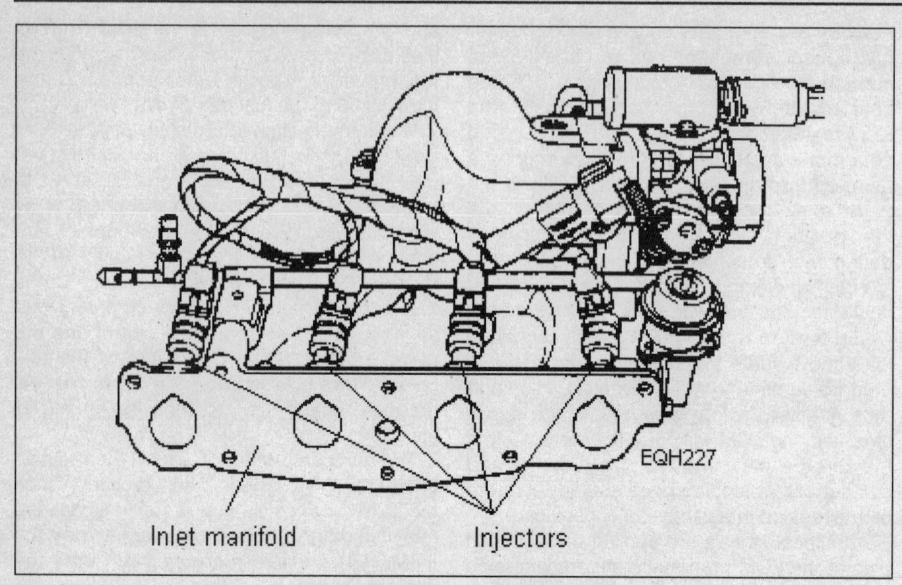

7.10 Multi-point injection system

Fuel pressure in the fuel rail is maintained at a constant 2.5 bar by a fuel pressure regulator. The fuel pump normally provides much more fuel than is required, and surplus fuel is thus returned to the fuel tank via a return pipe. Re-circulation of fuel helps to keep it cool. In fact, a maximum fuel pressure in excess of 5 bar is possible in this system. To prevent pressure loss in the supply system, a non-return valve is provided in the fuel pump outlet. When the ignition is switched off, and the fuel pump ceases operation, pressure is thus maintained for some time.

Fuel pressure system (internal pump, MPi and single-point)

From the middle of 1990, the fuel system consists of a fuel tank, with plastic anti-surge pot and a submerged fuel pump (mounted inside the fuel tank). The fuel pump draws fuel from the tank, and pumps it to the injector via a fuel filter **(see illustration 7.10)**.

Switching the ignition key on causes the ECM to energise the fuel pump relay for approximately one second so that the fuel system is pressurised. The fuel pump relay is then switched off, to await a cranking or running signal.

The fuel pump assembly comprises an outer and inner gear assembly, termed a 'gerotor'. Once the pump motor becomes energised, the gerotor rotates and as the fuel passes through the individual teeth of the gerotor, a pressure differential is created. Fuel is drawn through the pump inlet, to be pressurised between the rotating gerotor teeth and discharged from the pump outlet into the fuel supply line. The pump is of the 'wet' variety, in that fuel actually flows through the pump and the electric motor. There is no actual fire risk, because the fuel drawn through the pump is not in a combustible condition.

The anti-surge pot ensures that the pick-up strainer is always immersed in fuel during fuel movement, due to centrifugal forces acting upon the vehicle when the fuel level is low. This prevents air from entering the fuel supply line under these conditions. To reduce the effect of fluctuations in fuel pressure, a pulsation damper is provided in the pump outlet, thereby reducing pumping noise. The pump is protected from over-pressurising by a ball-type relief valve mounted in the inlet side of the pump. When pressure exceeds a pre-determined level, the valve opens and fuel is returned to the tank.

Fuel pressure in the fuel rail is maintained at a constant 2.5 bar by a fuel pressure regulator. The fuel pump normally provides much more fuel than is required, and surplus fuel is thus returned to the fuel tank via a return pipe. Re-circulation of fuel helps to keep it cool. In fact, a maximum fuel pressure in excess of 5 bar is possible in this system. To prevent pressure loss in the supply system, a non-return valve is provided in the fuel pump outlet. When the ignition is switched off, and the fuel pump ceases operation, pressure is thus maintained for some time.

Fuel pressure regulator (MPi, external and internal fuel pumps)

The pressure regulator is fitted on the outlet side of the fuel rail, and maintains an even pressure of 2.5 bar in the fuel rail. The pressure regulator consists of two chambers separated by a diaphragm. The upper chamber contains a spring which exerts pressure upon the lower chamber and closes off the outlet diaphragm. Pressurised fuel flows into the lower chamber, and this exerts pressure upon the diaphragm. Once the pressure exceeds 2.5 bar, the outlet diaphragm is opened, and excess fuel flows back to the fuel tank via a return line.

A vacuum hose connects the upper chamber to the inlet manifold, so that variations in inlet manifold pressure will not affect the amount of fuel injected. This means that the pressure in the rail is always at a constant pressure above the pressure in the inlet manifold. The quantity of injected fuel thus depends solely on injector opening time, as determined by the ECM, and not on a variable fuel pressure.

At idle speed with the vacuum pipe disconnected, or with the engine stopped and the pump running, or at full-throttle, the system fuel pressure will be around 2.5 bar. At idle speed (vacuum pipe connected), the fuel pressure will be approximately 0.5 bar under the system pressure.

Fuel pressure regulator (single-point injection)

Fuel pressure of approximately one bar is controlled by the pressure regulator, which is located within the throttle body next to the injector. As the pressure rises over the pre-determined level, excess fuel is returned to the fuel tank via a return pipe. To prevent pressure loss in the supply system, a non-return valve is provided in the fuel pump outlet. When the ignition is switched off, and the fuel pump ceases operation, pressure is thus maintained for some time.

7 Catalytic converter and emission control

Catalytic converter

Versions with a catalytic converter are fitted with an oxygen sensor, so that closed-loop control of emissions can be implemented. The OS is heated, so that it will reach optimum operating temperature as quickly as possible after the engine is started. The OS heater supply is made from the fuel injection main relay terminal number 87. This ensures that the heater will only operate whilst the engine is running. Some models are equipped with two OS's - one in the left-hand, and one in the right-hand exhaust pipe.

An CFSV and activated carbon canister is also be employed to aid evaporative emission control. The carbon canister stores fuel vapours until the CFSV is opened by the EMS under certain operating conditions. Once the CFSV is actuated by the EMS, fuel vapours are drawn into the inlet manifold, to be burnt by the engine during normal combustion. The CFSV is not activated when the engine is cold or during warm-up, when the engine is at idle speed, or during full-load (wide open throttle) operation.

An CFSV and activated carbon canister are not used on the V6 cat models, and a 1000-ohm resistor mounted close to the ECM is substituted in the wiring to the ECM CFSV connection.

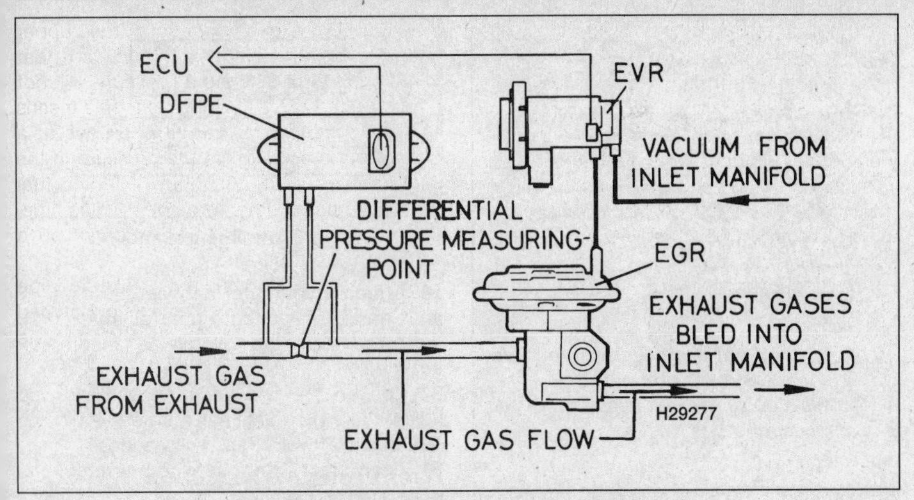

7.11 Exhaust gas recirculation system (EGR)

Exhaust gas recirculation (EGR)

Modern engines that run at high temperatures with high compression tend to produce a high level of NOx. NOx production can be reduced by recycling a small amount of exhaust gas into the combustion chamber. So long as the recycling of the exhaust gas is properly controlled, the engine operation will be little affected **(see illustration 7.11)**.

EGR operation only occurs after the engine has attained normal operating temperature and the engine is operating under part-load conditions. The ECM monitors the voltage returned from the DPFE or EPT sensor, and adjusts the signal to the EVR valve. The EVR applies vacuum to the EGR valve, which in turn opens to allow a finely-metered supply of exhaust gas to be introduced into the inlet manifold.

Electronic vacuum regulator (EVR)

The EVR regulates the vacuum that is applied to the EGR valve. Vacuum is piped from the inlet manifold to the EVR. A second pipe connects the EVR to the EGR valve. When the ECM signals the EVR, a channel is opened so that vacuum is applied to the EGR valve.

Delta pressure feedback electronic system (DPFE)

This sensor measures the differential pressure in a venturi pipe that connects the exhaust pipe and the EGR valve. The pressure drop is converted to a voltage and returned to the ECM, which actuates the EVR so that a finely-metered amount of exhaust gas is re-circulated into the inlet manifold by the EGR valve.

Electronic pressure transducer (EPT)

This sensor is a forerunner of the DPFE, and measures the exhaust flow in a pipe that connects the exhaust pipe and the EGR valve. The exhaust flow is converted to a voltage and returned to the ECM, which actuates the EVR so that a finely-metered amount of exhaust gas is re-circulated into the inlet manifold by the EGR valve.

Pulse air system

It is important that the catalytic converter and OS reach their respective operating temperatures as soon after the engine is started as possible. Bleeding fresh air into the exhaust system allows the rich cold start mixture to continue burning. This raises the exhaust temperature, and very quickly achieves the objective.

Fresh air from the inlet trunking (upstream of the AFS) is routed to the exhaust manifold though the pulse air valve (PAV). The air branches into two circuits, and enters the exhaust manifold through a non-return valve and connector pipe. Each circuit feeds air to two companion cylinders (1 & 4 and 2 & 3), and each cylinder is provided air from its own connector pipe.

A vacuum connection from the inlet manifold applies vacuum to the PAV. A solenoid (PASV) controls the vacuum applied to the PAV. Immediately after the engine starts from cold, the ECM actuates the PASV, which opens the air valve and air is thus introduced to the exhaust manifold. The pulse air system is switched off once the heated OS and catalyst reaches operating temperature. This occurs within 30 to 60 seconds from engine start. A silencer is provided in the PAV, to reduce noise from operation of the pulse air system (Mondeo only).

Adjustments

8 Adjustment pre-conditions

1 Ensure that all of these conditions are met before attempting to make adjustments:

a) Engine at operating temperature. Engine oil at a minimum temperature of 80°C. A 4-mile (minimum) journey is recommended (particularly so if equipped with AT).
b) Ancillary equipment (all engine loads and accessories) switched off.
c) AT models: Transmission in N or P.
d) Engine mechanically sound.
e) Engine breather hoses and breather system in satisfactory condition.
f) Induction system free from vacuum leaks.
g) Ignition system in satisfactory condition.
h) Air filter in satisfactory condition.
i) Exhaust system free from leaks
j) Throttle cable correctly adjusted
k) No fault codes logged by the ECM.
l) OS operating satisfactorily (catalyst vehicles with closed-loop control).
m) Stabilise the engine. Raise the engine speed to 3000 rpm for a minimum of 30 seconds and then let the engine idle. Allow the CO and idle speed to stabilise.
n) Make all checks and adjustments within 30 seconds. If this time is exceeded, re-stabilise the engine and recheck.

2 When setting the idle speed and CO, refer also to the following additional conditions:

a) Set the electric cooling fan running continuously:
Detach the multi-plug from the cooling system thermoswitch.
Use a jumper lead to bridge the multi-plug contacts.
b) Disconnect the service-set cables (if used)

9 Throttle adjustments

All vehicles

1 Clean the throttle valve and surrounding areas with carburettor cleaner. Blow-by from the breather system often causes sticking problems here.

2 Apart from the vehicles described below, the throttle valve and TPS on all other vehicles are non-adjustable. **Note:** *If the idle speed remains high after adjustment and cannot be set to the correct value, check for induction vacuum leaks.*

Throttle valve position (2.0 SOHC)

3 The throttle valve is critical, and should not normally be disturbed. A common fault is maladjustment of the idle speed by use of the throttle stop screw.

4 Where adjustment IS required, refer first to the adjustment pre-conditions in Section 8.

5 Check that the ignition timing is correct.

6 Disconnect the TPS multi-plug. Access is rather difficult.

7 Start the engine, without touching the throttle pedal, and allow it to idle. The engine should settle to its base idle speed of 1050 ± 20 rpm.

8 If the base idle speed is incorrect:

a) Remove the tamperproof cap from the throttle stop screw, and slacken the locknut.

b) Adjust the throttle stop screw until the base idle speed of 1050 ± 20 rpm is reached.

c) Carefully retighten the locknut.

d) Fit a new tamperproof cap to the throttle stop screw.

9 Reconnect the TPS multi-plug.

10 Adjust the TPS (see paragraph 28).

Throttle valve position (2.4, 2.8 and 2.9 V6 non-cat)

11 The throttle position is critical, and should not normally be disturbed. Where adjustment IS required, refer first to the adjustment pre-conditions in Section 8.

12 Attach a FCR to the serial port, and use it to place the engine into code 60, service-set mode. **Note:** *The 2.8 engine does not require the use of a FCR.*

13 Check that the ignition timing is correct.

14 Stop the engine.

15 Disconnect the ISCV multi-plug.

16 Start the engine, without touching the throttle pedal, and allow it to idle. The engine should settle to its base idle speed.

Base idle speed table

Model	Base rpm
2.4	875
2.8	675
2.9, MT up to 05/1988	800 ± 25
2.9, MT from 06/1988	875 ± 25
2.9, AT up to 11/1987	800 to 875
2.9, AT from 12/1987	900 ± 25

17 If the base idle speed is incorrect:

a) Remove the cover from the throttle housing.

b) Carefully loosen the roller bolt on the throttle camplate ***(see illustration 7.12)****.*

c) Remove the tamperproof cap from the throttle stop screw and slacken the locknut.

d) Adjust the throttle stop screw to obtain the base idle speed (see table above).

e) Carefully retighten the locknut.

f) Retighten the roller bolt, ensuring that the camplate is touching the throttle stop screw and there is no free play between the roller and the camplate.

g) Stop the engine and reconnect the ISCV multi-plug.

h) Fit a new tamperproof cap to the throttle stop screw.

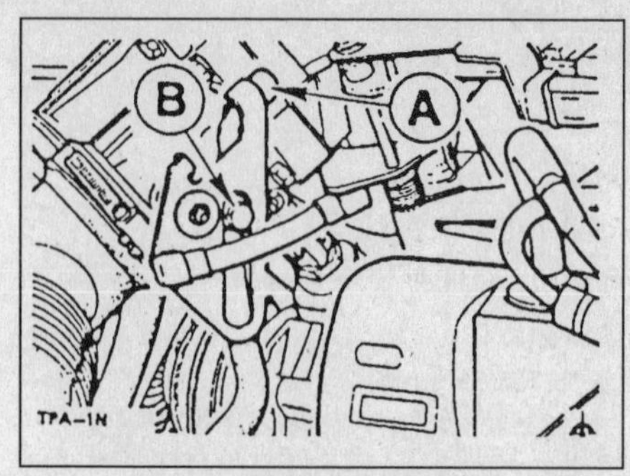

7.12 V6, non-cat engines throttle valve adjustment procedure

A Throttle stop screw with tamperproof cap
B Camplate roller bolt

18 Reconnect the service connection (where required).

19 Adjust the TPS (see paragraph 28).

Throttle valve position (2.4 and 2.9 V6 cat)

20 The throttle position is critical, and should not normally be disturbed. Where adjustment IS required, refer first to the adjustment pre-conditions in Section 8.

21 Attach a FCR to the serial port; use it to check that the ignition timing is correct, then disconnect the FCR. **Note:** *the following procedure MUST be made without the FCR being connected.*

22 Stop the engine.

23 Disconnect the ISCV multi-plug.

24 Start the engine and run it at 3000 rpm for approximately 30 seconds. Slowly close the throttle so that the engine rpm returns to idle speed. The engine should settle to its base idle speed.

Base idle speed table

Model	Regulated rpm	Base rpm
ARD	825 rpm	700 rpm
BRD	900 rpm	700 rpm
BRE	875 rpm	700 rpm
B4B	900 rpm	700 rpm
B4C	900 rpm	700 rpm

25 If the base idle speed is incorrect:

a) Loosen the throttle camplate roller bolt.

b) Remove the tamperproof cap, and adjust the throttle stop screw so that the engine idles at the base idle speed.

c) Tighten the throttle camplate roller bolt so that it gently abuts against the throttle stop screw. Ensure that there is no free play between camplate and roller.

d) Stop the engine and reconnect the ISCV.

e) Fit a new tamperproof cap to the throttle stop screw.

26 Reconnect the service connection (where required)

27 Adjust the TPS (see paragraph 28).

Throttle 'pot' sensor (TPS)

28 Test conditions: Throttle plate correctly set, engine stopped, throttle closed, ignition 'on'.

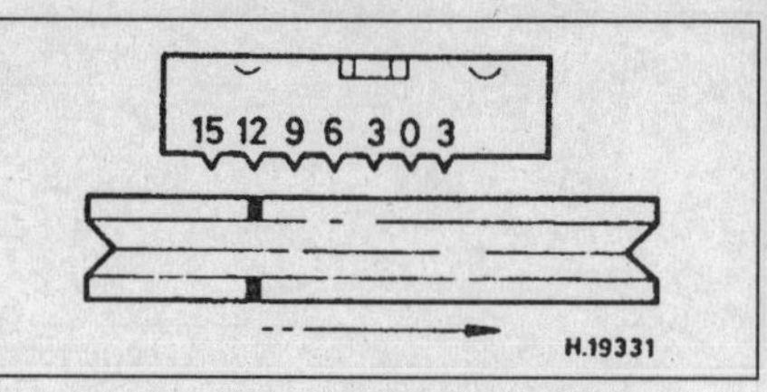

7.13 Ignition timing marks (V6)

29 Attach a voltmeter between terminal 47 and earth. A voltage greater than 0.70 indicates that the switch is incorrectly adjusted.

30 Loosen the two securing screws, and adjust the switch until the voltmeter indicates less than 0.70 volts (0.50 volts is ideal).

31 Reconnect the service connections (where necessary).

32 Check the Idle CO adjustment.

10 Ignition timing checks

Ignition timing (2.0 SOHC, 2.8 V6)

1 Refer to the adjustment pre-conditions in Section 8.

2 Set the ignition timing to the base figure: 12° for unleaded petrol, or 8° for leaded petrol **(see illustration 7.13)**. **Note:** *The ignition timing is adjustable by turning the distributor in the appropriate direction. However, it is strongly recommended that this adjustment should only be used to set the timing to the 12° base setting. Any alteration from the base setting should only be made by connecting one of the two octane leads to earth in the appropriate combination.*

3 Increase the engine speed. The timing marks should move apart as the timing advances.

Ignition timing (all other vehicles with distributor or DIS)

4 Refer to the adjustment pre-conditions in Section 8.

5 The base ignition timing should only be checked or adjusted with the aid of a FCR.

6 Attach a FCR to the serial port, and place the ECM into service-set mode: code 11 (2.4 and 2.9 cat only) or code 60 (all other vehicles). **Note:** *On later systems which use three-digit fault code procedures, enter service-set mode after seeing the flashing cursor.*

7 Set the ignition timing to the base figure (DIS models can be checked, but are non-adjustable) **(see illustration 7.14)**. **Note:** *The ignition timing is adjustable by turning the distributor in the appropriate direction. However, it is strongly recommended that this adjustment should only be used to set the timing to the base setting. If the distributor is turned arbitrarily (without the aid of the FCR),*

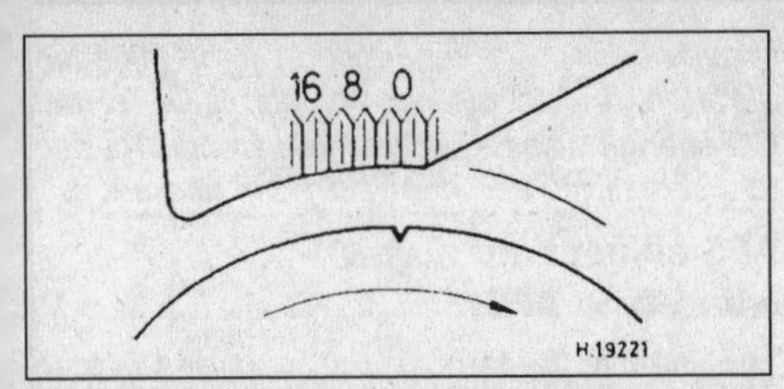

7.14 Ignition timing marks (CVH and CFi)

the base timing will be incorrectly set, even though the marks may appear to be correctly aligned. Any alteration from the base setting should only be made by connecting the service cables to earth in the appropriate combination.

Base timing table

Model	Base timing value
1.4 CFi	10°
2.4, 2.9 V6 non cat	12° unleaded
	8° leaded
2.4, 2.9 V6 cat	15° unleaded

8 Disconnect the FCR.
9 Increase the engine speed and check that the timing marks move apart. Typical timing advance at 3000 rpm is 30 to 40°. **Note:** *When under ECM control with a FCR attached to the serial port, the timing is locked to the base timing figure, and the timing marks will not move apart.*

11 Service cable adjustments

Note: *The service cable connections are usually located near the ignition coil.*

1.4 CFi

When terminal 5 (yellow) is connected to earth, the regulated idle speed will rise by 100 rpm.

When terminal 23 (red) is connected to earth, the ignition timing will be retarded by 2°.

When terminal 24 (blue) is connected to earth, the ignition timing will be retarded by 4°.

When terminal 23 and terminal 24 are both connected to earth, the ignition timing will be retarded by 6°.

1.6 CVH EFi

When terminal 3 (yellow) (not fitted to cat models) is connected to earth, the regulated idle speed will rise.

When terminal 23 (red) is connected to earth, the ignition timing will be retarded by no fixed value. The object of the connection is to prevent slight engine knock in partial and full-load conditions.

When terminal 24 (blue) is connected to earth, the ignition timing will be retarded by no fixed value. The object of the connection is to allow the engine to run on 91 octane fuel.

When terminal 23 and terminal 24 are both connected to earth, the ignition timing will be retarded by no fixed value. The object of the connection is to prevent slight engine knock in partial and full-load conditions with 91 octane fuel.

Escort, Orion and Fiesta 1.6/1.8 DOHC

When terminal 42 is connected to earth (by bridging the two connections in the service connector multi-plug), the ignition timing will be set for 95 octane unleaded fuel.

When terminal 42 is open-circuit, the ignition timing is retarded by no fixed value. The object of removing the connection is to prevent slight engine knock in partial and full-load conditions.

2.0 SOHC

When terminal 5 (yellow) is connected to earth, the regulated idle speed will rise by 75 rpm (MT only).

When terminal 23 (red) is connected to earth, the ignition timing will be retarded by 2°.

When terminal 24 (blue) is connected to earth, the ignition timing will be retarded by 4°.

When terminal 23 and terminal 24 is connected to earth, the ignition timing will be retarded by 6°.

2.0 DOHC, 8-valve

When terminal 5 (yellow) is connected to earth, the regulated idle speed will rise by 25 rpm.

When terminal 23 (red) is connected to earth, the ignition timing will be retarded by no fixed value. The object of the connection is to prevent slight engine knock in partial and full-load conditions.

When terminal 24 (blue) is connected to earth, the ignition timing will be retarded by no fixed value. The object of the connection is to allow the engine to run on 91 octane fuel.

When terminal 23 and terminal 24 are both connected to earth, the ignition timing will be retarded by no fixed value. The object of the connection is to prevent slight engine knock in partial and full-load conditions with 91 octane fuel.

2.0 DOHC, 16-valve

When terminal 30 (yellow) is connected to earth, the regulated idle speed will rise.

When terminal 23 (red) is connected to earth, the ignition timing will be retarded by no fixed value. The object of the connection is to prevent slight engine knock in partial and full-load conditions.

When terminal 24 (blue) is connected to earth, the ignition timing will be retarded by no fixed value. The object of the connection is to allow the engine to run on 91 octane fuel.

When terminal 23 and terminal 24 are both connected to earth, the ignition timing will be retarded by no fixed value. The object of the connection is to prevent slight engine knock in partial and full-load conditions with 91 octane fuel.

2.8 V6

When terminal 3 (yellow) is connected to earth, the regulated idle speed will rise by 75 rpm (MT only). **Note:** *Idle speed may be reduced by 75 rpm for some models with a particular ECM calibration.*

When terminal 23 (red) is connected to earth, the ignition timing will be retarded by 3°.

When terminal 24 (blue) is connected to earth, the ignition timing will be retarded by 6°.

Note: *Under no circumstances should the red and blue wires be connected to earth at the same time.*

2.4 and 2.9 V6 (non-cat)

When terminal 3 (yellow) is connected to earth, the regulated idle speed will rise by 75 rpm (MT only)

When terminal 23 (red) is connected to earth, the ignition timing will be retarded by 4°.

When terminal 24 (blue) is connected to earth, the ignition timing will be retarded by 6°.

Note: *Under no circumstances should the red and blue wires be connected to earth at the same time.*

2.4 and 2.9 V6 (cat)

When terminal 28 (yellow) is connected to earth, the regulated idle speed will rise by 50 rpm OR reduce by 75 rpm - depending on ECM calibration.

When terminal 23 (red) is connected to earth, the ignition timing will be retarded by 4°.

When terminal 24 (blue) is connected to earth, the ignition timing will be retarded by 6°.

Note: *Under no circumstances should the red and blue wires be connected to earth at the same time.*

12 Idle adjustments

Adjustment procedure

1 Refer to the adjustment pre-conditions in Section 8.
2 Check that the ignition timing is correct.
3 Check the regulated idle speed. **Note:** *Although the regulated idle speed is not adjustable, it is possible to adjust the base idle speed on some vehicles. Refer to the throttle valve adjustments in Section 9.*
4 2000 DOHC, 8-valve: This vehicle is the only one that is provided with an air by-pass screw for base idle adjustment **(see illustration 7.15)**. However, adjustment must be made during service-set mode in code 60.
5 If the idle speed remains high and cannot be set to the correct value, check for induction vacuum leaks.

Idle CO adjustment (non-cat models only)

6 Refer to the adjustment pre-conditions in Section 8.

7.15 Ford 2000 DOHC, 8-valve engine: idle speed adjustment must be made during service set mode in code 60

7 Start the engine and raise the engine speed to 3000 rpm. Hold the speed at this rpm for approximately 30 seconds, and then release the throttle.

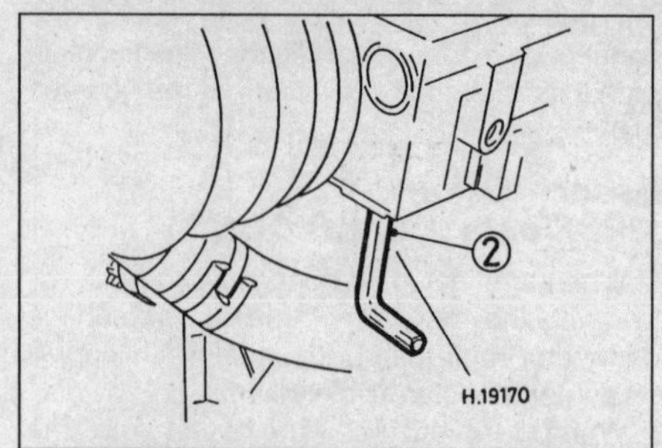

7.16 Ford V6 idle and CO adjustment
2 Allen key

8 Attach a gas analyser to the exhaust pipe, and check the idle CO value.

9 The idle CO is adjusted in one of two ways, depending upon vehicle **(see illustration 7.16)**. **Note:** *The CO adjustment purely affects the CO value at idle. The A/F mixture at speeds over idle is influenced by the injection duration, and this is not adjustable. Incorrect CO at engine speeds over idle can only be due to a sensor fault or incorrect ECM operation.*

AFS adjustment screw (vane-type AFS)

10 Remove the tamperproof cap, and use an Allen key to turn the CO adjustment screw; clockwise to increase CO level, anti-clockwise to reduce CO level.

11 V6 engines with two AFS's: First adjust the front AFS. Only adjust the rear AFS if the correct CO cannot be obtained by adjustment of the front AFS.

CO pot adjustment screw (MAP sensor)

12 Remove the tamperproof cap and turn the CO adjustment screw; clockwise to increase CO level, anti-clockwise to reduce CO level.

System sensor and actuator tests

Important note: *Please refer to Chapter 4, which describes common test procedures applicable to this system. The routines in Chapter 4 should be read in conjunction with the component notes and wiring diagrams presented in this Chapter. The wiring diagrams and other data presented in this Chapter are necessarily representative of the system depicted. Because of the variations in wiring and other data that often occurs, even between similar vehicles in any particular VM's range, the reader should take great care in identification of ECM pins, and satisfy himself that he has gathered the correct data before failing a particular component.*

13 Primary trigger - crank angle sensor (CAS)

1 Refer to the note at the start of this Section, and refer to the relevant Section of Chapter 4.

2 The CAS found in EEC IV systems may be connected directly to the ECM (2.0 DOHC, 8-valve), or connected to the EDIS unit.

3 The CAS resistance for all models is 200 to 450 ohms.

14 Primary trigger - Hall-effect sensor (HES)

1 Refer to the note at the start of Section 13, and refer to the relevant Section of Chapter 4.

2 The routines described in Chapter 4 are generally suitable. When testing the EEC IV Hall-effect sensor for a signal, the (O) output signal corresponds to the Ford PIP signal, and the ECM control signal corresponds to the Ford SPOUT signal.

3 When testing for a spark (Quick test) and where the TFI is directly connected to the distributor, it will need to be detached and the test carried out at the TFI terminals that directly engage the HES terminals in the distributor.

15 Primary ignition

1 Refer to the note at the start of Section 13, and refer to the relevant Section of Chapter 4.

2 When testing the ignition circuit for a primary signal, the routines described in 'Primary not available (separate external amplifier)' are generally suitable **(see illustration 7.17)**. The sequence of events is: The primary trigger (CAS or HES) signals the ECM, which triggers the amplifier (TFI), which switches the coil to provide ignition. In some models, the CAS is attached to an EDIS module, which passes the PIP signal to the ECM. The ECM returns a modified SAW signal to the EDIS, which then switches the coil to instigate ignition **(see illustrations 7.18 to 7.21)**.

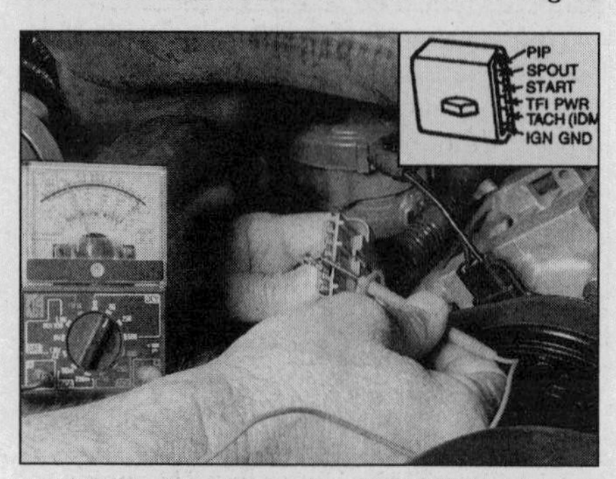

7.17 Check for nbv on V6 TFI unit (TFI PWR, terminal 3)

3 Distributor ignition: Primary resistance, 0.70 to 1.0 ohms. Secondary resistance, 4500 to 8600 ohms.

4 DIS ignition: Primary resistance, 0.50 ohms (approx.). Secondary resistance, 4500 to 16000 ohm.

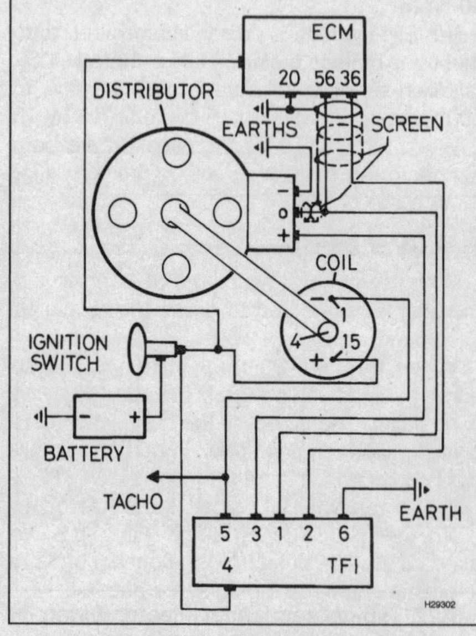

7.18 HES (CFi) ignition wiring diagram

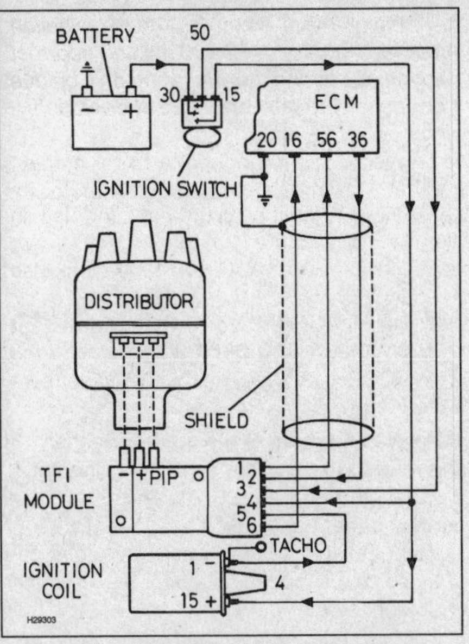

7.19 Typical ignition wiring: V6 engine

16 Fuel injector operation (MPi)

1 Refer to the note at the start of Section 13, and refer to the relevant Section of Chapter 4.
2 The injector resistance is normally 16 ohms **(see illustrations 7.22 to 7.24)**.

17 Fuel injector operation (SPi)

1 Refer to the note at the start of Section 13, and refer to the relevant Section of Chapter 4.
2 The injector resistance is normally 1.0 to 2.0 ohms.
3 The SPi system is current-controlled, and utilises a ballast resistor in the circuit. The ballast resistor resistance is normally 3.5 to 7.0 ohms.

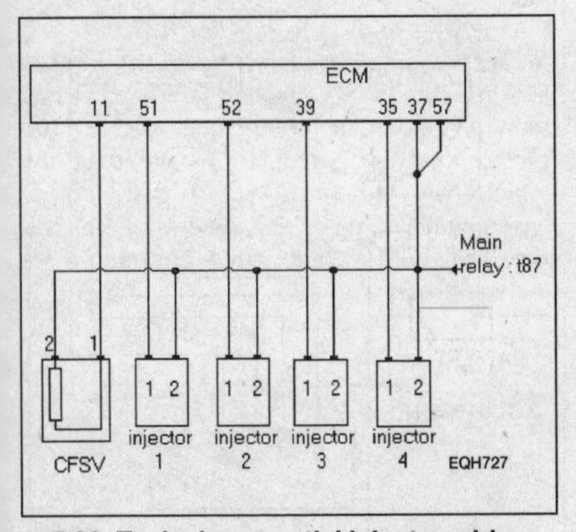

7.22 Typical sequential injector wiring

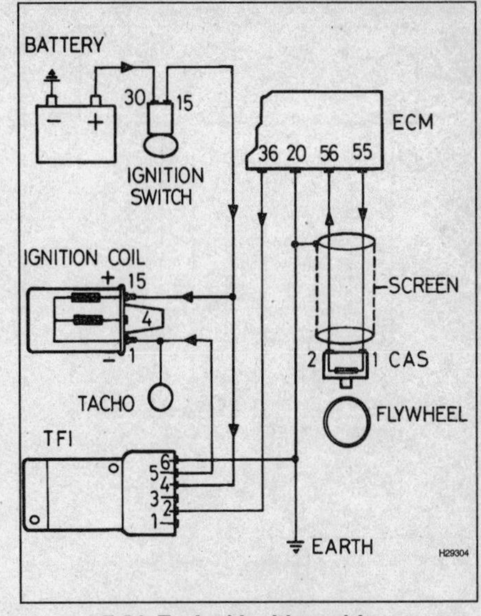

7.21 Typical ignition wiring: 2000 8-valve DOHC

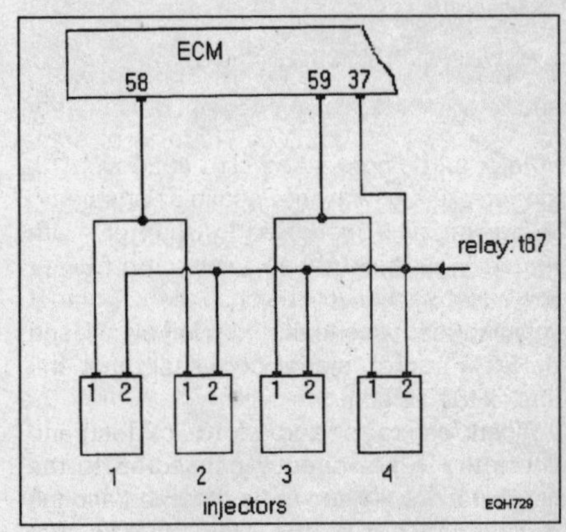

7.24 Typical injector wiring: 2000 8-valve DOHC

18 Phase sensor (CID)

1 Refer to the note at the start of Section 13, and refer to the relevant Section of Chapter 4.
2 The CID phase sensor is located in the distributor.
3 The CID resistance should lie between 200 and 900 ohms.

19 Airflow sensor (AFS)

1 Refer to the note at the start of Section 13, and refer to the relevant Section of Chapter 4.
2 The AFS may be of the Vane, Hot-wire or Hot-film type, depending on model.
3 Where an AFS of the vane type is found, the CO pot is of the mechanical type, and adjustment is effected by an Allen key.

20 MAP sensor

1 Refer to the note at the start of Section 13, and refer to the relevant Section of Chapter 4.
2 Unlike the MAP sensor fitted to the majority of other EMS's, the MAP sensor used in EEC IV systems is of a digital nature. It is also of the external type, and is fitted in the engine compartment.

21 Air temperature sensor (ATS)

1 Refer to the note at the start of Section 13, and refer to the relevant Section of Chapter 4.
2 The ATS may be located in the inlet tract of the AFS, or in the inlet manifold, depending on model.

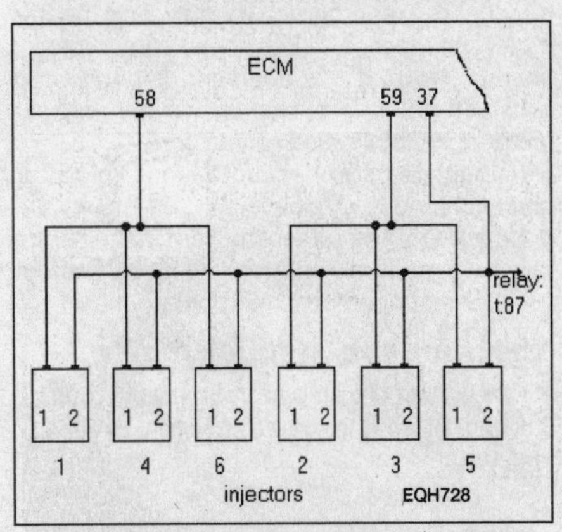

7.23 Typical injector wiring: V6 engine

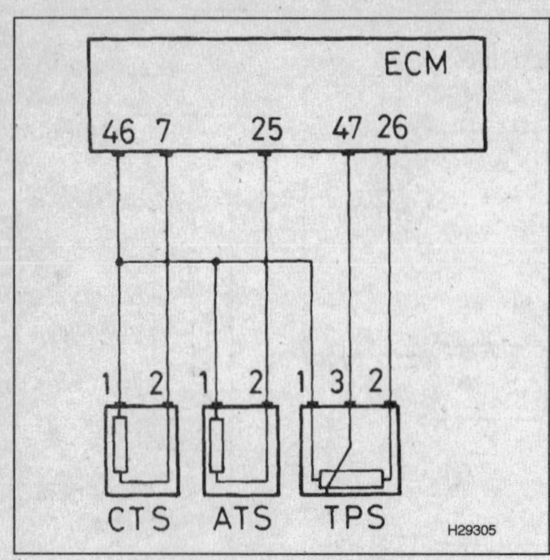

7.25 Typical sensor wiring

22 CO potentiometer ('pot')

1 Refer to the note at the start of Section 13, and refer to the relevant Section of Chapter 4.

2 The CO pot is of the external type, and is located in the engine compartment.

23 Coolant temperature sensor (CTS)

1 Refer to the note at the start of Section 13, and refer to the relevant Section of Chapter 4.

24 Throttle potentiometer sensor (TPS)

1 Refer to the note at the start of Section 13, and refer to the relevant Section of Chapter 4 **(see illustration 7.25)**.

25 ISCV (Hitachi type)

1 Refer to the note at the start of Section 13, and refer to the relevant Section of Chapter 4 for the two-pin ISCV. There are some fundamental difference in the ISCV found in EEC IV systems, and the routines in Chapter 4 should be read in careful conjunction with these component notes and the wiring diagrams portrayed in this Chapter.

2 During voltage tests, the average voltage, duty cycle and frequency will all change - unlike the Bosch two-wire type, where the frequency remains fixed.

3 Check the diode between the ECM terminal and the ISCV. **Note:** *In later models, the diode is integrated into the ISCV body. In this instance, a diode symbol will be stamped upon the ISCV body.*

Warning: When checking operation of the ISCV by applying battery voltage, it is essential that the battery and earth connections are attached to the correct ISCV connections (if the ISCV is equipped with the integral diode). If the connections are reversed, the diode and ISCV may be irreparably damaged. The connection should be made only briefly, in any case.

Resistance measurements

4 Remove the ISCV multi-plug, and measure the resistance of the ISCV between the two terminals, which should be between 6 and 14 ohms.

Note 1: *A defective ISCV will normally display an open-circuit or shorted winding (open-circuit or high resistance).*

Note 2: *When the diode is integral with the ISCV, the measurement value will differ slightly - depending on which way round the meter probes are connected.*

Diode resistance (when mounted in wiring loom)

5 Locate the diode in the loom close to the ISCV.

6 Disconnect the diode from the loom, and test it with the aid of a diode tester or ohmmeter.

7 Diode test results as follows:

a) *Normal diode: continuity in one direction and infinity in the other.*
b) *Shorted diode: continuity in both directions.*
c) *Open diode: infinity in both directions.*

26 Stepper motor

1 Warm the engine to normal operating temperature.

2 Start the engine and allow it to idle.

3 Check that the idle speed is within its operating limits.

4 Load the system by switching on the headlights, rear screen heater and heater motor onto high. The idle speed should barely change. **Note:** *If this operation is completed satisfactorily, it is probable that the stepper motor condition is also satisfactory.*

5 Inspect the stepper motor multi-plug for corrosion and damage.

6 Check that the connector terminal pins are fully pushed home and making good contact with the stepper motor multi-plug.

Checking the stepper motor

7 Disconnect the stepper motor multi-plug.

8 Connect an ohmmeter between terminal 2 and earth:

a) *Throttle closed: The ohmmeter should indicate infinity.*
b) *Throttle open: The ohmmeter should indicate less than one ohm.*

9 Use a jumper lead to connect stepper motor terminal 3 to a 12-volt supply.

10 Use a second jumper lead to connect stepper motor terminal 4 to an earth. The motor should actuate.

11 Reverse the connections to terminals 3 and 4. The motor should actuate in the opposite direction.

27 ECM voltage supplies and earths

1 Refer to the note at the start of Section 13, and refer to the relevant Section of Chapter 4.

2 ECM pin numbers 20, 40 and 60 are the earth connections for the Ford EEIC IV system. For this reason, where possible, one of these pins should be used for the voltmeter earth connection.

3 ECM pin number 1 is the KAM supply, and battery voltage should be available at all times.

4 ECM pins number 37 and 57 are connected to the main relay output terminal, and voltage should be available with the ignition on or the engine running.

5 ECM pin number 22 is the fuel pump relay driver. Nbv will be available with the ignition on, and this voltage will reduce to near zero when the engine is cranking or running.

Loss of stored values in KAM

6 When the vehicle battery or the EEC IV ECM is disconnected, the ECM supply to the KAM is also disconnected, and all stored values in KAM will be lost. This includes the KAM fault codes and the adaptive idle settings. On reconnection of the battery, the engine may temporarily lose its ability to idle, or the idle may become erratic and the engine may surge and hesitate. The EEC IV ECM must relearn the idle values as follows. **Note:** *The engine will also need to relearn the idle values if the base idle setting is changed.*

7 Allow the engine to idle for 3 minutes, if necessary keeping it running on the throttle lever. Once normal operating temperature has been reached, raise the engine speed to 1200 rpm for a further 2 minutes. Finally, drive the vehicle on the road for a distance of approximately 5 miles. By the end of the road test, the ECM should have completed its learning process.

28 Inertia switch

1 Refer to the note at the start of Section 13, and refer to the relevant Section of Chapter 4.

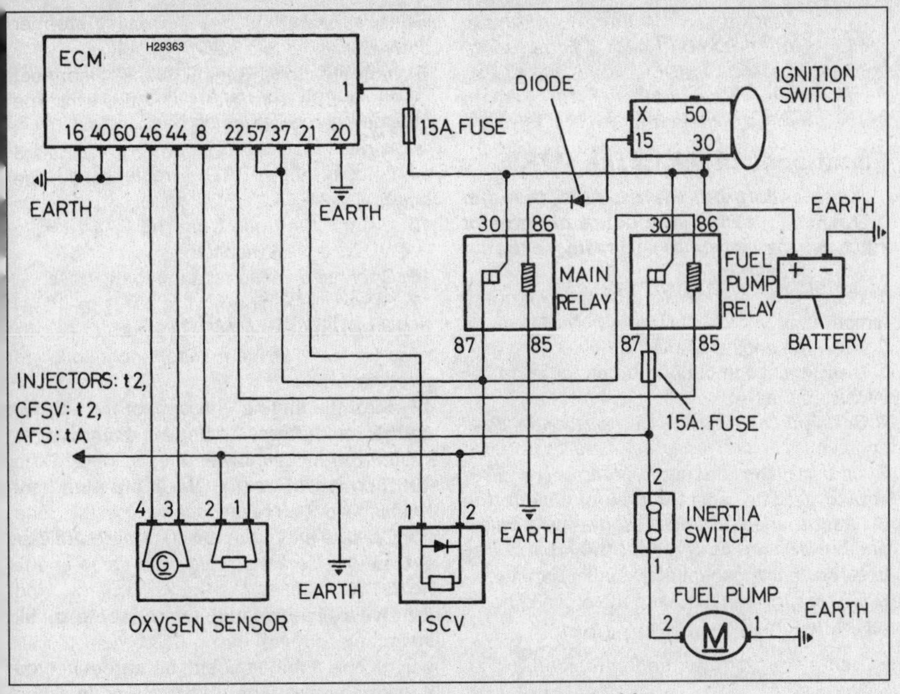

7.26 Typical relays and components wiring

29 System relays

1 Refer to the note at the start of Section 13, and refer to the relevant Section of Chapter 4.
2 The majority of Ford vehicles utilise a main relay and a fuel pump relay, each with single contacts. Pin numbering is along the DIN lines **(see illustration 7.26)**.

30 Fuel pump and circuit

1 Refer to the note at the start of Section 13, and refer to the relevant Section of Chapter 4.

31 Fuel pressure

1 Refer to the note at the start of Section 13, and refer to the relevant Section of Chapter 4.

32 Oxygen sensor (OS)

1 Refer to the note at the start of Section 13, and refer to the relevant Section of Chapter 4.
2 The OS found in the majority of EEC IV systems is a four-wire sensor.

33 Carbon filter solenoid valve (CFSV)

1 Refer to the note at the start of Section 13, and refer to the relevant Section of Chapter 4.

34 EGR system

1 Check the two DPFE pipes for leaks. The pipes connect the DPFE to the DPFE venturi in the exhaust system.
2 Inspect the DPFE and EVR multi-plugs for corrosion and damage.
3 Check that the DPFE and EVR connector terminal pins are fully pushed home and making good contact with their respective multi-plugs.

EGR valve functional check

4 Warm the engine to normal operating temperature.
5 Start the engine and allow it to idle.
6 Disconnect the vacuum connection to the EGR valve from the EVR.
7 Connect a vacuum pump to the EGR connection.
8 Operate the vacuum pump. The EGR valve should actuate, and the idle quality will deteriorate as vacuum is increased.
9 Release the vacuum, and the idle quality should return to normal.
10 If the system operates as described, the EGR valve is probably OK.

Poor idle condition

11 If the idle quality is poor, it could be the EGR system recycling exhaust gas at idle.
12 Locate the vacuum hose that connects the EVR to the EGR.
13 Disconnect the vacuum hose, and plug the connection that leads to the EGR:
a) If the idle quality improves, check the EVR and vacuum hose for leaks. See EVR tests.
b) If the idle quality is still poor, check the EGR valve.
14 Check the EGR valve for leaks:
a) Locate the pipe that connects the inlet manifold to the EGR.
b) Detach the pipe at the inlet manifold end, and plug the opening in the inlet manifold.
c) If the idle quality improves, the EGR is suspect.

Checking the DPFE

15 Roll back the rubber protection boot to the DPFE multi-plug (where possible).
16 Connect the voltmeter negative probe to an engine earth.
17 Connect the positive oscilloscope or voltmeter probe to the wire attached to DPFE signal terminal number 3.
18 Start the engine, and set the speed to approximately 2000 to 2500 rpm.
19 Open and close the throttle several times, and check that the voltage varies between approximately 0.40 volts and 4.0 volts. **Note:** *If a digital voltmeter is used, then it is useful for it to have a bar graph facility.*

Erratic signal output

20 An erratic output occurs when the voltage output is stepped, drops to zero, or becomes open-circuit.
21 When the DPFE signal output is erratic, this usually suggests a faulty potentiometer. In this instance, a new or reconditioned DPFE is the only cure.

Signal voltage not available

22 Check for the 5.0-volt reference voltage supply at the DPFE supply terminal.
23 Check the earth return connection at the DPFE earth terminal.
24 If the supply and earth are satisfactory, check for continuity of the signal wiring between the DPFE and the ECM.
25 If the supply and/or earth are unsatisfactory, check for continuity of the wiring between the DPFE and the ECM.
26 If the DPFE wiring is satisfactory, check all voltage supplies and earth connections to the ECM. If the voltage supplies and earth connections are satisfactory, the ECM is suspect.

Signal or supply voltage at nbv level

27 Check for a short to a wire connected to the battery positive (+) terminal or a switched supply voltage.

Checking the EVR operation

28 The two wires to the EVR connector are supply and actuated earth.

29 Connect the voltmeter negative probe to an engine earth.
30 Backprobe the EVR supply terminal with the voltmeter positive probe.
31 With the ignition on, check for nbv at the EVR supply terminal. If no voltage is obtained, trace the wiring back to terminal 87 of the main FI relay.
32 Check the EVR resistance (paragraph 43).
33 Detach the hose from the EVR (at the EVR) to the inlet manifold.
34 Connect a vacuum gauge to the hose.
35 Start the engine and allow it to idle.
36 If manifold vacuum is not obtained, check the hose for leaks or the manifold connection for a restriction.
37 Stop the engine, disconnect the vacuum gauge, and attach a vacuum pump to the vacuum connector (lower one).
38 Disconnect the ECM multi-plug (see Warning No 3 in Reference).
39 Operate the pump to 500 mm Hg. Release the handle, and the registered value should hold.
40 Use a jumper lead to very briefly touch the switching terminal in the ECM multi-plug to earth. The EVR should actuate, and the vacuum registered on the vacuum pump should fall to zero.
41 If the EVR actuates, check the ECM main voltage supplies and earths. If tests reveal no fault, the ECM is suspect.
42 If the EVR does not actuate, check for continuity of wiring between the EVR and the ECM switching terminal.

EVR resistance

43 Remove the multi-plug and measure the resistance of the EVR between the two terminals.

35 Pulse air system

Functional check of the PASV

Warning: Please note that the following procedure may result in damage to the exhaust system.

1 Warm the engine to normal operating temperature.
2 Allow the engine to idle.
3 Disconnect the vacuum connection to the PAV from the PASV.
4 Connect a vacuum pump to the PAV connection.
5 Operate the vacuum pump. The PAV should actuate, and the flow of air into the exhaust manifold should be detected by an audible hissing. In addition, the engine may backfire, which can cause exhaust damage.
6 Release the vacuum, and the engine should return to normal.
7 If the system operates as described, the PASV is probably OK.

Checking the PASV (general)

8 Inspect the PASV multi-plug for corrosion and damage.
9 Check that the connector terminal pins are fully pushed home and making good contact with the PASV multi-plug.

Checking the PASV operation

10 The two wires to the PASV connector are supply and actuated earth.
11 Connect the voltmeter negative probe to an engine earth.
12 Backprobe the PASV supply terminal with the voltmeter positive probe.
13 With the ignition on, check for nbv at the PASV supply terminal. If no voltage is obtained, trace the wiring back to terminal 87 of the main FI relay.
14 Check the PASV resistance (see paragraph 24).
15 Detach the hose from the PASV (at the PASV) to the inlet manifold.
16 Connect a vacuum gauge to the hose.
17 Start the engine and allow it to idle. If manifold vacuum is not obtained, check the hose for leaks or the manifold connection for a restriction.
18 Stop the engine, disconnect the vacuum gauge and attach a vacuum pump to the vacuum connector (lower one).
19 Disconnect the ECM multi-plug (*see Warning No 3 in Reference).*
20 Operate the pump to 500 mm Hg. Release the handle, and the registered value should hold.
21 Use a jumper lead to very briefly touch the switching terminal in the ECM multi-plug to earth. The PASV should actuate, and the vacuum registered on the vacuum pump should fall to zero.
22 If the PASV actuates, check the ECM main voltage supplies and earths. If tests reveal no fault, the ECM is suspect.
23 If the PASV does not actuate, check for continuity of wiring between the PASV and the ECM switching terminal.

PASV resistance

24 Remove the multi-plug and measure the resistance of the PASV between the two terminals.

Pin table - typical 60-pin ECM

Note: *Refer to* ***illustration 7.27.***

1 KAM supply
5 Idle speed adjustment
7 CTS supply /signal
10 Air conditioning LP switch
16 Earth
17 Diagnostic socket
20 Earth
21 ISCV signal
22 FP relay driver
23 Octane adjustment
24 Octane adjustment
25 ATS (AFS)
26 TPS supply
27 AFS signal
30 Neutral switch
36 SPOUT signal: TFI
37 FI Relay
40 Earth
43 AFS signal
44 OS signal
46 Sensor return (AFS/CTS/TPS)
47 TPS signal
48 Diagnostic socket
52 -
56 PIP signal: TFI
57 FI Relay
58 Injectors cyls 1, 2 (4-cyl) 1, 4, 6 (6-cyl)
59 Injectors cyls 3, 4 (4-cyl) 2, 3, 5 (6-cyl)
60 Earth

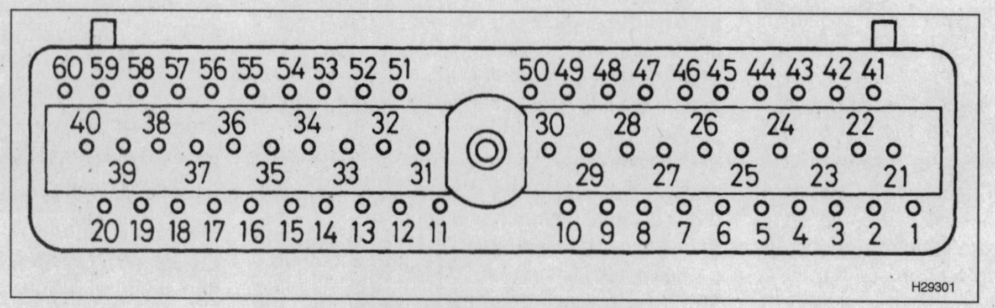

7.27 Typical 60-pin ECM multi-plug

Fault codes

36 Obtaining fault codes

1 If a fault code reader (FCR) is available, it could be attached to the SD serial connector and used for the following purposes:

a) *Obtain fault codes by running one of the diagnostic routines:*
Engine off.
Engine running.
Continuous running (not all vehicles).

b) *Clear fault codes.*

c) *Actuate the system actuators (three-digit codes only).*

2 The procedures detailing how to obtain codes will be described in the instruction manual for the equipment used.

3 If a FCR is not available, it is still possible to obtain fault codes.

Obtaining codes without a FCR

4 Attach an LED test lamp between terminal 3 at the plug (negative lead) and the battery positive terminal (positive lead).

5 Use a jumper lead to bridge terminals 1 and 2 in the serial port plug.

6 Switch on the ignition. The codes will now be output on the LED as flashes after about forty-five seconds. By counting the flashes and referring to the relevant fault code table for the vehicle in question, faults can thus be determined **(see illustration 7.28)**.

a) *Code digit pulses are 0.5 second on and 0.5 second off.*

b) *A two-second pause separates the digits of each code, and a four-second pulse separates one code from another.*

c) *After all codes have been transmitted, a pause of six to nine seconds is followed by single flash (separator code).*

d) *After a further six to nine seconds, followed by a flash, intermittent fault codes stored in KAM will be transmitted.*

Note: *A test lamp (LED) should be used that conforms to minimum standards for electronic vehicles - see Warning No 5 in Reference.*

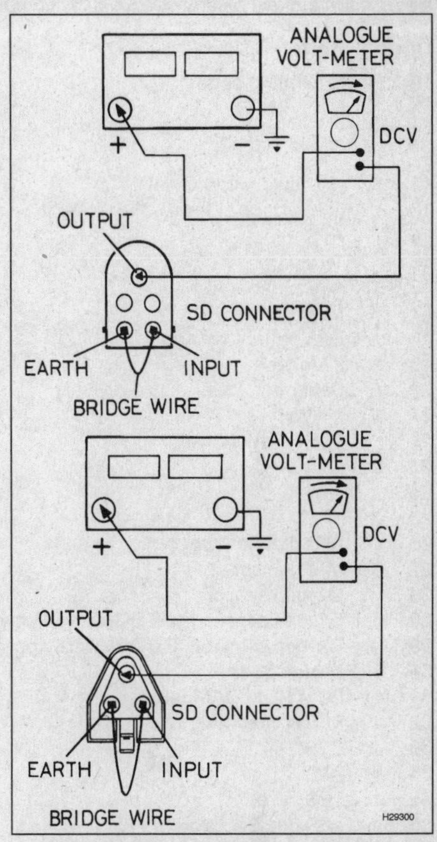

7.28 Obtaining flash codes: Connect an analogue voltmeter (see *Warning No 5 in Reference*). Bridge the wire as shown, switch on the ignition and then count the needle sweeps. It is also possible to use an LED lamp and count the flashes

Fault code table - EEC IV 'basic' (2.0 SOHC and 2.8 V6 engines)

Code	Item
11	No faults found
12	AFS number one
13	CTS
14	ATS (in AFS)
15	TPS
22	AFS number two
23	AFS number one and number two
31	Wiring/module fault
32	Wiring/module fault

Fault code table - EEC IV 'enhanced', two-digits (except 2.4/2.9 V6 cat)

Note: *A system test means checking the component as described in the test procedures.*

Code	Item	Fault/reason/action
10	Command code	Operator action required as follows: *Ignition key on, engine off: wiggle test* *Engine running: load engine by 'blipping' the throttle; the engine speed must exceed 2500 rpm.*
11	No faults found	System pass
13	CTS	Make CTS tests
14	ATS	Make ATS tests
15	TPS	Make TPS tests
16	AFS number two	
17	MAP sensor	Make MAP sensor tests
18	Low battery voltage	Check battery and charging system
19	KAM fault	End & restart SD test, if code repeats make ECM voltage & earth tests
20	Separator code	Separates soft KAM codes from hard codes (permanent codes)
21	ignition	Irregular signal
22	AFS number one	Voltage too high
23	CTS	Voltage too high; make CTS tests
24	ATS	Make ATS tests
25	TPS	Voltage too high; make TPS tests
26	AFS number two	Voltage too high
27	MAP sensor	Value too high; make MAP sensor tests
28	Oxygen sensor	Make OS tests
28	Oxygen sensor 1 (2.0 DOHC 16V only)	Lean mixture or failed sensor
29	Oxygen sensor 2 (2.0 DOHC 16V only)	Lean mixture or failed sensor
30	Marker code	Identifies ECM for 6-cyl engines
31	ECM ROM/RAM failure	Make ECM voltage & earth tests
32	AFS number two	Voltage too low
33	CTS	Voltage too low; make CTS tests
34	ATS	Make ATS tests
35	TPS	Voltage too low; make TPS tests
36	AFS number two	Voltage too low
37	MAP sensor	Value too low; make MAP sensor tests
38	Oxygen sensor 1 (2.0 DOHC 16V only)	Lean mixture or failed sensor
39	Oxygen sensor 2 (2.0 DOHC 16V only)	Lean mixture or failed sensor
42	MAP sensor	No change in sensor output during SD test: Repeat SD test, if same result, make MAP sensor tests
43	TPS	No response to blip test during SD test: Repeat SD test, if same result, make TPS tests
44	'Blip' test not performed or late response to message	Repeat SD test
45	VSS	Make VSS tests
46	ISCV failure	Max rpm not achieved **
47	ISCV failure	Min rpm not achieved **
48	ISCV	*** Make ISCV tests. If ISCV OK, test the fuel system*
50	European ECM fitted	must appear during test
51	Air conditioning 'on'	Switch A/C off and repeat SD test
52	AT: Vehicle in 'drive' during SD test	Select 'Neutral' or 'Park' and repeat SD test
53	Octane adjust wire number one earthed)	Disconnect service adjustment wires and repeat SD test
54	Octane adjust wire number two earthed)	Disconnect service adjustment wires and repeat SD test
55	Idle speed adjust wire earthed)	Disconnect service adjustment wires and repeat SD test
57	Throttle moved during SD test (prior to code 10)	Repeat SD test
58	PIP.SAW	Phasing of PIP.SAW
59	CO pot	Outside test limits; make CO pot tests
60	Start of service-set mode	Idle speed may be adjusted
61	Loss of power - cylinder 1	Check cylinder No 1 spark plug & compression
62	Loss of power - cylinder 2	Check cylinder No 2 spark plug & compression
63	Loss of power - cylinder 3	Check cylinder No 3 spark plug & compression
64	Loss of power - cylinder 4	Check cylinder No 4 spark plug & compression
65	Brake on/off switch	
66	Kickdown switch	
67	FTS	Make FTS tests
68	Boost pressure control valve	Check/adjust turbo
69	Boost pressure control valve	Check/adjust turbo
70	End of service-set mode	

Code	Item	Fault/reason/action
72	WCS (1.6 CVH EFi Turbo only)	
73	CFSV (cat model)	
74	3/4 shift solenoid	
75	Clutch converter lock-up solenoid	
76	Brake 'on' indicated	
77	Kickdown indicated	
78	PSPS	PSPS not activated during SD procedure. Check if PSPS fitted, if so, repeat SD procedure. If fault evident, carry out system test
91	OS connections	Connections interchanged (2.0 DOHC 16-valve engine)

Fault code table - EEC IV 'enhanced', two-digits (2.4/2.9 V6 cat)

Code	Item	Fault/reason/action
10	Command code	Separator code for KAM. Operator action required as follows: *Engine running: load engine by 'blipping' the throttle. The engine speed must exceed 2500 rpm.*
11	No faults found (system pass)	
12	ISCV	
13	ISCV	
14	Erratic PIP signal	
15	KAM/ROM (module failure)	
16	Engine test speed too low	
18	Ignition module operation (IDM)	
19	Voltage supply to module	
21	CTS	
22	MAP	
23	TPS	
24	ATS	
25	Knock sensor	
27	Cruise control delayed	
28	Cruise control - speed too advanced	
29	VSS	
30	Marker code	Identifies ECM for 6-cyl engines
31	EPT	Voltage too low
32	EPT	Outside specification
33	No EGR	
34	EPT	Outside specification
35	EPT	Voltage too high
36	No increase in engine test speed	
37	Decrease in engine test speed	
39	Torque converter lock-up clutch	
40	Unused	
41	HEGO sensor one (cyls 1,2,3)	Lean mixture
42	HEGO sensor one (cyls 1,2,3)	Rich mixture
46	Unused	
47	Cruise control switch	Operation
48	Cruise control switch	Sticking
49	Cruise control	Signal
50	Unused	
51	CTS	Voltage too high
52	PSPS	
53	TPS	Voltage too high
54	ATS	
55, 57	Unused	
57	Octane adjust - service loom connector	
58	Injection delayed through Service adjust facility	
59	Idle adjust - service loom connector	
60	Unused	
61	CTS	Voltage too low
62	AT shift solenoid 4/3	Closed
63	TPS	Voltage too low
64	ATS	Voltage too low
65, 66	Unused	
67	A/C switched on or AT in 'drive'	
69	Shift valve for 3/2 gear	Open

Fault code table - EEC IV 'enhanced', two-digits (2.4/2.9 V6 cat) - continued

Code	Item	Fault/reason/action
70	Unused	
72	MAP	
73	TPS	No reaction to test
74	Brake light switch	Circuit open
75	Brake light switch	Short-circuit
76	Unused	
77	Late response to 'blip throttle' command code	
78 to 80	Unused	
81	MAP - Transit V6	
82	Secondary air Feed Valve (Secondary combustion)	
83	Heavy Duty Fan Switch	
84	EVR - EGR system	
85	Canister Purge Valve	
86	Unused	
87	Electric fuel pump	
88	Electric fan - if fitted	
89	Solenoid torque converter lock-up clutch	
90	Unused	
91	HEGO sensor two (cyls 4,5,6)	Lean mixture
92	HEGO sensor two (cyls 4,5,6)	Rich mixture
98	ACT, ECT, MAP, TPS	Hard fault present
99	Unused	

Fault code table - EEC IV 'enhanced', three-digits

Note: *A system test means checking the component as described in the test procedures.*

Code	Item	Fault/reason/action
010	Separator/command code	Momentarily press accelerator fully
020	Command code	Momentarily press brake pedal fully
10	Cylinder No 1 low	Cylinder balance test
20	Cylinder No 2 low	Cylinder balance test
30	Cylinder No 3 low	Cylinder balance test
40	Cylinder No 4 low	Cylinder balance test
111	All systems OK	
112 to 124	ATS or CTS	Normal operating temperature not reached
125	TPS	
129	AFS	No change in AFS. Repeat SD procedure whilst depressing throttle during SD test
144	OS	
157 to 159	AFS	
167	TPS	No change in TPS whilst depressing throttle during SD test. Repeat SD procedure, then carry out system test
171 to 178	OS	Mixture too lean, or too rich
179	Fuel system	Mixture too lean; check EGR valve
181	Fuel system	Mixture too rich; check ISCV
182	Idle mixture too lean	
183	Idle mixture too rich	
184, 185	AFS (hot-wire type)	
186	Injector	Opening time (pulse width too long); carry out system test
187	Injector	Opening time (pulse width too short); carry out system test
194, 195	OS	
211	Ignition	PIP signal; carry out system test
212	Ignition	Tachometer circuit
213	Ignition	SAW signal
214	CID	CID circuit failure
215 to 218	EDIS ignition coil	Carry out system test
222	Tachometer circuit	
226	EDIS module	Carry out system test
227	CAS	
228	EDIS ignition coil	Winding 1; carry out system test
229	EDIS ignition coil	Winding 2
231	EDIS ignition coil	Winding 3
232	Primary circuit of ignition coil	

Code	Item	Fault/reason/action
233	EDIS module	Carry out system test
234 to 237	Ignition coil	Carry out system test
238	EDIS module	Carry out system test
239	PIP	PIP signal present under cranking; carry out system test
241	ECM	Incorrect SD data; repeat SD procedure
243	Coil	Failure
311 to 316	Pulse air system faulty	
326, 327	EPT or DPFE	
328	EVR	
332	EGR	Valve not opening
334	EVR	
335	EPT or DPFE	
336	Exhaust pressure too high	
337	EPT or DPFE/EVR	
338, 339	CTS	
341	OS	Circuit connected to earth
411	SD test	Engine speed during test too low; check that no induction leaks are present, then repeat SD procedure
412	SD test	Engine speed during test too high
413 to 416	ISCV	
452	VSS	
511	ROM fault	Check whether battery was disconnected; check KAM fuse
512	KAM fault	Check whether battery was disconnected; check KAM fuse
513	EEC IV	Reference voltage; carry out system test
519, 521	PSPS	PSPS not activated during SD test; check if PSPS fitted. If so, try SD test again, then carry out system test
522, 523	Drive/neutral switch	Carry out system test
528	Clutch switch error	
536	Brake on/off switch	Switch not activated during SD test; repeat SD procedure
538	Operating error during SD test	Repeat SD procedure
539	Air conditioning	Air conditioning on during SD test. repeat SD procedure
542, 543	Fuel pump	Fuel pump circuit; carry out system test
551	ISCV circuit	Failure
552	Pulse air circuit	Failure
556	Fuel pump	Fuel pump circuit; carry out system test
558	EVR	Electrical circuit; carry out system test
563	High-speed electronic drive fan	Circuit failure
564	Electronic drive fan relay/circuit	
565	CFSV circuit	
566	3rd/4th gear solenoid (AT)	Carry out system test
573	Electronic drive fan relay/circuit	
574	High-speed electronic drive fan circuit	
575	Fuel pump circuit/and or inertia switch	Carry out system test
576	Kickdown switch	Carry out system test
577	Kickdown switch	Not activated during SD test. Repeat SD procedure
612, 613	4/3 switch failed (AT)	Open-circuit
614, 615	3/2 switch failed (AT)	Open-circuit
621	Shift solenoid 1	Circuit failure
622	Shift solenoid 2	Circuit failure
624	EPC solenoid	Failure
625	EPC solenoid	Circuit failure
628	MLUS	
629	Torque converter lock-up clutch solenoid	Carry out system test
634	Drive/neutral switch	Carry out system test
635 to 638	Transmission temperature switch	Failure
639	TSS failure	
645	1st gear failure	
645	2nd gear failure	
645	3rd gear failure	
645	4th gear failure	
649	ETV	Failure
651	ETV	Intermittent failure
652	MLUS	Failure
653	transmission control switch	Not activated during SD test; repeat SD procedure
658	Performance/economy switch (AT)	Not activated during SD test
998	CTS/ATS/AFS/TPS	Sensor fault, rectify codes following 998, repeat SD procedure

Chapter 8
GM-Multec MPi/CFi (SPi)

Contents

Specifications

Vehicle	Year	Idle speed	CO%
Multec MPi			
Astra 1.4	1991 to 1994	820 to 980	less than 0.4
Astra-F 1.4i	1996 to 1997	820 to 890	0.3 max
Astra 1.6i	1992 to 1993	820 to 980	less than 0.4
Corsa 1.6i	1992 to 1993	820 to 920	less than 0.4
Corsa-B 1.6 GSi	1993 to 1995	820 to 930	1.5 ± 0.5
Nova 1.4i	1992 to 1993	850 to 1010	less than 0.4
Nova 1.6i	1992 to 1993	820 to 920	less than 0.4
Tigra 1.6i	1994 to 1997	820 to 890	1.5 ± 0.5
Multec CFi (SPi)			
Astra 1.4i cat	1990 to 1996	830 to 990	0.4 max
Astra 1.6i	1987 to 1993	820 to 980	0.4 max
Astra 1.8i	1991 to 1995	820 to 980	0.4 max
Astra-F 1.4i	1997	830 to 990	1.5 ± 0.5
Astra-F 1.6i E-Drive	1993 to 1996	770 to 930	0.3 max
Astra-F 1.6i	1996 to 1997	770 to 930	0.3 max
Belmont 1.4i cat	1990 to 1993	830 to 990	0.4 max
Belmont 1.6i	1987 to 1993	820 to 980	0.4 max
Belmont 1.8i cat	1990 to 1992	820 to 980	0.4 max
Cavalier 1.6i	1993 to 1995	770 to 930	1.5 ± 0.5
Cavalier 1.6i	1995 to 1997	830 to 990	0.3 max
Cavalier 1.6i (C16NZ)	1988 to 1994	720 to 880	0.4 max
Cavalier 1.6i (C16NZ2)	1993 to 1994	825 to 925	0.4 max
Cavalier 1.8 (C18NZ)	1989 to 1994	800 to 960	0.4 max
Corsa 1.2/1.4i cat	1990 to 1994	830 to 990	0.4 max
Corsa-B & Combo 1.2i	1993 to 1996	840 to 1000	0.4 max
Corsa-B 1.4i & Van	1993 to 1996	830 to 990	0.4 max
Corsa-B & Combo 1.4i	1996 to 1997	830 to 990	1.5 ± 0.5
Corsa 1.6i cat	1988 to 1991	800 to 950	0.4 max
Kadett-E 1.4i cat	1990 to 1993	830 to 990	0.4 max
Kadett-E 1.6 cat	1990 to 1993	720 to 880	0.4 max
Kadett-E 1.8i cat	1990 to 1991	800 to 960	0.4 max
Nova 1.2i/1.4i	1990 to 1994	830 to 990	0.4 max
Vectra 1.6i cat	1990 to 1993	825 to 925	0.4 max
Vectra 1.8i cat	1990 to 1994	800 to 960	0.4 max
Vectra-A 1.6i	1993 to 1995	770 to 930	1.5 ± 0.5
Vectra-A 1.6i	1995 to 1997	830 to 990	0.3 max

8

Overview of system operation

1 Introduction

The GM Multec (MULTiple TEChnology) EMS was developed by General Motors, and first appeared on vehicles in the USA. It had also been used in GM vehicles on mainland Europe before appearing in the UK in about 1989. Original applications were SPi, but MPi-equipped vehicles began to appear in 1992. Engine sizes vary from 1.4 litre through 1.6 to 1.8 litre **(see illustration 8.1)**.

GM Multec was designed as a modular system, capable of controlling a wide range of engines utilising both MPi and SPi. European vehicles with Multec were always equipped with a catalytic converter.

Multec has evolved from Multec-CFi (SPi) to Multec-M (MPi) and finally Multec-S (sequential injection).

Unlike many other modular systems, ECM pin number connections to common components may differ according to application, and care should be taken when making tests at the ECM multi-plug.

The GM Multec ECM is designed with three main areas of control. These are the ignition, fuel system and idle speed. The Multec ignition point and injection duration are jointly processed by the ECM, so that the best moment for ignition and fuelling are determined for every operating condition.

Primary ignition in early engines was initiated by either a distributor-mounted Hall-effect sensor, a distributor-mounted inductive trigger, or a flywheel-based CAS. From about 1992, all engines were equipped with DIS ignition, and the CAS became the standard primary trigger. The load sensor in Multec-CFi and Multec-M is a MAP sensor, but some Multec-S engines utilise an hot-wire type AFS. A stepper motor, located in the inlet manifold, is provided for Idle control. The injection system is either multi-point or single-point in operation, but Multec-S is sequential. Later versions of all three types practise an increasing level of emission control. Two multi-plugs (32- and 24-pin, or two 32-pin) connect the ECM to the battery, sensors and actuators.

Although an ECM of similar appearance is used in all vehicles, there are a number of vital internal differences between applications. In addition, the types of sensors used to provide base information also differ. This Chapter attempts to deal with the majority of variations which have appeared between the different years and vehicles.

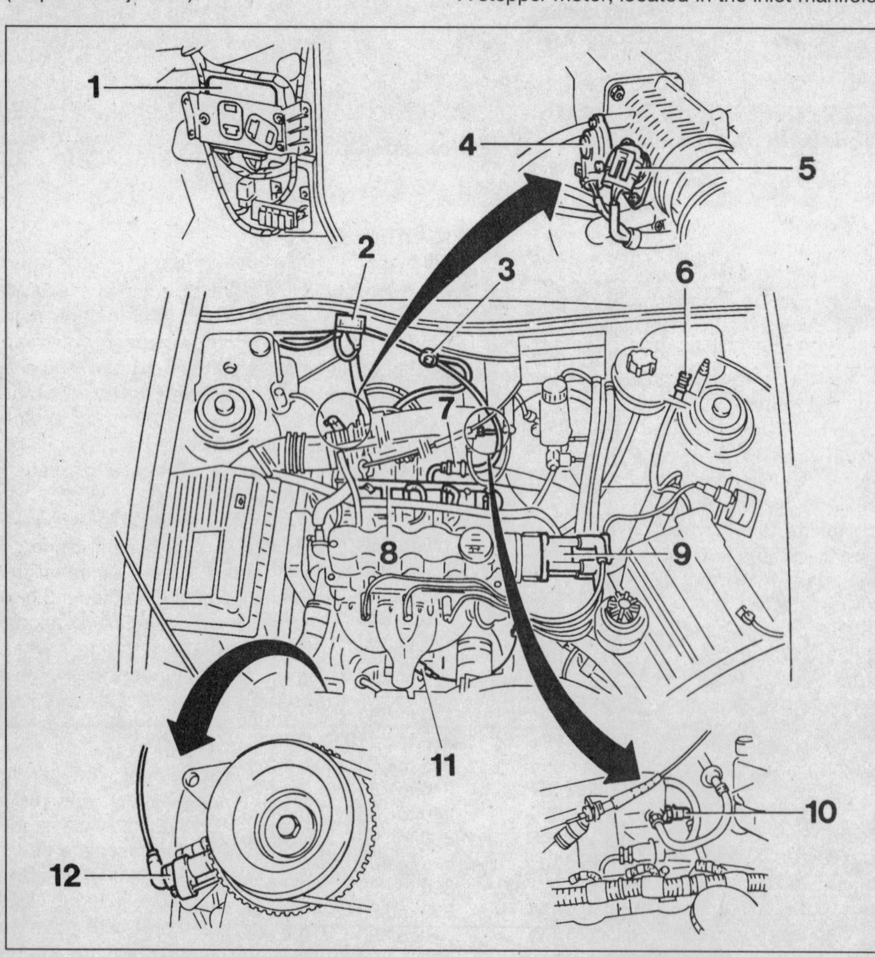

8.1 Typical Multec MPi system (1.4 engine with distributor)

1 ECM (in RH footwell)
2 MAP sensor
3 CFSV
4 TPS
5 Stepper motor
6 Octane plug
7 Fuel pressure regulator
8 Fuel injectors
9 Distributor
10 ATS
11 OS
12 CAS

2 Control functions

Signal processing

Basic ignition timing is stored by the ECM in a three-dimensional map, and the engine load and speed signals determine the ignition timing. The main engine load sensor is either a MAP sensor or a hot-wire AFS, and engine speed is determined from either the CAS, distributor-based inductive trigger or HES, as appropriate.

Correction factors are then applied for starting, idle, deceleration, and part- and full-load operation. The main correction factor is engine temperature (CTS). Minor corrections to timing and AFR are made with reference to the ATS and TPS signals. However, an ATS is not used in SPi models.

The basic AFR is also stored in a three-dimensional map, and the engine load and speed signals determine the basic injection pulse value. GM Multec calculates the AFR from the MAP sensor or AFS, and from the speed of the engine.

The AFR and pulse duration are then corrected on reference to the CTS, battery voltage and rate of throttle opening (TPS). The MPi system utilises the signal from an inlet manifold ATS, and this is not present in SPi systems. Other controlling factors are determined by operating conditions such as cold start and warm-up, idle condition, acceleration and deceleration.

Multec accesses a different map for idle running conditions, and this map is implemented whenever the engine speed is at idle. Idle speed during warm-up and normal hot running conditions is maintained by the idle control. Multec also makes small adjustments to the idle speed by advancing or retarding the timing, and this results in an ignition timing that is forever changing during engine idle.

Basic ECM operation (MPi and SPi)

Voltage is permanently applied to two of the ECM pins from the system battery. This allows the self-diagnostic function to retain data of an intermittent nature.

Once the ignition is switched on, voltage is applied to the ignition coil, VSS, injector, amplifier and to the ECM. The majority of sensors (other than those that generate a voltage such the CAS and OS), are now provided with a 5.0-volt reference supply from a relevant pin on the ECM. When the engine is cranked or run, a speed signal from the ignition causes the ECM to apply voltage to the relay so that the fuel pump will run. Ignition and injection functions are also activated. The injector circuit is completed by pulsing the relevant actuator wire to earth, and the stepper motor regulates the idle speed under ECM control when the engine is at idle.

Self-diagnostic function

The GM Multec system has a self-test capability that regularly examines the signals from engine sensors, and internally logs a code in the event of a fault being present. This code can be extracted from the serial port by a suitable fault code reader.

When the ECM detects that a fault is present, it earths an ECM pin, and the warning lamp on the dash will light. The lamp will stay lit until the fault is no longer present. If the fault clears, the code will remain logged until wiped clean with a suitable FCR, or until the engine has been started for more than 20 times when the fault code is self-initialising.

Limp-home facility (LOS)

GM Multec has a limp-home facility (LOS). In the event of a serious fault in one or more of the sensors, the EMS will substitute a fixed default value in place of the defective sensor.

This means that the engine may actually run quite well with failure of one or more minor sensors. However, since the substituted values are those of a hot engine, cold starting and running during the warm-up period may be less than satisfactory. Also, failure of a major sensor, ie the MAP sensor, will lead to a considerable reduction in performance.

Deceleration fuel cut-off

A reduction in the injection pulse is implemented during engine over-run to improve economy and reduce emissions.

Reference voltage

Voltage supply from the ECM to the engine sensors is made at a 5.0-volt reference level. This ensures a stable working voltage unaffected by variations in system voltage.

The earth return connection for most engine sensors is made through an ECM pin, and this pin is not directly connected to earth. The ECM internally connects all sensors to earth via an ECM earth pin that is directly connected to earth.

Signal shielding

To reduce RFI, a number of sensors (ie CAS, and OS) use a shielded cable.

Vehicle speed sensor (VSS)

The VSS is used to advise the ECM of vehicle speed. It operates upon the Hall-effect principle, and will be mounted directly on the gearbox or behind the dash.

A voltage of approximately 10 volts is applied to the VSS from the ignition switch when switched on. As the speedometer cable turns, the Hall switch is alternately turned on and off to return a square wave signal to the ECM. The frequency of the signal denotes the vehicle speed.

3 Primary trigger

The primary trigger in the GM Multec system is either a distributor-mounted Hall-effect sensor, a distributor-mounted inductive trigger, or a flywheel-mounted crank angle sensor (CAS). The operation of all types is described below.

CAS (1.8 SPi, 1.4 MPi with distributor, and all DIS models)

The primary signal to initiate both ignition and fuelling emanates from a CAS mounted in proximity to the flywheel. The CAS consists of an inductive magnet that radiates a magnetic field. The flywheel incorporates a reluctor disk containing 60 positions set at regular intervals. Fifty-eight of those positions contain reluctor teeth, with two positions vacant.

As the flywheel spins, and the teeth are rotated in the magnetic field, an AC voltage signal is generated to indicate speed of rotation. The two missing teeth (set at 180° intervals) are references to TDC, and indicate crankshaft position by varying the signal as the flywheel spins. One missing tooth indicates TDC for cylinders 1 and 4, and the other missing tooth indicates TDC for cylinders 2 and 3.

The peak-to-peak voltage of the speed signal can vary from 5 volts at idle to over 100 volts at 6000 rpm. The ECM uses an analogue-to-digital converter (ADC) to transform the AC pulse into a digital signal.

HES (1.4 SPi)

The amplifier supplies a voltage slightly under nbv to the Hall-effect switch in the distributor. An earth return wire completes the circuit to the amplifier, where it is internally connected to the amplifier main earth path.

Opposite the Hall switch is a magnet whose field causes the switch to return a small voltage back to the amplifier. Attached to the distributor shaft is a trigger vane with the same number of cut-outs as cylinders. Passing the trigger vane between the switch and the magnet will cause the Hall switch to be turned off and on. As the cut-out space proceeds past the switch, a voltage is returned to the module via a third wire termed the output wire.

When the solid portion comes between the switch and magnet, the voltage is turned off as the magnetic field is diverted. Essentially, the voltage signal is returned as either voltage or no voltage, and the waveform produced is that of a square wave.

Inductive trigger (1.6 SPi)

The primary signal to initiate both ignition and fuelling emanates from an inductive trigger mounted in the distributor. The inductive trigger consists of an inductive magnet that radiates a magnetic field. The distributor shaft incorporates a reluctor containing four lobes set at 90° intervals.

As the distributor spins, and the reluctor teeth are rotated in the magnetic field, an AC voltage signal is generated to indicate the ignition point.

The peak-to-peak voltage of the signal can vary from 5 volts at idle to over 100 volts at 6000 rpm. The ECM uses an ADC to transform the AC pulse into a digital signal.

4 Distributor ignition

Ignition

Data on engine load (MAP or AFS) and engine speed (CAS) are collected by the ECM, which then refers to a digital ignition map stored within its microprocessor. This map contains an advance angle for basic load and speed operating conditions. The advance angle is corrected after reference to engine temperature (CTS), so that the best ignition advance angle for a particular operating condition can be determined.

Dwell operation in GM Multec is based upon the principle of the 'constant-energy current-limiting' system. This means that the dwell period remains constant at about 3.0 to 3.5 ms, at virtually all engine running speeds. However, the dwell duty cycle, when measured in percent or degrees, will vary as the engine speed varies.

Amplifier

For 1.4 and 1.8 litre engines, a separate amplifier is mounted on a heat sink plate adjacent to the coil. For 1.6 litre engines, the amplifier is mounted on the baseplate under the distributor cap. The amplifier used in the HES system also supplies voltage to the HES, and provides a separate HES earth path. An internal connection completes the circuit through the main amplifier earth terminal.

The amplifier contains circuitry for amplifying a control signal, and switching the coil negative terminal at the correct moment to instigate ignition. Amplification is necessary because the control signal received by the amplifier from the ECM is of an insufficient level to complete the necessary coil switching. On receiving a speed and position signal from the primary trigger, the ECM looks up the correct ignition dwell time and timing advance, and sends a control signal to the amplifier which then switches the coil negative.

Ignition coil

The ignition coil utilises low primary resistance in order to increase primary current and primary energy. The amplifier limits the primary current to around 8 amps, and this permits a reserve of energy to maintain the required spark burn time (duration).

Distributor

In the GM Multec system, the distributor only serves to distribute the HT current from the coil secondary terminal to each spark plug in firing order. The distributor is located on the camshaft at the cylinder No 4 end. Either a Bosch or Lucas distributor may be used.

1.4 SPi models: The distributor also contains the HES and magnet.
1.6 SPi models: The distributor also contains the inductive trigger and the amplifier.
1.8 SPi and all MPi models: The distributor only contains the HT components, and ignition is triggered from a CAS mounted adjacent to the flywheel.

Ignition timing

Basic timing is set a few degrees before TDC, and the value is calculated to provide efficient combustion and maximum power output at a particular speed. It is only possible to adjust the ignition timing on vehicles equipped with a distributor, and the distributor can be moved in order to make timing adjustment. The timing marks are scribed upon the flywheel. When the marks are aligned at idle speed, the base ignition timing is correct. Timing is not adjustable in DIS models.

As the engine speed increases, combustion must occur earlier and the ignition point is advanced by the ECM with reference to its own mapped ignition table.

Octane coding

An octane coding plug is provided in most systems (not Multec-S) to enable the ECM to

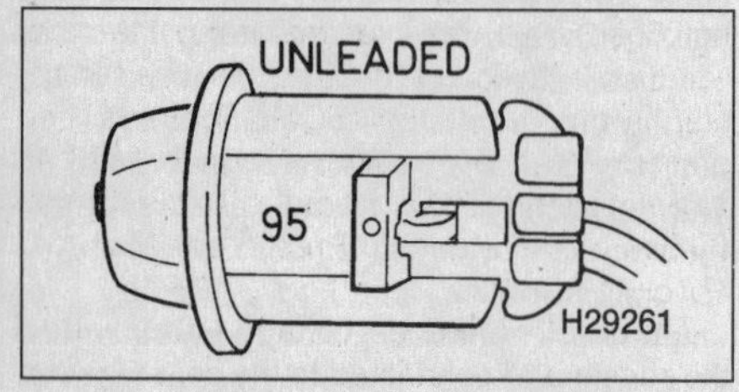

8.2 Octane coding plug

8.3 The DIS ignition system (the amplifier is integral with the dual coil unit)

adopt different characteristics to suit various grades of unleaded fuel. Simply turning the standard 95/91 octane plug to its alternative position fulfils the alternative condition **(see illustration 8.2)**.

5 DIS ignition

General

Although the ignition system is termed DIS, the basic operation is similar to models with conventional ignition **(see illustration 8.3)**. In a DIS or so-called 'wasted spark' system, a double-ended coil is used to fire two plugs at the same time. This means that the system can only be used where two cylinders rise and fall together. The ignition coils utilise low primary resistance in order to increase primary current and primary energy. The amplifier limits the primary current to around 8 amps, and this permits a reserve of energy to maintain the required spark burn time (duration).

One cylinder will fire on the compression stroke, and the companion cylinder will fire on the exhaust stroke where the spark is 'wasted'. Two pairs of coils are therefore required for a four-cylinder engine. About 3 KV is still needed to fire the 'wasted spark' plug, but this is far less than that required to bridge the rotor gap when a distributor is fitted.

Dwell operation in GM Multec is based upon the principle of the 'constant-energy current-limiting' system. This means that the dwell period remains constant at about 3.0 to 3.5 ms, at virtually all engine running speeds. However, the dwell duty cycle will vary as the engine speed varies. During engine start-up, dwell is based upon battery voltage and a fixed degree value. When 400 rpm is reached, the ECM changes to running mode, and dwell is based upon battery voltage and engine rpm.

In GM Multec DIS, the amplifier is integral with the twin coils. The ECM calculates the correct ignition dwell time and timing advance from data received from the CAS and other sensors, and sends a timed control signal to the amplifier, which then switches the coil negative terminal. Two control signals are sent, one to each coil, and the signals are alternately timed at 180° of crankshaft rotation. Four signals are therefore sent over 720°, and this results in all four spark plugs being fired during two revolutions of the engine.

The two control signals are termed EST (Electronic Spark Timing). The 'EST A' signal feeds the coil for cylinders one and four, and 'EST B' signal feeds the coil for cylinders two and three.

Knock sensor

The optimal ignition timing (at engine speeds greater than idle) for a given high compression engine is quite close to the point of onset of knock. However, running so close to the point of knock occurrence, means that knock will certainly occur on one or more cylinders at certain times during the engine operating cycle.

The knock sensor is mounted on the engine block, and consists of a piezoceramic measuring element that responds to engine noise oscillations. This signal is converted to a voltage signal by the knock sensor and returned to the knock control processor (KCP) for evaluation and action. The knocking frequency is in the 8 kHz frequency band.

Initially, timing will occur at its optimal ignition point. Once knock is identified, the ECM retards the ignition timing. After knocking ceases, the timing is advanced until the reference timing value is achieved or knock occurs once more. This procedure continually occurs so that the engine consistently runs at its optimum timing.

In Multec-S, cylinder-selective knock control is practised. Since knock may occur at a different moment in each individual cylinder, Multec knock control pinpoints the actual cylinder or cylinders that are knocking, and retards the cylinder or cylinders individually. This procedure continually occurs so that each cylinder consistently runs at its optimum timing.

6 Fuel injection

Fuel injection

The GM Multec injection system may be single-point, simultaneous multi-point, or sequential in operation. The ECM contains a fuel map with an injector opening time for basic conditions of load and speed. Information is then gathered from engine sensors such as the AFS or MAP sensor, CAS, CTS, and TPS. As a result of this information, the ECM will look up the correct injector pulse duration right across the engine rpm, load and temperature range. When the magnetic solenoid closes, a back-EMF voltage of up to 60 volts is induced.

8.4 Single-point injection system

8.5 Multi-point injection system

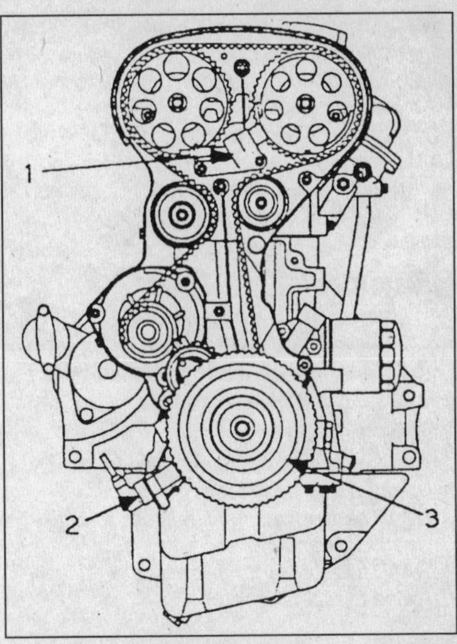

8.6 Cylinder identification sensor (CID)

1 *Camshaft sensor (CID)*
2 *CAS*
3 *58-tooth disc*

The amount of fuel delivered by the injector is determined by the fuel pressure and the injector opening time - otherwise known as the pulse duration. The ECM controls the period of time that the injector is held open, and this is determined by the signals from the various sensor inputs. During engine start-up from cold, the pulse duration is increased to provide a richer air /fuel mixture.

Fuel injector(s)

The fuel injector is a magnetically-operated solenoid valve that is actuated by the ECM. Voltage to the injectors is applied from the main relay and the earth path is completed by the ECM for a period of time (called pulse duration) of between 1.5 and 10 milliseconds.

Deceleration fuel cut-off

A reduction in the injection pulse is implemented during engine over-run conditions to improve economy and reduce emissions. Injection operation will become asynchronous with pulses every 12.5 ms. Under extreme deceleration the injector operation may be cut-off completely.

Single-point injection (SPi)

The single fuel injector is a magnetically-operated solenoid valve that is mounted in the throttle body **(see illustration 8.4)**.

The injector is switched using two circuits. Operation depends on the principle that more current is required to open an injector than to keep it open. This kind of system is often termed 'current-controlled injection system'.

Once the injector is open, a second circuit rapidly pulses the injector to earth. The switching is so rapid that the injector is effectively held open, and less current is required during the operation. Advantages of this arrangement include a reduction in injector operating temperature, and immediate injector closure once the holding circuit is switched off.

Injection operation can be synchronous or asynchronous. During normal operation ie during steady throttle cruise conditions - injection operation is synchronous. This means that the injector operation is synchronised with the ignition pulses, and four injection pulses occur for every two engine revolutions.

During sharp acceleration, injection operation becomes asynchronous. Injection operation is no longer synchronised with the ignition pulses, and injection pulses now occur every 12.5 milliseconds. Injection duration may also be increased. Asynchronous operation also occurs during operation where the injection duration is very small (less than one millisecond) and control of the mixture becomes poor.

Simultaneous MPi

The simultaneous MPi system consists of one injector for each cylinder mounted in the inlet port, so that a finely-atomised fuel spray is directed onto the back of each valve. The injectors are pulsed once per engine revolution, and fuel will briefly rest upon the back of a valve before being drawn into a cylinder **(see illustration 8.5)**.

In addition, the injectors are arranged in two banks, with injectors 1 and 2 comprising one bank, and injectors 3 and 4 making up the other bank. Each bank is connected to the ECM via a separate ECM pin.

Sequential MPi

The Multec-S system pulses the injectors sequentially - ie in firing order and once per engine cycle. Each injector is connected to the ECM via a separate ECM pin. A Hall-effect phase sensor (CID), mounted in proximity to the camshaft, identifies the position of No 1 cylinder for correct injector sequential timing **(see illustration 8.6)**.

Air temperature control (SPi models)

The air filter casing contains a thermal valve system to regulate the temperature of the air supply to the throttle body. The supply functions very much like those fitted to carburettor models.

Manifold vacuum is piped via a small hose to the thermal valve in the air filter casing. Another hose is connected to a vacuum motor which controls a flap in the air filter nozzle. The flap opens or closes according to under-bonnet air temperature. The thermal valve is a bi-metal valve which contains a passage to allow the passing of vacuum. As the temperature rises, the valve opens to form an air bleed in the passage, and this causes the vacuum in the passage to collapse.

When the under-bonnet air temperature is low, the bi-metal valve is closed, and vacuum acts to fully open the flap. Thus, heated air from the exhaust system enters the throttle body intake. As under-bonnet air temperature rises, the bi-metal air bleed begins to open, and the vacuum pull upon the flap is reduced. A mixture of heated and unheated air is thus fed to the throttle body. As the air temperature rises above a pre-determined value, the air bleed becomes fully open. The flap therefore fully closes to shut off the exhaust heated air. Unheated air now enters the throttle body. Air is thus introduced to the throttle body at a fairly constant temperature, irrespective of ambient temperature.

Load sensors

The main load sensor used in Multec-CFi and Multec-M systems is the MAP sensor. However, Multec-S may utilise an AFS of the hot-wire type or a MAP sensor, depending on model.

MAP sensor

The main engine load sensor is the MAP sensor **(see illustration 8.7)**. A vacuum hose connects the MAP sensor (located on the bulkhead) and the inlet manifold. Manifold vacuum acts upon the MAP sensor diaphragm, and the ECM converts the pressure into an electrical signal. MAP is calculated from the formula: Atmospheric Pressure less Manifold Pressure = Manifold Absolute Pressure.

A 5.0-volt reference voltage is applied to the sensor and connected to the sensor return circuit. MAP sensor output on the signal wire

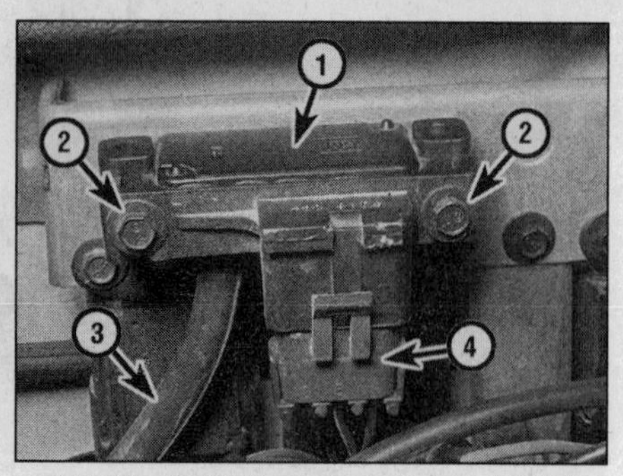

8.7 Manifold absolute pressure (MAP) sensor assembly

1 *MAP sensor*
2 *Mounting screws (some units are simply clipped into a bracket*
3 *MAP sensor vacuum line (goes to intake manifold vacuum)*
4 *MAP sensor electrical connector (usually goes to main harness)*

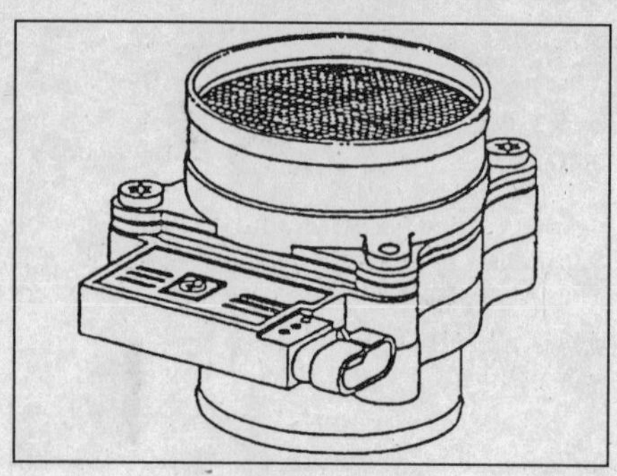

8.8 Hot-wire AFS

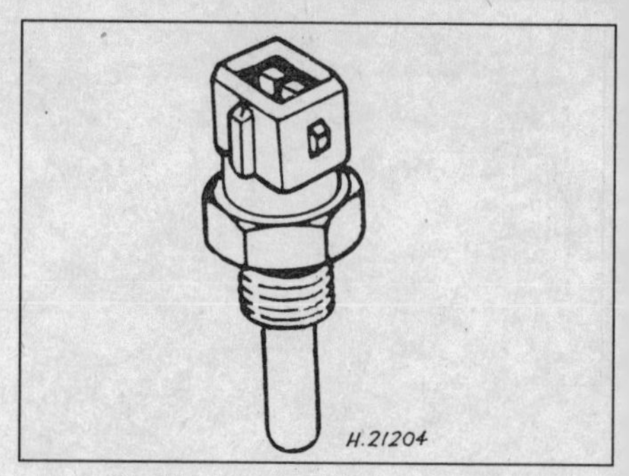

8.9 Coolant temperature sensor (CTS)

is returned to the ECM as a variable voltage signal. When the ignition is first turned on, the ECM reads and records the signal as a measure of atmospheric pressure at that moment. Since atmospheric pressure will vary every time the vehicle is used, the ECM is able to account for the changed pressure in its fuel requirement calculations.

Using the speed/density method, GM Multec calculates the AFR from the MAP signal and the speed of the engine. This method relies on the theory that the engine will draw in a fixed volume of air per revolution.

The inlet manifold on the SPi models is a 'wet' manifold. Fuel is injected into the inlet manifold, and there is a risk of fuel being drawn into the MAP sensor to contaminate the diaphragm. This is prevented by running the vacuum hose upward to the air filter, through a fuel trap and then to the ECM (which contains the MAP sensor).

Hot-wire air mass meter (AFS)

Some Multec-S models uses a hot-wire airflow sensor to measure the mass of air entering the engine **(see illustration 8.8)**. The hot-wire air mass meter is an alternative to the MAP type sensor fitted to other vehicles. The air mass meter measures the mass of air entering engine, which allows an accurate fuel injection pulse to be calculated. Hot-wire is a very accurate method of calculating the engine load (air input) and often excludes the need for additional sensors to measure air temperature and air pressure. Automatic compensation for altitude is thus provided. The absence of moving parts improves reliability and lessens maintenance requirements. The absence of moving parts improves reliability and lessens maintenance requirements.

Two heated semi-conductor elements and a temperature compensation sensor are placed in a by-pass to the main air intake.

The AFS module receives a voltage supply from the system main relay, and applies a constant voltage to the hot-wire sensors. As air passes over the hot-wire, it has a cooling effect. As air mass increases or decreases according to engine load, the AFS module adjusts the current flow to maintain the wire at its original resistance and temperature. The change in heating current is measured as a voltage drop over a precision resistor, and amplified by the AFS module as a measured value. This measured value is then returned to the ECM for evaluation as a load signal.

By measuring the change in current flow, the ECM is able to determine the mass of airflow into the engine. As the current varies on the signal wire, so does the voltage, and an indication of load can be assessed by measuring the variable voltage signal.

Air temperature sensor (ATS) - some models only

The ATS is mounted in the end of the inlet manifold, and measures the air temperature in the inlet manifold. Because the density of air varies in inverse proportion to the temperature, the ATS signal allows more accurate assessment of the volume of air entering the engine.

The ATS contains a variable resistance that operates on the NTC principle. When the air temperature is cold, the resistance is quite high. Once the engine is started and begins to warm up, the air temperature in the inlet manifold becomes hotter ,and this causes the resistance of the ATS to diminish. A variable voltage signal is thus returned to the ECM based upon the air temperature.

The open-circuit supply to the sensor is at a 5.0-volt reference level, and the earth path is through the sensor return. To increase sensitivity, the relationship between voltage and temperature is switched at a certain point. This will result in two different voltage measurements between certain temperatures. An ATS is not used in SPi systems or in Multec-S.

CO adjustment

There is no provision for CO adjustment on any of the models in this range.

Coolant temperature sensor (CTS)

The CTS is immersed in the coolant system, and contains a variable resistance that operates on the NTC principle. When the engine is cold, the resistance is quite high. Once the engine is started and begins to warm up, the coolant becomes hotter, and this causes a change in the CTS resistance. As the CTS becomes hotter, the resistance of the CTS reduces (NTC principle) and this returns a variable voltage signal to the ECM based upon the coolant temperature **(see illustration 8.9)**.

The open-circuit supply to the sensor is at a 5.0-volt reference level, and this voltage reduces to a value that depends upon the resistance of the CTS resistance. Normal operating temperature is usually from 80° to 100°C. The ECM uses the CTS signal as a main correction factor when calculating ignition timing and injection duration. To increase sensitivity, the relationship between voltage and temperature is switched at a certain point. This will result in two different voltage measurements between certain temperatures.

Throttle potentiometer sensor (TPS)

A TPS is provided to inform the ECM of idle position and rate of acceleration. The TPS is a potentiometer with three wires. A 5-volt reference voltage is supplied to a resistance track, with the other end connected to earth. The third wire is connected to an arm which wipes along the resistance track and so varies the resistance and voltage of the signal returned to the ECM.

Stepper motor

The air valve stepper motor is an actuator that the ECM uses to automatically control idle speed during normal idle and during engine warm-up **(see illustration 8.10)**. When the throttle is closed, the throttle valve is locked in a position where very little air passes by. The throttle position then, will have no effect upon the idle speed.

A by-pass port to the throttle plate is located in the inlet manifold. A valve is positioned in the port. As the valve moves, the

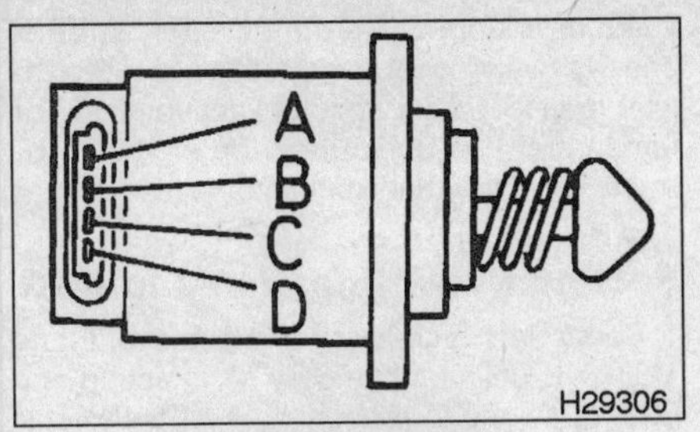

8.10 Stepper motor
Pin annotations shown

volume of air passing through the port will vary, and this directly affects the idle speed. The idle speed then, depends upon the position of the stepper air valve in the by-pass port.

The stepper motor is controlled by the ECM through two motor windings. The circuits for each winding both originate and terminate at the ECM. By pulsing these windings, the ECM is able to position the air valve exactly in its task to control the idle speed.

When an electrical load, such as headlights or heater fan etc are switched on, the idle speed would tend to drop. In this event, the ECM opens the stepper motor valve to maintain the previous idle speed. During periods of cold running, the stepper motor will regulate the valve position, so that the engine speed will be set to a suitable fast idle. On switching off the engine, the ECM actuates the air valve to its fully closed position (thus preventing engine run-on). After a few seconds more, the ECM actuates the air valve to a slightly open position, where it is ready for the next engine start.

At vehicle speeds over 16 mph, the stepper motor will position the air valve to completely shut off the air supply. During engine deceleration, the stepper motor will open the by-pass to allow additional air into the inlet manifold. This aids the reduction of excessive CO and HC emissions during deceleration.

Fuel pump relay

A single relay is utilised to provide voltage to the fuel injectors (MPi only) and fuel pump. Operation of the relay is similar on all engines, although a number of different methods may be used to provide voltage and energise the relay. Operation of two typical methods are described below.

All relays

The GM Multec fuel pump is controlled by a single relay. A permanent voltage supply is made to the fuel pump relay terminal 30 from the battery positive terminal.

Method one

When the engine is cranked or run, the ECM briefly applies voltage to relay terminal 86, which is directly connected to earth through terminal 85. This energises the fuel pump relay winding and causes the fuel pump relay contacts to close.

Method two

When the engine is cranked or run, a voltage supply from the ignition switch is applied to relay terminal 86 which is connected to an ECM pin through relay terminal 85. The ECM actuates the ECM pin by driving it to earth. This energises the fuel pump relay winding and causes the fuel pump relay contacts to close.

All relays

Whichever method is used to energise the relay winding, the result is closure of the relay contacts, and voltage is connected from terminal 30 to terminal 87, thereby providing output to the fuel pump circuit. Unlike other systems, from 1992 the relay in Multec 'M' is only actuated by the ECM during engine cranking or running operations. Prior to 1992, the relay was actuated by the ECM for several seconds to pressurise the fuel lines when the ignition was first switched on.

Voltage to the injectors in the MPi system is also applied from relay terminal 87. Voltage to the single injector in the SPi system is directly applied from the ignition switch.

Fuel pressure system (MPi and SPi)

The fuel system includes a fuel tank, with swirl pot and a submerged fuel pump. The fuel pump draws fuel from the tank, and pumps it to the fuel rail via a fuel filter **(see illustration 8.11)**.

Switching the ignition key on causes the ECM to energise the fuel pump relay for approximately one second, so that the fuel system is pressurised. The fuel pump relay is then switched off, to await a cranking or running signal.

The swirl pot prevents air from entering the fuel supply line by ensuring that the pick-up strainer is always immersed in fuel when the fuel level is low - even if the fuel moves due to centrifugal forces acting upon the vehicle during cornering.

The pump is of the 'wet' variety, in that fuel actually flows through the pump and the electric motor. There is no actual fire risk, because the fuel drawn through the pump is not in a combustible condition.

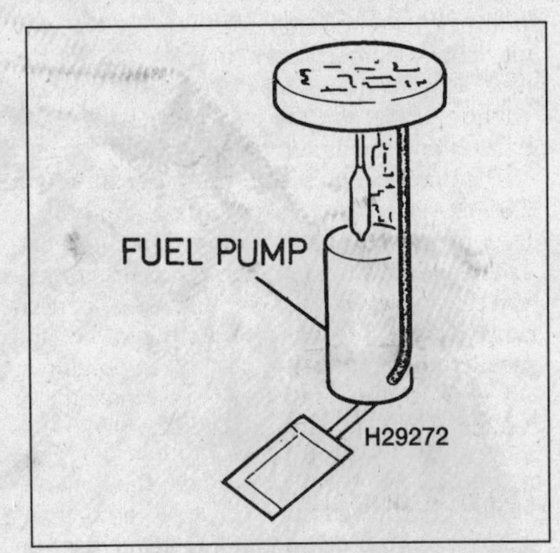

8.11 Internal fuel pump

The fuel pump assembly comprises an outer and inner gear assembly, termed a 'gerotor'. Once the pump motor becomes energised, the gerotor rotates and as the fuel passes through the individual teeth of the gerotor, a pressure differential is created. Fuel is drawn through the pump inlet, to be pressurised between the rotating gerotor teeth and discharged from the pump outlet into the fuel supply line.

To reduce the effect of fluctuations in fuel pressure, a pulsation damper is provided in the pump outlet, thereby preventing hydraulic knock. The pump is protected from over-pressurising by a relief valve mounted in the inlet side of the pump. Once the engine is running, fuel is fed through a non-return valve and fuel filter to the multi-point injector rail or to the single throttle body injector.

To prevent pressure loss in the supply system, a non-return valve is provided in the fuel pump outlet. When the ignition is switched off, and the fuel pump ceases operation, pressure is thus maintained for some time.

Fuel pressure regulator (MPi)

Fuel pressure in the fuel rail is maintained at a constant 3.0 bar by a fuel pressure regulator. The fuel pump normally provides much more fuel than is required, and surplus fuel is thus returned to the fuel tank via a return pipe. In fact, a maximum fuel pressure in excess of 5 bar is possible in this system. To prevent pressure loss in the supply system, a non-return valve is provided in the fuel pump outlet. When the ignition is switched off, and the fuel pump ceases operation, pressure is thus maintained for some time.

The pressure regulator is fitted on the outlet side of the fuel rail, and maintains an even pressure of 3.0 bar in the fuel rail. The pressure regulator consists of two chambers separated by a diaphragm. The upper chamber contains a spring which exerts pressure upon the lower chamber and closes off the outlet diaphragm. Pressurised fuel flows into the lower chamber, and this exerts pressure upon the diaphragm. Once the pressure exceeds 2.5 bar, the outlet diaphragm is opened and excess fuel flows back to the fuel tank via a return line.

A vacuum hose connects the upper chamber to the inlet manifold, so that variations in inlet manifold pressure will not affect the amount of fuel injected. This means that the pressure in the rail is always at a constant pressure above the pressure in the inlet manifold. The quantity of injected fuel thus depends solely on injector opening time, as determined by the ECM, and not on a variable fuel pressure.

At idle speed with the vacuum pipe disconnected, or with the engine stopped and the pump running, or at full-throttle, the system fuel pressure will be around 2.5 bar. At idle speed (vacuum pipe connected), the fuel pressure will be approximately 0.5 bar under the system pressure.

Fuel pressure regulator (SPi)

Fuel pressure of approximately 1.0 bar is controlled by the pressure regulator, which is located within the throttle body next to the injector. As the pressure rises over the pre-determined level, excess fuel is returned to the fuel tank via a return pipe. To prevent pressure loss in the supply system, a non-return valve is provided in the fuel pump outlet. When the ignition is switched off, and the fuel pump ceases operation, pressure is thus maintained for some time.

Fuel pressure regulation according to manifold vacuum is unnecessary in SPi vehicles. This is because injection is made into the airstream above the throttle plate, and injection is therefore unaffected by changes in manifold vacuum.

7 Catalytic converter and emission control

Catalytic converter

All UK models with the GM Multec EMS are fitted with a catalyst as standard equipment.

The GM Multec injection system fitted to catalyst vehicles implements a closed-loop control system so that exhaust emissions may be reduced. Closed-loop systems are fitted with an oxygen sensor which monitors the exhaust gas for its oxygen content. A low oxygen level in the exhaust signifies a rich mixture. A high oxygen level in the exhaust signifies a weak mixture.

The OS only produces a signal when the exhaust gas has reached a minimum temperature of approximately 300°C. However, an OS heater is not fitted to the Multec system, and the OS relies on exhaust heat to bring it to operating temperature.

Evaporative emission control

An activated carbon canister is employed to prevent petrol (hydrocarbon) fumes from escaping to atmosphere. Fumes from the fuel tank are routed to the carbon canister via the fuel tank ventilation line. When the engine is stopped or at idle, the fumes are trapped in the canister and cannot escape. A one-way valve, actuated by engine vacuum (early models), or the ECM (later models) is used to purge the canister according to certain operating conditions.

In the mechanically-controlled system, a vacuum line runs from above the throttle plate to the canister. As the throttle plate is opened, vacuum is applied to the canister, and the one-way valve opens a direct channel to the inlet manifold via a second vacuum line. The fumes are then drawn into the engine to be burnt during normal combustion.

Secondary air injection and EGR

Some late versions of Multec-CFi and Multec-S utilise secondary air injection and EGR functions to reduce exhaust emissions. Immediately after a cold engine start, and before the OS signal places the EMS under closed-loop control, the air/fuel mixture is rich. Under these conditions, secondary air injection is switched on by the EMS, and air is injected into the exhaust tract. The oxygen in the injected air reacts with the hot exhaust gas in the exhaust manifold, and CO and HC emissions are oxidised into CO_2 and H_2O. The exhaust temperature is raised so that the OS will reach its operating temperature more quickly. Once OS switching commences, secondary air injection is switched off.

EGR operation only occurs after the engine has attained normal operating temperature, and the engine is operating under part-load conditions. The ECM pulses open an EGR valve, which opens to allow a finely-metered supply of exhaust gas to be introduced into the inlet manifold. This reduces combustion chamber temperature, and reduces the production of NOx emissions.

Adjustments

8 Adjustment pre-conditions

1 Ensure that all of these conditions are met before attempting to make adjustments:

a) Engine at operating temperature. Engine oil at a minimum temperature of 80°C. A journey of at least 4 miles is recommended (particularly so if equipped with AT).
b) Ancillary equipment (all engine loads and accessories) switched off.
c) AT engines: Transmission in N or P.
d) Engine mechanically sound.
e) Engine breather hoses and breather system in satisfactory condition.
f) Induction system free from vacuum leaks.
g) Ignition system in satisfactory condition.
h) Air filter in satisfactory condition.
i) Exhaust system free from leaks.
j) Throttle cable correctly adjusted.
k) No fault codes logged by the ECM.
l) OS operating satisfactorily (catalyst vehicles with closed-loop control).

2 In addition, before checking the idle speed and CO values, stabilise the engine as follows:

a) Stabilise the engine. Raise the engine speed to 3000 rpm for a minimum of 30 seconds, and then let the engine idle.
b) Allow the CO and idle speed to settle.
c) Make all checks and adjustments within 30 seconds. If this time is exceeded, re-stabilise the engine and recheck.

9 Throttle adjustments

Throttle valve position and TPS

1 Clean the throttle valve and surrounding areas with carburettor cleaner. Blow-by from the breather system often causes sticking problems here.

2 The throttle valve position is critical, and must not be disturbed.

3 The TPS is not adjustable for this range of engines.

10 Ignition timing checks

1 The ignition timing is adjustable only on the early 1.2 and 1.4 SPi models with a distributor. For all other models, the ignition timing is non-adjustable. However, an octane adjuster is provided so that the timing may be altered to suit different fuel octane levels.

2 Timing marks are usually provided, even on DIS models, so that the timing can be checked.

3 Even if the timing is non-adjustable, it is useful to check that timing is being properly controlled by the ECM. Lack of timing control could indicate a serious sensor or ECM malfunction.

4 Refer to the pre-conditions in Section 8.

5 Allow the engine to idle.

6 Connect a stroboscopic light.

7 Check that the approximate base ignition timing is either 5° BTDC or 10° BTDC. This range of engines utilise timing marks that are aligned when the timing is correct **(see illustration 8.12)**. A TDC indicator is not normally provided. **Note:** *The marks will fluctuate by a few degrees as the ECM varies the timing to control the idle speed.*

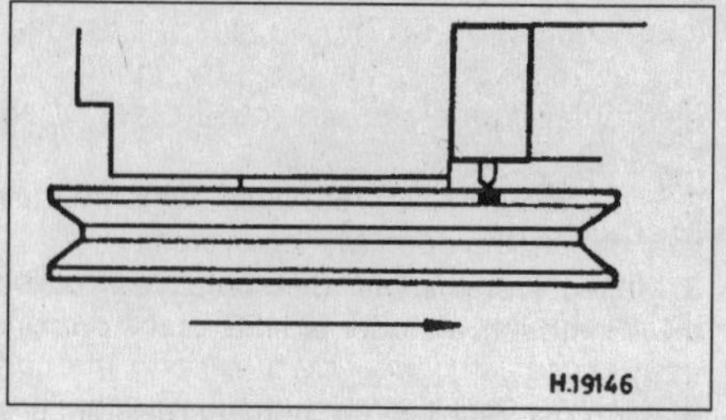

8.12 Ignition timing marks (1.6 engine, not DIS)

8 If the ignition timing is incorrect but adjustable, correct the timing by slackening the clamp bolts and turning the distributor. Tighten the bolts once the timing is correct.
9 Increase the engine speed. The timing marks should smoothly advance. Expect approximately 25 to 35° of timing advance at 3000 rpm.
10 If the timing is not being controlled properly by the ECM, suspect one of the following faults:

a) *The engine is in LOS, due to one or more serious sensor failures.*
b) *The ECM is faulty.*

11 Idle speed and CO checks

Note: *The idle speed and idle CO are non-adjustable on this range of vehicles.*
1 Refer to the test conditions described in Section 8.
2 Stabilise the engine. Raise the engine speed to 3000 rpm for a minimum of 30 seconds, and then allow the engine to idle. Make all checks and adjustments within 30 seconds. If this time is exceeded, re-stabilise the engine and recheck. *If the cooling fan operates during adjustment, wait until it stops, re-stabilise the engine and then restart the adjustment procedure.*
3 Allow the idle speed to settle, and check that the regulated idle speed is correct.
4 If the idle speed is outside of the specified parameters, check the system sensors for faults.
5 Connect a gas analyser to the exhaust system.
6 Stabilise the engine as above.
7 Allow the CO value to settle, and check the idle CO value.

System sensor and actuator tests

Important note: *Please refer to Chapter 4, which describes common test procedures applicable to this system. The routines in Chapter 4 should be read in conjunction with the component notes and wiring diagrams presented in this Chapter. The wiring diagrams and other data presented in this Chapter are necessarily representative of the system depicted. Because of the variations in wiring and other data that often occurs, even between similar vehicles in any particular VM's range, the reader should take great care in identification of ECM pins, and satisfy himself that he has gathered the correct data before failing a particular component.*

12 Primary trigger - CAS or inductive trigger

1 Refer to the note at the start of this Section, and refer to the relevant Section of Chapter 4.
2 The CAS resistance is 500 to 800 ohms for most vehicles.
3 Testing of the inductive trigger found in some models follows very similar lines to testing the CAS. The inductive resistance is 500 to 1500 ohms.

13 Primary trigger - Hall-effect sensor

1 Refer to the note at the start of Section 12, and refer to the relevant Section of Chapter 4.

14 Primary ignition (distributor models)

1 Refer to the note at the start of Section 12, and refer to the relevant Section of Chapter 4 **(see illustration 8.13)**. Although the primary trigger may differ, the primary ignition in distributor models is essentially that of an ECM with separate amplifier.
2 ECM and amplifier terminals numbers may vary depending upon Multec system.
3 Multec systems with distributor may utilise a CAS, inductive trigger or HES as the primary trigger.
4 For most vehicles, the primary resistance is 0.30 to 0.60, and the secondary resistance is 5000 ohms.

15 Ignition system (DIS models)

Note: *The primary ignition on the Multec DIS is rather unusual, in that the twin coil pack and the amplifier are combined in a finned unit on the left-hand side of the cylinder head, and it is not possible to make normal primary connections.*
1 For most vehicles, the secondary resistance is 6000 ohms. It is not possible to check the primary resistance.
2 Avoid damage to the coils unit by disconnecting the DIS coils multi-plug before making a compression test.

Engine non-runner test procedures

3 Switch the ignition on.
4 Check for a voltage supply to the DIS coils' positive (+) terminal number one **(see illustrations 8.14 to 8.16)**. No voltage: Check the wiring back to the supply from the ignition switch.
5 Check the DIS coils' earth connection at terminal number two.
6 Switch off the ignition, and disconnect the DIS coils' multi-plug *(refer to Warning No 3 in Reference)*.
7 Disconnect the HT leads from cylinders No 1 and 4, and use a spark jumper to attach each plug to the cylinder head.

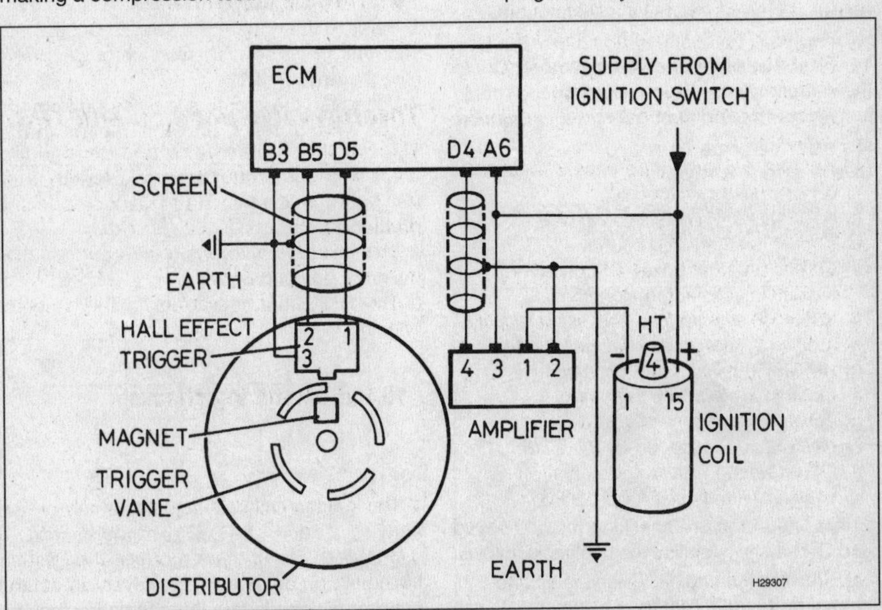

8.13 Typical Multec wiring: distributor ignition

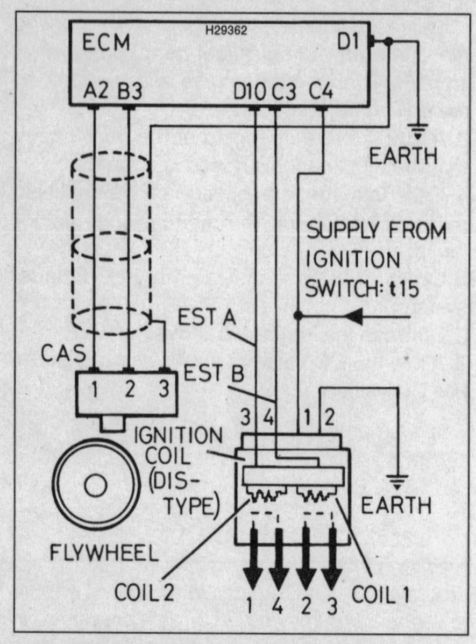

8.14 Typical Multec wiring: DIS ignition

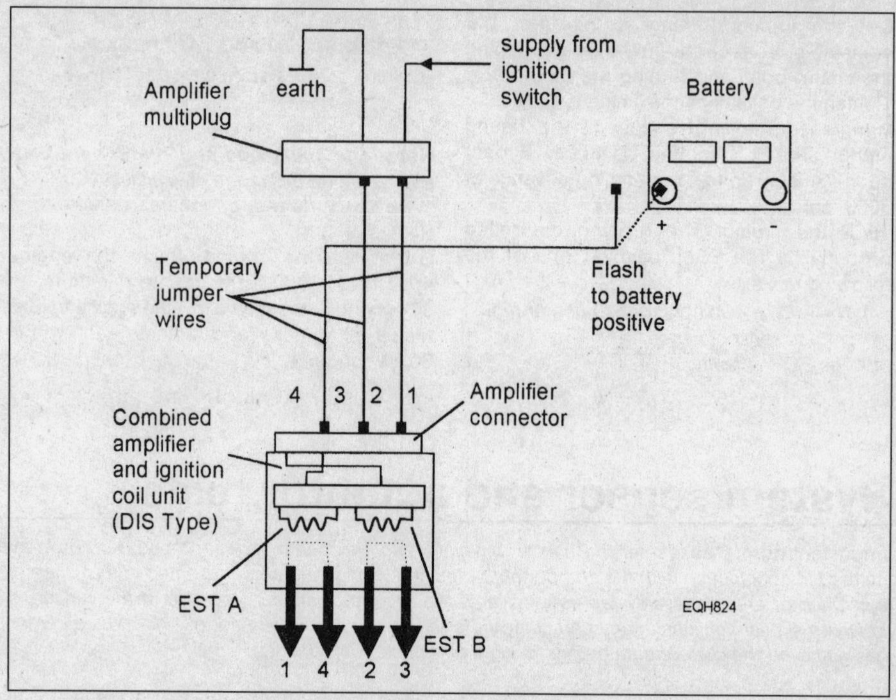

8.15 Testing DIS coil pack

8 Connect a temporary (fused) jumper wire between DIS coils multi-plug terminal one and DIS coils connector terminal one.

9 Connect a temporary (fused) jumper wire between DIS coils multi-plug terminal two and DIS coils connector terminal two.

10 Connect one end of a temporary jumper wire to the DIS coils connector terminal three.

11 Flash the other end of the jumper wire to the battery positive terminal. A spark should jump both spark jumper gaps.

12 Reconnect the HT leads to cylinders No 1 and 4. Disconnect the HT leads from the spark plugs to cylinders No 2 and 3, and use a spark jumper to attach each plug to the cylinder head.

13 Remove the temporary jumper wire from DIS coils' connector terminal three, and reconnect the wire to the DIS coils' connector terminal four.

14 Flash the other end of the jumper wire to the battery positive terminal. A spark should jump both spark jumper gaps.

No spark at one or more of the spark jumpers

a) If the HT lead resistance and connections are satisfactory, the DIS coils unit is suspect.

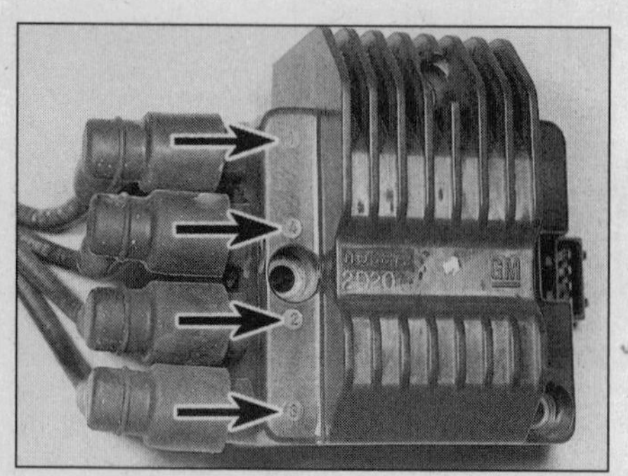

8.16 DIS coil number markings

A satisfactory spark at the spark jumpers

a) Check continuity of circuit, ECM to DIS coil connector.

b) If the wiring is satisfactory, check all ECM voltage supplies and earth connections. If tests find no faults, the ECM is suspect.

16 Fuel injector operation (MPi)

1 Refer to the note at the start of Section 12, and refer to the relevant Section of Chapter 4 **(see illustration 8.17)**.

2 Voltage to the injectors is provided from the single system relay, and this means that a supply is only available whilst the engine is cranking or running. However, voltage could be applied for test purposes by by-passing the relay (see Chapter 4).

3 The injector resistance is normally 11.8 to 12.6 ohms.

17 Fuel injector operation (SPi)

1 Refer to the note at the start of Section 12, and refer to the relevant Section of Chapter 4 **(see illustration 8.18)**.

2 The injector resistance is normally 1.4 to 2.0 ohms.

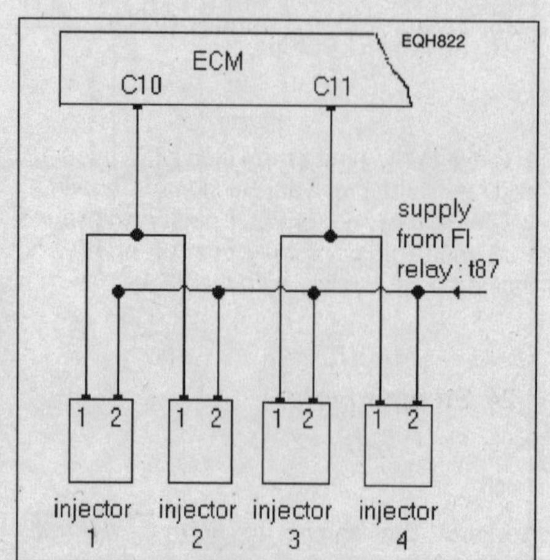

8.17 Typical Multec wiring: injectors, MPi

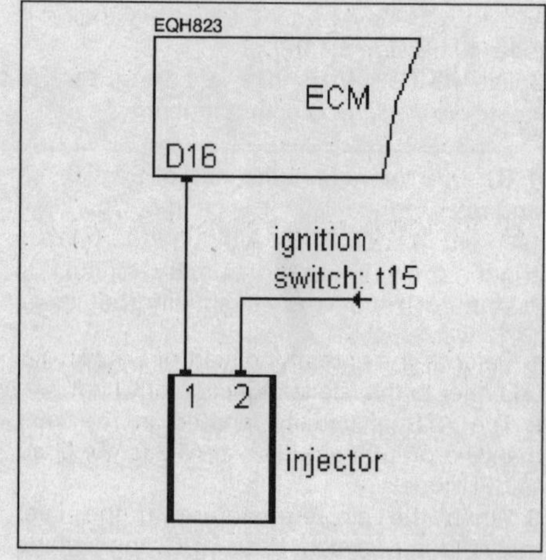

8.18 Typical Multec wiring: injector, SPi

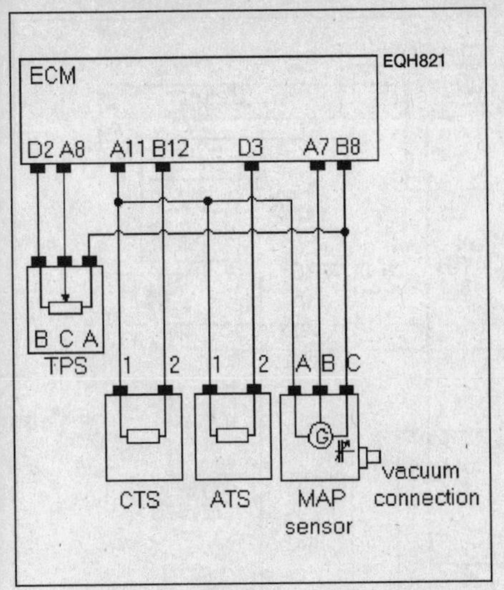

8.19 Typical Multec wiring: sensors

3 The SPi system is current-controlled and under rapid acceleration, the pulse should change to asynchronous operation with an injection pulse appearing every 12.5 ms. **Note:** *In asynchronous mode the injection pulse is no longer synchronised with the ignition. To measure the asynchronous pulse properly, an oscilloscope with a variable timebase function is required.*

18 Hot-wire AFS

1 Refer to the note at the start of Section 12, and refer to the relevant Section of Chapter 4.

19 MAP sensor

1 Refer to the note at the start of Section 12, and refer to the relevant Section of Chapter 4 **(see illustration 8.19).**

2 The MAP sensor is a separate sensor located in the engine compartment.

20 Air temperature sensor (ATS)

1 Refer to the note at the start of Section 12, and refer to the relevant Section of Chapter 4.

2 The ATS is usually located in the inlet manifold on MPi models. An ATS is not fitted to SPi models.

3 When the air temperature in the inlet manifold is between 40 to 50°C. the voltage will switch ranges as shown in the ATS table.

ATS resistance, voltage and temperature table

Temp	Resistance	Voltage
0	*9420*	*3.25 to 3.50*
5	*7280*	*3.00 to 3.25*
10	*5670*	*2.75 to 3.00*
15	*4449*	*2.50 to 2.75*
20	*3515*	*2.00 to 2.50*
30	*2237*	*1.75 to 2.00*
40 to 50	*1000*	*0.90 to 1.00*
40 to 50	*820*	*4.10 to 3.48*
60 to 80	*560*	*3.05 to 2.40*

21 Coolant temperature sensor (CTS)

1 Refer to the note at the start of Section 12, and refer to the relevant Section of Chapter 4.

2 When the coolant temperature is between 40 to 50°C. the voltage will switch ranges as shown in the CTS table.

CTS resistance, voltage and temperature table

Temp	Resistance	Voltage
0	*6000*	*2.75 to 3.25*
20	*3000*	*2.00 to 2.50*
30	*1800*	*1.50 to 2.00*
40	*1450*	*1.25 to 1.50*
45	*1000*	*1.20 and 3.70*
50	*820*	*3.48*
70	*450 to 500*	*2.75 to 3.00*
85	*400*	*2.21*
100 to 110	*300*	*1.43 to 2.00*

22 Throttle potentiometer sensor (TPS)

1 Refer to the note at the start of Section 12, and refer to the relevant Section of Chapter 4.

23 Vehicle speed sensor (VSS)

1 Refer to the note at the start of Section 12, and refer to the relevant Section of Chapter 4.

2 Check that the terminal pins in the round VSS multi-plug are fully pushed home and making good contact with the VSS.

24 Stepper motor

1 Warm the engine to normal operating temperature.

2 Start the engine and allow it to idle.

3 Check that the idle speed is within its operating limits.

4 Load the system by switching on the headlights, rear screen heater and heater motor onto high. The idle speed should barely change. **Note:** *If this operation is completed satisfactorily, it is probable that the stepper motor condition is also satisfactory.*

5 Inspect the stepper motor multi-plug for corrosion and damage.

6 Check that the connector terminal pins are fully pushed home and making good contact with the stepper motor multi-plug.

Stepper motor tests

7 Remove the stepper motor from the inlet manifold.

8 Check that the air passage in the inlet manifold is clear. Clean the passage as necessary.

9 Ensure that the shaft and cone will freely rotate in the motor armature.

10 Refit the stepper motor to the inlet manifold.

11 Detach the stepper motor multi-plug.

12 Measure the resistance of motor windings A to B and C to D. The resistance should be 50 to 65 ohms.

13 Reconnect all of the multi-plugs.

14 Connect the voltmeter negative probe to an engine earth.

15 Connect the voltmeter positive probe to the wire attached to stepper motor signal terminal number 'A'.

16 Allow the engine to idle.

17 Switch on and off a number of high electrical load components: ie heated rear window, headlights on high beam and the heater fan on maximum. The voltage should occasionally switch from zero to nbv as the motor winding is energised.

18 Repeat the test at stepper motor signal terminals B, C and D.

19 If the signal is absent, check continuity of the wiring between the ECM multi-plug and the stepper motor.

20 If the stepper motor wiring is satisfactory, check all voltage supplies and earth connections to the ECM. If the voltage supplies and earth connections are satisfactory, the ECM is suspect.

25 ECM voltage supplies and earths

1 Refer to the note at the start of Section 12, and refer to the relevant Section of Chapter 4.

2 The battery supply to the ECM is normally made to two separate ECM pins.

3 In some models, a voltage supply is applied to relay terminal 86 from the ECM, and voltage should be available with the engine cranking or running. Check for this condition where appropriate.

26 Single system relay

1 Refer to the note at the start of Section 12, and refer to the relevant Section of Chapter 4.
2 The Multec system utilises a single system relay that provides voltage to the injectors and the fuel pump **(see illustration 8.20)**.
3 In some models, a voltage supply is applied to relay terminal 86 from the ECM, and voltage should be available with the engine cranking or running. Check for this condition where appropriate.
4 Check for a supply voltage at these component(s) supplied by the relay; injectors (MPi only) or fuel pump.

27 Fuel pump and circuit

1 Refer to the note at the start of Section 12, and refer to the relevant Section of Chapter 4.

28 Fuel pressure

1 Refer to the note at the start of Section 12, and refer to the relevant Section of Chapter 4.

29 Oxygen sensor (OS)

1 Refer to the note at the start of Section 12, and refer to the relevant Section of Chapter 4.
2 The OS found in the majority of Multec systems is a single wire sensor without a heater.

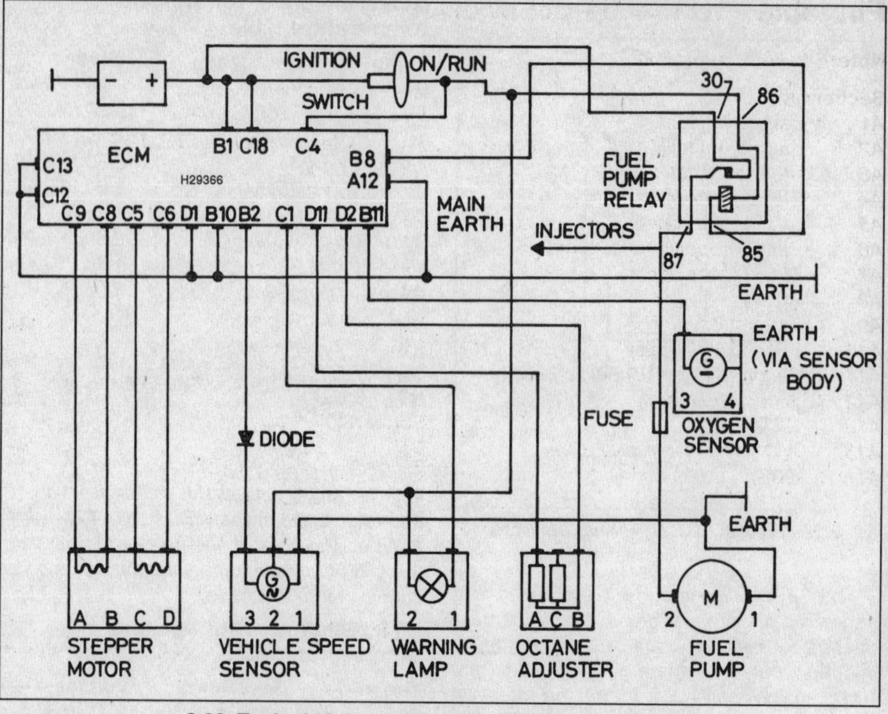

8.20 Typical Multec wiring: relays and components

Pin table - typical 56-pin (Multec-CFi and Multec-M)

Note: *See* ***illustration 8.21***

Section 'A'

A2	*CAS*
A7	*MAP sensor signal, terminal B*
A8	*TPS signal*
A11	*Sensor return, ATS, CTS, MAP*
A12	*Main ECM earth*

Section 'B'

B1	*Battery supply - fault memory*
B2	*VSS*
B3	*CAS*
B6	*Injection relay*
B7	*Diagnostic socket*
B8	*MAP sensor, TPS*
B10	*Earth*
B11	*OS signal*
B12	*CTS*

Section 'C'

C1	*Warning lamp*
C2	*Tachometer*
C4	*Ignition supply*
C5	*Stepper motor, terminal C*
C6	*Stepper motor*
C8	*Stepper motor*
C9	*Stepper motor*
C10	*Injectors pulse (1 + 2)*
C11	*Injectors pulse (3 + 4)*
C12	*Earth (inj 1+2)*
C13	*Earth (inj 3+4)*
C16	*Battery supply*

Section 'D'

D1	*Earth (final injector stage)*
D2	*Sensor return TPS*
D3	*ATS signal*
D6	*Diagnostic socket*
D10	*Amplifier control signal*
D11	*Octane adjuster*

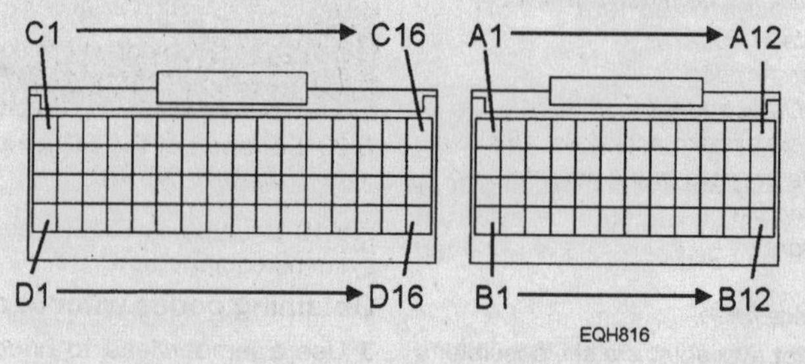

8.21 Typical Multec multi-plug (Multec-CFi and Multec-M)

Pin table - typical 64-pin (Multec-S)

Note: *See* ***illustration 8.22***

Section 'A'

A1	*Stepper motor*
A2	*Stepper motor*
A3	*Stepper motor*
A4	*Stepper motor*
A5	*CID sensor signal*
A6	*Battery supply - fault memory*
A7	*MAP sensor signal*
A8	*A/C*
A9	*AT control unit*
A10	*Secondary air relay*
A11	*Secondary air solenoid valve*
A12	*Fuel pump relay*
A13	*CFSV*
A15	*A/C compressor relay driver*
A16	*CAS*

Section 'B'

B1	*Main ECM earth*
B2	*Sensor return - CTS, TPS, EGR*
B3	*CTS*
B4	*ATS signal*
B5	*A/C pressure switch*
B6	*Injection relay*
B8	*P/N lever position switch (AT)*
B9	*Diagnostic socket*
B10	*Warning lamp*
B13	*Tachometer*
B14	*CAS*

Section 'E'

E1	*KS signal*
E2	*Injector 3 pulse*
E3	*Injector 2 pulse*
E4	*Injector 1 pulse*
E6	*Injector 4 pulse*
E7	*Earth (injectors final stage)*
E9	*Earth (OS)*
E10	*AT torque control signal*
E14	*Ignition control signal EST A*
E16	*Ignition supply*

Section 'F'

F1	*EGR solenoid valve ground pulse*
F2	*EGR solenoid valve signal*
F3	*Ignition supply*
F5	*TPS signal*
F7	*Earth (injectors final stage)*
F8	*MAP sensor supply*
F9	*OS signal*
F10	*VSS signal*
F11	*Diagnostic socket*
F14	*Ignition control signal EST B*
F15	*Sensor return, ATS*
F16	*Earth*

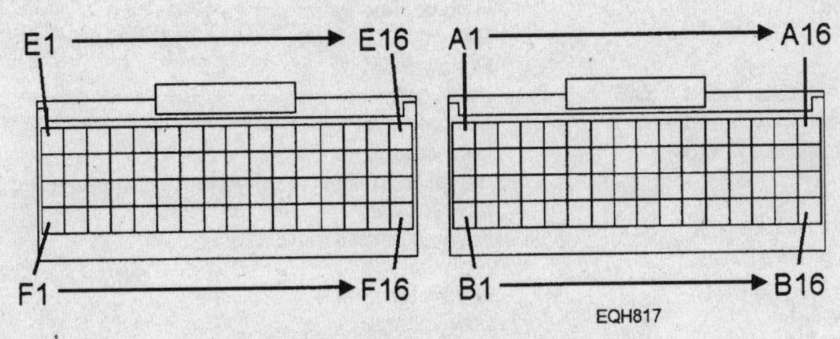

8.22 Typical Multec multi-plug (Multec-S)

Fault codes

30 Obtaining fault codes

1 If a FCR is available it could be attached to the SD serial connector (the Vauxhall term for the SD plug is ALDL) and used for the following purposes **(see illustration 8.23)**:

a) Obtaining fault codes.
b) Clearing fault codes.
c) Obtaining Datastream information.
d) Actuating the system actuators: This may include one or more of the actuators on the following list:
Fuel injectors
ISCV
CFSV (where fitted)

2 If a FCR is not available, it is still possible to obtain fault codes so long as the SD plug is of the 10-pin type. A FCR is required for those systems equipped with the 16-pin SD plug.

8.23 Location of the SD plug, late vehicles

Obtaining codes without a FCR

3 Use a jumper lead to bridge terminals A and B in the SD (ALDL) plug. The codes are then output on the instrument panel warning lamp. By counting the flashes and referring to the fault code table, faults can thus be determined **(see illustration 8.24)**.

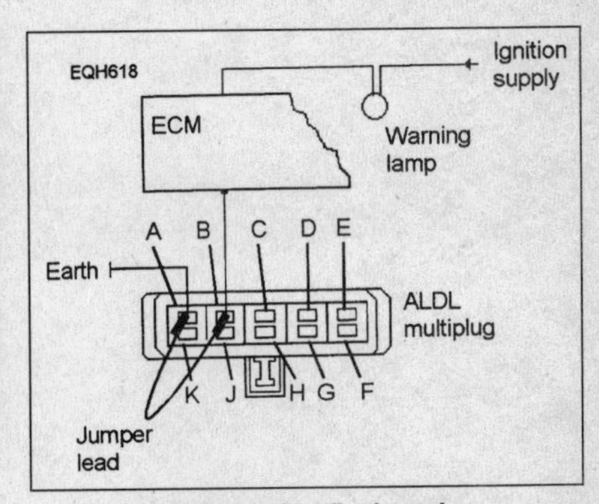

8.24 Obtaining flash codes: GM (Opel & Vauxhall)

Fault code table

Code	Item	Fault
12	Initiation of diagnosis	
13	Oxygen sensor	No change in voltage/open-circuit
14	CTS	Low voltage
15	CTS	High voltage
18	Knock control processor	
19	CAS	Incorrect rpm signal
21	TPS	High voltage
22	TPS	Low voltage
24	VSS	No speed signal
25	Injectors	Low voltage
28	Fuel pump relay contacts	
29	Fuel pump relay	Low voltage
32	Fuel pump relay	High voltage
33	MAP sensor	High voltage
34	MAP sensor	Low voltage
35	Idle stepper motor	Poor or no idle speed control
41	Amplifier control signal, cyls. 2 and 3 (DIS)	High voltage
42	Amplifier control signal, cyls. 1 and 4 (DIS)	High voltage
42	Primary ignition (distributor systems)	High voltage
44	Oxygen sensor	Air/fuel mixture too lean
45	Oxygen sensor	Air/fuel mixture too rich
46	Amplifier (DIS) control signal (A+B)	High voltage
49	Battery supply to ECM	High voltage (greater than 17.0 volts)
51	ECM	Defective ECM (disconnect and reconnect ECM, then recheck for fault codes)
55	ECM fault	Renew ECM
63	Amplifier control signal, cyls. 2 and 3 (DIS)	Low voltage
64	Amplifier control signal, cyls. 1 and 4 (DIS)	Low voltage
64	Primary ignition (distributor systems)	Low voltage
67	AFS (air mass meter)	Signal is outside normal operating parameters
69	ATS (MPi only)	Low voltage
69	AFS (air mass meter)	Faulty air mass meter signal
71	ATS (MPi only)	High voltage
72	Amplifier (DIS) control signal (A+B)	Lead interruption
75	Torque control (AT only)	Low voltage
76	Continuous torque control (AT only)	
81	Injectors	High voltage
93	Quad drive module (in ECM)	

Chapter 9
Honda / Rover PGM-Fi

Contents

Specifications

Vehicle	Year	Idle speed	CO%
Honda PGM-Fi			
Accord EFi A4 SOHC A20	1985 to 1989	800 ± 50	0.1 max
Accord 2.0i-16 A2 DOHC 16V B20	1987 to 1989	800 ± 50	0.1 max
Accord 2.0i & cat SOHC F20A4	1989 to 1992	770 ± 50	0.1 max
Accord 2.0i & cat F20A8	1992 to 1996	770 ± 50	0.1 max
Accord 2.0i Coupe cat F20A7	1992 to 1996	770 ± 50	0.1 max
Accord 2.2i cat F22A3/A7/A8	1989 to 1996	770 ± 50	0.1 max
Accord 2.3i cat DOHC H23A2	1993 to 1996	780 ± 50	0.1 max
Aerodeck EFi A4 SOHC A20	1985 to 1989	800 ± 50	0.1 max
Aerodeck 2.2i cat SOHC F22A3/A7/A8	1989 to 1996	770 ± 50	0.1 max
Ballade EXi SOHC 3W EW3	1986 to 1989	800 to 900	1.5 max
Civic CRX EW3	1984 to 1987	850 ± 50	0.5 to 2.0
Civic GT EW3	1984 to 1987	850 ± 50	0.5 to 2.0
Civic 1.5 LSi SOHC D15B2	1991 to 1995	750 ± 50	0.1 max
Civic Coupe cat SOHC D15B2	1991 to 1995	750 ± 50	0.1 max
Civic 1.5i VTEC-E SOHC D15Z3	1995 to 1996	750 ± 50	0.1 max
Civic 1.6i-16 DOHC 16V D16A9	1987 to 1992	800 ± 50	0.1 max
Civic 1.5 VEi SOHC VTEC cat D15Z1	1991 to 1995	600 ± 50	0.1 max
Civic 1.6 ESi SOHC VTEC cat D16Z6	1991 to 1996	750 ± 50	0.1 max
Civic/CRX 1.6 VTi DOHC VTEC cat	1990 to 1991	750 ± 50	0.1 max
CRX 1.6i-16 DOHC 16V D16A9	1987 to 1992	800 ± 50	0.1 max
CRX 1.6 ESi cat SOHC 16V D16Z6	1991 to 1996	750 ± 50	0.1 max
Civic 1.6 VTi cat DOHC 16V B16A2	1991 to 1995	750 ± 50	0.1 max
CRX 1.6 VTi c DOHC 16V B16A2	1991 to 1995	750 ± 50	0.1 max
Civic 1.6i SOHC 16V 83kW D16Y3	1995 to 1996	750 ± 50	0.1 max
Civic 1.6i VTEC SOHC 16VD16Y2	1995 to 1996	750 ± 50	0.1 max
Concerto 1.5i cat ZC 1 SOHC D15B2	1991 to 1995	800 ± 50	0.1 max
Concerto 1.6 DOHC D16A9 (AT:D16Z4)	1989 to 1991	800 ± 50	0.5+0.5-0.3
Concerto 1.6i SOHC 16V cat D16Z2	1992 to 1995	780 ± 50	0.1 max
Concerto 1.6i DOHC 16V cat D16A8	1992 to 1995	800 ± 50	0.1 max
Integra EX 16 A2 DOHC 16V D16	1986 to 1990	800 ± 50	0.1

Vehicle	Year	Idle speed	CO%
Legend C25A2	1986 to 1988	770 ± 50	1.0 ± 1.0
Legend 2.7 & Coupe SOHC C27A2	1988 to 1991	720 ± 50	2.0 max
Legend 2.7 cat SOHC C27A1	1990 to 1991	680 ± 50	0.1 max
Legend 3.2 cat SOHC 24V C32A2	1992 to 1996	650 ± 50	0.1 max
NSX cat DOHC 24V V-TEC C30A	1991 to 1996	800 ± 50	0.1 max
Prelude Fi B20A1	1985 to 1987	800 ± 50	1.0 ± 1.0
Prelude 4WS 2.0i-16 DOHC B20A7	1987 to 1992	800 ± 50	0.1
Prelude 4WS 2.0i-16 cat B20A9	1987 to 1992	750 ± 50	0.1 max
Prelude 2.0i 16V cat SOHC F20A4	1992 to 1996	770 ± 50	0.1 max
Prelude 2.2i VTECDOHC 16V H22A2	1994 to 1996	790 ± 50	0.1 max
Prelude 2.3i 16V cat DOHC 16V H23A2	1992 to 1996	780 ± 50	0.1 max
Shuttle 1.6i 4WD SOHC 16V D16A7	1988 to 1990	780 ± 50	0.1 max
Rover PGM-Fi			
216/416i SOHC non cat D16A6/7/Z2	1989 to 1992	780 ± 50	0.2 to 1.0
216/416i SOHC cat D16A6/7/Z2	1989 to 1994	780 ± 50	0.1 max
216/416 GTi DOHC non cat D16A9/8/Z4 (MT)	1990 to 1992	800 ± 50	0.5 ± 0.3
216/416 GTi DOHC non cat D16A9/8/Z4 (AT)	1990 to 1992	750 ± 50	0.5 ± 0.3
216/416 GTi DOHC non cat D16A9/8/Z4 (MT)	1992 to 1994	800 ± 50	0.1 max
216/416 GTi DOHC non cat D16A9/8/Z4 (AT)	1992 to 1994	750 ± 50	0.1 max
620i/Si/SLi/GSi F20Z1/2	1993 to 1996	770 ± 50	0.2 max
623i S/Si/SLi/GSi H23A3	1993 to 1996	770 ± 50	0.2 max
825i V6 SOHC 24V V6 2.5	1986 to 1988	720 to 820	0.25 to 0.75
827i V6 SOHC 24V V6 2.7	1988 to 1991	720 ± 50	0.5 ± 0.25
827i V6 SOHC 24V cat V6 2.7	1988 to 1991	720 ± 50	0.1 max
827i V6 SOHC 24V cat V6 2.7	1991 to 1996	680 ± 50	0.1 max
Sterling V6 SOHC 24V V6 2.5	1986 to 1988	770 ± 50	0.5 ± 0.25

Overview of system operation

1 Introduction

PGM-Fi (ProGraMmed Fuel Injection) is an EMS developed by Honda, and fitted to all Honda fuel-injected vehicles since the early 1980's. During a period of close collaboration between Honda and Rover, PGM-Fi was also fitted to a number of four- and six-cylinder Rover vehicles equipped with Honda fuel-injected engines. PGM-Fi first appeared on Rover six-cylinder engines in 1986, and on four-cylinder (200 and 400 series) engines in 1989. The PGM-Fi EMS is a fully integrated system that controls primary ignition, fuelling and idle speed from within the same ECM **(see illustration 9.1)**.

The basic PGM-Fi system fitted to all fuel-injected Honda vehicles is broadly of a similar type. However, there are a number of significant differences between the various vehicles and the components that are used. The early 2.5 V6 engine was more akin to a conventional electronic system with the ignition timing controlled by mechanical and vacuum means rather than by an ignition map as in the later 2.7 litre engine. For this reason, when considering the V6 engine, we have concentrated more on the 2.7 litre system. Apart from ignition control, inlet manifold control and the pin number connections to the ECM, the 2.5 and 2.7 variations are actually fairly similar. A control box is also provided in V6 applications, which contains timing and CO pots and also the majority of vacuum-controlled devices **(see illustration 9.2)**.

9.1 Typical PGM-Fi system component layout (four-cylinder engine)

1 *Throttle body*
2 *ISCV*
3 *Fuel pressure service connection*
4 *Fuel rail*
5 *Fuel pressure regulator*
6 *Distributor*
7 *Fuse and relay control centre*
8 *Air filter assembly*

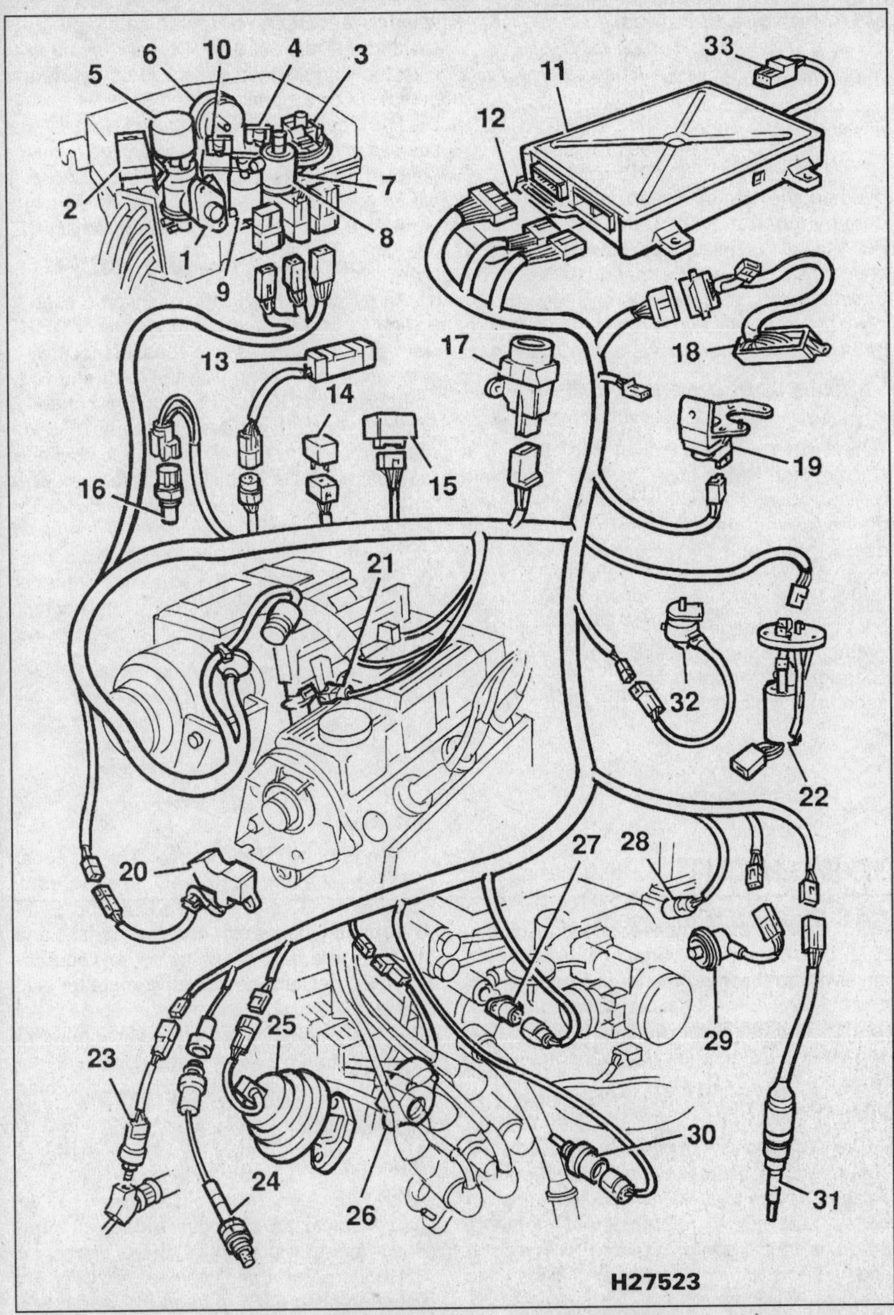

9.2 Typical PGM-Fi system component layout (Rover 827, V6 engine)

1 Ignition timing pot.
2 MAP sensor
3 Constant vacuum control valve
4 Air suction control solenoid valve
5 EGR control solenoid valve
6 Throttle dashpot filter
7 Air reservoir
8 Pressure regulator control cut-off solenoid valve
9 Manifold control solenoid valve A
10 Manifold control solenoid valve B
11 ECM
12 Cooling fan timer module
13 Injector resistor pack
14 Air conditioning clutch relay
15 Main system relay
16 Oil temperature sensor
17 Inertia switch
18 Transmission shift position switch
19 Atmospheric pressure sensor (APS)
20 CAS on camshaft
21 Fuel injectors
22 Fuel pump
23 Power steering pressure switch
24 Oxygen sensor
25 EGR valve lift sensor
26 CAS in distributor
27 ATS
28 ISCV
29 TPS
30 CTS
31 VSS
32 Air filter resonator control solenoid valve
33 ECM link connector 66

2 Control functions

Signal processing

Basic ignition timing is stored in a three-dimensional map, and the engine load and speed signals determine the ignition timing. The main engine load sensor is the MAP sensor; engine speed is determined from the crank angle sensor (CAS) signal.

Correction factors are then applied for starting, idle, deceleration, and part- and full-load operation. The main correction factor is engine temperature (CTS). Minor corrections to timing are made with reference to the ATS and TPS signals.

The basic AFR is also stored in a three-dimensional map, and the engine load and speed signals determine the basic injection pulse value. PGM-Fi calculates the AFR from the MAP sensor signal and the engine speed (CAS).

The AFR and the pulse duration are then corrected on reference to APS, ATS, CTS, battery voltage and position of the TPS. Other controlling factors are determined by operating conditions such as cold start and warm-up, idle condition, acceleration and deceleration.

PGM-Fi accesses a different map for idle running conditions, and this map is implemented whenever the engine speed is at idle. Idle speed during warm-up and normal hot running conditions are maintained by the ISCV.

Other input signals that PGM-Fi uses to influence the output signals are signals from the alternator, AT, A/C and battery voltage.

Basic ECM operation

The ignition point and injection duration are jointly processed by the ECM, so that the best moment for ignition and fuelling are determined for every operating condition. Three separate connectors and multi-plugs connect the ECM to the battery, sensors and actuators.

A permanent voltage supply is made from the vehicle battery to the ECM. This allows the self-diagnostic function to retain data of an intermittent nature. Once the ignition is switched on, a voltage supply is made to the ignition coil, amplifier, ECM, ISCV (some models) and the main relay. The main fuel injection relay actuates, and a relay-switched voltage supply is made to the fuel injector circuit, ECM and the ISCV (some models).

The majority of sensors (other than those that generate a voltage such the CAS, CID and OS), are now provided with a 5.0-volt reference supply from a relevant pin on the ECM. When the engine is cranked or run, a speed signal from the CAS causes the ECM to earth the relay driver, so that the fuel pump will run. Ignition and injection functions are also activated. All actuators (injectors, ISCV, CFSV etc), are supplied with nbv from the ignition or the main relay, and the ECM completes the circuit by pulsing the relevant actuator wire to earth.

Adaptive function

The ECM is adaptive to changing engine operating characteristics, and constantly monitors the data from the various sensors (ie MAP, ATS, CTS and TPS). As the engine or its components wear, the ECM reacts to new circumstances by adopting the changed values as a correction to the basic map.

Self-diagnostic function

The PGM-Fi system has a self-test capability that regularly examines the signals from engine sensors and internally logs a code in the event of a fault being present. Unlike other EMS's, PGM-Fi system does not include a serial port for interrogation by a FCR.

When the ECM detects that a fault is present, it earths pin A13, and the 'Check Engine' warning lamp on the dash will light. The lamp will stay lit until the fault is no longer present. If the 'Check Engine' warning lamp lights and then extinguishes, the fault is very likely an intermittent problem.

A red LED is incorporated into the ECM casing (not all models) and this will also begin to flash if a fault is present. When the ignition is switched off, the LED will extinguish. However, the LED will resume flashing once the ignition is switched on again. If the fault is corrected, the LED will continue to flash until the ECM memory is initialised by removing the 10-amp No 4 fuse in the fusebox for a period of 10 seconds.

In PGM-Fi, the SD system can only be used to obtain and clear codes, and other functions such as Datastream are not available.

Limited operating strategy (LOS)

PGM-Fi utilises two central processors (CPU) within the ECM. If one CPU fails, the other will assume control to maintain vehicle driveability. This mode is termed 'back-up'.

In the event of a serious fault in one or more of the sensors or their wiring circuits, PGM-Fi will substitute a fixed default value in place of the defective sensor. This mode is often termed 'limp home'. A serious fault occurs when the signal from the sensor is outside of its normal operating parameters.

Reference voltage

Voltage supply from the ECM to many of the engine sensors is at a 5.0-volt reference level. This ensures a stable working voltage, unaffected by variations in system voltage.

The earth return connection for most engine sensors is made through an ECM pin that is not directly connected to earth. The ECM internally connects that pin to earth via one of the ECM pins that are directly connected to earth.

Maximum speed cut-off

Once the engine speed reaches a pre-determined limit, PGM-Fi cuts off injector operation, thereby limiting the maximum rpm possible.

Deceleration fuel cut-off

When the engine speed is above a pre-determined rpm with the throttle closed, PGM-Fi cuts off injector operation as an aid to economy. As the engine speed falls below the threshold value, injection is re-instated. The point at which injection is re-instated depends upon engine temperature and the drop in rpm.

Vehicle speed sensor (VSS)

The VSS is used to advise the ECM of vehicle speed. In conjunction with other input signals, the ECM will use the VSS signal as a basis for controlling the variable valve timing during forward motion, and the ISCV during deceleration and as the vehicle slows to a stop.

The VSS functions on the Hall-effect principle. A voltage supplied from the ignition switch is connected to earth. As the speedometer cable turns, a pulse is generated which switches between 5.0 and zero.

3 Primary trigger

CAS (Inductive trigger)

The primary trigger signal to initiate both ignition and fuelling emanates from a crank angle sensor (CAS). Location and operation of the CAS differs according to whether the engine is a V6 or a 4-cylinder engine. Both types are described below.

V6 engines

The CAS consists of two inductive sensors, contained in one casing and mounted adjacent to the front camshaft. The camshaft pulley acts as a reluctor, and contains 24 poles to provide a TDC and RPM signal, and one pole to provide a signal to identify the position of cylinder No 1.

Four-cylinder engines

The CAS consists of two inductive sensors mounted in the distributor. Each sensor consists of a reluctor with a set number of teeth positioned within the field of an inductive magnet. The reluctors are mounted on the distributor shaft - one above the other, with the cylinder sensor in the lower position, the TDC sensor in the middle, and the rpm sensor uppermost. The rpm reluctor contains 16 teeth equally spaced at 22.5° intervals, the TDC sensor's four teeth at 90° degree intervals, and the cylinder reluctor has one tooth to indicate the position of No 1 cylinder. As the distributor spins, and the teeth are rotated in each magnetic field, an AC voltage signal is generated to indicate speed of rotation, a reference to TDC, and position of No 1 cylinder. Each sensor is connected to the ECM by a signal wire and earth return.

The peak-to-peak voltage of each signal can vary from 2.0 volts during engine cranking to over 100 volts at 6000 rpm. The ECM uses an analogue-to-digital converter (ADC) to transform each AC pulse into a digital signal.

Cylinder identification (CID)

An cylinder identification sensor is used to identify cylinder firing sequence. In SOHC four-cylinder engines, the sensor is located in the distributor (along with the TDC and RPM sensors). On DOHC models, the sensor is located on the exhaust camshaft. As the distributor rotates and No 1 cylinder approaches TDC, a small AC signal is induced in the sensor and returned to the ECM. The ECM utilises an ADC to transform the AC signal into a digital pulse. This signal is used to correctly time the sequential injection pulses. In V6 engines, cylinder identification is determined from the camshaft-mounted CAS.

4 Ignition

Ignition

Data on load (MAP sensor), engine speed (CAS), engine temperature (CTS) and throttle position (TPS) are collected by the ECM, which then refers to a three-dimensional digital map stored within its microprocessor. This map contains an advance angle for each operating condition, and thus the best ignition advance angle for a particular operating condition can be determined. However, the 2.5 V6 engine does not utilise an ignition map.

Distributor

Four-cylinder engines

The ignition coil, amplifier, CAS (incorporating an inductive trigger and rpm sensor) are all mounted inside the distributor. This reduces wiring and improves reliability. The system is often referred to as the 'coil in cap' system, and is identified by the lack of a main coil secondary HT lead **(see illustration 9.3)**. The secondary HT voltage passes directly from the coil to the rotor arm - which distributes the voltage to the spark plugs via HT leads in the conventional manner. In addition, the CID sensor for identifying cylinder sequence is mounted inside the distributor in SOHC applications. In DOHC systems, the CID sensor is mounted externally, and driven by the exhaust camshaft.

V6 engines

The distributor contains an inductive trigger and reluctor with six arms. How the signal is utilised depends upon whether the application is 2.5 or 2.7 litre.

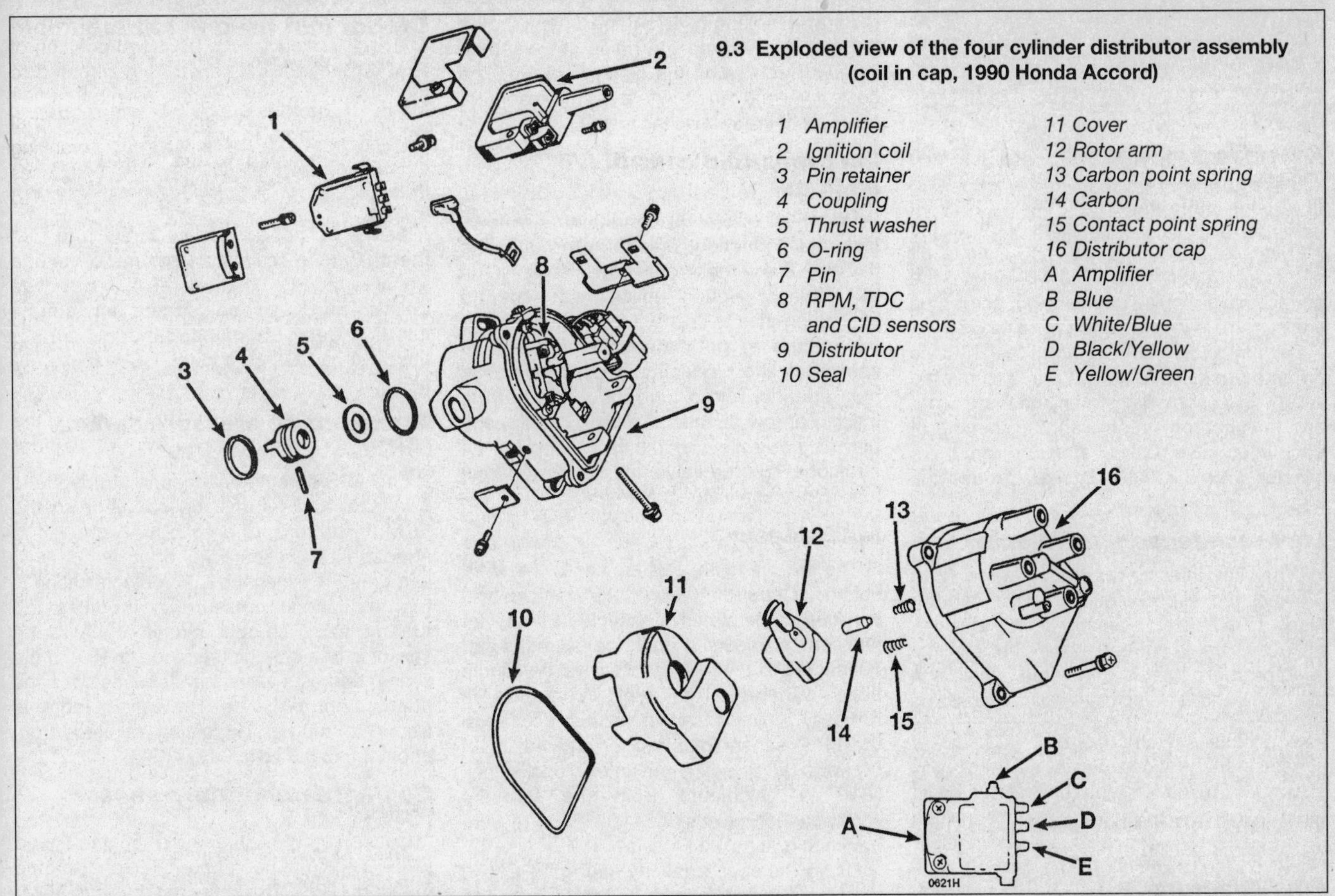

9.3 Exploded view of the four cylinder distributor assembly (coil in cap, 1990 Honda Accord)

1 *Amplifier*
2 *Ignition coil*
3 *Pin retainer*
4 *Coupling*
5 *Thrust washer*
6 *O-ring*
7 *Pin*
8 *RPM, TDC and CID sensors*
9 *Distributor*
10 *Seal*
11 *Cover*
12 *Rotor arm*
13 *Carbon point spring*
14 *Carbon*
15 *Contact point spring*
16 *Distributor cap*
A *Amplifier*
B *Blue*
C *White/Blue*
D *Black/Yellow*
E *Yellow/Green*

2.5 litre

The CAS is directly connected to the amplifier, which uses the signal to calculate the dwell angle and base timing value. Mechanical weights and springs that operate by centrifugal force cater for timing advance. In addition, an ECM-controlled vacuum advance is used to control ignition timing according to engine load.

2.7 litre

The distributor-based CAS is directly connected to the ECM, and the signal returned to the ECM during engine cranking is a fixed ignition timing reference of 10° BTDC. During engine running, the ECM disregards the distributor signal, and uses the camshaft signal to determine engine speed, position and cylinder No 1 position. If the camshaft signals fail, the ECM utilises the distributor signal to determine a basic ignition and injection duration.

Ignition timing

Four-cylinder engines

Unlike most EMS's, the base ignition timing is adjustable on the PGM-Fi system. The timing must only be adjusted after the ECM is placed into a service-set mode by bridging a test connector. If the RPM signal and/or the cylinder sequence signal are erroneous, the ECM will utilise the TDC signal for all timing functions.

During engine cranking, the ECM recognises cranking and the presence of RPM and TDC from the various signals, and sets the timing to a fixed value of 10° BTDC. During warm-up, the ECM advances the timing to improve cold engine driveabilty. Once the engine has reached normal operating temperature, the timing at idle will stabilise around 18° BTDC. The ECM makes small changes to the timing to control the idle speed, and the timing marks will normally vary by several degrees during engine idle when in normal operating mode (not service-set).

If air or coolant temperature become dangerously high, the ECM will retard the ignition timing in an attempt to reduce the engine temperature. Low and high temperature conditions are recognised from the input signal from primarily the CTS and additionally the ATS.

V6 engines

The base ignition timing is also adjustable on V6 engines, but a different method is used. Adjustment is made via a timing pot located in the control box.

Amplifier

The PGM-Fi amplifier (often termed an 'igniter' by the Japanese vehicle manufacturers) contains the circuitry for switching the coil negative terminal at the correct moment to instigate ignition. The ECM calculates the correct ignition dwell time and timing advance (not 2.5 V6) from data received from its sensors, and sends a signal to the amplifier, which then switches off the coil negative terminal. The amplifier is located within the distributor housing (four-cylinder engines) or on the left-hand inner wing (six-cylinder engines).

Dwell operation in PGM-Fi is based upon the principle of the 'constant-energy current-limiting' system. This means that the dwell period remains constant at about 3.0 to 3.5 ms, at virtually all engine running speeds. However, the dwell duty cycle, when measured in percent or degrees, will vary as the engine speed varies.

Ignition coil

The ignition coil utilises low primary resistance in order to increase primary current and primary energy. The amplifier limits the primary current to around 8 amps, and this permits a reserve of energy to maintain the required spark burn time (duration). The ignition coil is located within the distributor housing (four-cylinder engines) or on the left-hand inner wing (six-cylinder engines).

5 Fuel injection

The PGM-Fi ECM contains a fuel map with an injector opening time for basic conditions of speed and load. Information is then gathered from engine sensors such as the MAP sensor, CAS, CTS, and TPS. As a result of this information, the ECM will look up the correct injector pulse duration right across the engine rpm, load and temperature range.

Each injector is connected to the ECM via an independent ECM pin, and actuated sequentially according to engine firing order and in synchronisation with the opening of each inlet valve. During start-up from cold, injector pulse duration is increased to provide a richer air/fuel mixture.

Low-resistance type injector

When the injector resistance is low (2 to 3 ohms), the response rate is quicker and this leads to a faster opening time. However, because more current flows through the injector, more heat is generated, which can result in a shorter injector life span. By passing the voltage through a series resistor, a lower voltage is applied to the injector, which results in less heat and longer injector life. Voltage to each of the PGM-Fi injectors is thus passed through a 5 to 7 ohm resistor situated in the wiring circuit leading to the injector.

Fuel injectors

The fuel injector is a magnetically-operated solenoid valve that is actuated by the ECM. Voltage to the injectors is applied from the main relay, and the earth path is completed by the ECM for a period of time (called pulse duration) of between 1.5 and 10 milliseconds. The pulse duration is very much dependent upon engine temperature, load, speed and operating conditions. When the magnetic solenoid closes, a back-EMF voltage of up to 60 volts is initiated.

Each fuel injector utilises a pintle tip, in order that the fuel is atomised at maximum efficiency during the opening duration. The injectors are mounted in the inlet stubs to the engine inlet valves, so that the finely-atomised fuel spray is directed into each individual cylinder during its engine intake stroke. The injectors are retained by the fuel rail, and sealed by two sealing 'O' rings and a cushion 'O' ring.

Air intake

Intake air is drawn into the engine through a length of intake trunking and past two resonators. The resonator system reduces intake noise to a minimum. The resonators are situated before the air filter; the first one is a fixed resonator of small diameter. The second resonator is a two-stage device that is electronically controlled by the ECM via an electrical solenoid. The ECM actuates the resonator solenoid at engine speeds over 3000 rpm. Vacuum stored in the vacuum reservoir acts upon the diaphragm, and the control valve opens to increase the resonator aperture, thereby lowering intake noise.

Inlet manifold control (V6 engines)

Under all operating conditions, air flows into the induction manifold through the throttle valve in the throttle body. However, on V6 engines, Honda utilise two separate induction paths to improve the flow of air into the engine at both low and high engine speeds. A short induction path is utilised at high speeds, and a long induction path is utilised at low speeds. Airflow through each path is controlled by the ECM through an additional throttle valve (located in the inlet manifold) and a vacuum actuator.

MAP sensor

The main engine load sensor is the MAP sensor. Depending upon the vehicle, the sensor may be directly connected to the inlet manifold, or mounted upon the bulkhead and connected to the inlet manifold via a vacuum hose. Whatever the type, operation is basically similar. Manifold vacuum acts upon the MAP sensor diaphragm, and the ECM converts the pressure into an electrical signal. MAP is calculated from the formula: Atmospheric Pressure less Manifold Pressure = Manifold Absolute Pressure.

Using the speed/density method, PGM-Fi calculates the AFR from the MAP signal and the speed of the engine. This method relies on the theory that the engine will draw in a fixed volume of air per revolution.

The inlet manifold is a 'dry' manifold. Since fuel does not enter the manifold - due to injection being made onto the back of the inlet valve, there is no risk of fuel being drawn into the MAP sensor to contaminate the diaphragm, and a fuel trap is not used.

A 5.0-volt reference voltage is applied to the sensor, and an earth path is connected to the sensor return circuit. MAP sensor output on the PIM signal wire is returned to the ECM as a variable voltage signal. Voltage on the signal wire varies from about 1.0 volt at idle to approximately 4.5 volts at full load.

Air temperature sensor (ATS)

The ATS is mounted in the air inlet casing, and measures the air temperature before it enters the inlet manifold. Because the density of air varies in inverse proportion to the temperature, the ATS signal allows more accurate assessment of the volume of air entering the engine.

The open-circuit supply to the sensor is at a 5.0-volt reference level, and the earth path is through the sensor return. The ATS operates on the NTC principle. A variable voltage signal is returned to the ECM based upon air temperature. This signal is around 2.0 to 3.0 volts at an ambient temperature of 20°C.

CO pot (not used in cat models)

The CO pot mixture adjuster is a three-wire potentiometer that allows small changes to be made to the idle CO. A 5.0-volt reference voltage is applied to the sensor, and an earth path is connected to the PGM-Fi sensor return circuit. The third wire is the CO pot signal.

As the CO pot adjustment screw is turned, the change in resistance returns a voltage signal to the ECM that will result in a change in CO. The CO pot adjustment only affects idle CO. Catalyst-equipped models are not fitted with a CO pot, and the CO is thus non-adjustable.

Atmospheric pressure sensor (APS)

The APS detects changes in atmospheric pressure, and returns the condition to the ECM in the form of a voltage. A change in atmospheric pressure will affect air density and the AFR. When the ECM detects changes to atmospheric pressure, it modifies the fuelling map. The open-circuit supply to the sensor is at a 5.0-volt reference level, and the sensor returns a value that depends upon the atmospheric pressure. The sensor range is from 0 to 700 mm Hg, giving a voltage from about 3.5 to 0.5 volts.

Coolant temperature sensor (CTS)

The CTS is immersed in the cooling system, and contains a variable resistance that operates on the NTC principle. When the engine is cold, the resistance is quite high. Once the engine is started and begins to warm-up, the coolant becomes hotter and this causes a change in the CTS resistance. As the CTS becomes hotter, the resistance of the CTS reduces (NTC principle) and this returns a variable voltage signal to the ECM based upon the coolant temperature.

The open-circuit supply to the sensor is at a 5.0-volt reference level, and this voltage reduces to a value that depends upon the resistance of the CTS resistance. Normal operating temperature is usually from 80 to 100°C.

The ECM uses the CTS signal as a main correction factor when calculating ignition timing and injection duration.

Throttle potentiometer sensor (TPS)

A TPS is provided to inform the ECM of throttle position and rate of acceleration. PGM-Fi uses the TPS signal to determine engine idle, engine deceleration, acceleration and wide-open throttle conditions so that the correct timing and injection map may be used **(see illustration 9.4)**. The TPS is a potentiometer with three wires. A 5.0-volt reference voltage is supplied to a resistance track, with the other end connected to the sensor earth return. The third wire is connected to an arm which wipes along the

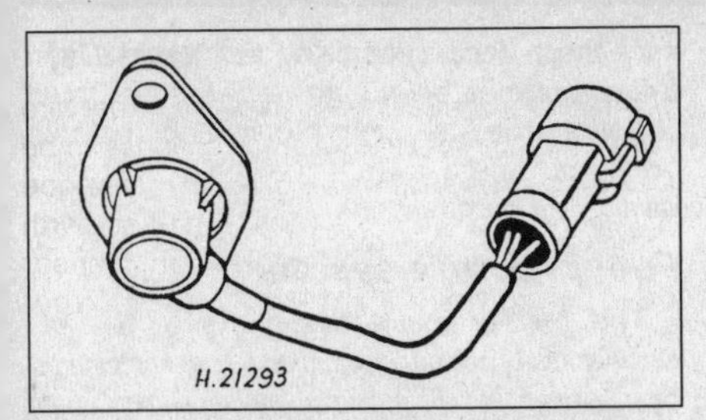

9.4 Throttle potentiometer sensor (TPS)

resistance track, and so varies the resistance and voltage of the signal returned to the ECM.

Throttle body, idle adjustment screw and throttle damper

The throttle body incorporates a by-pass passage and adjusting screw for idle speed adjustment.

A damper is attached to the throttle mechanism so that the throttle will close more slowly when the engine is decelerated. Slow throttle closure aids emissions by preventing the high vacuum present when the throttle is snapped shut. The high vacuum produced under these conditions tends to draw out the droplets of fuel that cling to the inlet manifold walls, and push them through the engine into the exhaust as unburned hydrocarbons.

Operation of the throttle damper is purely mechanical, and it is not controlled by the ECM. A vacuum-actuated spring acts upon the diaphragm, which is connected to the throttle mechanism. At rest with the engine stopped, the spring is relaxed and the diaphragm extends to push the throttle slightly open. When the engine is started, a depression acts upon the diaphragm to compress the spring, and the throttle closes. Idle speed is dependent on the position of the ISCV and base idle adjustment screw.

During engine operation above idle, there is little vacuum acting upon the diaphragm, and the spring relaxes to slightly hold open the throttle. When the throttle pedal is released during deceleration or gear changing, vacuum acts upon the diaphragm, and the throttle closes in a controlled manner, thereby preventing the emission of unburned fuel.

Idle speed control valve (ISCV)

The ISCV is a solenoid-controlled actuator that the PGM-Fi ECM uses to automatically control idle speed during normal idle and during engine warm-up. PGM-Fi detects the engine idle situation from the position of the TPS and the temperature of the engine from the CTS. The ISCV is located in a by-pass hose that connects the inlet manifold to the air filter side of the throttle plate. A voltage supply is applied from the main relay, and the ISCV earth is actuated by the ECM according to load and temperature. So that changes in the solenoid valve resistance will not affect operation, the valve body is connected to the cooling system.

When an electrical load, such as headlights, A/C, or heater fan etc are switched on, the idle speed would tend to drop. The ECM will sense the load, and open the ISCV against spring tension to increase the airflow through the valve, and thus increase the idle speed. When the load is removed, the ECM will pulse the valve so that the airflow is reduced. Normal idle speed should be maintained under all hot operating conditions, although the idle speed may be slightly higher during some load conditions.

During engine cranking and immediately after the engine starts, the ISCV is opened to increase idle speed by approximately 100 to 250 rpm. During engine warm-up, the ISCV is opened sufficiently to provide a fast idle until the engine approaches normal operating temperature.

When the engine is decelerating, the ECM pulses the ISCV further open, so reducing the formation of a depression in the inlet manifold. This prevents crankcase oil being drawn into the inlet manifold. The ECM maintains a faster idle for a brief period after returning to the idle condition before settling down to the controlled idle. The ECM also senses when the AT (where fitted) is in Park, Neutral or Drive, and will adjust the injection duration accordingly in order to control the idle speed.

Auxiliary air valve (AAV)

In order to prevent uneven idle and stalling when the engine is cold, PGM-Fi utilises a waxstat-actuated control valve to increase the idle speed during the engine warm-up period. When the coolant temperature is below 30°C. The AAV closes once the engine reaches normal operating temperature.

The AAV is mounted on the throttle body, and connected by hose to the coolant system so that the coolant temperature will determine the position of the waxstat. A drilling in the throttle body on the air filter side of the throttle valve allows incoming air to by-pass the throttle valve. The flow of by-pass air passes through the body of the AAV, and is returned to the throttle body on the engine side of the throttle valve. This flow of air cause the engine idle rpm to increase to a speed that is fully dependent on the volume of the additional air.

The waxstat responds to temperature by expanding and contracting. When the temperature is low, the waxstat is contracted and the valve is open so that engine idle speed is increased. The lower the temperature, the more open the valve will be. As the engine warms up and coolant acts upon the waxstat, the waxstat expands to gradually shut the AAV until it is fully closed at normal operating temperature.

Fast idle valve (some models)

When the coolant temperature is below -10°C and the idle speed is below 1800 rpm, the ECM actuates the fast idle solenoid valve in order to allow additional air to by-pass the throttle, which provides a high fast idle speed

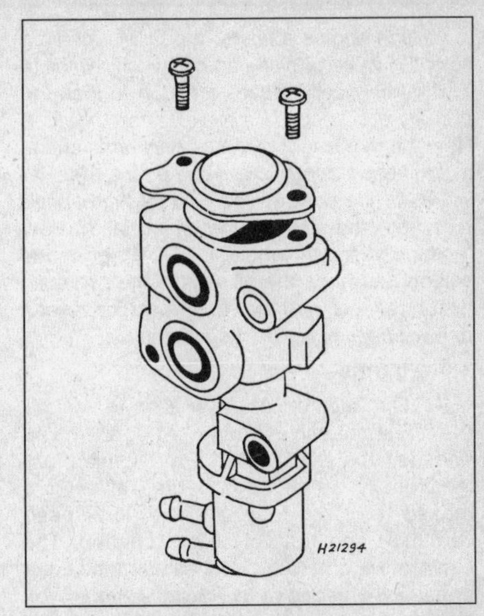

9.5 Fast idle valve (not controlled by ECM)

(see illustration 9.5). The fast idle valve has only two conditions - open or closed. The ISCV fine-tunes the idle speed during the time that the fast idle valve is open.

Variable valve timing and electronic control system (VTEC - some 1.5 & 1.6 models)

The Honda VTEC system is a method of varying the valve timing in order to improve engine efficiency at both high and low engine speeds. Standard valve opening time and the degree of valve lift in roadgoing engines is always a compromise between outright power, torque, emissions and economy. If the valve timing is set so that maximum lift and opening time is achieved at high engine speeds, then torque, emissions and economy will suffer at lower speeds. The Honda VTEC system allows the valve timing to be placed into one of two positions, so that engine efficiency is maximised. This allows maximum torque at low speeds (usually under 4800 rpm) and maximum power at high speeds.

There are two distinct mechanical methods used by Honda to open and close the valve gear fitted to 1.5 and 1.6 VTEC-equipped engines. Otherwise, there is no difference in the electrical circuit and hydraulic actuator action.

1.5 engines

VTEC utilises a camshaft with separate primary and secondary lobes and associated primary and secondary rocker arms to achieve the variable valve timing. The cam profiles are designed so that the secondary cam gives less lift than the primary. At low engine speeds, the rocker arm is moved by the secondary lobe on the camshaft, and the valves are opened enough to give good economy and performance suited to the moderate operating conditions.

9

At high engine speeds, the ECM signals a solenoid valve to close an oil switch, which in turn hydraulically moves a piston to lock the primary and secondary rocker arms together. Now the movement of the primary arms on the high-speed primary cam lobe opens the inlet valves to the position required for high-speed running. When the engine speed falls below the high-speed threshold, the ECM signals the solenoid to open the oil switch, the hydraulic piston retracts, and the valve operation reverts to low-speed secondary operation.

1.6 engines

VTEC utilises three rocker arms to achieve the variable valve timing. At low engine speeds, the two outer arms (which are individually connected to the valves) are moved by the lobe on the low-speed camshaft and the valves are opened. The inner rocker arm is not connected to the outer arms or the valves at this point. Although the inner arm is moved by the high cam lobe, the arm has no effect on valve operation during low-speed running.

At high engine speeds, the ECM signals a solenoid valve to close an oil switch, which in turn hydraulically moves a piston to lock all three rocker arms together. Now the movement of the inner arm on the high-speed cam lobe moves the outer arms to the higher position required for high-speed running. When the engine speed falls below the high-speed threshold, the ECM signals the solenoid to open the oil switch; the hydraulic piston retracts, and the valve operation reverts to low-speed operation.

All engines

In addition to rpm, the ECM controls the high-speed valve operation according to load (MAP sensor), coolant temperature (the CTS must signal an engine temperature above 60°C), and the vehicle must be moving at a speed above 13 mph (MT) or 3 mph (AT) as signalled by the VSS.

Power steering pressure switch (PSPS)

This switch is operated by a change in pressure when the power steering is in operation. The PSPS is located in the engine compartment, in the delivery pipe to the steering gear. The PSPS is closed when the steering gear fluid pressure is low (ie when the steering is straight). The switch opens when the steering is turned (ie when the fluid pressure rises above a pre-determined value).

A voltage slightly less than nbv is applied to the PSPS. When the steering is straight and the PSPS is closed, the voltage drops to near-zero. When the steering is turned and the steering gear pressure reaches its pre-determined value, the PSPS opens and the voltage on the PSPS pin rises to almost nbv. The ECM then increases the idle rpm to maintain the idle speed due to the increased load caused by the power steering coming into play.

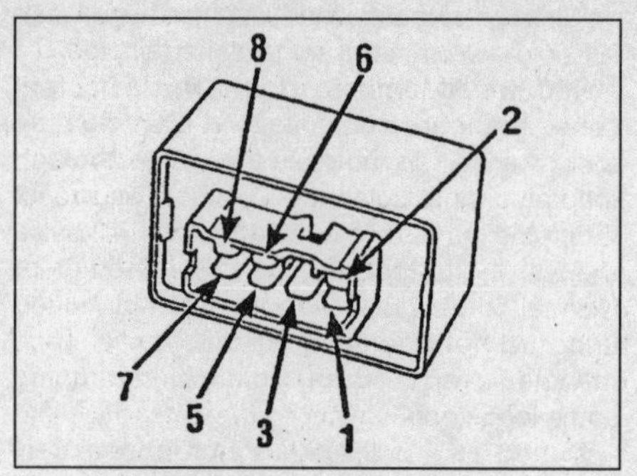

9.6 PGM-Fi system relay

1 Battery supply to relay
2 Relay earth
3 Relay output to injectors and ECM
5 Ignition supply to relay
6 Cranking supply to relay
7 Relay output to fuel pump
8 Relay drive

Relays

The PGM-Fi electrical system is controlled by a single system relay with dual contacts **(see illustration 9.6)**. A permanent voltage supply is made to relay terminals 1 from the battery positive terminal. When the ignition is switched on, a voltage supply is made to terminal 5, and this energises the first relay winding which is connected to earth. This causes the first relay contacts to close, and terminal 1 is connected to the output circuit at terminal 3 which supplies voltage to the injectors and to ECM: pins B11 and B12. In addition voltage is supplied to the second relay contact via a diode and resistor.

When the ignition is first switched on, the ECM briefly earths relay terminal 8 at ECM pins B3 and B4. This energises the second relay winding, which closes the second relay contact and connects voltage to output terminal 7, thereby providing voltage to the fuel pump circuit. After approximately one second, the ECM opens the circuit and the pump stops. This brief running of the fuel pump allows pressure to build within the fuel pressure lines, and provides for an easier start.

The fuel pump relay circuit will then remain open until the engine is cranked or run. Once the ECM receives a speed signal from the CAS, the second winding will again be energised by the ECM, and the fuel pump will run until the engine is stopped.

The voltage supply to the pump whilst the engine is running is applied to the pump via a ballast resistor incorporated into the fuel system relay. The ballast resistor reduces current flow through the fuel pump circuit to improve reliability. During cranking, this resistor is by-passed by voltage applied to relay terminal 6 from the starter circuit.

Inertia switch (Rover models)

The inertia switch is a safety cut-out switch used to isolate the fuel pump in the event of a very sharp deceleration - eg a collision. Once the switch has been activated, the electrical supply to the fuel pump remains open-circuit until the inertia switch has been reset by raising the button.

Fuel pressure system

The fuel pressure system is of the re-circulating type, and includes a fuel tank, swirl pot, submerged fuel pump, pressure regulator and a return line. The fuel pump draws fuel from the tank, and pumps it to the fuel rail via a fuel filter. When fuel in the rail exceeds a pre-determined pressure, the excess fuel is returned to the fuel tank. Re-circulation of fuel ensures that a fresh supply of cool fuel at a constant pressure is always available in the fuel rail. The swirl pot ensures that the fuel pick-up is always immersed in fuel - even when the fuel level is low and fuel is surging in the tank.

To reduce the effect of fluctuations in fuel pressure, a pulsation damper is connected to the fuel rail, thereby preventing hydraulic knock.

Switching the ignition key on causes the ECM to energise the fuel pump relay for approximately one second, so that the fuel system is pressurised. The fuel pump relay is then switched off, to await a cranking or running signal.

The fuel pump assembly comprises an impeller or roller type fuel pump, driven by a permanent magnet electric motor mounted inside the fuel tank, which draws fuel from the tank and pumps it to the fuel rail via a fuel filter. The pump is of the 'wet' variety, in that fuel actually flows through the pump and the electric motor. There is no actual fire risk, because the fuel drawn through the pump is not in a combustible condition.

Impeller type

The impeller is mounted upon the armature shaft, and contains a number of grooves set into its perimeter. As the pump is actuated and the impeller is rotated, it creates a differential pressure that forces fuel through the grooves to the pump pressure outlet. A relief valve is provided, to prevent over-pressurisation.

Roller type

Mounted on the armature shaft is an eccentric rotor, holding a number of pockets arranged around the circumference - each pocket containing a metal roller. As the pump is actuated, the rollers are flung outwards by centrifugal force to act as seals. The fuel between the rollers is forced to the pump pressure outlet. A relief valve is provided to prevent over-pressurisation.

All types

Fuel pressure in the fuel rail is maintained at a constant pressure (3.0, 2.7 or 2.4 bar depending on model) by a fuel pressure regulator. The fuel pump normally provides much more fuel than is required, and surplus fuel is thus returned to the fuel tank via a return pipe. In fact, a maximum fuel pressure in excess of 4.5 bar is possible in this system. To prevent pressure loss in the supply system, a non-return valve is provided in the fuel pump outlet. When the ignition is switched off, and the fuel pump ceases operation, pressure is thus maintained for some time.

Fuel pressure regulator

The pressure regulator is fitted on the outlet side of the fuel rail, and maintains an even pressure in the fuel rail.
At idle speed with the vacuum pipe disconnected, with the engine stopped and the pump running, or at full-throttle, the system fuel pressure will be approximately 2.4, 2.7 or 3.0 bar, depending on model. At idle speed (vacuum pipe connected), the fuel pressure will be approximately 0.5 bar under the system pressure.

In addition, an ECM-actuated cut-off valve is provided in V6 engines, to allow increased fuel pressure and therefore fuel enrichment under certain operating conditions. The facility may be required under hot starting conditions that could lead to fuel vaporisation. By cutting vacuum to the pressure regulator, the increased fuel pressure will lead to easier starting.

6 Catalytic converter and emission control

Catalytic converter

The PGM-Fi injection system fitted to Honda and Rover vehicles equipped with a catalytic converter implements a closed-loop control system so that exhaust emissions may be reduced. Closed-loop systems are equipped with an oxygen sensor which monitors the exhaust gas for oxygen content. A low oxygen level in the exhaust signifies a rich mixture. A high oxygen level in the exhaust signifies a weak mixture. The oxygen sensor closed-loop voltage is quite low, and switches between 100 millivolts (weak) to 1.0 volt (rich).

The signal switches from weak to rich at the rate of approximately 1 HZ. A digital voltmeter connected to the signal wire, would display an average voltage of approximately 0.45 volts. In the event of OS circuit failure, the ECM substitutes a constant voltage of 0.45 volts, and this should not be confused with the average voltage of 0.45 which occurs during switching from approximately 0.1 volt to 1.0 volt.

When the engine is operating under closed-loop control, the OS signal causes the ECM to modify the injector pulse so that the AFR is maintained close to the stoichiometric ratio. By controlling the injection pulse during most operating conditions, so that the air/fuel ratio is always in a small window around the Lambda point (ie Lambda = 0.98 to 1.04), almost perfect combustion is achieved. Thus the catalyst has less work to do, and it will last longer with fewer emissions at the tail pipe.

The closed-loop control is implemented during engine operation at engine normal operating temperature. When the coolant temperatures is below 70°C, or the engine is at full load, or is on the overrun, the ECM will operate in open-loop. When operating in open-loop, the ECM allows a richer or leaner AFR than the stoichiometric ratio. This prevents engine hesitation, for example, during acceleration with a wide-open throttle.

The OS only produces a signal when the exhaust gas, has reached a minimum temperature of approximately 300°C. In order that the OS will reach optimum operating temperature as quickly as possible after the engine has started, the OS contains a heating element. The OS heater is controlled by the ECM through an OS relay, or from the fuel pump relay, depending on vehicle. The ECM switches off the OS relay under certain conditions of speed and load. In V6 engines two OS's are utilised; one OS for each bank of cylinders.

LAF sensor (some engines only)

The linear airflow (LAF) sensor has a similar function to the OS, and the sensor is also installed in the exhaust system. However, the signal is digital, and switches between 5.0 volts and zero volts. The LAF sensor functions over a wide AFR range.

In common with the OS, the LAF sensor only produces a signal when the exhaust gas has reached a minimum temperature of approximately 300°C. In order that the LAF sensor will reach optimum operating temperature as quickly as possible after the engine has started, the LAF sensor contains a heating element. The LAF sensor heater also stabilises the LAF sensor temperature. The LAF sensor heater is supplied with voltage by the system relay, and switched off (earthed) by the ECM under certain conditions of speed and load.

Carbon filter solenoid valve (CFSV)

A CFSV, diaphragm valve, two-way valve and activated carbon canister all combine to aid evaporative emission control. The carbon canister stores fuel vapours until the CFSV is opened by PGM-Fi under certain operating conditions **(see illustration 9.7)**.

The supply to the CFSV is made from the ignition switch. The earth path is made through the ECM, and the ECM actuates the CFSV by connecting it to earth when required. The normal state of the CFSV is open, and it closes when actuated by the ECM.

After the engine has started and while the coolant temperature is below 70°C, the ECM actuates the CFSV to the closed position, so that fumes will be retained in the carbon canister. After the engine has attained 70°C, the ECM releases the CFSV so that vacuum is applied to the diaphragm valve. The valve then opens, and fuel vapours are drawn into the inlet manifold to be burnt by the engine during normal combustion.

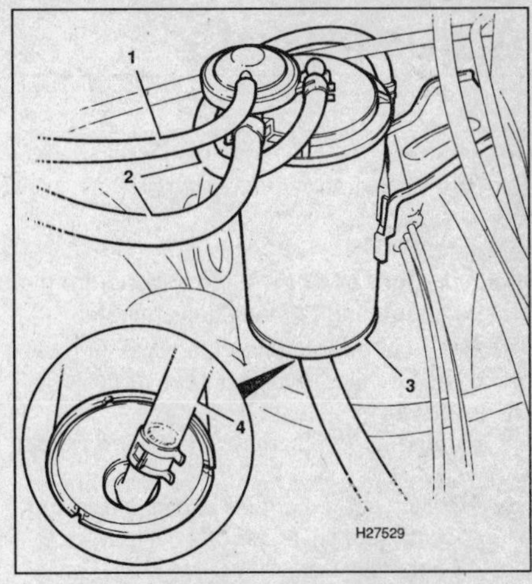

9.7 Typical carbon canister hose connections (V6 engine)

1 Vacuum hose
2 Vapour hose
3 Charcoal canister
4 Air inlet hose

EGR system

The EGR system used in the Honda PGM-Fi equipped vehicles is controlled essentially by the ECM according to signals received from the various sensors. Components used in the EGR control system include an EGR CS (EGR control solenoid), a constant vacuum control valve (CVC) and an combined EGR lift valve sensor and EGR valve.

The ECM contains a map detailing the amount of lift required to meter exhaust gas recycling. It signals the EGR control solenoid valve so that vacuum is applied to the EGR valve, which opens to introduce a metered volume of exhaust gas into the inlet manifold. The EGR sensor detects the actual amount of EGR lift and compares it to the stored map value. If the two values differ, the ECM signals the EGR control solenoid valve to make the requisite adjustment.

Vacuum is piped from the inlet manifold to the CVC valve. The CVC valve dampens the inlet manifold pulses according to throttle opening, and feeds a constant vacuum supply to the EGR CS valve. On receipt of a pulsed signal from the ECM, the solenoid varies its opening time to allow varying amounts of vacuum to act upon the EGR lift valve, which opens to allow a metered volume of exhaust gas into the inlet manifold.

The EGR lift valve sensor is an example of a three-wire sensor, with a resistance that varies according to the position of the lift valve. A 5.0-volt supply is connected to the sensor and to the ECM sensor return circuit. A signal voltage varying from 1.2 to 4.3 volts is returned to the ECM, depending upon the position of the lift valve. In turn, the EGR CS is pulsed open by the ECM with a duty cycle that varies according to the degree of control required.

Adjustments

7 Adjustment pre-conditions

1 Ensure that all of these conditions are met before attempting to make adjustments:

a) *Engine at operating temperature. Engine oil at a minimum temperature of 80°C. A journey of at least 4 miles is recommended (particularly so if equipped with AT).*
b) *Ancillary equipment (all engine loads and accessories) switched off.*
c) *AT engines: Transmission in N or P.*
d) *Engine mechanically sound.*
e) *Engine breather hoses and breather system in satisfactory condition.*
f) *Induction system free from vacuum leaks.*
g) *Ignition system in satisfactory condition.*
h) *Air filter in satisfactory condition.*
i) *Exhaust system free from leaks.*
j) *Throttle cable correctly adjusted.*
k) *No fault codes logged by the ECM.*
l) *OS operating satisfactorily (catalyst vehicles with closed-loop control).*

2 In addition, before checking the idle speed and CO values, stabilise the engine as follows:

a) *Stabilise the engine. Raise the engine speed to 3000 rpm for a minimum of 30 seconds, and then let the engine idle.*
b) *If the cooling fan operates during adjustment, wait until it stops, re-stabilise the engine, and then restart the adjustment procedure.*
c) *Allow the CO and idle speed to settle.*
d) *Make all checks and adjustments within 30 seconds. If this time is exceeded, re-stabilise the engine and recheck.*

8 Throttle adjustments

Throttle body checks and adjustments

1 Clean the throttle plate and surrounding areas with carburettor cleaner.
2 The throttle position is critical, and should not be disturbed. To that end, the throttle stop screw is pre-set and non-adjustable, and must not be tampered with.
3 Adjust the throttle cable.
4 Warm the engine to normal operating temperature.
5 Ensure that the cable operates smoothly and without binding over its full operating range.
6 Check the throttle cable free play. Carefully depress the cable, and check that the cable moves 10 to 12 mm before the throttle linkage begins to open.
7 If adjustment is required, slacken the locknut and move the cable until the deflection is correct.
8 Once the throttle cable adjustment is correct, depress the throttle pedal fully and check that the throttle is fully open.
9 Release the throttle pedal and check that the throttle fully closes against its stop.
10 The TPS is also non-adjustable, and must not be tampered with.
11 Check the throttle body; poor throttle action or the throttle binding at idle or an open throttle could result from excessive wear in the throttle housing or shaft areas.

9 Ignition timing

Four-cylinder models

Note: *The following procedure refers to the Rover 216/416, Honda models are similar.*
1 The base ignition timing is adjustable on the four-cylinder PGM-Fi equipped vehicles.
2 The ignition timing must only be adjusted after the ECM is placed into a service-set mode by bridging the terminals in the SD connector. **Note:** *The SD test connector is not fitted to cat versions of the 216/416, since the ECM pin has been re-allocated to the OS signal.*
3 Refer to the adjustment test conditions in Section 7. It is particularly important that the engine oil is at normal operating temperature before commencing.
4 Start the engine and allow it to idle.
5 Connect a tachometer and stroboscopic timing light.
6 Place the ECM into base timing mode.
7 Locate the SD connector, and remove the protective yellow cap (if fitted).
8 Use a jumper lead to bridge the two outside terminals at the SD connector.
9 Whilst the ECM is operating in base timing mode, the timing marks should remain steady, and must not fluctuate. If difficulty is experienced in setting the base timing, or the timing fluctuates, check for a faulty or maladjusted TPS or throttle plate.
10 Use the strobe light to check that the base timing is set at the specified value. Please note that the engine rotates in an anti-clockwise direction. The red timing mark is the datum value, and the marks either side of the red mark indicate the ± 2° tolerance. The yellow mark indicates TDC. Timing figure is 16 ± 2° BTDC for most engines **(see illustration 9.8)**.
11 If the timing is incorrect, slacken the distributor fixing bolts and rotate the distributor until the marks are aligned.
12 Carefully tighten the distributor bolts and recheck that the marks are still aligned.

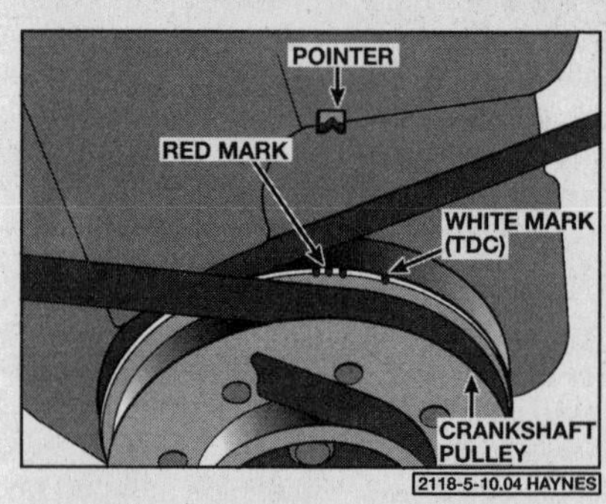

9.8 Typical ignition timing marks (most four-cylinder models). Note that engine rotates anti-clockwise

13 Remove the bridge wire from the SD plug.
14 Start the engine, point the strobe light at the timing marks (the strobe advance timing control must be set at zero) and slowly increase the engine speed to 3000 rpm. The marks should move smoothly apart as the timing advances.

V6 models

15 The base ignition timing is adjustable on V6 PGM-Fi equipped vehicles.
16 Start the engine and allow it to idle.
17 Connect a tachometer and stroboscopic timing light.
18 Use the strobe light to check that the base timing is set at the specified value. The red timing mark is 15° ± 2° BTDC, and is the correct mark for UK engines. The white mark indicates TDC **(see illustration 9.9)**.
19 If the timing is incorrect, turn the CO adjusting screw in the control box until the correct value is attained **(see illustration 9.10)**. The screw is turned clockwise to advance the timing, and anti-clockwise to retard the timing. **Note:** *On some engines, the adjuster may be fitted with an tamperproof cover retained by two rivets. Drill out the rivets to gain access to the adjuster.*
20 Start the engine, point the strobe light at the timing marks (the strobe advance timing control must be set at zero) and slowly

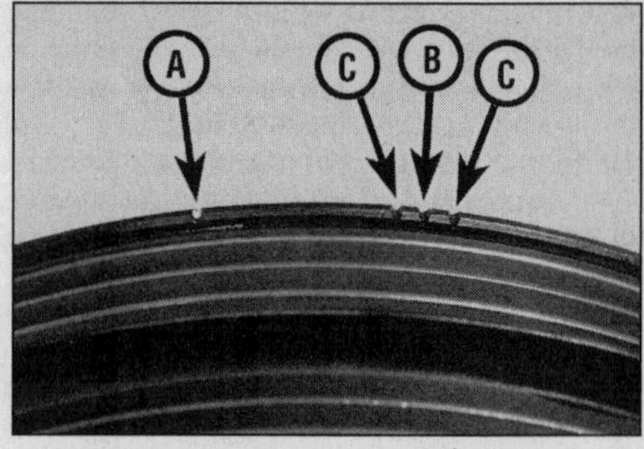

9.9 Typical ignition timing marks (most V6 models). Note that engine rotates clockwise

A TDC mark
B Timing mark
C Tolerance ± 2° marks

9.10 Adjustment of the ignition timing (V6 engines, non-cat). Locate adjustment pot in the control box, and turn the screw to advance or retard the timing

increase the engine speed to 3000 rpm. The marks should move smoothly apart as the timing advances.

10 Idle adjustments

1 PGM-Fi utilises an automatic ISCV to maintain a proper idle speed, irrespective of engine load conditions. However, it is important that the base idle speed is set within its operating limits, otherwise idle problems may occur.

2 Refer to the adjustment pre-conditions in Section 7. It is particularly important that the engine oil is at normal operating temperature before commencing.

3 Start the engine and allow it to idle.

4 Connect a tachometer and exhaust gas analyser.

5 Check that the ignition timing is correct.

6 Check that the TPS position is correct.

7 Check the normal idle speed. If the idle speed is outside of its operating limits or unstable, the base idle speed should be checked and adjusted.

Base idle speed adjustment

8 Switch off the ignition.

9 Disconnect the multi-plug to the ISCV.

10 Restart the engine and raise the engine speed to 2000 rpm for a period of 10 seconds, then allow the engine to idle.

11 Locate the adjustment screw in the throttle body **(see illustration 9.11)**.

12 Remove the tamperproof plug (if fitted).

13 Turn the base idle adjustment screw to obtain the specified rpm (550 ± 50 rpm).

14 Raise the engine speed to 1000 rpm for a few seconds, then slowly release the throttle and allow the engine to stabilise at idle.

15 Recheck the base idle speed and re-adjust if necessary.

16 Switch off the ignition and reconnect the ISCV multi-plug.

17 Remove fuse No 4 for about 30 seconds. Refer to Warning No 3 in Reference.

18 Reconnect the multi-plug to the ISCV.

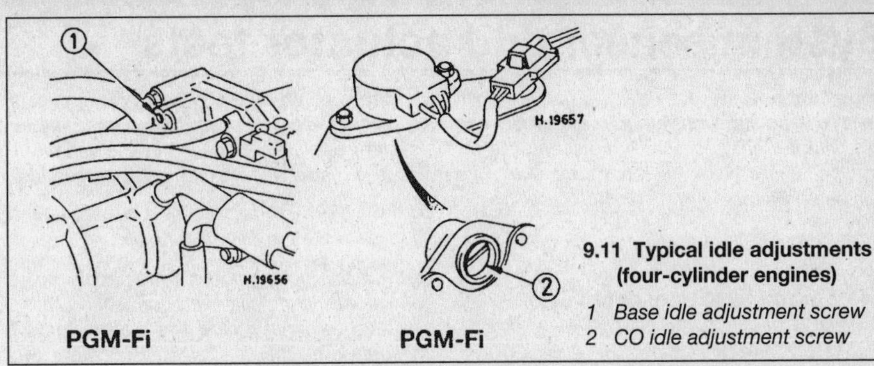

9.11 Typical idle adjustments (four-cylinder engines)

1 *Base idle adjustment screw*
2 *CO idle adjustment screw*

19 Restart the engine and raise the engine speed to 2000 rpm for a period of 10 seconds, then allow the engine to idle.
Check that the idle speed is within its operating limits. If not, repeat the procedure.

20 Check that the CO value is within its operating limits. If the CO level is incorrect, locate the CO adjustment screw in the CO pot (non-cat), adjust the CO and then recheck the base idle speed.

21 Repeat the CO and idle speed checks until both are within their respective operating limits.

22 Load the engine by switching on the heated rear window, and check that the idle speed is being controlled within its operating limits.

Idle adjustments (V6 engines)

Idle speed

23 Refer to the adjustment pre-conditions in Section 7. It is particularly important that the engine oil is at normal operating temperature before commencing.

24 Set the steering so that the front wheels are straight.

25 Connect a tachometer and record the idle speed which should be 720 ± 50 rpm (MT) or 680 ± 50 rpm (automatic transmission in Drive) or 720 ± 50 rpm (automatic transmission in Neutral or Park).

26 Locate the ECM under the front passenger seat and observe the yellow LED.

a) If the yellow LED is off the idle speed does not require adjustment.
b) If the yellow LED is on, turn the idle speed adjustment screw (located in the throttle body) anti-clockwise ***(see illustration 9.12)****.*
c) If the yellow LED is flashing, turn the idle speed adjustment screw clockwise.

27 If the yellow LED does not turn off within 30 seconds of adjustment, turn the idle speed adjustment screw in the same direction.

28 Continue adjustment until the yellow LED turns off.

29 Place the engine under load as follows:

a) Switch the headlights on main beam
b) Switch the heater blower on full power.
c) Switch on the heated rear window.

30 The idle speed should remain constant at 800 rpm under these conditions.

CO value (non-cat models only)

31 Refer to the adjustment test conditions in Section 7, and ensure that all engine loads are turned off.

32 Connect a gas analyser to the exhaust system.

33 The CO value should be 1.0 ± 1.0. Adjust as necessary by turning the CO adjustment screw in the CO pot (located under the dash).

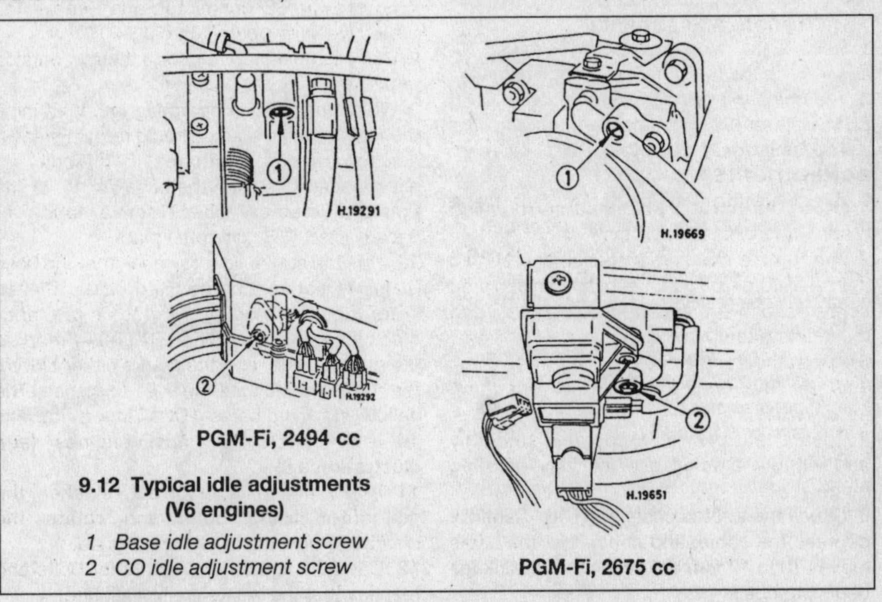

9.12 Typical idle adjustments (V6 engines)

1 *Base idle adjustment screw*
2 *CO idle adjustment screw*

System sensor and actuator tests

Important note: *Please refer to Chapter 4, which describes common test procedures applicable to this system. The routines in Chapter 4 should be read in conjunction with the component notes and wiring diagrams presented in this Chapter. The wiring diagrams and other data presented in this Chapter are necessarily representative of the system depicted. Because of the variations in wiring and other data that often occurs, even between similar vehicles in any particular VM's range, the reader should take great care in identification of ECM pins, and satisfy himself that he has gathered the correct data before failing a particular component.*

11 Crank angle sensor (CAS)

1 Refer to the note at the start of this Section, and refer to the relevant Section of Chapter 4.

2 The multi-plug to the CAS in V6 vehicles contains two sets of terminals, one set for each sensor. Treat each set of terminals as a separate CAS, and test accordingly. In addition, the inductive trigger in the distributor is tested in a similar fashion. The CAS resistance (both TDC and RPM sensors) should be between 500 and 1200 ohms. The CAS resistance (distributor based inductive signal) should be between 650 and 850 ohms.

3 The CAS in four-cylinder vehicles consists of two independent inductive triggers located in the distributor. The sensors separately measure TDC and RPM. Operation and test procedures are very similar to the flywheel-mounted CAS once the correct signal wires have been identified in the CAS multi-plug.

4 On Honda vehicles, the CAS resistance (both TDC and RPM sensors) should be between 350 and 700 ohms. On Rover models, the CAS resistance (both TDC and RPM sensors) should be between 500 and 1200 ohms.

12 Primary ignition

1 Refer to the note at the start of Section 11, and refer to the relevant Section of Chapter 4.

2 The primary ignition is essentially that of an ECM with an external amplifier. The amplifier is located inside the distributor in 'coil-in-cap' systems.

3 When testing the ignition circuit for a primary signal, the routines described in 'Primary signal not available (external amplifier)' are generally the most suitable.

4 Ignition coil resistances will usually be one of the following values:

a) *Primary resistance 0.6 to 0.8, secondary resistance 13200 to 19800*

b) *Primary resistance 0.4 to 0.5, secondary resistance 940 to 14160*

5 Probe for amplifier voltages at the seven-pin distributor multi-plug, or the two-pin multi-plug, or at the ECM **(see illustrations 9.13 and 9.14)**. **Note:** *Although a primary signal may be obtained at the tachometer terminal in the two-pin connector to the distributor, the signal so obtained is not a genuine primary signal, and connecting to the negative terminal inside the distributor will give better results.*

6 Connect the dwell meter positive probe to the coil negative terminal. The ignition coil terminal is not easy to access, and the following method could be used to attach the instrument.

Connecting a test instrument probe to the primary ignition

7 Remove the distributor cap and identify the coil negative terminal.

8 Remove the screw fixing the LT wire to the coil negative terminal.

9 Construct a temporary LT lead out of a length of LT wire with a small eyelet at one end and a terminal at the other end.

10 Refit the screw so that it secures the original LT wire and the new temporary LT wire to the coil negative connection.

11 Carefully route the temporary lead over the rubber grommet that carries the primary leads into the distributor. Ensure the new lead does not interfere with the rotor arm, and is not crushed when the distributor cap is refitted.

12 Another method to ease the passage of the temporary lead is to file a tiny nick with a small round file into the lip of the distributor cap base.

13 Refit the distributor cap with care.

14 Connect the test apparatus probe to the terminal at the exposed end of the new lead.

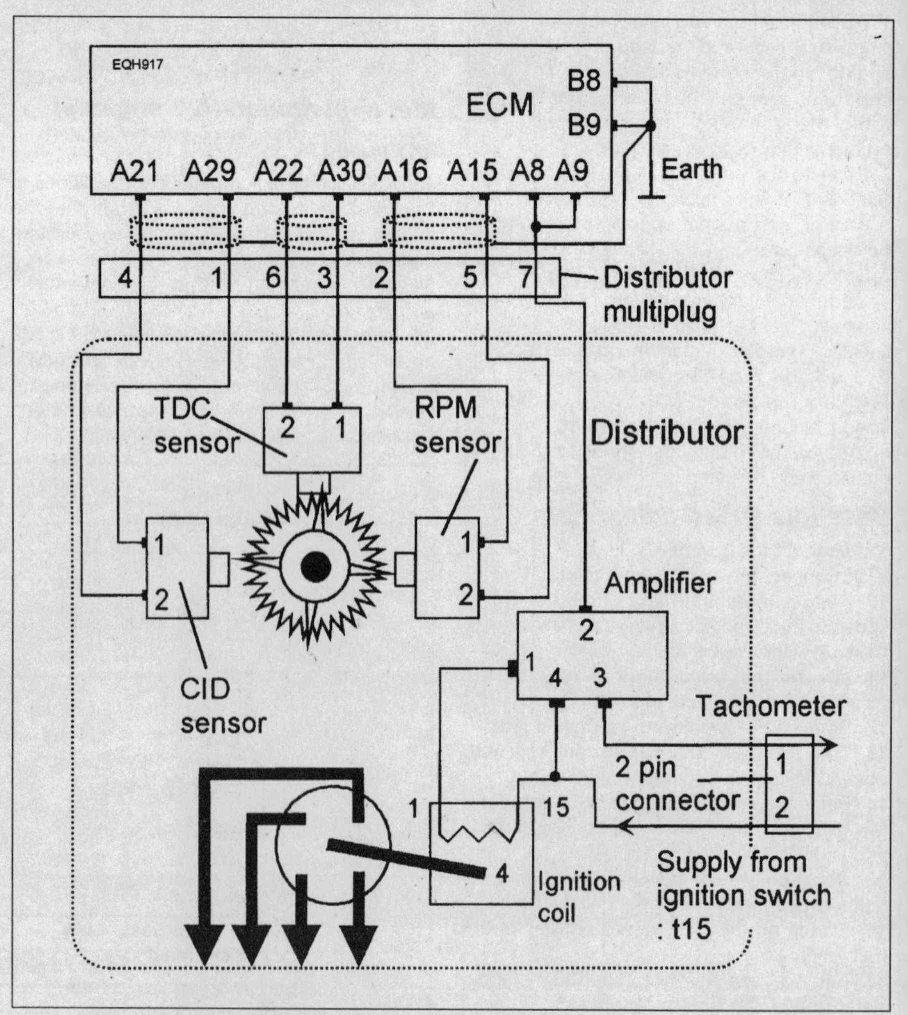

9.13 Typical ignition wiring (four-cylinder engines)

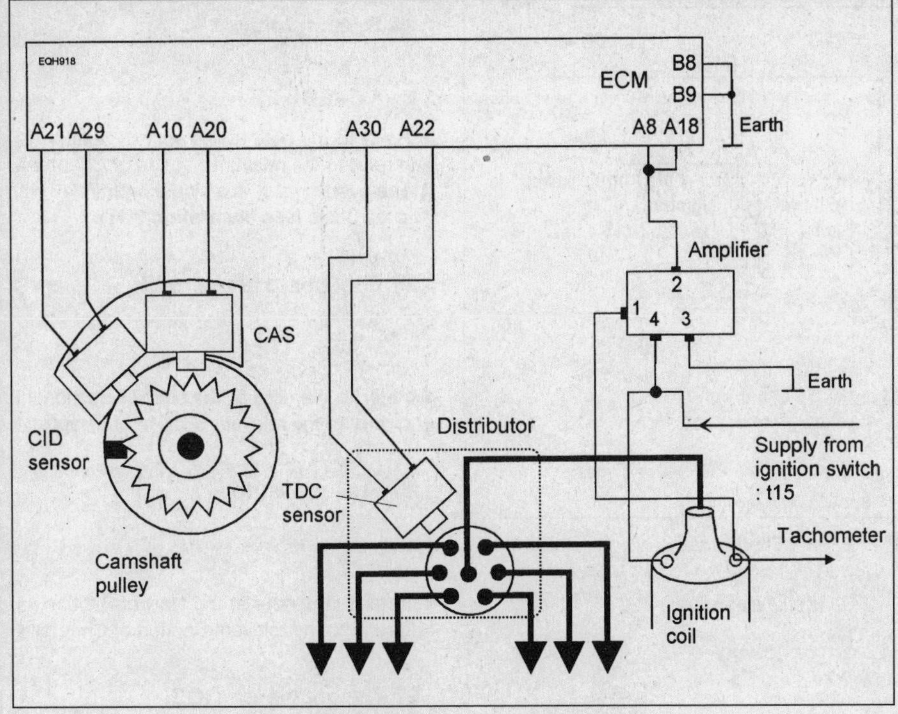

9.14 Typical ignition wiring (V6 engines)

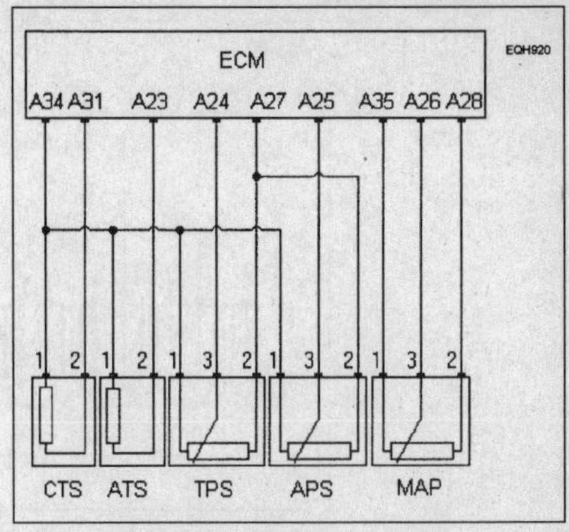

9.15 Typical sensor wiring

13 Fuel injector operation

1 Refer to the note at the start of Section 11, and refer to the relevant Section of Chapter 4.
2 Voltage to the injectors is normally provided from the system relay.
3 Injector operation is sequential.
4 The PGM-Fi injector resistance is normally 10.0 to 13.0 ohms (no resistor pack) or 1.5 to 2.0 ohms (through 5.0 to 7.0 ohm resistor pack).

14 Phase sensor (CID)

1 Refer to the note at the start of Section 11, and refer to the relevant Section of Chapter 4.
2 The CID sensor may be located in the distributor or connected to the exhaust camshaft.
3 Honda: The CID resistance should be between 350 and 700 ohms. Rover: The CID resistance should be between 500 and 1200 ohms.

15 MAP sensor

1 Refer to the note at the start of Section 11, and refer to the relevant Section of Chapter 4.
2 The MAP sensor is located on the bulkhead, or directly bolted to the inlet manifold (no vacuum hose).
3 Where the MAP sensor is directly connected to the inlet manifold, check for a vacuum leak at the mating surfaces. Renew the 'O' ring if necessary.

16 Atmospheric pressure sensor (APS)

1 A thin probe could be used to probe through the rubber insert on the APS multi-plug. Great care must be taken to avoid damage to the boot or terminal.
2 Connect the voltmeter negative probe to an engine earth.
3 Connect the voltmeter positive probe to the wire attached to the APS sensor signal terminal.
4 Switch the ignition on.
5 The voltage signalled by atmospheric pressure at sea level will be around 1.0 to 3.0 volts. The voltage will change slightly to reflect changes in pressure and also when the vehicle operates at different altitudes. The changes in voltage are likely to be relatively small. The important point is that the voltage falls within the expected parameters. Erroneous values would indicate a faulty sensor.

17 CO potentiometer ('pot')

1 Refer to the note at the start of Section 11, and refer to the relevant Section of Chapter 4.
2 The CO pot is of the external type, and is located in the passenger footwell, below the ECM.

18 Air temperature sensor (ATS)

1 Refer to the note at the start of Section 11, and refer to the relevant Section of Chapter 4.
2 The ATS is normally mounted in the inlet manifold **(see illustration 9.15)**.

19 Coolant temperature sensor (CTS)

1 Refer to the note at the start of Section 11, and refer to the relevant Section of Chapter 4.

20 Throttle potentiometer sensor (TPS)

1 Refer to the note at the start of Section 11, and refer to the relevant Section of Chapter 4.

21 Idle speed control valve (ISCV)

1 Refer to the note at the start of Section 11, and refer to the relevant Section of Chapter 4.
2 Continuity should be measured between the two ISCV terminals with an ohmmeter **(see illustration 9.16)**.

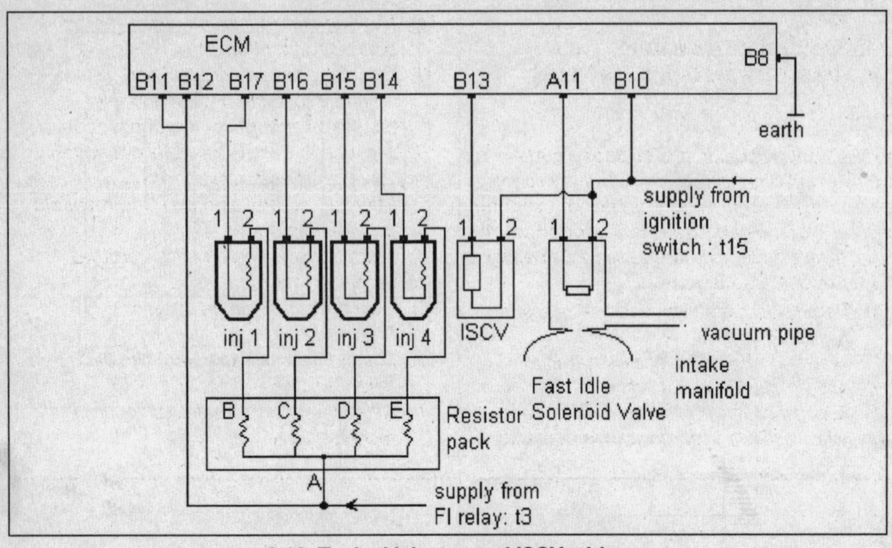

9.16 Typical injector and ISCV wiring

3 Duty cycle with the engine hot:

No load condition	*30% approx.*
Under load condition	*37% approx.*

22 ECM voltage supplies and earths

1 Refer to the note at the start of Section 11, and refer to the relevant Section of Chapter 4.

23 Inertia switch

1 Refer to the note at the start of Section 11, and refer to the relevant Section of Chapter 4.

2 The inertia switch is only fitted to Rover models (not Honda), and is usually located behind the radio.

24 System relays

1 Refer to the note at the start of Section 11, and refer to the relevant Section of Chapter 4.

2 The system relay is a single 8-pin relay with dual contacts **(see illustration 9.17)**.

25 Fuel pump and circuit

1 Refer to the note at the start of Section 11, and refer to the relevant Section of Chapter 4.

26 Fuel pressure

1 Refer to the note at the start of Section 11, and refer to the relevant Section of Chapter 4.

27 Oxygen sensor (OS)

1 Refer to the note at the start of Section 11, and refer to the relevant Section of Chapter 4.

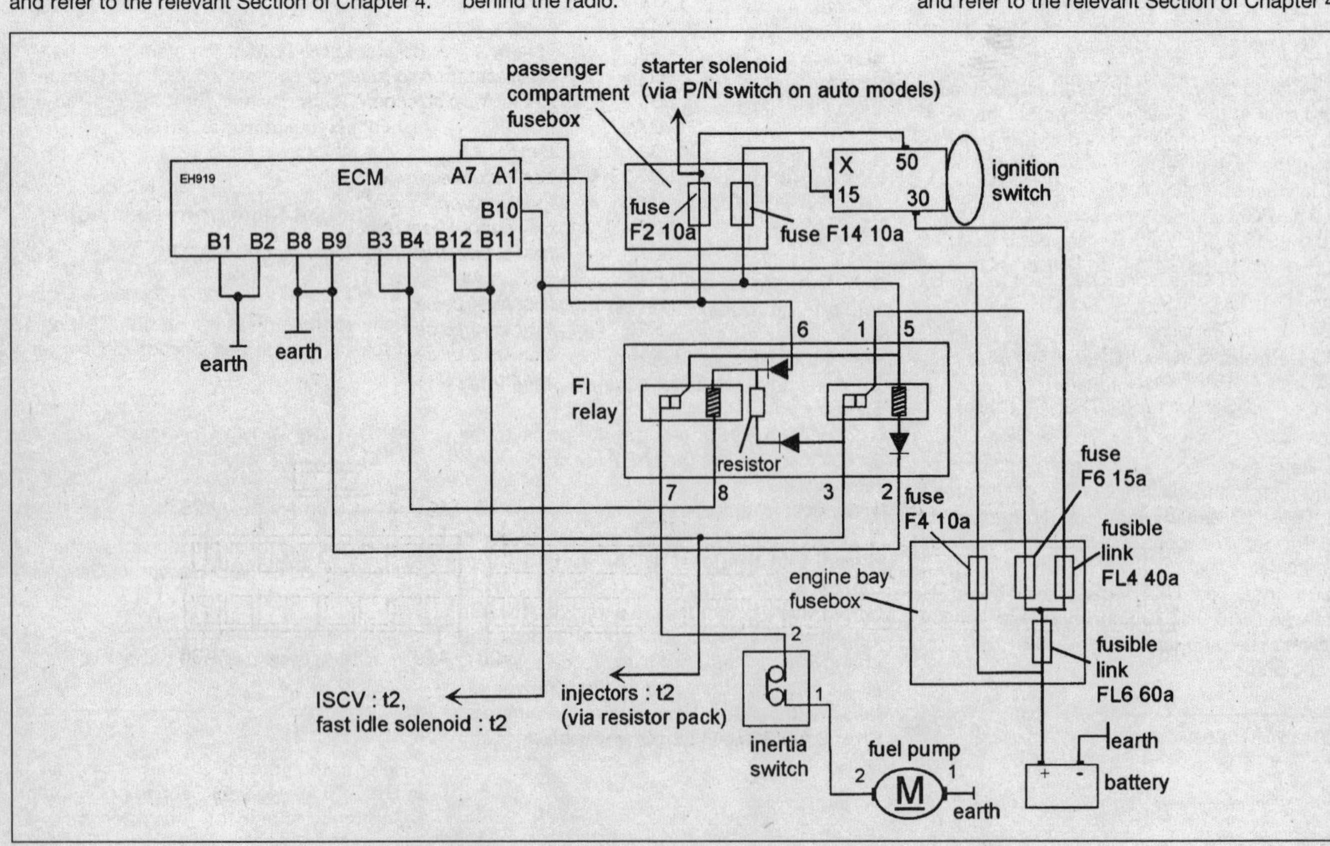

9.17 Typical relay and components wiring

2 The OS found in the majority of Honda PGM-Fi vehicles is a four-wire sensor with a heater. However, some models utilise a LAF sensor that switches digitally from 5.0 volts to zero volts.

28 Carbon filter solenoid valve (CFSV)

1 Refer to the note at the start of Section 11, and refer to the relevant Section of Chapter 4.

29 Control box vacuum connections (V6, 2.7 engine)

1 The control box on the bulkhead contains a number of components - mainly control solenoids that are connected by vacuum hoses. The hose number is inscribed on the side of the hose and the correct connections by number are as follows:-

1) *Regulator cut-off valve to fuel pressure regulator*
2) *Manifold control solenoids A & B to manifold control diaphragm unit.*
3) *Fuel pressure regulator cut-off valve to inlet manifold vacuum source connection.*
4) *MAP sensor to inlet manifold vacuum source connection.*
5) *Constant vacuum control and air reservoir to vacuum tank and inlet manifold vacuum source connection.*
6) *Air suction control valve to air suction valve (air injection systems only).*
7) *Manifold control solenoid B to manifold control diaphragm.*
8) *Throttle damper air filter to throttle damper diaphragm.*
9) *EGR control solenoid valve to EGR valve.*
10) *Manifold control solenoid A to vacuum reservoir tank.*
11) *Air suction control valve to vacuum reservoir tank.*

Pin table - typical 53-pin (Rover)

Note: *Refer to* ***illustration 9.18***

A1	Battery supply (fused)
A2	A/C clutch relay driver
A3	-
A4	P/N switch (AT models)
A5	-
A6	P/N switch (AT models)
A7	Cranking supply (fused) ignition switch
A8	Ignition output to amplifier
A9	Ignition output to amplifier (connected to ECM)
A10	-
A11	Fast idle solenoid driver
A12	-
A13	SD warning lamp
A14	A/C pressure switch
A15	Rpm sensor signal
A16	Rpm sensor return
A17	Alternator
A18	VSS signal
A19	-
A20	CO pot signal
A21	CID sensor signal
A22	TDC sensor signal
A23	ATS signal
A24	TPS signal
A25	APS sensor signal + sea level
A26	MAP sensor signal
A27	Sensor supply TPS, PA sensor
A28	Sensor supply MAP
A29	CID return
A30	TDC sensor return
A31	CTS signal
A32	-
A33	-
A34	Sensor return ATS, CTS, TPS, PA sensor
A35	MAP sensor return
A36	SD connector
B1	Earth
B2	Earth (connected to ECM)
B3	FI relay driver
B4	FI relay driver (connected to ECM)
B5	Resonator control solenoid
B6	A/T lock-up solenoid
B7	-
B8	Earth
B9	Earth (connected to ECM)
B10	Ignition supply (fused)
B11	Nbv supply from relay
B12	Nbv supply from relay (connected to ECM)
B13	ISCV pulse
B14	Injector 4 pulse
B15	Injector 3 pulse
B16	Injector 2 pulse
B17	Injector 1 pulse

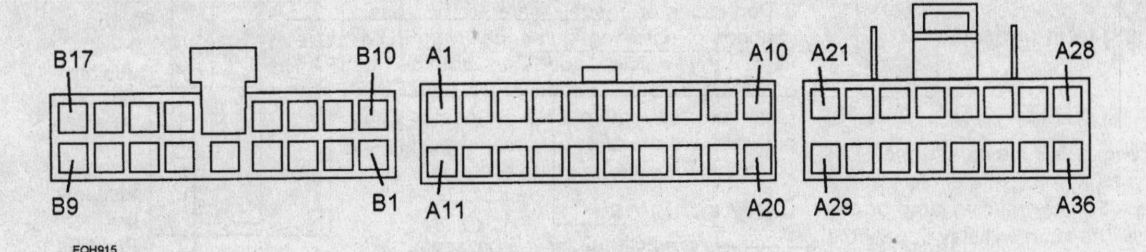

9.18 PGM-Fi 53-pin multi-plug

9

Pin table - typical 76-pin (Honda)

Note:** Refer to **illustration 9.19

Pin	Function	Pin	Function
A1	Injector 1 driver	B7	P/N switch (auto models)
A2	Injector 4 driver	B8	PSPS
A3	Injector 2 driver	B9	Ignition switch
A4	Spool solenoid valve	B10	VSS
A5	Injector 3 driver	B11	CID sensor signal
A6	OS heater driver	B12	CID sensor return
A7	FI relay driver	B13	TDC sensor signal
A8	FI relay driver	B14	TDC sensor return
A9	ISCV driver	B15	RPM sensor signal
A10	-	B16	RPM sensor return
A11	-	D1	Battery
A12	Radiator fan relay	D2	Brake switch
A13	SD warning lamp driver	D3	-
A14	-	D4	SD connector
A15	A/C relay driver	D5	-
A16	Alternator	D6	VTEC oil pressure switch
A17	AT lock-up solenoid	D7	Data link connector
A18	-	D8	-
A19	AT lock-up solenoid	D9	Alternator
A20	CFSV driver	D10	ELD unit
A21	Amplifier control signal	D11	TPS signal
A22	Amplifier control signal	D12	-
A23	Earth	D13	CTS signal
A24	Earth	D14	OS signal
A25	FI relay output	D15	ATS signal
A26	Earth	D16	-
B1	FI relay output	D17	MAP signal
B2	Earth	D18	AT interlock control unit, upshift indicator
B3	Instrument cluster (AT only)	D19	Sensor supply MAP
B4	Instrument cluster (AT only)	D20	Sensor supply TPS
B5	A/C switch	D21	MAP sensor return
B6	-	D22	Sensor return ATS, CTS, OS, SD connector TPS

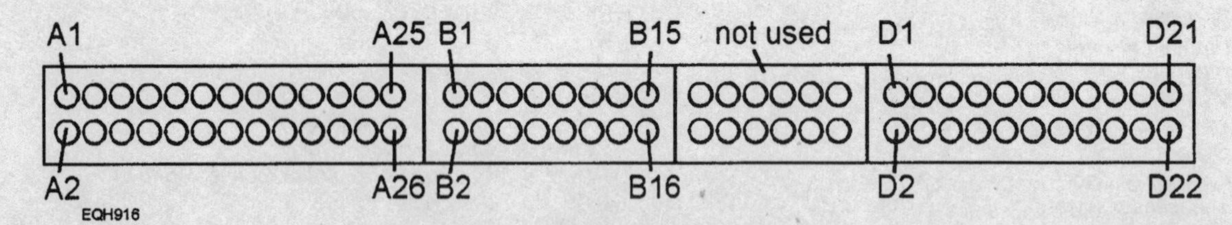

9.19 PGM-Fi 76-pin multi-plug

Fault codes

30 Obtaining fault codes

1 When the engine is running and the ECM detects that a fault present, a pin is earthed and the 'Check Engine' warning lamp on the dash will light. The lamp will stay lit until the fault or faults are no longer present. If the warning lamp lights and then extinguishes, the fault is very likely an intermittent problem.

2 In PGM-Fi, the self-diagnostic (SD) system can only be used to obtain and clear codes, and other functions such as Datastream are not available.

3 Depending on model, there are two basic methods of obtaining fault codes from PGM-Fi. In early vehicles, codes are obtained by observing the flashes of the LED on the ECM. Later vehicles require a SD connector to be bridged, and the codes observed as flashes on the dash-located warning lamp.

Early vehicles

4 Access the ECM under the passenger side footwell.

5 Switch on the ignition.

6 View the red LED in the centre of the ECM.

7 Count the number of flashes emitted by the LED. The flashes are emitted as a straight count: ie 15 flashes indicates code number 15 **(see illustration 9.20)**.

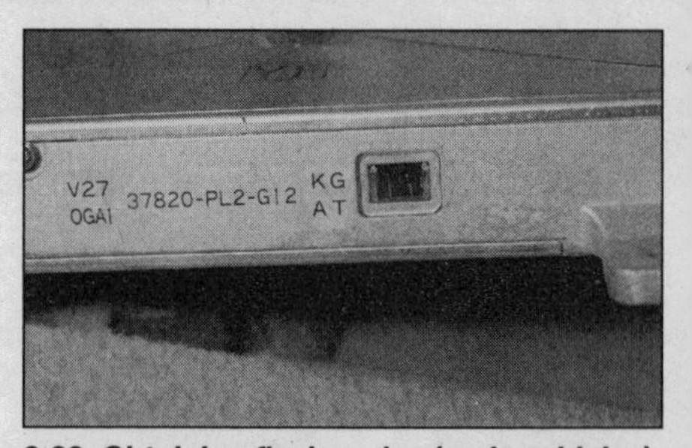

9.20 Obtaining flash codes (early vehicles). Observe the flashes of the LED on the ECM. The yellow LED will be extinguished if the idle speed value is correct. If the yellow LED is constantly on or is flashing, the idle speed requires adjustment

8 The LED will then pause for two seconds and then transmit the next code. When all codes have been transmitted, the LED will pause for two seconds and then repeat the sequence.
9 If the number of flashes indicate a number for which there is no code, the ECM is suspect. Recheck several times, and then check the earth and supply voltages to the ECM before fitting a replacement.
10 When the ignition is switched off, the LED will extinguish. However, the LED will resume flashing once the ignition is switched on again.
11 If the fault(s) are corrected, the LED will continue to flash until the ECM memory is initialised. The method is detailed below.

Clearing fault codes

12 Clear the fault codes by removing the 10 amp number 4 fuse in the fusebox for a period of 10 seconds. **Note:** *Removing the fuse will also reset the adaptive values.*

Later vehicles

13 Inspect the 'Check Engine' warning lamp on the dash. If it is illuminated, one or more codes are logged by PGM-Fi, and the ECM should be interrogated as follows.
14 Use a jumper lead to bridge the two terminals at the SD connector.
15 Switch on the ignition.
16 View the warning lamp on the dash. If the warning lamp remains on and does not flash, the ECM is in back-up mode. In this instance, the ECM should be removed and checked by one of the specialist ECM testing companies.
17 Count the number of flashes emitted by the warning lamp. The flashes are emitted as a straight count of short flashes for the first nine codes, eg 8 flashes indicates code number 8. The numbers from 10 to 48 are indicated by a series of long and short flashes separated by short pauses. The first digit of the number is transmitted by the long flashes, and the second digit by the short flashes, eg 41 would be signalled by four long flashes and one short flash **(see illustration 9.21)**.
18 After the first code is transmitted, the warning lamp will pause and then transmit the next code.
19 When all codes have been transmitted, the warning lamp will pause and then repeat the sequence.

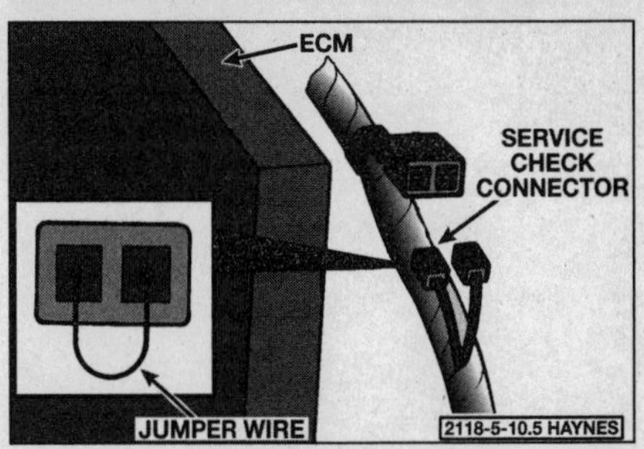

9.21 Obtaining flash codes (later vehicles). Bridge the terminals in the service check connector (behind the kick panel, to the left of the glovebox)

20 If the number of flashes indicate a number for which there is no code, the ECM is suspect. Recheck the code output several times, and then check the earth and supply voltages before fitting a replacement ECM.

Clearing fault codes

21 Clear the fault codes by removing the 7.5 amp back-up fuse in the fusebox for a period of 30 seconds. **Note:** *Removing the fuse will also reset the adaptive values.*

Fault code table

Code	Fault
0	*ECM*
1	*Oxygen sensor (except D16A9 engine)*
3	*Manifold absolute pressure (MAP sensor)*
4	*Crank angle sensor (CAS)*
5	*Manifold absolute pressure (MAP sensor)*
6	*Coolant temperature sensor (CTS)*
7	*Throttle pot sensor (TPS)*
8	*TDC position (TDC sensor)*
9	*No 1 cylinder position (CID sensor)*
10	*Air temperature sensor (ATS)*
11	*CO pot*
12	*Exhaust gas recirculation system (EGR)*
13	*Atmospheric pressure sensor (APS)*
14	*Idle speed control valve (ISCV)*
15	*Ignition output signal*
16	*Fuel injector (D15B2 engine)*
17	*Vehicle speed sensor (VSS)*
18	*Ignition timing*
19	*AT lock-up control solenoid valve A/B*
20	*Electronic load detector (ELD)*
21	*Spool solenoid valve*
22	*Valve timing oil pressure switch*
30	*A/T Fi signal A*
31	*A/T Fi signal B*
41	*Oxygen sensor heater (D16Z6, D16Z7, B16A2 engine)*
41	*LAF sensor heater (D15Z1 engine)*
43	*Fuel supply system (D16Z6, D16Z7, B16Z2 engine)*
48	*LAF sensor (D15Z1 engine)*

Notes

Chapter 10
Magneti-Marelli G5/G6/8F/8P MPi/SPi

Contents

Specifications

Vehicle	Year	Idle speed	CO%
Magneti-Marelli G5 & G6 (Citroën/Peugeot)			
AX 1.1i cat TU1M/Z (HDZ/HDY)	1992 to 1995	850 ± 50	0.5 max
BX 1.6i cat XU5M3Z (BDY)	1991 to 1994	850 ± 50	0.5 max
ZX 1.6i XU5M (B4A)	1991 to 1993	875 ± 25	1.0 to 2.0
ZX 1.6i XU5M.3/4K (B4A)	1991 to 1993	875 ± 25	1.0 to 2.0
ZX 1.6i cat XU5M.3L/Z (BDY)	1992 to 1993	850 ± 50	0.5 max
106 1.1i cat TU1M/Z (HDZ)	1993 to 1995	800 ± 50	0.4 max
205 1.1i cat TU1M/Z (HDZ)	1992 to 1995	800 ± 50	0.4 max
205 1.6i cat XU5M2Z (BDY)	1990 to 1991	800 ± 50	0.5 max
205 1.6i cat XU5M3Z (BDY)	1992 to 1995	800 ± 50	0.5 max
309 1.6i cat XU5MZ (BDZ)	1989 to 1991	800 ± 50	0.5 max
309 1.6i cat XU5M2Z (BDY)	1991 to 1992	850 ± 50	0.5 max
309 1.6i cat XU5M3Z (BDY)	1992 to 1994	800 ± 50	0.5 max
405 1.6i cat XU5MZ (BDZ)	1989 to 1991	800 ± 50	0.5 max
405 1.6i cat XU5M2Z (BDY)	1989 to 1991	800 ± 50	0.5 max
405 1.6i cat XU5M3Z (BDY)	1991 to 1992	800 ± 50	0.5 max
405 1.6i cat XU5M3L/Z (BDY)	1992 to 1993	800 ± 50	0.5 max
Magneti-Marelli 8F (Fiat)			
Punto 75, 1.2 176 A8.000	1994 to 1995	850 ± 50	0.35 max
Tipo 1.8i cat 159 A4.046	1992 to 1994	850 ± 50	0.35 max
Magneti-Marelli 8P (Citroën/Peugeot)			
Evasion 2.0i cat RFU (XU10J2CZ/L)	1994 to 1996	850 ± 50	0.3 max
Synergie 2.0i cat RFU (XU10J2CZ/L)	1994 to 1996	850 ± 50	0.3 max
Xantia 1.6i cat XU5JP/Z (BFZ)	1993 to 1995	850 ± 50	0.5 max
Xantia 2.0i cat XU10J2C/Z (RFX)	1993 to 1995	850 ± 50	0.5 max
ZX 2.0i cat XUJ10J2/C/L/Z (RFX)	1992 to 1995	850 ± 50**	0.4 max
ZX 1.6i & Break cat BFZ(XU7JPL/Z)	1994 to 1995	850 ± 50	0.4 max
ZX 1.8i & Break cat LFZ(XU7JPL/Z)	1995 to 1996	850 ± 50	0.4 max
106 1.4i 8V SOHC TU2J2L/Z (MFZ)	1993 to 1996	950 ± 50	0.3 max
106 1.6 MPi TU5J2L/Z/K (NFY)	1994 to 1996	850 ± 50	0.3 max
306 1.8i Cabrio & cat XU7JPL/Z (LFZ)	1993 to 1996	850 to 900	0.3 max
306 2.0i cat XU10J2C (RFX)	1994 to 1995	850 ± 50	0.5 max
405 2.0i & 4X4 cat XU10J2C/Z (RFX)	1992 to 1995	850 ± 50	0.5 max
Boxer 2.0i cat XU10J2.U (RFW)	1994 to 1995	850 ± 50	0.5 max
806 2.0i XU10J2CL/Z (RFU)	1995 to 1996	850 ± 50	0.3 max

*** A/C models: 900 ± 50 rpm*

Overview of system operation

1 Introduction

Please read this overview of Magneti-Marelli operation in conjunction with Chapter 2, which describes some of the functions in more detail.

The Magneti-Marelli (MM) family of engine management systems evolved from the Weber-Marelli system fitted to Fiat and other vehicles. Although some components in MM are similar to Weber-Marelli, there are enough differences to allow the systems to be treated separately.

G5 is an early MM system fitted to various Citroën and Peugeot vehicles, soon replaced by G6. The 8P variant has now generally replaced G6, although G5, G6 and 8P are very similar in construction and in operation. The main difference between the systems is the numbering of the ECM pins used for sensor and actuator control.

Generally, both G5 and G6 systems are SPi, although an MPi version of G5 was fitted to some 2.0i models of the Citroën XM and Peugeot 605. Some early versions of G5 fitted to Peugeot 309 and 405 had a distributor, but all later versions of both G5 & G6 are equipped with DIS ignition systems. The 8P system is an MPi system with DIS; 8F is also MPi with DIS, and was fitted to some Fiat vehicles from model year 1993 to replace the Weber-Marelli system. The 8F system is very similar to 8P, including similar numbering of the ECM pins used for sensor and actuator control.

Magneti-Marelli G5, G6, 8P and 8F are fully integrated systems that control primary ignition, fuelling and idle control from within the same ECM. The correct ignition dwell, timing and injection duration for all engine operating conditions are calculated from data provided by the CAS (crankshaft position and speed), and the MAP sensor (engine load). A 35-pin connector and multi-plug connects the ECM to the battery, sensors and actuators. Most versions employ a catalytic converter and a carbon canister for containing exhaust emissions.

2 Control functions

Signal processing

Basic ignition timing is stored in a three-dimensional map, and the engine load and speed signals determine the ignition timing. The main engine load sensor is the MAP sensor; engine speed is determined from the crank angle sensor (CAS) signal.

Correction factors are then applied for starting, idle, deceleration, and part- and full-load operation. The main correction factor is engine temperature (CTS). Minor correction to timing and AFR are made with reference to the ATS and TPS signals.

The basic AFR is also stored in a three-dimensional map, and the engine load and speed signals determine the basic injection pulse value. Using the speed/density method, MM calculates the AFR from the pressure in the inlet manifold (MAP) and the speed of the engine (CAS). This method relies on the theory that the engine will draw in a fixed volume of air per revolution. The AFR and the pulse duration are then corrected on reference to ATS, CTS, battery voltage and rate of throttle opening (TPS). Other controlling factors are determined by operating conditions such as cold start and warm-up, idle condition, acceleration and deceleration.

MM accesses a different map for idle running conditions, and this map is implemented whenever the engine speed is at idle. Idle speed during all warm-up and normal hot running conditions is maintained by the ISCV. However, MM makes small adjustments to the idle speed by advancing or retarding the timing, and this results in an ignition timing that is forever changing during engine idle.

When the engine is equipped with an oxygen sensor (OS), the OS signal causes the ECM to modify the injector pulse so that the AFR is maintained close to the stoichiometric ratio.

Basic ECM operation

The permanent voltage supply from the vehicle battery to the ECM is slightly different depending on model. A description of each type follows.

G5 and G6

A permanent voltage supply is made from the vehicle battery to the ECM. This allows the self-diagnostic function to retain data of an intermittent nature. Once the ignition is switched on, power is applied to the main relay, and the relay in turn applies a voltage supply to ECM pin 35 (most models).

8P

A permanent voltage supply is made from the vehicle battery to pin 4 of the ECM. The connection is made via the 15-pin relay, and is unusual in that the connection doubles as the main relay driver. Once the ignition is switched on, power is applied to the main relay, and the relay in turn provides a switched voltage supply to ECM pin 35. The supply to pin 35 now takes over the task of supplying voltage to the ECM.

All models

The majority of sensors such as the ATS, CTS, TPS and MAP sensor are now provided with a 5.0-volt reference supply from a relevant pin on the ECM. When the engine is cranked or run, a speed signal from the CAS causes the ECM to earth the pump relay driver pin, so that the fuel pump will run. Ignition and injection functions are also activated. All actuators (ignition coil, injector, ISCV, CFSV etc), are supplied with nbv from the fuel pump relay, and the ECM completes the circuit by pulsing the relevant actuator wire to earth.

Self-diagnostic function

MM provides a serial port for diagnostic purposes. The port allows two-way communication, so that certain output components can be actuated. Datastream information (live values) on the status of system components is also available. In Peugeot and Citroën systems, the idle/CO values (non-cat models) and timing advance can also be altered by the FCR.

In addition, a self-test capability regularly examines signals from the engine sensors, and internally logs a code in the event of a fault being present. In Citroën and Peugeot systems, this code can be extracted from the MM serial port by a suitable FCR. In addition, the codes can be output as flash codes, by counting the flashes upon the dash-mounted warning lamp.

In Fiat systems, details of which components are at error can also be extracted from the MM 8F serial port by a dedicated FCR. Flash codes are not available in this system.

If both systems, if the fault clears, the code will remain logged until the FCR is used to erase it from memory.

The operation of the dash-mounted warning lamp also differs between Fiat and Citroën/Peugeot vehicles.

Citroën/Peugeot models

When the ECM detects that a major fault is present, it earths the appropriate ECM pin and the warning lamp on the dash will light. The lamp will stay lit until the fault is no longer present. However, if a minor fault is present, the warning lamp will not light, although a fault code will be logged by the ECM. Where the fault is intermittent, the lamp will light whilst the fault is present and extinguish when the fault is not present. A fault code will be logged under these circumstances, and the presence of a fault code denotes that a fault was detected on the appropriate circuit at some past juncture.

Fiat models

When the ECM detects that a major fault is present, it earths ECM pin 6, and the warning lamp on the dash will light. The lamp will stay lit until the fault is no longer present. Where the fault is intermittent, the lamp will light whilst the fault is present, and extinguish when the fault is not present. An error will be logged under these circumstances, and the presence of an error denotes that a fault was detected on the appropriate circuit at some past juncture.

Limited operation strategy (limp-home)

In the event of a serious fault in one or more of the sensors, the EMS will substitute a fixed default value in place of the defective sensor. The engine will still run, albeit inefficiently, when in limp-home mode.

This means that the engine may actually run quite well with failure of one or more minor sensors. Since the substituted values are those of a hot engine, cold starting and running during the warm-up period may be less than satisfactory. Also, failure of a major sensor, ie the MAP sensor, will lead to a considerable reduction in performance.

Faults identified by the self-diagnostic function will also be stored in memory, and will remain there until erased by a suitable FCR. This allows the self-diagnostic function to retain data of an intermittent nature.

Adaptive memory

Over a period of time, the ECM will learn the best idle position for a particular engine - irrespective of age, engine condition and load, so that the correct idle speed is always maintained. The adaptive idle settings are stored in memory.

Adaptive idle measurements and fault codes retained in memory will be lost if the vehicle battery is disconnected. This could mean that idle quality will deteriorate until the ECM relearns the optimum settings.

Reference voltage

Voltage supply from the ECM to the engine sensors is made at a 5.0-volt reference level. This ensures a stable working voltage, unaffected by variations in system voltage.

The earth return connection for most engine sensors is made through one or more ECM pins, and these pins are not directly connected to earth. The ECM internally connects these pins to earth via the ECM earth pin that is directly connected to earth.

Signal shielding

To reduce RFI, a number of sensors (G5: CAS, MAP and OS), (G6: CAS, and OS), (8P: CAS, KS and OS) use a shielded cable. The shielded cable for the OS is connected to the main ECM earth wire at terminal 12 (G5) or terminal 31 (G6) to reduce interference to a minimum. The CAS shielded wire is connected to ECM pin number 24 (G6), and ECM pin number 17 (8P). The other shielded wires are directly connected to earth or ECM earth pin 34 (8P).

Vehicle speed sensor (VSS)

The VSS is used to advise the ECM of vehicle speed. It operates upon the Hall-effect principle, and is mounted directly upon the gearbox speedometer connection.

A voltage of approximately 12 volts is applied to the VSS from the ignition switch when switched on. As the speedometer cable turns, the Hall switch is alternately turned on and off to return a square wave signal to the ECM. The frequency of the signal (8 pulses per revolution) denotes the vehicle speed.

3 Primary trigger

Crank angle sensor (CAS)

The primary signal to initiate both ignition and fuelling emanates from a CAS mounted close to the flywheel. The CAS consists of an inductive magnet that radiates a magnetic field. The flywheel incorporates a reluctor disc containing steel pins set at intervals. As the flywheel spins, the pins are rotated in the magnetic field, and an AC voltage signal is generated to indicate speed of rotation. The two missing pins (set at 180° intervals) are references to TDC, and indicate crankshaft position by varying the signal as the flywheel spins. One missing pin indicates TDC for cylinders 1 and 4, and the other missing pin indicates TDC for cylinders 2 and 3.

The peak-to-peak voltage of the speed signal can vary from 5.0 volts at idle to over 100 volts at 6000 rpm. The ECM uses an analogue-to-digital converter (ADC) to transform the AC pulse into a digital signal.

4 Ignition

Data on engine load (MAP) and engine speed (CAS) are collected by the ECM, which then refers to a three-dimensional digital ignition map stored within its microprocessor. This map contains an advance angle for basic load and speed operating conditions. The advance angle is corrected after reference to engine temperature (CTS), so that the best ignition advance angle for a particular operating condition can be determined.

Amplifier

The MM amplifier contains the circuitry for switching the coil negative terminal at the correct moment to instigate ignition. The amplifier circuitry is contained within the ECM itself, and the microprocessor controls the ignition dwell period for each condition of engine speed and battery voltage.

Dwell operation in MM is based upon the principle of the 'constant-energy current-limiting' system. This means that the dwell period remains constant at about 3.0 to 4.0 ms, at virtually all engine running speeds. However, the dwell duty cycle, when measured in percent or degrees, will vary as the engine speed varies.

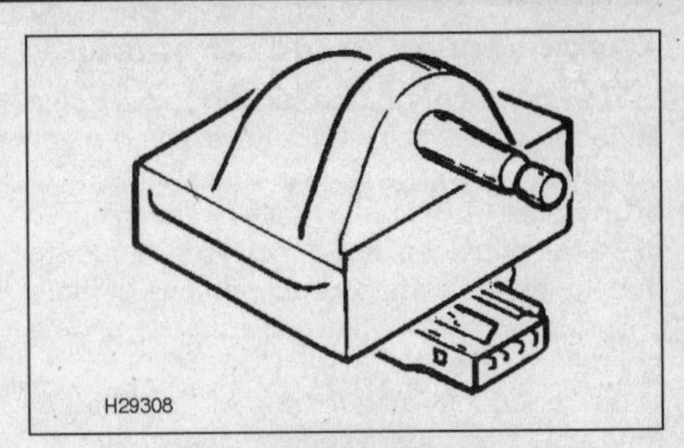

10.1 Ignition coil in G5 system with distributor

Ignition coil

The ignition coil utilises low primary resistance in order to increase primary current and primary energy. The amplifier limits the primary current to around 8 amps, and this permits a reserve of energy to maintain the required spark burn time (duration). In DIS systems, two ignition coils are utilised. Voltage to the ignition coil is applied from the fuel pump contact of the relay, and voltage is therefore only available with the engine cranking or running **(see illustration 10.1)**.

Distributor (where fitted)

In the MM system, the distributor only contains secondary HT components (distributor cap and rotor), and serves to distribute the HT current from the coil secondary terminal to each spark plug in firing order.

DIS ignition

Although the ignition system is termed DIS, the basic operation is much the same as on models with conventional ignition. In a DIS or so-called 'wasted spark' system, a double-ended coil is used to fire two plugs at the same time. This means that the system can only be used where two cylinders rise and fall together.

One cylinder will fire on the compression stroke, and the companion cylinder will fire on the exhaust stroke where the spark is 'wasted'. Two pairs of coils will therefore be required for a four-cylinder engine. About 3 kV is still needed to fire the 'wasted spark' plug, but this is far less than that required to bridge the rotor gap. Each ignition coil requires a voltage supply from the ignition switch and a separate dwell connection to the ECM, so that the ECM can switch each coil individually.

Ignition timing

The ignition timing on MM G5/G6 Monopoint models is not normally adjustable. However, it is possible to adjust the ignition advance curve with the aid of a suitable FCR. This task should not be undertaken lightly, and all other engine and system functions should be checked and evaluated before attempting advance adjustment. The ignition timing on MM 8F models is not adjustable under any circumstances.

Knock sensor (some 8P models)

The optimal ignition timing (at engine speeds greater than idle) for a given high-compression engine is quite close to the point of the onset of knock. However, running so close to the point of knock occurrence, means that knock will certainly occur on one or more cylinders at certain times during the engine operating cycle.

Since knock may occur at a different moment in each individual cylinder, MM 8P employs a knock control microprocessor (in the ECM) to pinpoint the actual cylinder or cylinders that are knocking. The knock sensor is mounted on the engine block, and consists of a piezoceramic measuring element that responds to engine noise oscillations. Engine knock is converted to a voltage signal by the knock sensor, and returned to the KCU for evaluation and action. The knocking frequency is in the 8 to 15 kHz frequency band.

The ECM will analyse the noise from each individual cylinder, and set a reference noise level for that cylinder based upon the average of the noise over a pre-determined period. If the noise level exceeds the reference level by a certain amount, the ECM identifies the presence of engine knock.

Initially, timing will occur at its optimal ignition point. Once knock is identified, the knock control microprocessor retards the ignition timing for that cylinder or cylinders by degrees. After knocking ceases, the timing is advanced until the reference timing value is achieved, or knock occurs once more. This process continually occurs so that all cylinders will consistently run at their optimum timing.

5 Fuel injection

Fuel injection (MPi)

The MM 8P ECM contains a fuel map with an injector opening time for basic conditions of speed and load. Information is then gathered from engine sensors such as the MAP sensor, CAS, CTS, ATS and TPS. As a result of this information, the ECM will look-up the correct injector pulse duration right across the engine rpm, load and temperature range.

The MM 8P MPi system has one injector for each cylinder, mounted in the inlet port so that a finely-atomised fuel spray is directed onto the back of each valve. The injectors are all pulsed simultaneously, twice per engine cycle. Half of the required fuel per engine cycle is therefore injected at each engine revolution.

Fuel will briefly rest upon the back of a valve before being drawn into a cylinder.

The amount of fuel delivered by the injector is determined by the fuel pressure and the injector opening time - otherwise known as the pulse duration. The ECM controls the period of time that the injector is held open, and this is determined by the signals from the various sensor inputs. During engine start-up from cold, the pulse duration is increased to provide a richer air /fuel mixture. During engine start-up, the injectors are pulsed at twice the normal engine running rate.

Voltage to the injectors is applied from the fuel pump contact of the relay, and voltage is therefore only available with the engine cranking or running.

Fuel injector

The fuel injector is a magnetically-operated solenoid valve actuated by the ECM. Voltage to the injectors is applied from the main relay, and the earth path is completed by the ECM for a period of time (called pulse duration) of between 1.5 and 10 milliseconds. The pulse duration is very much dependent upon engine temperature, load, speed and operating conditions. When the magnetic solenoid closes, a back-EMF voltage of up to 60 volts is induced.

Single-point fuel injection (SPi)

The SPi system consists of a single injector mounted in the throttle body. The amount of fuel delivered by the injector is determined by the fuel pressure and the injector opening time - otherwise known as the pulse duration. The ECM controls the period of time that the injector is held open, and this is determined by the signals from the various sensor inputs. Voltage to the injector is applied from the fuel pump contact of the relay, and voltage is therefore only available with the engine cranking or running.

During engine start-up from cold, the pulse duration is increased to provide a richer air/fuel mixture, and the ECM injects fuel in asynchronous mode (ie not synchronised with the firing of the ignition). Once the engine has started, the ECM switches to synchronised injection mode, so that injection is synchronised with the ignition pulses. Pulses of 1.5 to 2.0 ms at 60° ATDC are delivered 4 times per engine cycle in normal operation. During periods of engine idling, where the pulse falls below a threshold of 1.5 ms, the ECM reverts to asynchronous mode until injection exceeds 1.5 ms again. Asynchronous mode is also adopted during engine acceleration.

During engine deceleration, the pulse reduces to zero as the ECM cuts off injection.

Fuel injector

The fuel injector is a magnetically-operated solenoid valve that is actuated by the ECM. Voltage to the injectors is applied from the fuel pump relay, and the earth path is completed by the ECM for a period of time (called pulse duration) of between 1.5 and 10 milliseconds. The pulse duration is very much dependent upon engine temperature, load, speed and operating conditions. When the magnetic solenoid closes, a back-EMF voltage of up to 60 volts is initiated.

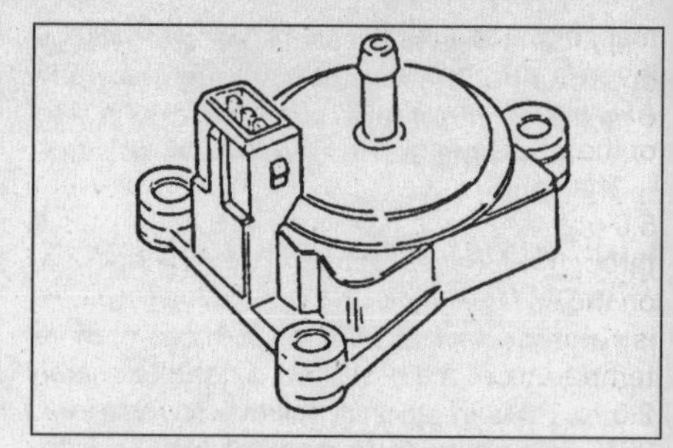

10.2 MAP sensor (all MM systems)

In SPi engines, fuel is injected into the inlet manifold, where it mixes with air. The depression produced by a descending piston causes the resulting air/fuel mixture to be drawn into each cylinder.

MAP sensor

The main engine load sensor is the MAP sensor. A vacuum hose connects the MAP sensor and the inlet manifold. Manifold vacuum acts upon the MAP sensor diaphragm, and the ECM converts the pressure into an electrical signal. The signal output is thus proportional to the depression in the inlet manifold **(see illustration 10.2)**.

MAP is calculated from the formula: Atmospheric Pressure less Manifold Pressure = Manifold Absolute Pressure. The ECM records the atmospheric (barometric) pressure at ignition switch-on and during full-load low-speed operation. The pressure is then used for subsequent MAP calculations.

Using the speed/density method, the ECM uses the MAP signal and the speed of the engine (CAS) to calculate the mass of air entering the engine. This method relies on the theory that the engine will draw in a fixed volume of air per revolution. When manifold vacuum is high (ie idle condition), MAP is moderately low, and the ECM provides less fuel. When manifold vacuum is low (ie wide open throttle), MAP is high and the ECM provides more fuel.

A 5.0-volt reference voltage is applied to the sensor and connected to the sensor return circuit. The third wire is connected to a transducer which converts the manifold pressure signal into a voltage. As the pressure in the manifold varies, so too does the signal voltage returned to the ECM.

The inlet manifold on SPi models is a 'wet' manifold. Fuel is injected into the inlet manifold, and there is a risk of fuel being drawn into the MAP sensor to contaminate the diaphragm. The inlet manifold on MPi models is a 'dry' manifold. Fuel is injected onto the back of an inlet valve, and there is no risk of fuel being drawn into the MAP sensor to contaminate the diaphragm.

Air temperature sensor (ATS)

The ATS is mounted in the inlet manifold, where it measures the air temperature in the manifold. Because the density of air varies in inverse proportion to the temperature, the ATS signal allows more accurate assessment of the volume of air entering the engine.

The open-circuit supply to the sensor is at a 5.0-volt reference level, and the earth path is through the sensor return. The ATS operates on the NTC principle. A variable voltage signal is returned to the ECM based upon the air temperature. This signal is approximately 2.0 to 3.0 volts at an ambient temperature of 20°C and reduces to about 1.5 volt as the temperature rises to around 40°C.

CO adjustment

The CO value at idle speeds can only be adjusted through the medium of a FCR attached to the serial port. It is not possible to make this adjustment by any other means. On catalyst-equipped models, the CO is non-adjustable.

Coolant temperature sensor (CTS)

The CTS is incorporated in the cooling system, and operates on the NTC principle. As the resistance of the CTS varies, this returns a variable voltage signal to the ECM based upon the coolant temperature. The signal is approximately 2.0 to 3.0 volts at an ambient temperature of 20°C, and reduces to between 0.5 to 1.0 volt at a normal operating temperature of 80 to 100°C.

The open-circuit supply to the sensor is at a 5.0-volt reference level, and the earth path is through the sensor return. The ECM uses the CTS signal as a main correction factor when calculating ignition timing and injection duration.

Throttle potentiometer sensor (TPS)

A TPS is provided to inform the ECM of rate of acceleration and throttle position. During engine idle, acceleration, deceleration and full-load engine conditions, the ECM uses the throttle position to modify the basic fuel map. If the MAP sensor becomes faulty, the TPS signal is used as a basis for engine load calculation.

The TPS is a potentiometer with three wires. A 5.0-volt reference voltage is supplied to a resistance track with the other end connected to earth. The third wire is connected to an arm which wipes along the resistance track, and so varies the resistance and voltage of the signal returned to the ECM.

Idle speed control valve (ISCV) - G5 and some G6 systems

The ISCV is a solenoid-controlled actuator that the ECM uses to automatically control idle speed during normal idle and during engine warm-up. The ISCV is located in a hose that connects the inlet manifold to the air filter side of the throttle plate **(see illustration 10.3)**.

When an electrical load, such as headlights or heater fan etc are switched on, the idle

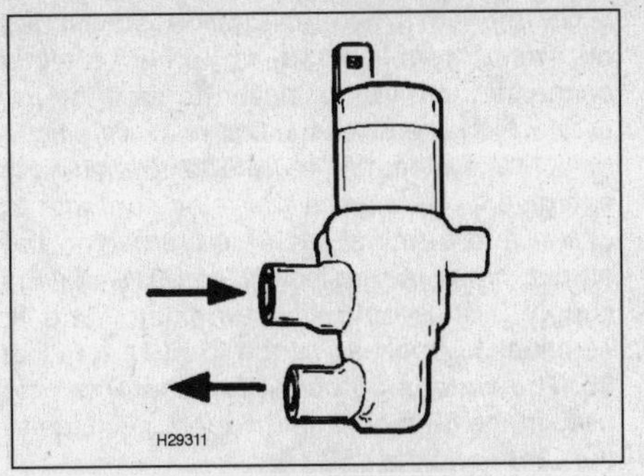

10.3 Typical ISCV

speed would tend to drop. The ECM will sense the load, and rotate the ISCV against spring tension to increase the airflow through the valve, and thus increase the idle speed. When the load is removed, the ECM will pulse the valve so that the airflow is reduced. Normal idle speed should be maintained under all cold and hot operating conditions. If the ISCV fails, it will fail-safe, with the aperture almost closed. This will provide a basic idle speed.

During engine deceleration, the ISCV acts like a dashpot and performs a controlled return to idle speed, so that emissions are reduced during this period.

Stepper motor (some G6 and 8P systems)

The air valve stepper motor is an actuator that the ECM uses to automatically control idle speed during normal idle and during engine warm-up. When the throttle is closed, the throttle plate is locked in a position where very little air passes by. The throttle position then, will have no effect upon the idle speed.

A by-pass port to the throttle plate is located in the throttle body. A valve is positioned in the port. As the valve moves, the volume of air passing through the port will vary, and this directly affects the idle speed. The idle speed then, depends upon the position of the stepper air valve in the by-pass port.

The stepper motor is controlled by the ECM through two motor windings. The circuits for each winding both originate and terminate at the ECM. By pulsing these windings, the ECM is able to position the air valve exactly, in its task to control the idle speed. Each pulse from the ECM causes the stepper motor to rotate by one step (ie 1/10th of a turn or 0.04 mm).

When an electrical load, such as headlights or heater fan etc are switched on, the idle speed would tend to drop. In this event, the ECM opens the stepper motor valve to maintain the previous idle speed.

During periods of cold running, the stepper motor will regulate the valve position so that the engine speed will be set to a suitable fast idle.

On switching off the engine, power remains applied to the stepper motor for 4 to 5 seconds,

10.4 Throttle body heater

so that the ECM can actuate the air valve to its fully closed position (thus preventing engine run-on). After a few seconds, the ECM actuates the air valve to a slightly open position, ready for the next engine start.

At engine speeds above idle, the stepper motor will position the air valve to completely shut off the air supply. During engine deceleration, the stepper motor will open the by-pass to allow additional air into the inlet manifold. This aids the reduction of excessive CO and HC emissions during deceleration.

Throttle body heater

This heater is provided to warm the throttle body so that icing does not occur during cold and humid atmospheric conditions. The heater is operating at all times whilst the engine is running. The heater works on the PTC principle and allows a greater current to quickly heat throttle body during the warm-up period. As the heater becomes hotter, the resistance increases and the current reduces **(see illustration 10.4)**.

Relays

The MM electrical system utilises either separate main and fuel pump relays, or a single 15-pin relay with dual contacts. Both types are described as follows **(see illustration 10.5)**.

Main and fuel pump relays (separate relays)

The MM electrical system is controlled by a main relay and a fuel pump relay. A permanent voltage supply is made to the main relay terminal 3 and the fuel pump relay terminal 3 from the battery positive terminal.

When the ignition is switched on, a voltage supply is made to main relay terminal 1 and fuel pump relay terminal 1 from ignition switch terminal 15. The ECM earths main relay terminal 2 through ECM pin number 5, which energises the relay winding. This causes the

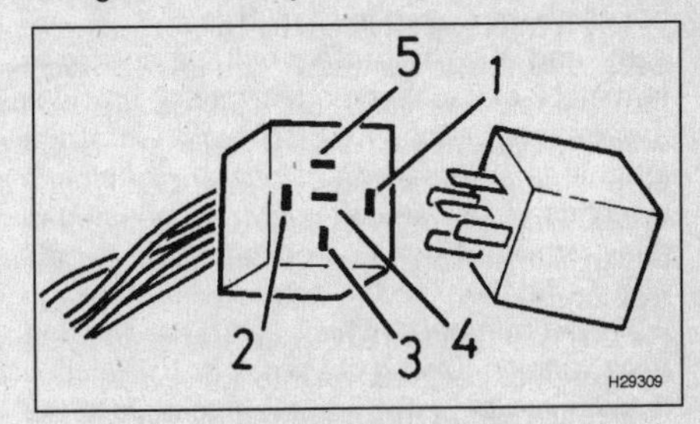

10.5 Relay block (4 to 5 pin relay)

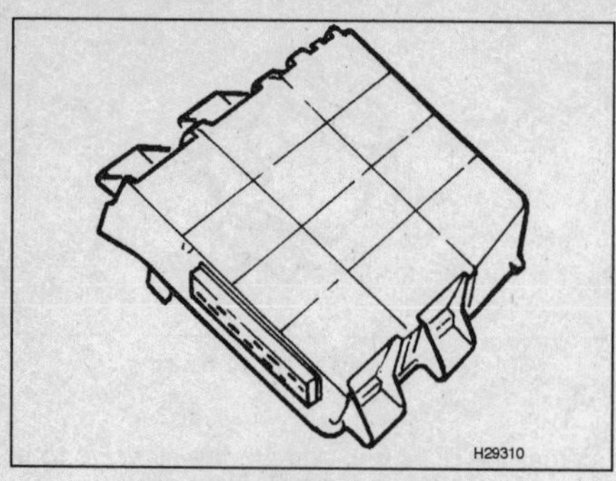

10.6 ECM (Magneti Marelli)

main relay contacts to close, and relay terminal 3 is connected to the output circuit at terminal 5. A voltage supply is thus output at terminal 5. Terminal 5 applies voltage to ECM terminal 35.

When the ignition is switched on, a voltage supply is made to fuel pump relay terminal 1, and the ECM briefly earths relay contact 2, which energises the fuel pump relay winding. This causes the fuel pump relay contacts to close, and connects voltage from relay terminal 3 to terminal 5. Voltage is thereby output to the fuel pump circuit. After approximately one second, the ECM opens the circuit and the pump stops. This brief running of the fuel pump allows pressure to build within the fuel pressure lines, and provides for an easier start.

The fuel pump circuit will then remain open until the engine is cranked or run. Once the ECM receives a speed signal from the CAS, the fuel pump winding will again be energised by the ECM, and the fuel pump will run until the engine is stopped **(see illustration 10.6)**.

Terminal 5 of the pump relay also provides voltage to the ignition coil, ISCV, OS, CFSV and the single injector. Voltage will only be available at any of these components whilst the engine is being cranked or is running. In addition, during engine cranking or running, the ECM will actuate all of these components in accordance with its internal program.

Main and fuel pump relays (single 'dual' relay)

In later G5 and G6 models and all 8P and 8Fmodels, the electrical system is controlled by a single 15-terminal relay with dual contacts. A permanent voltage supply is made to relay terminals 2, 3, 8, 11 and 15 from the battery positive terminal, although not all pins are used in all models.

8P and 8F: The battery voltage supply to terminal 2 or 3 (depending on model) provides a permanent supply to ECM pin 4 whilst the ignition is switched off. When the ignition is switched on, a voltage supply is connected to relay terminal 14 or 12 (depending on model). The ECM then earths terminal 10 through ECM pin number 4 which energises the first relay winding. During the time that the ignition is switched on, pin 35 applies voltage to the ECM.

G5 and G6: When the ignition is switched on, relay terminal 10 is either directly connected to earth, or driven to earth by the ECM which energises the first relay winding.

All MM systems: When the relay winding is energised, this causes the relay contacts to close, and terminal 11 is connected to the output circuit at terminals 1 and 9. A voltage supply is thus output at terminal 1 and 9. Terminal 1 supplies voltage to ECM terminal 35. The voltage output at terminal 9 is only used in the 8P model, and supplies voltage to the CFSV and the VSS.

When the ignition is switched on, the ECM briefly earths relay contact 7 at an ECM pin. This energises the second relay winding, which closes the second relay contact, and connects voltage from terminal 8 to terminal 13, thereby providing voltage to the fuel pump circuit. After approximately one second, the ECM opens the circuit and the pump stops. This brief running of the fuel pump allows pressure to build within the fuel pressure lines, and provides for an easier start. In addition, voltage is applied to the ignition coils, injectors and where fitted, ISCV, throttle body heater and the OS heater, via relay output terminals 4, 5 and 6.

The second circuit will then remain open until the engine is cranked or run. Once the ECM receives a speed signal from the CAS, the second winding will again be energised by the ECM, and the fuel pump, ignition and injection will run until the engine is stopped.

Fuel pressure system

Switching on the ignition causes the ECM to energise the fuel pump relay for approximately one second so that the fuel system is pressurised. The fuel pump relay is then switched off, to await a cranking or running signal. Once the engine is running, fuel is fed through a non-return valve and fuel filter to the MPi fuel rail, or to the single throttle body injector.

To prevent pressure loss in the supply system, a non-return valve is provided in the fuel pump outlet. When the ignition is switched off, and the fuel pump ceases operation, pressure is thus maintained for some time.

The fuel pump may be mounted externally or internally, and both types are described as follows.

External pump (where used)

A roller type fuel pump, driven by a permanent magnet electric motor mounted close to the fuel tank draws fuel from the tank, and pumps it to the fuel rail or the single fuel injector via a fuel filter. The pump is of the 'wet' variety, in that fuel actually flows through the pump and the electric motor. There is no actual fire risk, because the fuel drawn through the pump is not in a combustible condition.

Mounted upon the armature shaft is an eccentric rotor holding a number of pockets arranged around the circumference - each pocket containing a metal roller. As the pump is actuated, the rollers are flung outwards by centrifugal force to act as seals. The fuel between the rollers is forced to the pump pressure outlet.

Internal pump (Citroën)

The two-stage fuel pump is mounted horizontally on the floor of the fuel tank. The fuel pump first stage comprises a turbine which supplies fuel to the high-pressure gear-driven second stage. Fuel is drawn through the pump inlet, to be pressurised and discharged from the pump outlet into the fuel supply line.

Internal pump (Fiat and Peugeot)

The fuel pump is mounted vertically in the fuel tank, and comprises an outer and inner gear assembly, termed a 'gerotor'. Once the pump motor becomes energised, the gerotor rotates, and as the fuel passes through the individual teeth of the gerotor, a pressure differential is created. Fuel is drawn through the pump inlet, to be pressurised between the rotating gerotor teeth and discharged from the pump outlet into the fuel supply line.

Fuel pressure regulator (MPi)

Fuel pressure in the fuel rail is maintained at a constant 2.5 bar by a fuel pressure regulator. The fuel pump normally provides much more fuel than is required, and surplus fuel is thus returned to the fuel tank via a return pipe. Re-circulation of the fuel helps to keep it cool. In fact, a maximum fuel pressure in excess of 5 bar is possible in this system. To prevent pressure loss in the supply system, a non-return valve is provided in the fuel pump outlet. When the ignition is switched off, and the fuel pump ceases operation, pressure is thus maintained for some time.

The pressure regulator is fitted on the outlet side of the fuel rail, and maintains an even pressure of 2.5 bar in the fuel rail. The pressure regulator consists of two chambers separated by a diaphragm. The upper chamber contains a spring, which exerts pressure upon the lower chamber and closes off the outlet diaphragm. Pressurised fuel flows into the lower chamber, and this exerts pressure upon the diaphragm. Once the pressure exceeds 2.5 bar, the outlet diaphragm is opened, and excess fuel flows back to the fuel tank via a return line.

A vacuum hose connects the upper chamber to the inlet manifold, so that variations in inlet manifold pressure will not affect the amount of fuel injected. This means that the pressure in the rail is always at a constant pressure above the pressure in the inlet manifold. The quantity of injected fuel thus depends solely on injector opening time, as determined by the ECM, and not on a variable fuel pressure.

At idle speed with the vacuum pipe disconnected, with the engine stopped and the pump running, or at full-throttle, the system fuel pressure will be approximately 2.5 bar. At idle speed (vacuum pipe connected), the fuel pressure will be approximately 0.5 bar under the system pressure.

Fuel pressure regulator (SPi)

Fuel pressure of approximately one bar is controlled by the pressure regulator, which is located within the throttle body next to the injector. As the pressure rises over the pre-determined level, excess fuel is returned to the fuel tank via a return pipe. To prevent pressure loss in the supply system, a non-return valve is provided in the fuel pump outlet. When the ignition is switched off, and the fuel pump ceases operation, pressure is thus maintained for some time.

6 Catalytic converter and emission control

Catalytic converter

The MM injection system fitted to catalyst vehicles implements a closed-loop control system, so that exhaust emissions may be reduced. Closed-loop systems are equipped with an oxygen sensor which monitors the exhaust gas for oxygen content. A low oxygen level in the exhaust signifies a rich mixture. A high oxygen level in the exhaust signifies a weak mixture.

When the engine is operating in closed-loop control, the OS signal causes the ECM to modify the injector pulse so that the AFR is maintained close to the stoichiometric ratio. By controlling the injection pulse during most operating conditions, so that the air/fuel ratio is always in a small window around the Lambda point (ie Lambda = 0.97 to 1.03), almost perfect combustion could be achieved. Thus the catalyst has less work to do, and will last longer, with fewer emissions at the tail pipe.

10.7 Carbon canister on Peugeot 205

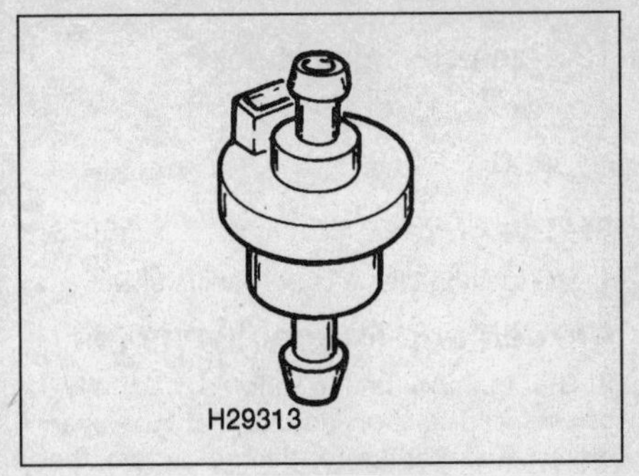

10.8 Typical CFSV

The closed-loop control is implemented during engine operation at coolant temperatures above 45°C. When the coolant temperatures is below 45°C, or the engine is at full load, or is on the overrun, the ECM will operate in open-loop. When operating in open-loop, the ECM allows a richer or leaner AFR than the stoichiometric ratio. This prevents engine hesitation, for example, during acceleration with a wide-open throttle.

The OS only produces a signal when the exhaust gas has reached a minimum temperature of approximately 300°C. In order that the OS will reach optimum operating temperature as quickly as possible after the engine has started, the OS contains a heating element.

The OS heater supply is made from fuel pump relay terminal number 5. This ensures that the heater will only operate whilst the engine is running.

Carbon filter solenoid valve (CFSV)

A CFSV and activated carbon canister is employed in catalyst-equipped vehicles, to aid evaporative emission control. The carbon canister stores fuel vapours until the CFSV is opened by the ECM under certain operating conditions **(see illustrations 10.7 and 10.8)**.

When the engine is stopped, the CFSV is open. As soon as the ignition is switched 'on', the CFSV closes until the engine reaches normal operating temperature and the throttle is partially open (normal cruise conditions with a hot engine). Once the CFSV is actuated by the ECM, fuel vapours are drawn into the inlet manifold, to be burnt by the engine during normal combustion.

So that engine performance will not be affected, the CFSV remains closed during cold engine operation and also during engine idle. Once the engine coolant reaches normal operating temperature and the throttle position is in the mid range (between 11° and 89°) the CFSV will be modulated on and off by the ECM with a duty cycle of 54%.

An additional CFSV is utilised in the XU5M3Z engine fitted to the Citroën ZX. When the engine is stopped, this valve is normally closed. Once the engine has started, the valve opens and remains open until the ignition is switched off and the engine is stopped.

After the engine is switched off, the relay maintains power to the CFSV for 4 to 5 seconds so that the valve will remain closed during engine shut-down. This should ensure that the engine does not run-on during this period.

Adjustments

7 Adjustment pre-conditions

1 Ensure that all of these conditions are met before attempting to make adjustments:

a) Engine at operating temperature. Engine oil at a minimum temperature of 80°C; a journey of at least 4 miles is recommended (particularly so if equipped with AT).
b) Ancillary equipment (all engine loads and accessories) switched off.
c) AT vehicles: Transmission in N or P.
d) Engine mechanically sound.
e) Engine breather hoses and breather system in satisfactory condition.
f) Induction system free from vacuum leaks.
g) Ignition system in satisfactory condition.
h) Air filter in satisfactory condition.
i) Exhaust system free from leaks.
j) Throttle cable correctly adjusted.
k) No fault codes logged by the ECM.
l) OS operating satisfactorily (catalyst vehicles with closed-loop control).

2 In addition, before checking the idle speed and CO values, stabilise the engine as follows:

a) Stabilise the engine. Raise the engine speed to 3000 rpm for a minimum of 30 seconds, and then let the engine idle.
b) If the cooling fan operates during adjustment, wait until it stops, re-stabilise the engine and then restart the adjustment procedure.
c) Allow the CO and idle speed to settle.
d) Make all checks and adjustments within 30 seconds. If this time is exceeded, re-stabilise the engine and recheck.

8 Throttle adjustments

Throttle valve position and TPS

1 Clean the throttle valve and surrounding areas with carburettor cleaner. Blow-by from the breather system often causes sticking problems here.

2 The throttle valve position is critical, and must not be disturbed.

3 The TPS in not adjustable for this range of engines.

9 Ignition timing checks

Fiat vehicles

1 The ignition timing is non-adjustable.

Citroën and Peugeot vehicles

2 The ignition timing should normally be considered as non-adjustable. However, if adverse operating conditions dictate that a change is necessary, the timing advance curve can be altered with the aid of the FCR. Timing retardation must be performed as a last resort, and all other reasons for poor engine performance must first be investigated.

3 Conditions where timing retardation may be necessary:-

a) Engine knock under part- or full-load conditions.
b) Use of poor-quality unleaded fuel.
c) Use of RON 91 unleaded fuel. In this instance, reduce the advance by three steps (6°).
d) Timing advance adjustment will affect the ignition timing at 3/4 load, during vehicle cruising and under acceleration conditions.

10 Idle adjustments

1 The CO value should normally be considered as non-adjustable. However, if operating conditions dictate that a change is necessary, the CO value (non-cat vehicles only) can be altered with the aid of a FCR. CO adjustment must be performed as a last resort, and all other reasons for an incorrect fuel mixture must first be investigated.

2 The idle speed is not adjustable. However, the idling speed can be re-initialised as follows (models with stepper motor only).

Initialising idle speed

3 Switch on the ignition.

4 Wait 10 seconds and then start the engine. The ECM will automatically re-initialise the idle speed. **Note:** *The idle speed should be re-initialised after the battery or ECM have been disconnected, or after the TPS or stepper motor have been renewed.*

System sensor and actuator tests

Important note: *Please refer to Chapter 4, which describes common test procedures applicable to this system. The routines in Chapter 4 should be read in conjunction with the component notes and wiring diagrams presented in this Chapter. The wiring diagrams and other data presented in this Chapter are necessarily representative of the system depicted. Because of the variations in wiring and other data that often occurs, even between similar vehicles in any particular VM's range, the reader should take great care in identification of ECM pins, and satisfy himself that he has gathered the correct data before failing a particular component.*

11 Crank angle sensor (CAS)

1 Refer to the note at the start of this Section, and refer to the relevant Section of Chapter 4.

2 Citroën/Peugeot vehicles: CAS resistance is between 300 and 500 ohms. Fiat vehicles: CAS resistance is between 612 and 748 ohms.

12 Primary ignition

1 Refer to the note at the start of Section 10, and refer to the relevant Section of Chapter 4 **(see illustrations 10.9 and 10.10)**.

2 When testing the ignition circuit for a primary signal, the routines described in 'Primary signal not available (amplifier inside the ECM)' are generally the most suitable.

3 ECM and component pin numbers may vary depending upon the Magneti-Marelli system under test.

4 A supply to the ignition coil(s) is applied from the fuel pump relay, and voltage is only available with the engine cranking or running. However, voltage could be applied for test purposes by by-passing the relay (see Chapter 4).

5 Where the ignition is DIS, test both coils in a similar fashion.

6 Citroën/Peugeot vehicles: Primary resistance is 0.80 ohms. Secondary resistance is 8600 ohms.

7 Fiat vehicles: Primary resistance is 0.495 to 0.605 ohms. Secondary resistance is 6660 to 8140 ohms.

13 Knock sensor (KS)

1 Refer to the note at the start of Section 10, and refer to the relevant Section of Chapter 4.

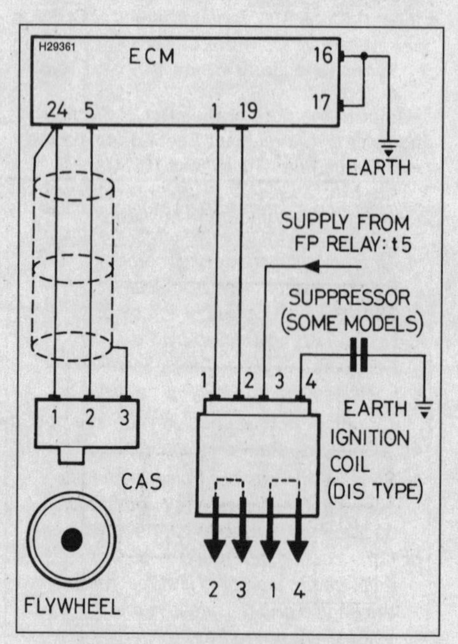

10.9 Typical G5, G6 ignition wiring

14 Fuel injector operation (MPi)

1 Refer to the note at the start of Section 10, and refer to the relevant Section of Chapter 4 **(see illustrations 10.11 and 10.12)**.

2 Voltage to the injectors is provided from the single system relay, and this means that a supply is only available whilst the engine is cranking or running. However, voltage could be applied for test purposes by by-passing the relay (see Chapter 4).

3 The injector resistance is normally 16.2 ohms (Fiat), or 13 to 17 ohms (Citroën & Peugeot 8P).

10.10 Typical 8P, 8F ignition wiring

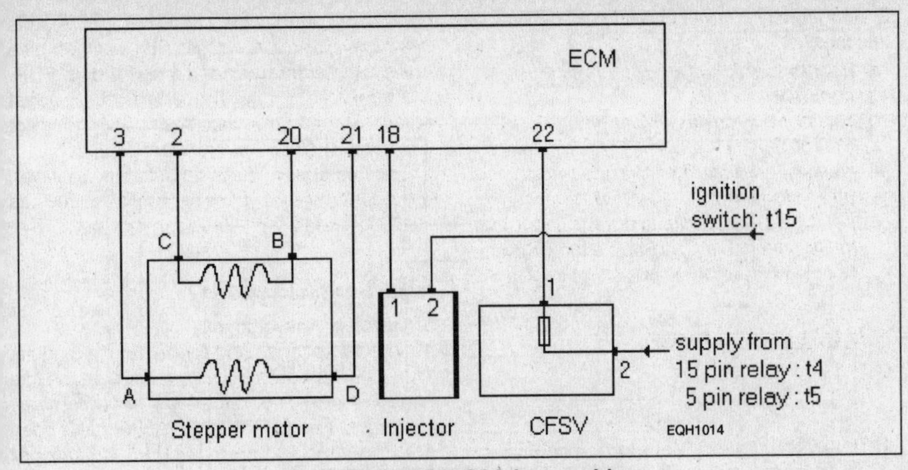

10.11 Typical G5, G6 injector wiring

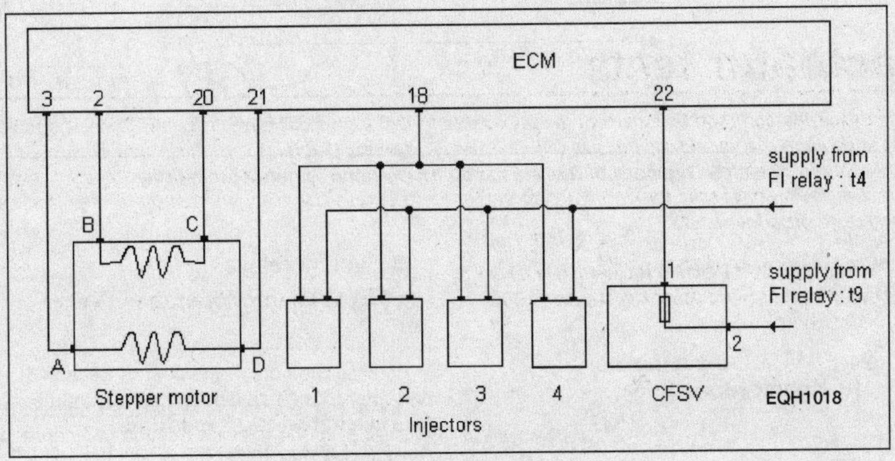

10.12 Typical 8P, 8F injector wiring

15 Fuel injector operation (SPi)

1 Refer to the note at the start of Section 10, and refer to the relevant Section of Chapter 4.
2 Voltage to the injectors is provided from the single system relay, and this means that a supply is only available whilst the engine is cranking or running. However, voltage could be applied for test purposes by by-passing the relay (see chapter 4).
3 The injector resistance is normally 1.4 to 1.6 ohms.
4 The SPi system is current-controlled; under certain operating conditions, the pulse will change to asynchronous operation. **Note:** *In asynchronous mode, the injection pulse is no longer synchronised with the ignition. To measure the asynchronous pulse properly, an oscilloscope with a variable timebase function is required.*

16 MAP sensor

1 Refer to the note at the start of Section 10, and refer to the relevant Section of Chapter 4 **(see illustrations 10.13 and 10.14).**
2 The MAP sensor is a separate sensor located in the engine compartment.

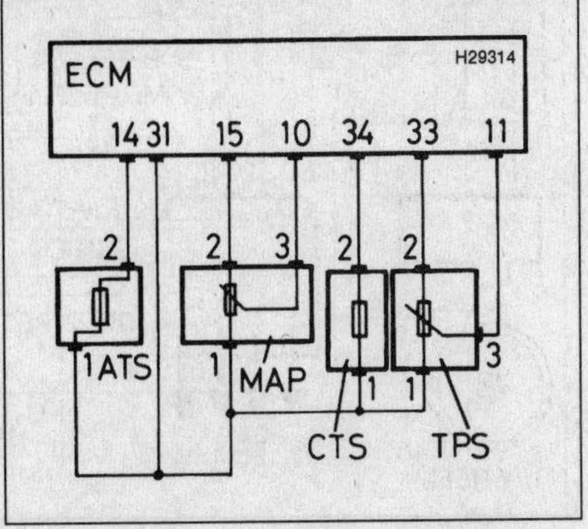

10.13 Typical G5, G6 sensor wiring

17 Air temperature sensor (ATS)

1 Refer to the note at the start of Section 10, and refer to the relevant Section of Chapter 4.
2 The ATS may be located in the inlet manifold or on the throttle body.

18 Coolant temperature sensor (CTS)

1 Refer to the note at the start of Section 10, and refer to the relevant Section of Chapter 4.

19 Throttle potentiometer sensor (TPS)

1 Refer to the note at the start of Section 10, and refer to the relevant Section of Chapter 4.

20 Vehicle speed sensor (VSS)

1 Refer to the note at the start of Section 10, and refer to the relevant Section of Chapter 4.

21 Idle speed control valve (ISCV)

1 Refer to the note at the start of Section 10, and refer to the relevant Section of Chapter 4.
2 The ISCV resistance is 6.5 to 8.0 ohms.
3 The ISCV is an example of a two-wire valve.
4 Voltage to the ISCV is provided from the system relay, and this means that a supply is only available whilst the engine is cranking or running. However, voltage could be applied for test purposes by by-passing the relay (see Chapter 4).

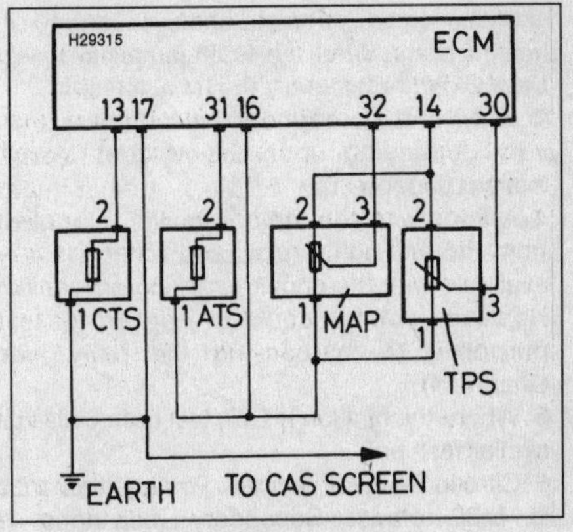

10.14 Typical 8P, 8F sensor wiring

22 Stepper motor

1 Warm the engine to normal operating temperature.
2 Start the engine and allow it to idle.
3 Check that the idle speed is within its operating limits.
4 Load the system by switching on the headlights, rear screen heater and heater fan; the idle speed should barely change. **Note:** *If this operation is completed satisfactorily, it is probable that the stepper motor condition is also satisfactory.*
5 Inspect the stepper motor multi-plug for corrosion and damage.
6 Check that the connector terminal pins are fully pushed home and making good contact with the stepper motor multi-plug.

Stepper motor tests

7 Remove the stepper motor from the inlet manifold.
8 Check that the air passage in the inlet manifold is clear. Clean the passage as necessary.
9 Ensure that the shaft and cone will freely rotate in the motor armature.
10 Refit the stepper motor to the inlet manifold.
11 Detach the stepper motor multi-plug.
12 Measure the resistance of motor windings A to D and B to C. The resistance should be approximately 53 ohms.
13 Reconnect all of the multi-plugs.
14 Connect the voltmeter negative probe to an engine earth.
15 Connect the voltmeter positive probe to the wire attached to stepper motor signal terminal 'A'.
16 Allow the engine to idle.
17 Switch on and off a number of high electrical load components, eg heated rear window, headlights main beam and the heater fan on maximum. The voltage should occasionally switch from zero to nbv as the motor winding is energised.
18 Repeat the test at stepper motor signal terminals B, C and D.
19 If the signal is absent, check continuity of the wiring between the ECM multi-plug and the stepper motor.
20 If the stepper motor wiring is satisfactory, check all voltage supplies and earth connections to the ECM. If the voltage supplies and earth connections are satisfactory, the ECM is suspect.

23 Throttle body heater (TBH)

1 Refer to the note at the start of Section 10; and refer to the relevant Section of Chapter 4.
2 Voltage to the TBH is provided from the single system relay, and this means that a supply is only available whilst the engine is running.

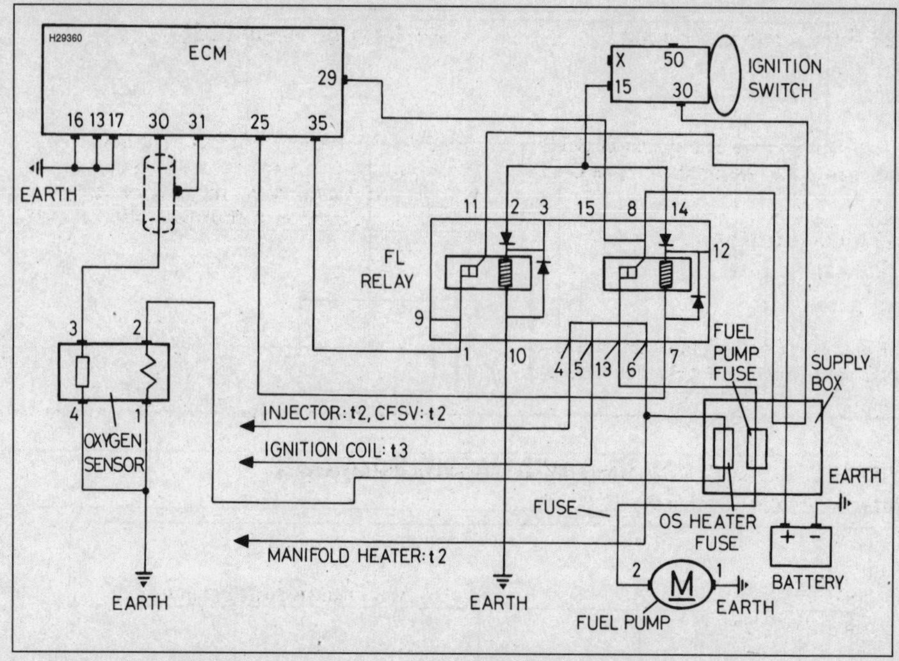

10.15 Typical G5, G6 relay and components wiring (15-pin relay)

24 ECM voltage supplies and earths

1 Refer to the note at the start of Section 10, and refer to the relevant Section of Chapter 4.

25 System relays

1 Refer to the note at the start of Section 10, and refer to the relevant Section of Chapter 4 **(see illustration 10.15 and 10.16).**
2 The Magneti-Marelli system utilises either separate main and pump relays, or a single 15-pin system relay.

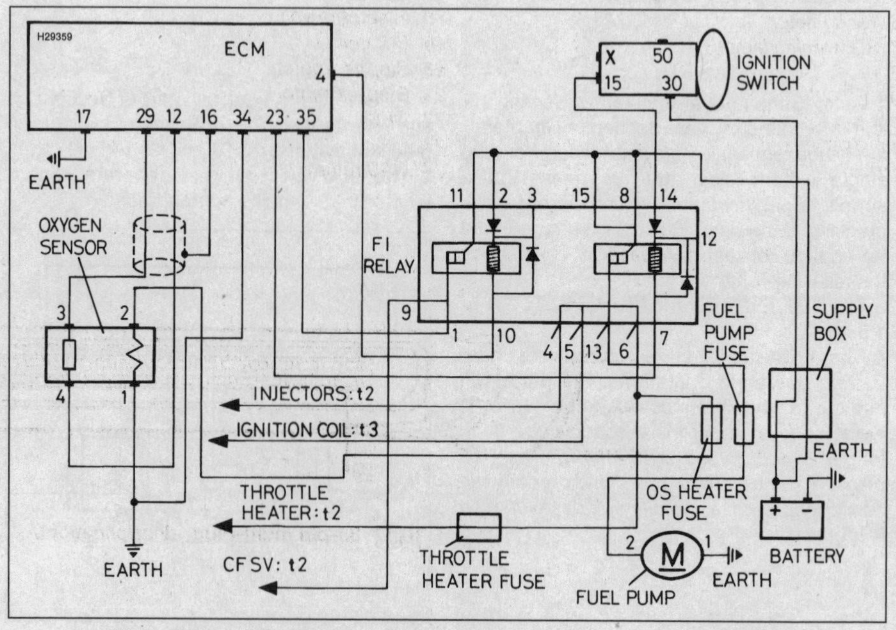

10.16 Typical 8P, 8F relay and components wiring - 4 to 5-pin relays)

26 Fuel pump and circuit

1 Refer to the note at the start of Section 10, and refer to the relevant Section of Chapter 4.

27 Fuel pressure

1 Refer to the note at the start of Section 10, and refer to the relevant Section of Chapter 4.

28 Oxygen sensor (OS)

1 Refer to the note at the start of Section 10, and refer to the relevant Section of Chapter 4.
2 The OS found in the majority of Magneti-Marelli systems is a four-wire sensor with heater.

29 Carbon filter solenoid valve (CFSV)

1 Refer to the note at the start of Section 10, and refer to the relevant Section of Chapter 4.
2 Voltage to the CFSV is provided from the system relay, and this means that a supply is only available whilst the engine is cranking or running. However, voltage could be applied for test purposes by by-passing the relay (see Chapter 4).

Pin table - typical 35-pin (MM G5, Peugeot)

Note: *Refer to* ***illustration 10.17***

1 Coil
2 ISCV
3 Tachometer
4 Diagnostic socket
5 Main relay driver
6 A/C compressor relay
7 TPS supply
8 -
9 MAP supply
10 -
11 Sensor return CTS, TPS
12 Sensor return ATS, MAP
13 OS signal return
14 CAS signal
15 Park - neutral switch (auto)
16 Earth
17 Earth
18 Injector driver
19 Ignition coil
20 CFSV
21 FP relay driver
22 SD warning lamp
23 -
24 CTS signal
25 TPS signal
26 ATS signal
27 MAP signal
28 Diagnostic socket
29 Battery supply
30 OS signal
31 CAS return
32 Air conditioning switch
33 Air conditioning switch
34 -
35 Nbv supply from main relay

Pin table - typical 35-pin (MM G6, Citroën/Peugeot)

Note: *Refer to* ***illustration 10.17***

1 DIS coil
2 Stepper motor
3 Stepper motor
4 Diagnostic socket
5 CAS signal
6 Tachometer
7 SD warning lamp
8 -
9 -
10 MAP signal
11 TPS signal
12 -
13 Earth, OS signal
14 ATS signal
15 MAP supply
16 Earth
17 Earth
18 Injector driver
19 DIS coil
20 Stepper motor
21 Stepper motor
22 CFSV
23 -
24 CAS return
25 FI relay driver
26 -
27 -
28 Diagnostic socket
29 Battery supply
30 OS signal
31 Sensor return TPS, ATS, CTS, MAP
32 -
33 TPS supply
34 CTS signal
35 Nbv supply from FI relay

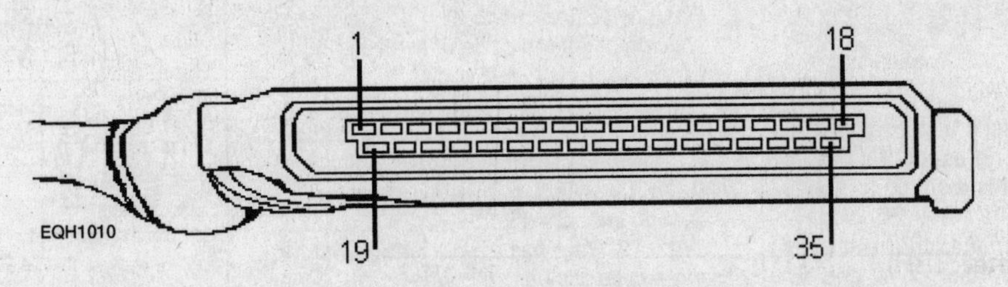

10.17 35-pin multi-plug, all applications

Pin table - typical 35-pin (MM 8F, Fiat)

Note:** Refer to **illustration 10.17

1 DIS coil
2 Stepper motor
3 Stepper motor
4 diagnostic socket
5 CAS signal
6 Tachometer
7 SD warning lamp
8 -
9 -
10 MAP signal
11 TPS signal
12 -
13 Earth, OS signal
14 ATS signal
15 MAP supply
16 Earth
17 Earth
18 Injector driver
19 DIS coil
20 Stepper motor
21 Stepper motor
22 CFSV
23 -
24 CAS return
25 FI relay driver
26 -
27 -
28 Diagnostic socket
29 Battery supply
30 OS signal
31 Sensor return TPS, ATS, CTS, MAP
32 -
33 TPS supply
34 CTS signal
35 Nbv supply from FI relay

Pin table - typical 35-pin (MM 8P, Citroën/Peugeot)

Note:** Refer to **illustration 10.17

1 Ignition coil
2 Stepper motor
3 Stepper motor
4 Main relay driver
5 -
6 SD warning lamp
7 -
8 A/C
9 A/C
10 Diagnostic socket
11 CAS return
12 OS signal return
13 CTS signal
14 Sensor supply, TPS
15 Diagnostic socket
16 Sensor return (TPS, MAP, ATS)
17 Earth
18 Injector driver
19 Ignition coil
20 Stepper motor
21 Stepper motor
22 CFSV
23 FI relay driver
24 A/C
25 -
26 -
27 VSS signal
28 CAS signal
29 OS signal
30 TPS signal
31 ATS signal
32 MAP signal
33 -
34 Earth
35 Nbv supply from main relay

Fault codes

30 Obtaining fault codes

Citroën and Peugeot vehicles

1 If a FCR is available, it could be attached to the SD serial connector and used for the following purposes:

a) Obtaining fault codes.
b) Clearing fault codes.
c) Obtaining Datastream information.
d) Actuating the system actuators: This may include one or more of the actuators on the following list:
Fuel injectors
ISCV
CFSV (where fitted)

2 If a FCR is not available, it is still possible to obtain fault codes, so long as the SD plug is of the 2-pin type. A FCR is required for those systems equipped with the 16-pin SD plug.

3 When the ECM determines that a fault is present, it internally logs a fault code, and will also light the diagnostic warning lamp if the fault is regarded by the system as major. Faults regarded as minor will not light the warning lamp, although a code will still be logged. All of the various two-digit fault codes in Citroën and Peugeot vehicles are of the 'slow' variety, and can be output as flash codes on the dash-mounted warning lamp. The first series of flashes indicates the number of tens, the second series of flashes indicates the single units.

Obtaining codes without a FCR

*a) Attach an on/off accessory switch between the FCR green multi-plug terminal 2 and earth **(see illustration 10.18)**.*
b) Switch on the ignition.
c) Close the switch for three seconds (the dash warning lamp will remain off).
d) Open the switch, the warning lamp will:
Flash once (indicating 10).
Pause for 1.5 seconds.
Flash twice (indicating 2).
This indicates the code of twelve (12) which is the test start code.
e) The warning lamp will extinguish.
f) Close the switch for three seconds (the dash warning lamp will remain off).
g) Open the switch, the warning lamp will flash to indicate a code.
h) Once the lamp has extinguished, wait for three seconds before continuing.
i) Close the switch for three seconds & repeat the test to obtain further codes. When code 11 is obtained, this indicates End of Test.
j) After code 11 is obtained the complete test may be repeated.
k) If code 11 is the first code obtained after code 12, no faults are logged by the ECM.

Clearing fault codes from the memory of the ECM

a) Repair all circuits indicated by the fault codes.
b) Switch on the ignition.
c) Perform the test as detailed above to reveal code 11 with no fault codes (optional).

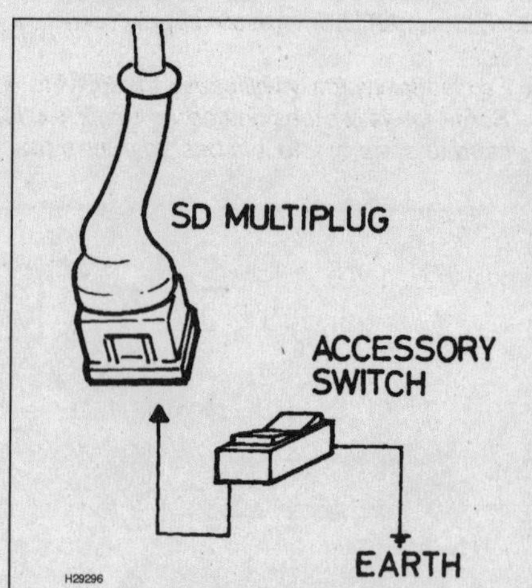

10.18 Obtaining flash codes: Citroën and Peugeot

d) Close the accessory switch for more than ten seconds.
e) The warning lamp will remain extinguished.

Checking operation of the fuel injectors and ISCV without a FCR

a) Close the accessory switch
b) Switch the ignition on.
c) Wait 3 seconds.
d) After a moment the fuel injectors will function. This can be determined by vibration and the sound of the injectors clicking.

Warning: Avoid the injection of excess fuel into the cylinders by completing the test quickly.

e) If the injectors fail to operate, refer to the fuel injector tests.
f) Continue with the next test to check the ISCV.
g) Close the accessory switch for three seconds once more.
h) After a moment the ISCV will function and vibrate to the touch.
i) If the ISCV fails to operate, refer to the ISCV tests.

Fiat vehicles

5 If a FCR is available it could be attached to the SD serial connector and used for the following purposes:

a) Obtaining fault codes.
b) Clearing fault codes.
c) Obtaining Datastream information.
d) Actuating the system actuators: This may include one or more of the actuators on the following list:
Fuel injectors
ISCV
CFSV (where fitted)

6 The Magneti-Marelli 8F system fitted to Fiat vehicles requires a dedicated FCR to access fault codes. Flash codes are not available for output from this system. For the sake of completeness, we have provided a list of components that will provide errors for readout upon a FCR.

Fault code table (MM G5, G6, 8P - Citroën/Peugeot)

Code	Item
11	End of diagnosis
12	Initiation of diagnosis
13x	ATS
14x	CTS
15	Fuel pump control
21x	TPS
22	Stepper motor or ISCV
23	ISCV
27x	VSS
31x	Lambda control
33x	MAP
34	CFSV
41	CAS
42	Injector control
44x	KS
45	Ignition coil control (coil one)
52	Lambda control
53x	Battery voltage
54	ECM
57	Ignition coil (coil two)
Actuator selection code	
91	Fuel pump or fuel pump relay
92	Injector
93	ISCV
94	CFSV
95	A/C compressor supply relay

x Faults that typically will cause the ECM to enter LOS, and use a default value in place of the sensor.
Some faults are designated as major faults, and will light the warning lamp. However, major faults that will light the warning lamp vary from system to system, and it is best to interrogate the ECM for codes if a fault is suspected.

Fault conditions (MM 8F - Fiat)

Code	Item	Fault
-	CAS	Loss of signal
-	TPS	
-	MAP	No correlation between MAP signal and the TPS & CAS signals
-	ATS	
-	CTS	
-	Voltage	Voltage less than 6.2 volts or greater than 15.5 volts
-	Lambda control	
-	Injector control	
-	Ignition coils control	
-	Stepper motor	
-	CFSV	
-	Relay control	
-	ECM	Memories
-	Adaptive	Limits of adaptive control reached - suggests a serious engine (mechanical) condition

Note: *Fault conditions, not fault codes, are logged in the MM 8F system, and a FCR is required to read the fault conditions.*

Chapter 11
Mazda EGI

Contents

Specifications

Vehicle	Year	Idle speed	CO%
3231.3i cat B3	1991 to 1995	850 ± 50	0.3 maximum
323 1.3i B3	1994 to 1997	850 ± 50	0.3 maximum
323 1.5i Z5	1994 to 1997	700 ± 50	0.5 ± 0.5
323 1600i B6	1985 to 1989	1000 ± 50	0.3 maximum
323 1.6i Turbo 4x4 B6	1986 to 1989	850 ± 50	0.3 maximum
323 1.6i cat B6	1991 to 1994	750 ± 50	0.3 maximum
323 1.6i Estate cat B6E	1991 to 1994	850 ± 50	0.3 maximum
323 1.8 GTi BP	1989 to 1991	850 ± 50	0.3 maximum
323 1.8 cat BP	1991 to 1994	800 ± 100	N/A
323 1.8i BP	1994 to 1997	750 ± 50	0.3 maximum
323 2.0 V6 KF	1994 to 1995	800 ± 50	0.3 maximum
323 2.0i KF	1996 to 1997	800 ± 50	0.3 maximum
626 1.8i cat FP	1991 to 1997	725 ± 50	0.3 maximum
626 2000i fwd FE	1985 to 1987		
626 2.0i GT FE	1987 to 1990	750 ± 50	1.5 ± 0.5
626 2.0i FE	1990 to 1993	825 ± 25	2.0 ± 0.5
626 2.0i cat FE	1990 to 1995	750 ± 50	1.5 ± 0.5
626 2.0i cat FS	1991 to 1997	700 ± 50	0.3 maximum
626 2.2i 4x4 cat F2	1990 to 1993	750 ± 25	0.5 maximum
626 2.5i V6 cat KL	1991 to 1997	650 ± 50	0.5 ± 0.5
MX-3 1.6i B6	1991 to 1996	700 ± 50	0.3 maximum
MX-3 1.8i V6 K8	1991 to 1996	670 ± 30	0.5 ± 0.5
MX-5 1.6i B6-ZE	1990 to 1996	850 ± 50	0.3 maximum
MX-5 1.8i BP	1994 to 1997	850 ± 50	0.5 ± 0.5
MX-6 2.5i cat KL	1992 to 1996	650 ± 50	0.5 ± 0.5
Xedos 6 1.6i B6	1994 to 1996	700 ± 50	0.3 maximum
Xedos 6 2.0i KF	1992 to 1996	670 ± 50	0.3 maximum
Xedos 9 2.0i KF	1994 to 1995	670 ± 50	0.3 maximum
Xedos 9 2.5i KL	1994 to 1996	650 ± 50	0.3 maximum
RX7 Rotary RE13B	1986 to 1990	750 ± 25	0.1 maximum
RX7 Rotary Turbo cat RE13B	1989 to 1993	750 ± 25	0.1 maximum
RX7 Rotary 2x turbo RE13B	1992 to 1996	725 ± 25	0.1 maximum

Ignition timing and primary resistance

Vehicle	Year	Idle speed	Primary resistance	Ignition timing
323 1.3i cat B3	1991 to 1995	850 ± 50	0.81 to 0.99	10 ± 1
323 1.3i B3	1994 to 1997	850 ± 50	0.81 to 0.99	10 ± 1
323 1.5i Z5	1994 to 1997	700 ± 50	0.49 to 0.73	5 ± 1
323 1.6i Turbo 4x4 B6	1986 to 1989	850 ± 50	3.1	6 ± 1
323 1.6i cat B6	1991 to 1994	750 ± 50	0.81 to 0.99	10 ± 1
323 1.6i Estate cat B6E	1991 to 1994	850 ± 50	1.04 to 1.27	2 ± 1
323 1.8 GTi BP	1989 to 1991	850 ± 50	0.81 to 0.99	10 ± 1
323 1.8 cat BP	1991 to 1994	800 ± 100	0.81 to 0.99	10 ± 1
323 1.8i BP	1994 to 1997	750 ± 50	0.49 to 0.73	10 ± 1
323 2.0 V6 KF	1994 to 1995	800 ± 50	0.49 to 0.73	10 ± 1
323 2.0i KF	1996 to 1997	800 ± 50	0.49 to 0.73	10 ± 1
626 1.8i cat FP	1991 to 1997	725 ± 50	0.64 to 0.96	12 ± 1
626 2.0i GT FE	1987 to 1990	750 ± 50	1.03 to 1.27	6 ± 1
626 2.0i FE	1990 to 1993	825 ± 25	1.03 to 1.27	6 ± 1
626 2.0i cat FE	1990 to 1995	750 ± 50	0.72 to 0.88	12 ± 1
626 2.0i cat FS	1991 to 1997	700 ± 50	0.64 to 0.96	12 ± 1
626 2.2i 4x4 cat F2	1990 to 1993	750 ± 25	0.72 to 0.88	6 ± 1
626 2.5i V6 cat KL	1991 to 1997	650 ± 50	0.49 to 0.73	10 ± 1
MX-3 1.6i B6	1991 to 1996	700 ± 50	0.49 to 0.73	10 ± 1
MX-3 1.8i V6 K8	1991 to 1996	670 ± 30	0.49 to 0.73	10 ± 1
MX-5 1.6i B6-ZE	1990 to 1996	850 ± 50	0.78 to 0.94	10 ± 1
MX-5 1.8i BP	1994 to 1997	850 ± 50	0.78 to 0.94	10 ± 1
MX-6 2.5i cat KL	1992 to 1996	650 ± 50	0.49 to 0.73	10 ± 1
Xedos 6 1.6i B6	1994 to 1996	700 ± 50	0.72 to 0.88	10 ± 1
Xedos 6 2.0i KF	1992 to 1996	670 ± 50	0.81 to 0.99	10 ± 1
Xedos 9 2.0i KF	1994 to 1995	670 ± 50	0.49 to 0.73	10 ± 1
Xedos 9 2.5i KL	1994 to 1996	650 ± 50	0.49 to 0.73	10 ± 1
RX7 RE13B	1986 to 1990	750 ± 25	0.20 to 1.0	-
RX7 Turbo cat RE13B	1989 to 1993	750 ± 25	0.20 to 1.0	-
RX7 2x turbo RE13B	1992 to 1996	725 ± 25	0.20 to 1.0	-

Overview of system operation

1 Introduction

Please read this overview of Mazda EGI operation in conjunction with Chapter Two which describes some of the functions in more detail.

In common with other vehicle manufacturers, Mazda developed their fuel injected system, EGI (Electronic Gas Injection) in the mid 1980's.

EGI has evolved into a fully integrated system that controls primary ignition, fuelling and idle speed from within the same ECM. In addition, when so equipped, EGI monitors and controls the Self Diagnostics, fuel pressure, air conditioning, coolant fans, automatic transmission and emission control including EGR and carbon canister purging. It was not always so and first versions of EGI did little more than fire the fuel injectors since the distributor was more akin to a conventional electronic system with the ignition timing controlled by mechanical and vacuum means rather than by an ignition map as in the later engines. Early engines also utilised a thermal operated AAV rather than an automatic control of idle speed.

The basic EGI system is broadly similar in all of its forms. However, there are a number of significant differences between the various vehicles and the components that are used - even when allowing for evolution.

EGI is connected to the battery, sensors and actuators by between one and four multi-plugs. The pin numbers in each multi-plug remains generally constant. However, there is some variation in which ECM pin is connected to which component. For example: In one vehicle the CTS is connected to pin 2C. In another vehicle 2C is an earth connection and the CTS is connected to pin 2D.

2 Control functions

Signal processing (description covers later models)

Basic ignition timing is stored in a map stored in the ROM part of the ECM, and engine load and speed signals determine the ignition timing. The main engine load sensor is the airflow sensor (AFS), and engine speed is determined from the crank angle sensor (CAS) signal.

Correction factors are then applied for starting, idle, deceleration and part and full-load operation. The main correction factor is engine temperature (CTS). Minor corrections to timing and AFR are made with reference to the ATS and TPS signals.

The basic AFR is also stored in a three-dimensional map, and the engine load and speed signals determine the basic injection pulse value. The AFR and the pulse duration are then corrected on reference to ATS, CTS, battery voltage and rate of throttle opening (TPS). Other controlling factors are determined by operating conditions such as cold start and warm-up, idle condition, acceleration and deceleration.

EGI accesses a different map for idle running conditions, and this map is implemented whenever the idle switch is closed and the engine speed is at idle.

Basic ECM operation (typical)

A permanent voltage supply is made from the vehicle battery to the ECM via one or more fusible links. Once the ignition is switched on, voltage is output to the EFi main relay and the ignition coil and amplifier.

The supply to the EFi main relay is directly connected to earth through an energising coil, and once the relay energises, a voltage is output to the ECM, fuel pump relay, fuel injectors and the various solenoid valves.

The engine sensors (AFS, APS, ATS, CO pot, CTS, TPS etc) are now provided with a 5.0-volt reference supply from a relevant pin on the ECM.

In some early models, a voltage is applied to the ECM when the ignition switch is turned to the start (engine cranking) position. This connection is not used in later models. When the engine is cranked or run, a speed signal from the ignition causes the ECM to earth the pump relay driver, so that the fuel pump will run. Ignition and injection functions are also activated. The injectors are supplied with nbv from the main relay, and the ECM completes the circuit by pulsing the injector driver pin to earth. The ISCV regulates the idle speed under ECM control by pulsing the ISCV driver when the engine is at idle.

The ECM also receives signals from a number of sensors including clutch, neutral position, brake switch, power steering, heater blower, air conditioning, heated rear window, etc. These signals are used to determine engine electrical load so that idle control can act accordingly.

Deceleration fuel cut-off

A deceleration fuel cut-off is implemented during engine over-run conditions, to improve economy and reduce emissions. Conditions when over-run is implemented are:

a) Throttle closed (idle switch contacts closed).
b) Engine speed above 3000 rpm.
c) Once the engine speed drops below 1500 to 1000 rpm, fuel injection is reinstated.

Clear flood

If the throttle is held fully open during engine cranking, the ECM will inhibit fuel injector operation, and no fuel will be injected. This is useful, for example, if the engine has flooded during an engine start procedure.

Reference voltage

Voltage supply from the ECM to the engine sensors is made at a 5.0-volt reference level. This ensures a stable working voltage, unaffected by variations in system voltage.

The earth return connection for most engine sensors is made through one or more ECM pins, but these pins are not directly connected to earth. The ECM internally connects the pins to earth via ECM earth pins that are directly connected to earth.

Self-diagnostic function

Mazda EGI has a self-test capability that continuously examines signals from the engine sensors. When a fault is detected, the 'Check Engine' warning lamp on the dashboard lights (where fitted), and the ECM internally logs an appropriate code or codes. These codes can be output on the 'Check Engine' warning lamp by bridging the appropriate terminals in the self-test connector. If a warning lamp is not fitted, the codes can be output from the check connector on an analogue voltmeter or LED lamp. Faults are also logged for output (actuated) components, but only for three seconds after the ignition is switched on when the SD connector is earthed.

If the fault clears, the warning lamp will extinguish but the codes will remain logged until a routine is initiated to erase them from memory. There are several different routines available, and these would include removing the 'Check Engine' warning lamp fuse, disconnecting the battery negative terminal, or utilising a suitable FCR.

Limited operating strategy (LOS)

In addition to the self-test capability, EGI has a limp-home facility. In the event of a serious fault in one or more of the sensors, the EMS will substitute a fixed default value in place of the defective sensor.

For example, in limp-home mode, the CTS value is set to 50°C and the ATS is set to 20°C. This means that the engine may actually run quite well with failure of either the ATS or the CTS. However, since the substituted values are those of a semi-hot engine, cold starting and running during the warm-up period may be less than satisfactory.

Adaptive memory

Over a period of time, the ECM will learn the best idle position for a particular engine - irrespective of age, engine condition and load, so that the correct idle speed is always maintained. The adaptive idle settings are stored in memory. Consequently, when the battery is disconnected, the ECM will need some time to re-learn the system parameters before proper idle control is restored.

Vehicle speed sensor (VSS)

The VSS is located in the speedometer. An AC pulse generated by the speedometer sensor is sent to the VSS, which converts the pulse to a digital value. The resulting square waveform pulse is then returned to the ECM as a vehicle speed signal.

3 Primary trigger

General

The primary trigger to initiate both ignition and fuelling in the EGI system is a distributor-mounted Hall-effect sensor. In addition, some later models also utilise a flywheel-mounted CAS to provide two sensor inputs. The operation of both types is described below.

Crank angle sensor (CAS)

The CAS is mounted in proximity to the flywheel, and consists of an inductive magnet that radiates a magnetic field. The flywheel incorporates a reluctor disk containing steel pins set at intervals. As the flywheel spins, and the pins are rotated in the magnetic field, an AC voltage signal is generated. The peak-to-peak voltage of the speed signal can vary from 5 volts at idle to over 100 volts at 6000 rpm. The ECM uses an analogue-to-digital converter (ADC) to transform the AC pulse into a digital signal. This signal is not used in all Mazda systems, and is an additional signal to the distributor-based HES.

Hall-effect sensor (HES)

The ignition supplies nbv to the Hall-effect sensor in the distributor. The HES circuit is completed by a connection to earth.

Opposite the Hall sensor is a magnet, whose field causes the switch to return a small voltage back to the ECM. Attached to the distributor shaft is a trigger vane with the same number of cut-outs as cylinders. Passing the trigger vane between the switch and the magnet will cause the Hall switch to be turned off and on. As the cut-out space proceeds past the switch, a voltage is returned to the ECM via a third wire termed the output wire.

When the solid portion comes between the switch and magnet, the voltage is turned off as the magnetic field is diverted. Essentially, the voltage signal is returned to the ECM as either voltage or zero voltage, and the waveform produced is that of a square wave. The HES signal is necessary for initiation of ignition, injection and idle control. The engine will not run without the HES signal.

Depending on model, the Hall signals returned to the ECM may differ. One common method sends one signal (180° of crankshaft rotation in four-cylinder engines) for every cylinder, plus an additional signal to indicate the position of TDC on No 1 cylinder. The second signal is returned to the ECM on a separate signal wire. A second method sends one signal for every cylinder, but the cut-out is elongated for No 2 cylinder to indicate the position of TDC on that cylinder.

4 Ignition

Data on engine load (AFS) and engine speed (CAS) are collected by the ECM, which then refers to a digital ignition map stored within its microprocessor. This map contains an advance angle for basic load and speed operating conditions. The advance angle is corrected after reference to engine temperature (CTS), so that the best ignition advance angle for a particular operating condition can be determined.

Amplifier

The Mazda EGI amplifier (often termed an 'igniter' by the Japanese vehicle manufacturers) contains the circuitry for switching the coil negative terminal at the correct moment to instigate ignition. The ECM calculates the correct ignition dwell time and timing advance from data received from its sensors, and sends a control signal to the amplifier, which then switches off the coil negative terminal.

The amplifier location differs according to the particular vehicle to which it is fitted. Some amplifiers are located in the engine compartment (mainly early models with a distributor) and others are contained within the distributor housing.

Dwell operation in Mazda EGI is based upon the principle of the 'constant-energy current-limiting' system. This means that the dwell period remains constant at about 3.0 to 3.5 ms, at virtually all engine running speeds. However, the dwell duty cycle, when measured in percent or degrees, will vary as the engine speed varies.

Ignition coil

The ignition coil utilises low primary resistance in order to increase primary current and primary energy. The amplifier limits the primary current to around 8 amps, and this permits a reserve of energy to maintain the required spark burn time (duration). The coil is located in the distributor in the majority of EGI-equipped vehicles.

Distributor

In the EGI system, the distributor contains the HES, which provides a speed and TDC signal, and also the secondary HT components (distributor cap, rotor and HT coil) and serves to distribute the HT current from the coil secondary terminal to each spark plug in firing order.

Integrated ignition assembly

In some models, the coil and amplifier are integrated inside the distributor. This reduces wiring and improves reliability. The system is often referred to as the 'coil in cap' system, and is identified by the lack of a main coil secondary HT lead. The secondary HT voltage passes directly from the coil to the rotor arm - which distributes the voltage to the spark plugs via the HT leads in the conventional manner.

Knock sensor (some vehicles only)

The optimal ignition timing (at engine speeds greater than idle) for a given high-compression engine is quite close to the point of onset of knock. However, running so close to the point of knock occurrence, means that knock will certainly occur on one or more cylinders at certain times during the engine operating cycle.

Since knock may occur at a different moment in each individual cylinder, EGI employs a knock control processor (in the ECM) to pinpoint the actual cylinder or cylinders that are knocking. The knock sensor is mounted on the engine block, and consists of a piezo-ceramic measuring element that responds to engine noise oscillations. This signal is converted to a voltage signal that is proportional to the level of knock, and returned to the ECM for evaluation and action.

The ECM will analyse the noise from each individual cylinder, and uses a sophisticated technique to recognise knock as distinct to general engine noise.

5 Fuel injection

Fuel injection

Mazda has adopted two distinct methods for providing fuel to the engines equipped with EGI. The methods are simultaneous multi-point injection (MPi) and sequential multi-point injection (MPi). In addition, the sequential injection may be synchronised or non-synchronised with the opening of the inlet valves.

Because of EGI modularity, little difference exists between layout of each type on the various engines. It is in implementation that contrasts are found. First a description of common features, followed by a description of each type.

Mazda EGI is mapped with a basic injector opening time according to various load and speed conditions. Information is then gathered from engine sensors such as the AFS sensor, RPM and TDC sensors, CTS, and combined TPS & TS. As a result of this information, the ECM will look up the correct injector pulse duration right across the engine rpm, load and temperature range.

The fuel injector is a magnetically-operated solenoid valve that is actuated by the ECM. Voltage to the injectors is applied from the main relay, and the earth path is completed by the ECM for a period of time (called pulse duration) of between 1.5 and 10 milliseconds. The pulse duration is very much dependent upon engine temperature, load, speed and operating conditions. When the magnetic solenoid closes, a back-EMF voltage of up to 60 volts is initiated.

The amount of fuel delivered by the injector(s) is determined by the fuel pressure and the injector opening time. The ECM controls the period of time that the injector is held open, and this is determined by the signals from the various sensor inputs. During engine start-up from cold, the pulse duration is increased to provide a richer air/fuel mixture.

Over-speed fuel cut-off (rev limiter)

To prevent over-revving the engine, EGI inhibits the injector earth path above a pre-determined engine speed (which varies according to individual engines), thereby cutting off the fuel supply. As the engine speed drops below the value, fuel injection is reinstated.

Deceleration fuel cut-off

A deceleration fuel cut-off is implemented during engine over-run conditions, to improve economy and reduce emissions. The conditions for over-run to be implemented vary according to engine speed, coolant temperature and other factors. Once the engine speed drops below a pre-determined threshold, fuel injection is reinstated. In addition, on models with automatic transmission, fuel injection is reduced during upward gear changes, in order to smooth out the change.

Multi-point injection (MPi - simultaneous)

The simultaneous MPi system consists of one injector for each cylinder, mounted in the inlet port, so that a finely-atomised fuel spray is directed onto the back of each valve. The injectors are all pulsed simultaneously, twice per engine cycle. Half of the required fuel per engine cycle is therefore injected at each engine revolution.

Fuel will briefly rest upon the back of a valve before being drawn into a cylinder. Unlike other simultaneous systems, the injectors are all connected to the ECM via separate wires to separate ECM driver pins.

Multi-point injection (MPi - sequential)

The sequential system functions in a similar manner to the simultaneous system. However, with reference to the signal from the cylinder identification (CID) sensor, the injectors are actuated as the inlet valve opens. The ECM controls the period of time that the injector is held open, and this is determined by the signals from the various sensor inputs.

However, under certain operating conditions, fuel is injected simultaneously or even non-sequentially (out of sequence with the crankshaft position). When the engine is at idle speed and the throttle switch is closed, injection is sequential. As the throttle is opened, injection changes to non-sequential simultaneous operation for a brief period that depends upon the coolant temperature.

When the engine is accelerating with the rate of throttle opening angle exceeding a specific value, injection changes to non-sequential simultaneous operation for a brief period that depends upon the coolant temperature.

Variable resonance induction system (VRIS)

Under all operating conditions, air flows into the induction manifold through the throttle valve in the throttle body. However, on some engines, Mazda utilise two separate induction paths, to improve the flow of air into the engine at both low and high engine speeds. A short induction path is utilised at high speeds, and a long induction path is utilised at low speeds. Airflow through each path is controlled by the ECM, through an additional throttle valve (located in the inlet manifold) and either one or two solenoid valve-controlled vacuum actuators.

Load sensors

The ECM requires a load sensor to detect the flow of air into the engine. Once the volume of air is known, the correct fuel injection duration can be looked up in the map. In early Mazda EGI systems, the vane-type AFS was prominent. In later systems, the hot-wire air mass meter is utilised as the main means to measure load.

Vane-type AFS

The AFS is located between the air filter and the throttle body. As air flows through the sensor, it deflects a vane (flap). The greater the volume of air, the more will the flap be deflected. The vane is connected to a wiper arm, which wipes a potentiometer resistance track and so varies the resistance of the track. This allows a variable voltage signal to be returned to the ECM.

The EGI AFS is based upon the now-outdated Bosch 'L' Jetronic design. Overall operation of the sensor is similar to the modern three-wire AFS as fitted to modern Motronic systems. However, the wiring circuitry is somewhat different **(see illustration 11.1)**. Battery voltage from the system relay is applied through connection VB to a resistance within the AFS body. The resistance reduces the nbv to between 5.0 and 10.0 volts, and the resulting voltage is termed the reference voltage. The reference voltage is applied to both the ECM and the AFS resistance track within the AFS body. The other end of the resistance track is connected to the AFS earth return at connection E2. AFS signal output is made from the wiper arm to the ECM, via AFS connection VS.

From the signal voltage returned, the ECM is able to calculate the volume of air (load) entering the engine, and this is used to calculate the main fuel injection duration. To smooth out inlet pulses, a damper is

THA VS VC VB E2 FC E1

H.21402.

11.1 Vane-type AFS terminals

THA	*Air temperature sensor*
VS	*AFS signal*
VB	*Voltage supply*
E1 & E2	*Earth connections*
FC	*Fuel pump earth contact (closed engine running, open engine stopped)*

connected to the AFS vane. The AFS exerts a major influence on the amount of fuel injected.

The vane type AFS also contains a set of fuel pump earth contacts. Refer to 'fuel pump relay' below for an operational description.

Hot-wire air mass meter (AFS)

The hot-wire air mass meter has replaced the vane-type AFS fitted to earlier vehicles. The hot-wire air mass meter measures the mass of air entering engine, which allows an accurate fuel injection pulse to be calculated. Hot-wire is a very accurate method of calculating the engine load (air input) and the air temperature function is incorporated into the sensor. Automatic compensation for altitude is also provided. The absence of moving parts improves reliability and lessens maintenance requirements.

Essentially, the hot-wire is so called because a heated wire is placed in the air intake. As air passes over the wire, it has a cooling effect in proportion to the mass of air. As air mass increases or decreases according to engine load, the ECM adjusts the current flow to maintain the wire at its original resistance and temperature. By measuring the change in current flow, the ECM is able to determine the mass of airflow into the engine. As the current varies on the signal wire, so does the voltage, and an indication of load can be assessed by measuring the variable voltage signal. Voltage is applied to the sensor from the system relay.

Air temperature sensor (ATS)

In the hot-wire AFS, there is no separate temperature sensor, and the function is incorporated into the hot-wire circuitry.

The ATS is mounted in the AFS inlet tract in the vane-type AFS. The ATS measures the air temperature before it enters the inlet manifold. Because the density of air varies in inverse proportion to the temperature, the ATS signal allows more accurate assessment of the volume of air entering the engine. However, the ATS has only a minor correcting effect on ECM output. The ATS operates on the NTC principle. A variable voltage signal is returned to the ECM based upon the air temperature.

CO adjustment (vane-type AFS only)

The mechanical type of AFS utilises an air bleed screw to trim the CO value. An air channel allows a small volume of air to by-pass the air flowing through the vane when it is in the idle position. As the by-pass screw is moved, the air volume acting upon the vane is altered, and the vane moves its position. The changed position results in an altered signal to the ECM, and a change in fuel volume injected. The air by-pass has no effect at engine speeds above idle. It is not possible to adjust the idle CO value in later vehicles without the vane AFS.

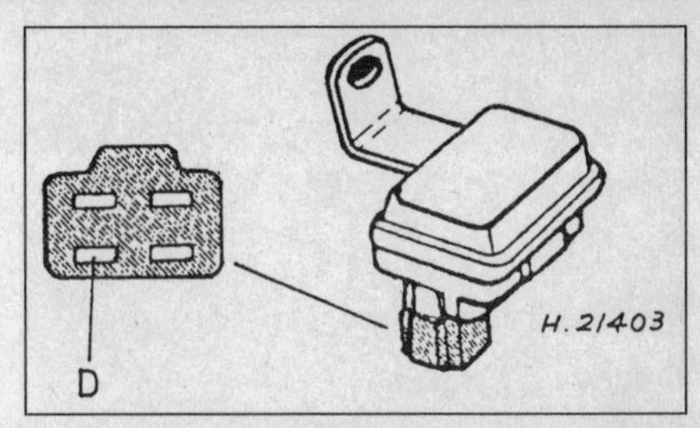

11.2 Atmospheric pressure sensor (APS)
At terminal D, a voltage of around 4 volts should be available with the ignition on

Atmospheric pressure sensor (APS)

On some vehicles, an APS may be fitted. Its purpose is to inform the ECM of changes in atmospheric pressure, so that minor changes can be made to the AFR **(see illustration 11.2)**.

Coolant temperature sensor (CTS)

The CTS is incorporated in the cooling system, and operates on the NTC principle. As the resistance of the CTS varies, this returns a variable voltage signal to the ECM based upon the coolant temperature. The signal is around 2.0 to 3.0 volts at an ambient temperature of 20°C, and reduces to 0.4 to 0.8 volts at a coolant temperature of 80°C.

The open-circuit supply to the sensor is at a 5.0-volt reference level, and the earth path is through the sensor return. The ECM uses the CTS signal as a main correction factor when calculating ignition timing and injection duration.

Throttle potentiometer sensor/throttle switch (TPS/TS)

In most models, the TPS and TS are combined into a sensor that is essentially a potentiometer with a separate set of idle contacts. The TPS provides the ECM with data on rate of acceleration and throttle position, and the TS indicates idle position. A common earth return connects both TPS and TS to the ECM. In some models, the TPS does not utilise the throttle switch contacts.

Voltage at the 5.0-volt reference level is applied to the TS idle contact terminal from the ECM. This voltage drops to zero when the idle contact is closed.

The TPS is a potentiometer with three wires. A 5.0-volt reference voltage is supplied to a resistance track with the other end connected to earth. The third wire is connected to an arm which wipes along the resistance track, and so varies the resistance and voltage of the signal returned to the ECM, which is able to calculate just how quickly the throttle is opened.

Engine idle control

Over the evolution period of EGI, a number of different components and methods have been used to control the engine idle speed at various engine temperatures and loads.

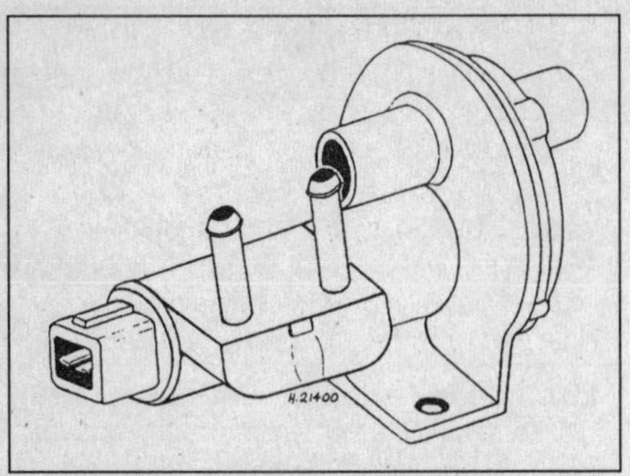

11.3 Auxiliary air valve (AAV). Used in very early systems which have no form of automatic idle control, or as a fast idle valve for engine warm-up, in association with the ISCV

Early models

EGI did not control the idle speed in early models, and an idle by-pass adjustment screw is provided upon the throttle body. During engine start-up from cold and during the warm-up period, the idle speed is raised by virtue of an auxiliary air valve (AAV) **(see illustration 11.3)**. When fairly heavy electrical loads are switched on, the idle speed would tend to drop. This is overcome by utilising an associated air valve ('idle-up' valve) that is actuated when the load is switched on. In addition to the AAV then, idle-up valves may be provided for air conditioning, power steering and general electrical loads **(see illustration 11.4)**.

Later models

A solenoid-controlled idle speed control valve (ISCV) actuated by the ECM according to engine load is used to automatically control idle speed during normal idle and during engine warm-up. The ISCV is located in an air passage that connects the inlet manifold to the air filter side of the throttle plate. The ECM pulses the valve at a fixed frequency of 160 Hz and with a variable duty cycle of between 40 and 100%. The greater the duty cycle, the further open is the valve.

The ECM also receives signals from a number of sensors including clutch, neutral position, brake switch, power steering, heater blower, air conditioning, heated rear window etc. These signals are used to determine engine electrical load, so that the ECM can act accordingly. If the ISCV fails, the valve will fail closed, to leave a small opening for a basic idle speed.

In addition, a waxstat-actuated control valve is used to increase the idle speed during the engine warm-up period. The valve closes once the engine coolant rises above 50°C.

In most models, it is still possible to adjust the base idle speed. However, the SD connector must be used to place the ECM into service-set mode before this operation can be attempted.

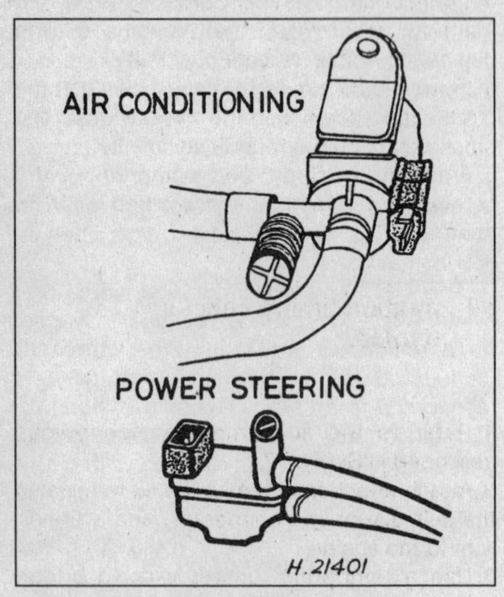

11.4 Idle-up solenoid valves. The valves are actuated by the ECM to provide a faster idle when air conditioning or power steering, for example, are in use

Main and fuel pump relays

The Mazda EGI electrical system is controlled by a main fuel injection relay and a fuel pump relay, and the method of operation does vary between the different models. In some vehicles (usually later models with a hot-wire air mass meter) the fuel pump relay is actuated much as in the majority of European systems, with a supply feed from the main relay, and actuation of the pump relay driver by the ECM. This means that failure of the main relay will prevent the fuel pump relay from operating. In other models, the fuel pump relay operates independently, and is not dependent on the main relay for a supply. In this instance, the relay is either earthed through the AFS fuel pump contact (early models with an vane-type AFS) or by actuation of the pump relay driver by the ECM.

Fuel pump relay operation in AFS system

The fuel pump relay uses two energising coils to control the relay circuit - one coil during cranking, and the other coil during normal engine running. Once the relay receives a cranking voltage, the first relay winding - which is connected to earth - will be energised, and the fuel pump will run during the cranking operation.

When cranking ceases, the fuel pump relay energising coil will de-energise, and the contacts will open to cut the voltage to the fuel pump. The second energising coil is connected to earth through a set of contacts in the AFS relay. Once the key is released from the start position, if the engine has started, the FC contacts in the AFS will close to earth and thus energise the second relay winding, so that the fuel pump will continue running. The FC contacts act as a safety feature. When the engine stops for whatever reason and the AFS returns to the closed position, the FC contacts will open. In turn, the fuel pump relay will de-energise, which will shut down the fuel pump.

Fuel pressure system

The fuel system consists of a fuel tank, a fuel pump, fuel filter, fuel rail, pressure regulator and return line. The fuel pump may be a submerged impeller type pump mounted in the fuel tank, or a roller type mounted externally. The pump draws fuel from the tank, and pumps it to the fuel rail via a fuel filter. In four-wheel-drive vehicles, installation of the propeller shaft causes the fuel tank to be designed in two sections. A transfer pump is provided to pump fuel from the left section to the right, where the system pump is located. The transfer pump is operated by its own control unit and switch.

Switching the ignition key on causes the ECM to energise the fuel pump relay for approximately one second so that the fuel system is pressurised. The fuel pump relay is then switched off, to await a cranking or running signal.

Once the engine is running, fuel is fed through a fuel filter to the fuel injector rail. To prevent pressure loss in the supply system, a non-return valve is provided in the fuel pump outlet. When the ignition is switched off, and the fuel pump ceases operation, pressure is thus maintained for some time so that vaporisation and poor hot starting is much reduced.

Fuel pressure regulator

Fuel pressure in the fuel rail is maintained at a constant 2.5 bar by a fuel pressure regulator. The fuel pump normally provides much more fuel than is required, and surplus fuel is thus returned to the fuel tank via a return pipe. In fact, a maximum fuel pressure in excess of 5 bar is possible in this system. To prevent pressure loss in the supply system, a non-return valve is provided in the fuel pump outlet. When the ignition is switched off, and the fuel pump ceases operation, pressure is thus maintained for some time.

At idle speed with the vacuum pipe disconnected, or with the engine stopped and the pump running, or at full-throttle, the system fuel pressure will be around 2.4 to 3.3 bar. At idle speed (vacuum pipe connected), the fuel pressure will be approximately 0.5 bar under the system pressure.

In addition, an ECM-actuated cut-off valve (PRC) is provided to allow increased fuel pressure and therefore fuel enrichment under certain operating conditions. The facility may be required under hot starting conditions that could lead to fuel vaporisation. By cutting vacuum to the pressure regulator, the increased fuel pressure will lead to easier starting.

6 Catalytic converter and emission control

The Mazda EGI system fitted to catalyst vehicles implements a closed-loop control system, so that exhaust emissions may be reduced. Closed-loop systems are fitted with an oxygen sensor which monitors the exhaust gas for its oxygen content. A low oxygen level in the exhaust signifies a rich mixture. A high oxygen level in the exhaust signifies a weak mixture.

When the engine is operating in closed-loop control, the OS signal causes the ECM to modify the injector pulse so that the AFR is maintained close to the stoichiometric ratio. By controlling the injection pulse during most operating conditions, so that the air/fuel ratio is always in a small 'window' around the Lambda point (ie Lambda = 0.97 to 1.03), almost perfect combustion could be achieved. Thus the catalyst has less work to do, and will last longer, with fewer emissions at the tail pipe.

The closed-loop control is implemented during engine operation at normal engine operating temperatures. When the coolant temperature is low, or the engine is at full load, or on the overrun, the ECM will operate in open-loop. When operating in open-loop, the ECM allows a richer or leaner AFR than the stoichiometric ratio. This prevents engine hesitation, for example, during acceleration with a wide-open throttle.

The OS only produces a signal when the exhaust gas has reached a minimum temperature of approximately 300°C. The OS contains a heating element so that once the engine has started, the sensor can rapidly attain optimum operating temperature. The OS heater supply is applied from the main relay. In V6 engines, two oxygen sensors are used.

Evaporation control

A carbon filter solenoid valve (CFSV), diaphragm valve, two-way valve and activated carbon canister all combine to aid evaporative emission control. The carbon canister stores fuel vapours until the CFSV is opened by EGI under certain operating conditions. Once the CFSV is actuated by the EMS, fuel vapours are drawn into the inlet manifold to be burnt by the engine during normal combustion. The CFSV is often termed a purge valve.

The supply to the CFSV is made from the main relay. The earth path is made through the ECM, and the ECM actuates the CFSV by pulsing it to earth when required. So that engine performance will not be affected, the CFSV remains closed during cold engine operation, and also during engine idle. Once the engine coolant reaches normal operating temperature, the OS is functioning, the vehicle is being driven in gear and the throttle is partially open (normal cruise conditions with a hot engine) the CFSV will be modulated (pulsed) on and off by the ECM.

Exhaust gas recirculation (EGR)

EGR operation only occurs after the engine has attained normal operating temperature, and the engine is operating under part-load conditions. Exhaust gas is piped from the exhaust manifold to the inlet manifold via an EGR control valve. In addition, an solenoid vent valve and solenoid vacuum valve are utilised to control vacuum applied to the control valve.

The ECM monitors engine conditions, and moves the control valve more open by pulsing the vacuum solenoid valve by duty cycle and turning the solenoid vent valve on. This applies more vacuum to the EGR control valve, and increases the flow of exhaust gas. The control valve is moved towards the closed position when the ECM pulses the vent solenoid valve by duty cycle and turns the solenoid vacuum valve on. This applies less vacuum to the EGR control valve, and decreases the flow of exhaust gas. Varying amounts of vacuum are therefore applied to the EGR control valve, which opens to allow a finely-metered supply of exhaust gas to be introduced into the inlet manifold. As the exhaust gas passes through the control valve, a variable signal is returned to the ECM on how much EGR lift is attained. In turn, the ECM adjusts the signal to the solenoid valves to 'tune' the amount of exhaust gas that is recycled into the inlet manifold.

Adjustments

7 Adjustment pre-conditions

1 Ensure that all of these conditions are met before attempting to make adjustments:

a) Engine at operating temperature. Engine oil at a minimum temperature of 80°C; a journey of at least 4 miles is recommended (particularly so if equipped with AT).
b) Ancillary equipment (all engine loads and accessories) switched off.
c) AT vehicles: Transmission in N or P.
d) Engine mechanically sound.
e) Engine breather hoses and breather system in satisfactory condition.
f) Induction system free from vacuum leaks.
g) Ignition system in satisfactory condition.
h) Air filter in satisfactory condition.
i) Exhaust system free from leaks.
j) Throttle cable correctly adjusted.
k) No fault codes logged by the ECM.
l) OS operating satisfactorily (catalyst vehicles with closed-loop control).

2 In addition, before checking the idle speed and CO values, stabilise the engine as follows:

a) Stabilise the engine. Raise the engine speed to 3000 rpm for a minimum of 30 seconds, and then let the engine idle.
b) If the cooling fan operates during adjustment, wait until it stops, re-stabilise the engine and then restart the adjustment procedure.
c) Allow the CO and idle speed to settle.
d) Make all checks and adjustments within 30 seconds. If this time is exceeded, re-stabilise the engine and recheck.

8 Throttle adjustments

1 The throttle valve position is not adjustable.
2 Detach the TPS multi-plug and identify the TS contacts.
3 Connect an ohmmeter between the two TS contacts. With the throttle closed, the ohmmeter should indicate continuity.
4 Insert a 0.50 mm feeler gauge between the throttle stop screw and the throttle lever. The ohmmeter should now indicate infinity.
5 Adjust the TS by slackening the fixing screws and turning the combined TPS/TS assembly.

9 Ignition timing checks (typical)

1 Refer to the adjustment pre-conditions described in Section 7.
2 Attach a tachometer (use the IG terminal in the self-diagnostic connector) and a timing light to the engine.
3 Use a temporary jumper wire to bridge terminals GND and TEN in the SD connector **(see illustration 11.5)**.
4 Check the idle speed and adjust if necessary.

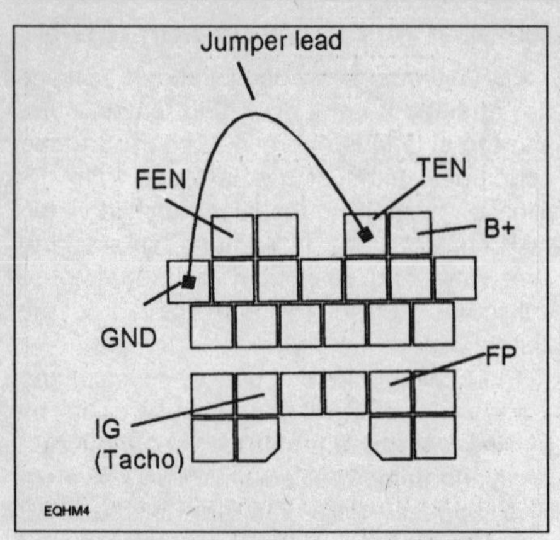

11.5 RPM is obtained by attaching the tachometer lead to the IG terminal in the SD connector. Bridge terminals TEN and GND in the SD connector. This causes EGI to enter service-set mode

5 Check the base ignition timing. Refer to the specifications at the start of this Chapter **(see illustration 11.6)**.
6 If the ignition timing is incorrect, correct the timing by slackening the clamp bolts and turning the distributor. Tighten the bolts once the timing is correct.
7 Remove the temporary jumper wire from the SD connector.
8 Increase the engine speed. The timing marks should smoothly advance. Expect approximately 25 to 35° of timing advance.

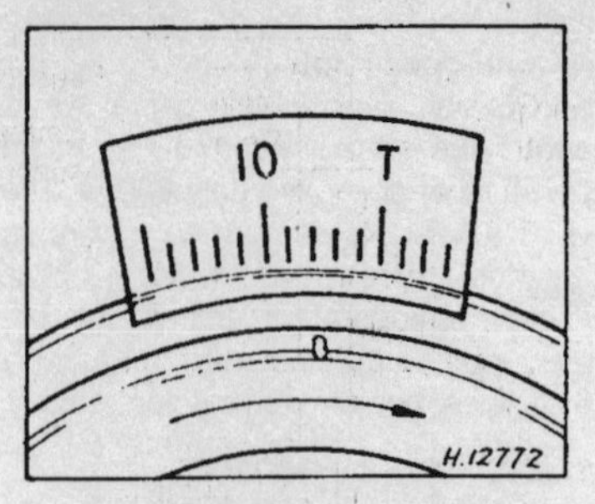

11.6 Ignition timing marks (most Mazda models)

10 Idle adjustments (typical)

1 Refer to the adjustment pre-conditions described in Section 7.
2 Attach a tachometer (use the IG terminal in the SD connector).
3 Use a temporary jumper wire to bridge terminals GND and TEN in the SD connector. **Note:** *This procedure is unnecessary on the earliest models without idle speed control.*
4 Check the idle speed and adjust if necessary by turning the air by-pass adjusting screw **(see illustrations 11.7 and 11.8)**.
5 Remove the temporary jumper wire from the SD connector.
6 Check and adjust the idle CO value (vane-type AFS only).

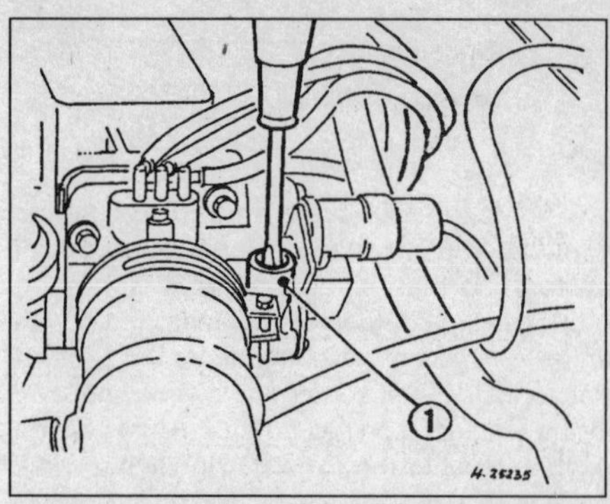

11.7 Adjustment of the idle speed (typical)
1 Adjustment screw

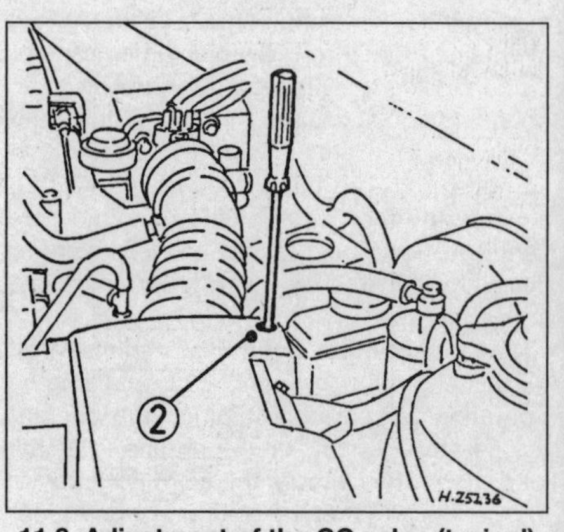

11.8 Adjustment of the CO value (typical)
2 Adjustment screw

System sensor and actuator tests

Important note: *Please refer to Chapter 4, which describes common test procedures applicable to this system. The routines in Chapter 4 should be read in conjunction with the component notes and wiring diagrams presented in this Chapter* **(see illustration 11.9)**. *The wiring diagrams and other data presented in this Chapter are necessarily representative of the system depicted. Because of the variations in wiring and other data that often occurs, even between similar vehicles in any particular VM's range, the reader should take great care in identification of ECM pins, and satisfy himself that he has gathered the correct data before failing a particular component.*

11 Crank angle sensor (CAS) - at crankshaft pulley, when fitted

1 Refer to the note at the start of this Section, and refer to the relevant Section of Chapter 4.
2 The CAS resistance is between 520 and 580 ohms.

12 Primary trigger - Hall-effect sensor (HES)

1 Refer to the note at the start of Section 11, and refer to the relevant Section of Chapter 4.
2 Two HES signals or one signal are generated depending on model. The signals switch from 5.0 volts to zero.

13 Primary ignition

1 Refer to the note at the start of Section 11, and refer to the relevant Section of Chapter 4.
2 The primary ignition is essentially that of an ECM with an external amplifier. However, the amplifier is combined with the coil, and the following additional test should be made.
3 ECM and component pin numbers may vary depending upon the Mazda EGI system under test.
4 The primary resistance varies according to model. Refer to the specifications at the start of this Chapter.
5 To measure the primary resistance, disconnect the three-pin connector to the distributor. Connect an ohmmeter between terminals A and B **(see illustration 11.10)**.
6 Secondary resistance should be between 20 000 and 31 000 ohms.
7 RPM readings can be obtained by attaching the tachometer to the IG terminal in the SD connector.

14 Knock sensor (KS)

1 Refer to the note at the start of Section 11, and refer to the relevant Section of Chapter 4.

15 Fuel injector operation (MPi)

1 Refer to the note at the start of Section 11, and refer to the relevant Section of Chapter 4.

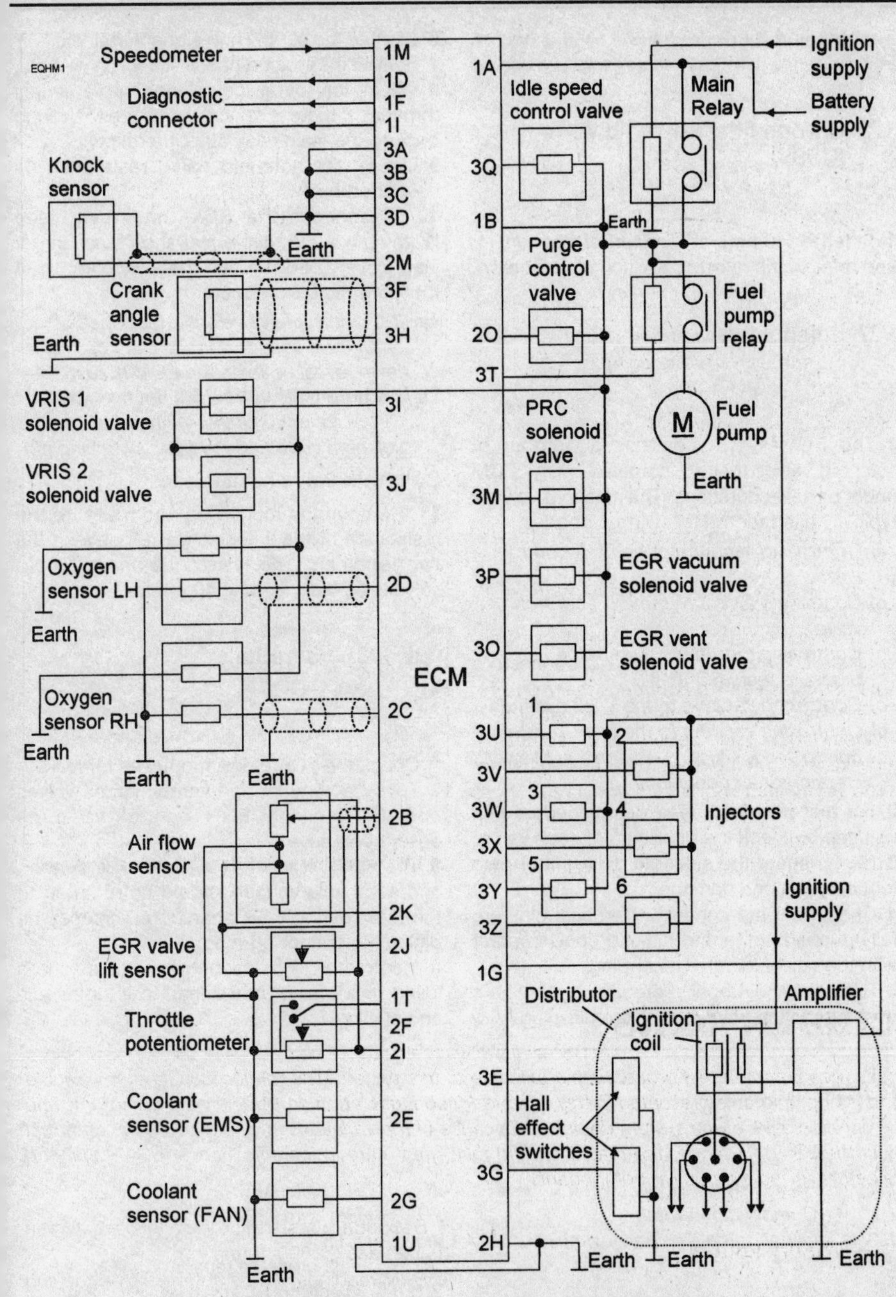

11.9 Typical EGI system wiring (626, V6 model shown)

2 Voltage to the injectors is provided from the system relay.
3 Injector operation is either simultaneous or sequential.
4 The injector resistance is normally 12.0 to 16.0 ohms.

16 Airflow sensor (AFS)

1 Refer to the note at the start of Section 11, and refer to the relevant Section of Chapter 4.
2 The AFS may be of the vane or hot-wire type, depending on vehicle.

17 Air temperature sensor (ATS)

1 Refer to the note at the start of Section 11, and refer to the relevant Section of Chapter 4.
2 The ATS is mounted in the vane-type AFS inlet.

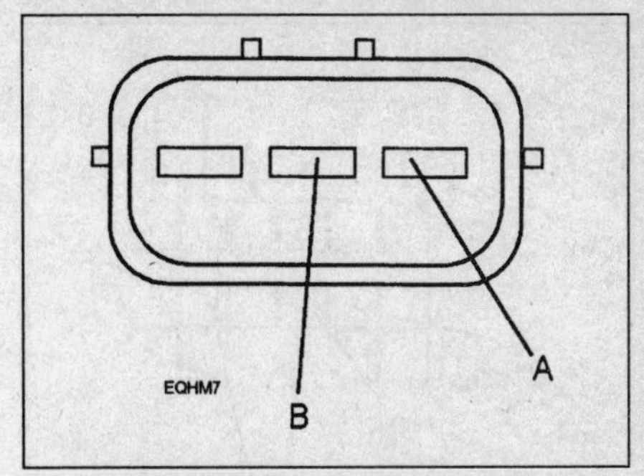

11.10 Disconnect the three-pin connector to the distributor, and connect an ohmmeter between terminals A and B to measure the primary resistance

18 Coolant temperature sensor (CTS)

1 Refer to the note at the start of Section 11, and refer to the relevant Section of Chapter 4.

19 Throttle potentiometer sensor/throttle switch (TPS/TS)

1 Refer to the note at the start of Section 11, and refer to the relevant Section of Chapter 4.

20 Idle speed control valve (ISCV)

1 Refer to the note at the start of Section 11, and refer to the relevant Section of Chapter 4.
2 ISCV resistance is 7.7 to 9.3 ohms.

21 ECM voltage supplies and earths

1 Refer to the note at the start of Section 11, and refer to the relevant Section of Chapter 4.

22 System relays

1 Refer to the note at the start of Section 11, and refer to the relevant Section of Chapter 4.

23 Fuel pump and circuit

1 Refer to the note at the start of Section 11, and refer to the relevant Section of Chapter 4.

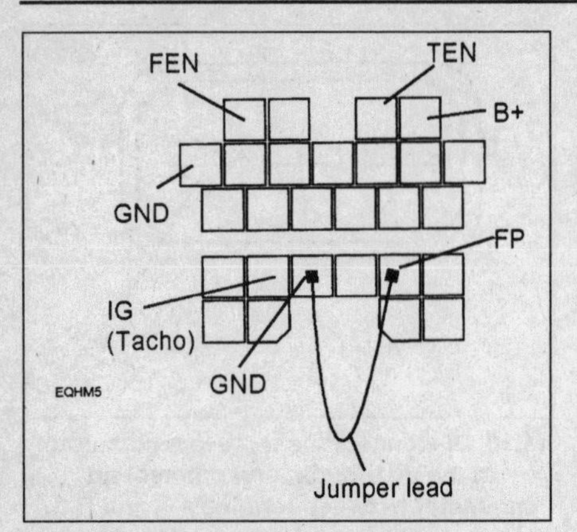

11.11 Run the fuel pump for pressure tests by bridging the FP and GND terminals in the SD connector

24 Fuel pressure

1 Refer to the note at the start of Section 11, and refer to the relevant Section of Chapter 4.

2 The fuel pump relay can be energised for pressure tests by bridging the FP and GND terminals in the self-diagnostic (SD) connector **(see illustration 11.11)**.

25 Oxygen sensor (OS)

1 Refer to the note at the start of Section 11, and refer to the relevant Section of Chapter 4.

2 The OS found in the majority of Mazda EGI systems is a four-wire sensor with a heater. In V6 engines, two oxygen sensors are used.

26 Carbon filter solenoid valve (CFSV)

1 Refer to the note at the start of Section 11, and refer to the relevant Section of Chapter 4.

27 Solenoid valves

1 The EGI system contains a number of solenoid valves that are actuated by the ECM under certain conditions. The solenoid valve is typically used for the following purposes:

a) Controlling vacuum to the EGR control valve.
b) Controlling a vent to the EGR control valve.
c) Controlling cut-off vacuum to the pressure regulator (PRC).
d) Controlling vacuum to the VRIS system.
e) Controlling vacuum to the idle-up valves during various load conditions, eg power steering or air conditioning.

2 For test purposes, a similar procedure can be used to check the operation of each valve.

3 First inspect the solenoid valve multi-plug for corrosion and damage.

4 Check that the connector terminal pins are fully pushed home and making good contact with the solenoid valve multi-plug.

5 Roll back the rubber protection boot (where possible) to the solenoid valve multi-plug.

6 Identify the supply and signal terminals.

7 Switch the ignition on.

8 Check for nbv at the solenoid valve supply terminal. If there is no voltage, trace the wiring back to the main relay output terminal.

9 Check the solenoid valve resistance as described below.

10 Disconnect the ECM multi-plug *(see Warning No 3 in Reference)* and use a jumper lead to very briefly touch the switching pin in the ECM multi-plug to earth:

a) If the solenoid valve actuates: Check the ECM main voltage supplies and earths. If tests reveal no fault, the ECM is suspect.
b) If the solenoid valve does not actuate: Check for continuity of wiring between the solenoid valve and the ECM switching pin.

Solenoid valve resistance

11 Remove the multi-plug and measure the resistance of the solenoid valve between the two terminals. The resistance of a solenoid valve is typically around 40 ohms.

28 EGR operation

1 Check the EGR pipes and hoses for leaks.

2 Test the vacuum and vent solenoid valves operation to the EGR control valve as described above.

3 The EGR lift valve is a three-wire sensor, and a variable voltage should be returned to the ECM during EGR operation. This may be difficult to test for off-load.

4 Incorrect EGR operation whilst the engine is idling or warming up will lead to a lumpy idle and stalling.

Pin table - two-segment ECM multi-plug

Note:** Refer to **illustration 11.12

1A	*Battery*	*1S*	*Heater/air conditioning motor switch*	*2N*	*OS*
1B	*Main relay*	*1T*	*Heated rear window switch*	*2O*	*Hot-wire AFS*
1C	*Fuel pump relay*	*1U*	*Combination switch*	*2P*	*Hot-wire AFS*
1D	*SD connector*	*1V*	*Clutch pedal position switch*	*2Q*	*CTS*
1F	*SD connector*	*2A*	*Earth*	*2T*	*Fuel pressure regulator*
1G	*Ignition amplifier*	*2B*	*Earth*	*2U*	*Injector no.1*
1J	*Air conditioning relay*	*2C*	*Earth*		*Injector no.3*
1K	*SD connector*	*2D*	*Earth*	*2V*	*Injector no.2*
1N	*TPS*	*2E*	*Distributor ignition*		*Injector no.4*
1O	*Stop lamps switch*	*2J*	*Engine control module*	*2W*	*ISCV*
1P	*Power steering fluid pressure switch*	*2K*	*Hot-wire AFS*	*2X*	*CFSV*
1Q	*Air conditioning control module*	*2L*	*TPS*		
1R	*Engine coolant blower motor relay*	*2M*	*TPS*		

2Y	2W	2U	2S	2Q	2O	2M	2K	2I	2G	2E	2C	2A	1U	1S	1Q	1O	1M	1K	1I	1G	1E	1C	1A
2Z	2X	2V	2T	2R	2P	2N	2L	2J	2H	2F	2D	2B	1V	1T	1R	1P	1N	1L	1J	1H	1F	1D	1B

EQHM3

11.12 Typical EGI two-segment ECM multi-plug

Pin table - three-segment ECM multi-plug

Note: *Refer to* ***illustration 11.13***

Pin	Function
1A	*Battery*
1B	*Main relay*
1C	*Ignition switch*
1D	*SD connector*
1F	*SD connector*
1G	*Amplifier control signal*
1I	*SD connector*
1J	*Air conditioning relay*
1K	*SD connector*
1L	*Combination control module/relay*
1M	*VSS*
1O	*Stop lamps switch*
1P	*Power steering fluid pressure switch*
1Q	*Heater/air conditioning motor switch*
1R	*Heater/air conditioning motor switch*
1S	*Engine coolant blower motor relay*
1T	*Closed throttle position switch*
1U	*Earth*
1V	*Clutch pedal position switch*
2B	*Hot-wire AFS*
2C	*OS, RH*
2D	*OS, LH*
2E	*CTS*
2F	*TPS*
2G	*Coolant sensor (fan)*
2H	*Earth*
2I	*Reference voltage to sensors*
2J	*EGR valve lift signal*
2K	*Hot-wire AFS*
2M	*Knock sensor*
2O	*CFSV*
3A	*Earth*
3B	*Earth*
3C	*Earth*
3D	*Earth*
3E	*Distributor HES signal*
3F	*CAS*
3G	*Distributor HES signal*
3H	*CAS*
3I	*VRIS solenoid valve 1*
3J	*VRIS solenoid valve 2*
3M	*Fuel pressure regulator (PRC)*
3O	*EGR vent solenoid valve*
3P	*EGR vacuum solenoid valve*
3Q	*ISCV*
3T	*Fuel pump relay driver*
3U	*Injector no. 1*
3V	*Injector no. 2*
3W	*Injector no. 3*
3X	*Injector no. 4*
3Y	*Injector no. 5*
3Z	*Injector no. 6*

3Y	3W	3U	3S	3Q	3O	3M	3K	3I	3G	3E	3C	3A
3Z	3X	3V	3T	3R	3P	3N	3L	3J	3H	3F	3D	3B

2O	2M	2K	2I	2G	2E	2C	2A
2P	2N	2L	2J	2H	2F	2D	2B

1U	1S	1Q	1O	1M	1K	1I	1G	1E	1C	1A
1V	1T	1R	1P	1N	1L	1J	1H	1F	1D	1B

EQHM2

11.13 Typical EGI three-segment ECM multi-plug

Fault codes

29 Obtaining fault codes

1 The two-digit fault codes emitted in Mazda vehicles equipped with EGI are of the 'slow' variety, and can be output as flash codes on an analogue voltmeter, LED or warning lamp, depending on model.

2 The flashes are emitted as a straight count of short flashes for the first nine codes (eg 8 flashes indicates code number 8). The numbers from 10 to 69 are indicated by a series of long and short flashes separated by short pauses. The first digit of the number is denoted by the long flashes, and the second digit by the short flashes (eg 41 would be signalled by four long flashes and one short flash).

3 One of two methods are available to capture fault codes. In early models, a green single-pin terminal is provided. In later models, a multi-pin SD connector is provided. The SD connector is usually located upon the left-hand inner wing, or near the AFS.

Early models

4 Locate the green single-pin terminal, and use a jumper wire to connect it to a good earth **(see illustration 11.14)**.

5 Switch on the ignition, and codes will be output on the dash-mounted warning lamp.

Later models

6 If a FCR is available, it could be attached to the SD serial connector and used for the following purposes:

a) Obtaining fault codes.
b) Clearing fault codes.

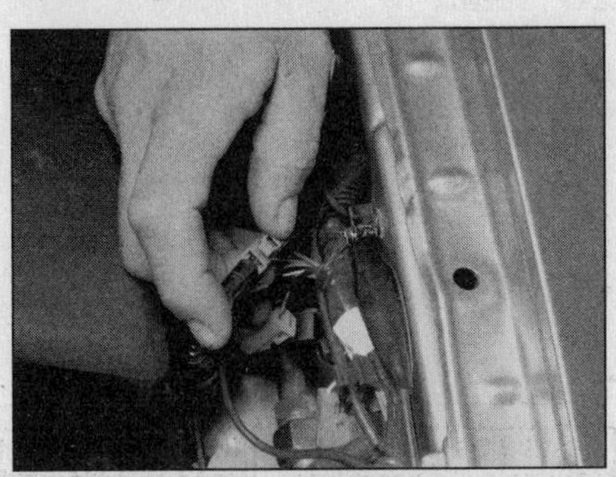

11.14 Early models: Locate the green single-pin terminal, and use a jumper wire to connect it to a good earth. Switch on the ignition, and codes will be output on the dash-mounted warning lamp

c) Obtaining Datastream information.
d) Actuating the system actuators and switches.

7 If a FCR is not available, it is still possible to obtain fault codes.

Obtaining codes without a FCR

8 Turn on the ignition, do not start the engine.

9 Use a jumper lead to bridge terminals TEN and GND in the SD plug **(see illustration 11.15)**. A warning lamp is not provided on later models, so connect an analogue voltmeter or LED lamp (*refer to the Warnings in Reference*) between terminal FEN and the battery positive terminal.

10 The flashes are output as a two-digit code, as described above. By counting the flashes and referring to the fault code table, faults can thus be determined.

Erasing codes

11 The codes will remain logged until the following action is performed.

12 The vehicle battery negative cable should be disconnected for at least 20 seconds (beware of losing other data, such as the radio code, clock setting, etc) and the brake pedal depressed for a period of five seconds.

13 Reconnect the battery cable and recheck the ECM for codes.

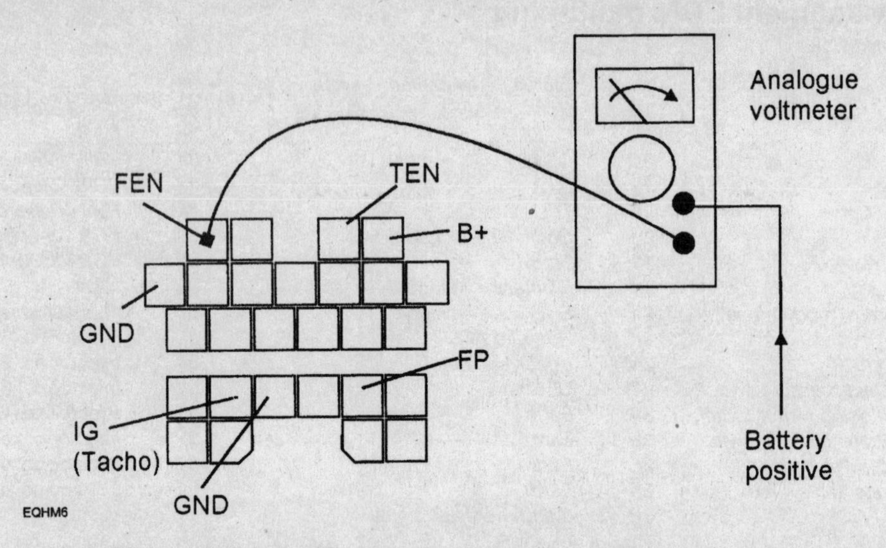

11.15 Bridge terminals TEN and GND in the SD connector. Connect a voltmeter or LED lamp between terminal FEN and the battery positive terminal to gather fault codes

Fault code table

Code	Fault
1	Ignition pulse
2	RPM sensor
3	RPM sensor
4	RPM sensor
5	Knock sensor
6	VSS
8	AFS
9	CTS
10	ATS
12	TPS
14	ECM
15	OS
16	EGR sensor
17	Lambda sensor
23	OS
24	Lambda sensor
25	Fuel pressure regulator solenoid valve
26	CFSV
28	Solenoid valve, EGR vacuum
29	Solenoid valve, EGR vent
34	Idle air control valve A
35	Idle air control valve B
41	Solenoid valve - variable induction system 1
46	Solenoid valve - variable induction system 2
55	Vehicle speed sensor
56	Temperature sensor AT
60	Solenoid valve - 1-2 shift AT
61	Solenoid valve - 2-3 shift AT
62	Solenoid valve - 3-4 shift AT
63	Solenoid valve - lock-up AT
64	Solenoid valve - 3-2 shift AT
64	Cooling fan relay
65	Lock-up solenoid AT
66	Line pressure solenoid AT
67	Cooling fan relay (low temperature)
68	Cooling fan relay (high temperature)
69	Cooling fan thermosensor

Chapter 12
Nissan ECCS

Contents

Specifications

Vehicle	Year	Idle speed	CO%
4WD pick-up 2.4i cat Z24i	1990 to 1994	800 ± 50	1.0 ± 0.5
4WD Wagon 3.0i cat VG30E	1990 to 1994	750 ± 50	0.2 to 0.8
100NX 2.0 cat SOHC 16V SR20DE	1991 to 1994	850 ± 50	0.5 ± 0.5
200 SX cat DOHC 16V Turbo CA18DET	1989 to 1994	850 ± 50	2.0 max
200 SX DOHC 16V turbo SR20DET	1994 to 1996	800 ± 50	0.5 max
300 CX VG30E	1984 to 1991	700 ± 50	1.0 max
300 ZX VG30E	1984 to 1990	900 ± 50	1.0 max
300 ZX Turbo VG30ET	1984 to 1990	900 ± 50	1.0 max
300 ZX Turbo cat DOHC 2x turbo	1990 to 1995	750 ± 50	0.2 to 0.8
Bluebird ZX Turbo SOHC CA 18T	1986 to 1990	650 ± 100	2.0 max
Bluebird 2.0i SOHC CA 20E	1988 to 1990	850 ± 50	1.5 ± 0.5
Micra 1.0i cat DOHC 16V 40kw CG10DE	1993 to 1996	650 ± 50	1.0 max
Micra 1.3i cat DOHC 16V 55kwCG13DE	1993 to 1996	650 ± 50	1.0 max
Maxima VG30E	1989 to 1994	900 ± 50	1.0 max
Maxima cat VG30E	1989 to 1994	900 ± 50	1.0 max
Prairie 2.0i cat SOHC CA20E	1989 to 1991	750 ± 50	0.5 max
Primera 1.6i GA16DE	1994 to 1996	700 ± 50	0.5 max
Primera 2.0 SPi SR20Di	1991 to 1995	850 ± 50	0.3 to 0.5
Primera 2.0 cat DOHC 16V SR20Di	1990 to 1995	850 ± 50	0.5 ± 0.5
Primera Estate 2.0 cat DOHC 16V	1990 to 1996	850 ± 50	0.5 max
Primera 2.0e ZX DOHC 16V SR20DE	1991 to 1995	850 ± 50	0.5 max
Primera 2.0e GT SR20DE	1991 to 1995	850 ± 50	0.5 max
Primera 2.0e cat SR20DE	1991 to 1995	850 ± 50	0.5 max
Primera 2.0i DOHC 16V SR20DE	1994 to 1996	850 ± 50	0.5 max
Primera 2.0i GT DOHC 16V SR20DE	1994 to 1996	850 ± 50	0.5 max
QX 2.0 DOHC 24v V6 VQ20DE	1994 to 1996	675 ± 50	0.3 max
QX 3.0DOHC 24v V6 VQ30DE	1994 to 1996	625 ± 50	0.3 max
Serena 1.6i DOHC 16V 71kw GA16DE	1993 to 1996	750 ± 50	0.5 max
Serena 2.0i DOHC 16V 93kw SR20DE	1993 to 1996	800 ± 50	0.5 max
Silvia Turbo ZX CA18ET	1984 to 1990	750 ± 100	2.0 max
Sunny 1.6i cat SOHC 12V GA16i	1989 to 1991	850 ± 50	0.5 max
Sunny ZX Coupe DOHC 16V CA16DE	1987 to 1989	800 ± 50	2.0 max
Sunny 1.8 ZX cat DOHC 16V CA18DE	1989 to 1991	800 ± 50	0.5 max
Sunny GTi-R DOHC 16V 164kw	1991 to 1994	925+25-75	0.7 ± 0.5
Sunny 2.0 GTi cat DOHC 16V 105kw	1991 to 1994	850 ± 50	0.5 ± 0.5
Terrano II 2.4 KA24EBF	1993 to 1996	800 ± 50	0.5 max
Patrol 4.2i OHV 128kw TB42E	1992 to 1996	650 ± 50	0.5 max
Urvan 2.4i cat Z24i	1989 to 1994	700 ± 50	0.7 to 1.0
Vanette 2.4i cat OHV 52 kW Z24i	1987 to 1994	800 ± 50	N/A

Overview of system operation

1 Introduction

Please read this overview of Nissan ECCS operation in conjunction with Chapter 2, which describes some of the functions in more detail.

The electronic system used to control the majority of Nissan engines equipped with fuel injection is labelled Nissan ECCS. Nissan ECCS has been used for about 10 years, and has evolved greatly over that period of time. Although ECCS is fitted to both MPi and SPi-equipped vehicles, components and ECM connections are similar, and the main differences centre around the crank angle sensor (CAS).

The Nissan ECCS system is a fully-integrated EMS that controls primary ignition, fuelling and idle speed from within the same ECM. In addition, the ECM controls the radiator fan and the air conditioning. A 54-pin connector and multi-plug connects the ECM to the battery, sensors and actuators.

2 Control functions

Signal processing

The ignition point and injection duration are jointly processed by the ECM so that the best moment for ignition and fuelling is determined for every operating condition.

Basic ignition timing is stored in a three-dimensional map, and the engine load and speed signals determine the ignition timing. The main engine load sensor is the hot-wire or hot-film AFS, and engine speed is determined from the crank angle sensor (CAS) signal. Correction factors are then applied for starting, idle, deceleration, and part- and full-load operation. The main correction factor is engine temperature (CTS). Minor corrections to timing and AFR are made with reference to the ATS and TPS signals.

The basic AFR is also stored in a three-dimensional map, and the engine load and speed signals determine the basic injection pulse value. Nissan ECCS calculates the AFR from the AFS signal and the speed of the engine (CAS). The AFR and the pulse duration are then corrected on reference to ATS, CTS, battery voltage, and position of the TPS. Other controlling factors are determined by operating conditions such as cold start and warm-up, idle condition, acceleration and deceleration.

Nissan ECCS accesses a different map for idle running conditions, and this map is implemented whenever the engine speed is at idle. Idle speed during warm-up and normal hot running conditions is maintained by the ISCV. However, Nissan ECCS makes small adjustments to the idle speed by advancing or retarding the timing, and this results in an ignition timing that is forever changing during engine idle.

During wide-open throttle engine operation, the ECM shuts off the A/C (where fitted) for several seconds to improve acceleration.

Basic ECM operation

A permanent voltage supply is made from the vehicle battery to one or more of the ECM pins. This allows the self-diagnostic function to retain data of an intermittent nature. Once the ignition is switched on, a voltage supply is directly made to the ECM from the ignition switch. The ignition switch also supplies voltage to the ignition coil, OS heater, CFSV, EGR valve, and fuel pump relay. On receiving the ignition on signal, the ECM switches on the main relay, which supplies voltage to one or more ECM pins, the AFS and the CAS.

The majority of sensors (other than those that generate a voltage such the CAS and OS), are now provided with a 5.0 volt reference supply from a relevant pin on the ECM. When the engine is cranked or run, a speed signal from the CAS causes the ECM to earth the pump relay driver pin, so that the fuel pump will run. A cranking signal from the ignition switch is also received by the ECM. Ignition and injection functions are activated during cranking and running. Actuators such as the ISCV, CFSV and EGR are supplied with nbv from the ignition switch, and the injector receives its own voltage supply directly from the battery positive terminal. The ECM completes the circuit by pulsing the relevant actuator wire to earth according to vehicle operating conditions of the moment.

Self-diagnostic function

The Nissan ECCS system has a self-test capability that regularly examines the signals from engine sensors and internally logs a code in the event of a fault being present. If the fault clears, the code will remain logged until erased by procedure, or when the battery is disconnected.

The codes emitted are of the 'slow code' variety. This means that the codes can be displayed on the dash warning lamp by bridging two of the terminals in the self-test connector, or by connecting a suitable fault code reader to the ECCS serial port.

When the ECM detects a major fault whilst the engine is running, ECM pin 24 is earthed, and the warning lamp on the dash will light. The lamp will stay lit until the fault is corrected.

In addition to the self-test capability, Nissan ECCS has a limp-home mode, or limited operation strategy (LOS). In the event of a serious fault in the ECM or one of the sensors circuits, the EMS will enter LOS. The degree of LOS depends upon the nature of the fault.

The ECM will initiate the following LOS action during failure of the ECM. LOS will only occur whilst the ignition is 'on'. If the ignition is switched off, LOS is discontinued and will only be reactivated if the fault condition is still present when the ignition is next switched on. Otherwise, the ECM will revert to normal operation.

Failure of main CPU in ECM:

a) The dash warning lamp is illuminated.
b) Fuel injection is limited to once every engine revolution.
c) The ignition timing set to a pre-determined fixed value.
d) The fuel pump relay is switched 'on' when the engine is running and switched 'off' when the engine is stopped.
e) The ISCV is fully opened.
f) The radiator fans relay is switched on.

The ECM will initiate the following actions during the failure of a particular sensor.

AFS or AFS circuit outside of normal operating parameters:

a) Signal from the TPS provides the ECM with substitute load signal.
b) A pre-determined injector value is used during engine starting.
c) Engine speed is limited to a maximum of 2400 rpm.

Failure of CTS, or CTS circuit outside of normal operating parameters:

a) The CTS value is set to 20°C on ignition switch-on or engine start.
b) The CTS value is slowly changed from 20°C to 80°C during the 6 minutes after ignition switch-on or engine start.
c) The CTS value is set to 80°C 6 minutes after ignition switch-on or engine start.

Failure of TPS, or TPS circuit outside of normal operating parameters:

a) The TPS signal is totally disregarded, and engine performance during acceleration will be poor. Idle position is determined from rpm and injector duration.

Failure of KS or KS circuit outside of normal operating parameters:

a) The ignition timing will be retarded according to operating conditions.

Reference voltage

Voltage supply from the ECM to many of the engine sensors is at a 5.0-volt reference level. This ensures a stable working voltage, unaffected by variations in system voltage.

The earth return connection for some engine sensors is made through an ECM pin that is not directly connected to earth. The ECM internally connects that pin to earth via one of the ECM pins that are directly connected to earth.

Signal shielding

To reduce interference (RFI), the airflow sensor, crank angle sensor, knock sensor, throttle pot and oxygen sensor are protected with a shielded cable. The shielded cable is connected to the ECM earth wires at pins 39 and 48 to reduce interference to a minimum.

Vehicle speed sensor (VSS)

The VSS is used to advise the ECM of vehicle speed. A reed switch is installed opposite a magnetic plate in the speedometer housing. As the speedometer cable rotates, the VSS generates an AC pulse which the ECM then converts to a digital value. Vehicle speed is thus converted to a pulse signal.

3 Primary trigger

Crank angle sensor (CAS)

The primary trigger to initiate both ignition and injection emanates from a CAS mounted in an optical distributor. The optical distributor and the CAS operate on a different principle to the conventional CAS or Hall-effect sensor (HES) that are used in the majority of European vehicles. The optical distributor consists of two LED's (light-emitting diodes), a thin disk or rotor with two rows of slits, and two optical diodes or pick-ups **(see illustration 12.1)**.

The following description concerns a typical ECCS CAS. However, the number of slits, ECM pin connections, and operation does vary between the different four- and six-cylinder models.

Primera P10 SPi

The outer row of slits are cut into the circumference of the rotor, fairly close to the edge, with a total of 360 slits cut at intervals of 1°. The inner row of slits consists of one slit for every cylinder (4 slits for a four-cylinder engine, cut at 90° intervals). Because the distributor rotates at half engine speed, the slits that are cut at 90° correspond to a crankshaft angle of 180°. One of the four inner slits is elongated, and this marks the position of No 1 cylinder. Equivalent six-cylinder slits are cut at 60° angles corresponding to 120° crankshaft angles. Because the position of No 1 cylinder is identified, a separate cylinder identification (CID) sensor for the sequential multi-point injection is unnecessary.

12.1 Crank angle sensor (CAS) assembly mounted in a Nissan distributor (6-cylinder engine shown). The arrow points to the optical pick-up. Beneath the pick-up is the rotor disk containing the two rows of slits. The large rectangular slit indicates the position of No 1 cylinder

A voltage supply from the main relay switches the LED's on when the ignition switch is turned to the 'on' position, and a second wire completes the earth circuit. The LED's are mounted in the distributor above the rotor which is attached to the distributor shaft. The pick-ups are mounted under the rotor, and connected to the ECM by two separate signal wires.

When a slit is opposite the LED, a circuit is completed as the light from the LED shines through the slit to energise the pick-up. As the rotor rotates and the two rows of slits pass under the two LED's, the pick-ups are switched on and off. Waveforming circuitry in the distributor transforms these signals into a series of on/off pulses, and two distinctive square waveform signals are returned to the ECM by the two signal wires. The outer slits send a speed signal, and the inner slits send a position signal to the ECM. Sometimes the speed signal is termed the 'high resolution' signal, and the position signal termed the 'low resolution' signal.

4 Ignition

Data on load (AFS), engine speed and position (CAS), engine temperature (CTS) and throttle position (TPS) are collected by the ECM, which then refers to the digital map stored within its microprocessor. This map contains an advance angle for each operating condition, and thus the best ignition advance angle for a particular operating condition can be determined. The ECM looks up the correct dwell duration and timing point, and signals the amplifier - which in turn switches the coil negative terminal to achieve ignition. Unusually for an engine equipped with an EMS, the base ignition timing is adjustable. However, the correct setting procedure must be followed.

Amplifier

The amplifier contains the circuitry for switching the coil negative terminal to instigate ignition. ECCS utilises a separate amplifier mounted on the bulkhead adjacent to the EGR valve **(see illustration 12.2)**. The ECM timing signal is of an insufficient level to complete the necessary coil switching, and the signal is thus amplified to a level capable of switching the coil negative terminal. The ECM thus calculates the correct ignition dwell time and timing advance from data received from its sensors, and sends a control signal to the amplifier, which then switches the coil negative terminal. In addition, a resistor is wired into the coil negative/amplifier and ECM circuit to facilitate amplifier switching. In other systems, this resistor may be located internally in the amplifier.

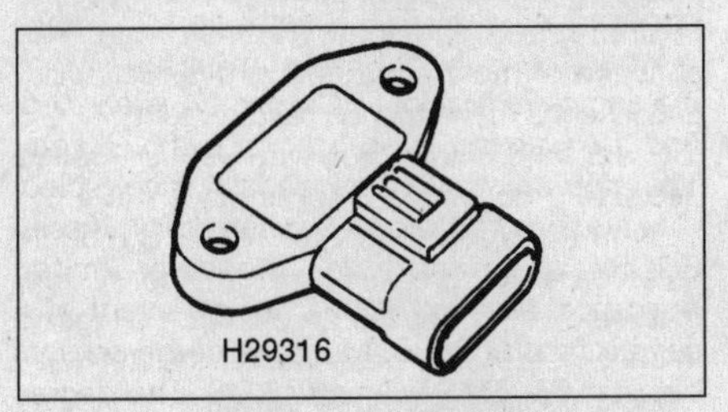

12.2 External amplifier

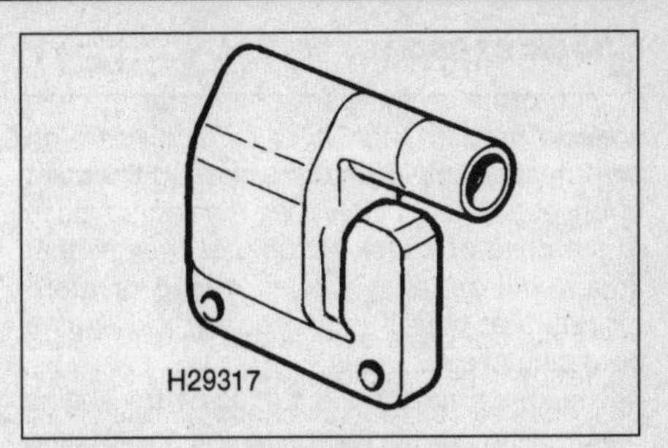

12.3 Ignition coil

Ignition dwell

Dwell operation in Nissan ECCS is based upon the principle of the 'constant-energy current-limiting' system. This means that the dwell period remains constant at around 4.0 to 5.0 ms, at virtually all engine running speeds. However, the dwell duty cycle, when measured in percent or degrees, will vary as the engine speed varies.

Ignition coil

The ignition coil utilises low primary resistance in order to increase primary current and primary energy **(see illustration 12.3)**. The amplifier limits the primary current to around 8 amps, and this permits a reserve of energy to maintain the required spark burn time (duration).

Optical distributor

In the Nissan system, the optical distributor contains the primary trigger rotor and LED's and the secondary HT components, and serves to distribute the HT current from the coil secondary terminal to each spark plug in firing order **(see illustration 12.4)**.

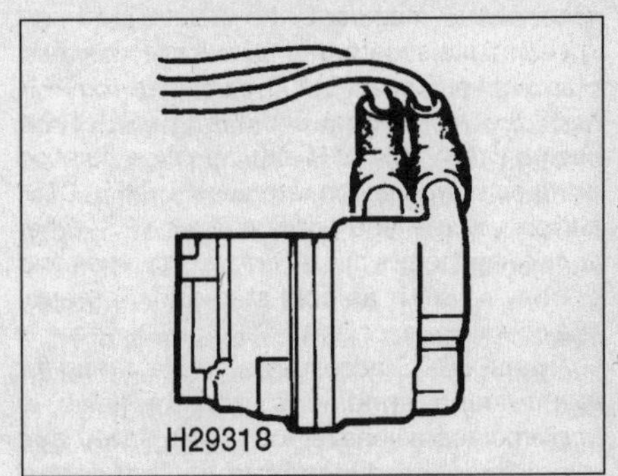

12.4 ECCS distributor

Knock sensor

The optimal ignition timing (at engine speeds greater than idle) for a given high compression engine is quite close to the point of onset of knock. However, running so close to the point of knock occurrence, means that knock will certainly occur on one or more cylinders at certain times during the engine operating cycle.

The knock sensor is mounted on the engine block, and consists of a piezo-ceramic measuring element that responds to engine noise oscillations. Engine knock is converted to a voltage signal by the knock sensor, and returned to the knock control processor for evaluation and action. The knocking frequency is in the 8 to 15kHz frequency band.

Initially, timing will occur at its optimal ignition point. Once knock is identified, the knock control processor retards the ignition timing.

5 Fuel injection

General

Nissan has adopted two distinct methods for providing fuel to the engines equipped with ECCS. The methods are sequential multi-point injection (MPi) and single-point injection (SPi).

Because of the modularity of ECCS, very little difference exists between the control system on the various engines. Differences in implementation are described below.

The ECCS ECM contains a fuel map with an injector opening time (or pulse duration) for basic conditions of speed and load. Information is then gathered from engine sensors such as the airflow sensor (AFS), crank angle sensor (CAS), coolant temperature sensor (CTS), air temperature sensor (ATS) and throttle pot (TPS). As a result of this information, the ECM will look up the correct injector pulse duration right across the engine rpm, load and temperature range.

The amount of fuel delivered by the injector(s) is determined by the fuel pressure and the pulse duration. During engine start-up from cold, the pulse duration and number of pulses (frequency) are increased to provide a richer air/fuel mixture.

The fuel injector is a magnetically-operated solenoid valve, with voltage applied from the battery positive terminal and an earth path through the ECM. The injector is switched using two circuits. Operation depends on the principle that more current is required to open an injector than to keep it open. This kind of system is often termed 'current-controlled injection system'. Once the injector is open, a second circuit rapidly pulses the injector to earth. The switching is so rapid that the injector is effectively held open, and less current is required during the operation. Advantages of this arrangement include a reduction in injector operating temperature, and immediate injector closure once the holding circuit is switched off.

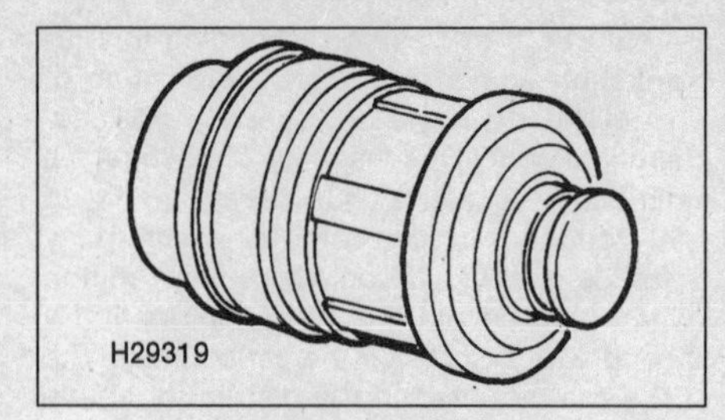

12.5 Single-point injector

During engine start-up from cold, the pulse duration is increased to provide a richer air/fuel mixture. During engine deceleration, the pulse reduces to zero as the ECM cuts off the injection pulse. At excessive engine speeds, the ECM cuts off injector operation as a safety precaution.

Single-point fuel injection (SPi)

The SPi system consists of a single injector mounted in the throttle body **(see illustration 12.5)**. In SPi engines, fuel is injected into the inlet manifold where it mixes with air. The depression produced by a descending piston causes the resulting air/fuel mixture to be drawn into each cylinder. The injector is normally actuated twice per engine revolution. However, during low or high load engine operation, or if a fault develops that causes the ECM to enter LOS, the injector is actuated once per engine revolution.

Multi-point injection (MPi - sequential)

The sequential MPi system consists of one injector for each cylinder, mounted in the inlet port, so that a finely-atomised fuel spray is directed onto the back of each valve. With reference to the No 1 cylinder signal from the CAS sensor, the injectors are actuated as the inlet valve opens.

Hot-wire air mass meter (AFS)

Nissan ECCS utilises a hot-wire airflow sensor, incorporated into the throttle body, to measure the mass of air entering the engine **(see illustration 12.6)**. Measuring the air mass means that corrections for a change in air density are unnecessary, since the density is now a known quantity. This is a more accurate method of assessing the engine load from air input, and ensures more precise metering of the fuel injection pulse over the engine speed and temperature range. The absence of moving parts improves reliability and lessens maintenance requirements.

Essentially, the hot-wire is so-called because a hot-wire sensor is placed in a by-pass to the main air intake. The AFS module receives a voltage supply from the system main relay, and applies a constant voltage to the hot-wire. As air passes over the hot-wire, it has a cooling effect. As air mass increases or decreases according to engine load, the AFS module adjusts the current flow to maintain the wire at its original resistance and temperature. The change in heating current is measured as a voltage drop over a precision resistor, and amplified by the AFS module as a measured value. This measured value is then returned to the ECM for evaluation as a load signal.

12.6 Hot-wire or hot-film air mass meter (AFS)

By measuring the change in current flow, the ECM is able to determine the mass of air flowing into the engine. As current varies on the signal wire, so too does voltage, and an accurate indication of load can be assessed by measuring the variable voltage signal.

Air temperature sensor (ATS)

The ATS is part of the AFS, and measures the air temperature passing through the throttle body. Because the density of air varies in inverse proportion to the temperature, the ATS signal allows more accurate assessment of the volume of air entering the engine. Since the ATS operates in conjunction with the AFS, the two sensors should be considered as one.

Where a separate ATS signal wire is provided (some models), a variable voltage signal is returned to the ECM based upon the air temperature. This signal is approximately 5.0 to 7.0 volts depending upon temperature.

Coolant temperature sensor (CTS)

The CTS is incorporated in the cooling system, and contains a variable resistance that operates on the NTC principle. When the engine is cold, the resistance is quite high. Once the engine is started and begins to warm-up, the coolant becomes hotter, and this causes a change in the CTS resistance. As the CTS becomes hotter, the resistance of the CTS reduces (NTC principle), and this returns a variable voltage signal to the ECM based upon the coolant temperature.

The open-circuit supply to the sensor is at a 5.0-volt reference level, and this voltage reduces to a value that depends upon the resistance of the CTS resistance. Normal operating temperature is usually from 80 to 100°C. The ECM uses the CTS signal as a main correction factor when calculating ignition timing and injection duration.

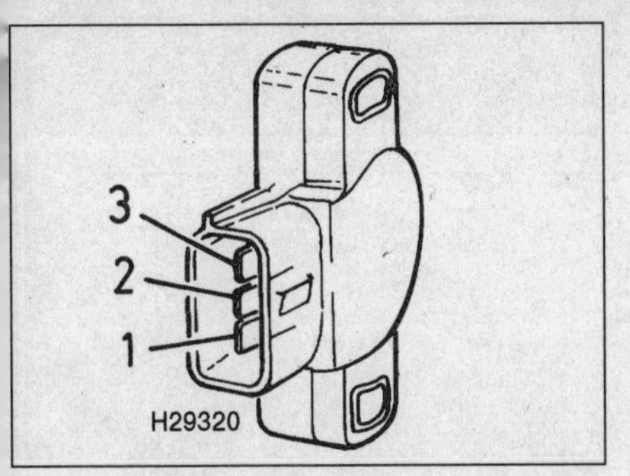

12.7 Throttle potentiometer sensor (TPS)

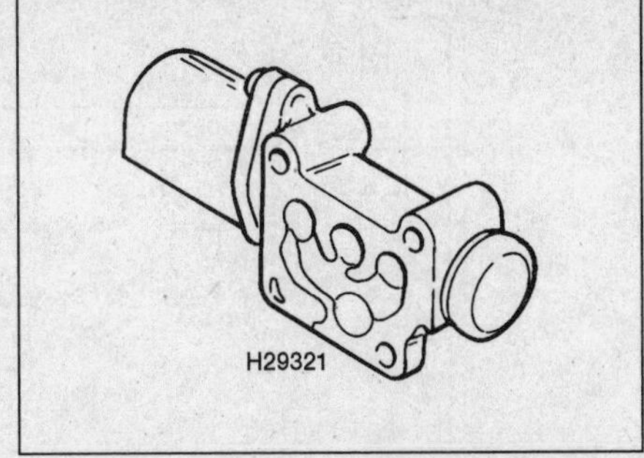

12.8 Idle speed control valve (ISCV)

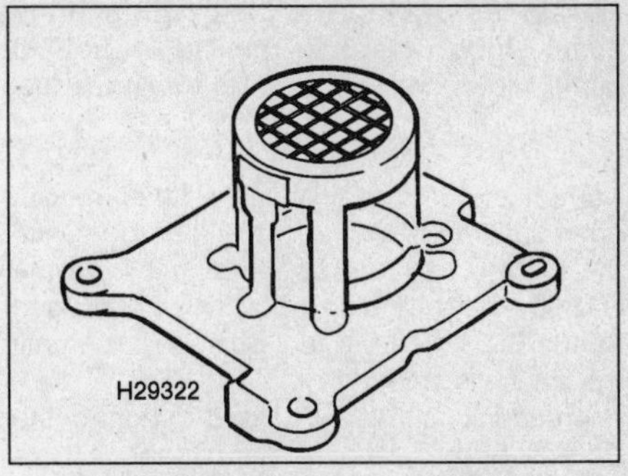

12.9 Throttle body heater (TBH)

Throttle potentiometer sensor (TPS)

A TPS is provided to inform the ECM of throttle position, and rate of acceleration **(see illustration 12.7)**. The TPS is a potentiometer with three wires. A 5.0-volt reference voltage is supplied to a resistance track, with the other end connected to earth. The third wire is connected to an arm which wipes along the resistance track, and so varies the resistance and voltage of the signal returned to the ECM.

Power steering pressure switch (PSPS)

This switch is operated by a change in pressure when the power steering is in operation. The PSPS is located in the engine compartment, in the delivery pipe to the steering gear. The PSPS is open when the steering gear fluid pressure is low (ie when the steering is straight). The switch closes when the steering is turned (ie when the fluid pressure rises above a pre-determined value).

A voltage of approximately 7 to 9 volts is applied to the PSPS. When the steering is straight and the PSPS is open, the voltage is at nbv level. When the steering is turned and the steering gear fluid pressure reaches its pre-determined value, the PSPS closes, and the voltage on the PSPS pin drops to near zero. The ECM then increases the idle speed, as the increased load caused by the power steering comes into play.

Idle control

ECCS uses two methods to control the idle speed during the various operating conditions. When the engine is first started from cold, an FIC (fast idle cam) raises the idle speed until the engine has warmed up. At normal operating temperature, the ECM regulates a solenoid-controlled actuator to maintain normal idle speed according to loads placed upon the engine.

FIC

The FIC is a throwback to the days of the carburettor, and is very similar in operation to the type fitted to many Japanese-designed carburettors. A waxstat element that is influenced by coolant temperature bears against the FIC. When the engine is cold, the waxstat pushes the cam against the throttle stop, and the throttle is forced open enough to give a fast idle. As the engine warms up, the coolant temperature heats the waxstat, and the FIC rotates toward the 'off' position. In turn, the idle speed returns to the normal hot idle position.

Idle speed control valve (ISCV)

The ISCV is a solenoid-controlled actuator used to automatically control engine idle at normal engine operating temperatures **(see illustration 12.8)**. The ISCV is located in a hose that connects the inlet manifold to the air filter side of the throttle plate.

The target idle speed is logged in a map situated in the ECM memory. When the ECM senses the idle situation from the closed TPS, it controls the idle speed by pulsing the ISCV to maintain an engine speed as close to the target value as possible, depending on load or temperature.

When an electrical load, such as headlights or heater fan etc are switched on, the idle speed would tend to drop. The idle ECM will sense the load, and rotate the ISCV to increase the airflow through the valve and thus maintain the idle speed. When the load is removed, the ECM will pulse the valve so that the airflow is reduced. Normal idle speed should be maintained under all hot operating conditions.

A duty cycle can be measured on the earth circuit, to determine the opening or closing time period as a percentage of the total time available. The more open the valve, the greater the duty cycle, and the lower the average voltage.

Throttle body heater (SPi models only)

The throttle body heater (TBH) is located between the lower throttle body and the inlet manifold **(see illustration 12.9)**. This heater is provided to heat the throttle body, so that icing does not occur during cold and humid atmospheric conditions.

The heater works on the PTC principle, and allows a greater current to quickly heat throttle body during the warm-up period. As the heater warms up, the resistance increases and the current reduces. Voltage supply is controlled by the ECM, which switches the heater on and off as required. The ECM switches the heater 'on' when the engine is running at a coolant temperature below 65°C and the battery voltage is above 13 volts. Once the engine temperature rises above 65°C for more than a few seconds, the heater is switched off.

Relays

The Nissan ECCS system is controlled by a main fuel injection relay and a fuel pump relay **(see illustration 12.10)**. A permanent voltage supply is made to the main relay terminals 3 and 2 from the battery positive terminal. When the ignition is switched on, the ECM earths terminal 1 through ECM pin number 4, which energises the first relay winding. This causes the first relay contacts to close, and terminal 3 is connected to the output circuit at terminal 5. Terminal 5 supplies voltage to ECM pins 38 and 47, the AFS and the CAS. When the ignition is switched off, the ECM will hold the relay driver on for a further 15 seconds before the circuit is switched off.

When the ignition is switched on, a switched voltage supply is made to pump relay terminals 3 and 2, and the ECM briefly earths fuel pump relay contact 1 (usually at ECM pin number 104). This energises the relay winding, which closes the relay contact and connects voltage from pump relay terminal 3 to terminal 5, thereby providing voltage to the fuel pump circuit. After approximately five seconds (if there is no CAS

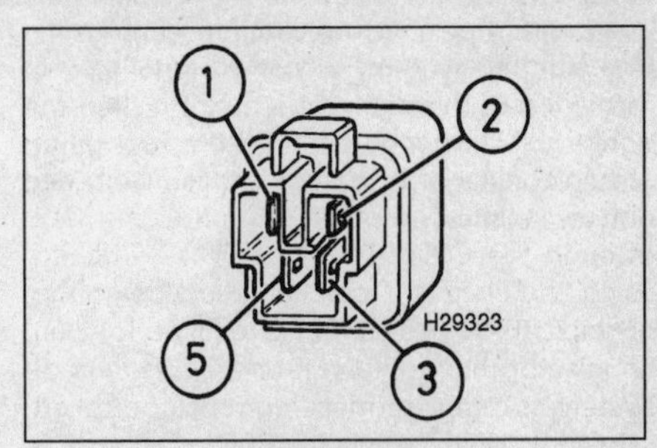

12.10 ECCS relay

1 Relay driver, ECM
2 Battery supply to relay
3 Battery supply to relay
5 Relay output

signal), the ECM opens the circuit and the pump stops. This brief running of the fuel pump allows pressure to build within the fuel pressure lines, and provides for an easier start.

The fuel pump relay circuit will then remain open until the engine is cranked or run. Once the ECM receives a speed signal from the CAS, the relay winding will again be energised by the ECM, and the fuel pump will run until the engine is stopped.

An additional relay is utilised to control the throttle body heater. A permanent voltage supply is made to main relay terminal 3 from the battery positive terminal. When the ignition is switched on, a switched voltage supply is made to relay terminal 2. Once the engine is running under certain conditions, the ECM earths relay contact 1. This energises the relay winding, which closes the relay contact and connects voltage from relay terminal 3 to terminal 5, thereby providing voltage to the throttle body heater. Voltage supply is controlled by the ECM, which switches the heater on and off as required. Refer to the paragraph on the TBH for an explanation of the ECM control process.

Fuel pressure system

Switching the ignition key on causes the ECM to energise the fuel pump relay for approximately five seconds so that the fuel system is pressurised. The fuel pump relay is then switched off, to await a cranking or running signal. Once the engine is running, fuel is fed through a non-return valve and fuel filter to the single throttle body injector or the multi-point fuel rail.

The fuel pump is mounted vertically in the fuel tank. Fuel is drawn through the pump inlet, to be pressurised and discharged from the pump outlet into the fuel supply line **(see illustration 12.11)**.

Fuel pressure regulator

A system fuel pressure of approximately 2.5 bar is controlled by the pressure regulator, which is located within the throttle body next to the injector (SPi) or on the fuel rail (MPi). As the pressure rises over the pre-determined level, excess fuel is returned to the fuel tank via a return pipe. To prevent pressure loss in the supply system, a non-return valve is provided in the fuel pump outlet. When the ignition is switched off, and the fuel pump ceases operation, pressure is thus maintained for some time.

6 Catalytic converter and emission control

Catalyst versions of the Nissan ECCS injection system are equipped with a closed-loop control system, so that exhaust emissions may be reduced. Closed-loop systems have an oxygen sensor (OS) which monitors the exhaust gas for oxygen content. A low oxygen level in the exhaust signifies a rich mixture. A high oxygen level in the exhaust signifies a weak mixture.

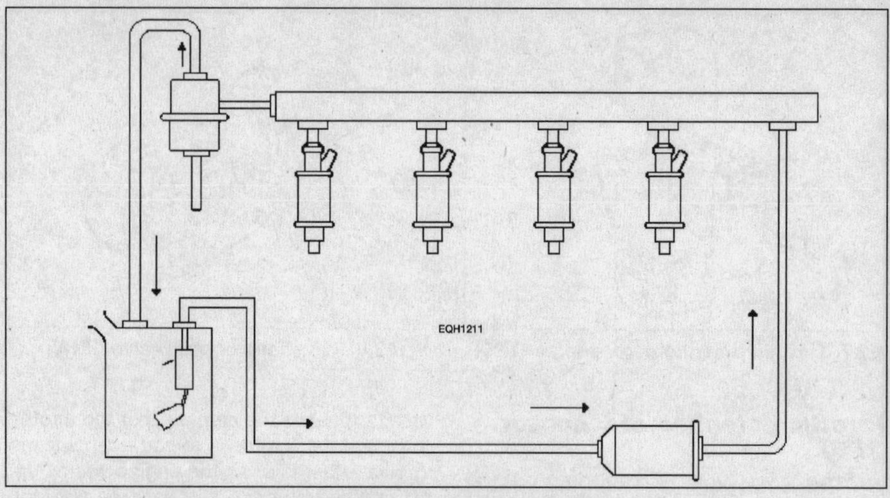

12.11 Fuel pressure circuit

The OS used in the Nissan system is constructed from ceramic titania. At the ideal AFR, ie stoichiometric, the resistance changes dramatically to provide a switching action. The ECM provides a voltage of 1.0 volt to the sensor, and the switching resistance of the OS causes this to fluctuate between zero and 1.0 volt at a frequency of about 8 times per 10 seconds.

When the engine is operating under closed-loop control, the OS signal causes the ECM to modify the injector pulse so that the AFR is maintained close to the stoichiometric ratio. By controlling the injection pulse during most operating conditions, so that the air/fuel ratio is always in a small 'window' around the Lambda point (ie Lambda = 0.97 to 1.03), almost perfect combustion could be achieved. Thus the catalyst has less work to do, and will last longer, with fewer emissions at the tail pipe.

The closed-loop control is implemented during engine operation at normal coolant temperatures. When the coolant temperature is low, the engine is idling, at full load, or on the overrun, the ECM will operate in open-loop. In addition, the ECM will fall into open-loop if the OS circuit develops a fault. When operating in open-loop, the ECM allows a richer or leaner AFR than the stoichiometric ratio. This prevents engine hesitation, for example, during acceleration with a wide-open throttle.

The OS only produces a signal when the exhaust gas has reached a minimum temperature of approximately 300°C. In order that the OS will reach optimum operating temperature as quickly as possible after the engine has started, the OS contains a heating element.

The OS heater supply is made from the ignition switch, and this ensures that the heater will operate whilst the ignition is switched on.

Carbon filter and EGR vacuum switching valve (VSV)

The ECCS ECM controls basic operation of both the carbon filter and EGR system by actuating a single vacuum switching valve (VSV) which cuts vacuum to both the CFCV and EGR components **(see illustration 12.12)**. When the VSV is switched 'off', vacuum is piped to the EGR and CFCV. When the VSV is switched 'on', an outlet channel bleeds the vacuum away to atmosphere (via the air filter). The operating conditions under which the ECM switches 'on' the VSV to disconnect the carbon filter and EGR vacuum control are as follows:

a) AFS fault.
b) Low engine temperature.
c) High engine temperature.
d) Engine start-up.
e) Engine idling.
f) High speed engine operation.

Carbon filter control valve (CFCV)

A CFCV and activated carbon canister is employed in catalyst-equipped vehicles, to aid evaporative emission control **(see illustration 12.13)**. Unlike many modern vehicles, the main method of opening the canister for vapour purging is controlled by a mechanical valve (CFCV) whose actuation

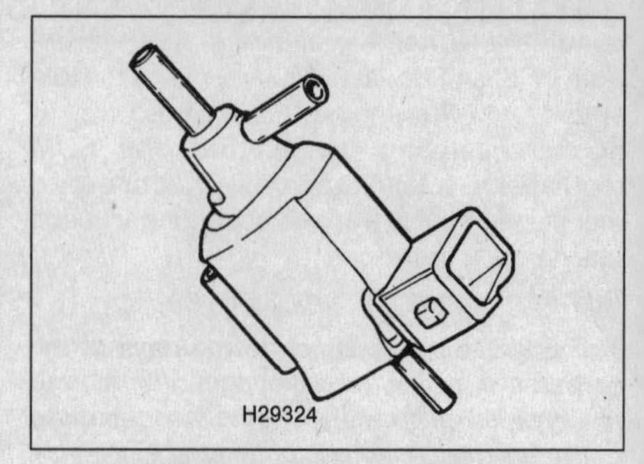

12.12 Carbon filter and EGR vacuum switching valve (VSV)

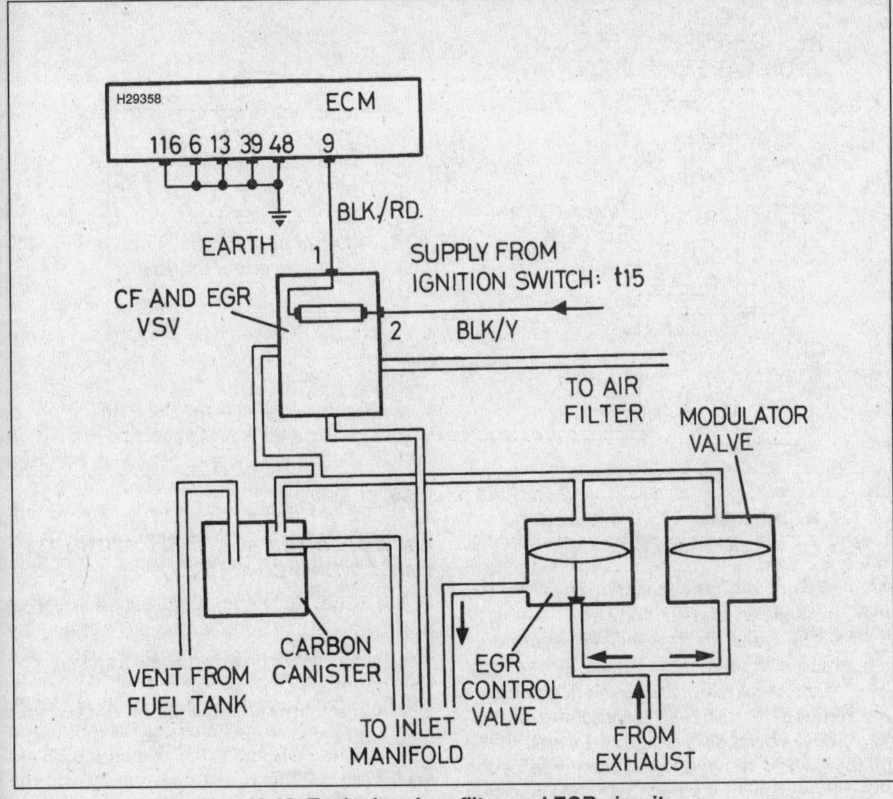

12.13 Typical carbon filter and EGR circuit

depends upon an increasing level of manifold vacuum.

The carbon canister is filled with active charcoal, and stores fuel vapours from the sealed fuel tank during the time that the engine is stopped. Two methods are then used to purge the canister of vapours once the engine is started. A vacuum hose from the inlet manifold connects to a constant purge valve with a small permanently-open orifice. At engine idle speed, a small amount of air is drawn through the air inlet opening at the bottom of the canister, and the air combines with a small volume of vapour to be drawn into the inlet manifold.

The vacuum hose to the CFCV is routed through the carbon filter and EGR VSV. Vacuum is only applied to the CFCV under certain operating conditions determined by the ECM and described above.

Once the carbon filter and EGR VSV is deactivated, vacuum is applied from a ported vacuum channel in the throttle body adjacent to the throttle valve. As the throttle is opened and the vacuum pull becomes greater, air is drawn through the air inlet opening at the bottom of the canister, and air and fuel vapours are drawn into the inlet manifold through both the open CFCV and the constant purge valve, to be burnt during normal combustion.

Exhaust gas recirculation (EGR)

Modern high-compression engines running at high temperatures tend to produce a high level of NOx. Production of NOx can be reduced by recycling a small amount of exhaust gas into the combustion chamber. So long as the recycling of the exhaust gas is properly controlled, engine operation will be little affected. If the exhaust gas was recycled in a cold engine, its performance and idle would be adversely affected.

The EGR system used in Nissan ECCS-equipped vehicles is a mechanical system controlled by engine vacuum. However, the ECM exercises overall control by using the combined carbon filter and EGR VSV to control the vacuum applied to the EGR valve.

By this means, EGR operation only occurs after the engine has attained normal operating temperature and the engine is operating under part-load conditions.

The EGR system consists of a modulator valve and EGR valve. When operating conditions are suitable, vacuum is piped to the EGR modulator valve. The EGR modulator valve controls the vacuum supply to the EGR valve. A channel from the exhaust system pipes exhaust gases to the modulator. A combination of engine vacuum and exhaust gas pressure allows the modulator to control the opening of the EGR valve, which in turn opens to allow a finely-metered supply of exhaust gas to be introduced into the inlet manifold.

Engine operating under part-load conditions

The throttle is partly open, and the vacuum signal acting on the modulator is quite strong. The exhaust gases acting upon the modulator are also strong, which opens the modulator exhaust valve against a spring. In turn, this seals the vacuum channel, and allows the vacuum signal to be directed to the modulator outlet, where it actuates the EGR valve which opens in turn to allow a finely-metered supply of exhaust gas to be introduced into the inlet manifold.

12

Adjustments

7 Adjustment pre-conditions

1 Ensure that all of these conditions are met before attempting to make adjustments

a) Engine at operating temperature. Engine oil at a minimum temperature of 80°C; a journey of at least 4 miles is recommended (particularly so if equipped with AT).
b) Ancillary equipment (all engine loads and accessories) switched off.
c) AT vehicles: Transmission in N or P.
d) Engine mechanically sound.
e) Engine breather hoses and breather system in satisfactory condition.
f) Induction system must be free from vacuum leaks.
g) Ignition system in satisfactory condition.
h) Air filter in satisfactory condition.
i) Exhaust system free from leaks.
j) Throttle cable correctly adjusted.
k) No fault codes logged by the ECM.
l) OS operating satisfactorily (catalyst vehicles with closed-loop control).

2 In addition, before checking the idle speed and CO values, stabilise the engine as follows:

a) Stabilise the engine. Raise the engine speed to 3000 rpm for a minimum of 30 seconds, and then let the engine idle.
b) If the cooling fan operates during adjustment, wait until it stops, re-stabilise the engine and then restart the adjustment procedure.
c) Allow the CO and idle speed to settle.
d) Make all checks and adjustments within 30 seconds. If this time is exceeded, re-stabilise the engine and recheck.

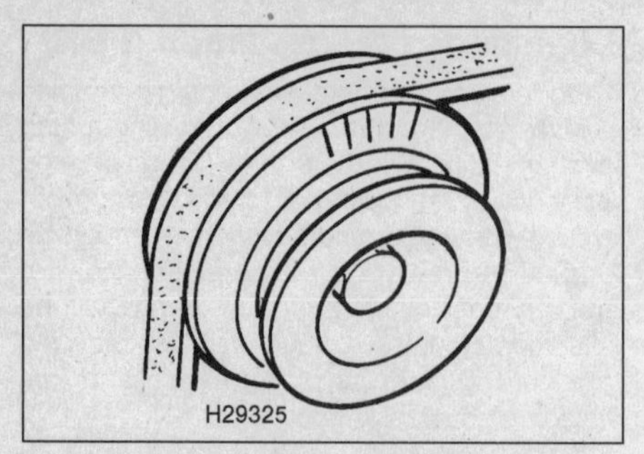

12.14 Typical Nissan ignition timing marks

8 Throttle adjustments

1 Setting conditions: Engine stopped, throttle closed, ignition 'on'.
2 Attach a voltmeter between terminal 3 and earth. A voltage between 0.52 and 0.62 volts should be obtained. A higher voltage indicates that the TPS is incorrectly adjusted.
3 Loosen the two securing screws and adjust the switch until the voltmeter indicates a voltage within the specified parameters.

9 Ignition timing checks

1 Unlike the majority of EMS's, the ignition timing is adjustable on the Nissan ECCS.
2 Refer to the adjustment pre-conditions in Section 7.
3 Allow the engine to idle at normal operating temperature.
4 Raise the engine speed to 2000 rpm for a period of 2 minutes, and then allow the engine to idle.
5 The ignition timing may be adjusted with the aid of a FCR, or by using the following method.
6 Stop the engine.
7 Disconnect the multi-plug to the TPS.
8 Restart the engine and allow it to idle.
9 Connect a stroboscopic timing light and tachometer.
10 Check the ignition timing, and compare to specification (15 ± 2°) **(see illustration 12.14)**.

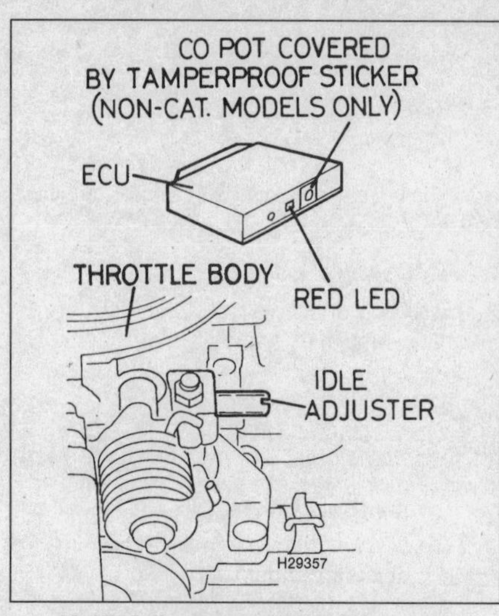

12.15 Adjustment of the idle speed and CO (SPi)

11 If the timing is incorrect, loosen the distributor bolts and rotate the distributor until it is correct. Tighten the distributor bolts.
12 Stop the engine.
13 Reconnect the multi-plug to the TPS.
14 Restart the engine and allow it to idle.
15 Increase the engine speed. The timing marks should advance. No values are stated, but expect the timing mark to advance smoothly.

10 Idle adjustments

Base idle speed

1 Refer to the adjustment pre-conditions in Section 7.
2 Check that the TPS is correctly adjusted (see Section 8).
3 Check that the ignition timing is correctly adjusted.
4 Allow the engine to idle at normal operating temperature.
5 Raise the engine speed to 2000 rpm for a period of 2 minutes, and then allow the engine to idle.
6 The base idle speed may be adjusted with the aid of a FCR, or by using the following method.

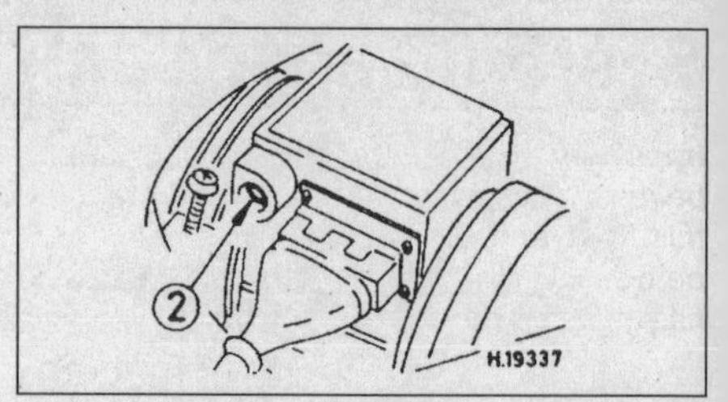

12.16 CO pot adjuster (2) is located in AFS on some models

7 Stop the engine.
8 Disconnect the multi-plug to the TPS.
9 Restart the engine and allow it to idle.
10 Check that the base idle speed is within its normal operating parameters (800 ± 50 rpm).
11 If the idle speed requires adjustment, turn the adjustment screw **(see illustration 12.15)** on the throttle body until the correct idle speed is attained.
12 Stop the engine and reconnect the TPS multi-plug.
13 Restart the engine and allow it to idle.
14 Check that the regulated idle speed is within its normal operating parameters (850 ± 50 rpm).

CO adjustment (non-cat models only)

15 Refer to the adjustment pre-conditions in Section 7.
16 Check that the TPS, ignition timing and idle speed are all correctly adjusted.
17 Connect a gas analyser.
18 Check the idle CO value. If the CO value is outside of its operating parameters, it will require adjustment.
19 Remove the sealing label from the side of the ECM, where applicable. On some models, a CO pot is provided on the AFS **(see illustration 12.16)**.
20 Turn the CO adjustment screw until the correct value is attained.
21 Recheck the idle speed. If the idle speed is incorrect, the whole idle speed and CO adjustment procedure must be restarted from the beginning.
22 When both idle speed and CO adjustment are correct, seal the ECM with a new seal.

System sensor and actuator tests

Important note: *Please refer to Chapter 4, which describes common test procedures applicable to this system. The routines in Chapter 4 should be read in conjunction with the component notes and wiring diagrams presented in this Chapter. The wiring diagrams and other data presented in this Chapter are necessarily representative of the system depicted. Because of the variations in wiring and other data that often occurs, even between similar vehicles in any particular VM's range, the reader should take great care in identification of ECM pins, and satisfy himself that he has gathered the correct data before failing a particular component.*

11 Crank angle sensor (CAS)

General

1 Remove the distributor cap and visually inspect the rotor plate for damage and eccentricity. If necessary, remove the distributor from the engine and rotate the shaft. The shaft and rotor plate must rotate without deviation or distortion.
2 Check the CAS shield wire.
3 The CAS and ECM multi-plug must remain connected during signal output tests.
4 A voltmeter, dwell meter or frequency meter can be used for signal output tests.
Note: *The following method is typical where two distinct signals are produced by the CAS. Where one signal wire is utilised, the method will need to be modified. However, the principle of testing is sound.*

RPM signal output tests

5 Connect the equipment between terminals 1 and 4 (RPM signal) at the CAS multi-plug or the corresponding multi-plug terminals at the ECM.
6 Crank or run the engine (if preferred, it is also possible to remove the distributor from the engine, switch the ignition on, and rotate the distributor shaft by hand). A high frequency signal that switches between zero and 5.0 volts should be obtained. The voltmeter should indicate switching between 0 and 5 volts. Duty cycle, rpm and frequency meters should indicate a signal output. The frequency should be more than that obtained when testing the TDC sensor output. If there is no signal, or a very weak or intermittent signal, refer to the test routines below.

TDC signal output tests

7 Connect the meter between terminals 1 and 3 (RPM signal) at the CAS multi-plug or the corresponding multi-plug terminals at the ECM connections.
8 Crank or run the engine (if preferred, it is also possible to remove the distributor from the engine, switch the ignition on, and rotate the distributor shaft by hand). A low frequency signal that switches between zero and 5 volts should be obtained. The voltmeter should indicate switching between 0 and 5 volts. The duty cycle, rpm and frequency meters should indicate a signal output. The frequency should be less than that obtained when testing the RPM sensor output. If there is no signal, or a very weak or intermittent signal, refer to the test routines below.

CAS shield connection

9 The CAS signal wires are shielded against RFI. Locate the wiring multi-plug connector, or disconnect the ECM multi-plug.
10 Attach an ohmmeter probe to the wire attached to sensor signal terminal 3.
11 Attach the other ohmmeter probe to earth. A reading of infinity should be obtained.
12 Move the first ohmmeter probe to the wire attached to sensor signal terminal 4. A reading of infinity should also be obtained.
13 If there is no signal, or a very weak or intermittent signal:

a) Check for a voltage supply to CAS terminal 2.
b) Check the CAS earth at terminal 1.
c) Check the sensor for damage, dirt or oil.
d) Check the distributor and rotor plate for damage
e) Check for continuity between the CAS signal terminal and the ECM pin.

12 Primary ignition

1 Refer to the note at the start of Section 11, and refer to the relevant Section of Chapter 4.
2 The primary ignition is essentially that of an ECM with an external amplifier. However, the amplifier is combined with the coil, and the following additional test should be made.
3 When testing the ignition circuit (with distributor) for a primary signal, the routines described in 'Primary signal not available (external amplifier)' are generally the most suitable.
4 ECM and component pin numbers may vary depending upon the Nissan ECCS system under test.
5 Coil primary resistance for most ECCS systems is 0.60 to 1.0 ohms. Secondary resistance is 6000 to 14 600 ohms.
6 Coil terminal 1 is connected to the amplifier terminal 2, and to ECM pin number 3 via a 3-ohm resistor. Check the resistance of the resistor.

Quick check on primary operation

7 Detach the distributor from the engine (the CAS wires must remain connected).
8 Place a spark jumper between the king HT lead and the cylinder block.
9 Switch on the ignition.
10 Rotate the distributor shaft by hand; observe the spark jumper, and also monitor the injector operation.
11 If the injector fires, the CAS must be providing a good signal.
12 If a good spark jumps the gap, the ECM and amplifier operation must be satisfactory. A poor spark would probably indicate a poor amplifier or resistor - but also check the ECM control signal.

13 Knock sensor (KS)

1 Refer to the note at the start of Section 11, and refer to the relevant Section of Chapter 4.

14 Fuel injector operation (SPi)

1 Refer to the note at the start of Section 11, and refer to the relevant Section of Chapter 4 **(see illustration 12.17)**.
2 Voltage to the injector(s) is provided from the battery supply terminal.
3 The injection system is current-controlled.
4 SPi injector resistance is normally 1.0 to 2.0 ohms. MPi injector resistance is normally 10 to 14 ohms.

Quick check on injector operation

5 Detach the distributor from the engine (the CAS wires must remain connected).
6 Place a spark jumper between the king HT lead and the cylinder block.
7 Switch on the ignition.
8 Rotate the distributor shaft by hand; observe the spark jumper, and also monitor the injector operation.
9 If the injector fires, the CAS must be providing a good signal.

15 Airflow sensor (AFS)

1 Refer to the note at the start of Section 11, and refer to the relevant Section of Chapter 4.
2 The AFS may be of the hot-wire or hot-film type, depending on vehicle.

16 Air temperature sensor (ATS)

1 Refer to the note at the start of Section 11, and refer to the relevant Section of Chapter 4.
2 The ATS is part of the hot-wire AFS, and it is not always possible to test it separately.

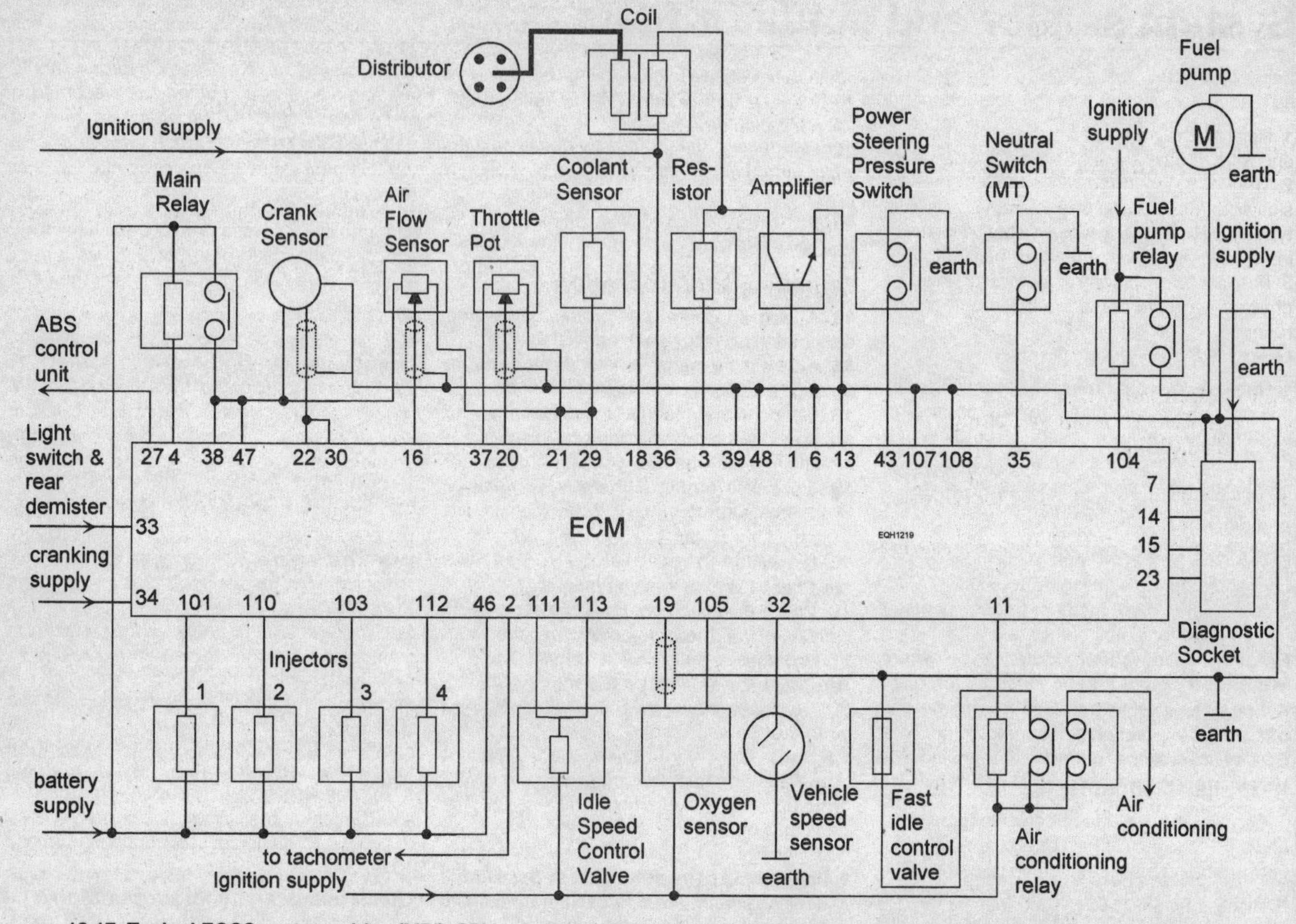

12.17 Typical ECCS system wiring (MPi). SPi is similar, and the single-point injector is usually connected to pin number 101

17 Coolant temperature sensor (CTS)

1 Refer to the note at the start of Section 11, and refer to the relevant Section of Chapter 4.

18 Throttle potentiometer sensor (TPS)

1 Refer to the note at the start of Section 11, and refer to the relevant Section of Chapter 4.

19 Idle speed control valve (ISCV)

1 Refer to the note at the start of Section 11, and refer to the relevant Section of Chapter 4.

2 ISCV resistance for a 2-wire unit would be approximately 10 ohms.

3 Remove two screws and detach the ISCV from the throttle body. Check that the ISCV spring is not broken, and that the plunger is not sticking or seized.

20 Throttle body heater (SPi engines only)

1 Refer to the note at the start of Section 11, and refer to the relevant Section of Chapter 4.

2 Carry out the tests when the engine coolant temperature is less than 65°C. **Note:** *If the engine is hot, a variable potentiometer could be connected to the CTS multi-plug so that a cold engine could be simulated.*

3 If a FCR is available, the manifold heater relay can be actuated via the serial port. This would prove the integrity of the relay and associated wiring.

21 ECM voltage supplies and earths

1 Refer to the note at the start of Section 11, and refer to the relevant Section of Chapter 4.

2 In addition to relay drivers for the main relay and pump relay, relay drivers may be available for the throttle body heater relay.

22 System relays

1 Refer to the note at the start of Section 11, and refer to the relevant Section of Chapter 4.

2 In the Nissan ECCS (SPi) system, the throttle body heater is also supplied from a relay.

23 Fuel pump and circuit

1 Refer to the note at the start of Section 11, and refer to the relevant Section of Chapter 4.

24 Fuel pressure

1 Refer to the note at the start of Section 11, and refer to the relevant Section of Chapter 4.

25 Oxygen sensor (OS)

1 Refer to the note at the start of Section 11, and refer to the relevant Section of Chapter 4.
2 The OS found in the Nissan ECCS may be similar to those found elsewhere, ie a zirconia type four-wire sensor with a heater. However, in some applications, a titania type is utilised.
3 The closed-loop control system can also be checked whilst in SD mode II with the engine running.

26 Carbon filter (CF) and EGR vacuum switching valve (VSV)

1 Inspect the VSV multi-plug for corrosion and damage.
2 Check that the connector terminal pins are fully pushed home and making good contact with the VSV multi-plug.
3 Check the vacuum hoses for leaks and poor connections.

Quick test of VSV operation

4 Start the engine and run it until normal operating temperature is reached.
5 Allow the engine to idle. At idle speed, the VSV should be switched on.
6 Disconnect the VSV outlet vacuum hose 'A' and 'B'.
7 Place a finger over VSV connector 'A'. Vacuum should be felt.
8 Place a finger over VSV connector 'B'. No vacuum should be felt.
9 Raise the engine speed above 2000 rpm. Above 2000 rpm, the VSV should switch off.
10 Place a finger over VSV connector 'A'. No vacuum should be felt.
11 Place a finger over VSV connector 'B'. Vacuum should be felt.
12 Return the engine speed to idle and switch the ignition off. Reconnect the vacuum hoses.
13 If the VSV functions as described, it is unlikely to be faulty.

Checking VSV operation

14 Run the engine until normal operating temperature is reached.
15 Connect the negative test meter probe to an engine earth.
16 Connect the positive test meter probe to the wire attached to VSV terminal number 2.
17 Switch on the ignition; the voltmeter should indicate nbv. If there is no voltage, check the supply voltage from the ignition switch.
18 Move the positive probe to the wire attached to VSV terminal number 1.
19 With the ignition on, the voltmeter should indicate nbv. If there is no voltage, connect an ohmmeter between VSV terminals 1 and 2, and check the VSV for continuity.
20 Start the engine and allow it to idle; the voltmeter should display a voltage less than 1.0 volt. If nbv is obtained, the VSV is not actuated; check that conditions for VSV actuation have been met, then check the continuity of the wiring back to the ECM. If the VSV wiring is satisfactory, check all voltage supplies and earth connections to the ECM. If the voltage supplies and earth connections are satisfactory, the ECM is suspect.
21 Raise the engine speed above 2000 rpm. The voltage should rise from less than 1.0 volt to nbv. If not, the ECM is suspect.

Checking the VSV mechanical operation

22 Disconnect the electrical multi-plug from the Idle up VSV.
23 Connect a vacuum pump to the VSV inlet pipe C.
24 Place a finger over the outlet at connector B.
25 Operate the pump to apply a vacuum of 500 mm Hg to connector C. On releasing the pump handle, the vacuum should hold.
26 Remove your finger from the outlet; the vacuum should collapse. If a vacuum pump is not available, try to blow through connectors C to B. The attempt should be successful.
27 Connect a temporary jumper lead from the positive terminal of the VSV to the battery positive terminal (the polarity of the VSV terminals must be observed, to avoid damage to the VSV).
28 Connect a temporary jumper lead from the negative terminal of the VSV to the battery negative terminal.
29 Place a finger over the outlet at connector A.
30 Operate the pump to apply a vacuum of 500 mm Hg to connector C. On releasing the pump handle, the vacuum should hold.
31 Remove the finger from connector A. The pent-up vacuum should release. If a vacuum pump is not available, try to blow through connectors C to A. The attempt should be successful.

Pin table - typical 64-pin

Note: *Refer to* **illustration 12.18**

1	Amplifier trigger signal
2	-
3	Ignition coil (via resistor)
4	Main relay driver
5	-
6	Earth
7	SD connector
8	AFS
9	Combined EGR/CFSV
10	-
11	A/C relay driver
12	-
13	Earth
14	SD connector
15	SD connector
16	AFS signal
17	AFS signal return
18	CTS signal
19	OS signal
20	TPS signal
21	Sensor return: CTS, TPS
22	CAS output
23	SD connector
24	SD warning lamp
25	-
26	-
27	Tachometer
28	-
29	Sensor return : CTS,TPS
30	CAS output
31	CAS output (some models)
32	VSS signal
33	-
34	Ignition switch
35	Neutral switch MT models, inhibitor switch AT models
36	Ignition switch
37	TPS supply
38	Main relay supply
39	Earth
40	CAS output (some models)
41	A/C pressure switch and blower switches on
42	KS signal
43	PSPS signal
44	-
45	-
46	Battery supply
47	Main relay supply
48	Earth
101	Injector driver, MPi number one (SPi when used)
102	Radiator fan relay no1 driver running, fan on
103	Injector driver, MPi number three
104	FP relay driver
105	Radiator fan relay no2 driver
106	Throttle body heater (SPi)
107	Earth
108	Earth
109	Battery supply
110	Injector driver, MPi number two
111	ISCV (some models)
112	Injector driver, MPi number four
113	ISCV (some models)
114	ISCV driver
115	AT lock-up solenoid valve
116	Earth

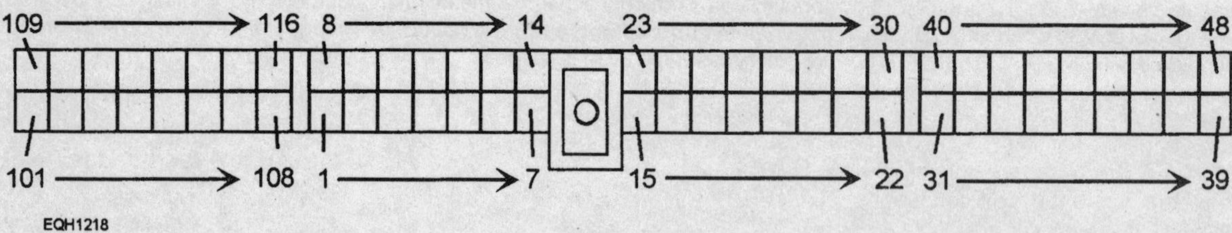

12.18 ECCS 64-pin multi-plug

Fault codes

27 Obtaining fault codes

1 If a FCR is available, it could be attached to the SD serial connector and used for the following purposes:

a) Obtaining fault codes.
b) Clearing fault codes.
c) Obtaining Datastream information.
d) Checking the closed-loop mixture control
e) Actuating the system actuators: This may include some of the following list:
Idle speed control valve
Fuel injectors
Fuel pump relay
EGR & carbon filter VSV
Radiator fan
f) Returning adaptive function to original default values
g) Making adjustments:
Set TPS position
Set ignition timing advance
Adjust CO value (non-cat models only)
Set base idle speed.
h) Change the following parameters (engine running):
ISCV duty cycle
Fuel injection pulse duration
Ignition timing retard
CTS (change temperature)

2 If a FCR is not available, it is still possible to display flash codes on the ECM LED (see note below) or on the dash-mounted warning lamp. Other than Datastream and component actuation, many of the above functions can be accomplished without the aid of the FCR. Adjustments are also possible without resorting to the FCR. Refer to the adjustments section.

Note: *In some models, one red LED is provided on the ECM, while in other models, one red and one green LED are provided. Where two LED's are provided, the red LED flashes the 'tens', whilst the green LED flashes the 'units' Four red flashes followed by three green flashes indicates code '43'.*

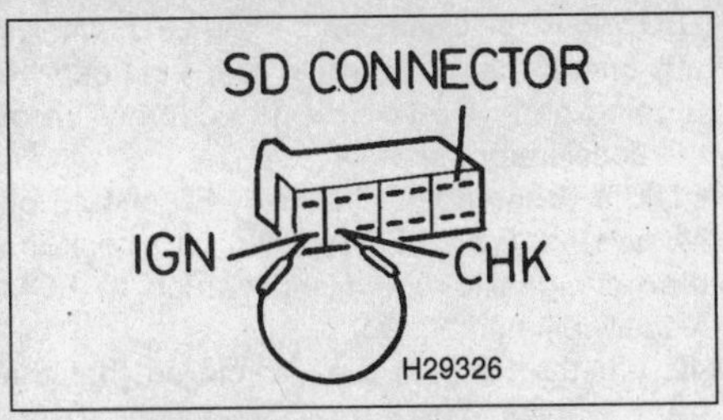

12.19 Obtaining flash codes

Obtaining flash codes

Note: *The following method is typical, and variations may be necessary in some systems.*

3 There are two modes to obtaining codes and associated information: mode I and mode II. Output from each mode differs according to whether the ignition is 'on' or the engine is running.

Mode I, ignition on: Check of warning lamp bulb and LED in the ECM. If the vehicle is not equipped with a warning lamp, observe the codes on the ECM.

Mode I, Engine running: Illumination of warning bulb or red LED indicates a system fault.

Mode II, Ignition on: Output of fault codes.

Mode II, Engine running: Check of closed-loop control system.

4 Switching off the ignition or stopping the engine will return the SD system to mode I.

5 Turn on the ignition, but do not start the engine.

6 Start the engine and allow it to idle. If a fault is present, the warning lamp or LED will light.

7 Stop the engine. Turn on the ignition, but do not start the engine.

8 Use a jumper lead to bridge the terminals in the SD plug **(see illustration 12.19)**. Remove the bridge after two seconds. The codes are then output on the instrument panel warning lamp as coded flashes. By counting the flashes and referring to the fault code table, faults can thus be determined.

9 The flashes are output as a two digit code in the following fashion.

10 One or more faults: A flash lasting 0.6 seconds, with a pause for 0.6 seconds between each flash, indicates the first digit of the two-digit fault code. After a 0.9 seconds pause, a second series of flashes with each flash lasting 0.3 seconds, and with a pause for 0.3 seconds between each flash, indicates the second digit. After the first fault is emitted, the lamp will pause for 2.1 seconds and then flash the next code. Once all faults have been emitted in numerical order of smallest code first and greatest code last, the lamp will pause for 2.1 seconds and then repeat the sequence. This will continue until the test connector connections are bridged once more.

11 If there are no faults, the lamp will flash code 55.

12 Use a jumper lead to bridge the terminals in the SD plug. Remove the bridge after two seconds. The ECM will revert to mode I.

Erasing codes

13 The codes will remain logged until one of the following actions is performed:

a) *The codes are displayed (mode II) and then the SD function is switched back to mode I.*

b) *The vehicle battery is disconnected for 24 hours (beware of losing other data, such as the radio code, clock setting, etc) or a FCR is used to erase the codes.*

c) *The fault is automatically erased once the engine has been started for a total of 50 times after the fault has cleared. If the fault re-occurs before 50 starts have been made, the counter will be reset to zero, and another 50 starts must occur before the fault is automatically erased. This procedure occurs on an individual fault code basis, and each code will only be erased after 50 starts have occurred with no re-occurrence of that particular fault.*

Checking the closed-loop mixture control (cat models only)

14 With the engine stopped, and the ignition on, use a jumper lead to bridge the terminals in the SD plug. Remove the bridge after two seconds. The codes are then output on the warning lamp or red LED as coded flashes. See above for evaluation of flashes.

15 Start the engine and run it to normal operating temperature.

16 Raise the engine speed to 2000 rpm for a period of 2 minutes.

17 Observe the warning lamp or LED display.

a) *Lamp or LED switches off and on at a frequency of 5 in 10 seconds. Engine is in closed-loop control.*

b) *Lamp or LED remains off. Engine is in open-loop control.*

c) *When the lamp or LED is on, the fuelling is lean.*

d) *When the lamp or LED is off, the fuelling is rich.*

18 The lamp or LED will reflect the current condition of lean or rich by staying on or off immediately before switching to open-loop control.

28 Alternative fault code gathering methods - certain models only

Note: *A mode selector is provided on the ECM casing to select the correct SD mode for emitting fault codes and (in some models) other functions. Use a screwdriver to carefully turn the mode selector as required during the following procedures. Be warned that harsh treatment can damage the mode selector* ***(see illustration 12.20)***.

Alternative method number one (typically, Nissan 300 ZX models)

1 Turn the mode selector fully anti-clockwise.

2 Turn on the ignition.

12.20 For some models a mode selector is provided on the ECM casing. Use a screwdriver to carefully turn the mode selector as described in the text. Be warned that harsh treatment can damage the mode selector

3 Ensure that the ECM LED's turn on and remain on (bulb check).

4 Turn the mode selector fully clockwise.

5 The ECM LED's should flash code number 23, 24 (some models) or 31. These codes signify no fault found. Record any other code emitted, and continue.

6 Depress fully and release the accelerator pedal.

7 The LED's should flash code number 24 (some models) or 31. These codes signify no fault found. Record any other code emitted, and continue.

8 Start the engine and allow it to idle.

9 The LED's should flash code number 31. The code signifies no fault found. Record any other code emitted, and continue.

10 Turn the air conditioning switch on and on (where fitted).

11 The LED's should flash code number 44. The code signifies no fault found. Record any other code emitted, and continue.

12 Turn the mode selector fully anti-clockwise, and then turn off the engine.

13 Refer to the code chart for any codes emitted, and check the relevant circuits as described elsewhere.

Erasing the fault codes

14 Turn on the ignition.

15 Turn the mode selector fully clockwise for a period exceeding two seconds.

16 Turn the mode selector fully anti-clockwise for a period exceeding two seconds.

17 Turn off the ignition.

Alternative method number two (typically, Nissan 200 SX and Primera models)

18 Turn on the ignition.

19 Turn the mode selector clockwise.

20 Both green and red LED's will begin to flash, and will cycle through five modes signified by one, two, three, four and five flashes.

21 A mode is selected by turning the mode selector fully anti-clockwise immediately after it has flashed the mode required. To select mode III, turn the mode selector fully anti-clockwise immediately after it has flashed three times.

22 Once the ignition switch is turned off, the ECM will return to mode I.

23 After self-diagnosis is completed, ensure that the mode selector is returned to the normal running position by turning it fully anti-clockwise. **Note:** *Mode I and mode II are only available in catalyst-equipped engines. The engine must be at operating temperature, and functioning in closed-loop control.*

Mode I (OS monitor)

24 The green LED's will turn on during lean running conditions, and turn off during rich running conditions. With the engine running, the LED will flash.
25 During open-loop control, the green LED will remain either off or on.
26 If the ECM is operating in LOS, the red LED will turn on.

Mode II (mixture ratio feedback control monitor)

27 The green LED will function exactly as it did in mode I.
28 The red lamp will turn on during lean running conditions, and turn off during rich running conditions, in sequence with the green LED during the time that the mixture ratio is controlled within its operating parameters.
29 During open-loop control, the red LED will remain either off or on.

Mode III (SD code output)

30 Initiate mode III as described above.
31 Record all codes that are transmitted. If code 55 is transmitted, no fault is logged.
32 Erase codes by switching to mode IV.

Erasing the fault codes/ initiating mode IV

33 Turn the mode selector clockwise.
34 The green and red LED's will begin to flash, and cycle through the five modes signified by one, two, three, four and five flashes.
35 To select mode IV, turn the mode selector fully anti-clockwise immediately after it has flashed four times.
36 Once the ECM has entered mode IV, it will erase the logged codes.
37 Switch off the ignition.

Mode IV (switch on or off monitor)

38 Initiate mode IV as described above.
39 The red LED should be off.
40 Depress the accelerator pedal; the red LED should be illuminated. If the LED remains off, check the idle switch. The LED can be toggled on and off with every depression of the accelerator pedal.
41 Start the engine; the red LED should be illuminated. If the LED remains off, check the starter signal circuit from ignition to ECM (usually pin number 34).
42 Lift the front of the vehicle so that the front wheels can turn. Observe all safety principles.
43 Engage a gear and drive the wheels so that 12 mph is exceeded. The green LED will illuminate at speeds over 12 mph, and extinguish at speeds below 12 mph. If the green LED does not behave as described, check the VSS circuit.

Mode V (Dynamic test in real time)

44 Start the engine and initiate mode V as described above.
45 Run the engine under various operating conditions and observe the LED's.
46 If the LED's begin to flash, count the flashes to determine the fault. The fault code is flashed once, and is not logged in memory.

Fault code table

Code	Fault
11	CAS in distributor, rpm or crankshaft position sensor
12	Vane/hot-wire AFS
13	CTS
14	Vehicle speed sensor
21	Ignition signal circuit
22	Fuel pump
23	Throttle position sensor - idle
24	Throttle position sensor - full load or neutral/park switch
25	Auxiliary air valve
26	Turbo boost pressure sensor
31	Air conditioning (A/C)
31	No faults detected (non A/C)
31	ECM - GA16i/CA18DE engines
32	Starter signal
33	Oxygen sensor
34	Knock sensor circuit
34	Throttle position sensor - SR20Di engines
41	Air temperature sensor
42	Fuel temperature sensor
43	TPS circuit
44	No faults detected
51	Injectors
54	AT signal lost
55	No malfunction in the above circuits

Note: *If code No. 11 and code No. 21 are both displayed in the same incident, check the CAS circuit before checking other circuits.*

Chapter 13
Renix MPi/SPi

Contents

Specifications

Vehicle	Year	Idle speed	CO%
Renix MPi			
5 F3N 702	1989 to 1992	800 ± 50	0.5 max
9/11 F3N 708	1986 to 1989	800 ± 50	0.5 max
19 F7P 700	1991 to 1993	900 ± 50	1.5 ± 0.5
19 F3N 746	1992 to 1993	850 ± 50	1.5 ± 0.5
19 AT cat F3N 743	1990 to 1992	800 ± 50	0.5 max
19 cat F7P 704	1991 to 1995	900 ± 50	0.5 max
21 cat F3N 722	1991 to 1995	800 ± 50	0.5 max
21 cat J7R740	1991 to 1995	900 ± 50	0.5 max
21 cat J7R 746,747	1991 to 1995	800 ± 50	0.5 max
21 J7R 750,751	1986 to 1993	775 ± 50	1.5 ± 0.5
21 J7R754	1989 to 1994	850 ± 75	1.8 ± 0.2
21 cat J7T754,755	1992 to 1995	800 ± 50	1.5 ± 0.5
21 turbo J7R 752	1991 to 1992	800 ± 25	1.5 ± 0.5
25 J7R 722,723	1986 to 1993	775 ± 50	1.5 ± 0.5
25 J7R	1991 to 1993	850 ± 75	1.8 ± 0.2
25 cat J7T 732, 733	1990 to 1991	800 ± 50	0.5 max
25 J7T 706/7,714/5,730/1	1984 to 1987	800 ± 25	1.5 ± 0.5
25 cat J7R 726	1991 to 1993	900 ± 50	0.5 max
25 V6 Z7W 700	1989 to 1993	700 ± 50	1.5 ± 0.5
25 V6 cat Z7W 706	1991 to 1992	800 ± 50	0.5 max
25 V6 turbo Z7U 702	1985 to 1990	700 ± 25	1.0 ± 0.25
25 V6 turbo cat Z7U 700	1991 to 1993	700 ± 50	0.5 max
Alpine V6 turbo Z7U 730	1986 to 1992	700 ± 25	1.0 ± 0.25
Alpine V6 turbo cat Z7U 734	1990 to 1992	700 ± 50	0.5 max
Clio cat F7P 720	1991 to 1992	900 ± 50	1.5 ± 0.5
Clio cat F7P 722	1991 to 1996	900 ± 50	0.5 max
Espace J7R 760	1988 to 1991	775 ± 50	1.5 ± 0.5
Espace cat J7R768	1991 to 1996	775 ± 50	0.5 max
Espace cat J7T 772	1991 to 1995	775 to 825	0.5 max
Espace cat J7T 770	1991 to 1992	800 ± 50	0.5 max
Espace V6 cat Z7W 712	1991 to 1995	800 ± 25	0.5 max
Laguna cat F3R 722	1994 to 1995	730 ± 50	0.3 max
Safrane cat J7R 732/3	1993 to 1996	750 ± 50	0.5 max
Safrane cat J7R 734/5	1993 to 1994	825 ± 50	0.5 max
Trafic cat J7T780	1991 to 1993	800 ± 25	0.5 max

Vehicle	Year	Idle speed	CO%
Renix SPi			
5 1.4 cat C3J 700 (B/C/F407)	1986 to 1990	850	0.5 max
5 1.4 cat C3J 760 (B/C/F407)	1990 to 1996	850	0.5 max
5 1.7i cat F3N G716 (B/C408)	1987 to 1991	700	0.5 max
5 1.7i cat F3N G717 (B/C409)	1987 to 1991	700	0.5 max
9 1721 cat F3N 718 (L42F/BC37F)	1986 to 1989	700	2.0 max
11 1721 cat F3N 718 (L42F/BC37F)	1986 to 1989	700	2.0 max
19 1.4i cat C3J 710 (B/C/L532)	1990 to 1992	850 ± 50	0.5 max
19 1.4i cat C3J 700	1991 to 1992	850 ± 50	0.5 max
19 1.7i cat F3N 740 B/C/L53B)	1990 to 1992	750 ± 50	0.5 max
19 1.7i AT cat F3N 741 B/C/L53B)	1990 to 1992	750 ± 50	0.5 max
21 1.7i cat F3N 723 (X48F)	1991 to 1995	800 ± 50	0.3 max
Chamade 1.4i cat C3J 710 (B/C/L532)	1990 to 1992	850 ± 50	0.5 max
Chamade 1.4i cat C3J 700	1991 to 1992	800 ± 50	0.5 max
Chamade 19 1.7i cat F3N 741	1990 to 1992	750 ± 50	0.5 max
Chamade 19 1.7i AT cat F3N 740	1990 to 1992	750 ± 50	0.5 max
Extra 1.4 cat C3J 760 (B/C/F407)	1990 to 1995	850	0.5 max
Extra 1.4 cat C3J 762 (F407)	1992 to 1995	850	0.5 max
Express 1.4 cat C3J 762 (F407)	1992 to 1995	850	0.5 max

Overview of system operation

1 Introduction

Renix was first fitted to the Renault 25 in 1984, and is a fully-integrated system that controls primary ignition, fuelling and idle control from within the same ECM. The basic Renix system is used on most Renault four- and six-cylinder engines with and without catalyst - including the turbo models - although there are a number of variations in each application. Renix may be MPi or SPi in operation, and this Chapter deals with both types. Despite a number of differences in the sensors used in the various Renault vehicles, the basic Renix configuration is very similar - even between MPi and SPi models, and the ECM pin numbers used are often identical **(see illustrations 13.1 and 13.2)**.

Although this system is termed 'Renix', it is also known as Bendix, Fenix or Siemens. Essentially, the basic wiring, specification and configuration of components are similar; the major components are supplied from a number of sources, and tend to lend their name to the system. For example, the ECM may be manufactured by Bendix, Fenix, Renix or Siemens. The injection components may be Bendix or Renix, and the throttle body Weber or Solex (MPi) or Weber, GM or Bosch (SPi). The ignition system utilises the commonplace AEI combined coil and amplifier used for many years to supply ignition in carburettor engines. A 35-pin connector and multi-plug connects the ECM to the battery, sensors and actuators.

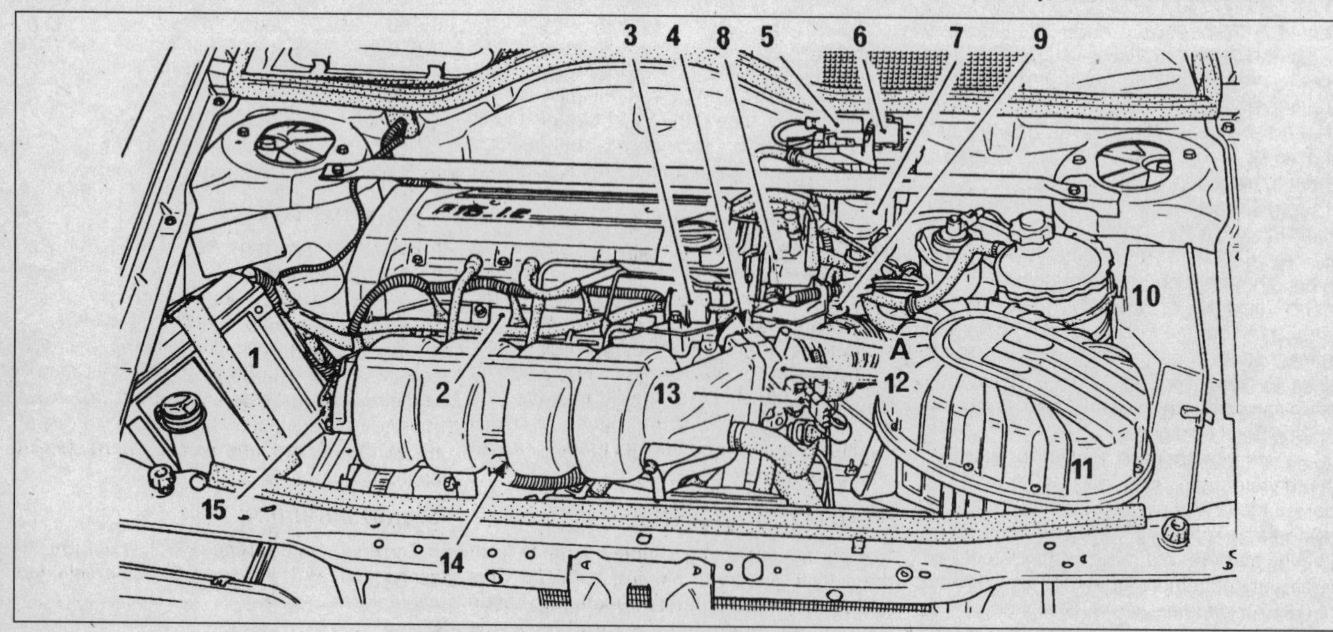

13.1 Multi-point injection system layout (Renault 19, F7P)

1 ECM
2 Fuel rail and injectors
3 Fuel pressure regulator
4 CTS
5 CO pot (non-cat models)
6 MAP sensor
7 Amplifier
8 Distributor
9 ISCV
10 Relay
11 Air filter
12 Throttle body
13 TPS
14 KS
15 ATS
A Idle speed adjusting screw

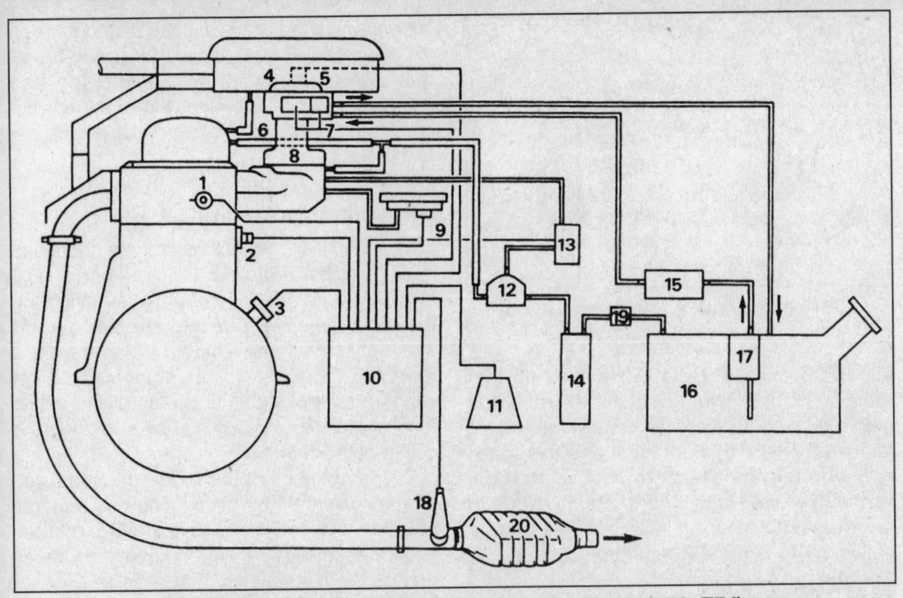

13.2 Single-point injection system layout (Renault 19, E7J)

1 CTS
2 KS
3 CAS
4 Fuel injector
5 ATS
6 TPS
7 ISCV
8 Throttle body
9 MAP sensor
10 ECM
11 Amplifier
12 Vacuum bleed valve
13 CFSV
14 Charcoal canister
15 Fuel filter
16 Fuel tank
17 Fuel pump
18 Oxygen sensor
19 Non-return valve
20 Catalytic converter

2 Control functions

Signal processing

Renix is designed with three main areas of control. These are ignition, fuel system and idle speed. The ignition point and injection duration are jointly processed by the ECM so that the best possible ignition and fuelling parameters are determined for every operating condition.

Basic dwell and ignition timing are stored in a three-dimensional map, and the engine load and speed signals determine the ignition timing. The main engine load sensor is the MAP sensor (MPi systems, and some SPi systems without the Bosch throttle body) and engine speed is determined from the CAS signal. The load signal in SPi engines with the Bosch throttle body is determined from the TPS and full-load signals.

Correction factors are applied for starting, idle, deceleration, and part- and full-load operation. The main correction factor is engine temperature (CTS). Minor corrections to timing and AFR are made with reference to the air temperature sensor (ATS) and throttle pot (TPS) or throttle switch (TS) signals.

The basic AFR is also stored in a three-dimensional map, and the engine load and speed signals determine the basic injection pulse value. Using the speed/density method, Renix calculates the AFR from the pressure in the inlet manifold (MAP) or the throttle angle (TPS) and the speed of the engine (CAS). The AFR and the pulse duration are then corrected on reference to ATS, coolant temperature sensor (CTS), battery voltage and rate of throttle opening (TPS). Other controlling factors are determined by operating conditions such as cold start and warm-up, idle condition, acceleration and deceleration.

The battery voltage also has an important influence upon the injector opening time. As the voltage changes, the ECM compensates by increasing or decreasing the injector opening time. A lower voltage will result in an increase in injection duration.

Renix accesses a different map for idle running conditions, and this map is implemented whenever the TS, TPS or stepper motor idle contacts indicate idle condition. Idle speed during warm-up and normal hot running conditions is maintained by the idle speed control valve (ISCV). However, Renix makes small adjustments to the idle speed by advancing or retarding the timing, and this results in an ignition timing that is forever changing during engine idle.

Basic ECM operation

A permanent voltage supply is made from the vehicle battery to pin 4 of the ECM. This allows the self-diagnostic function to retain data of an intermittent nature. Once the ignition is switched on, a voltage supply to the combined ignition coil/amplifier is made from the ignition switch. This causes the ECM to connect pin 7 to earth, so actuating the main fuel injection relay. A relay switched voltage supply is thus made to ECM pin 19, from terminal 5 of the main fuel injection relay.

The majority of sensors (other than those that generate a voltage such the crank angle sensor, knock sensor and oxygen sensor), are now provided with a 5.0-volt reference supply from a relevant pin on the ECM.

When the engine is cranked, a feed from terminal 50 of the starter circuit provides a voltage to pin 29 of the ECM. This voltage feed is only present during engine cranking, and informs the ECM of the need to increase injection frequency. This feed is discontinued on later systems, which use the engine speed signal to determine cranking speed.

When the engine is cranked or run, a speed signal from the CAS causes the ECM to earth pin 6 so that the fuel pump will run. Ignition and injection functions are also activated. All actuators (injectors, ISCV, CFSV etc), are supplied with nbv from the pump relay, and the ECM completes the circuit by pulsing the relevant actuator wire to earth.

Over-speed fuel cut-off (rev limiter)

Renix prevents excessive engine speeds by inhibiting the injector earth path above a certain rpm. Engine speed cut-off varies according to the engine code. Typical values are as follows:

a) Z7X engines: 6300 rpm in 1st and 2nd gear, 6200 rpm in 3rd, 4th and 5th gear.
b) J7R and J7T (12-valve) engines: 6350 rpm.
c) J7R and J7T (8-valve) engines: 6000 rpm.

Deceleration fuel cut-off

Deceleration fuel cut-off is implemented during engine over-run conditions, to improve economy and reduce emissions. The conditions for over-run to be implemented are:

a) Throttle closed.
b) Engine speed above 2000 rpm.
c) Once the engine speed drops below 1100 rpm, fuel injection is reinstated.

Reference voltage

Voltage supply from the ECM to many of the engine sensors is at a 5.0-volt reference level. This ensures a stable working voltage, unaffected by variations in system voltage.

The earth return connection for most engine sensors is made through an ECM pin that is not directly connected to earth. The ECM internally connects that pin to earth via one of the ECM pins that are directly connected to earth.

Signal shielding

To reduce interference (RFI), a number of sensors (ie CAS, KS and OS) use a shielded cable.

Self-diagnostic function

The Renix system has a self-test capability that regularly examines the signals from the engine sensors, and internally logs a code in the event of a fault being present. This code can be extracted from the Renix serial port by a suitable fault code reader. When the ECM detects that a fault is present, it earths ECM pin 18, and the warning lamp on the dash will light. The lamp will stay lit until the fault is no longer present.

If the fault clears, the code will remain logged until wiped clean with a suitable FCR, or until the battery or ECM have been disconnected. As the ECM retains codes for faults of an intermittent nature, this is a valuable aid to fault diagnosis.

Limited operating strategy (LOS)

Renix has a limp-home (LOS) facility. In the event of a serious fault in one or more of the sensors, the EMS will substitute a fixed default value in place of the defective sensor.

This means that the engine may actually run quite well with failure of one or more minor sensors. However, since the substituted values are those of a hot engine, cold starting and running during the warm-up period may be less than satisfactory. Also, failure of a major sensor, ie the MAP sensor, will tend to make driving conditions less easy.

Default values when operating in LOS

a) Air temperature sensor (ATS): 20° C.
b) Coolant temperature sensor (CTS): During engine cranking, the ATS value is used. After starting, 90 to 100° C (hot engine)
c) CO pot: Mean CO pot value.

Vehicle speed sensor (VSS)

The VSS is used to advise the ECM of vehicle speed. It operates upon the Hall-effect principle, and may be mounted directly upon the gearbox or behind the dash.

A voltage of approximately 10 volts is applied to the VSS from the ignition switch. As the speedometer cable turns, the Hall switch is alternately turned on and off, to return a square wave signal to the ECM. The frequency of the signal denotes the vehicle speed.

3 Primary trigger

Crank angle sensor (CAS)

The primary signal to initiate both ignition and fuelling emanates from a CAS mounted next to the flywheel **(see illustration 13.3)**. The CAS consists of an inductive magnet that radiates a magnetic field. The peak-to-peak voltage of the speed signal can vary from 5 volts at idle to over 100 volts at 6000 rpm. An analogue-to-digital converter (located in the ECM microprocessor) transforms the AC pulse into a digital signal.

Four-cylinder engines

Forty-four evenly-spaced steel teeth are set into the periphery of the flywheel. Two teeth are then removed at each of the positions

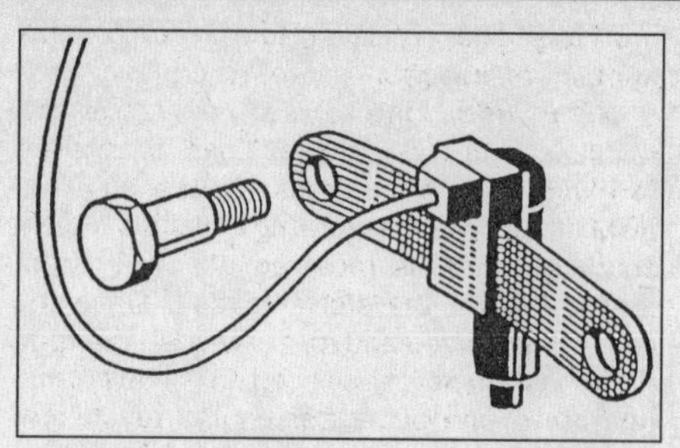

13.3 Renix crank angle sensor (CAS)

90° BTDC and 90° BBDC. The 40 teeth that remain include two double teeth set just before the space where the smaller teeth were removed. The two larger teeth and the space acts as a reference mark to TDC. In addition, as the flywheel spins, and the teeth rotate in the magnetic field, an AC voltage signal is delivered to the ECM to indicate speed of rotation.

Six-cylinder engines

Sixty-six evenly-spaced steel teeth are set into the periphery of the flywheel. Two teeth are then removed at each third of a turn (120° apart). The 60 teeth that remain includes three double teeth set just before the space where the smaller teeth were removed. The two larger teeth and the space acts as a reference mark to TDC. In addition, as the flywheel spins, and the teeth rotate in the magnetic field, an AC voltage signal is delivered to the ECM to indicate speed of rotation.

4 Ignition

Ignition operation

Data on load (MAP) engine speed (CAS), engine temperature (CTS) and throttle position (TS or TPS) are collected by the ECM, which then refers to a three-dimensional digital map stored within its microprocessor. This map contains an advance angle for each operating condition, and thus the best ignition advance angle for a particular operating condition can be determined.

When the ignition is switched on, voltage is applied to the ECM and to the combined amplifier/ignition coil unit. The circuit then lies dormant to await a cranking or running signal.

When the engine is cranked and run, the ECM receives a signal from the CAS, and in turn applies a control signal to the combined amplifier/coil unit so that ignition can be initiated.

The amplifier controls the coil dwell circuit by turning the coil current on and off to initiate ignition.

Once the amplifier turns the coil current off, the magnetic field in the coil primary windings quickly collapses, and a high voltage is induced in the coil secondary windings. The secondary output travels to the distributor cap via the main HT lead, through the medium of the rotor arm. From the distributor, the secondary output is distributed to the correct spark plug, in the firing order of the engine, via an HT lead.

Combined amplifier and ignition coil unit

The amplifier and ignition coil are contained in a combined unit, to reduce wiring. The amplifier contains the circuitry for switching the coil negative terminal at the correct moment to instigate ignition. When the ECM receives the CAS trigger signal, the ECM sends a control signal to the amplifier, which then completes the process by switching the coil negative terminal.

The amplifier applies current to the coil primary windings by connecting coil terminal number one to earth for a period of time known as the dwell time. During this dwell period, the coil builds a magnetic field within the primary coil windings. While the engine is running, the Renix ECM calculates the coil turn-on time so that the correct dwell period is maintained.

Dwell operation in Renix is based upon the principle of the 'constant-energy current-limiting' system. This means that the dwell period remains constant at about 3.0 to 3.5 ms, at virtually all engine running speeds. However, the dwell duty cycle, when measured in percent or degrees, will vary as the engine speed varies.

The ignition coil utilises low primary resistance in order to increase primary current and primary energy. The amplifier limits the primary current to around 8 amps, and this permits a reserve of energy to maintain the required spark burn time (duration).

Distributor

In the Renix system, the distributor only serves to distribute the HT current from the coil secondary terminal to each spark plug in firing order.

Ignition timing

It is not possible to adjust the ignition timing on the Renix system.

Knock sensor (not all engines)

The optimal ignition timing (at engine speeds greater than idle) for a given high-compression engine is quite close to the point of onset of knock. However, running so close to the point of knock occurrence means that knock will certainly occur on one or more cylinders at certain times during the engine operating cycle.

Since knock may occur at a different moment in each individual cylinder, Renix employs a knock control microprocessor (in the ECM) to pinpoint the actual cylinder or cylinders that are knocking. The knock sensor is mounted on the engine block, and consists of a piezo-ceramic measuring element, that responds to engine noise oscillations. Engine knock is converted to a voltage signal by the knock sensor and returned to the knock control processor for evaluation and action. The knocking frequency is in the 8 to 15 kHz frequency band. Some Renix-equipped engines may utilise twin knock sensors.

The ignition advance map within the ECM is divided into two zones - a non-critical zone and a critical zone. The non-critical zone is defined as the period when the engine load is low and the engine speed is also low. The critical zone is defined as the period when the engine load varies from partial load to high load. Engine speed in the critical zone could be either high or low.

Initially, timing will occur at its optimal ignition point, as defined in the advance map. Once knock is identified, the ECM takes action depending on the engine's operating zone. During operation in the non-critical zone, the ECM rapidly retards the timing by 7°. After about 10 seconds, the advance returns in small increments to its optimal ignition point as defined in the advance map.

During operation in the critical zone, the ECM operates in two phases. During the first phase, the ECM rapidly retards the timing in a similar fashion to the non-critical zone. After several seconds, the second phase - termed the 'slow correction' phase, returns the advance in small increments to its optimal ignition point as defined in the advance map.

This procedure continually occurs so that all cylinders will consistently run at their optimum timing.

If a fault exists in the knock sensor or wiring, an appropriate code is logged in the self-diagnostic unit, and the ignition timing in the critical zone is retarded 3° from the nominal setting.

5 Fuel injection

Two distinct methods are utilised for providing fuel to engines equipped with Renix. The methods are Multi-point injection (MPi) and Single-point injection (SPi).

Because of the modularity of Renix, little difference exists between the control system on the various engines. However, there are a number of differences in implementation as described below.

The Renix ECM contains a fuel map with an injector opening time (or pulse duration) for basic conditions of speed and load. Information is then gathered from engine sensors such as the MAP sensor, CAS, CTS, ATS and TPS. As a result of this information, the ECM will look up the correct injector pulse duration right across the engine rpm, load and temperature range.

The amount of fuel delivered by the injector(s) is determined by the fuel pressure and the pulse duration. During engine start from cold, the pulse duration is increased to provide a richer air/fuel mixture. In addition, the number of injection pulses (frequency) are doubled from one pulse per crankshaft revolution to two pulses per crankshaft revolution during the cranking operation. The ECM determines the cranking condition when a cranking signal is received at pin 29 from terminal 50 of the starter circuit. Once the engine has started and rpm exceeds 1000 rpm, or the ignition key is released, injection pulsing returns to one pulse per engine revolution. During engine deceleration, the pulse reduces to zero as the ECM cuts off the injection pulse. At excessive engine speeds, the ECM cuts off injector operation as a safety precaution.

Fuel injector(s)

The fuel injector is a magnetically-operated solenoid valve, with voltage applied from the main relay and an earth path through the ECM. The injector is switched using two circuits. Operation depends on the principle that more current is required to open an injector than to keep it open. This kind of system is often termed 'current-controlled injection system'. Once the injector is open, a second circuit rapidly pulses the injector to earth. The switching is so rapid that the injector is effectively held open, and less current is required during the operation. Advantages of this arrangement include a reduction in injector operating temperature, and immediate injector closure once the holding circuit is switched off.

Multi-point injection (MPi - sequential)

The MPi system consists of one injector for each cylinder, mounted in the inlet port, so that a finely-atomised fuel spray is directed onto the back of each valve. Since the injectors are all pulsed simultaneously, fuel will briefly rest upon the back of a valve before being drawn into a cylinder.

Single-point fuel injection (SPi)

The SPi system consists of a single injector, mounted in the throttle body. In SPi engines, fuel is injected into the inlet manifold, where it mixes with air. The depression produced by a descending piston causes the resulting air/fuel mixture to be drawn into each cylinder. The injector is normally actuated twice per engine revolution. However, during low or high load engine operation, or if a fault develops that causes the ECM to enter LOS, the injector is actuated once per engine revolution.

Cold start valve (CSV)

In some models, a CSV is provided to spray additional fuel into the inlet manifold at low temperatures. Unlike previous versions of this valve in other applications, the valve is NOT connected to the starter circuit, and does not rely on a thermal time switch to complete the valve earth circuit. In fact, the CSV functions in a similar fashion to the fuel injectors, and is actuated for a period of time determined by the coolant temperature.

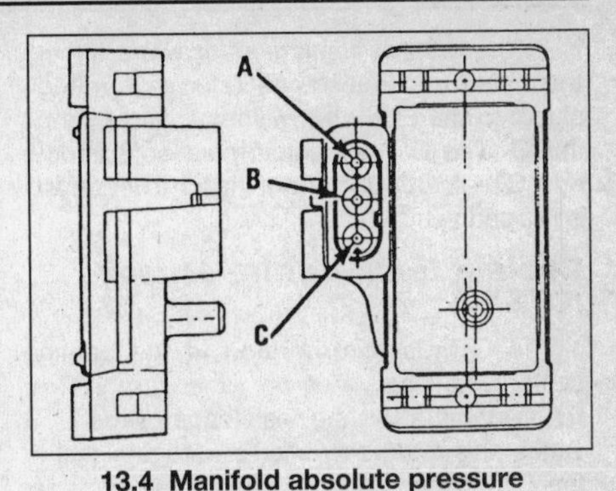

13.4 Manifold absolute pressure (MAP) sensor assembly
A Earth B Signal C 5-volt supply

MAP sensor

The main engine load sensor for MPi systems and engines without the Bosch throttle body is the MAP sensor **(see illustration 13.4)**. A vacuum hose connects the MAP sensor (located on the bulkhead close to the ECM) and the inlet manifold. Manifold vacuum acts upon the MAP sensor diaphragm, and the ECM converts the pressure into an electrical signal. MAP is calculated from the formula: Atmospheric Pressure less Manifold Pressure = Manifold Absolute Pressure.

Using the speed/density method, the Renix ECM calculates the AFR from the MAP signal and the speed of the engine (CAS). This method relies on the theory that the engine will draw in a fixed volume of air per revolution.

Air temperature sensor (ATS)

The ATS is mounted in the air inlet trunking (MPi) or on top of the single-point injector (SPi), and measures the air temperature before it enters the inlet manifold. Because the density of air varies in inverse proportion to the temperature, the ATS signal allows more accurate assessment of the volume of air entering the engine. However, the ATS has only a minor correcting effect on ECM output.

The open-circuit supply to the sensor is at a 5.0-volt reference level, and the earth path is through the ATS earth return. Essentially, two completely different types of ATS are employed - depending on vehicle:

a) *NTC: This signal is approximately 2.0 to 3.0 volts at an ambient temperature of 20°C, and reduces to about 1.5 volt as the temperature rises to around 40°C.*
b) *PTC: This signal is approximately 0.5 volts at an ambient temperature of 20°C, and rises to about 1.5 volt as the temperature rises to around 40°C.*

CO potentiometer ('pot')

The CO pot mixture adjuster is a two-wire potentiometer that allows small changes to be made to the idle CO. A 5.0-volt reference voltage is applied to the sensor, and an earth connection is made via the AFS earth return circuit. The CO pot signal voltage varies according to the position of the adjuster screw.

As the CO pot adjustment screw is turned, the change in resistance returns a voltage signal to the ECM that will result in a change in CO. The CO pot adjustment only affects idle CO. A CO pot is not fitted to catalyst-equipped vehicles.

Coolant temperature sensor (CTS)

The CTS is incorporated in the cooling system, and operates on either the NTC or PTC principle. As the resistance of the CTS varies, this returns a variable voltage signal to the ECM based upon the coolant temperature:

a) *NTC: The signal is approximately 1.5 to 2.2 volts at an ambient coolant temperature of 20°C, and reduces to between 0.1 to 0.2 volts at a normal operating temperature of 80 to 100°C.*
b) *PTC: This signal is approximately 0.5 volts at an ambient coolant temperature of 20°C, and rises to about 1.2 volts as the temperature rises to around 80°C.*

The open-circuit supply to the sensor is at a 5.0-volt reference level, and the earth path is through the sensor return. The ECM uses the CTS signal as a main correction factor when calculating ignition timing and injection duration.

Throttle switch (some vehicles)

A throttle switch with dual contacts is provided to inform the ECM of idle position, deceleration, cruising and full-load (WOT) conditions. In SPi engines without the Bosch throttle body, the TS is fitted as an alternative to the TPS. When the engine is at idle, the idle contact is closed and the full-load contact is open. As the throttle is moved to the fully-open position, the full-load contact closes and the idle contact becomes open. Under cruising conditions with a part-open throttle, both contacts are open. During full-load operation, when the switch is less than 10° from the fully-open position, the ECM provides additional enrichment. During closed throttle operation above a certain rpm (deceleration), the ECM will cut off fuel injection. Injection will be reintroduced once the rpm returns to idle or the throttle is opened. One of two different types of TS may be used, and the TS has generally been replaced by the TPS in later vehicles.

TPS (some MPi vehicles)

The TPS is an alternative to the TS, and is provided to inform the ECM of the exact throttle position. The TPS is a potentiometer with three wires. A 5.0-volt reference voltage is supplied to a resistance track, with the other end connected to earth. The third wire is connected to an arm which wipes along the resistance track, and so varies the resistance and voltage of the signal returned to the ECM.

TPS (SPi with Bosch throttle body)

A throttle potentiometer with dual resistance tracks is provided, to inform the ECM of acceleration, throttle position, and full load. Some early models had a 7-pin connector, and later models a 5-pin connector. The extra pins in the 7-pin connector provided throttle position information to the automatic transmission ECM, where applicable. In later models, information on throttle position is sent directly to the automatic transmission ECM by the Renix ECM **(see illustration 13.5)**.

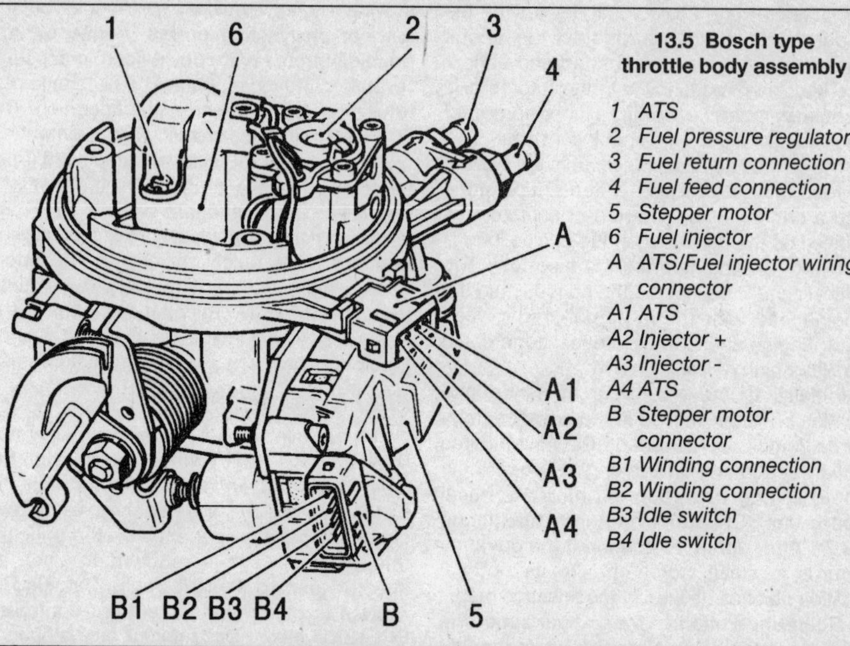

13.5 Bosch type throttle body assembly

1 ATS
2 Fuel pressure regulator
3 Fuel return connection
4 Fuel feed connection
5 Stepper motor
6 Fuel injector
A ATS/Fuel injector wiring connector
A1 ATS
A2 Injector +
A3 Injector -
A4 ATS
B Stepper motor connector
B1 Winding connection
B2 Winding connection
B3 Idle switch
B4 Idle switch

The TPS is a potentiometer with four wires. A common 5.0-volt reference voltage is applied to each resistance track, with the other end connected to a common earth. Each signal output wire is connected to an arm which wipes along the resistance track, and so varies the resistance and voltage of the signal returned to the ECM.

The more sensitive signals produced by two TPS signals enable the ECM to more accurately assess engine load. There is a strong correlation between throttle position, rpm and volume of air (load) entering the engine, and with reference to the mapped values, the ECM is able to calculate fuel injection duration. The first resistance covers the angles from 0° to 24°, and the second resistance covers the angles from 18° to 90°. When the throttle position exceeds an angle of 70°, the resistance at the full load track becomes open-circuit and the ECM lengthens the injection pulse to provide an enriched full-load mixture.

The TPS terminals and connectors are gold-plated, to prevent erroneous signals that may come from poor contact of the surfaces. In addition, the TPS body is vented to prevent condensation.

Idle control

When an electrical load, such as headlights, heater fan or other load are switched on or applied to the engine, the idle speed would tend to drop. The idle speed in Renix-equipped vehicles is not adjustable, and the ECM utilises an ISCV (MPi applications) or stepper motor (SPi applications) to maintain a stable idle speed under all operating conditions.

ISCV (MPi applications)

The idle speed control valve (ISCV) is a solenoid-controlled actuator that the ECM uses to automatically control idle speed during normal idle and engine warm-up. The ISCV is located in a hose that connects the inlet manifold to the air filter side of the throttle plate.

The ECM senses engine loads (such as additional electrical loads from headlights, heated rear window, etc) and pulses the ISCV to increase the airflow through the valve and thus increase the idle speed. When the load is removed, the ECM pulses the valve so that the airflow is reduced. Normal idle speed is thus maintained under all cold and hot operating conditions. One of two different types of ISCV are fitted to Renix-equipped vehicles - a two-wire connector and a three-wire connector. Each type can be identified by counting the number of wires to the ISCV multi-plug.

Three-wire ISCV (MPi applications)

The three-wire ISCV is a DC motor that the ECM can rotate either clockwise or anti-clockwise **(see illustration 13.6)**. Rotating in one direction will open the valve, and rotating in the opposite direction will cause it to close. A voltage supply is applied to the ISCV from the fuel pump relay, and the earth for the motor is made through two connections to the ECM.

Rotation of the motor in the appropriate direction is accomplished by actuating the motor through one or the other of the two earth circuits. In reality, the two circuits are opposed. This prevents the valve from being

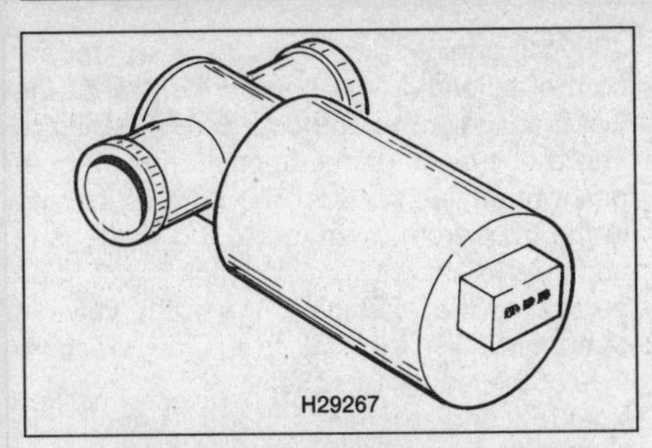

13.6 Idle speed control valve (ISCV), three-wire

fully opened of closed in one particular direction. The valve will thus take up an average position that reflects circuit bias to be open or closed. Normally, this bias would be towards the open position.

A duty cycle may be measured on each earth circuit, to determine the opening or closing time period as a percentage of the total time available.

Two-wire ISCV (MPi applications)

The two-wire ISCV is a solenoid-controlled actuator that the ECM pulses against spring tension to increase the airflow through the valve, and thus increase the idle speed **(see illustration 13.7)**. When the load is removed, the ECM will pulse the valve so that the airflow is reduced. Normal idle speed should be maintained under all cold and hot operating conditions. If the ISCV fails, it will fail-safe, with the aperture almost closed. This will provide a basic idle speed.

Stepper motor (SPi applications)

The ECM constantly monitors the idle rpm, and compares the engine speed to a look-up map tabling rpm against temperature and load. If the difference between the actual engine rpm and the idle map are more than 25 rpm apart, the ECM indexes the stepper motor to bring the idle speed into alignment.

In addition, the ECM makes small adjustments to the idle speed by advancing or retarding the timing if the deviation between rpm and idle map is more than 10°. This results in a more stable idle speed, and an ignition timing that is forever changing during engine idle. During periods of cold running, the stepper motor will set the throttle position to provide a suitable fast idle.

The stepper motor is a DC motor that operates a pushrod. The pushrod contacts the throttle lever, which actuates the throttle plate and so maintains the correct idle speed.

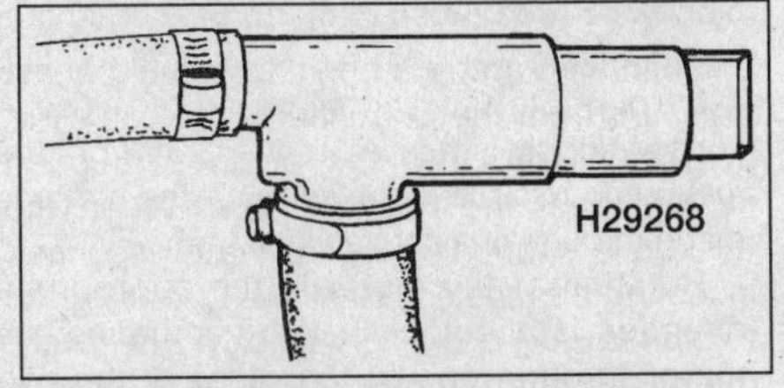

13.7 Idle speed control valve (ISCV), two-wire

The stepper motor consists of a helical-toothed gear and pinion which is controlled by the ECM through a motor winding. The circuit for the winding originates and terminates at the ECM. Pulsing the winding, causes the pushrod to move in one direction. The ECM moves the pushrod in the reverse direction by reversing the polarity of the winding, and the ECM is thus able to position the stepper motor pushrod exactly in its task to control the idle speed.

In addition, a set of contacts is used to signal idle position. When the throttle is closed, the contacts are closed and an ECM pin is connected to earth. When the throttle is opened, the contacts open and the earth is removed from the ECM pin.

Fast idle thermostat (R25, B29E only)

The early version of Renix fitted to the Renault 25 utilised a thermostatic control that operated in a similar fashion to the automatic choke controls on some carburettors. The device acts upon the second throttle valve in the throttle housing. A thermostatic bi-metal spring is arranged in a cast aluminium housing. Heating of the spring is by running water from the cooling system.

Fast idle is achieved with the aid of a variable cam attached to the throttle spindle. When the engine is cold, the cam acts upon the spindle to open the throttle, so giving a suitably fast idle. As the bi-metal coil is heated, and gradually relaxes, the cam will withdraw to progressively reduce the idle speed. Once the coolant temperature has reached 70° C, the spindle is released and the idle speed returns to normal.

Relays

The Renix electrical system is controlled by a main fuel injection relay and a fuel pump relay. Described is a typical wiring arrangement; but variations are present in many of the applications.

A permanent voltage supply is made to the main relay and pump relay terminals 3 from the battery positive terminal. When the ignition is switched on, a voltage supply is applied to terminal 1, and the ECM earths terminal 2 through ECM terminal number 7, which energises the first relay winding. This causes the first relay contacts to close, and terminal 3 is connected to the output circuit at terminal 5. A voltage supply is thus output at terminal 5. Terminal 5 supplies voltage to ECM terminal 19 and to the fuel pump relay terminal 1.

When the ignition is switched on, the ECM briefly earths fuel pump relay contact 2 at ECM terminal 6. This energises the relay winding, which closes the relay contact and connects voltage from terminal 1 to terminal 5, thereby providing voltage to the fuel pump circuit. After approximately one second, the ECM opens the circuit and the pump stops. This brief running of the fuel pump allows pressure to build within the fuel pressure lines, and provides for an easier start.

In some instances, the relay terminal connections 1 and 2 are reversed, to reduce interference (RFI) as the relay coil is actuated.

The fuel pump relay circuit will then remain open until the engine is cranked or run. Once the ECM receives a speed signal from the CAS, the relay winding will again be energised by the ECM, and the fuel pump will run until the engine is stopped. In addition, the fuel pump output terminal 5 also supplies voltage to the injectors, ISCV and the OS heater and CFSV when fitted.

Electric water pump (F3N743 & F3N746)

The purpose of the electric water pump is to pump water through the coolant system after the ignition has been switched off and the engine has stopped. This helps to prevent poor hot starting that can occur due to fuel vaporisation and percolation in the fuel lines.

Once the ignition has been switched off, the ECM holds the main relay on so that power to the ECM is maintained for two minutes. During this period, the CTS signal is monitored, and if the voltage returned indicates a coolant temperature over 107°C, the ECM drives pin 13 to earth, which actuates the electric water pump relay.

The electric pump relay earths the electric water pump, and also the cooling fan relay, which in turn powers up the radiator cooling fan. The two components work together to reduce the coolant temperature. Once the temperature has fallen to 70°C, the ECM releases pin 13, the electric pump relay de-activates, which cuts off the electric water pump and also the coolant fan relay and coolant fan. After 13 minutes of operation, the ECM releases pin 13, even if the temperature has not fallen to the threshold minimum.

The fan relay is attached to the electric water pump earth. When the fan actuates during the normal running of the engine, this connects the electric water pump to earth and it will run. So that this situation is avoided, a diode is fitted to the coolant fan earth line and the electric water pump will not run.

Some Renault models (eg Clio) utilise a timed relay to control the circuit, and the relay is not controlled by the engine management system.

Fuel pump ballast resistor

The F3P704 engine utilises a ballast resistor to control the current applied to the fuel pump. Full battery voltage is applied to the fuel pump, via the ballast resistor relay, during engine cranking.

Injection cut-off relay (B295)

In this model, an additional relay known as an injector cut-off relay is utilised to control the pump relay driver circuit. The pressure switch is positioned in the earth to the cut-off relay coil winding. When the pressure switch closes, the cut-off relay activates and the pump relay driver circuit becomes open-circuit. This results in the pump relay ceasing operation.

Fuel pressure system

Switching on the ignition key causes the ECM to energise the fuel pump relay for approximately one second, so that the fuel system is pressurised. The fuel pump relay is then switched off, to await a cranking or running signal. Once the engine is running, fuel is fed through a non-return valve and fuel filter to the MPi fuel rail or to the single throttle body injector.

To prevent pressure loss in the supply system, a non-return valve is provided in the fuel pump outlet. When the ignition is switched off, and the fuel pump ceases operation, pressure is thus maintained for some time.

The fuel pump may be mounted externally or internally, and both types are described as follows.

External pump

A roller-type fuel pump, driven by a permanent magnet electric motor, is mounted close to the fuel tank. The pump draws fuel from the tank, and pumps it to the fuel rail or the single fuel injector via a fuel filter. The pump is of the 'wet' variety, in that fuel actually flows through the pump and the electric motor. There is no actual fire risk, because the fuel drawn through the pump is not in a combustible condition.

Mounted upon the armature shaft is an eccentric rotor, holding a number of pockets arranged around the circumference - each pocket containing a metal roller. As the pump is actuated, the rollers are flung outwards by centrifugal force to act as seals. The fuel between the rollers is forced to the pump pressure outlet.

Internal pump (SPi)

The fuel pump is mounted vertically in the fuel tank, and comprises an outer and inner gear assembly, termed a 'gerotor'. Once the pump motor becomes energised, the gerotor rotates, and as the fuel passes through the individual teeth of the gerotor, a pressure differential is created. Fuel is drawn through the pump inlet, to be pressurised between the rotating gerotor teeth and discharged from the pump outlet into the fuel supply line.

Fuel pressure regulator (MPi)

Fuel pressure in the fuel rail is maintained at a constant 2.5 bar by a fuel pressure regulator. The fuel pump normally provides much more fuel than is required, and surplus fuel is thus returned to the fuel tank via a return pipe. Re-circulation of the fuel helps to keep it cool. In fact, a maximum fuel pressure in excess of 5 bar is possible in this system. To prevent pressure loss in the supply system, a non-return valve is provided in the fuel pump outlet. When the ignition is switched off, and the fuel pump ceases operation, pressure is thus maintained for some time.

Fuel pressure regulator (SPi)

Fuel pressure of approximately one bar is controlled by the pressure regulator, which is located within the throttle body next to the injector. As the pressure rises over the pre-determined level, excess fuel is returned to the fuel tank via a return pipe. To prevent pressure loss in the supply system, a non-return valve is provided in the fuel pump outlet. When the ignition is switched off, and the fuel pump ceases operation, pressure is thus maintained for some time.

6 Turbocharger

The power output for any given engine is limited by the volume of air that the engine can 'inhale'. Simply put, the more air that an engine can cram into a cylinder, the greater is the volumetric efficiency, and the more power will be produced. Obviously, as the air intake is increased, so too must the fuel intake, so that the AFR is maintained.

Turbocharging is a method of compressing the inlet air so that the maximum charge can be forced into a cylinder under high pressure, or 'boost'.

Exhaust gases are used to drive a turbine and impeller to compress the intake air. The turbine is mounted in the exhaust system, fairly close to the exhaust manifold. The compressing of air generates heat, and the air tends to expand, so losing some of its efficiency. Renault use an intercooler, or 'air radiator', so that the air is cooled on its way to the inlet manifold, and this ensures maximum compression of the air charge.

Boost control

As the volume of exhaust gases increase, the turbine is driven ever faster, and at high engine speeds there is a danger of over-high turbine speeds and over-pressurisation, causing engine damage. This is overcome by using a wastegate control valve to actuate a wastegate flap in the exhaust system - upstream of the turbo.

A hose connects the turbo compressor to the diaphragm of the wastegate actuating valve. As pressure rises to a pre-determined level, the compressed air acts upon the wastegate diaphragm, which mechanically actuates a flap inside the exhaust pipe. Some of the exhaust gases flow through the flap and by-pass the turbine, so that the boost pressure is reduced.

In its simplest form, this provides adequate turbo protection from over-pressurisation, and this arrangement is used in the Renault B295 engines. However, in the B29G and J7R752 engines, by utilising a wastegate control solenoid (WCS) under control of the ECM, maximum turbo boost can be varied to improve power under acceleration and at different engine speeds. The WCS is located in the hose from the turbo to the wastegate, and acts to allow all or part of the boost to be applied to the wastegate. When the valve is open, air is vented back to the low pressure side of the induction system.

At low engine speeds, boost is negligible and the valve is not actuated until rpm rises above a certain level. The ECM tends to pulse the valve with a fixed frequency (12 Hz) and the duration of the pulse is varied, so that the valve is open for longer or shorter time periods as desired.

Boost pressure safety switch

Although the wastegate control will protect the engine from over-high boost pressures under normal circumstances, the engine could be at risk under certain circumstances. For example a seized or inoperative wastegate control could be a recipe for disaster. For this reason, the Renault turbo incorporates a safety pressure switch in the relay circuit. The switch remains closed until the boost pressure reaches a certain pre-determined level, when the pressure switch opens to cut off the fuel pump relay. The wiring of the various turbo models is all slightly different, but the effect is the same for all models.

J7R 752 (Renault 25 four-cylinder)

The pressure switch is positioned in the supply from the ignition switch to one of the pump relay supply terminals. When the switch opens, the pump relay stops operating.

B29G (Renault 25 V6)

The pressure switch is positioned in the pump relay driver terminal to ECM pin number 6. When the switch opens, the pump relay stops operating.

B295 (Renault 25 V6 and Alpine V6)

In these models, an additional relay known as an injector cut-off relay is utilised to control the pump relay driver circuit. The pressure switch is positioned in the earth to the cut-off relay coil winding. When the pressure switch closes, the cut-off relay activates and the pump relay driver circuit becomes open-circuit. This results in the pump relay ceasing operation.

By-pass valve

When the throttle is open, increasing boost pressure from the turbocharger forces air at great pressure into the engine induction system past the open throttle. When the throttle is suddenly closed, the pressurised incoming air meets a blank wall, causing the turbine to slow down very quickly. Effectively, the closed throttle also means that there is very little exhaust gas to keep the turbine moving, and this compounds the problem.

If the throttle is now opened and the engine accelerated, because the turbine is moving very slowly, it can be some little time before the turbo comes back to speed. This so-called 'turbo-lag' can cause a dramatic hesitation between the time that the throttle is opened to the time that the engine responds.

Renault employ a vacuum-controlled air by-pass valve to overcome this problem. The valve is normally closed. During engine deceleration, high vacuum exists in the inlet manifold, and this vacuum is piped to the by-pass valve, causing it to open. Once the valve opens, the high pressure in the inlet tract is vented into the low pressure trunking from the air filter.

7 Catalytic converter and emission control

Models with a catalytic converter will also be fitted with an oxygen sensor (OS), so that closed-loop control of emissions can be implemented. Early versions employed an unheated OS, although later versions utilise the heated type.

The advantage of heating the OS is that it will reach optimum operating temperature very quickly after the engine is started. The OS heater supply is made from the fuel pump relay terminal number 5. This ensures that the heater will only operate whilst the engine is running.

A carbon filter solenoid valve (CFSV) and activated carbon canister are also employed to aid evaporative emission control. The carbon canister stores fuel vapours until the CFSV is opened by the EMS under certain operating conditions. Once the CFSV is actuated by the EMS, fuel vapours are drawn into the inlet manifold, to be burnt by the engine during normal combustion. The CFSV supply is made from the fuel pump relay terminal number 5 or directly from terminal 15 of the ignition switch.

Operating conditions under which the ECM will actuate the carbon canister include:

a) Coolant temperature above 60°C.
b) An engine speed greater than 1200 rpm.
c) A stable manifold pressure less than 900 mbar.

Evaporative emission control (mechanical type)

Although many early models with a catalyst are also equipped with a carbon canister, operation was mechanical, and venting was not controlled by the ECM. In this instance, the canister outlet valve is connected to the throttle body upstream of the throttle valve. When the throttle is opened and the volume of air reaches a certain pre-determined value, the canister valve is drawn open, and this allows manifold vacuum to vent the canister.

Adjustments

8 Adjustment pre-conditions

1 Ensure that all of these conditions are met before attempting to make adjustments

a) Engine at operating temperature. Engine oil at a minimum temperature of 80°C. A journey of at least 4 miles is recommended (particularly so if equipped with AT).
b) Ancillary equipment (all engine loads and accessories) switched off.
c) AT engines: Transmission in N or P.
d) Engine mechanically sound.
e) Engine breather hoses and breather system in satisfactory condition.
f) Induction system free from vacuum leaks.
g) Ignition system in satisfactory condition.
h) Air filter in satisfactory condition.
i) Exhaust system free from leaks.
j) Throttle cable correctly adjusted.
k) No fault codes logged by the ECM.
l) OS operating satisfactorily (catalyst vehicles with closed-loop control).

2 In addition, before checking the idle speed and CO values, stabilise the engine as follows:

a) Stabilise the engine. Raise the engine speed to 3000 rpm for a minimum of 30 seconds, and then let the engine idle.
b) If the cooling fan operates during adjustment, wait until it stops, re-stabilise the engine, and then restart the adjustment procedure.
c) Allow the CO and idle speed to settle.
d) Make all checks and adjustments within 30 seconds. If this time is exceeded, re-stabilise the engine and recheck.

9 Throttle adjustments (MPi)

1 Renault engines with the Renix/Bendix 'R' MPi system are equipped with a number of different throttle bodies as follows:

Solex single-barrel.
Weber twin-barrel.
Pierburg twin-barrel.

2 The Solex throttle body could be equipped with either a throttle switch (TS) or a throttle potentiometer sensor (TPS).

3 Both the Weber and Pierburg throttle bodies are usually equipped with a TPS. In addition, the Pierburg throttle body is usually heated by a PTC heater, although this heater is not controlled by the ECM.

4 Irrespective of the type of throttle body fitted to the vehicle, the adjustments will normally be effected in the following manner.

Throttle body with TPS

5 The TPS is adjustable. However, adjustments can only be effected through the aid of a suitable FCR attached to the serial port. Values obtained by the FCR will fall into the following ranges. These ranges are digital values, and are not obtainable by other means.

Throttle body with TPS (values for FCR)

Condition	Typical value
Idle speed (MT)	*5 to 15*
Idle speed (AT)	*12 to 28*
Part-load:	*20 to 190*
Full-load:	*225 to 245*

Throttle body with TS

Voltmeter

6 Conditions: engine stopped, throttle closed, ignition 'on'.

7 Attach a voltmeter between terminal 2 and earth. A voltage greater than zero indicates that the switch is open, and therefore incorrectly adjusted.

8 Loosen the two screws, and adjust the switch until the voltmeter indicates zero.

Ohmmeter

9 Conditions: TS multi-plug disconnected.

10 Attach an ohmmeter to terminals 2 and 18. The ohmmeter should indicate zero (continuity).

11 Open the throttle. The ohmmeter should indicate an open-circuit (infinity) as soon as the throttle moves off its stop. An audible 'click' should also be heard.

12 Adjust as necessary.

10 Throttle adjustments (SPi)

1 Adjustment of the TPS is not possible. However, the base position can be checked using a suitable FCR.

2 If the TPS is judged defective, the lower part of the throttle body must be replaced.

11 Ignition timing checks

1 Base timing and timing advance figures are not quoted for this system, and in any case the timing is non-adjustable.

Checking for an incorrect flywheel position

2 It is possible to fit the flywheel in the wrong position. If this occurs, the engine will run very badly with a very low manifold vacuum and consequent rich mixture.
3 Set No 1 piston at TDC.
4 Use white paint to mark the tooth on the flywheel that is directly located under the CAS.
5 Slowly turn the engine in a clockwise direction whilst counting the teeth. Eight teeth (including the one that is marked) should pass the under the CAS before the large double tooth reaches the CAS.

12 Idle adjustments

CO pot adjustment (non-cat MPi models only)

1 Remove the tamperproof cap from the CO pot, and turn the CO adjustment screw **(see illustration 13.8)**:

Clockwise to increase CO level and raise voltage.
Anti-clockwise to reduce CO level and reduce voltage.

2 After adjustment is complete, record the CO level, and disconnect the breather hose from the rocker cover.
3 If the CO level decreases by more than 1%, readjust the level with the hose disconnected. When the hose is reconnected, the CO value is likely to rise to a level greater than the specified upper limit. In this instance, adjusting the CO level with the breather hose connected will lead to hesitation and poor engine performance due to a weak mixture.
4 The high CO level with the breather hose is connected is due to contaminated engine oil (short journeys or need for an oil change).
5 Change the engine oil. If the CO level remains high, the engine pistons/rings may be excessively worn, creating engine blow-by.

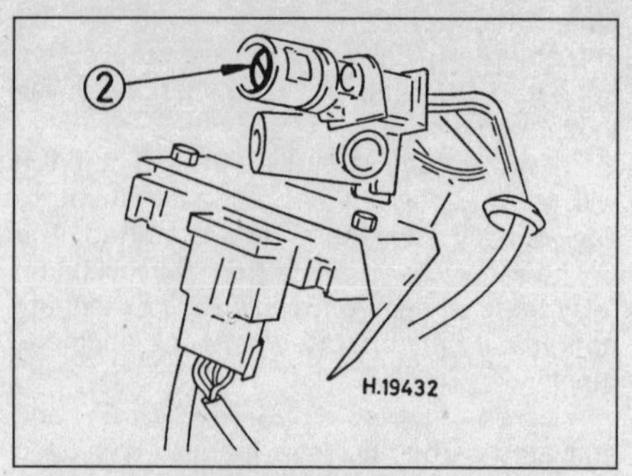

13.8 CO adjustment at the CO pot screw
2 CO adjustment screw

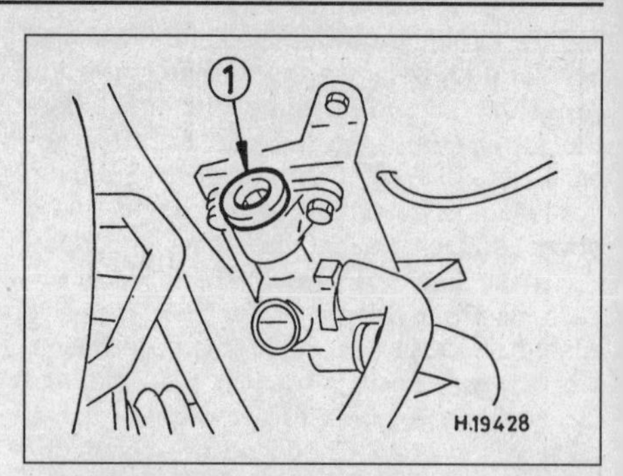

13.9 Some vehicles are equipped with an air by-pass screw to allow a small amount of adjustment
1 Idle by-pass adjustment screw

Idle speed adjustment

6 The idle speed is normally non-adjustable on all models equipped with an ISCV.
7 However, some vehicles are equipped with an air by-pass screw, to allow a small amount of adjustment due to engine wear and sensor ageing **(see illustration 13.9)**.
8 When the engine is new, the air by-pass must be completely shut-off.
9 Before attempting air by-pass adjustment, check for the following faults:

Vacuum leak.
Dirty throttle body or throttle valve.
Sticking throttle, or maladjusted throttle cable or TS.

10 Refer to the adjustment test conditions before making adjustments.
11 Attach a suitable FCR to the serial port. **Note:** *It may be possible to make this adjustment with a dwell meter connected to the ISCV terminal 1 (2-wire ISCV) or terminal 3 (3-wire ISCV).*
12 Display the ISCV pulse width or duty cycle on the FCR screen.
13 Record the idle speed.
14 Record the ISCV pulse width or duty cycle.
15 Unscrew the air by-pass screw until the idle speed increases. As the idle speed increases, the pulse width will reduce.
16 Continue unscrewing the air by-pass screw until the minimum duty cycle or pulse width is attained.
17 Record the minimum value.
18 Tighten the by-pass screw until the duty cycle or pulse width increases by 0.2 to 0.3 ms, or by 4 to 5%. For example: minimum value 2.85 ms/30.2% - adjust to 3.1 ms/35%. **Note:** *If an air leak or another fault is present resulting in more air by-passing the throttle, the ISCV pulse will be at a lower value than normal as the ECM pulses the ISCV less open. When more load is placed upon the engine, the ECM pulses the ISCV more open to increase the idle speed. In addition, if the engine is mechanically unsound or the throttle body plate is dirty, the ECM may pulse the ISCV more open to increase the idle speed. This may result in an uneven idle, and a larger than normal duty cycle or pulse width.*

System sensor and actuator tests

Important note: *Please refer to Chapter 4, which describes common test procedures applicable to this system. The routines in Chapter 4 should be read in conjunction with the component notes and wiring diagrams presented in this Chapter. The wiring diagrams and other data presented in this Chapter are necessarily representative of the system depicted. Because of the variations in wiring and other data that often occurs, even between similar vehicles in any particular VM's range, the reader should take great care in identification of ECM pins, and satisfy himself that he has gathered the correct data before failing a particular component.*

13 Crank angle sensor (CAS)

1 Refer to the note at the start of this Section, and refer also to the relevant Section of Chapter 4.
2 The CAS resistance is 200 ohms approximately.
3 Use a rod to measure the CAS air gap. If the gap is outside of the specification (1.0 ± 0.5 mm), renew the CAS assembly.
4 Check that the CAS is fixed with the proper shouldered bolts. Incorrect fixing bolts can fix the CAS in the wrong position.

14 Primary ignition

1 Refer to the note at the start of Section 13, and refer to the relevant Section of Chapter 4 **(see illustration 13.10)**.
2 The primary ignition is essentially that of an ECM with an external amplifier, and the amplifier is part of a combined amplifier and coil unit.
3 When testing the ignition circuit (with distributor) for a primary signal, the routines described in 'Primary signal not available (external amplifier)' are generally the most suitable.
4 Ignition coil primary resistance is 0.40 to 0.80 ohms; secondary resistance is 2000 to 12 000 ohms.
5 Disconnect the coil from the AEI unit in order to check the coil primary resistance.

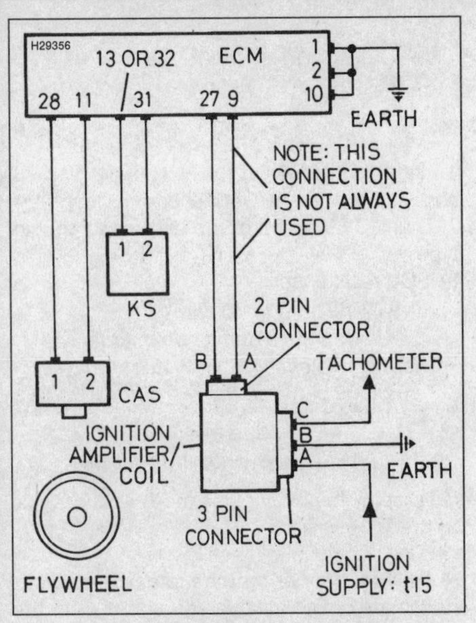

13.10 Typical ignition wiring

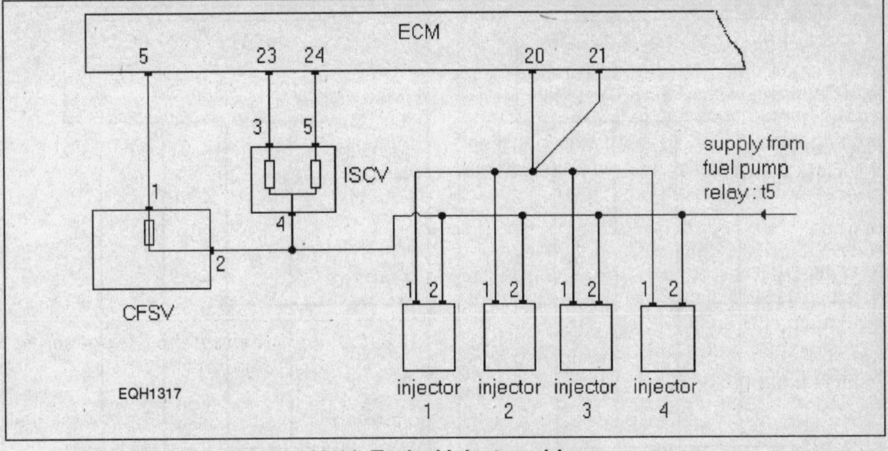

13.11 Typical injector wiring

15 Knock sensor (KS)

1 Refer to the note at the start of Section 13, and refer to the relevant Section of Chapter 4.

16 Fuel injector operation (MPi)

1 Refer to the note at the start of Section 13, and refer to the relevant Section of Chapter 4 **(see illustration 13.11)**.

2 Voltage to the injectors is usually provided from the fuel pump relay, and voltage is therefore only available with the engine cranking or running. However, voltage could be applied for test purposes by by-passing the relay (see Chapter 4).

3 The MPi system is current-controlled, and the opening voltage and holding voltage circuits are completed through ECM pins 20 and 21 (F3N746 models, terminal 21 alone).

4 Injector operation is simultaneous.

5 The injector resistance is normally 14.0 to 15.0 ohms. If not, it's possible an incorrect injector may be fitted (injectors are built with different resistance values, and one with the incorrect resistance for the Renix fuel injection ECM can sometimes be erroneously fitted).

17 Fuel injection operation (SPi)

1 Refer to the note at the start of Section 13, and refer to the relevant Section of Chapter 4.

2 Voltage to the injectors is usually provided from the fuel pump relay, and voltage is therefore only available with the engine cranking or running. However, voltage could be applied for test purposes by by-passing the relay (see Chapter 4).

3 The SPi system is current-controlled.

4 The injector resistance is 1.2 ohms.

18 MAP sensor

1 Refer to the note at the start of Section 13, and refer to the relevant Section of Chapter 4 **(see illustration 13.12)**.

2 Performance of the MAP sensor can be quickly evaluated by a suitable FCR attached to the serial port. Select Datastream; the values should be similar to those in the MAP table (Chapter 4, Section 18).

3 Check that the calibrated restrictor jet is fitted in the hose between the manifold and the MAP sensor (manifold end), and then check that the jet is not blocked. The restrictor size varies according to vehicle type.

19 Air temperature sensor (ATS)

1 Refer to the note at the start of Section 13, and refer to the relevant Section of Chapter 4.

2 Identify the type of sensor ie NTC or PTC:

a) NTC sensor: As the engine compartment air rises in temperature, the voltage signal passed to the ECM will reduce.

b) PTC sensor: As the engine compartment air rises in temperature, the voltage signal passed to the ECM will increase.

3 The air temperature sensor is mounted in the air inlet casing (MPi) or on top of the injector (SPi).

13

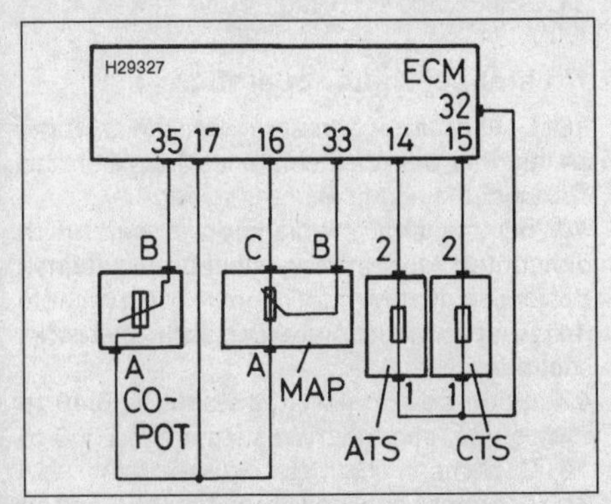

13.12 Typical sensor wiring

Air temperature sensor (ATS)

Sensor type	P.T.C.		N.T.C	
Engine codes	F3N, J7R, J7T, Z7U, J7T780		J7R (732,740,746/7, 752), Z7W, F7P, J7T 754/5,760, Z7X (722,723)	
Temp (°C)	**Resistance**	**Volts**	**Resistance**	**Volts**
0	*254 - 266*		*7469 - 11970*	
20	*283 - 297*	*0.5 - 1.5*	*3061 - 4045*	*2.2 - 2.8*
40	*315 - 329*		*1289 - 1654*	
Open-circuit		*5.0 ± 0.1*		*5.0 ± 0.1*
Short to earth		*zero*		*zero*

Note: *If the sensor is not listed amongst the above engine codes, measure the resistance and compare to the above tables. It should then be obvious which sensor is fitted.*

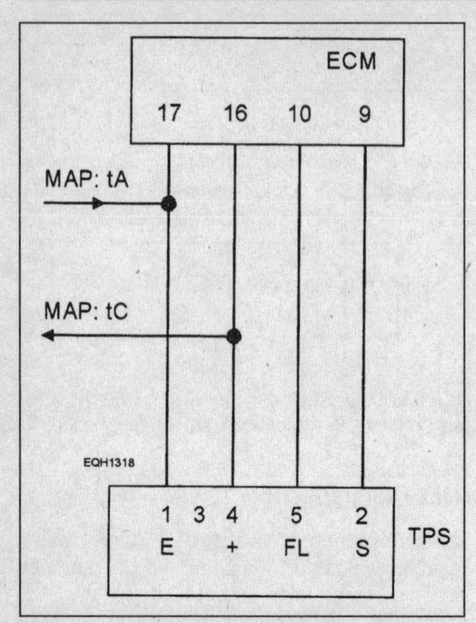

13.13 Bosch SPi throttle body TPS wiring (5-pin)

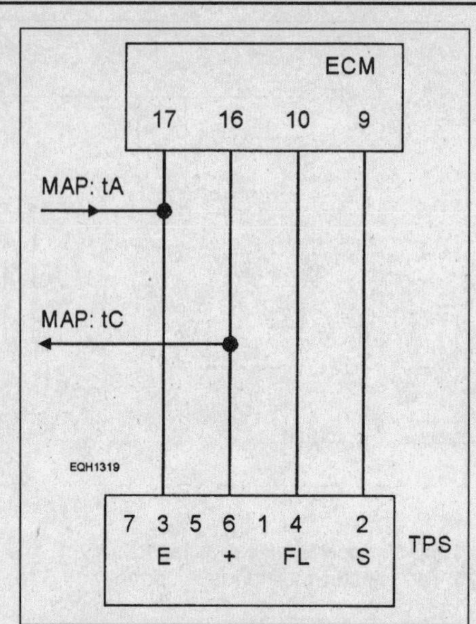

13.14 Bosch SPi throttle body TPS wiring (7-pin)

20 Coolant temperature sensor (CTS)

1 Refer to the note at the start of Section 13, and refer to the relevant Section of Chapter 4.
2 Identify the type of sensor ie NTC or PTC:

a) *NTC sensor: As the coolant rises in temperature, the voltage signal passed to the ECM will reduce.*
b) *PTC sensor: As the coolant rises in temperature, the voltage signal passed to the ECM will increase.*

21 Throttle switch (TS)

1 Refer to the note at the start of Section 13, and refer to the relevant Section of Chapter 4.

22 Throttle potentiometer sensor (TPS)

1 Refer to the note at the start of Section 13, and refer to the relevant Section of Chapter 4.
2 MPi: TPS terminal connections:

TPS signal at terminal A.
Reference voltage supply at terminal B.
Earth return at terminal C.

3 SPi: TPS terminal connections, 5-terminal connector **(see illustration 13.13)**:

TPS signal at terminal 2.
Reference voltage supply at terminal 4.
Earth return at terminal 1.
Full-load contact at terminal 5.

4 SPi: TPS terminal connections, 7-terminal connector **(see illustration 13.14)**:

TPS signal at terminal 2.
Reference voltage supply at terminal 6.
Earth return at terminal 3.
Full-load contact at terminal 4.

Coolant temperature sensor (CTS)

Sensor type	P.T.C (Bendix)		N.T.C. (Bosch)		N.T.C (Bendix)	
Engine codes 746/7,	F3N, J7R, J7T, Z7U		J7T (706,707, 714,715)		F7P, J7R (732,740, 752), J7T 760, J7T780, Z7W, Z7X (722,723)	
Temp (°C)	**Resistance**	**Volts**	**Resistance**	**Volts**	**Resistance**	**Volts**
20	*283 - 297*	*0.6 - 0.8*	*2200 - 2800*	*1.5 - 2.2*	*3061 - 4045*	*1.6 - 2.5*
80	*383 - 397*	*1.0 - 1.2*	*280 - 370*	*0.1 - 0.2*	*301 - 367*	*0.2 - 0.5*
90	*403 - 417*	*212 - 273*				
Open-circuit		*5.0 ± 0.1*		*5.0 ± 0.1*		*5.0 ± 0.1*
Short to earth		*zero*		*zero*		*zero*

Note: *The CTS employed in Renault vehicles may be one of three different types: two of these types function as NTC sensors, and one type functions as a PTC sensor. If the sensor is not listed amongst the above engine codes, measure the resistance and compare to the above specifications.*

23 Idle speed control valve (ISCV)

1 Refer to the note at the start of Section 13, and refer to the relevant Section of Chapter 4.
2 The ISCV may be of the two- or three-wire type.
3 ISCV resistances:

2-wire ISCV: 8 to 10 ohms
3-wire ISCV: 40 ohms from middle terminal to either of the outer terminals. 80 ohms between the two outer terminals.

24 Stepper motor (SPi models)

Note: *The stepper motor and associated idle switch are not adjustable.*
1 Inspect the stepper motor multi-plug for corrosion and damage.
2 Check that the connector terminal pins are fully pushed home and making good contact with the stepper motor multi-plug.
3 Place a shim between the throttle stop and the stepper motor plunger.
4 Switch the ignition key to the 'on' position, and then switch to the 'off' position. The stepper motor plunger should step to the cold start position.
5 Remove the shim and repeat the procedure.
6 If a suitable FCR is available, the base position of the motor can now be checked.

Stepper motor operational test

Note: *this test will result in the ECM storing a fault code. After testing is completed, the fault code memory should be cleared.*
7 Turn on the ignition.
8 Disconnect the CTS multi-plug.
9 Connect a resistance of 15 k-ohms across the two terminals in the CTS multi-plug. The stepper motor should extend to further open the throttle.
10 Disconnect the resistance and reconnect the multi-plug to the CTS. The stepper motor should return to its original position.
11 Cancel the CTS fault code stored in the ECM.

No stepper motor operation

12 Backprobe terminal 1 at the stepper motor with the positive probe of a voltmeter. Connect the negative probe to earth.
13 Switch the ignition key on and off. A voltage should be briefly seen as the stepper motor is actuated.
14 Repeat the above procedure at stepper motor terminal 2.
15 Disconnect the multi-plug to the stepper motor.
16 Connect an ohmmeter between terminals 1 and 2. A resistance of between 5 and 50 ohms should be obtained.

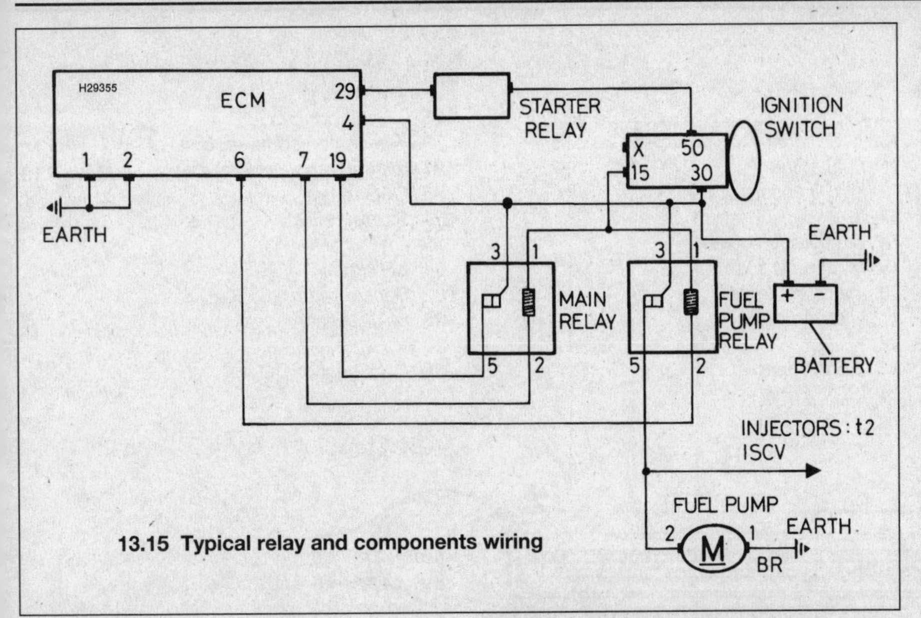

13.15 Typical relay and components wiring

Checking the stepper motor idle contacts

17 Ignition on, throttle closed.

18 Attach the voltmeter negative probe to stepper motor terminal 4.

19 Attach the voltmeter positive probe to stepper motor terminal 3. A maximum voltage of 0.25 volts should be obtained.

20 Open the throttle, the voltage should increase to nbv.

21 If the voltage is nbv, throttle open or closed, the stepper motor idle contacts are suspect.

22 If there is no voltage when the throttle is open, check the continuity of the wiring from the stepper motor terminals to the ECM terminals.

25 ECM voltage supplies and earths

1 Refer to the note at the start of Section 13, and refer to the relevant Section of Chapter 4.

2 In addition to relay drivers for the main relay and pump relay, relay drivers may be available for the electric water pump and other relays.

26 System relays

1 Refer to the note at the start of Section 13, and refer to the relevant Section of Chapter 4 **(see illustration 13.15)**.

2 In the Renix system, the electric water pump is also supplied from a relay.

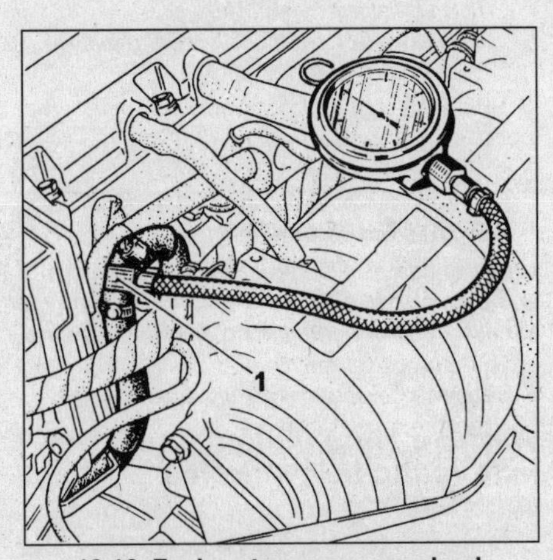

13.16 Fuel system pressure check (MPi, 1.8 F7P engine shown)

1 T-piece

27 Fuel pump and circuit

1 Refer to the note at the start of Section 13, and refer to the relevant Section of Chapter 4 **(see illustrations 13.16 and 13.17)**.

28 Fuel pressure

1 Refer to the note at the start of Section 13, and refer to the relevant Section of Chapter 4.

29 Oxygen sensor (OS)

1 Refer to the note at the start of Section 13, and refer to the relevant Section of Chapter 4.

2 The OS found in the majority of Renix systems is a four-wire sensor with a heater.

30 Carbon filter solenoid valve (CFSV)

1 Refer to the note at the start of Section 13, and refer to the relevant Section of Chapter 4.

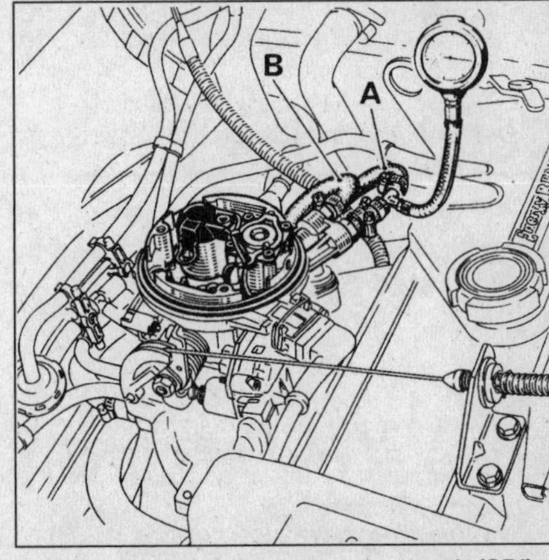

13.17 Fuel system pressure check (SPi)

A Fuel feed pipe *B Fuel return*

Pin table - typical 35-pin

Note: *Refer to* ***illustration 13.18.***

1 Earth
2 Earth
3 -
4 Battery supply
5 CFSV (where fitted)
6 FP relay driver
7 Main relay driver
8 TS full load contact
9 Ignition amp/coil assy
10 earth (some models)
11 CAS signal
12 -
13 KS return (or 32)
14 ATS signal
15 CTS signal
16 MAP sensor supply
17 MAP sensor return
18 Diagnostic socket
19 Main relay output
20 Injectors driver
21 Injectors driver
22 -
23 ISCV signal
24 ISCV signal
25 TS idle contact
26 Flowmeter (some models)
27 Ignition amplifier/coil assy
28 CAS return
29 Starter relay
30 -
31 KS signal
32 Sensor return (CTS, ATS)
33 MAP sensor signal
34 -
35 OS signal or CO pot

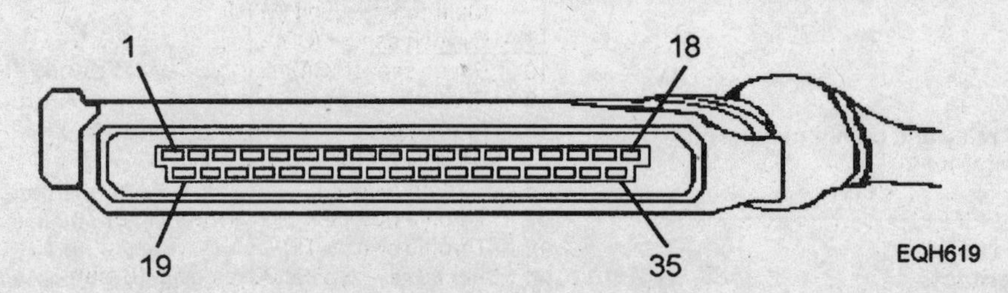

13.18 Renix 35-pin multi-plug

Fault codes

31 Obtaining fault codes

Fault code reader (FCR) analysis

1 If a FCR is available, it could be attached to the SD serial connector and used for the following purposes:

a) Obtaining fault codes.
b) Clearing fault codes.
c) Obtaining Datastream information.
d) Actuating one or more of the system actuators.
e) Making service adjustments.

2 Flash codes are not available for output from this system. For the sake of completeness, we have provided a list of components that will provide errors for readout upon a FCR.

3 When the vehicle is equipped with a TPS (not all vehicles) the TPS base position can be set with the aid of the FCR. Because the values used in the FCR setting process are digital values, it is difficult to make this adjustment manually.

Clearing fault codes

4 Disconnect the battery *(refer to Warnings 3 and 8 in Reference).*

5 Leave disconnected for a minimum period of 15 minutes.

6 Reconnect the battery.

Warning lamp illuminated (automatic transmission vehicles)

7 On automatic transmission vehicles, the reason for an illuminated warning lamp could be due to a fault either in the transmission or in the EMS.

8 Disconnect the ECM multi-plug to the transmission *(see Warning No 3 in Reference).*

9 If the warning lamp is extinguished, the fault lies in the transmission.

10 If the warning lamp remains illuminated, the fault lies in the EMS.

Fault codes

11 In the Renix/Bendix R Engine Management System (EMS), internal fault codes are used to designate faults in the system component circuits. A fault code reader (FCR) such as the Renault XR25 or a suitable proprietary FCR, is required to read the codes. No actual code numbers are available, although the component circuits checked by the EMS include the following:

Faulty circuit

Air conditioning
ATS
Battery supply to ECU
CAS
CO pot (where used - non-cat only)
CTS
Fuel pump control (relay driver circuit)
Heated windscreen (if so equipped)
Ignition signal
Injector
ISCV
KS
MAP sensor
Oxygen sensor
Power assisted steering (if so equipped)
Main relay
Serial communication
TPS or TS (depending on which type fitted)
VSS (if so equipped)

Note: *Not all components are fitted to all vehicles.*

Chapter 14
Rover MEMS - MPi/SPi

Contents

Specifications

Vehicle	Year	idle speed	CO%
Rover MEMS MPi			
114 1.4 GTi 16V cat	1991 to 1994	850 ± 50	0.75 max
214 1.4 DOHC 16V cat	1992 to 1996	875 ± 50	0.5 max
220 2.0 DOHC 16V cat	1991 to 1994	850 ± 50	0.5 to 2.0
220 2.0 DOHC 16V cat	1992 to 1996	850 ± 50	0.5 to 2.0
220 2.0 DOHC 16V turbo cat	1992 to 1996	850 ± 50	0.5 to 2.0
414 1.4 DOHC 16V cat	1992 to 1996	875 ± 50	0.5 max
414 1.4 DOHC 16V	1995 to 1996	875 ± 50	0.5 max
416 1.6 DOHC 16V	1995 to 1996	875 ± 50	0.5 max
420 2.0 DOHC 16V cat	1991 to 1994	850 ± 50	0.5 to 2.0
420 2.0 DOHC 16V cat	1992 to 1996	850 ± 50	0.5 to 2.0
420 2.0 DOHC 16V turbo cat	1992 to 1996	850 ± 50	0.5 to 2.0
620 2.0 DOHC 16V turbo	1994 to 1996	800 ± 50	0.3 max
820i 2.0 DOHC 16V cat	1991 to 1996	850 ± 50	0.5 to 2.0
820 2.0 DOHC 16V turbo cat	1992 to 1996	850 ± 50	0.5 to 2.0
Metro 1.4 GTi DOHC 16V cat	1991 to 1994	850 ± 50	0.5 to 2.0
MGF 1.8 DOHC 16V	1995 to 1996	875 ± 50	0.3 max
MGF 1.8 VVC DOHC 16V	1995 to 1996	875 ± 50	0.3 max
Montego 2.0 EFi	1989 to 1992	750 ± 50	2.0 to 2.5
Montego 2.0 EFi AT	1989 to 1992	750 ± 50	2.0 to 2.5
Rover MEMS SPi			
Metro 1.4 16V	1990 to 1992	850 ± 50	0.5 to 2.0
Metro 1.4 16V cat	1990 to 1992	850 ± 50	0.5 to 2.0
Metro 1.4 16V cat	1993 to 1997	850 ± 50	0.5 to 2.0
Mini Cooper 1.3i MT	1991 to 1992	850 ± 50	0.5 to 2.0
Mini Cooper 1.3i AT	1991 to 1992	850 ± 50	0.5 to 2.0
Mini Cooper 1.3i Cabriolet	1993 to 1997	850 ± 50	0.5 to 2.0
Mini 1.3	1996 to 1997	850 ± 50	0.4 max
111	1995 to 1997	850 ± 50	0.4 max
114	1995 to 1997	875 ± 50	0.4 max
114 1.4i & Cabrio cat	1991 to 1994	875 ± 50	0.75 max
114 1.4i 16V cat	1991 to 1993	875 ± 50	0.75 max
214/414 non cat	1989 to 1992	850 ± 50	0.5 to 2.0
214/414 cat	1990 to 1992	850 ± 50	0.5 to 2.0
214 1.4 16V cat	1992 to 1996	850 ± 50	0.5 to 2.0
414 1.4 16V cat	1992 to 1996	850 ± 50	0.5 to 2.0
414 1.4 16V	1995 to 1996	850 ± 50	0.5 to 2.0

Overview of system operation

1 Introduction

Please read this overview of Rover MEMS operation in conjunction with Chapter 2, which describes some of the functions in more detail.

The Rover MEMS (Modular Engine Management System) was developed jointly by Rover and Motorola, and first appeared in 1989 on Montego 2.0 carburettor and then MPi vehicles. MEMS is a fully-integrated system that controls primary ignition, fuelling and idle control from within the same ECM **(see illustration 14.1)**. When fitted to carburetted engines, it is known as the ERIC system.

MEMS was designed as a modular system that was capable of controlling a wide range of engines equipped with either MPi or SPi. Additionally, the ECM is designed for a harsh environment. It is robustly built, and incorporates short-circuit protection in consideration of its location in the engine compartment.

Prior to 1994, there were three main production versions of MEMS. These are labelled versions 1.2, 1.3 and 1.6. From mid-1994, version 1.8 was fitted.

The differences between the versions are as follows:

a) *Version 1.2 (the first production version) was designed for non-catalyst engines. Although a catalyst could be fitted to the exhaust system of vehicles with v1.2, the catalyst would be of the non-regulated type. Version 1.2 is identified by a single 36-pin multi-plug connector to the ECM.*

b) *Version 1.3 is a fully-regulated catalyst version with ECM control of emission controls. Version 1.3 is identified by two multi-plug connectors (36-pin and 18-pin) to the ECM.*

Improvements in internal organisation released vital areas of MEMS, and allowed the return of a single 36-pin multi-plug connector to the ECM. However, turbocharged vehicles retain the twin multi-plug connectors.

From mid-1994, MEMS version 1.8 has been in production. Main changes are fitment of a plastic inlet manifold and a new stepper motor. The new stepper motor no longer acts upon the linkage to the throttle plate, but uses the motor to actuate a valve mounted within the inlet manifold. Very late versions ııtted to KR6 and MGF vehicles utilise wasted spark DIS and variable valve control (VVC).

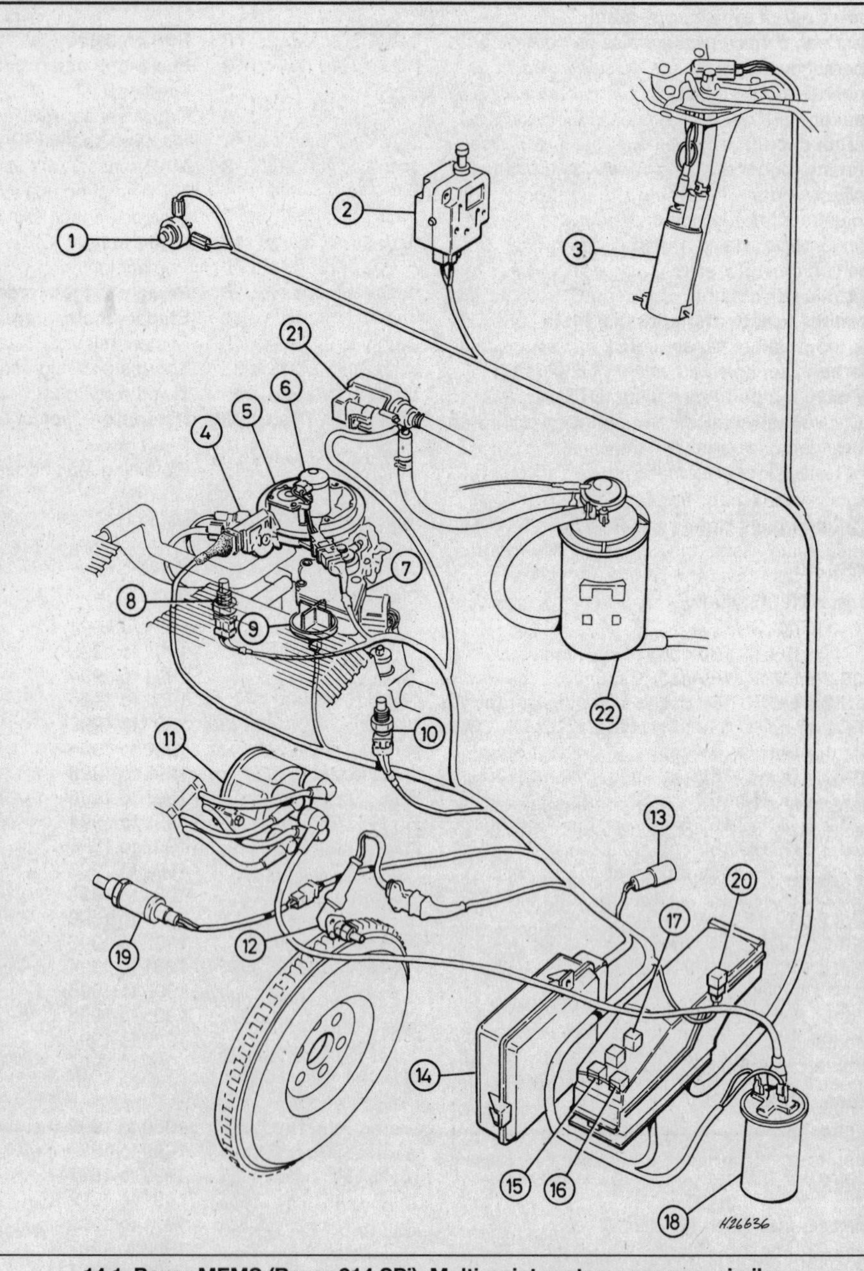

14.1 Rover MEMS (Rover 214 SPi). Multi-point systems are very similar

1 Throttle pedal switch
2 Inertia switch
3 Fuel pump
4 TPS
5 Fuel pressure regulator
6 Fuel injector
7 Stepper motor
8 ATS
9 Throttle body heater (inlet manifold)
10 CTS
11 Distributor
12 CAS
13 SD connector plug
14 ECM
15 Main relay
16 Fuel pump relay
17 Throttle body heater (inlet manifold) relay
18 Ignition coil
19 OS
20 OS relay
21 CFSV
22 Charcoal canister

2 Control functions

Signal processing

The MEMS ECM is designed with three main areas of control. These are the ignition, fuel system and idle speed. The correct ignition dwell and timing for all engine operating conditions are calculated from data provided by the CAS (crankshaft position and speed), and the MAP sensor (engine load).

Basic ignition timing is stored in a three-dimensional map, and the engine load and speed signals determine the ignition timing. The main engine load sensor is the MAP sensor, and engine speed is determined from the CAS signal.

Correction factors are then applied for starting, idle, deceleration, and part- and full-load operation. The main correction factor is engine temperature (CTS). Minor corrections to timing and AFR are made with reference to the air temperature sensor (ATS) and throttle potentiometer sensor (TPS) signals.

The basic AFR is also stored in a three-dimensional map, and the engine load and speed signals determine the basic injection pulse value. Using the speed/density method, MEMS calculates the AFR from the pressure in the inlet manifold (MAP) and the speed of the engine (CAS).

This method relies on the theory that the engine will draw in a fixed volume of air per revolution. The AFR and the pulse duration are then corrected on reference to ATS, CTS, battery voltage and rate of throttle opening (TPS). Other controlling factors are determined by operating conditions such as cold start and warm-up, idle condition, acceleration and deceleration. During acceleration, additional injection pulses are provided at 80° crankshaft intervals.

MEMS accesses a different map for idle running conditions, and this map is implemented whenever the idle switch is closed and the engine speed is at idle. Idle speed during all warm-up and normal hot running conditions is maintained by the idle speed stepper motor. However, MEMS makes small adjustments to the idle speed by advancing or retarding the timing, and this results in an ignition timing that is forever changing during engine idle.

Basic ECM operation

Once the ignition is switched on, a voltage supply to ECM pin 11 is made from the ignition switch. This causes the ECM to connect pin 4 to earth, so actuating the main fuel injection relay. A relay switched voltage supply is thus made to ECM pin 28, from terminal 87 of the main fuel injection relay. Depending on model, the coil is supplied with voltage from either the main relay or from the ignition switch direct.

The majority of sensors (other than those that generate a voltage such the CAS, KS and CID sensor), are now provided with a 5.0-volt reference supply from a relevant pin on the ECM. When the engine is cranked or run, a speed signal from the CAS causes the ECM to earth pin 20 so that the fuel pump will run. Ignition and injection functions are also activated. All actuators (Injectors, ISCV, FTVV etc), are supplied with nbv from the main relay, and the ECM completes the circuit by pulsing the relevant actuator wire to earth.

Self-diagnostic function

MEMS provides a serial port for diagnostic and system tuning purposes. The port allows two-way communication, so that certain parameters can be changed (ie CO value) and actuation of various output components.

In addition, a self-test capability regularly examines signals from the engine sensors, and internally logs a code in the event of a fault being present. This code can be extracted from the MEMS serial port by a suitable FCR. If the fault clears, the code will remain logged until the FCR is used to erase it from memory.

LOS (limp-home mode)

MEMS has a limited operating strategy (LOS) or limp-home facility, and in the event of a serious fault in one or more of the sensors, the EMS will substitute a fixed default value in place of the defective sensor.

For example, in limp-home mode the coolant temperature sensor (CTS) value is set to 60°C, the ATS is set to 35°C, and engine load is based on rpm. The engine may actually run quite well with failure of one or more minor sensors. However, since the substituted values are those of a hot engine, cold starting and running during the warm-up period are likely to be less than satisfactory. Also, failure of a major sensor, ie the MAP sensor, will lead to a considerable reduction in performance.

Adaptive and non-volatile memory

Over a period of time, the ECM will learn the best idle position for a particular engine - irrespective of age, engine condition and load, so that the correct idle speed is always maintained. The adaptive idle settings are stored in non-volatile memory. Consequently, a replacement ECM will need some time to re-learn the system parameters before proper idle control is restored. A tune-up with a suitable FCR is recommended whenever a new ECM is fitted.

Faults identified by the self-diagnostic function will also be stored in non-volatile memory, and will remain there until erased by a suitable FCR. This allows the self-diagnostic function to retain data of an intermittent nature.

Adaptive idle measurements and fault codes retained in non-volatile memory cannot be lost - even if the vehicle battery is removed. If the ECM from one vehicle is transferred to another vehicle, the contents of non-volatile memory will also be transferred, unless a FCR is used to erase the codes and tune the engine to the new set-up.

Reference voltage

Voltage supply from the ECM to the engine sensors is made at a 5.0-volt reference level. This ensures a stable working voltage, unaffected by variations in system voltage.

The earth return connection for most engine sensors is made through ECM pin number 30, and this pin is not directly connected to earth. The ECM internally connects pin number 30 to earth via the ECM earth pin that is directly connected to earth.

Signal shielding

To reduce interference (RFI), a number of sensors (eg the crank angle sensor, knock sensor and oxygen sensor) use a shielded cable. The shielded cable is connected to the main ECM earth wire at terminal 29 to reduce interference to a minimum.

3 Primary trigger

Crank angle sensor (CAS)

The primary signal to initiate both ignition and fuelling emanates from a CAS mounted next to the flywheel. The CAS consists of an inductive magnet that radiates a magnetic field. The flywheel incorporates a reluctor disk containing 34 steel pins set at 10° intervals. As the flywheel spins, and the pins are rotated in the magnetic field, an AC voltage signal is generated to indicate speed of rotation. The two missing pins (set at 180° intervals) are a reference to TDC, and indicate crankshaft position by varying the signal as the flywheel spins. One missing pin indicates TDC for cylinders 1 and 4, and the other missing pin indicates TDC for cylinders 2 and 3.

The peak-to-peak voltage of the speed signal can vary from 5 volts at idle to over 100 volts at 6000 rpm. The ECM microprocessor contains an analogue-to-digital converter to transform the AC pulse into a digital signal.

4 Ignition

Data on engine load (MAP) and engine speed (CAS) are collected by the ECM, which then refers to a three-dimensional digital ignition map stored within its microprocessor. This map contains an advance angle for basic load and speed operating conditions. The advance angle is corrected after reference to engine temperature (CTS), so that the best ignition advance angle for a particular operating condition can be determined.

Amplifier

The MEMS amplifier contains the circuitry for switching the coil negative terminal at the correct moment to instigate ignition. The signal received by the amplifier from the CAS trigger is of an insufficient level to complete the necessary coil switching. The signal is thus amplified to a level capable of switching the coil negative terminal.

The amplifier circuitry is contained within the ECM itself, and the microprocessor controls the ignition dwell period for each condition of engine speed and battery voltage.

Dwell operation in MEMS is based upon the principle of the 'constant-energy current-limiting' system. This means that the dwell period remains constant at about 3.0 to 3.5 ms, at virtually all engine running speeds. However, the dwell duty cycle, when measured in percent or degrees, will vary as the engine speed varies.

Ignition coil

The ignition coil utilises low primary resistance in order to increase primary current and primary energy. The amplifier limits the primary current to around 8 amps, and this permits a reserve of energy to maintain the required spark burn time (duration). In DIS systems, the coils are double-ended, and fire two spark plugs together. The KR6 utilises three DIS coils, and the MGF two DIS coils.

Distributor

In the MEMS system, the distributor only serves to distribute the HT current from the coil secondary terminal to each spark plug in firing order. The distributor is located on the inlet camshaft at the cylinder No 4 end. The distributor contains a rotor arm, and also has a deflector plate and oil drain to prevent oil seal leakage from contaminating the distributor cap and rotor arm.

Distributorless ignition system (DIS)

Vehicles with the KR6 V6 engine, and those with the four-cylinder MGF VVC engine utilise wasted spark DIS ignition. The MGF without VVC is equipped with a distributor. Refer to Chapter 2 for a detailed description of wasted spark and DIS.

Knock sensor (some MPi vehicles)

The optimal ignition timing (at engine speeds greater than idle) for a given high-compression engine is quite close to the point of onset of knock. However, running so close to the point of knock occurrence means that knock will certainly occur on one or more cylinders at certain times during the engine operating cycle.

Since knock may occur at a different moment in each individual cylinder, MEMS employs a knock control processor (KCP) built into the ECM to pinpoint the actual cylinder or cylinders that are knocking. The knock sensor is mounted on the engine block, and consists of a piezo-ceramic measuring element that responds to engine noise oscillations. This signal is converted to a voltage signal that is proportional to the level of knock, and returned to the ECM for evaluation and action.

The ECM will analyse the noise from each individual cylinder, and uses a sophisticated technique to recognise knock as distinct to general engine noise.

Initially, timing will occur at its optimal ignition point. Once knock is identified, the microprocessor retards the ignition timing for that cylinder in steps of 0.625° until either knock ceases or a maximum retard of 10° is reached. The timing is then advanced in 0.65° increments until the reference timing value is achieved or knock occurs again, when the processor will retard the timing once more. This procedure continually occurs so that all cylinders will consistently run at their optimum timing.

If a fault exists in the KCP, knock control sensor or wiring, an appropriate code will be logged in the self-diagnostic unit, and the ignition timing retarded by 10.5° by the LOS program.

5 Fuel injection

Rover has adopted three distinct methods for providing fuel to the engines equipped with MEMS. The methods are simultaneous multi-point injection (MPi), sequential multi-point injection (MPi) and single-point injection (SPi).

Because of the modularity of MEMS, very little difference exists between the implementation of each system on the various engines. First, a description of common features and a description of each type follows.

The injector(s) are switched using two circuits. Operation depends on the principle that more current is required to open an injector than to keep it open. This kind of system is often termed 'current-controlled'. Once the injector is open, a second circuit rapidly pulses the injector to earth. The switching is so rapid that the injector is effectively held open, and less current is required during the operation. Advantages of this arrangement include a reduction in injector operating temperature, and immediate injector closure once the holding circuit is switched off.

The MEMS ECM contains a fuel map with an injector opening time for basic conditions of speed and load. Information is then gathered from engine sensors such as the MAP sensor, CAS, CTS, ATS and TPS. As a result of this information, the ECM will look up the correct injector pulse duration right across the engine rpm, load and temperature range.

The fuel injector is a magnetically-operated solenoid valve that is actuated by the ECM. Voltage to the injectors is applied from the fuel pump relay, and the earth path is completed by the ECM for a period of time (called pulse duration) of between 1.5 and 10 milliseconds. The pulse duration is very much dependent upon engine temperature, load, speed and operating conditions. When the magnetic solenoid closes, a back-EMF voltage of up to 60 volts is initiated.

The amount of fuel delivered by the injector(s) is determined by the fuel pressure and the injector opening time - otherwise known as the pulse duration. The ECM controls the period of time that the injector is held open, and this is determined by the signals from the various sensor inputs. During engine start-up from cold, the pulse duration and number of pulses (frequency) are increased to provide a richer air/fuel mixture.

Over-speed fuel cut-off (rev limiter)

To prevent over-high engine speeds, which might otherwise lead to engine damage, above 6250 rpm (MPi) and 6860 rpm (SPi), MEMS inhibits the injector earth path. As the engine speed drops below 6150 rpm and 6820 rpm respectively, fuel injection is reinstated.

Deceleration fuel cut-off

A deceleration fuel cut-off is implemented during engine over-run conditions, to improve economy and reduce emissions. The conditions for over-run to be implemented are:

a) Throttle closed (throttle pedal contacts closed).
b) Engine speed above 2600 rpm (MPi) or 1500 rpm (SPi).
c) Coolant temperature above 80°C.
d) Once the engine speed drops below 2600 rpm or 1500 rpm respectively, fuel injection is reinstated.

Multi-point injection (MPi - simultaneous)

The MPi system consists of one injector for each cylinder, mounted in the inlet port, so that a finely-atomised fuel spray is directed onto the back of each valve. The injectors are all pulsed simultaneously, twice per engine cycle. Half of the required fuel per engine cycle is injected at each engine revolution.

Fuel will briefly rest upon the back of a valve before being drawn into a cylinder. Unlike other simultaneous systems, the injectors are all connected to the ECM via separate wires to separate ECM driver pins.

Multi-point injection (MPi - sequential)

The sequential system functions in a similar manner to the simultaneous system. However, with reference to the signal from the cylinder identification (CID) sensor (only present in sequential systems), each injector is actuated as its inlet valve opens, in firing order.

Single-point fuel injection (SPi)

The SPi system consists of a single injector mounted in the throttle body. The amount of fuel delivered by the injector is determined by the fuel pressure and the injector opening time - otherwise known as the pulse duration.

In SPi engines, fuel is injected into the inlet manifold, where it mixes with air. The depression produced by a descending piston causes the resulting air/fuel mixture to be drawn into each cylinder. Otherwise, operation of the injector is very similar to operation of the injector fitted to the MPi systems.

Cylinder identification sensor (sequential injection only)

In simultaneous MPi systems, the ECM does not have to recognise No 1 cylinder, or indeed even the firing order. When the crankshaft or distributor provides a timing signal, the correct cylinder is identified by the mechanical position of the crankshaft, camshaft, valves and ignition rotor.

On models fitted with sequential injection, the ECM must determine which cylinder is on its firing stroke, and the CID sensor provides the appropriate signal. The CID sensor operates on the inductive principle, and is a permanent magnet device mounted adjacent to the camshaft. A reluctor is attached to the camshaft, divided into four equal quadrants. Each quadrant contains a unique number of teeth, numbering from one to four. Because the AC-generated signal from each quadrant is unique, the ECM is able to determine the camshaft position and cylinder sequence.

The reluctor should be handled with extreme care, due to the fragile sintered material used in its construction. Any impact may cause cracking or a stress fracture.

MAP sensor

The main engine load sensor is the MAP sensor. A vacuum hose connects the MAP sensor (located within the ECM) and the inlet manifold **(see illustration 14.2)**. Manifold vacuum acts upon the MAP sensor diaphragm, and the ECM converts the pressure into an electrical signal. MAP is calculated from the formula: Atmospheric Pressure less Manifold Pressure = Manifold Absolute Pressure.

Using the speed/density method, MEMS calculates the AFR from the MAP signal and the speed of the engine (CAS). This method relies on the theory that the engine will draw in a fixed volume of air per revolution.

The inlet manifold on the MPi models is a 'dry' manifold. Since fuel does not enter the manifold - due to injection being made onto the back of the inlet valve, there is no risk of fuel being drawn into the MAP sensor to contaminate the diaphragm, and a fuel trap is not used. However, on Rover 820 models

14.2 SPi: The MAP sensor vacuum hose connections to the fuel trap at the air filter. The hoses are colour coded to ensure correct refitting

under certain operating conditions, fumes are drawn from the rocker box into the MAP sensor vacuum hose and then to the ECM, where contamination can occur. This can be prevented by fitting the fuel trap used on SPi models.

The inlet manifold on the SPi models is a 'wet' manifold. Fuel is injected into the inlet manifold, and there is a risk of fuel being drawn into the MAP sensor to contaminate the diaphragm. This is prevented by running the vacuum hose upward to the air filter, through a fuel trap and then to the ECM (which contains the MAP sensor).

Air temperature sensor (ATS)

The ATS is mounted in the air inlet casing (MPi) or air filter casing (SPi), and measures the air temperature before it enters the inlet manifold. Because the density of air varies in inverse proportion to the temperature, the ATS signal allows more accurate assessment of the volume of air entering the engine.

The open-circuit supply to the sensor is at a 5.0-volt reference level, and the earth path is through the sensor return. The ATS operates on the NTC principle. A variable voltage signal is returned to the ECM based upon the air temperature. This signal is approximately 2.0 to 3.0 volts at an ambient temperature of 20°C, and reduces to about 1.5 volt as the temperature rises to around 40°C.

Although the air filter casing used on SPi models contains a thermal valve system, the thermal valve has no bearing on the AFR, and the air temperature is calculated solely by reference to the ATS.

CO adjustment

The CO value at idle speeds can only be adjusted through the medium of a FCR attached to the serial port. It is not possible to make this adjustment by any other means. On catalyst-equipped models, the CO is non-adjustable.

Coolant temperature sensor (CTS)

The CTS is incorporated in the cooling system, and contains a variable resistance that operates on the NTC principle. When the engine is cold, the resistance is quite high. Once the engine is started and begins to warm-up, the coolant becomes hotter, and this causes a change in the CTS resistance. As the CTS becomes hotter, the resistance of the CTS reduces (NTC principle), and this returns a variable voltage signal to the ECM based upon the coolant temperature.

The open-circuit supply to the sensor is at a 5.0-volt reference level, and this voltage reduces to a value that depends upon the CTS resistance. Normal operating temperature is usually from 80° to 100° C. The ECM uses the CTS signal as a main correction factor when calculating ignition timing and injection duration.

Throttle potentiometer sensor (TPS)

A TPS is provided to inform the ECM of rate of acceleration. The TPS is a potentiometer with three wires. A 5.0-volt reference voltage is supplied to a resistance track, with the other end connected to earth. The third wire is connected to an arm which wipes along the resistance track, and so varies the resistance and voltage of the signal returned to the ECM.

From the voltage returned, the ECM is able to calculate just how quickly the throttle is opened. From model year 1993 onwards, the TPS also informs the ECM of idle position with a voltage of approximately 0.6 volts.

Throttle pedal switch

Until the 1993 model year, the throttle pedal switch indicated a closed throttle to the ECM. The ECM was then able to recognise the idle speed condition and also deceleration. From 1993 models year, MEMS recognised the closed throttle condition with reference to the TPS signal.

Stepper motor

The stepper motor is an actuator that the ECM uses to automatically control idle speed during normal idle and during engine warm-up **(see illustration 14.3)**. When electrical loads, such as headlights or heater fan etc are switched on, the idle speed would tend to drop. In this event, the ECM advances the ignition timing to make a small speed change, and indexes the stepper motor for a greater change in idle speed. During periods of cold

14.3 Rover 820 stepper motor
1 Stepper motor 2 Ignition coil 3 ECM

running, the stepper motor will open the throttle so that the engine rpm will be set to a suitable fast idle speed. Also, on sensing low battery voltage, the ECM will increase the idle speed to allow greater alternator output.

The stepper motor is a DC motor, provided with a voltage supply from the system relay. The motor windings are earthed through four earth wires. By earthing various combinations of the four wires, the ECM is able to index the motor to its correct position. The ECM controls idle speed by using the stepper motor in one of two diverse ways.

Throttle plate actuator

The stepper motor controls a cam and pushrod through a reduction gear. The pushrod contacts the throttle lever, which actuates the throttle plate and so maintains the correct idle speed. Maximum movement of the stepper motor is 3.75 revolutions, and this is accomplished by 180 steps of 7.5°. The reduction gear reduces the actual cam movement to 150°.

Inlet manifold air valve

The air valve stepper motor is an actuator that the ECM uses to automatically control idle speed during normal idle and during engine warm-up. When the throttle is closed, the throttle valve is locked in a position where very little air passes by. The throttle position then, will have no effect upon the idle speed.

A by-pass port to the throttle plate is located in the inlet manifold. A valve is positioned in the port. As the valve moves, the volume of air passing through the port will vary, and this directly affects the idle speed. The idle speed then, depends upon the position of the stepper air valve in the by-pass port. This method of idle control is fitted to some models (principally those with the plastic inlet manifold) from the middle of 1994.

Adaptive idle control

Since the idle control is adaptive, over a period of time, the ECM will learn the best position for a particular engine - irrespective of age, engine condition and load, so that the correct idle speed is always maintained. Consequently, a replacement ECM will need some time to re-learn the system parameters before proper idle control is restored.

Adaptive idle measurements are retained in non-volatile memory and cannot be lost - even if the vehicle battery is removed. On models prior to 1993, idle position was determined by an idle switch located on the accelerator pedal. From 1993, this switch has been discontinued, and the idle position is now determined by the TPS.

Manifold heater (SPi)

The ECM controls the manifold heater through a relay. This heater works on the PTC principle, and allows a greater current to quickly heat the inlet manifold during the warm-up period. This allows better driveability during engine warm-up. Once a preset temperature of approximately 75° C is reached, the ECM turns off the relay. If the ignition is switched to the 'on' position and the engine is not cranked, the ECM will turn off the manifold heater after a few seconds. The manifold heater will also be turned off to prevent battery overload during engine cranking.

14.4 Rover 820 MEMS multi-function unit (MFU)
MFU multi-plug disconnected

MEMS relays and MFU

The MEMS electrical system is controlled by a number of relays. The relays utilised in some vehicles are conventional in construction and operation. However, some models are equipped with an MFU (multi-function unit).

Main and fuel pump relays (Rover 214, 414, 220 and 420 models)

A permanent voltage supply is made to main relay terminals 30 and 86, and fuel pump relay terminal 30, from the battery positive terminal. When the ignition is switched on, the ECM earths terminal 85 through ECM terminal number 4, which energises the relay winding. This causes the main relay contacts to close, and terminal 30 is connected to the output circuit at terminal 87. A voltage supply is thus output at terminal 87. Terminal 87 supplies voltage to the injector(s), ECM terminal 28, the ignition coil terminal 15 (some models) and the stepper motor. In addition, voltage is supplied to the manifold heater relay terminal 86 on SPi vehicles.

When the ignition is switched on, a voltage supply is made to fuel pump relay terminal 86, and the ECM briefly earths relay contact 85 at ECM terminal 20, which energises the fuel pump relay winding. This causes the fuel pump relay contacts to close, and connects voltage from terminal 30 to terminal 87. Voltage is thereby output to the fuel pump circuit. After approximately one second, the ECM opens the circuit and the pump stops. This brief running of the fuel pump allows pressure to build within the fuel pressure lines, and provides for an easier start.

The fuel pump circuit will then remain open until the engine is cranked or run. Once the ECM receives a speed signal from the CAS, the fuel pump winding will again be energised by the ECM, and the fuel pump will run until the engine is stopped.

Multi-function unit (MFU) main and fuel pump relays (all Rover models other than 214, 414, 220, and 420)

The MFU is a sealed box that contains four sets of relay contacts. The two relays always used are a main and fuel pump relay, and the other two will be chosen from the starter, OS or manifold heater relays **(see illustration 14.4)**.

If any one of the relays fails, the whole MFU must be replaced. However, the relay contacts are heavy-duty, and failure is a fairly rare occurrence.

Two multi-plugs of 8-pin and 6-pin configuration connect the MFU with MEMS wiring. The multi-plug terminal designations are identified by the prefix 8 or 6 for the multi-plug, and the suffix 1 to 8 or 1 to 6 for the actual terminal. So 8/1 would identify the terminal as number one terminal in the eight 8-pin multi-plug. There follows a typical description, but be warned that wiring of some MFU's may differ.

A permanent voltage supply is made to the MFU main relay terminals 8/6 and 8/7 from the battery positive terminal. When the ignition is switched on, the ECM earths terminal 6/3 through ECM terminal number 4, which energises the relay winding. This causes the main relay contacts to close, and output voltage is available at MFU terminal 8/1, 8/3 and 8/8. These output terminals supply voltage to the injector(s), ECM terminal 28, the ignition coil terminal 15 models) and the stepper motor. Connections to individual components vary according to vehicle. In addition, voltage is internally supplied to the manifold heater relay inside the MFU on SPi vehicles.

When the ignition is switched on, a voltage supply is made to MFU terminal 6/2, and the ECM briefly earths MFU contact 6/1 at ECM terminal 20. This energises the fuel pump relay, and causes the fuel pump relay contacts to close. Terminal 8/6 is thus connected to terminal 8/4, and voltage is thereby output to the fuel pump circuit. After approximately one second, the ECM opens the circuit, and the pump stops. This brief running of the fuel pump allows pressure to build within the fuel pressure lines, and provides for an easier start.

The fuel pump circuit will then remain open until the engine is cranked or run. Once the ECM receives a speed signal from the CAS, the fuel pump winding will again be energised by the ECM, and the fuel pump will run until the engine is stopped.

Engine shut down

On switching off the engine, the ECM keeps the relay (or MFU) earth energised for up to 30 seconds. This holds the voltage supply to the ECM, which then actuates the stepper motor to its fully closed position (thus preventing engine run-on). After a few seconds more, the ECM actuates the stepper motor to a position where it slightly opens the throttle plate, ready for the next engine start.

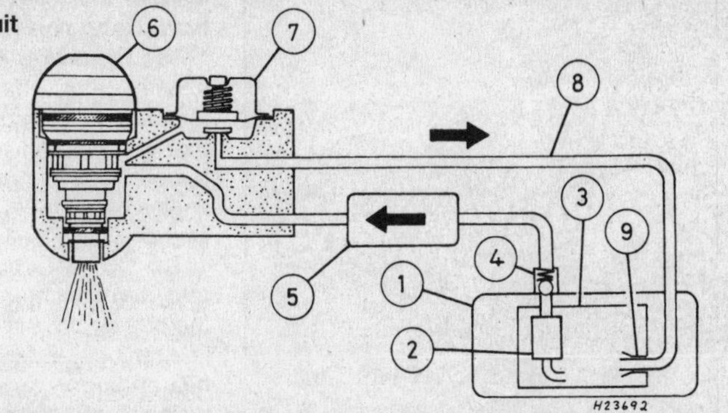

14.5 Fuel delivery circuit for SPi engines

1 *Fuel tank*
2 *Fuel pump*
3 *Swirl pot*
4 *Non-return valve*
5 *Fuel filter*
6 *Fuel injector*
7 *Fuel pressure regulator*
8 *Fuel return line*
9 *Venturi*

Fuel pressure system

Note: *Uniquely, the Montego utilises a roller-type fuel pump mounted outside the fuel tank. Voltage to the fuel pump is applied through a 1.0 ohm ballast resistor. This reduces the voltage and current applied to the fuel pump, and ensures cooler running. During cranking, when a higher voltage level is required, voltage is applied directly to the pump from the starter solenoid and the resistor is by-passed. Full nbv is thus applied to the fuel pump.*

The fuel system includes a fuel tank, with swirl pot and a submerged fuel pump. The fuel pump draws fuel from the tank and pumps it to the fuel rail via a fuel filter **(see illustration 14.5)**.

Switching the ignition key on causes the ECM to energise the fuel pump relay for approximately one second so that the fuel system is pressurised. The fuel pump relay is then switched off, to await a cranking or running signal. The swirl pot prevents air from entering the fuel supply line, by ensuring that the pick-up strainer is always immersed in fuel when the fuel level is low - even during fuel movement due to centrifugal forces acting upon the vehicle.

The pump is of the 'wet' variety, in that fuel actually flows through the pump and the electric motor. There is no actual fire risk, because the fuel drawn through the pump is not in a combustible condition. The fuel pump assembly comprises an outer and inner gear assembly, termed a 'gerotor'. Once the pump motor becomes energised, the gerotor rotates, and as the fuel passes through the individual teeth of the gerotor, a pressure differential is created. Fuel is drawn through the pump inlet, to be pressurised between the rotating gerotor teeth, and discharged from the pump outlet into the fuel supply line.

To reduce the effect of fluctuations in fuel pressure, a pulsation damper is provided in the pump outlet, thereby preventing hydraulic knock. The pump is protected from over-pressurising by a relief valve mounted in the inlet side of the pump. Once the engine is running, fuel is fed through a non-return valve and fuel filter to the multi-point injector rail or the single throttle body injector.

To prevent pressure loss in the supply system, a non-return valve is provided in the fuel pump outlet. When the ignition is switched off, and the fuel pump ceases operation, pressure is thus maintained for some time. Temperature in the fuel rail is monitored by a fuel rail temperature sensor (FRTS) in manual transmission models; a fuel restrictor and fuel temperature sensor (FTS) is used in automatic transmission models.

Fuel pressure regulator (MPi)

Fuel pressure in the fuel rail is maintained at a constant 2.5 bar by a fuel pressure regulator fitted on the outlet side of the fuel rail. The fuel pump normally provides much more fuel than is required, and surplus fuel is thus returned to the fuel tank via a return pipe. In fact, a maximum fuel pressure in excess of 5 bar is possible in this system.

The pressure regulator consists of two chambers, separated by a diaphragm. The upper chamber contains a spring, which exerts pressure upon the lower chamber and closes off the outlet diaphragm. Pressurised fuel flows into the lower chamber, and this exerts pressure upon the diaphragm. Once the pressure exceeds 2.5 bar, the outlet diaphragm is opened, and excess fuel flows back to the fuel tank via a return line.

A vacuum hose connects the upper chamber to the inlet manifold, so that variations in inlet manifold pressure will not affect the amount of fuel injected. This means that the pressure in the rail is always at a constant pressure above the pressure in the inlet manifold. The quantity of injected fuel thus depends solely on injector opening time, as determined by the ECM, and not on a variable fuel pressure.

At idle speed with the vacuum pipe disconnected, or with the engine stopped and the pump running, or at full-throttle, the system fuel pressure will be around 2.5 bar. At idle speed (vacuum pipe connected), the fuel pressure will be approximately 0.5 bar under the system pressure.

Fuel pressure regulator (SPi)

Fuel pressure of approximately one bar is controlled by the pressure regulator, which is located within the throttle body next to the injector. As the pressure rises over the pre-determined level, excess fuel is returned to the fuel tank via a return pipe.

Fuel rail temperature sensor (FRTS) - some MPi models with manual transmission

The FRTS senses the temperature of the fuel in the fuel rail, and the value is logged by the ECM at the time that the engine is shut down. When the engine is restarted, the ECM compares the start-time temperature with the temperature recorded at shut-down. If the new temperature is higher, the injection pulse is lengthened during the cranking operation to provide hot start enrichment. This enrichment decays at a fixed rate.

Fuel temperature sensor (FTS) and fuel restrictor solenoid (FRS) - MPi models with automatic transmission)

In vehicles with automatic transmission, the FRTS is replaced with a fixed resistance so that after-start enrichment will never be implemented. When the fuel rail temperature exceeds 90°C, the FTS closes to complete the earth circuit to the FRS. The FRS is energised to cause a restriction in the fuel return line. The increased fuel pressure thereby improves starting.

Inertia switch

The inertia switch is a safety cut-out switch, used to isolate the fuel pump in the event of a very sharp deceleration - eg a collision. Once the switch has been activated, the electrical supply to the fuel pump remains open-circuit until the inertia switch has been reset by raising the button **(see illustration 14.6)**.

Temperature gauge (Montego only)

The engine coolant temperature gauge on the instrument panel is connected to earth through the ECM. MEMS actuates the gauge and warning lamp by rapidly pulsing the ECM connection to earth. This produces a square waveform of variable frequency and duty cycle. The frequency increases as the engine temperature increases, and the hotter the engine, the lower will the average voltage become. In addition, the duty cycle will also change.

14.6 Reset inertia switch by depressing plunger

Turbocharger

Refer to Chapter 2 for a detailed description of turbocharger operation. An intercooler, which is a kind of air radiator, for cooling is used in Rover turbo models. Boost control is controlled by the ECM so that maximum use is made of the turbo during appropriate operating conditions.

Air by-pass (turbo models)

Turbo lag is reduced on Rover turbo models by use of an air by-pass valve. A sensing pipe connects the by-pass valve with the inlet manifold. When the turbine supplies compressed air to the manifold, the compressed air pushes upon the air by-pass valve, and it remains shut. During deceleration or light load when the turbo is inactive, the manifold contains depressed air (a vacuum) and the depression will open the air by-pass valve. Air pressure from the impeller wheel is circulated throughout the turbocharger housing, and prevents a back pressure forming. The turbine slows very little, and turbo lag is much reduced when the accelerator is re-applied.

6 Catalytic converter and emission control

From January 1993, all new cars in the UK are fitted with a catalyst as standard equipment.

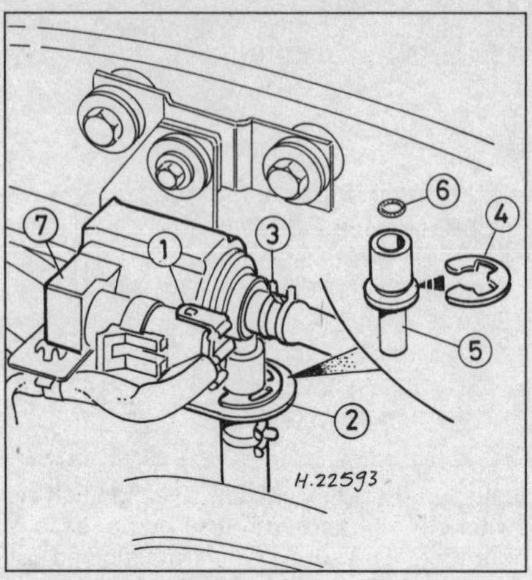

14.7 Carbon filter solenoid valve (CFSV)

1 Wiring connector
2 Inlet hose, charcoal canister to CFSV
3 Outlet hose, CFSV to throttle body
4 C-clip
5 Inlet hose, connector
6 O ring
7 CFSV

The MEMS injection system fitted to catalyst vehicles implements a closed-loop control system, so that exhaust emissions may be reduced. Closed-loop systems are fitted with an oxygen sensor (OS) which monitors the exhaust gas for its oxygen content. A low oxygen level in the exhaust signifies a rich mixture. A high oxygen level in the exhaust signifies a weak mixture.

The OS only produces a signal when the exhaust gas, has reached a minimum temperature of approximately 300°C. In order that the OS will reach optimum operating temperature as quickly as possible after the engine has started, the OS contains a heating element.

The OS heater supply is made from the OS relay terminal number 87. This ensures that the heater will only operate whilst the engine is running. Under full-load conditions, the heater supply is cut-off by the ECM by inhibiting the earth path of the OS relay. The KR6 engine utilises twin oxygen sensors, one for each bank.

Carbon filter solenoid valve (CFSV)

A CFSV and activated carbon canister will also be employed to aid evaporative emission control **(see illustration 14.7)**. The carbon canister stores fuel vapours until the CFSV is actuated by MEMS. CFSV actuation occurs when the engine temperature is above 70°C, the engine speed above 1500 rpm and the MAP sensor returns less than 30 kPa.

When the CFSV is actuated by MEMS, the valve is modulated on and off, and fuel vapours are drawn into the inlet manifold to be burnt by the engine during normal combustion. So that engine performance will not be affected, the CFSV remains closed during cold engine operation and also during engine idle.

Adjustments

7 Adjustment pre-conditions

1 Ensure that all of these conditions are met before attempting to make adjustments:

a) Engine at operating temperature. Engine oil at a minimum temperature of 80°C. A journey of at least 4 miles is advised (particularly so if equipped with AT).
b) Ancillary equipment (all engine loads and accessories) switched off.
c) AT engines: Transmission in N or P.
d) Engine mechanically sound.
e) Engine breather hoses and breather system in satisfactory condition.
f) Induction system free from vacuum leaks.
g) Ignition system in satisfactory condition.
h) Air filter in satisfactory condition.
i) Exhaust system free from leaks.
j) Throttle cable correctly adjusted.
k) No fault codes logged by the ECM.
l) OS operating satisfactorily (catalyst vehicles with closed-loop control).

2 In addition, before checking the idle speed and CO value stabilise the engine as follows.

a) Stabilise the engine. Raise the engine speed to 3000 rpm for a minimum of 30 seconds, and then let the engine idle.
b) If the cooling fan operates during adjustment, wait until it stops, re-stabilise the engine, and then restart the adjustment procedure.
c) Allow the CO and idle speed to settle.
d) Make all checks and adjustments within 30 seconds. If this time is exceeded, re-stabilise the engine and recheck.

8 Throttle adjustments

1 Clean the throttle valve and surrounding areas with carburettor cleaner. Blow-by from the breather system often causes sticking problems here **(see illustration 14.8)**.
2 The throttle valve position is critical, and must not be disturbed.
3 The TPS in not adjustable for this range of engines.

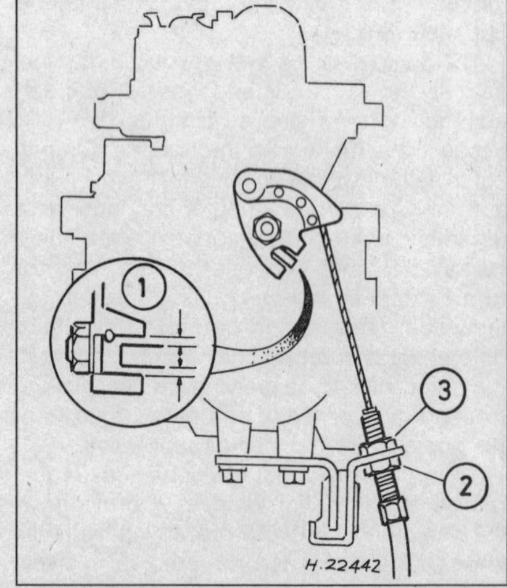

14.8 Adjust the throttle lost motion gap - see text

1 The clearance should be equal on both sides
2 Adjustment nut
3 Locknut

9 Ignition timing checks

1 The ignition timing is not adjustable on these models, and timing marks are not provided.

10 Idle adjustments

Adjustments (idle tune)

1 Idle speed and CO level (non-cat models only) are only adjustable through the use of a suitable FCR connected to the serial port.
2 Before connecting the FCR, check the throttle lost motion gap.
3 After completing the idle tune, recheck the throttle lost motion gap.

Adjustment of the throttle lost motion gap (typical)

4 Switch the ignition on.
5 From within the engine compartment, use the throttle lever to fully open the throttle valve. The ECM will index the stepper motor to 25 steps.
6 Allow the throttle valve to fully close.
7 Adjust the throttle cable so that an equal gap exists either side of the lost motion lever.
8 Switch off the ignition key. The stepper motor will revert to normal control.

System sensor and actuator tests

Important notes

Please refer to Chapter 4, which describes common test procedures applicable to this system. The routines in Chapter 4 should be read in conjunction with the component notes and wiring diagrams presented in this Chapter. The wiring diagrams and other data presented in this Chapter are necessarily representative of the system depicted. Because of the variations in wiring and other data that often occurs, even between similar vehicles in any particular VM's range, the reader should take great care in identification of ECM pins, and satisfy himself that he has gathered the correct data before failing a particular component.

MEMS ECM terminals

The multi-plug terminals at the MEMS ECM are gold-plated, and care must be taken that the plating is not removed during procedures that involve probing or back-probing. The terminal wires are sealed with a rubber plug, and you should not back-probe through these plugs, or pierce them with a sharp object. If the rubber plug is damaged, it will lose its water-sealant qualities. The following method is strongly recommended to prevent damage to terminal or sealing plug.

First, disconnect the multi-plug and detach the white cover. Carefully insert a small jeweller's-type screwdriver into the recess at the top of the terminal pin. Gently lever out the plastic retainer leg, and gently pull on the wire from behind the multi-plug. Once the clip is disengaged, the terminal should slide easily from its holder. Slide the rubber plug up the wire, and then push the terminal back into the multi-plug. Repeat this procedure for all terminal pins that will be back-probed during a test. After testing is completed, the procedure should be reversed, and all sealant plugs refitted into their original position.

Moulded component multi-plugs

From about 1994, many Rover models are fitted with moulded multi-plugs to the components. This means that it is no longer possible to backprobe the component. Live voltage or oscilloscope tests must therefore be made at the ECM or with the aid of a break-out box (BOB). Component BOB's suitable for this purpose are available from the suppliers of engine test equipment.

11 Primary trigger - crank angle sensor (CAS)

1 Refer to the notes at the start of this Section, and refer to the relevant Section of Chapter 4.
2 The CAS resistance is 1100 to 1700 ohms

12 Primary ignition

1 Refer to the notes at the start of Section 11, and refer to the relevant Section of Chapter 4 **(see illustration 14.9)**.
2 The primary ignition is essentially that of an ECM with internal amplifier.
3 Primary resistance (distributor ignition) is 0.71 to 0.81 ohms. Secondary resistance is 5000 to 15 000 ohms.
4 Primary resistance (DIS ignition) is 0.63 to 0.77 ohms.

13 Knock sensor (KS)

1 Refer to the notes at the start of Section 11, and refer to the relevant Section of Chapter 4.
2 A knock sensor is only used in 2.0 litre engines with MPi.

14 Fuel injector operation (MPi)

1 Refer to the notes at the start of Section 11, and refer to the relevant Section of Chapter 4.
2 Voltage to the injectors is provided from either the system relay or MFU.
3 MEMS fuel injector operation is current-controlled.
4 Injector operation is either simultaneous or sequential.
5 The injector resistance is normally 15.0 to 17.0 ohms.

15 Fuel injector operation (SPi)

1 Refer to the notes at the start of Section 11, and refer to the relevant Section of Chapter 4.

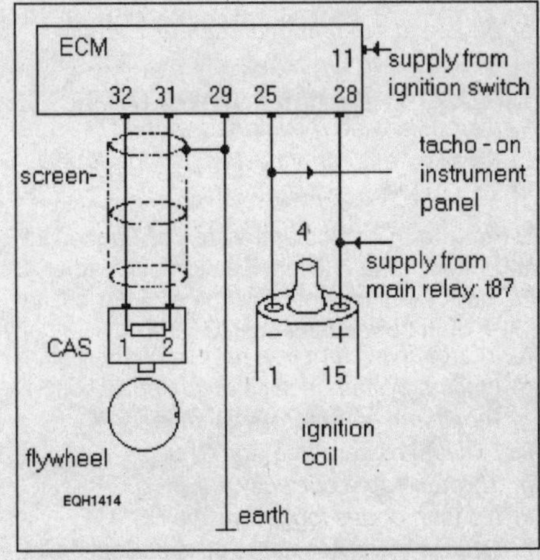

14.9 Typical local wiring diagram: ignition

14

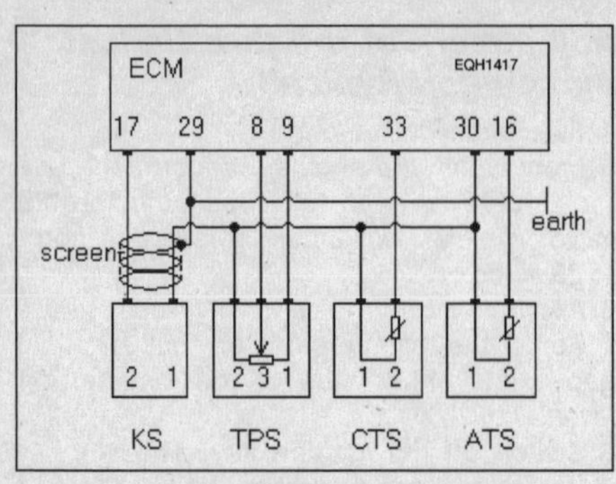

14.10 Typical local wiring diagram: sensors

2 Voltage to the injectors is provided from either the system relay or MFU.
3 The SPi system is current-controlled.
4 The injector resistance is normally 1.1 to 1.5 ohms.

16 Phase sensor (CID)

1 Refer to the notes at the start of Section 11, and refer to the relevant Section of Chapter 4.
2 The CID phase sensor is located adjacent to the camshaft.
3 Unfortunately, no data is available for CID resistance, but failure is likely to be indicated by a short- or open-circuit reading.

17 MAP sensor

1 Refer to the notes at the start of Section 11, and refer to the relevant Section of Chapter 4 **(see illustration 14.10)**.
2 The MAP sensor is incorporated into the ECM, and separate voltage tests are not possible.
3 Performance of the MAP sensor can be quickly evaluated by a suitable FCR attached to the serial port. Select Datastream; the values should be similar to those detailed in the MAP table (see Chapter 4, Section 18).

18 Air temperature sensor (ATS)

1 Refer to the notes at the start of Section 11, and refer to the relevant Section of Chapter 4.
2 The ATS is mounted in the air inlet casing (MPi) or in the air filter casing (SPi).

19 Coolant temperature sensor (CTS)

1 Refer to the notes at the start of Section 11, and refer to the relevant Section of Chapter 4.

20 Throttle switch (TS)

1 On pre-1993 models equipped with the throttle pedal-mounted 'idle switch', the engine will gasp, die and fail to respond properly if the engine speed is increased by moving the throttle lever directly from under the bonnet. This is because the ECM links the idle switch closed condition with rpm, and enters fuel deceleration cut-off mode. The engine rpm should only be increased by use of the accelerator pedal from inside the car.
2 However, during testing it is sometimes more convenient to be able to control the engine speed by moving the throttle lever directly. It is possible to by-pass the idle switch by disconnecting one of the wires on the pedal switch. MEMS will assume a fault, and set a default value. The engine will then respond to throttle lever movement.
3 Once testing is complete, the pedal switch wire must be reconnected, and a FCR used to clear the ECM of any logged faults.
4 Check that the terminal pins are pushed home and making good contact with the pedal switch.

Checking pedal switch operation

5 The two wires to the pedal switch multi-plug connector are earth and idle signal.
6 With the engine stopped, and ignition on, connect the voltmeter negative probe to an engine earth.
7 Connect the voltmeter positive probe to the wire attached to the pedal switch signal terminal number 2. The meter should indicate zero volts.
8 If zero volts cannot be obtained:

a) Check the pedal switch earth connection.
b) Make the pedal switch resistance tests (below).

9 Crack open the throttle. The voltage should rise to 5.0 volts.
10 If the voltage is low or non-existent:

a) Check that the pedal switch idle terminal is not shorted to earth.
b) Disconnect the pedal switch connections, and check for 5.0 volts at the signal terminal. If there is no voltage, check for continuity of the signal wiring between the pedal switch and the ECM.

11 If the pedal switch wiring is satisfactory, check all voltage supplies and earth connections to the ECM. If the voltage supplies and earth connections are satisfactory, the ECM is suspect.

Pedal switch resistance tests

12 Connect an ohmmeter between the earth terminal 1 and terminal 2.
13 With the pedal switch closed, the ohmmeter should indicate very close to zero ohms.
14 Slowly open the throttle, and as the pedal switch cracks open, the resistance should

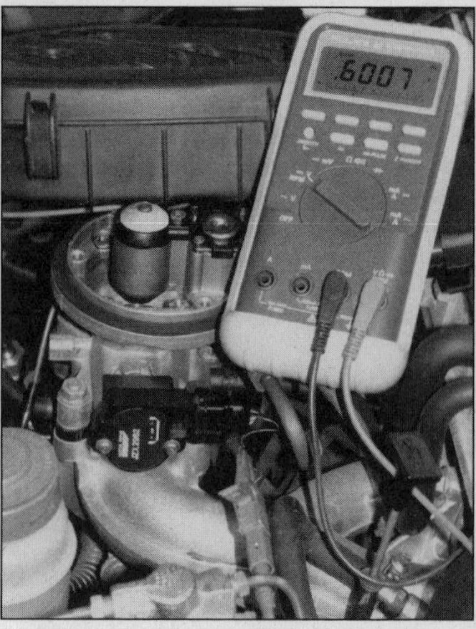

14.11 Check the throttle pot voltage output with the aid of a voltmeter

become open-circuit and remain so - even as the throttle is opened fully.
15 If the pedal switch does not behave as described, and if it is not prevented from opening or closing fully by a binding throttle linkage, the ECM pedal switch is suspect.

21 Throttle potentiometer sensor (TPS)

1 Refer to the notes at the start of Section 11, and refer to the relevant Section of Chapter 4 **(see illustration 14.11)**.

22 Stepper motor

1 Switch the ignition key to the 'on' position.
2 After 5 seconds, switch the ignition key to the 'off' position. The stepper motor plunger should fully retract, and then step to the correct position (according to temperature), ready for the next engine start. After 15 seconds, the main relay will audibly 'click out'. If this operation is completed satisfactorily, it is probable that the stepper motor condition is also satisfactory.

Stepper motor tests

3 Check for nbv to the stepper motor supply.
4 Connect a DC voltmeter to each of the earth pins in turn **(see illustrations 14.12 and 14.13)**.
5 Switch the ignition key on and off. A voltage should be briefly seen as the stepper motor actuates.
6 Disconnect the stepper motor multi-plug, and check the resistance from pin 5 to pins 1, 2, 3 and 4 in turn; 16 ohms should be obtained between pin 5 and each earth pin.

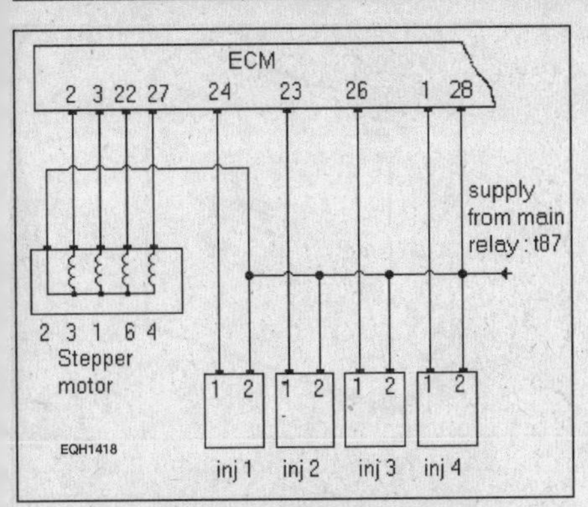

14.12 Typical local wiring diagram: injectors, stepper motor

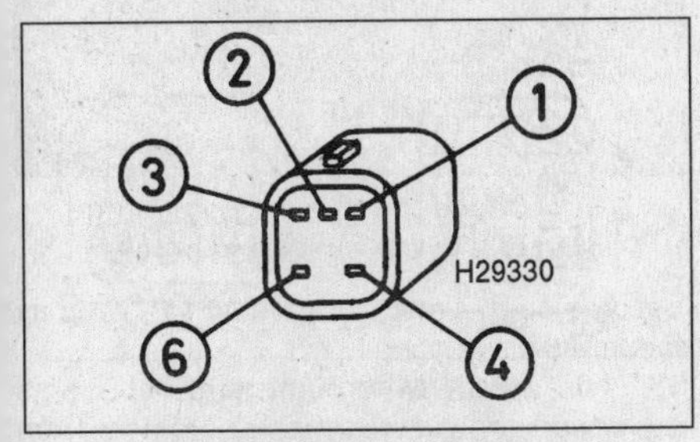

14.13 Stepper motor multi-plug pin numbers

7 Disconnect the ECM multi-plug (*refer to Warning No 3 in Reference)*
8 Switch the ignition key 'on'.
9 Connect a jumper lead from ECM pin 4 to battery earth (this energises the main relay with the ECM disconnected).
10 Connect a voltmeter between earth and ECM pins 22, 2, 27 and 3 in turn, nbv should be obtained.
11 If nbv is not obtained at one or more of the ECM pins, check the continuity of the wiring between the relevant ECM and stepper motor pins.
12 If the stepper motor wiring is satisfactory, check all voltage supplies and earth connections to the ECM. If the voltage supplies and earth connections are satisfactory, the ECM is suspect.

23 Manifold heater (SPi engines only)

1 Refer to the notes at the start of Section 11, and refer to the relevant Section of Chapter 4.
2 Make tests when the engine coolant temperature is less than 75°C. **Note:** *If the engine is hot, a variable potentiometer could be connected to the CTS multi-plug so that a cold engine could be simulated.*
3 If a FCR is available, the manifold heater relay can be actuated via the serial port. This would prove the integrity of the relay and associated wiring.

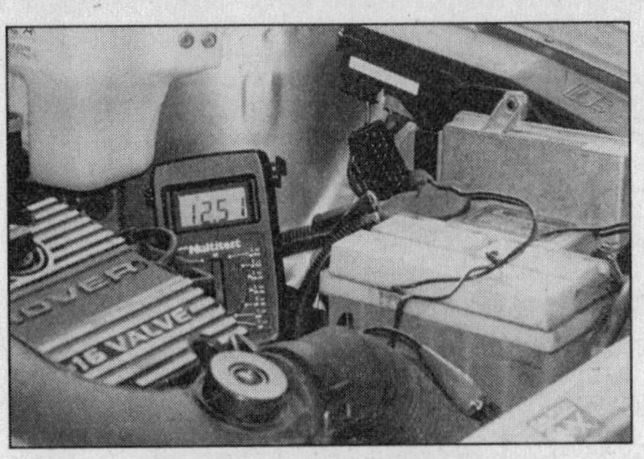

14.14 Probing for nbv at the ECM multi-plug

24 ECM voltage supplies and earths

1 Refer to the notes at the start of Section 11, and refer to the relevant Section of Chapter 4 **(see illustration 14.14).**
2 In addition to relay drivers for the main relay and pump relay, relay drivers may be available for the manifold heater and OS relays.

25 Inertia switch

1 Refer to the notes at the start of Section 11, and refer to the relevant Section of Chapter 4.
2 Montego models only: check the ballast resistor by-pass.
3 The inertia switch may be located behind the radio (early models) or in the engine compartment, close to the bulkhead.

26 System relays

1 Power to the MEMS electrical circuits is provided by either a number of conventional relays or an MFU (multi-function unit).
2 When a conventional set of relays are used, testing also follows conventional lines. In this instance, please refer to Chapter 4, which describes common test procedures applicable to checking standard system relays found in Rover MEMS systems. The routines in Chapter 4 should be read in conjunction with these component notes and the wiring diagrams portrayed in this Chapter **(see illustration 14.15).**
3 In the Rover MEMS system, the OS and manifold heater are also supplied from a relay.

27 Multi-function unit (MFU)

Quick relay test

1 A quick method of determining whether the relay is defective would be:
- *a) By-pass the MFU and attempt to run the engine.*
- *b) Check for voltages at the MFU output terminals or at the components supplied by the relay.*

2 If the wiring and MFU operation are satisfactory, yet the ECM fails to operate one or more of the relays, the ECM is suspect.

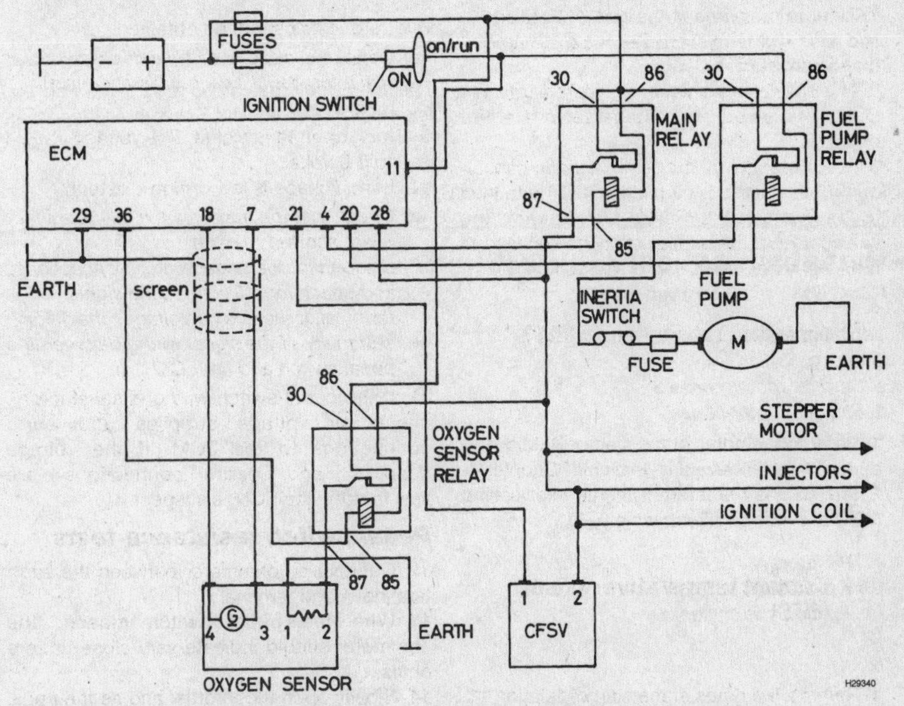

14.15 Typical local wiring diagram: relays and components

14

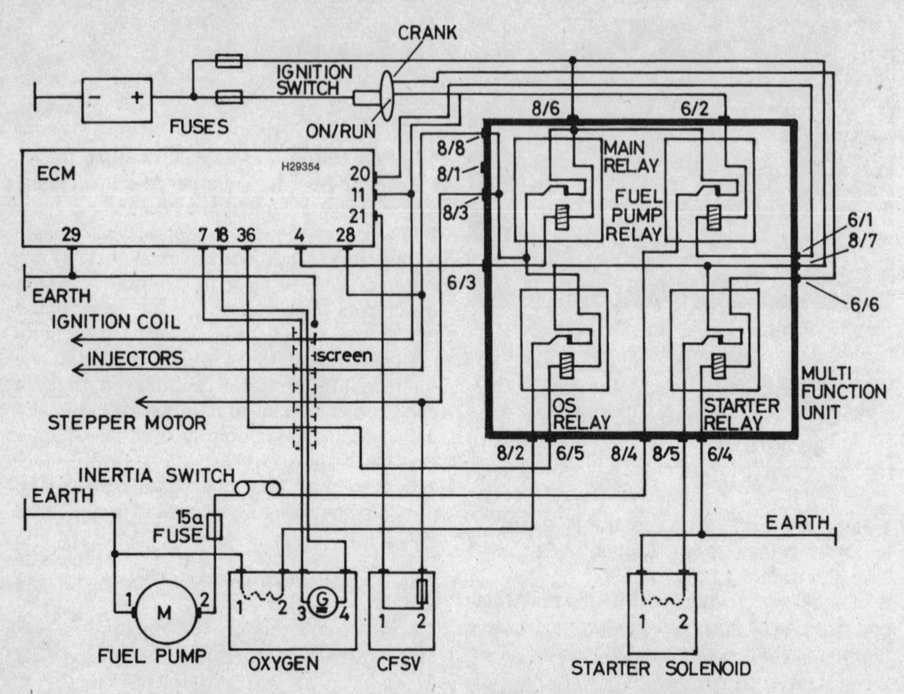

14.16 Typical local wiring diagram: relays (MFU) and components

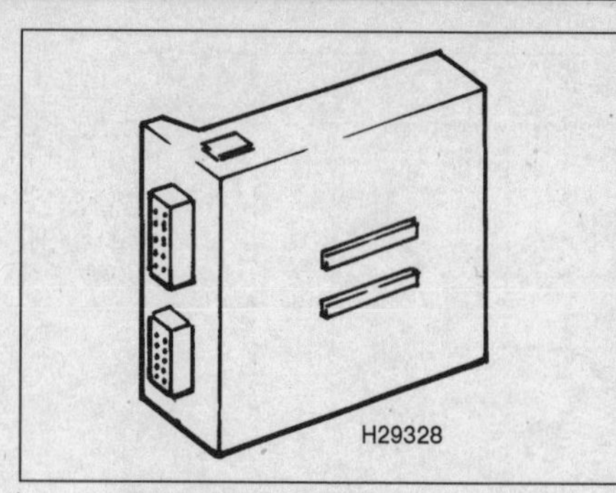

14.17 Multi-function unit (MFU)

14.18 MFU multi-plug

Testing the MFU

3 Ignition key on, relay connected.

4 Backprobe or probe for voltages at components supplied by the relay. If there is no output, backprobe at the appropriate MFU output terminal. If there is still no output, and all supply and earth voltages are satisfactory, the MFU is suspect **(see illustrations 14.16 to 14.18)**.

5 If one of the MFU relays is judged faulty, the MFU must be renewed complete.

28 Fuel pump and circuit

1 Refer to the notes at the start of Section 11, and refer to the relevant Section of Chapter 4.

29 Fuel pressure

1 Refer to the notes at the start of Section 11, and refer to the relevant Section of Chapter 4.

30 Oxygen sensor (OS)

1 Refer to the notes at the start of Section 11, and refer to the relevant Section of Chapter 4.

2 The OS found in the majority of Rover MEMS systems is a four-wire sensor with a heater.

31 Carbon filter solenoid valve (CFSV)

1 Refer to the notes at the start of Section 11, and refer to the relevant Section of Chapter 4.

Pin table - typical 36-pin/18-pin

Note: *Refer to* ***illustration 14.19.***

Terminal 'A'

1 Injector cylinder 4
2 Stepper motor phase 2
3 Stepper motor phase 1
4 Main relay driver
5 -
6 -
7 Oxygen sensor signal
8 TPS signal
9 TPS supply
10 Diagnostics output
11 Ignition switch supply
12 -
13 -
14 Earth
15 Diagnostics input
16 ATS
17 KS
18 Oxygen sensor return
19 AC magnetic clutch relay
20 Fuel pump relay driver
21 CFSV
22 Stepper phase 3
23 Injector pulse cyl 2
24 Injector pulse cyl 1
25 Ignition coil
26 Injector pulse cyl 3
27 Stepper motor phase 4
28 Supply from main relay
29 ECM earth
30 Sensor return
31 CAS +
32 CAS return
33 CTS
34 FRTS
35 AC high press safety sw
36 Oxygen sensor relay driver

Terminal 'B'

3 Alternator
5 OS relay driver
6 Turbo boost valve
8 Turbo air pressure solenoid
13 OS return
14 OS signal
15 Camshaft sensor
18 Camshaft sensor

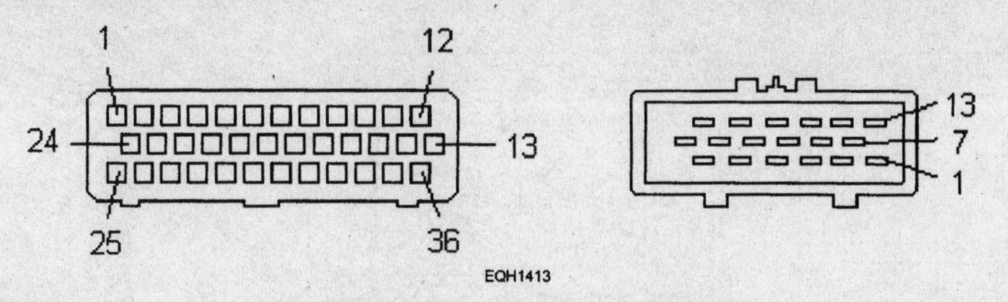

14.19 Typical 36-pin and 18-pin multi-plugs

Fault codes

32 Obtaining fault codes

1 Rover MEMS requires a dedicated FCR to access fault codes and Datastream, actuate components and make service adjustments. Flash codes are not available for output from this system.

2 MEMS does not provide too many codes, since a programmed test procedure (when using a Rover dedicated tester) will check the sensor and actuator circuits and report on all faults found.

Code	Fault
1	CTS circuit fault
2	ATS circuit fault
10	Fuel pump circuit fault
16	TPS circuit fault
17	TPS supply voltage fault
19	Oxygen sensor heater circuit fault (cat models only)

Chapter 15
Rover SPi

Contents

Specifications

Vehicle	Year	Idle speed	CO%
Rover 2.0 DOHC 20HE M16e	1986 to 1990	750 ± 50	2.5 to 3.5

Overview of system operation

1 Introduction

The Rover SPi (single-point injection) engine management system was developed jointly by Rover and Lucas, and appeared in 1986 on the Rover 2.0 820E and 820SE vehicles **(see illustration 15.1)**. Rover SPi (Lucas 10 CU) is a fully-integrated system that controls primary ignition, fuelling and idle speed from within the same ECM. Although the system is now obsolete, sufficient numbers exist for the interest to run at a high level in both workshops and from owners.

The Rover SPi ECM is designed with three main areas of control. These are the ignition, fuel system and idle speed. The correct ignition dwell and timing for all engine operating conditions are calculated from data provided by the CAS (crankshaft position and speed), and the MAP sensor (engine load).

2 Control functions

Signal processing

Basic ignition timing is stored in a three-dimensional map, and the engine load and speed signals determine the ignition timing. The main engine load sensor is the MAP sensor; engine speed is determined from the crank angle sensor (CAS) signal.

Correction factors are then applied for starting, idle, deceleration, and part- and full-load operation. The main correction factor is engine temperature (CTS). Minor corrections to timing and AFR are made with reference to the air temperature sensor (ATS) and throttle potentiometer sensor (TPS) signals.

The basic AFR is also stored in a two-dimensional map, and the engine load and speed signals determine the basic injection pulse value. Using the speed/density method, the ECM calculates the AFR from the pressure in the inlet manifold (MAP) and the speed of the engine (CAS).

This method relies on the theory that the engine will draw in a fixed volume of air per revolution. The AFR and the pulse duration are then corrected on reference to ATS, CTS, battery voltage and rate of throttle opening (TPS). Other controlling factors are determined by operating conditions such as cold start and warm-up, idle condition, acceleration and deceleration. During acceleration, four pulses are provided at 90° crankshaft intervals. During sustained acceleration, further pulses of larger duration are introduced at 270∞ crankshaft intervals.

The ECM accesses a different map for idle running conditions, and this map is implemented whenever the idle switch is closed and the engine speed is at idle. Idle speed during all warm-up and normal hot running conditions is maintained by the idle speed stepper motor. However, small adjustments to the idle speed are made by advancing or retarding the timing, and this results in an ignition timing that is forever changing during engine idle.

Basic ECM operation

A permanent voltage is applied to pin 3 of the ECM from the vehicle battery.
Once the ignition is switched on, a voltage supply to ECM pin 18 is made from the ignition switch. This causes the ECM to earth relay terminal 85 through ECM terminal number 30 which energises the relay winding. In turn, the main relay contacts close, and relay terminal 30 is connected to the output circuit at terminal 87. A voltage supply is thus output at terminal 87 which supplies voltage to the injector, ECM terminal 25 and ignition coil terminal 15.

The majority of sensors (other than those that generate a voltage such the CAS, KS and CID sensor), are now provided with a 5.0-volt reference supply from a relevant pin on the ECM. The ECM also applies voltage to the stepper motor, which sets the throttle position according to the engine temperature.

When the engine is cranked, voltage is applied to the fuel pump from terminal 50 of the ignition switch. Once the engine runs, voltage is applied to the fuel pump via the oil pressure relay.

Ignition and injection functions are also activated. All actuators (injectors, stepper motor etc), are supplied with nbv from the main relay, and the ECM completes the circuit by pulsing the relevant actuator wire to earth.

Over-speed fuel cut-off

Engine speeds above 6700 rpm are prevented by inhibiting the injector earth path. As the engine speed drops below 6400 rpm, fuel injection is reinstated.

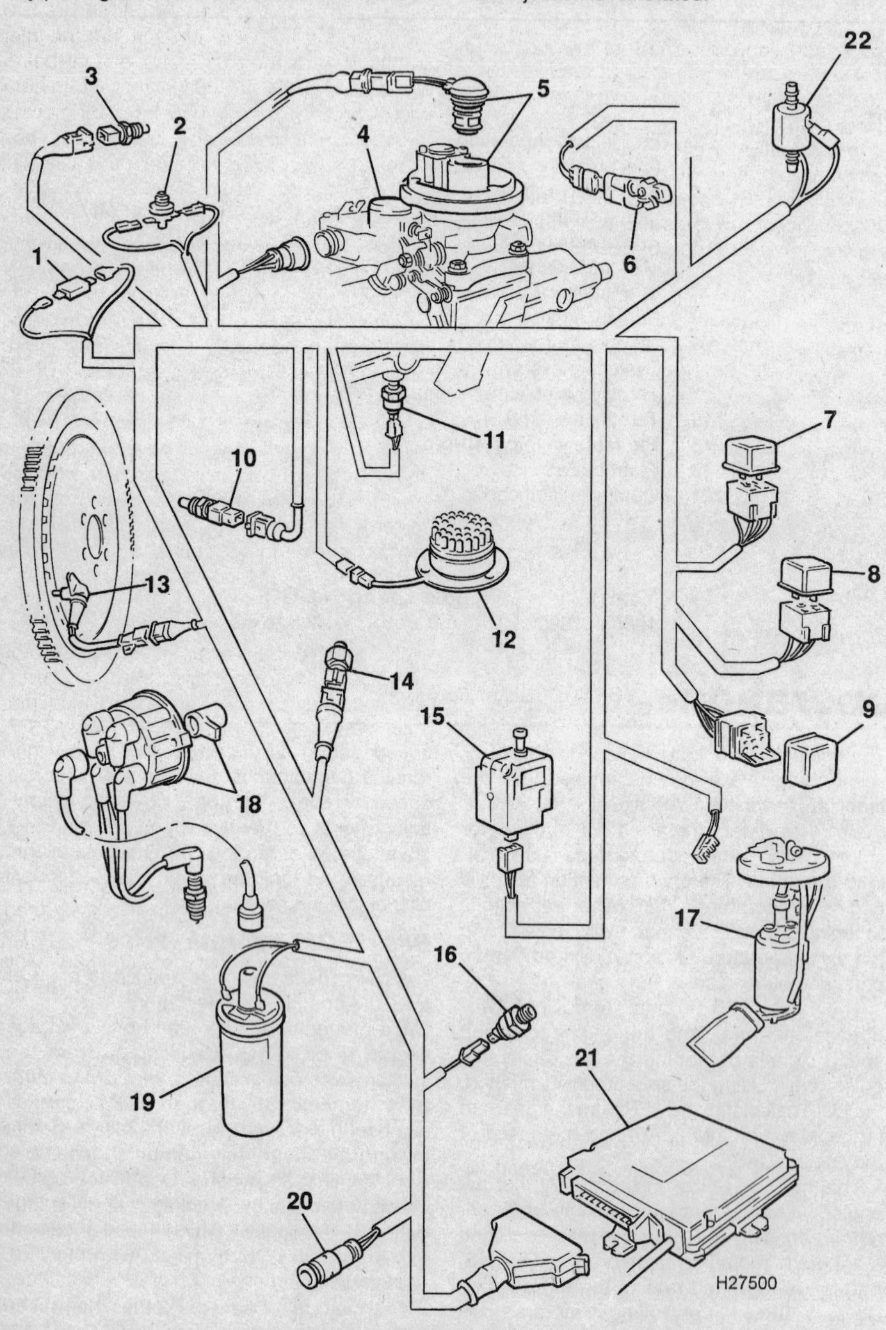

15.1 Components of the Rover SPi system

1 *Ambient ATS*
2 *Throttle pedal switch*
3 *ATS*
4 *Throttle body and stepper motor*
5 *Fuel injector and fuel pressure regulator*
6 *TPS*
7 *Main relay*
8 *Fuel pump relay*
9 *Oil pressure relay*
10 *CTS*
11 *Manifold heater temperature sensor*
12 *Manifold heater*
13 *CAS*
14 *Knock sensor*
15 *Inertia switch*
16 *Oil pressure switch*
17 *Fuel pump*
18 *Distributor cap and rotor arm*
19 *Ignition coil*
20 *SD connector*
21 *ECM*
22 *Idle solenoid (models with air conditioning)*

Deceleration fuel cut-off

A deceleration fuel reduction is implemented during engine over-run conditions, to improve economy and reduce emissions. The conditions for over-run reduction to be implemented are:

a) Throttle closed (throttle pedal contacts closed).
b) Engine speed above 1500 rpm.
c) Coolant temperature above 80°C.
d) Once the engine speed drops below 1500 rpm, fuel injection is reinstated.

Reference voltage

Voltage supply from the ECM to the engine sensors is made at a 5.0-volt reference level. This ensures a stable working voltage, unaffected by variations in system voltage.

The earth return connection for most engine sensors is made through ECM pin number 9, although this pin is not directly connected to earth. The ECM internally connects pin number 9 to earth via the ECM pin that is directly connected to earth.

Self-diagnostic function

A serial port is provided for diagnostic and system tuning purposes. The port allows two-way communication, so that the idle CO value can be changed when necessary.

In addition, a self-test capability regularly examines signals from the engine sensors, and internally logs a code in the event of a fault being present. This code can be extracted from the serial port by a suitable fault code reader (FCR). However, this code is only available when the fault is actually present, and will be erased from memory if the fault clears. Faults of an intermittent nature will not be retained.

LOS (limp-home mode)

Rover SPi has a limited operation strategy (LOS, or 'limp-home' mode). In the event of a serious fault in one or more of the sensors, the EMS will substitute a fixed default value in place of the defective sensor.

For example, in limp-home mode, the CTS value is set to 60°C, and the ATS is set to 20°C. The engine will still run, albeit less efficiently, when in limp-home mode.

Since the substituted values are those of a semi-hot engine, cold starting and running during the warm-up period may be less than satisfactory. Also, failure of a major sensor, ie the MAP sensor, will lead to a considerable reduction in performance.

3 Primary trigger

Crank angle sensor (CAS)

The primary signal to initiate both ignition and fuelling emanates from a CAS mounted next to the flywheel. The CAS consists of an inductive magnet that radiates a magnetic field. The flywheel incorporates a reluctor disk containing 34 steel pins set at 10° intervals. As the flywheel spins, the pins are rotated in the magnetic field, and an AC voltage signal is generated to indicate speed of rotation. The two missing pins (at 180° intervals) indicate crankshaft TDC position by varying the signal as the flywheel spins. One missing pin gives TDC for cylinders 1 and 4, and the other missing pin gives TDC for cylinders 2 and 3.

The peak-to-peak voltage of the speed signal (when viewed upon an oscilloscope), can vary from 5 volts at idle to over 100 volts at 6000 rpm. The ECM uses an analogue-to-digital converter to transform the AC pulse into a digital signal.

4 Ignition

Data on engine load (MAP) and engine speed (CAS) are collected by the ECM, which then refers to a three-dimensional digital ignition map stored within its microprocessor. This map contains an advance angle for basic load and speed operating conditions. The advance angle is corrected after reference to engine temperature (CTS), so that the best ignition advance angle for a particular operating condition can be determined.

Amplifier

The Rover SPi amplifier contains the circuitry for switching the coil negative terminal at the correct moment to instigate ignition. The amplifier circuitry is contained within the ECM itself, and the microprocessor controls the ignition dwell period for each condition of engine speed and battery voltage.

Ignition dwell operation in Rover SPi is based upon the principle of the 'constant-energy current-limiting' system. This means that the dwell period remains constant at about 3.0 to 3.5 ms, at virtually all engine running speeds. However, the duty cycle, when measured in percent or degrees, will vary as the engine speed varies.

Ignition coil

The ignition coil utilises low primary resistance in order to increase primary current and primary energy. The amplifier limits the primary current to around 8 amps, and this permits a reserve of energy to maintain the required spark burn time (duration).

Distributor

In the Rover SPi system, the distributor only serves to distribute the HT current from the coil secondary terminal to each spark plug in firing order. The distributor is located on the exhaust camshaft, at the cylinder No 4 end. The distributor contains a rotor arm, and also a deflector plate and oil drain to prevent oil from contaminating the cap and rotor arm.

Knock sensor

The knock sensor is mounted on the engine block, and consists of a piezo-ceramic measuring element that responds to engine noise oscillations. This signal is converted to a voltage signal that is proportional to the level of knock, and returned to the ECM for evaluation and action. The ECM will analyse the noise from each individual cylinder, and uses a sophisticated technique to recognise knock as distinct to general engine noise.

Initially, timing will occur at its optimal ignition point. Once knock is identified, the microprocessor retards the ignition timing for that cylinder in steps of 1.875° until either knock ceases or a maximum retard of 10° is achieved. The timing is then advanced in 0.625° increments every 16 rpm until the reference timing value is achieved or knock occurs again, when the processor will retard the timing once more. This procedure continually occurs so that all cylinders will consistently run at their optimum timing.

5 Fuel injection

Single-point injection (SPi)

The SPi system consists of a single injector mounted in the throttle body. The amount of fuel delivered by the injector is determined by the fuel pressure and the injector opening time - otherwise known as the pulse duration. The ECM controls the period of time that the injector is held open, and this is determined by the signals from the various sensor inputs. During engine start-up from cold, the pulse duration and number of pulses (frequency) are increased to provide a richer air/fuel mixture.

Fuel injector

The fuel injector is a magnetically-operated solenoid valve that is actuated by the ECM. Voltage to the injectors is applied from the main relay, and the earth path is completed by the ECM for a period of time (called pulse duration) of between 1.5 and 10 milliseconds. The pulse duration is very much dependent upon engine temperature, load, speed and operating conditions. When the magnetic solenoid closes, a back-EMF voltage of up to 60 volts is initiated.

In SPi engines, fuel is injected into the inlet manifold, to be drawn into a cylinder by the action of a descending piston.

MAP sensor

The main engine load sensor is the MAP sensor. A vacuum hose connects the MAP sensor (located within the ECM) and the inlet manifold. Manifold vacuum acts upon the MAP sensor diaphragm, and the ECM converts the pressure into an electrical signal. MAP is calculated from the formula: Atmospheric Pressure less Manifold Pressure = Manifold Absolute Pressure.

Using the speed/density method, the ECM calculates the AFR from the MAP signal and the speed of the engine (CAS). This method relies on the theory that the engine will draw in a fixed volume of air per revolution.

The inlet manifold on the SPi models is a 'wet' manifold. Fuel is injected into the inlet manifold, and there is a risk of fuel being drawn into the MAP sensor to contaminate the diaphragm. This is prevented by running the vacuum hose through a fuel trap and then to the ECM (which contains the MAP sensor).

Air temperature sensor (ATS)

The ATS is mounted in the air filter casing, and measures the air temperature before it enters the inlet manifold. Because the density of air varies in inverse proportion to the temperature, the ATS signal allows more accurate assessment of the volume of air entering the engine.

The open-circuit supply to the sensor is at a 5.0-volt reference level, and the earth path is through the sensor return. The ATS operates on the NTC principle. A variable voltage signal is returned to the ECM based upon the air temperature. This signal is around 2.0 to 3.0 volts at an ambient temperature of 20°C, and reduces to about 1.5 volt as the temperature rises to around 40°C.

An additional ambient ATS to monitor the general engine compartment temperature is located behind the left-hand headlight. Operation is similar to that of the main ATS.

CO adjustment

The CO value at idle speed can only be adjusted through the medium of a FCR attached to the serial port. It is not possible to make this adjustment by any other means. If the battery supply to the ECM is interrupted, the idle CO programming will be lost, and the ECM will implement a default value. This usually results in a richer-than-normal idle CO value.

Coolant temperature sensor (CTS)

The CTS is incorporated in the cooling system, and contains a variable resistance that operates on the NTC principle. When the engine is cold, the resistance is quite high. Once the engine is started and begins to warm up, the coolant becomes hotter, and this causes a change in the CTS resistance. As the CTS becomes hotter, the resistance of the CTS reduces (NTC principle), and this returns a variable voltage signal to the ECM based upon the coolant temperature.

The open-circuit supply to the sensor is at a 5.0-volt reference level, and this voltage reduces to a value that depends upon the resistance of the CTS resistance. Normal operating temperature is usually from 80° to 100°C. The ECM uses the CTS signal as a main correction factor when calculating ignition timing and injection duration.

Throttle potentiometer sensor (TPS)

A TPS is provided to inform the ECM of rate of acceleration. The TPS is a potentiometer with three wires. A 5.0-volt reference voltage is supplied to a resistance track, with the other end connected to earth. The third wire is connected to an arm which wipes along the resistance track, and so varies the resistance and voltage of the signal returned to the ECM. From the voltage returned, the ECM is able to calculate just how quickly the throttle is opened.

Throttle switch (TS)

The throttle pedal switch indicates idle position to the ECM. During closed-throttle operation above a certain rpm (deceleration), the ECM will cut off fuel injection. Injection will be reintroduced once the rpm returns to idle or the throttle is opened.

Stepper motor

The stepper motor is an actuator that the ECM uses to automatically control idle speed during normal idle and during engine warm-up. When electrical loads such as the headlights or heater fan are switched on, the idle speed would tend to drop. In this event, the ECM indexes the stepper motor so that the correct idle speed is always maintained.

During periods of cold running, the stepper motor will set the throttle position so that the idle speed will be set to a suitable fast idle. On sensing low battery voltage, the ECM will increase the idle speed to allow greater alternator output.

The stepper motor is a DC motor that operates a cam and pushrod through a reduction gear. The pushrod contacts the throttle lever, which actuates the throttle plate and so maintains the correct idle speed. Maximum movement of the stepper motor is 3.75 revolutions and this is accomplished by 180 steps of 7.5°. The reduction gear reduces the actual cam movement to 150°.

The stepper motor contains a voltage supply wire and four earth wires. By using various combinations of the four earth wires, the ECM is able to index the motor to its correct position.

Manifold heater

The ECM controls the manifold heater through a relay. This heater works on the PTC principle, and allows a greater current to quickly heat the inlet manifold during the warm-up period. This allows better driveability during engine warm-up.

The manifold heater earth path is made through the oil pressure relay terminal 87. When the relay is switched off, terminals 30 and 87 are connected. When the relay is energised, terminals 30 and 87 are open-circuit. This means that energising of the relay contacts are in reverse of the other relays in this system.

When the ignition is switched 'on' and the engine is not cranked, the oil pressure relay is energised through the closed oil pressure switch (situated in the relay earth path), which opens the manifold heater earth circuit. Once the engine runs, the oil pressure switch opens, which opens the relay earth path and de-energises the oil pressure relay. This closes the manifold heater earth circuit and allows it to function.

Once a predetermined temperature of around 50°C is reached, the manifold heater switch opens to turn off the earth path to the relay. This de-energises the relay and switches off the voltage to the manifold heater.

Main relay

A permanent battery voltage is applied to the main relay terminals 30 and 86.

Once the ignition is switched on, a voltage supply is applied to ECM pin 18 from the ignition switch. This causes the ECM to earth relay terminal 85 through ECM terminal number 30, which energises the relay winding. This causes the main relay contacts to close and relay terminal 30 is connected to the output circuit at terminal 87. A voltage supply is thus output at terminal 87 which supplies voltage to the injector, ECM terminal 25 and ignition coil terminal 15.

Fuel pump relay

When the ignition is switched on, a voltage supply is made to fuel pump relay terminals 30 and 86. In addition, voltage is applied to the oil pressure relay terminal 86.

Since oil pressure relay terminal 85 is connected to earth through the oil pressure switch, the oil pressure relay winding is energised, which opens the contacts between terminal 30 and 87. The fuel pump relay is earthed through oil pressure relay contacts terminal 30 and 87, and so the fuel pump remains inoperative. The oil pressure warning lamp is on.

When the engine is cranked, voltage is applied to terminal 50 of the fuel pump relay, and thus to the fuel pump through pump relay terminal 87; the pump runs.

When the engine starts, increased oil pressure opens the oil pressure switch. The oil pressure warning light loses its earth and the warning light goes out. In addition, the loss of the earth to terminal 85 causes the oil pressure relay to de-energise, and contact is again made between terminals 30 and 87. This completes the earth circuit for terminal 85 of the fuel pump relay, which energises and joins terminal 30 and 87 through the contacts. Voltage is thus output to the fuel pump, and the pump runs until the engine is stopped.

If oil pressure drops below a certain value, the oil pressure switch will activate and energise the oil pressure relay to inhibit the earth to the fuel pump relay. The voltage to the pump will cease, and the pump will stop.

In the event of a sharp deceleration, such as in a collision, the inertia switch will activate to cut the voltage supplies to the fuel pump relay. The pump will stop.

Engine shutdown

On switching off the engine, the ECM keeps the main relay earth energised for 5 or 6 seconds. This holds the voltage supply to the ECM, which then actuates the stepper motor to its fully closed position (thus preventing engine run-on). After a few seconds more, the ECM actuates the stepper motor to a position where it slightly opens the throttle plate, ready for the next engine start.

Fuel pressure system

The fuel system includes a fuel tank, with swirl pot and a submerged fuel pump. The fuel pump draws fuel from the tank, and pumps it to the fuel rail via a fuel filter. A reduced voltage is applied to the pump via an 0.82 ohm resistor cable, 91 cm in length.

The swirl pot prevents air from entering the fuel supply line by ensuring that the pick-up strainer is always immersed in fuel when the fuel level is low - even during fuel movement due to centrifugal forces acting upon the vehicle.

The pump is of the 'wet' variety, in that fuel actually flows through the pump and the electric motor. There is no actual fire risk, because the fuel drawn through the pump is not in a combustible condition.

The fuel pump assembly comprises an impeller containing a number of grooves cut into its circumference. Once the pump motor becomes energised, the impeller rotates and as the fuel passes through the impeller, a pressure differential is created. Fuel is drawn through the pump inlet, to be pressurised between the grooves and discharged from the pump outlet into the fuel supply line.

The pump is protected from over-pressurising by a relief valve mounted in the outlet side of the pump.

Once the engine is running, fuel is fed through a non-return valve and fuel filter to the single throttle body injector. To prevent pressure loss in the supply system, a non-return valve is provided in the fuel pump outlet. When the ignition is switched off, and the fuel pump ceases operation, pressure is thus maintained for some time.

Fuel pressure regulator

Fuel pressure of approximately one bar is controlled by a diaphragm-actuated pressure regulator located in the upper reaches of the throttle body. As the pressure rises over the pre-determined level, the diaphragm moves against spring pressure to allow the return of excess fuel to the fuel tank via a return pipe. To prevent pressure loss in the supply system, a non-return valve is provided in the fuel pump outlet. When the ignition is switched off, and the fuel pump ceases operation, pressure is thus maintained for some time.

Inertia switch

The inertia switch is a safety cut-out switch used to isolate the fuel pump in the event of a very sharp deceleration - eg a collision. Once activated, the fuel pump remains open-circuit until the switch is reset by raising the button.

Adjustments

6 Adjustment pre-conditions

1 Ensure that all of these conditions are met before attempting to make adjustments:

a) Engine at operating temperature. Engine oil at a minimum temperature of 80°C; a journey of at least 4 miles is advised (particularly so if equipped with AT).
b) Ancillary equipment (all engine loads and accessories) switched off.
c) AT vehicles: Transmission in N or P.
d) Engine mechanically sound.
e) Engine breather hoses and breather system in satisfactory condition.
f) Induction system free from vacuum leaks.
g) Ignition system in satisfactory condition.
h) Air filter in satisfactory condition.
i) Exhaust system free from leaks.
j) Throttle cable correctly adjusted.
k) No fault codes logged by the ECM.
l) OS operating satisfactorily (catalyst vehicles with closed-loop control).

2 In addition, before checking the idle speed and CO values, stabilise the engine as follows:

a) Stabilise the engine. Raise the engine speed to 3000 rpm for a minimum of 30 seconds, and then let the engine idle.
b) If the cooling fan operates during adjustment, wait until it stops, re-stabilise the engine and then restart the adjustment procedure.
c) Allow the CO and idle speed to settle.
d) Make all checks and adjustments within 30 seconds. If this time is exceeded, re-stabilise the engine and recheck.

7 Throttle adjustments

1 Engine stopped, throttle closed, ignition on.
2 Connect a voltmeter between the TPS terminal 2 and earth.
3 Record the voltage, which should be between 0.3 and 0.7 volts.
4 If the voltage is incorrect: Slacken the two adjustment screws and rotate the TPS unit until the voltage is between 0.3 and 0.7 volts.

8 Ignition timing checks

1 The Ignition timing is controlled by the ECM, and is not adjustable. However a stroboscopic timing gun could be used on the mark on the front pulley, to check that timing advance occurs as the throttle is opened and the engine rpm increases.

9 Idle adjustments

1 Adjustments to idle speed and CO should be made through the medium of a suitable FCR connected to the serial port.
2 A procedure for adjusting the CO without an FCR is detailed below.
3 The base idle speed adjustment screw must only be moved during the FCR tuning procedure, or during the base idle setting procedure described below.
4 Any adjustment made to the CO level will only affect the level at idle, and will not affect the CO level during engine operation at speeds above idle.

Adjustment of idle CO without a FCR (some models)

5 Start the engine and allow it to warm up to normal operating temperature (coolant temperature at 80°C minimum).
6 Allow the cooling fan to cut in. As the cooling fan stops, turn off the ignition.
7 Turn the ignition back on.
8 Pump the throttle five times; this will open and close the switch on the throttle pedal. Ensure that the pedal returns to the closed position between pumps.
9 The coolant high temperature warning lamp on the dash will start to flash. Wait for the lamp to stop flashing before continuing with the next step.
10 Start the engine without touching the throttle. Touching the throttle between this point and completion of the CO calibration will cause the ECM to abort the adjustment procedure. Operation of any electrical device will also cause the ECM to abort the procedure.
11 The idle speed will rise and fall while the ECM calibrates the CO level. This should take approximately two minutes. The process is over when the coolant temperature warning lamp begins to flash once more.
12 The CO should be between 2.5 and 3.5%.

Lost motion gap adjustment

13 Engine stopped and throttle pedal closed.
14 The lost motion gap should be between 0.2 and 0.5 mm; this is the amount of travel required by the throttle cable before the throttle starts to open **(see illustrations 15.2 and 15.3).**

Basic idle speed adjustment

15 Allow the engine to idle.
16 Increase the engine speed to about 1200 rpm using the throttle lever on the throttle body.
17 Wait for the stepper motor piston to retract completely.
18 As soon as the piston is fully retracted, disconnect the stepper motor multi-plug, and then release the throttle lever so that the engine will return to idle.
19 Check the base idle speed against the following values:

a) Manual transmission: 650 ± 50 rpm.
b) Automatic transmission: 600 ± 50 rpm.

20 If required, use the idle speed adjustment screw to adjust the basic idle speed **(see illustrations 15.4 and 15.5).**

15.2 Lost motion gap: Insert a feeler gauge of 0.2 to 0.5 mm between the throttle lever and stop . . .

15.3 . . . and adjust the length of the accelerator cable until the correct setting is achieved

15.4 Slacken the locknut to the base idle adjustment screw . . .

15.5 . . . and turn the screw (arrowed) until the base idle speed is achieved

21 Reconnect the stepper motor multi-plug.
22 Switch off the ignition, wait for 3 seconds and then switch on the ignition again. Wait another 3 seconds and then switch off the ignition once more. The stepper motor should now be set ready for the next engine start.
23 Check the lost motion gap adjustment.

System sensor and actuator tests

Important note: *Please refer to Chapter 4, which describes common test procedures applicable to this system. The routines in Chapter 4 should be read in conjunction with the component notes and wiring diagrams presented in this Chapter. The wiring diagrams and other data presented in this Chapter are necessarily representative of the system depicted. Because of the variations in wiring and other data that often occurs, even between similar vehicles in any particular VM's range, the reader should take great care in identification of ECM pins, and satisfy himself that he has gathered the correct data before failing a particular component.*

10 Crank angle sensor (CAS)

1 Refer to the note at the start of this Section, and refer to the relevant Section of Chapter 4.
2 The CAS resistance is between 1250 and 1550 ohms.

11 Primary ignition

1 Refer to the note at the start of Section 10, and refer to the relevant Section of Chapter 4 **(see illustration 15.6)**.
2 When testing the ignition circuit for a primary signal, the routines described in 'Primary signal not available (amplifier inside the ECM)' are generally the most suitable.
3 Primary resistance is 0.71 to 0.81 ohms; secondary resistance is 5000 to 15000 ohms.

12 Knock sensor (KS)

1 Refer to the note at the start of Section 10, and refer to the relevant Section of Chapter 4.

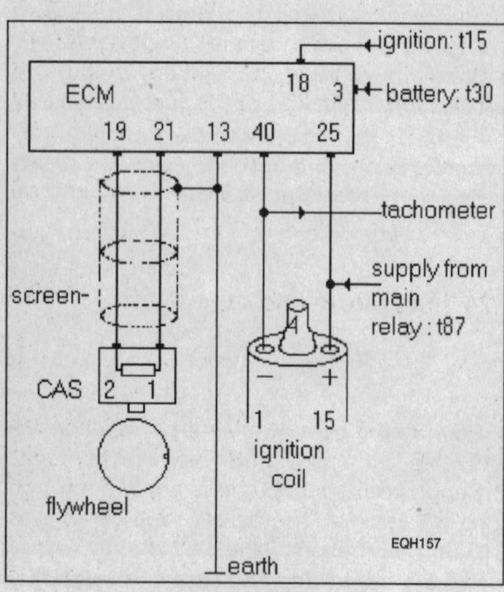

15.6 Ignition wiring

13 Fuel injector operation

1 Refer to the note at the start of Section 10, and refer to the relevant Section of Chapter 4.
2 Voltage to the injector is provided from the main system relay.
3 The SPi system is current-controlled.
4 The injector resistance is normally 1.0 to 2.0 ohms.
5 If injection does not cut off during deceleration, check the throttle pedal switch for correct operation. Noise from the injector should also temporarily disappear as the cut-off operates.

14 MAP sensor

1 Refer to the note at the start of Section 10, and refer to the relevant Section of Chapter 4 **(see illustration 15.7)**.
2 The MAP sensor is incorporated into the ECM, and separate voltage tests are not possible.

15 Air temperature sensor (ATS)

1 Refer to the note at the start of Section 10, and refer to the relevant Section of Chapter 4.

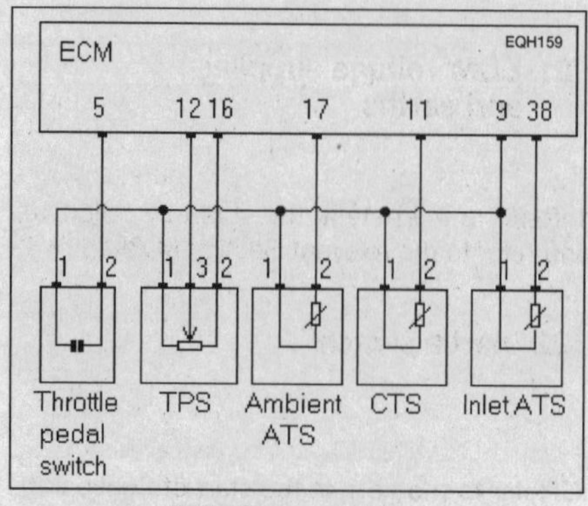

15.7 Sensor wiring

2 The ATS is mounted in the intake of the air filter casing.

16 Coolant temperature sensor (CTS)

1 Refer to the note at the start of Section 10, and refer to the relevant Section of Chapter 4.

17 Throttle switch (TS)

1 Check that the terminal pins are fully pushed home and making good contact with the pedal switch.

Checking pedal switch operation

2 The two wires to the pedal switch multi-plug connector are earth and idle signal.
3 With the engine stopped, and ignition on, connect the voltmeter negative probe to an engine earth.
4 Connect the voltmeter positive probe to the wire attached to the pedal switch signal terminal number 2; the meter should indicate zero volts.
5 If zero volts cannot be obtained, check the pedal switch earth connection, then carry out the pedal switch resistance tests below.
6 Crack open the throttle; the voltage should rise to 5.0 volts.
7 If the voltage is low or non-existent, check that the pedal switch idle terminal is not shorted to earth. disconnect the pedal switch connections, and check for 5.0 volts at the signal terminal. If there is no voltage, check for continuity of the signal wiring between the pedal switch and the ECM.
8 If the pedal switch wiring is satisfactory, check all voltage supplies and earth connections to the ECM. If the voltage supplies and earth connections are satisfactory, the ECM is suspect.

Pedal switch resistance tests

9 Connect an ohmmeter between the earth terminal 1 and terminal 2.
10 With the pedal switch closed, the ohmmeter should indicate very close to zero ohms.

11 Slowly open the throttle; as the pedal switch cracks open, the resistance should become open-circuit and remain so - even as the throttle is opened fully.

12 If the pedal switch does not behave as described, and it is not prevented from opening or closing fully by any binding of the throttle linkage, the ECM pedal switch is suspect.

18 Throttle potentiometer sensor (TPS)

1 Refer to the note at the start of Section 10, and refer to the relevant Section of Chapter 4.

19 Stepper motor

1 Switch the ignition key to the 'on' position.

2 After 5 seconds, switch the ignition key to the 'off' position. The stepper motor plunger should fully retract, and then step to the correct position (according to temperature), ready for the next engine start. After 15 seconds, the main relay will audibly 'click out'. If this operation is completed satisfactorily, it is probable that the stepper motor condition is also satisfactory.

Stepper motor tests

3 Check for nbv to the stepper motor supply **(see illustration 15.8)**.

4 Connect a DC voltmeter to each of the earth pins in turn.

5 Switch the ignition key on and off. A voltage should be briefly seen as the stepper motor actuates.

6 Disconnect the stepper motor multi-plug, and check the resistance from pin 5 to pins 1, 2, 3 and 4 in turn; 16 ohms should be obtained between pin 5 and each earth pin.

7 Disconnect the ECM multi-plug (*refer to Warning No 3 in Reference).*

8 Switch the ignition 'on'.

9 Connect a jumper lead from ECM pin 4 to battery earth (this energises the main relay with the ECM disconnected).

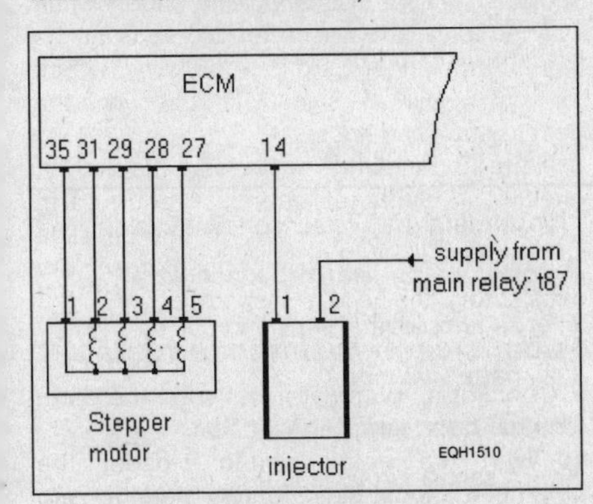

15.8 Injector and stepper motor wiring

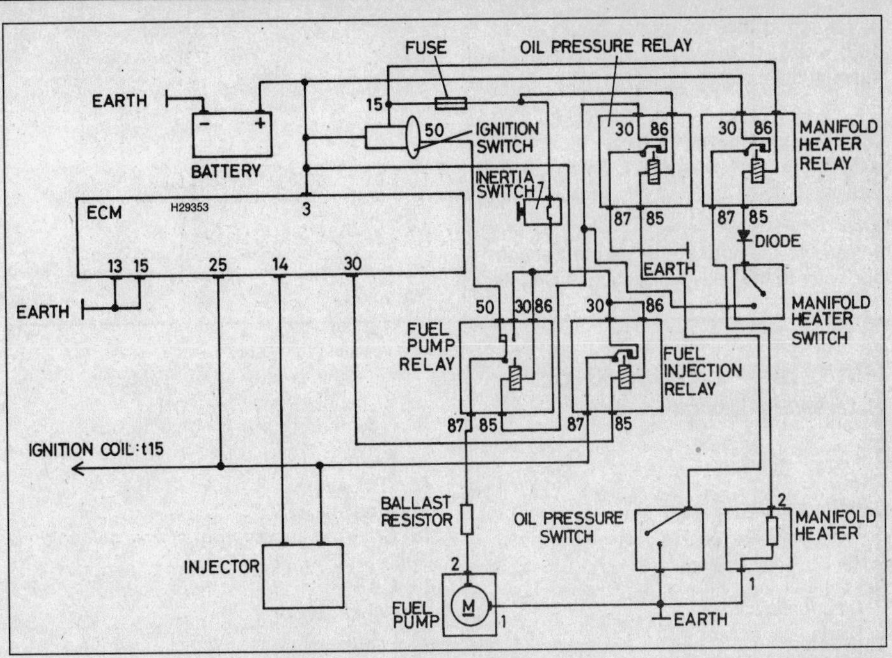

15.9 Relay and components wiring

10 Connect a voltmeter between earth and ECM pins 22, 2, 27 and 3 in turn; nbv should be obtained.

11 If nbv is not obtained at one or more of the ECM pins, check the continuity of wiring between the relevant ECM and stepper motor pins.

12 If the wiring is satisfactory, check all voltage supplies and earth connections to the ECM. If the voltage supplies and earths are satisfactory, the ECM is suspect.

13 Stepper motor resistance is 15.0 ohms.

20 Manifold heater

1 Refer to the note at the start of Section 10, and refer to the relevant Section of Chapter 4.

2 Carry out the tests when the engine coolant temperature is less than 50°C. **Note:** *If the engine is hot, a variable potentiometer could be connected to the CTS multi-plug so that a cold engine could be simulated.*

21 ECM voltage supplies and earths

1 Refer to the note at the start of Section 10, and refer to the relevant Section of Chapter 4.

22 Inertia switch

1 Refer to the note at the start of Section 10, and refer to the relevant Section of Chapter 4.

2 The inertia switch is located under the dash, behind the centre console near the radio.

23 System relays

1 Refer to the note at the start of Section 10, and refer to the relevant Section of Chapter 4.

2 Power to the Rover SPi electrical circuits is provided by a main relay and fuel pump relay. The earth to the fuel pump relay is made through an oil pressure relay and oil pressure switch. Refer to the description of relay operation for a detailed description of this very complex relay set-up **(see illustration 15.9)**.

3 A manifold heater relay applies voltage to the manifold heater. Earth to the manifold heater relay is made through a temperature switch (50°C) and the oil pressure switch.

4 When the engine is cranked, voltage is applied to terminal 50 of the fuel pump relay and thus to the fuel pump through pump relay terminal 87; the pump runs. If the fuel pump will only run during cranking, check the oil pressure relay and oil pressure switch.

24 Fuel pump and circuit

1 Refer to the note at the start of Section 10, and refer to the relevant Section of Chapter 4.

2 Supply to the fuel pump is applied through a ballast resistor. The ballast resistor cable is 910 mm long (resistance 0.82 ohms), and is located in the fuel pump supply wire near the front of the vehicle.

3 Voltage at the fuel pump should be 9.0 to 10.0 volts. If the voltage is much lower, suspect the resistor.

25 Fuel pressure

1 Refer to the note at the start of Section 10, and refer to the relevant Section of Chapter 4.

Pin table - typical 40-pin

Note: *Refer to **illustration 15.10**.*

1 -
2 -
3 Battery supply
4 Ignition supply
5 TS
6 -
7 Diagnostic socket
8 Diagnostic socket
9 Sensor earth return
10 -
11 CTS
12 TPS signal
13 Earth
14 Injector
15 Earth
16 TPS supply
17 Ambient ATS
18 Cranking supply from starter solenoid via diode
19 CAS
20 Knock sensor
21 CAS return
23 -
24 Diagnostic socket
25 Main relay
26 -
27 Stepper motor phase 5
28 Stepper motor phase 4
29 Stepper motor phase 3
30 Main relay
31 Stepper motor phase 2
32 -
33 Temperature gauge
34 -
35 Stepper motor supply
36 -
37 -
38 ATS
39 -
40 Ignition coil

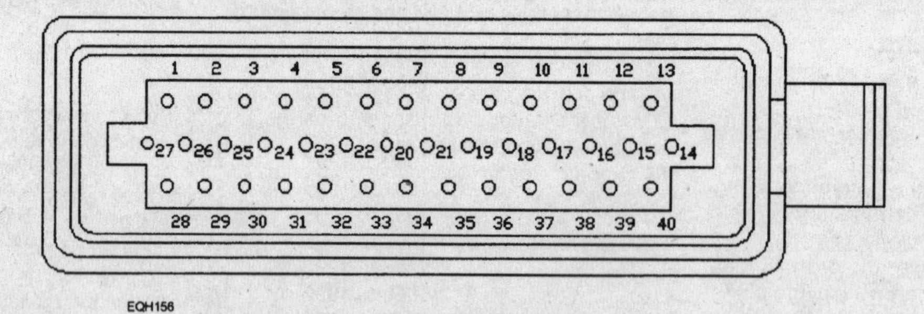

15.10 Rover 40-pin multi-plug

Fault codes

26 Obtaining fault codes

1 Rover SPi requires a dedicated FCR to access fault codes and Datastream, actuate components and make service adjustments. Flash codes are not available for output from this system.

2 Rover SPi does not log traditional fault codes. However, during a system check with the aid of a FCR, each sensor and actuator circuit is tested, and a report made on all faults found.

3 If the system and circuits check out fault-free, the FCR will step into an adjustment and tune routine, when CO adjustments can be made. Below are listed a number of the faults that may be indicated during the test procedures.

Coolant temperature sensor circuit fault

Ambient air temperature sensor circuit fault

Inlet air temperature sensor circuit fault

Low battery voltage

Throttle pedal switch circuit fault

Knock sensor circuit fault

Coil circuit fault

Chapter 16
Toyota TCCS

Contents

Specifications

Vehicle	Year	Idle speed	CO%
Camry cat 5S-FE (SXV10)	1992	750 ± 50	0.5 max
Camry 2.0i OHC 3S-FE	1987 to 1991	700 ± 50	1.5 ± 0.5
Camry 2.0i OHC 4WD 3S-FE	1988 to 1989	700 ± 50	1.5 ± 0.5
Camry 2.0i OHC 4WD 3S-FE	1988 to 1989	700 ± 50	1.5 ± 0.5
Camry 2.2i 16V DOHC cat 5S-FE	1991 to 1996	750 ± 50	0 to 0.5
Camry 2.2	1997	750 ± 50	0.5 max
Camry 2.5i V6 OHC cat 2VZ-FE	1989 to 1991	700	0.5 max
Camry 3.0i V6 24V DOHC cat 3VZ-FE	1991 to 1995	700 ± 50	0 to 0.5
Carina E 1.6i 16V DOHC 4A-FE	1992 to 1996	750 ± 50	0.3 max
Carina E 1.6i 16V DOHC cat 4A-FE	1992 to 1996	750 ± 50	0.3 max
Carina II 2.0i OHC 3S-FE	1988 to 1992	700 ± 50	1.5 ± 0.5
Carina II 2.0i OHC cat 3S-FE	1988 to 1992	700 ± 50	0 to 0.5
Carina E 2.0i DOHC cat 3S-FE	1992 to 1996	800 ± 50	0.5 max
Carina E 2.0i DOHC cat 3S-GE	1992 to 1995	800 ± 50	0.5 max
Celica 2.0 16V DOHC 3S-GE	1990 to 1994	800 ± 50	1.0 ± 0.5
Celica 2.0 16V DOHC cat 3S-GE	1990 to 1994	800 ± 50	1.0 ± 0.5
Celica 2.0 16V DOHC 3S-GEL	1985 to 1990	800	1.0 ± 0.5
Celica 2.0 GT-4 turbo 16V 3S-GTE	1988 to 1990	750 ± 50	0 to 0.5
Celica 2.0 GT-4 turbo 16V 3S-GTE	1990 to 1993	800 ± 50	0 to 0.5
Celica 2.2i 16V DOHC cat 5S-FE	1991 to 1994	700 ± 50	0 to 0.5
Corolla 1.3i OHC cat 2E-E	1990 to 1992	800 ± 50	0.5 to 2.0
Corolla 1.3i 16V DOHC cat 4E-FE	1992 to 1995	700 ± 50	0.3 max
Corolla non cat 4A-GE	1987 to 1992	800	1.5 ± 0.5
Corolla cat 4A-GE	1987 to 1992	800	0.5 max
Corolla non cat 4A-FE (AE101)	1992 to 1997	800 ± 50	1.5 ± 0.5
Corolla 1.6 GTi OHC cat 4A-GE	1989 to 1992	850 ± 50	1.5 ± 0.5
Corolla cat 4A-FE (AE101)MT	1992 to 1997	750 ± 50	0.5 max
Corolla cat 4A-FE (AE101) AT	1992 to 1997	800 ± 50	0.5 max
Corolla 1.6i 16V DOHC cat 4A-FE	1992 to 1996	750 ± 50	0.5 max
Corolla 1.6 GTi OHC 4A-GE	1987 to 1992	800 ± 50	1.5 ± 0.5
Corolla 1.8i 16V DOHC cat 7A-FE	1993 to 1995	750 ± 50	0.5 max
Hi-Ace 2.4i OHC 2RZ-E	1989 to 1994	750	1.0 ± 0.5
Hi-Ace 2.4i 4x4 OHC 2RZ-E	1989 to 1994	750	1.0 ± 0.5
MR2 1.6 OHC 4A-GEL	1984 to 1990	800 ± 50	1.5 ± 0.5
MR2 2.0 16V DOHC GT cat 3S-GE	1990 to 1995	800 ± 50	0.5 max
MR2 2.0 16V DOHC cat 3S-FE	1990 to 1994	700 ± 50	0 to 0.5

Vehicle	Year	Idle speed	CO%
Previa 2.4i 16V DOHC cat 2TZ-FE	1990 to 1996	700 ± 50	0.5 max
Supra 3.0i 24V DOHC 7M-GE	1986 to 1993	850 ± 50	1.0 ± 0.5
Supra 3.0i 24V DOHC cat 7M-GE	1986 to 1993	800 ± 50	1.0 ± 0.5
Supra 3.0i turbo DOHC DIS cat7M-GTE	1989 to 1993	800 ± 50	0 to 0.5
Supra 3.0i turbo DOHC DIS 2JZ-GTE	1993 to 1994	650 ± 50	0.5 max
Tarago 2.4i 16V DOHC cat 2TZ-FE	1990 to 1995	700 ± 50	0.5 max
4 Runner 3.0i 4WD V6 SOHC 12V cat	1991 to 1995	700 ± 50	0 to 0.5

Overview of system operation

1 Introduction

Please read this overview of Toyota TCCS operation in conjunction with Chapter 2, which describes some of the functions in more detail.

Toyota developed their first electronic fuel injection (EFi) system in 1971, and this was fitted in volume to the 1979 Toyota Crown with the 5M-E engine, and to the Cressida with the 4M-E engine. Toyota EFi was an analogue system that controlled the injection of fuel by reference to the time taken to charge and discharge a capacitor. Toyota also refer to the fuel injection function of TCCS as EFi, and this can sometimes lead to confusion.

1983 saw the appearance of the first digital system - designated TCCS (Toyota Computer Controlled System). TCCS is a fully-integrated system that controls primary ignition (ESA), fuelling (MPi) and engine idle from within the same ECM. In contrast to the early EFi system, digital reference tables stored in ROM and a self-diagnostic function are utilised.

Toyota TCCS was designed as a modular system, capable of controlling a wide range of engines. Essentially, TCCS can be divided into two different types, according to the method of measuring engine load. One type utilises a MAP sensor, and the other an AFS to measure load. Within each type there are a number of other differences, including the design of the ECM multi-plug connections **(see illustrations 16.1 and 16.2)**.

The TCCS ECM is connected to the battery, sensors and actuators by a multi-plug which has a different number and position of pins according to the various models. A common method of annotating the various pins used in TCCS is practised, and this Chapter refers to those pin codes in text and illustrations.

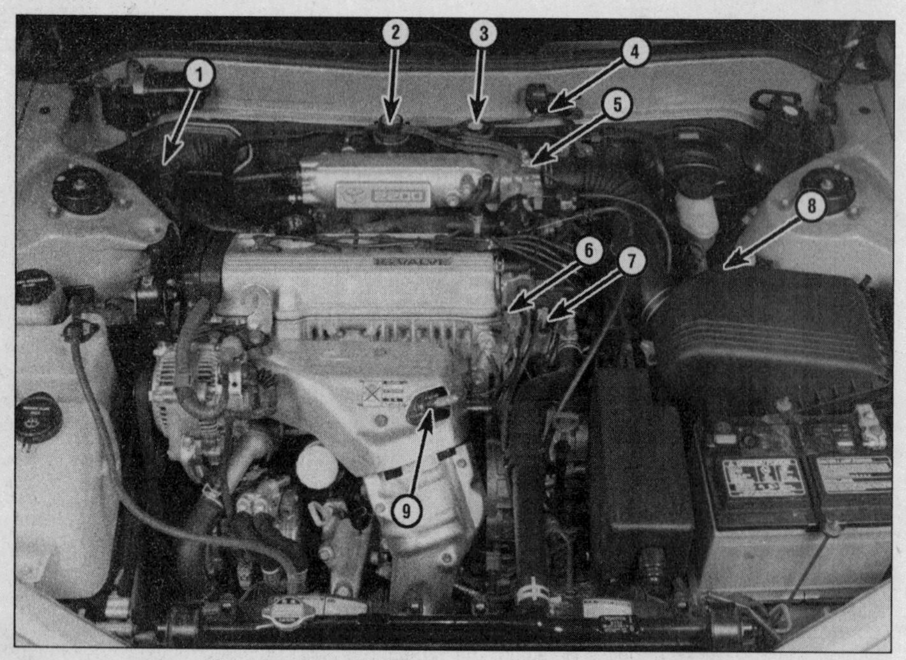

16.1 Location of TCCS components (Toyota Camry)

1 *SD connector*
2 *EGR vacuum modulator*
3 *EGR valve*
4 *MAP sensor*
5 *TPS (behind throttle body)*
6 *CTS*
7 *Distributor*
8 *Amplifier (igniter), behind air filter housing*
9 *Oxygen sensor (OS)*

2 Control functions

Signal processing

Basic ignition timing is stored in a map stored in ECM ROM, and the engine load and speed signals determine the ignition timing. The main engine load sensor is the MAP sensor (or AFS); engine speed is determined from the crank angle sensor (CAS) signal.

Correction factors are then applied for starting, idle, deceleration, and part- and full-load operation. The main correction factor is engine temperature (CTS). Minor corrections to timing and AFR are made with reference to the air temperature sensor (ATS) and throttle potentiometer sensor (TPS) signals.

The basic AFR is also stored in a three-dimensional map, and the engine load and speed signals determine the basic injection pulse value. The AFR and the pulse duration are then corrected on reference to ATS, CTS, battery voltage and rate of throttle opening (TPS). Other controlling factors are determined by operating conditions such as cold start and warm-up, idle condition, acceleration and deceleration.

TCCS accesses a different map for idle running conditions, and this map is implemented whenever the idle switch is closed and the engine speed is at idle.

Basic ECM operation (typical)

A permanent voltage supply is made from the vehicle battery to pin BATT of the ECM, via one or more fusible links. Once the ignition is switched on, voltage is output at ignition switch terminals IG1 and IG2. IG1 is connected to ECM pin W via the 'Check Engine' warning lamp, and IG2 supplies voltage to the EFi main relay, the ignition coil and amplifier and the injector circuit.

The supply to the EFi main relay is directly connected through the energising coil to earth, and the relay outputs a voltage to ECM pins +B and +B1, the fuel pump relay, the fuel injectors and the VSV for the T-VIS (where used). Once the ECM receives voltage at pin +B, the pin W is connected to earth pin E1 and the 'Check Engine' warning lamp will light.

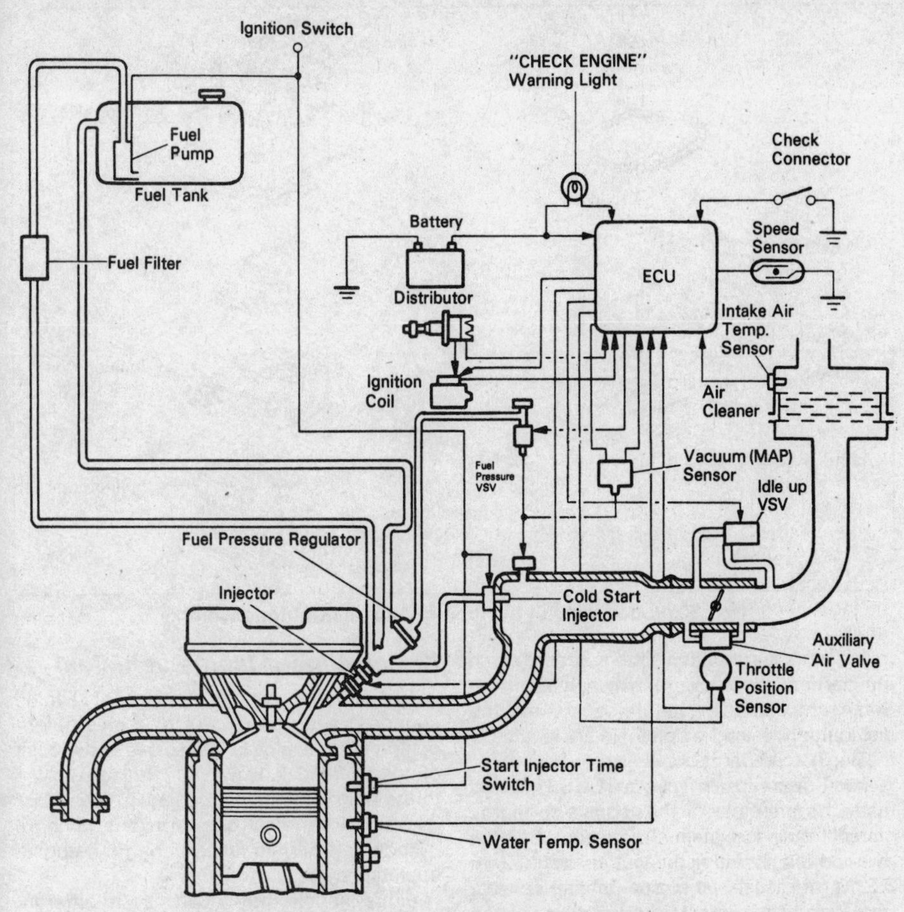

16.2 Schematic of TCCS (Corolla, 1989 on)

The engine sensors (eg ATS, CO pot, CTS, MAP (or AFS) and TPS, are now provided with a 5.0-volt reference supply from a relevant pin on the ECM.

When the ignition switch is turned to the ST1 position (crank engine) a voltage is supplied to the starter solenoid, ECM pin STA, the CSI and the fuel pump relay energising coil. The fuel pump will run, and when the ECM recognises the cranking signal at pin STA, ignition and injection functions are activated. In addition, if the engine temperature is low, the cold start injector (CSI) will operate for a few seconds until the thermo-time switch (TTS) opens to break the CSI circuit.

Once the key is released from the start position, if the engine has not started, the voltage supply from terminal ST1 of the ignition switch will stop and the starter solenoid, ECM pin STA, the CSI and the fuel pump relay energising coil will all cease operation.

Once the key is released from the start position and if the engine has started, pin FC at the ECM will energise the fuel pump relay coil and the fuel pump will continue running.

Deceleration fuel cut-off

A deceleration fuel cut-off is implemented during engine over-run conditions, to improve economy and reduce emissions. Conditions when over-run is implemented are:

a) Throttle closed (idle switch contacts closed).
b) Engine speed above 1800 rpm.
c) Once the engine speed drops below 1400 rpm, fuel injection is reinstated.

Reference voltage

Voltage supply from the ECM to the engine sensors is made at a 5.0-volt reference level. This ensures a stable working voltage, unaffected by variations in system voltage.

The earth return connection for most engine sensors are made through ECM pin numbers E1 and E2, but these pins are not directly connected to earth. The ECM internally connects pins E1 and E2 to earth via ECM earth pins EO1 and E02 that are directly connected to earth.

Self-diagnostic function

The TCCS has a self-test capability that continuously examines signals from the engine sensors. When a fault is detected, the 'Check Engine' warning lamp located on the dashboard lights, and the ECM internally logs an appropriate code or codes. These codes can be output on the 'Check Engine' warning lamp by bridging the appropriate terminals in the self-test connector. Some later vehicles are equipped with a TDCL (total diagnostic communication link) located under the driver's side dash. Codes may be obtained by attaching a FCR to the TDCL connector.

In some earlier versions of TCCS, not all codes caused the 'Check Engine' warning lamp to light, although the ECM still logged an appropriate code or codes. When the lamp is triggered, it will begin to flash. By counting the flashes, the fault code can be determined. Codes can also be extracted from the diagnostic link (TDCL) when so equipped, with the aid of a suitable FCR. Where more than one code is stored, the codes will be output in numerical order from the smallest value code to the largest.

If the fault clears, the warning lamp will extinguish, but the codes will remain logged until a routine is initiated to erase them from memory. There are several different routines available, and these include removing the 'Check Engine' warning lamp fuse, disconnecting the battery negative terminal, or utilising a suitable FCR (for the type with TDCL).

Limited operating strategy (LOS, or 'limp-home' mode)

In addition to the self-test capability, Toyota TCCS has a limp-home facility. In the event of a serious fault in one or more of the sensors, the EMS will substitute a fixed default value in place of the defective sensor.

For example, in limp-home mode, the coolant temperature sensor (CTS) value is set to 80°C, and the air temperature sensor (ATS) is set to 20°C. This means that the engine may actually run quite well with failure of either the ATS or the CTS. However, since the substituted values are those of a hot engine, cold starting and running during the warm-up period may be less than satisfactory.

Adaptive memory

Over a period of time, the ECM will learn the best idle position for a particular engine - irrespective of age, engine condition and load, so that the correct idle speed is always maintained. The adaptive idle settings are stored in memory. Consequently, when the battery is disconnected, the ECM will need some time to re-learn the system parameters before proper idle control is restored.

Vehicle speed sensor (VSS)

The VSS is used to advise the ECM of vehicle speed. The VSS in early models generates an AC pulse which the ECM then converts to a digital value. Some later models may utilise a Hall-effect type VSS which produces a square waveform. The VSS is mounted upon the speedometer drive behind the dash.

With the Hall-effect type of VSS, a voltage of approximately 10 volts is applied to the VSS from the ignition switch when it is switched on. As the speedometer cable turns, the Hall switch is alternately turned on and off, to return a square wave signal to the ECM. The frequency of the signal denotes the engine speed.

3 Primary trigger

Crank angle sensor (CAS)

The primary signal to initiate both ignition and fuelling emanates from two inductive sensors mounted in the distributor. Each sensor consists of a reluctor with a set number of teeth, positioned within the field of an inductive magnet. Both reluctors are mounted on the distributor shaft - one above the other, with the TDC sensor uppermost. The rpm reluctor contains 24 teeth and the TDC reluctor 4 teeth - one for each cylinder. As the distributor spins, and the teeth are rotated in each magnetic field, an AC voltage signal is generated to indicate speed of rotation and a reference to TDC. Each sensor is connected to the ECM by a signal wire and earth return.

The peak-to-peak voltage of each signal (when viewed upon an oscilloscope) can vary from 2.0 volts during engine cranking to over 100 volts at 6000 rpm. The ECM uses an analogue-to-digital converter to transform each AC pulse into a digital signal.

4 Ignition

Data on engine load (MAP or AFS) and engine speed (CAS) are collected by the ECM, which then refers to a digital ignition map stored within its microprocessor. This map contains an advance angle for basic load and speed operating conditions. The advance angle is corrected after reference to engine temperature (CTS), so that the best ignition advance angle for a particular operating condition can be determined.

Amplifier

The Toyota TCCS amplifier (often termed an 'igniter' by the Japanese vehicle manufacturers) contains the circuitry for switching the coil negative terminal at the correct moment to instigate ignition. The ECM calculates the correct ignition dwell time and timing advance from data received from its sensors, and sends a signal (IGt) to the amplifier, which then switches off the coil negative terminal.

The amplifier then monitors the primary switching and if this is satisfactory, passes a confirmation signal (IGf) to the ECM. If the ECM does not detect the IGf signal from the amplifier, it will switch off the fuel pump driver at pin FC as a safety precaution.

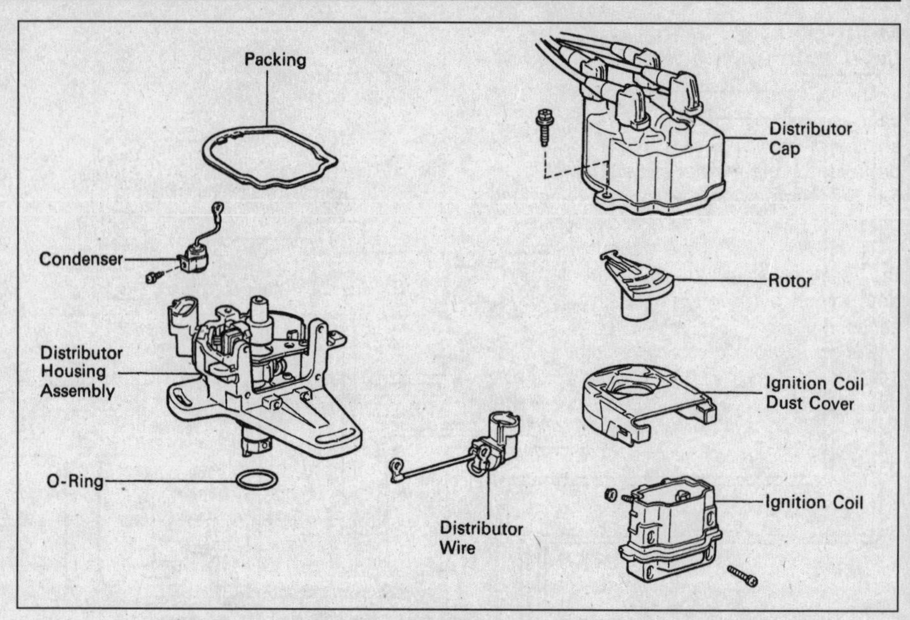

16.3 Exploded view of the 'coil-in-cap' distributor assembly

The amplifier location differs according to the particular vehicle to which it is fitted. Some amplifiers are contained within the distributor housing, while others are located in the engine compartment.

Dwell operation in Toyota TCCS is based upon the principle of the 'constant-energy current-limiting' system. This means that the dwell period remains constant at about 3.0 to 3.5 ms, at virtually all engine running speeds. However, the dwell duty cycle, when measured in percent or degrees, will vary as the engine speed varies.

Ignition coil

The ignition coil utilises low primary resistance in order to increase primary current and primary energy. The amplifier limits the primary current to around 8 amps, and this permits a reserve of energy to maintain the required spark burn time (duration).

Distributor

In the TCCS system, the distributor contains the RPM and TDC sensors, and also the secondary HT components (distributor cap, rotor and HT coil) and serves to distribute the HT current from the coil secondary terminal to each spark plug in firing order. The distributor is located on the exhaust camshaft, at the cylinder No 1 end **(see illustration 16.3)**.

Integrated ignition assembly (IIA)

In some models, the coil and amplifier are integrated inside the distributor. This reduces wiring and improves reliability. The system is often referred to as the 'coil-in-cap' system, and is identified by the lack of a main coil secondary HT lead. The secondary HT voltage passes directly from the coil to the rotor arm - which distributes the voltage to the spark plugs via HT leads in the conventional manner.

Knock sensor (some vehicles)

The optimal ignition timing (at engine speeds greater than idle) for a given high-compression engine is quite close to the point of onset of knock. However, running so close to the point of knock occurrence means that knock will certainly occur on one or more cylinders at certain times during the engine operating cycle.

Since knock may occur at a different moment in each individual cylinder, TCCS employs a knock control processor (in the ECM) to pinpoint the actual cylinder or cylinders that are knocking. The knock sensor is mounted on the engine block, and consists of a piezo-ceramic measuring element that responds to engine noise oscillations. This signal is converted to a voltage signal that is proportional to the level of knock, and returned to the ECM for evaluation and action.

The ECM will analyse the noise from each individual cylinder, and uses a sophisticated technique to recognise knock as distinct to general engine noise.

5 Fuel injection

The Toyota TCCS ECM is mapped with a basic injector opening time according to various load and speed conditions. Information is then gathered from engine sensors such as the MAP sensor, RPM and TDC sensors, CTS, and combined TPS & TS. As a result of this information, the ECM will look up the correct injector pulse duration right across the engine rpm, load and temperature range.

Multi-point injection (MPi - simultaneous)

The MPi system consists of one injector for each cylinder, mounted in the inlet port adjacent to its inlet valve. The amount of fuel delivered by the injector is determined by the fuel pressure and the injector opening time - otherwise known as the pulse duration.

The ECM controls the period of time that the injector is held open, and this is determined by the signals from the various sensor inputs.

During simultaneous fuel injection, the TCCS ECM opens all the injectors once every one or two revolutions of the crankshaft. Normally, the injectors operate twice per complete engine cycle (eg 4A-GE engine). Half of the fuel required is injected onto the back of a closed inlet valve, waiting for it to open, and the other half is injected as the valve opens for the intake stroke. Once the valve has opened, the fuel enters the cylinder in the normal way.

In some engines, the injectors are wired in two banks of two. Even so, the injection is still simultaneous, although here injection occurs once every two revolutions of the crankshaft. The injection pulse in this instance is approximately twice the duration of those engines that pulse every revolution.

Fuel injector

The fuel injector is a magnetically-operated solenoid valve that is actuated by the ECM. Voltage to the injectors is either applied from nbv or through a ballast resistor, and the earth path is completed by the ECM for a period of time (called pulse duration) of between 1.5 and 10 milliseconds. The pulse duration is very much dependent upon engine temperature, load, speed and operating conditions. When the magnetic solenoid closes, a back-EMF voltage of up to 60 volts is initiated.

On the MPi engines, the fuel injectors are mounted in the inlet stubs to the engine inlet valves, so that a finely-atomised fuel spray is directed onto the back of each valve. Some early models also utilise a cold start injector and thermo-time switch to provide extra fuel during engine cranking.

The injectors used in the TCCS system may be the high-resistance type (13.8 ohms) or low-resistance type (2.3 ohms).

Low-resistance injector

When the injector resistance is low, the response rate is quicker, and this leads to a faster opening time. However, because more current flows through the injector, more heat is generated, which can result in a shorter injector life span. By passing the voltage through a series (ballast) resistor, a lower voltage is applied to the injector, which results in less heat and longer injector life.

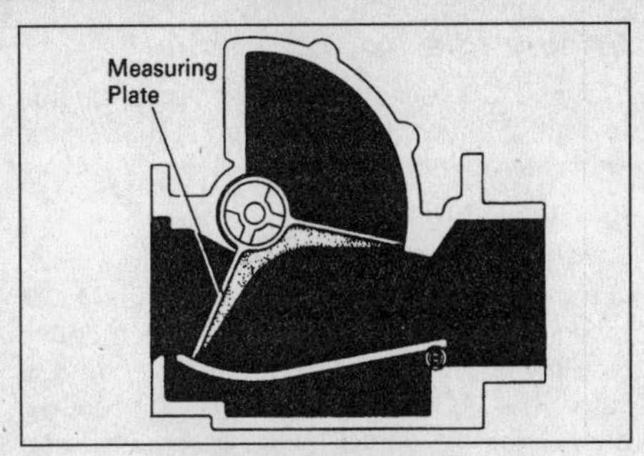

16.4 Vane-type AFS

Airflow sensor (AFS) - where fitted

The AFS is located between the air filter and the throttle body **(see illustration 16.4)**. As air flows through the sensor, it deflects a vane (flap). The greater the volume of air, the more will the flap be deflected. The vane is connected to an arm which wipes a potentiometer resistance track, and so varies the resistance of the track. This allows a variable voltage signal to be returned to the ECM.

The TCCS AFS is based on the now outdated Bosch 'L' Jetronic design. Overall operation of the sensor is similar to the modern three-wire AFS as fitted to modern Motronic systems. However, the wiring circuitry is somewhat different. Battery voltage from the system relay is applied through connection VB to a resistance within the AFS body. The resistance reduces the nbv to between 5.0 and 10.0 volts, and the resulting voltage is termed the reference voltage. The reference voltage is applied to both the ECM at pin VC and the AFS resistance track within the AFS body. The other end of the resistance track is connected to the AFS earth return at connection E2. AFS signal output is made from the wiper arm to the ECM pin VS, via AFS connection VS.

From the signal voltage returned, the ECM is able to calculate the volume of air (load) entering the engine, and this is used to calculate the main fuel injection duration. To smooth out inlet pulses, a damper is connected to the AFS vane. The AFS exerts a major influence on the amount of fuel injected.

The TCCS AFS also contains a set of fuel pump earth contacts. Refer to the fuel pump relay details for an operational description.

MAP sensor - where fitted

Where the main engine load sensor is the MAP sensor, a vacuum hose connects the MAP sensor (located on the bulkhead) and the inlet manifold. Manifold vacuum acts upon the MAP sensor diaphragm, and the ECM converts the pressure into an electrical signal. MAP is calculated from the formula: Atmospheric Pressure less Manifold Pressure = Manifold Absolute Pressure.

A 5.0-volt reference voltage is applied to the sensor, and the earth return is via the sensor return circuit. MAP sensor output on the PIM signal wire is returned to the ECM as a variable voltage signal. Voltage on the signal wire varies from about 1.0 volt at idle to approximately 4.5 volts at full load. Using the speed/density method, Toyota TCCS calculates the AFR from the MAP signal and the speed of the engine. This method relies on the theory that the engine will draw in a fixed volume of air per revolution.

The inlet manifold is a 'dry' manifold. Since fuel does not enter the manifold - due to injection being made onto the back of the inlet valve, there is no risk of fuel being drawn into the MAP sensor to contaminate the diaphragm, and a fuel trap is not used.

Air temperature sensor (ATS)

The ATS is either mounted in the AFS inlet tract or in the air inlet casing, and measures the air temperature before it enters the inlet manifold. Because the density of air varies in inverse proportion to the temperature, the ATS signal allows more accurate assessment of the volume of air entering the engine. However, the ATS has only a minor correcting effect on ECM output.

The open-circuit supply to the sensor is at a 5.0-volt reference level, and the earth path is through the earth return. The ATS operates on the NTC principle. A variable voltage signal is returned to the ECM based upon the air temperature. This signal is approximately 2.0 to 2.8 volts at an ambient temperature of 20°C, and reduces to about 1.5 volt as the air temperature rises to around 40°C.

CO 'pot' (not used in cat models)

The CO pot mixture adjuster is a three-wire potentiometer that allows small changes to be made to the idle CO level. A 5.0-volt reference voltage is applied to the sensor, and earth return is made via the TCCS sensor return circuit. The third wire is the CO pot signal.

As the CO pot adjustment screw is turned, the change in resistance returns a voltage signal to the ECM that will result in a change in CO. The CO pot adjustment only affects idle CO. Catalyst-equipped models are not fitted with a CO pot, and the CO is thus non-adjustable.

Coolant temperature sensor (CTS)

The CTS is incorporated in the cooling system, and operates on the NTC principle. As the resistance of the CTS varies, this returns a variable voltage signal to the ECM based upon the coolant temperature. The signal is approximately 2.0 to 3.0 volts at an ambient temperature of 20°C, and reduces to between 0.4 to 0.8 volts at a coolant temperature of 80°C.

The open-circuit supply to the sensor is at a 5.0-volt reference level, and the earth path is through the sensor return. The ECM uses the CTS signal as a main correction factor when calculating ignition timing and injection duration.

Throttle potentiometer sensor/throttle switch (TPS/TS)

The TPS and TS are combined into a sensor that is essentially a potentiometer with a separate set of idle contacts. The TPS provides the ECM with data on rate of acceleration and throttle position, and the TS indicates idle position. A common earth return connects both TPS and TS to the ECM.

Voltage at the 5.0-volt reference level is applied to the TS idle contact terminal from the ECM. This voltage drops to zero when the idle contact is closed.

The TPS is a potentiometer with three wires. A 5.0-volt reference voltage is supplied to a resistance track, with the other end connected to earth. The third wire is connected to an arm which wipes along the resistance track, and so varies the resistance and voltage of the signal returned to the ECM.

From the voltage returned, the ECM is able to calculate just how quickly the throttle is opened.

Idle speed control valve (ISCV) - 4A-FE engine

The ISCV is a solenoid-controlled actuator that the ECM uses to automatically control idle speed during normal idle and during engine warm-up. The ISCV is controls a channel that connects the inlet manifold to the air filter side of the throttle plate.

The ISCV is a DC motor that the ECM can rotate either clockwise or anti-clockwise. Rotating in one direction will open the valve, and rotating in the opposite direction will cause it to close. A voltage supply is applied to the ISCV from the main relay, and the earth for the motor is made through two connections to the ECM.

Rotation of the motor in the appropriate direction is accomplished by actuating the motor through one or the other of the earth circuits. In reality, the two circuits are opposed. This prevents the valve from being fully opened of closed in one particular direction. The valve will thus take up an average position that reflects circuit bias to be open or closed. Normally, this bias would be towards the open position.

A duty cycle can be measured on each earth circuit, to determine the opening or closing time period as a percentage of the total time available.

When electrical loads such as the headlights or heater fan are switched on, the idle speed would tend to drop. The ECM will sense the load, and rotate the ISCV to increase the airflow through the valve, and thus increase the idle speed. When the load is removed, the ECM will pulse the valve so that the airflow is reduced. Normal idle speed should be maintained under all cold and hot operating conditions. If the ISCV fails, it will fail-safe, with the aperture almost closed. This will provide a basic idle speed.

Engine idle (4A-GE engine)

The TCCS uses three different components to control the engine idle speed at the various engine temperatures.

Idle-up system

When the engine is first started from cold, voltage at the ECM pin STA causes the ECM to signal the V-ISC idle-up VSV, which opens to allow additional air to by-pass the throttle valve. The VSV remains open for 10 seconds, after which the control signal is removed and the VSV closes. The position of the auxiliary air valve (AAV) then determines the idle speed during the remainder of the warm-up period.

Auxiliary air valve (AAV)

The AAV is a waxstat-actuated control valve that is used to increase the idle speed during the engine warm-up period. The AAV closes once the engine reaches normal operating temperature.

The AAV is mounted on the throttle body, and connected by hose to the coolant system so that the coolant temperature will determine the position of the waxstat. A drilling in the throttle body on the air filter side of the throttle valve allows incoming air to by-pass the throttle valve. The flow of by-pass air passes through the body of the AAV, and is returned to the throttle body on the engine side of the throttle valve. This flow of air causes the engine idle rpm to increase to a speed that is fully dependent on the volume of the additional air.

The waxstat responds to temperature by expanding and contracting. When the temperature is low, the waxstat is contracted and the valve is open, so that engine idle speed is increased. The lower the temperature, the more open the valve will be. As the engine warms-up and coolant acts upon the waxstat, the waxstat expands to gradually shut the AAV until it is fully closed at normal operating temperature.

However, even when nominally closed, it is normal for a very small volume of air to pass through the AAV by-pass channel. Since idle speed is set by adjustment of the idle speed air screw, it is easy to compensate for this additional air bleed.

Idle speed

The throttle valve and also the AAV are both almost completely closed when the engine is at idle speed. In order for the engine to idle satisfactorily, an adjustable by-pass passage is provided in the throttle body. An adjustment screw is located in this passage, so that the idle speed may be set to the correct value by varying the air which passes through the passage.

T-VIS (Toyota - variable induction system)

Under all operating conditions, air flows into the induction manifold through the throttle valve in the throttle body. However, on some models, Toyota utilise a variable induction system to improve the flow of air into the engine at both low and high engine speeds.

At low engine speeds, airflow is comparatively slow, and this can lead to inefficient fuel atomisation when the inlet port to the inlet valve is large. Ideally the port should be small, which leads to higher air speeds, much better atomisation and a more efficient engine.

Conversely, at high engine speeds, the volume of air into the engine needs to be high, which demands a larger inlet port. A small port at high engine speeds would restrict engine performance. For efficient engine operation over the entire engine rpm range then, a variable inlet port would seem to be required.

Some carburettor engines overcome this particular problem with the aid of a twin-venturi air inlet. A number of fuel-injected engines have used a similar arrangement in the throttle barrel. However, the TCCS uses a somewhat different solution.

The inlet port to each set of inlet valves is divided into two inlet ports. One of these ports is provided with a throttle valve, whilst the other is left open. At low engine speeds, air will pass into the engine through the open inlet port. The diameter is large enough to satisfy engine demand at low engine speed, yet small enough to provide good fuel atomisation.

As engine speed rises, the ECM actuates the control system, and the throttle valve in the second inlet port opens to provide the additional air required for high speed engine operation.

A vacuum supply from the inlet manifold is piped to the T-VIS control valve via a vacuum tank and the T-VIS vacuum switching valve (VSV). The vacuum tank 'stores' vacuum so that when the VSV is actuated, the secondary throttle action will be more controlled. Voltage is applied to the VSV from the main relay, and the earth path is completed through the ECM. When engine rpm is low the VSV is switched 'on' by the ECM, so that vacuum will act upon the control valve. This in turn will pull the secondary throttle valves into the closed position.

As engine rpm exceeds the pre-determined limit, the ECM switches the VSV 'off' so that the vacuum supply to the control valve is interrupted, and the secondary throttles will open. The engine thus receives the correct volume of air for all operating conditions of speed and load.

As engine rpm increases, the ECM switches off the VSV and as vacuum pull decreases, air is allowed to bleed through a filter open to atmosphere. This gradual decay of vacuum allows the throttles to open in a controlled manner. Once the engine rpm falls below the pre-determined limit and vacuum is re-introduced, the secondary throttles will gently close until the rpm rises again.

Air conditioning ASV (air switching valve)

When the A/C is switched on at idle rpm, a load is placed upon the engine which could result in a great reduction in engine speed. The lower idle speed could result in poor idle quality, and a tendency to stall. The A/C ASV is used to allow extra air to by-pass the throttle, which will result in the idle speed returning to a figure close to the normal idle speed. The ECM monitors the A/C load and opens the A/C ASV whenever the A/C is in operation during engine idle.

A by-pass hose from the inlet manifold is piped through the A/C VSV. Voltage is applied to the ASV from the main relay, and the earth path is completed through the ECM. When engine rpm is low, the ASV is opened by the ECM so that the flow of air into the inlet manifold will maintain the correct idle speed.

Once the A/C is switched off, the ECM switches the ASV 'off' so that flow of air is stopped and the correct idle speed is once more maintained.

Main and fuel pump relays

The Toyota TCCS electrical system is controlled by a main fuel injection relay and a fuel pump relay. A permanent voltage supply, via one or more fusible links, is made to the main relay terminal 3 from the battery positive terminal.

Once the ignition is switched on, a voltage supply from the ignition switch is applied to main relay terminal 2. Terminal 2 is connected to the relay winding, which is connected to earth through terminal 1. When voltage is applied to the winding, it is energised to close the relay contacts, and thus connect terminals 3 and 4 (or 5). The supply to terminal 3 is output from terminal 4 (or 5) and voltage is thereby applied to ECM terminals +B and +B1, the fuel pump relay, the fuel injectors and the VSV for the T-VIS.

The fuel pump relay contains two windings and a set of contacts. When the ignition is switched on, voltage is applied to terminal +B of the contacts, and to the second winding which is connected to pin FC at the ECM (MAP sensor) or terminal FC at the AFS. What happens next depends on whether the system utilises a MAP sensor or an AFS. Refer to the appropriate following section.

Fuel pump relay operation in MAP sensor system

When the ignition is switched on, the ECM briefly earths the fuel pump relay contact at ECM pin FC. This energises the second relay winding, which closes the relay contact and connects voltage from terminal +B to terminal FP, thereby providing voltage to the fuel pump circuit. After approximately one second, the ECM opens the circuit and the pump stops. This brief running of the fuel pump allows pressure to build within the fuel pressure lines, and provides for an easier start.

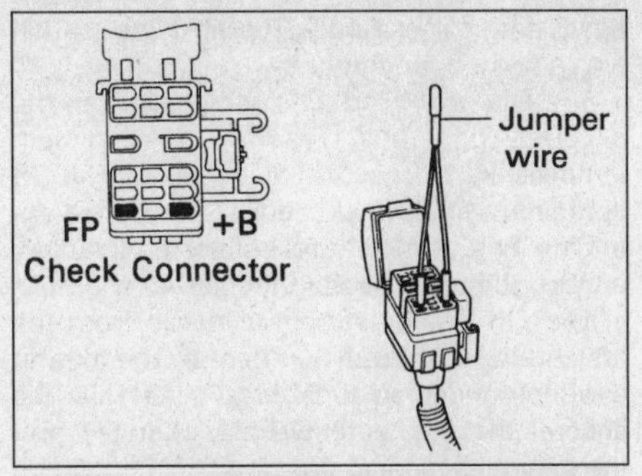

16.5 Check the fuel pump relay. Apply battery voltage to terminals STA and E1 and check for continuity across terminals B+ and FP

The fuel pump relay circuit will then remain open until the engine is cranked or run. Once the relay receives a cranking voltage at terminal STA, the first relay winding - which is connected to earth at terminal E1 - will be energised, and the fuel pump will run until during the cranking operation **(see illustration 16.5)**.

Once the key is released from the start position, if the engine has not started, the voltage supply from terminal ST1 of the ignition switch will stop, the fuel pump relay energising coil will de-energise, and the contacts will open to cut the voltage to the fuel pump.

Once the key is released and the engine has started, pin FC at the ECM will energise the second relay winding and the fuel pump will continue running.

Fuel pump relay operation in AFS system

The fuel pump relay uses two energising coils to control the relay circuit - one coil during cranking, and the other coil during normal engine running. Once the relay receives a cranking voltage at terminal STA, the first relay winding - which is connected to earth at terminal E1 - will be energised, and the fuel pump will run until during the cranking operation.

When cranking ceases, the fuel pump relay energising coil will de-energise, and the contacts will open to cut the voltage to the fuel pump

The second coil is connected to earth through a set of contacts in the AFS relay. Once the key is released from the start position, if the engine has started, the FC contacts in the AFS will earth and thus energise the second relay winding so that the fuel pump will continue running. The FC contacts act as a safety feature. When the engine stops for whatever reason and the AFS returns to the closed position, the FC contacts will open. In turn, the fuel pump relay will de-energise, which will shut down the fuel pump.

Fuel pressure system

The fuel system consists of a fuel tank, a submerged fuel pump, fuel filter, fuel rail, pressure regulator and return line. The fuel pump is an impeller-type pump, mounted in the fuel tank and driven by a permanent magnet electric motor. The pump draws fuel from the tank, and pumps it to the fuel rail via a fuel filter.

Switching the ignition key 'on' causes the ECM to energise the fuel pump relay for approximately one second, so that the fuel system is pressurised. The fuel pump relay is then switched off, to await a cranking or running signal.

The pump is of the 'wet' variety, in that fuel actually flows through the pump and the electric motor. There is no actual fire risk, because the fuel drawn through the pump is not in a combustible condition. Mounted upon the pump armature shaft is an impeller which rotates when the pump is actuated. Placed around the circumference of the impeller are located a number of blades. As the pump impeller rotates, the blades draw fuel from the inlet port, and pump it to the pump pressure outlet via a non-return valve. The pump is protected from over-pressurising by a relief valve mounted in the inlet side of the pump.

Once the engine is running, fuel is fed through a fuel filter to the fuel injector rail. To prevent pressure loss in the supply system, a non-return valve is provided in the fuel pump outlet. When the ignition is switched off, and the fuel pump ceases operation, pressure is thus maintained for some time, so that vaporisation and poor hot starting is much reduced.

Fuel pressure regulator

Fuel pressure in the fuel rail is maintained at a constant 2.5 bar by a fuel pressure regulator. The fuel pump normally provides much more fuel than is required, and surplus fuel is thus returned to the fuel tank via a return pipe. In fact, a maximum fuel pressure in excess of 5 bar is possible in this system. To prevent pressure loss in the supply system, a non-return valve is provided in the fuel pump outlet. When the ignition is switched off, and the fuel pump ceases operation, pressure is thus maintained for some time.

At idle speed with the vacuum pipe disconnected, or with the engine stopped and the pump running, or at full-throttle, the system fuel pressure will be around 2.5 bar. At idle speed (vacuum pipe connected), the fuel pressure will be approximately 0.5 bar under the system pressure.

6 Catalytic converter and emission control

The Toyota TCCS injection system fitted to catalyst vehicles implements a closed-loop control system, so that exhaust emissions may be reduced. Closed-loop systems are fitted with an oxygen sensor (OS), which monitors the exhaust gas for its oxygen content. A low oxygen level in the exhaust signifies a rich mixture. A high oxygen level in the exhaust signifies a weak mixture.

When the engine is operating in closed-loop control, the OS signal causes the ECM to modify the injector pulse, so that the AFR is maintained close to the stoichiometric ratio. By controlling the injection pulse during most operating conditions, so that the air/fuel ratio is always in a small 'window' around the Lambda point (ie Lambda = 0.98 to 1.04), almost perfect combustion could be achieved. Thus the catalyst has less work to do, and will last longer, with fewer emissions at the tail pipe.

The closed-loop control is implemented during engine operation at normal engine operating temperatures. When the coolant temperature is low, or the engine is at full load or on the overrun, the ECM will operate in open-loop. When operating in open-loop, the ECM allows a richer or leaner AFR than the stoichiometric ratio. This prevents engine hesitation, for example, during acceleration with a wide-open throttle.

The OS only produces a signal when the exhaust gas has reached a minimum temperature of approximately 300°C. The OS contains a heating element so that once the engine has started, the sensor can rapidly attain optimum operating temperature.

The OS heater supply is made from the main relay terminal number 4. The heater earth is connected to ECM terminal HT. This ensures that the heater will only operate whilst the engine is running. Under certain operating conditions, the heater supply is cut off by the ECM.

VF learned value voltage

TCCS employs a digital conversion of the analogue signal from the OS. This digital conversion is termed the 'VF learned value' and is available at ECM pin VF, or terminal VF at the SD check connector. The VF voltage is more easily checked, and is an excellent indication of the correct functioning of the OS. When the OS switches between 0.2 and 0.8 volts, the VF voltage will switch between zero and 5.0 volts at a frequency of 8 to 10 switches in 10 seconds.

EGR (some engines only)

Modern engines that run at high temperatures with high compression tend to produce a high level of NOx. Production of NOx can be reduced by recycling a small amount of exhaust gas into the combustion chamber. So long as the recycling of the exhaust gas is properly controlled, the engine operation will be little affected.

EGR operation only occurs after the engine has attained normal operating temperature and the engine is operating under part-load conditions. The ECM monitors engine conditions, and adjusts the signal to the VSV. Vacuum is applied to the VSV via a vacuum modulator. The VSV applies vacuum to the EGR valve, which opens to allow a finely-metered supply of exhaust gas to be introduced into the inlet manifold.

Adjustments

7 Adjustment pre-conditions

1 Ensure that all of these conditions are met before attempting to make adjustments:

a) Engine at operating temperature. Engine oil at a minimum temperature of 80°C. A journey of at least 4 miles is recommended (particularly so if equipped with AT).
b) Ancillary equipment (all engine loads and accessories) switched off.
c) AT engines: Transmission in N or P.
d) Engine mechanically sound.
e) Engine breather hoses and breather system in satisfactory condition.
f) Induction system free from vacuum leaks.
g) Ignition system in satisfactory condition.
h) Air filter in satisfactory condition.
i) Exhaust system free from leaks.
j) Throttle cable correctly adjusted.
k) No fault codes logged by the ECM.
l) OS operating satisfactorily (catalyst vehicles with closed-loop control).

2 In addition, before checking the idle speed and CO values, stabilise the engine as follows:

a) Stabilise the engine. Raise the engine speed to 3000 rpm for a minimum of 30 seconds, and then let the engine idle.
b) If the cooling fan operates during adjustment, wait until it stops, re-stabilise the engine, and then restart the adjustment procedure.
c) Allow the CO and idle speed to settle.
d) Make all checks and adjustments within 30 seconds. If this time is exceeded, re-stabilise the engine and recheck.

3 Toyota routines to adjust the throttle, ignition timing, and CO and idle speed vary between the different models. The following adjustments are typical, and based upon engine code 4-GE. The routines may need to be varied in individual cases.

8 Throttle adjustments (typical)

1 Initiate fault code gathering, and check for code 11 (code 51 on models with AFS). If code 11 (51) is output, it is likely that the TS is out of adjustment or faulty.

2 Look for a disturbed paint seal on the throttle stop screw, which could indicate that the screw has been tampered with. The throttle valve position must not be altered by maladjustment of the TSS (throttle stop screw).

3 If throttle valve adjustment is required because the TSS setting has been disturbed, proceed with the following routines.

4 The throttle body should first be cleaned. Carbon deposits may be keeping the throttle partially open.

5 Loosen the TSS locknut, and turn in the screw until it touches the bellcrank. Turn in the screw an additional 1/4-turn and tighten the locknut.

Adjusting the TS

6 With the engine stopped, throttle closed, and ignition 'on', attach a voltmeter between terminal 2 and earth. A voltage greater than zero indicates that the switch is incorrectly adjusted (open).

7 Loosen the two securing screws, and adjust the switch until the voltmeter indicates zero. Tighten the screws and recheck the voltmeter. If the TS will not retain the base adjustment after about three attempts, the TS may be faulty.

9 Ignition timing checks (typical procedure)

1 The timing is adjustable on TCCS models.

2 Refer to the adjustment pre-conditions in Section 7. It is particularly important that the engine oil is at normal operating temperature before commencing.

3 Start the engine and allow it to idle.

4 Connect a tachometer and stroboscopic timing light. On some models, the tachometer connection can be attached to the coil negative terminal, otherwise the IG terminal in the SD connector should be used **(see illustrations 16.6 and 16.7)**.

5 Check that the engine idle speed and CO values are within the specified limits.

6 Open the throttle to advance the timing. This can prevent an apparent advance fault later in the procedure. Close the throttle and allow the engine to idle.

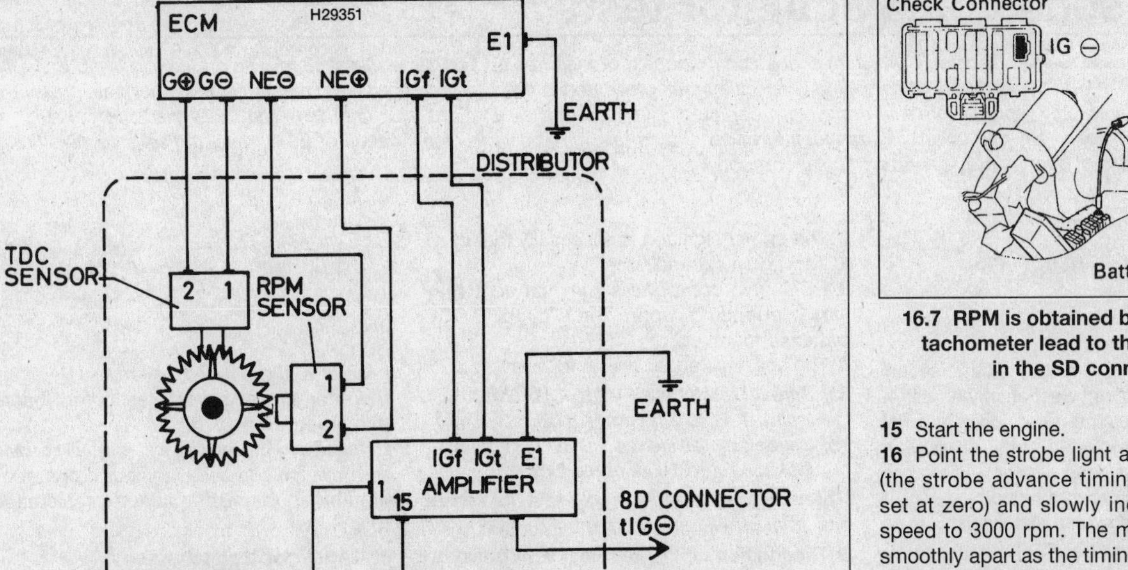

16.6 Typical ignition wiring

7 Check that the TS contacts in the TS/TPS are closed.

8 Place the ECM into base timing mode. This can be accomplished by using a jumper lead to connect terminals T (or TE1) and E1 at the SD connector **(see illustration 16.8)**.

9 Check for fault codes, particularly for code 11, which indicates a TS problem. All faults should be corrected before continuing with the timing check and adjustment.

10 Use the strobe to check that the base timing is set at the specified value (marks aligned) **(see illustration 16.9)**.

11 If the timing is incorrect, slacken the distributor fixing bolts and rotate the distributor until the marks are aligned.

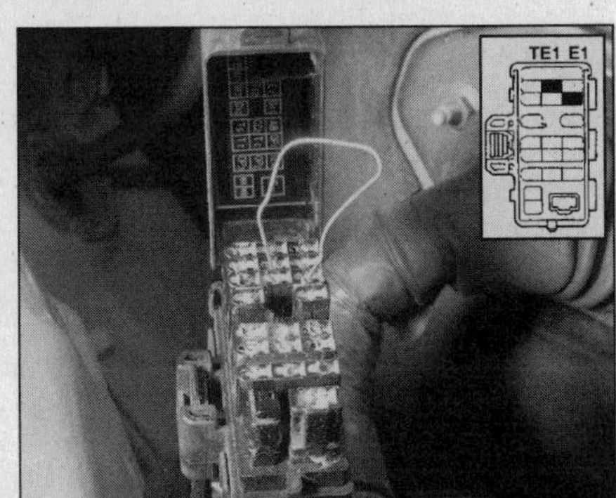

16.8 Bridge terminals TE1 (or T1) in the SD connector. This causes TCCS to enter service-set mode and to emit fault codes on the warning lamp

12 Carefully tighten the distributor bolts, and recheck that the marks are still aligned.

13 If difficulty is experienced in setting the base timing, or the timing fluctuates, check for code 11 (51 if AFS model) and for a faulty or maladjusted TS.

14 Remove the bridge wire from the SD connector. At idle, the timing should advance by 16° or more. **Note:** *The timing may not advance above the base setting. This may be because the throttle was not opened before the SD check connector was bridged. Even if the correct procedure was followed, the timing may not temporarily advance above the base setting, and this may be considered as normal.*

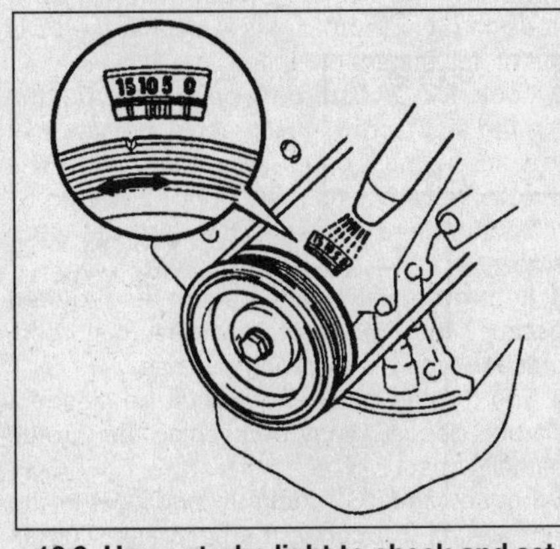

16.9 Use a strobe light to check and set the base ignition timing

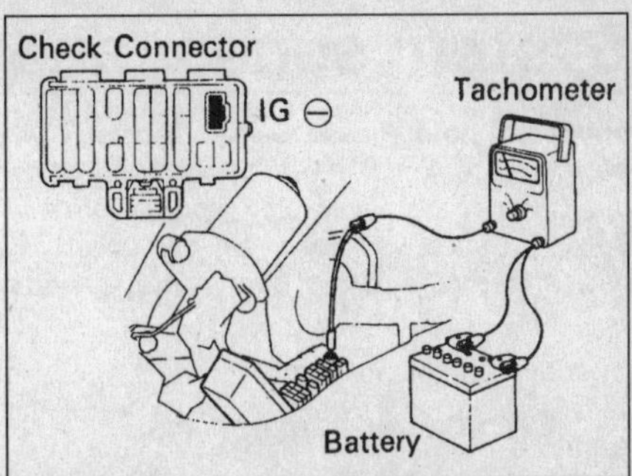

16.7 RPM is obtained by attaching the tachometer lead to the IG terminal in the SD connector

15 Start the engine.

16 Point the strobe light at the timing marks (the strobe advance timing control must be set at zero) and slowly increase the engine speed to 3000 rpm. The marks should move smoothly apart as the timing advances.

17 If the timing does not advance, check the TS. If the TS contacts remain closed during acceleration, the timing will not advance.

10 Idle adjustments

1 Refer to the adjustment pre-conditions in Section 7. It is particularly important that the engine oil is at normal operating temperature before commencing.

2 Start the engine and allow it to idle.

3 Connect a tachometer and stroboscopic timing light. Attach the tachometer connection to the IG terminal in the SD connector.

Warning: The amplifier and ignition coil may be damaged if the tachometer connection becomes shorted to earth.

4 Check that the ignition timing is set correctly.

5 Check the AAV operation (where fitted). A faulty AAV will not allow correct setting of the idle speed.

6 Check that the TS position is correct.

7 Check the idle speed. If adjustments are necessary, locate the adjustment screw in the throttle body.

8 Remove the tamperproof plug (if fitted).

9 Turn the idle adjustment screw to obtain the specified rpm.

CO level

10 If adjustments are necessary, locate the CO adjustment screw in the CO pot (non-cat models only).

11 Remove the tamperproof plug (if fitted).

12 Turn the adjustment screw until the correct CO value is achieved. Do not force the screw, as it is easily damaged.

13 Recheck the idle speed.

14 Repeat the CO and idle speed adjustments until both are correct.

System sensor and actuator tests

Important note: *Please refer to Chapter 4, which describes common test procedures applicable to this system. The routines in Chapter 4 should be read in conjunction with the component notes and wiring diagrams presented in this Chapter. The wiring diagrams and other data presented in this Chapter are necessarily representative of the system depicted. Because of the variations in wiring and other data that often occurs, even between similar vehicles in any particular VM's range, the reader should take great care in identification of ECM pins, and satisfy himself that he has gathered the correct data before failing a particular component.*

11 Crank angle sensor (CAS)

1 Refer to the note at the start of this Section, and refer to the relevant Section of Chapter 4.
2 The CAS is represented by individual RPM and TDC sensors mounted in the distributor. Individual testing of each sensor is similar to testing the flywheel mounted type.
3 The CAS resistances are as follows:

a) Terminals G - and G+ (TDC sensor), 185 - 275 ohms (cold), 240 - 325 ohms (hot).
b) Terminals NE+ and NE (RPM sensor), 370 - 550 ohms (cold), 475 - 650 ohms (hot).

Note: *The change from a cold to a hot sensor occurs at 50°C, measured at the component.*

12 Primary ignition

1 Refer to the note at the start of Section 11, and refer to the relevant Section of Chapter 4.
2 The primary ignition is essentially that of an ECM with an external amplifier.
3 ECM and component pin numbers may vary depending upon the Toyota TCCS system under test.
4 The coil resistances are as follows:

a) Primary resistance 1.11 to 1.75 ohms (cold), 1.41 to 2.05 ohms (hot).
b) Secondary resistance 9.0 to 15.7k ohms (cold), 11.4 to 18.4k ohms (hot).

Note: *The change from a cold to a hot sensor occurs at 50°C, measured at the component.*

5 The ignition coil (-) terminal is not easy to access, and the ignition primary signal should be obtained at the IG- terminal in the SD test connector.
6 Voltage and earth connections to the coil are made via a two-pin connector plug.
7 The ECM control signal to the amplifier emanates from ECM terminal IGt.
8 If the IGt signal is satisfactory, but there is no primary signal and the amplifier earth and supply voltages are OK, the amplifier is suspect. In this instance the IGf confirmation signal, amplifier to ECM, is also likely to be missing.
9 If the IGt signal is OK, but there is no IGf signal and the amplifier earth and supply voltages are OK, the amplifier is suspect.

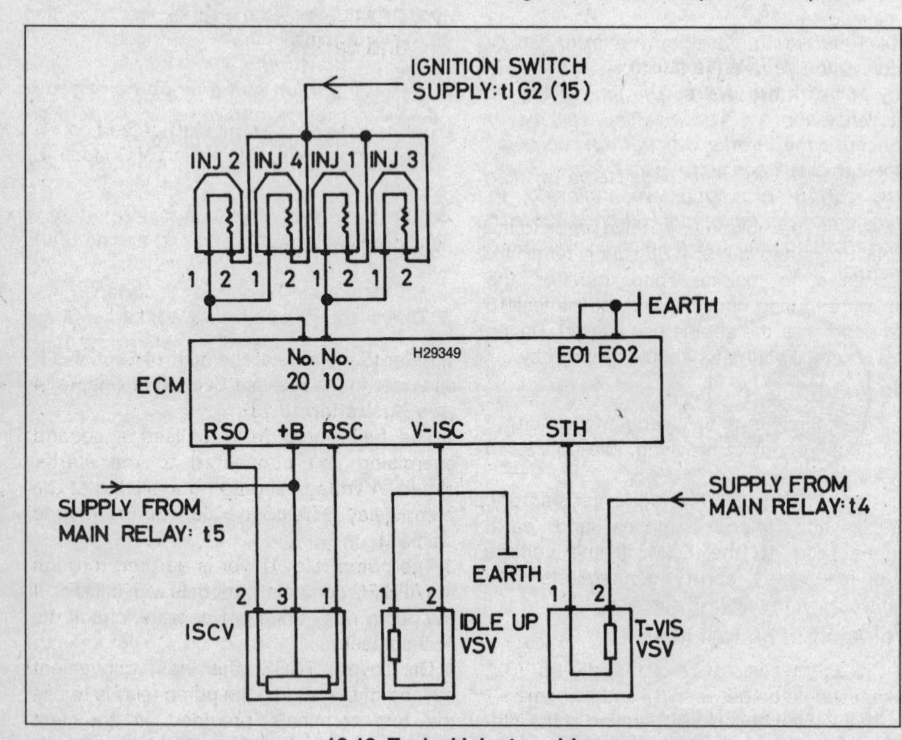

16.10 Typical injector wiring

13 Fuel injector operation

1 Refer to the note at the start of Section 11, and refer to the relevant Section of Chapter 4 **(see illustration 16.10)**.
2 Voltage to the injectors is normally provided from the ignition switch, injector operation is simultaneous and the injector resistance is 13.8 ohms.

Voltage-controlled pulse

3 When a voltage-controlled pulse via a series resistor is utilised, the opening voltage and holding voltage circuits are completed through ECM pins No 10 and No 20. In this case, the injector resistance is 2.0 to 3.0 ohms.
4 Because of the interconnection of the voltage-controlled circuit through the series resistor, and also at ECM pins No 10 & No 20, it is possible for a signal to be obtained at an injector, even if the voltage feed to that injector is missing. If an injector fault is suspected, the following tests should be made in all circumstances:

a) Check the CAS for a good signal.
b) Disconnect the series resistor multi-plug.
c) Check for nbv at terminal IG2.
d) Check for nbv at terminal No 10.
e) Check for nbv at terminal No 20.
f) Reconnect the series resistor multi-plug.
g) Disconnect three of the injector multi-plugs and carry out the following tests at the remaining injector plug that is still connected.
h) Crank the engine.
i) Either an acceptable waveform or a duty cycle reading should be obtained.
j) No waveform, check for a voltage supply to the injector multi-plug.
k) No voltage, check the injector resistance and the injector voltage supply.
l) Repeat the above procedure on all of the other injectors.

14 Vane-type AFS

1 Refer to the note at the start of Section 11, and refer to the relevant Section of Chapter 4 **(see illustration 16.11)**.
2 Terminal VS is the AFS signal wire.
3 Terminal VC is the AFS reference voltage supply.

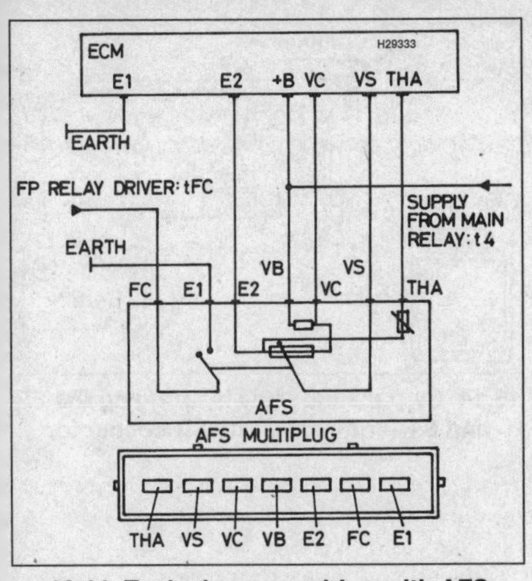

16.11 Typical sensor wiring with AFS

4 Terminal VB is the AFS voltage supply from the relay.
5 Terminal E2 is the AFS earth return connection.
6 Terminal FC is the AFS fuel pump contacts in the AFS.

15 MAP sensor

1 Refer to the note at the start of Section 11, and refer to the relevant Section of Chapter 4 **(see illustration 16.12)**.

16 Air temperature sensor (ATS)

1 Refer to the note at the start of Section 11, and refer to the relevant Section of Chapter 4.
2 The ATS is mounted in the vane-type AFS inlet, or in the air filter casing if a MAP sensor is fitted.

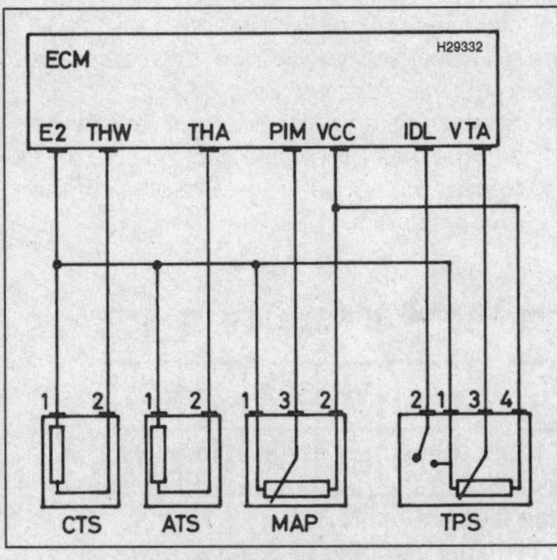

16.12 Typical sensor wiring with MAP sensor

17 CO potentiometer ('pot')

1 Refer to the note at the start of Section 11, and refer to the relevant Section of Chapter 4.
2 The CO pot is of the external type, and is located in the engine compartment.

18 Coolant temperature sensor (CTS)

1 Refer to the note at the start of Section 11, and refer to the relevant Section of Chapter 4.

19 Throttle potentiometer sensor/throttle switch (TPS/TS)

1 Refer to the note at the start of Section 11, and refer to the relevant Section of Chapter 4.
2 The four wires to the TPS/TS multi-plug connector are 5.0 volt supply, return, TPS signal and idle contact.
3 The measured values from the 5.0 volt supply, return and TPS signal are identical to the values given in Chapter 4.
4 Zero volts should be obtained on the idle contact wire (IDL) when the throttle is closed. If a voltage is obtained, loosen the screws and adjust the TS so that zero volts is obtained.
5 Crack open the throttle. The switch should 'click' and the voltage rise to between 4.50 to 5.50 volts.

20 Idle-up VSV (vacuum switching valve)

1 Connect the voltmeter negative probe to an engine earth.
2 Connect the voltmeter positive probe to the wire attached to idle-up VSV supply terminal.
3 Crank the engine, and monitor the voltmeter during cranking and for the first 10 seconds after the engine has started. During this time, the voltmeter should display nbv.

No voltage

4 Check the idle-up VSV earth connection.
5 Check continuity of wiring, idle-up VSV to ECM pin.
6 If the idle-up VSV wiring is satisfactory, check all voltage supplies and earth connections to the ECM. If the voltage supplies and earth connections are satisfactory, the ECM is suspect.

Voltage but no fast idle

7 Check the resistance of the idle-up VSV, which should be between 37 and 44 ohms.
8 Check the mechanical operation of the idle-up VSV.

21 Toyota variable induction system (T-VIS)

1 Connect the voltmeter negative probe to an engine earth.
2 Connect the oscilloscope or voltmeter positive probe to the wire attached to T-VIS VSV supply terminal.
3 Switch on the ignition; the voltmeter should indicate nbv. If there is no voltage, check the supply voltage from the main relay terminal 4.
4 Move the voltmeter positive probe to the wire attached to T-VIS VSV terminal 1.
5 With the ignition on, the voltmeter should indicate nbv. If there is no voltage, check the resistance of the T-VIS VSV, which should be between 37 and 44 ohms.
6 Start the engine and allow it to idle. The voltmeter should display a voltage less than 3.0 volts. If nbv is obtained, but the T-VIS VSV is not actuated, check the continuity of wiring back to the main ECM pin STH.
7 If the T-VIS VSV wiring is satisfactory, check all voltage supplies and earth connections to the ECM. If the voltage supplies and earth connections are satisfactory, the ECM is suspect.
8 Raise the engine speed. The voltage should rise from less than 3.0 volts to nbv. If not, the ECM is suspect.
9 Check the mechanical operation of the T-VIS VSV.

22 ECM voltage supplies and earths

1 Refer to the note at the start of Section 11, and refer to the relevant Section of Chapter 4.

23 System relays

1 Refer to the note at the start of Section 11, and refer to the relevant Section of Chapter 4 **(see illustration 16.13)**.
2 The fuel pump relay utilises a second energising coil connected to the starter circuit. A voltage should be available at the pump relay STA connection during engine cranking.
3 The pump relay driver is earthed through the AFS FC contacts in models with an AFS. If the pump relay does not operate, check the AFS contacts.
4 On Toyota TCCS, the most convenient method of by-passing the pump relay is to use the two terminals provided in the test connector (+B and FP) **(see illustration 16.14)**.

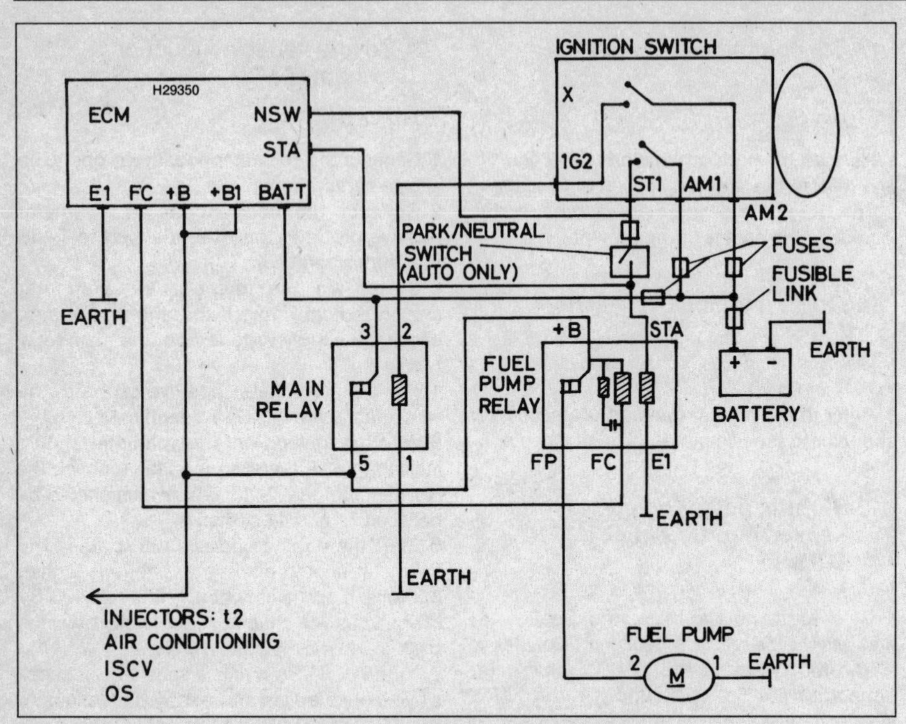

16.13 Typical relay and components wiring

16.14 By-pass the relay by bridging the FP and B+ terminals in the SD connector

Pin table - typical 42-pin

Note: *Refer to* ***illustration 16.15.***

14-pin plug

Pin	Component
+B1	*Main relay supply*
BATT	*Battery supply*
THA	*ATS sensor, AFS*
VS	*AFS signal*
VC	*AFS reference voltage*
+B	*Main relay supply*
SPD	*VSS*
STP	*Stop-light switch*
E21	*Sensor return*

18-pin plug

Pin	Component
NE	*RPM sensor*
G	*TDC sensor*
G -	*TDC, RPM sensor return*
IGF	*Amplifier*
IDL	*TPS idle contact*
T	*SD connector*
W	*SD warning lamp*
FPU	*Fuel pressure VSV*
THW	*CTS*
VTA	*TPS*
VCC	*Sensor supply*
OX	*Oxygen sensor*
E2	*Sensor return*
A/C	*A/C magnetic switch*
R/P	*Fuel control switch*
HT	*Oxygen sensor*
V-	*ISCV idle-up VSV*

10-pin plug

Pin	Component
VF	*SD connector*
STA	*Ignition switch*
No.10	*Injectors*
E01	*Earth*
STH	*T-VIS VSV*
No.20	*Injectors*
E1	*Earth*
IGT	*Amplifier*
EO2	*Earth*

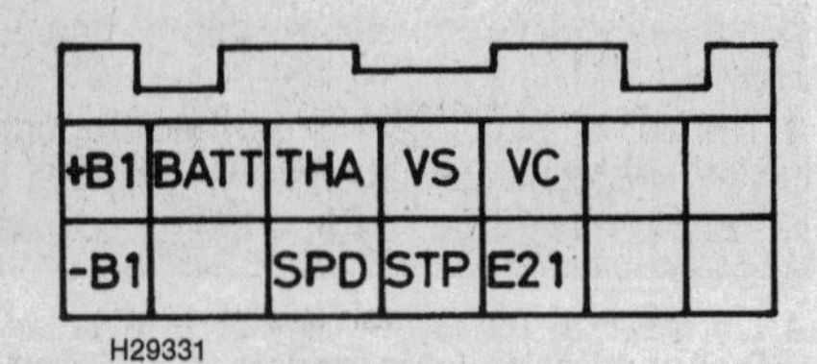

NE		G	G⊖	IGF	IDL	T	W	FPU
THW	VTA	VCC		E2	A/C	R/P	HT	V -18C

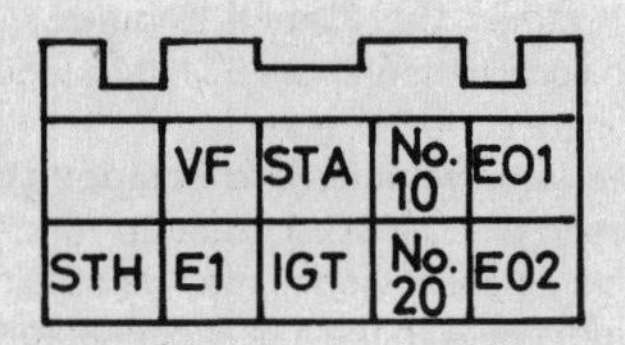

16.15 Typical TCCS 42-pin multi-plug

Pin table - typical 54-pin

Note: *Refer to* ***illustration 16.16****.*

12-pin plug

Pin	Component
+B1	*Main relay supply*
BATT	*Battery supply*
FC	*FP relay*
ACT	*Air conditioning*
+B	*Main relay supply*
W	*SD warning lamp*
ED	*ED monitor*
AC1	*A/C amplifier*
SPD	*VSS*
ELS	*Tail-light relay demister switch*

16-pin plug

Pin	Component
PIM	*MAP signal*
THA	*ATS signal*
THW	*CTS signal*
OX	*Oxygen sensor*
TE2	*SD connector*
VF	*SD connector*
E2	*Sensor return*
VTA	*TPS*
VC	*MAP, TPS supply voltage*
IDL	*TPS idle contact*
KNK	*Knock sensor*
TE1	*SD connector*
E21	*Sensor return*

26-pin plug

Pin	Component
O/D	
STA	*Ignition switch*
IGF	*Amplifier*
NE+	*RPM sensor*
G1	*TDC sensor*
RSC	*ISCV*
RSO	*ISCV*
No.10	*Injectors*
E01	*Earth*
HT	*Oxygen sensor heater*
NSW	*Ignition supply*
NE-	*RPM sensor*
G -	*TDC sensor return*
IGT	*Amplifier*
ISC	*A/C idle-up VSV*
E1	*Earth*
No.20	*Injectors*
EO2	*Earth*

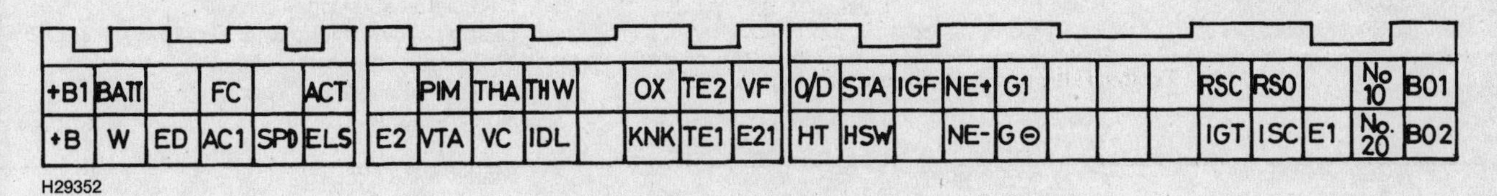

16.16 Typical TCCS 54-pin multi-plug

Fault codes

24 Obtaining fault codes

1 Fault codes can be extracted from the TCCS ECM by bridging the T1 and TE1 connections in the self-test connector. Once the connections are bridged, the 'Check Engine' warning lamp will flash to indicate the codes. See below for the procedure.

2 The earliest vehicles emitted codes in a straight count. Later vehicles emitted codes in two-digit format.

3 In some earlier versions of TCCS, not all codes caused the 'Check Engine' warning lamp to light, although the ECM still logged an appropriate code or codes.

4 Some later vehicles are equipped with a diagnostic link (TDCL) located under the driver's side dash. Codes may be obtained by attaching a FCR to the TDCL connector.

5 When the lamp is triggered, it will begin to flash. By counting the flashes, the fault code can be determined. Where more than one code is stored, the codes will be output in numerical order, from the smallest value code to the largest.

Pre-conditions

a) Battery voltage above 11.0 volts.
b) Throttle switch closed (idle position).
c) Transmission in neutral.
d) Accessories switched off.
e) Engine at normal operating temperature.

6 Turn on the ignition, but do not start the engine.

7 Use a jumper lead to bridge terminals T1 (or TE1) and E1 in the SD plug **(see illustration 16.17)**. The codes are then output on the instrument panel warning lamp as coded flashes. By counting the flashes and referring to the fault code table, faults can thus be determined.

8 The flashes are output either as a straight count of the digits, or as a two-digit code. The codes are output in the following fashion.

Straight count of the digits

9 One or more faults: A flash every 0.5 second to indicate the code for the fault. After the first fault is emitted, the lamp will pause for 2.5 seconds and then flash the next code. Once all faults have been emitted in numerical order of smallest code first and greatest code last, the lamp will pause for 4.5 seconds and then repeat the sequence. This will continue for so long as the test connector connections are bridged.

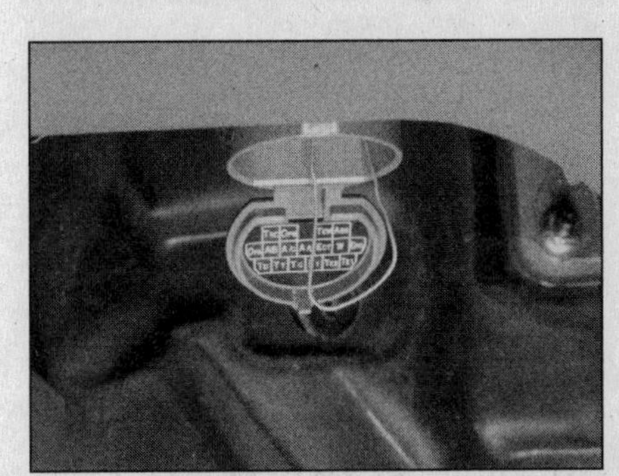

16.17 Under-dash location of SD connector on later models. A FCR can be attached or the TE1 and E1 terminals bridged as before (TDCL)

Examples

Code 1: No fault: one flash every five seconds
Code 3: three flashes, pause for 4.5 seconds and then repeat.
Code 4 and code 5: four flashes, pause for 2.5 seconds and then five flashes, pause for 4.5 seconds and then repeat.

Two-digit code output

10 One or more faults: A flash every 0.5 seconds to indicate the first digit of the two-digit code for the fault.

11 After a 1.5 second pause, a second series of similar flashes will indicate the second digit.

12 After the first fault is emitted, the lamp will pause for 2.5 seconds and then flash the next code.

13 Once all faults have been emitted in numerical order of smallest code first and greatest code last, the lamp will pause for 4.5 seconds and then repeat the sequence. This will continue for so long as the test connector connections are bridged.

14 No fault: the lamp will flash continually on and off every 0.26 seconds.

Erasing codes

15 The codes will remain logged until one of the following actions is performed:

a) The 15 amp EMS (EFi) STOP fuse is disconnected for a period of at least 30 seconds ***(see illustration 16.18)****.*

b) The vehicle battery is disconnected (beware of losing other data, eg the radio code, clock etc).

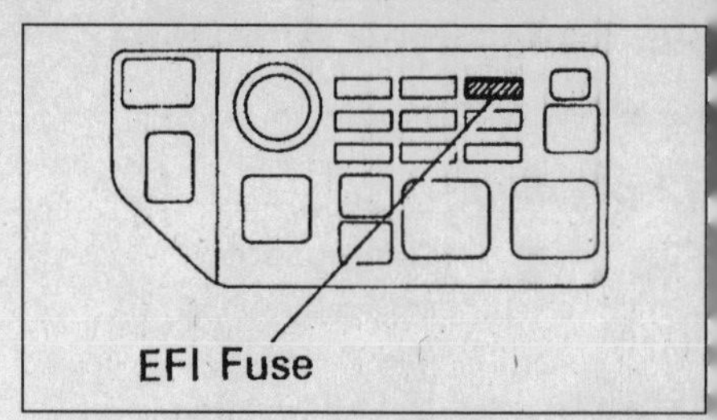

16.18 Typical location of the 15 amp EFi fuse. Remove to erase the fault codes from TCCS memory

16 Road test the vehicle after clearing the codes.

17 If the same codes return, this suggests that a fault still exists on a particular circuit.

Fault code table (MAP sensor system, straight count)

Code	Item	Fault	Component or circuit
1	System OK		
2	MAP sensor	MAP	MAP circuit short/open-circuit
3	Ignition signal	Ignition/amplifier	No signal from amplifier four times in succession
4	CTS	CTS	CTS circuit short/open-circuit
6	RPM signal	No RPM, TDC signal	Distributor/amplifier/starter circuit
7	TPS	TPS	TPS circuit short/open-circuit
8	ATS	ATS	ATS circuit short/open-circuit
9	VSS	2000 to 5000 rpm, coolant temp over 80°C, MAP over certain value and no VSS signal	No VSS signal
10	Cranking signal	No cranking signal	Starter relay circuit
11	Switch signal	A/C switch on, idle switch off, or shift in 'D'	A/C switch, TPS, start/neutral switch or ECM

Fault code table (two-digits)

Code	Fault	Reason	Component or circuit
12	RPM signal	No RPM, TDC signal	Distributor/amplifier/starter circuit
13	RPM signal	No RPM, TDC signal to ECM within several seconds of engine reaching 1500 rpm	Distributor/amplifier/starter circuit
14	Ignition signal	Ignition/amplifier	No signal from igniter four times in succession
16	ECT control signal	Abnormal signal output from ECM	ECM
21	OS	OS signal decreases	OS, OS circuit
22	CTS	CTS	CTS circuit short/open-circuit
24	ATS	ATS	ATS circuit short/open-circuit
25	Lean signal	OS indicates a lean signal	Injector/AFS/CTS/ATS/OS
26	Rich signal	OS indicates a lean signal	Injector/AFS/CTS/ATS/OS
27	OS	LH or single	
28	OS	RH (V6)	
31	AFS (when fitted)	Open-circuit in VC, VS, VB or short-circuit in VC	AFS/ATS circuit
31	MAP (when fitted)	Open-circuit in MAP or short-circuit in VC	MAP circuit
32	Vane airflow sensor		
34	Turbo pressure signal		
35	Turbo pressure signal	MAP sensor	
41	TPS	TPS	TPS circuit short/open-circuit
42	VSS	2000 to 5000 rpm, coolant temp over 80°C, injector duration over certain value, and no VSS signal	No VSS signal
43	Cranking signal	No cranking signal	Starter relay circuit
47	Throttle position sensor		
51	Switch signal	A/C switch on, idle switch off or TPS shift position in 'D' during diagnosis check	A/C switch, start/neutral switch or ECM
52	Knock sensor	Engine speed between 1200 and 6000 rpm, but no KS signal input to ECM	KS circuit
53	Knock control (ECM)		
54	Turbo intercooler signal		
55	Knock sensor RH (V6)		
78			

Note: *Codes 16, 42, 43 and 51 are only available whilst the ignition is on. Once the ignition is switched off, these codes will be erased.*

Chapter 17
VW Digifant

Contents

Specifications

Vehicle	Year	Idle speed	CO %
25-pin ECM			
Corrado 1.8i (PG)	1989 to 1990	800 ± 50	0.7 ± 0.4
Corrado 1.8i (G60 Supercharger) cat	1988 to 1992	800 ± 50	0.7 ± 0.4
Golf 1.8i cat (1P)	1988 to 1992	750 to 850	0.7 ± 0.4
Golf 1.8i, 1.8i cat (PB)	1987 to 1992	750 to 850	1.0 ± 0.5
Golf 1.8i cat (PF)	1987 to 1992	750 to 850	0.7 ± 0.4
Golf GTi (G60 Supercharger) cat (PG)	1990 to 1992	800 ± 50	0.7 ± 0.4
Golf Rallye (G60 Supercharger) cat (IH)	1989 to 1992	800 ± 50	0.7 ± 0.4
Golf 1.8i cat (PF)	1990 to 1992	800 ± 50	0.7 ± 0.4
Golf 1.8i Cabrio cat (2H)	1990 to 1993	750 to 850	0.3 to 1.1
Jetta 1.8i, 1.8i cat (1P, PB, PF)	1987 to 1992	800 ± 50	0.7 ± 0.4
LT van 2.4i cat (1E)	1988 to 1995	750 to 850	0.5 max
Passat 1.8i cat (PF)	1988 to 1992	750 to 850	0.7 ± 0.4
Passat 1.8i GT (PB)	1988 to 1990	750 to 850	1.0 ± 0.5
Passat 1.8i cat (PB, PF)	1988 to 1992	950 ± 50	0.3 to 1.0
Polo 1.3 G40 & cat	1987 to 1990	920 ± 25	0.7 ± 0.2
Polo 1.3 GT cat (3F)	1990 to 1994	920 ± 25	1.0 ± 0.2
Polo 1.3 G40 & cat (PY)	1991 to 1994	920 ± 25	0.7 ± 0.2
Transporter 2.1i cat	1987 to 1991	880 ± 50	0.7 ± 0.4
38-pin ECM			
Caravelle 2.0 & cat (AAC)	1990 to 1992	775 to 825	0.5 max
Caravelle 2.5i cat (AAF)	1991 to 1995	800 ± 25	0.5 max
Corrado (G60 Supercharger) cat (PG)	1992 to 1993	800 ± 50	0.7 ± 0.4
Passat 2.0i & 4x4 cat (2E)	1990 to 1992	800 ± 50	0.7 ± 0.4
Transporter 2.0 & cat (AAC)	1990 to 1992	775 to 825	0.7 ± 0.4
Transporter 2.5i cat (AAF)	1991 to 1995	775 to 825	0.5 max
38-pin ECM with self-diagnostics			
Caravelle 2.0 & cat (AAC)	1990 to 1992	775 to 825	0.5 max
Caravelle 2.5i cat (AAF)	1991 to 1995	775 to 825	0.5 max
Corrado (G60 Supercharger) cat	1992 to 1993	800 ± 50	0.7 ± 0.4
Passat 2.0i & 4x4 cat (2E)	1992 to 1994	800 ± 50	0.7 ± 0.4
Transporter 2.0 & cat (AAC)	1990 to 1992	775 to 825	0.7 ± 0.4
Transporter 2.5i cat (AAF)	1991 to 1995	775 to 825	0.5 max

45-pin ECM

Vehicle	Year	Idle speed	CO %
Caravelle 2.0i & cat (AAC)	1994 to 1995	775 to 825	0.5 max
Corrado 2.0i cat (2E)	1993 to 1995	770 to 870	0.2 to 1.2
Golf 2.0i cat (2E)	1991 to 1995	770 to 870	0.5 max
Transporter 2.0i cat (AAC)	1994 to 1995	775 to 825	0.5 max
Transporter 2.5i cat (ACU)	1994 to 1995	775 to 825	0.5 max
Vento 2.0i cat (2E)	1992 to 1995	770 to 870	0.5 max
68-pin ECM			
Golf 2.0i 16V cat (ABF)	1992 to 1995	775 to 875	0.5 max
Passat 2.0i cat (ABF)	1994 to 1995	775 to 875	0.5 max
Vento 2.0i 16V cat (ABF)	1992 to 1995	750 to 850	0.5 max

Overview of system operation

1 Introduction

VW Digifant is a fully-integrated engine management system that controls primary ignition, fuelling and idle functions from within the same ECM.

There are a wide number of variations to Digifant, which was first manufactured in early 1987. Early variations include 25-pin, 38-pin and 45-pin ECM's with internal or external amplifier, with and without self-diagnostics, and with a vane-type AFS or MAP sensor. The primary trigger used in the majority of Digifant systems is a Hall-effect sensor mounted in the distributor. In later systems, the amplifier is combined with the coil, and the 68-pin system utilises a flywheel-based trigger and sequential fuel injection **(see illustration 17.1)**.

2 Control functions

Signal processing

The Digifant ECM contains an ignition map and a fuel map. The ignition map contains a table of basic values for ignition timing, and the fuel map contains a table of basic injection pulse values.

When the ECM is supplied with data on engine speed and engine load from the engine sensors, the ECM looks up the correct values for dwell, timing and injector opening time. Correction factors are then applied for starting, deceleration, and part- and full-load operation.

The Digifant ignition timing point and injection duration are jointly processed by the ECM so that the best moment for ignition and fuelling is determined for every operating condition. In Digifant, the main engine load sensor is either the AFS or MAP sensor; engine speed is determined from the ignition signal (Hall-effect sensor). The main correction factors are determined from the engine temperature (CTS), air temperature sensor (ATS), throttle switch/sensor (TS or TPS) and oxygen sensor (OS) signals.

As a result of the input data, the ECM will look up the correct injector pulse duration right across the engine rpm, load and temperature range.

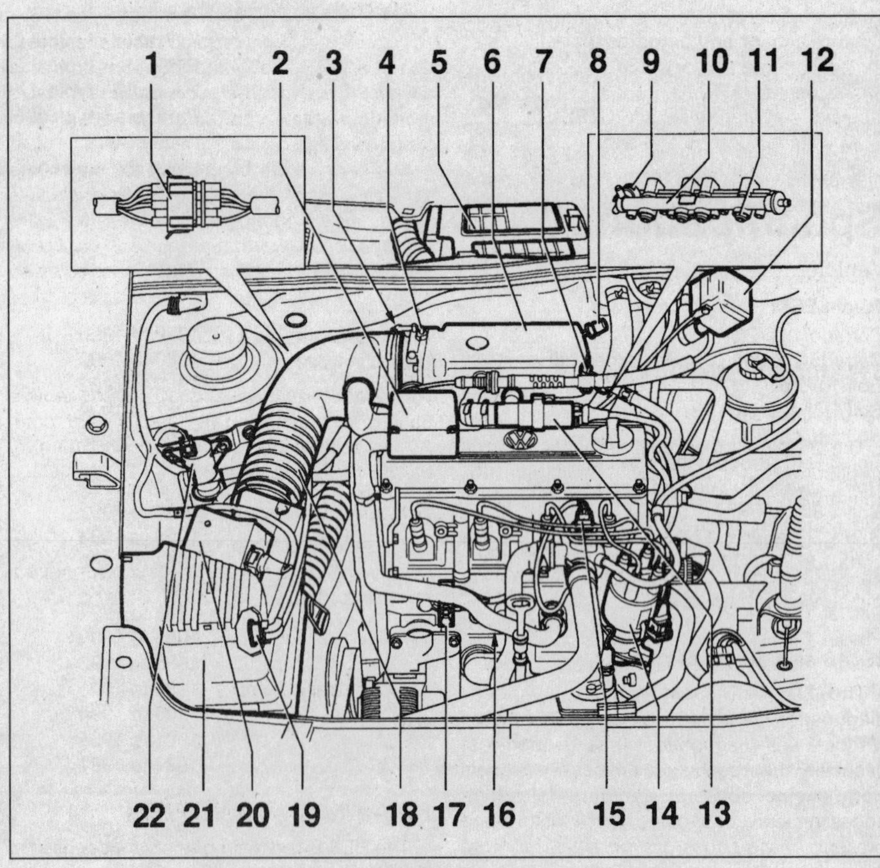

17.1 Typical VW Digifant component locations

1 *Multi-plug connector for OS*
2 *Crankcase breather control valve*
3 *TPS*
4 *Throttle body*
5 *ECM*
6 *Inlet manifold*
7 *Cold start valve*
8 *Sealing cap for CO measuring pipe*
9 *Fuel pressure regulator*
10 *Fuel rail*
11 *Fuel injectors*
12 *Combined ignition amplifier and coil unit*
13 *ISCV*
14 *Distributor*
15 *CTS with coolant gauge sender*
16 *Knock sensor*
17 *Engine earth connection*
18 *Inlet air trunking*
19 *Inlet air pre-heating temperature regulator*
20 *AFS (incorporating ATS)*
21 *Air filter*
22 *CFSV*

Basic ECM operation

No permanent voltage supply is made to the ECM in these versions of Digifant. Once the ignition is switched on, a voltage feed is supplied to the ignition coil, the amplifier and the main relay energising coil. The main relay energises, and a voltage supply is applied to an ECM pin.

When voltage is first applied to the ECM, it briefly connects the pump relay driver pin, so actuating the fuel pump relay and pressurising the fuel system.

The majority of sensors (other than those that generate a voltage such the HES, and OS), are now provided with a 5.0-volt reference supply from a relevant pin on the ECM. The ISCV is supplied with approximately 12 volts from ECM pin 22.

When the engine is cranked, a feed from terminal 50 of the starter circuit (not later models) provides a voltage to the ECM. This voltage feed is only present during engine cranking and informs the ECM of the need to increase injection frequency. When the engine is cranked or run, a speed signal from the HES causes the ECM to earth the pump relay driver so that the fuel pump will run. Ignition and injection functions are also activated. The injectors are supplied with nbv from either the main relay or the pump relay and the ECM completes the circuit by pulsing the injector driver pin to earth. The ISCV regulates the idle speed under ECM control by pulsing the ISCV driver when the engine is at idle.

Self-diagnostic function

25-pin Digifant

The 25-pin Digifant system with external amplifier has no self-test capability. An adjustment (service-set) mode is provided, and this is triggered by removing the CTS multi-plug. Adjustments to distributor and idle speed should only be attempted after moving into service-set mode.

38, 45 and 68-pin Digifant

The 38-pin Digifant system with self-diagnostics (early 38-pin systems were without self-diagnostics) has a self-test capability that regularly examines the signals from engine sensors, and internally logs codes in the event of one or more faults being present. These codes can be extracted from the serial port by a suitable fault code reader (FCR). If the fault clears, the code will remain logged until wiped clean with a suitable FCR. If the fault occurs intermittently - ie for less than 5 seconds - and then clears, the code will still be logged, but in this case will be logged as an SP (sporadic) fault.

An adjustment (service-set) mode is provided and this is triggered by removing the CTS multi-plug. Adjustments to distributor and idle speed should only be attempted after moving into service-set mode.

Adaptive memory

Later models have an adaptive capability. Over a period of time, the ECM will learn the best idle position for a particular engine - irrespective of age, engine condition and load, so that the correct idle speed is always maintained. The adaptive idle settings are stored in memory.

LOS (limited operating strategy, or 'limp-home')

Digifant has a limp-home facility. In the event of a serious fault in one or more of the sensors, the EMS will substitute a fixed default value in place of the defective sensor.

This means that the engine may actually run quite well with failure of one or more minor sensors. However, since the substituted values are those of a hot engine, cold starting and running during the warm-up period may be less than satisfactory.

Reference voltage

Voltage supply from the ECM to the engine sensors (ATS, CTS and TS) is made at a 5.0-volt reference level. This ensures a stable working voltage, unaffected by variations in system voltage.

The earth return connection for the engine sensors is made through an ECM pin which is not directly connected to earth. The ECM internally connects that pin to earth via one of the ECM pins that are directly connected to earth.

Over-speed fuel cut-off (rev limiter)

Digifant prevents engine speeds above 6500 rpm by inhibiting the injector earth path. As the engine speed drops below 6500 rpm, fuel injection is reinstated.

Signal shielding

To reduce interference (RFI), the knock sensor (KS) and oxygen sensor (OS) have a shielded cable.

3 Primary trigger

Hall-effect switch (HES)

The HES is the main primary trigger used in VW Digifant systems. The ECM supplies a voltage slightly under nbv to the Hall-effect switch in the distributor. The HES circuit is completed by a connection to earth.

Opposite the Hall switch is a magnet whose field causes the switch to return a small voltage back to the ECM. Attached to the distributor shaft is a trigger vane with the same number of cut-outs as cylinders. Passing the trigger vane between the switch and the magnet will cause the Hall switch to be turned off and on. As the cut-out space proceeds past the switch, a voltage is returned to the ECM via a third wire termed the output wire.

When the solid portion comes between the switch and magnet, the voltage is turned off as the magnetic field is diverted. Essentially, the voltage signal is returned as either voltage or no voltage, and the waveform produced is that of a square wave. The cut-out in the trigger vane is cut to provide a signal at 60° before TDC (leading edge) and 5° or 6° depending on vehicle (trailing edge). The HES signal is necessary for initiation of both ignition, injection and idle control. The engine will not run without the HES signal.

Although the sensor is usually located in the distributor, in 68-pin models the HES is located upon the flywheel. The distributor-located HES is retained, but the function is changed. A single shutter in the distributor ensures that a single signal is returned to the ECM. This signal identifies the position of No 1 cylinder for correct operation of the sequential fuel injection and dual selective knock sensors.

4 Distributor ignition

Ignition operation

When the ignition is switched on, voltage is applied to the ECM, and to the amplifier and ignition coil. The circuit then lies dormant to await a cranking or running signal **(see illustration 17.2)**.

When the engine is cranked and run, the ECM receives a signal from the HES primary trigger, and in turn applies a control signal to the amplifier so that ignition can be initiated.

The amplifier controls the coil dwell circuit by turning the coil current on and off to initiate ignition.

Once the amplifier turns the coil current off, the magnetic field in the coil primary windings quickly collapses, and a high voltage is induced in the coil secondary windings. The secondary output travels to the distributor cap via the main HT lead through the medium of the rotor arm. From the distributor, the secondary output is distributed to the correct spark plug, in the firing order of the engine, via an HT lead.

Distributor

The VW distributor assembly includes the secondary HT components (distributor cap, rotor and HT leads) and serves to distribute the HT current from the coil secondary terminal to each spark plug in firing order. The distributor is usually located on the block at the cylinder No 4 end.

The distributor also contains the HES and magnet.

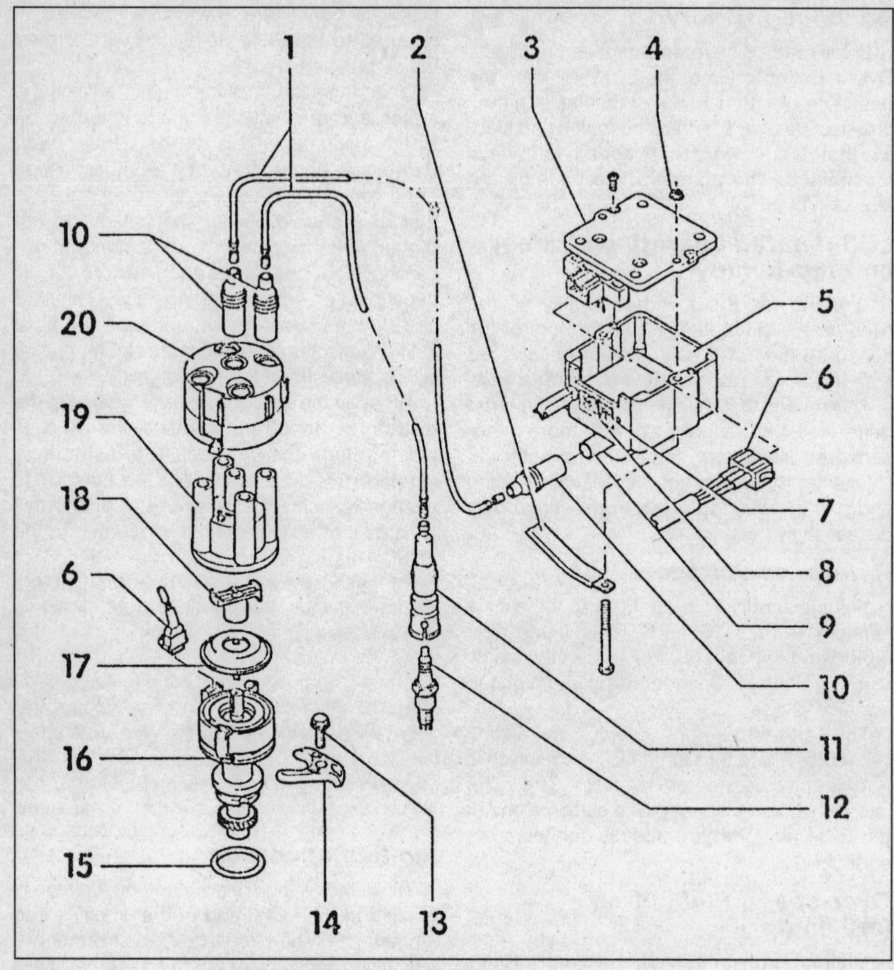

17.2 Exploded view of ignition system components

1 *HT leads*
2 *Earthing strap to rocker box cover*
3 *Amplifier*
4 *Fixing screw*
5 *Ignition coil*
6 *Ignition multi-plug*
7 *Coil supply terminal 15 (+)*
8 *Coil terminal 1 (-)*
9 *Coil terminal 4 (output to distributor)*
10 *HT suppressers*
11 *Shielded HT connectors*
12 *Spark plugs*
13 *Fixing bolt*
14 *Distributor retaining clamp*
15 *'O' ring*
16 *Distributor complete with HES*
17 *Dust cap*
18 *Rotor arm*
19 *Distributor cap*
20 *Screen cap*

Amplifier

The amplifier contains the circuitry for switching the coil negative terminal at the correct moment to instigate ignition. When the ECM receives the Hall-effect trigger signal, the ECM sends a control signal to the amplifier, which then completes the process by switching the coil negative terminal. In many models, the amplifier and ignition coil are contained in a combined unit to reduce wiring.

The amplifier applies current to the coil primary windings by connecting coil terminal number one to earth for a period of time known as the dwell time. During the dwell period, the coil builds a magnetic field within the primary coil windings. While the engine is running, Digifant calculates the coil turn-on time so that the correct dwell period is maintained.

Dwell operation in Digifant is based upon the principle of the 'constant-energy current-limiting' system. This means that the dwell period remains constant at about 4.5 ms, at virtually all engine running speeds. However, the dwell duty cycle, when measured in percent or degrees, will vary as the engine speed varies.

Ignition coil

The ignition coil utilises low primary resistance in order to increase primary current and primary energy. The amplifier limits the primary current to around 8 amps, and this permits a reserve of energy to maintain the required spark burn time (duration).

Ignition timing

Basic timing is set a few degrees before TDC, and the value is calculated to provide efficient combustion and maximum power output at a particular speed.

The base ignition timing in 25 and 38-pin variants is not maintained under ECM control, and the distributor can be moved in order to make timing adjustment. The timing marks are scribed upon the flywheel. When the marks are aligned at idle speed, the base ignition timing is correct.

As the engine speed increases, combustion must occur earlier, and the ignition point is advanced by the ECM with reference to its own mapped ignition table. The Digifant distributor does not contain a vacuum advance facility. The load factor is calculated by the ECM with reference to the AFS, and the ignition timing is adjusted accordingly.

Knock sensor

The optimal ignition timing (at engine speeds greater than idle) for a given high-compression engine is quite close to the point of onset of knock. However, running so close to the point of knock occurrence means that knock will certainly occur on one or more cylinders at certain times during the engine operating cycle.

The knock sensor is mounted on the engine block, and consists of a piezo-ceramic measuring element that responds to engine noise oscillations. This signal is converted to a voltage signal by the knock sensor, and returned to the knock control processor for evaluation and action. The knocking frequency is in the 8 to 15 kHz frequency band.

Initially, timing will occur at its optimal ignition point. Once knock is identified, the ECM retards the ignition timing. After knocking ceases, the timing is advanced until the reference timing value is achieved or knock occurs once more, when the timing is again retarded. This procedure continually occurs, so that the engine consistently runs at its optimum timing.

In 68-pin models, two knock sensors are utilised, and cylinder-selective knock control is practised with the aid of the distributor-based HES. Since knock may occur at a different moment in each individual cylinder, Digifant knock control pinpoints the actual cylinder or cylinders that are knocking, and retards the cylinder or cylinders individually. This procedure continually occurs, so that each cylinder always runs at its optimum timing.

5 Fuel injection

The Digifant ECM contains a fuel map with an injector opening time for basic conditions of load and speed. Information is then gathered from engine sensors such as the HES, AFS, ATS, CTS, and TPS or TS. As a result of this information, the ECM will look up the correct injector pulse duration right across the engine rpm, load and temperature range.

The Digifant system is a multi-point injection system, and the majority of models pulse all injectors at the same time - ie simultaneously and twice per engine cycle. Half of the required fuel per engine cycle is injected at each engine revolution. During engine start from cold, the pulse duration is increased to provide a richer air/fuel mixture. In addition, the number of injection pulses (frequency) are doubled from one pulse per crankshaft revolution to two pulses per crankshaft revolution during the first 20 seconds of cranking. This occurs irrespective of whether the engine is hot or cold. The ECM determines the cranking condition when a cranking signal is received from the starter circuit. The 68-pin ECM pulses the injectors sequentially in the firing order of the engine.

Fuel injectors

The fuel injector is a magnetically-operated solenoid valve that is actuated by the ECM. Voltage to the injectors is applied from the either the main or pump relay, and the earth path is completed by the ECM for a period of time (called pulse duration) of between 1.5 and 10 milliseconds. The pulse duration is very much dependent upon engine temperature, load, speed and operating conditions. When the magnetic solenoid closes, a back-EMF voltage of up to 60 volts is initiated.

The fuel injectors are mounted in the inlet stubs to the engine inlet valves, so that a finely-atomised fuel spray is directed onto the back of each valve. Since the injectors are all pulsed simultaneously, fuel will briefly rest upon the back of a valve before being drawn into a cylinder.

Deceleration fuel cut-off

During engine over-run conditions (oil temperature over 80°C), the ECM cuts off the injection pulse to improve economy and reduce emissions.

Cold start valve (CSV)

In some early models, a CSV is provided to spray additional fuel into the inlet manifold at temperatures below 15°C. Unlike previous versions of this valve in other applications, the valve is NOT connected to the starter circuit, and does not rely on a thermal time switch to complete the valve earth circuit. In fact the CSV functions in a similar fashion to the fuel injectors, and is actuated by the ECM for a period of time determined by the coolant temperature.

Airflow sensor (AFS)

The main engine load sensor used with Digifant is the vane-type AFS. The AFS is located between the air filter and the throttle body. As air flows through the sensor, it deflects a vane (flap). The greater the volume of air, the more will the flap be deflected. The vane is connected to a wiper arm which wipes a potentiometer resistance track, and so varies the resistance of the track. This allows a variable voltage signal to be returned to the ECM.

Three wires are used by the circuitry of this sensor, and it is often referred to as a three-wire sensor. A 5.0-volt reference voltage is applied to the resistance track, with the other end connected to the AFS earth return. The third wire is connected to the wiper arm.

From the voltage returned, the ECM is able to calculate the volume of air (load) entering the engine, and this is used to calculate the main fuel injection duration. To smooth out inlet pulses, a damper is connected to the AFS vane. The AFS exerts a major influence on the amount of fuel injected.

MAP sensor

The MAP sensor is an alternative load sensor used in the some models of Digifant. A vacuum hose connects the MAP sensor (located within the ECM) and the inlet manifold. Manifold vacuum acts upon the MAP sensor diaphragm, and the ECM converts the pressure into an electrical signal. MAP is calculated from the formula: Atmospheric Pressure less Manifold Pressure = Manifold Absolute Pressure.

Using the speed/density method, Digifant calculates the AFR from the MAP signal and the speed of the engine (HES). This method relies on the theory that the engine will draw in a fixed volume of air per revolution.

Air temperature sensor (ATS)

The ATS may be mounted in the AFS inlet tract, or in a combined ATS and CO pot, or on its own in the inlet manifold. The ATS either measures the air temperature in the inlet tract or in the inlet manifold. Because the density of air varies in inverse proportion to the temperature, the ATS signal allows more accurate assessment of the volume of air entering the engine. However, the ATS has only a minor correcting effect on ECM output.

The open-circuit supply to the sensor is at a 5.0-volt reference level, and the earth path is either through the AFS earth return or the combined CO pot and AFS return. The ATS operates on the NTC principle. A variable voltage signal is returned to the ECM based upon the air temperature. This signal is approximately 2.0 to 3.0 volts at an ambient temperature of 20°C, and reduces to about 1.5 volt as the temperature rises to around 40°C.

CO adjustment (25-pin)

The mechanical type of AFS utilises an air bleed screw to trim the CO value. An air channel allows a small volume of air to by-pass the air flowing through the vane. As the by-pass is moved, the air volume acting upon the vane is altered and the vane moves its position. The changed position results in an altered signal to the ECM, and a change in fuel volume injected.

CO pot (not fitted to late cat engines)

The CO pot mixture adjuster is a two-wire potentiometer that allows small changes to be made to the idle CO. A 5.0-volt open-circuit reference voltage is applied to the sensor. When this wire is connected to the CO pot resistance, the voltage returned to the ECM is determined by the position (and therefore resistance) of the pot. The earth side of the CO pot is connected to the Digifant sensor return circuit.

As the CO pot adjustment screw is turned, the change in resistance returns a voltage signal to the ECM that will result in a change in CO. The CO pot adjustment only affects idle CO. The CO pot may be part of the vane AFS, or part of a combined ATS and CO pot component.

Coolant temperature sensor (CTS)

The CTS is incorporated in the cooling system, and contains a variable resistance that operates on the NTC principle. When the engine is cold, the resistance is quite high. Once the engine is started and begins to warm up, the coolant becomes hotter and the CTS resistance decreases (NTC principle); this returns a variable voltage signal to the ECM based upon the coolant temperature.

The signal is approximately 1.0 to 1.5 volts at an ambient temperature of 20°C, and reduces to between 0.2 and 0.5 volts at a normal operating temperature of 80 to 100°C.

The open-circuit supply to the sensor is at a 5.0-volt reference level. The ECM uses the CTS signal as a main correction factor when calculating ignition timing and injection duration.

Throttle switches

Two throttle switches are provided, to inform the ECM of idle position and full-load (WOT) conditions. The switches are usually used in models without a TPS **(see illustration 17.3)**.

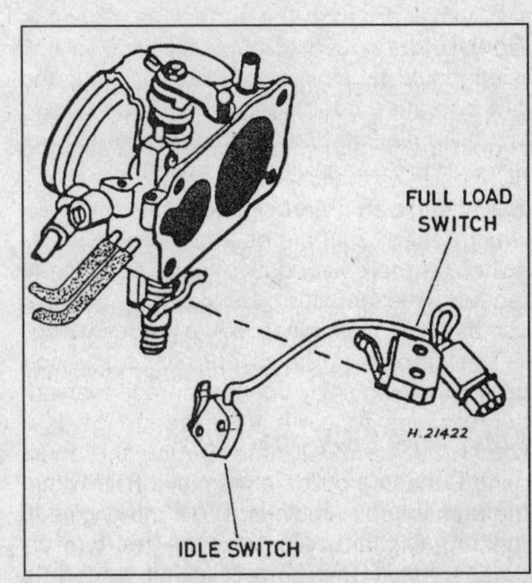

17.3 Idle speed and full-load switches

A 5.0-volt supply is applied from the ECM to the switches. When either switch is closed (idle or full load throttle position), the circuit is earthed and the ECM recognises the condition. When the engine is at idle, the idle switch is closed and the full-load contact is open. As soon as the throttle is opened, the idle switch opens.

As the throttle is moved to the fully open position, the full-load contact closes. Under cruising conditions with a part-open throttle, both switches are open. During full-load operation, the ECM provides additional enrichment. During closed throttle operation above a certain rpm (deceleration), the ECM will cut off fuel injection. Injection will be reintroduced once the rpm returns to idle or the throttle is opened.

Throttle potentiometer sensor (TPS)

A TPS is provided to inform the ECM of idle position and rate of acceleration. The TPS is a potentiometer with three wires. A 5.0-volt reference voltage is supplied to a resistance track, with the other end connected to earth. The third wire is connected to an arm which wipes along the resistance track, and so varies the resistance and voltage of the signal returned to the ECM.

Idle speed control valve (ISCV)

Two slightly different types of ISCV are used in Digifant systems. Basic operation of the two types is very similar. The ISCV is a solenoid-controlled actuator that the ECM uses to automatically control idle speed during normal idle and during engine warm-up. The ISCV is located in a hose that connects the inlet manifold to the air filter side of the throttle plate.

When electrical loads such as the headlights or heater fan are switched on, the idle speed would tend to drop. The ECM will sense the load, and rotate the ISCV against spring tension to increase the airflow through the valve and thus increase the idle speed. When the load is removed, the ECM will pulse the valve so that the airflow is reduced. Normal idle speed of (typically) 750 to 850 rpm should be maintained under all cold and hot operating conditions. If the ISCV fails, it will fail-safe, with the aperture almost closed. This will provide a basic idle speed.

Early-type ISCV operation

When the ignition is switched on, the ECM provides the ISCV with voltage, and the ISCV earth circuit is completed through an earth return connection to the ECM. Unusually, the ECM controls the ISCV by pulsing the voltage feed wire.

Later-type ISCV operation

On the more common type of ISCV, a voltage supply is applied from the ignition switch, and the ECM actuates the ISCV by pulsing the ISCV earth terminal to earth for a certain period of time at a frequency of 100 Hz. The period of time can be measured as a duty cycle, and the duty cycle varies according to the load on the engine.

Relays

The Digifant electrical system is controlled by a main fuel injection relay and a fuel pump relay. Numbering of the relays may not always be in accordance with the DIN system.

Main relay (typical)

A permanent voltage supply is made to the main relay terminal 30 from the battery positive terminal. When the ignition is switched on, a voltage supply is made to terminal 86, and this energises the main relay winding which is connected to earth via terminal 85. This causes the relay contacts to close; terminal 30 is connected to the output circuit at terminal 87, and a voltage supply is output to the injectors and ECM terminal 35.

Fuel pump relay (typical)

A permanent voltage supply is made to the main relay terminal 30 from the battery positive terminal. When the engine is running, the ECM earths terminal 85 through an ECM driver pin, which energises the relay winding. This causes the relay contacts to close; terminal 30 is connected to the output circuit at terminal 87, and a voltage supply is output to the fuel pump(s), OS heater, and also to the injectors in some models.

When the ignition is switched on, the ECM briefly earths fuel pump relay contact 85 at ECM terminal 3. This energises the relay winding, which closes the relay contact and connects voltage from terminal 30 to terminal 87, thereby providing voltage to the fuel pump circuit. After approximately one second, the ECM opens the circuit and the pump stops. This brief running of the fuel pump allows pressure to build within the fuel pressure lines, and provides for an easier start.

The fuel pump relay circuit will then remain open until the engine is cranked or run. Once the ECM receives a speed signal from the HES, the relay winding will again be energised by the ECM, and the fuel pump will run until the engine is stopped.

Fuel pressure system

VW vehicles may employ an external fuel pump, or alternatively, an in-tank fuel pump in conjunction with an external fuel pump. Where used, the in-tank fuel transfer pump is used to pump fuel from the fuel tank. Excess fuel is returned to the fuel tank via a return pipe.

Both pumps are of the 'wet' variety, in that fuel actually flows through the pump and the electric motor. There is no actual fire risk, because the fuel drawn through the pump is not in a combustible condition.

The external roller-type fuel pump is driven by a permanent magnet electric motor, and mounted close to the fuel tank. It draws fuel from the tank, and pumps it to the fuel rail via a fuel filter. Mounted upon the armature shaft is an eccentric rotor holding a number of pockets arranged around the circumference - each pocket containing a metal roller. As the pump is actuated, the rollers are flung outwards by centrifugal force to act as seals. The fuel between the rollers is forced to the pump pressure outlet.

Fuel pressure in the fuel rail is maintained at a constant 2.5 bar by a fuel pressure regulator. The fuel pump normally provides much more fuel than is required, and surplus fuel is thus returned to the fuel tank via a return pipe. In fact, a maximum fuel pressure in excess of 5 bar is possible in this system. To prevent pressure loss in the supply system, a non-return valve is provided in the fuel pump outlet. When the ignition is switched off, and the fuel pump ceases operation, pressure is thus maintained for some time.

Fuel pressure regulator

The pressure regulator is fitted on the outlet side of the fuel rail, and maintains an even pressure of 2.5 bar in the fuel rail. The pressure regulator consists of two chambers separated by a diaphragm. The upper chamber contains a spring which exerts pressure upon the lower chamber and closes off the outlet diaphragm. Pressurised fuel flows into the lower chamber, and this exerts pressure upon the diaphragm. Once the pressure exceeds 2.5 bar, the outlet diaphragm is opened and excess fuel flows back to the fuel tank via a return line.

A vacuum hose connects the upper chamber to the inlet manifold, so that variations in inlet manifold pressure will not affect the amount of fuel injected. This means that the pressure in the rail is always at a constant pressure above the pressure in the inlet manifold. The quantity of injected fuel thus depends solely on injector opening time, as determined by the ECM, and not on a variable fuel pressure.

At idle speed with the vacuum pipe disconnected, or with the engine stopped and the pump running, or at full-throttle, the system fuel pressure will be around 2.5 bar. At idle speed (vacuum pipe connected), the fuel pressure will be approximately 0.5 bar under the system pressure.

6 Catalytic converter and emission control

The Digifant injection system fitted to catalyst vehicles implements a closed-loop control system so that exhaust emissions may be reduced. Closed-loop systems are fitted with an oxygen sensor (OS) which monitors the exhaust gas for its oxygen content. The OS signal oscillates between 100 and 1000 mV. A low oxygen level in the exhaust signifies a rich mixture. A high oxygen level in the exhaust signifies a weak mixture. The ECM will then drive the mixture to the opposite extreme, so that a weak signal may create a rich mixture and vice versa.

The OS only produces a signal when the exhaust gas has reached a minimum temperature of approximately 300°C. An OS heater is fitted to the Digifant system, so that the OS reaches its operating temperature every quickly (within 20 to 30 seconds) after the engine is started.

Adjustments

7 Adjustment pre-conditions

1 Ensure that all of these conditions are met before attempting to make adjustments:

- *a) Engine at operating temperature. Engine oil at a minimum temperature of 80°C. A journey of at least 4 miles is advised (particularly so if equipped with AT).*
- *b) Ancillary equipment (all engine loads and accessories) switched off.*
- *c) AT engines: Transmission in N or P.*
- *d) Engine mechanically sound.*
- *e) Engine breather hoses and breather system in satisfactory condition.*
- *f) Induction system free from vacuum leaks.*
- *g) Ignition system in satisfactory condition.*
- *h) Air filter in satisfactory condition.*
- *i) Exhaust system free from leaks.*
- *j) Throttle cable correctly adjusted.*
- *k) No fault codes logged by the ECM.*
- *l) OS operating satisfactorily (catalyst vehicles with closed-loop control).*

2 In addition, before checking the idle speed and CO values, stabilise the engine as follows:

- *a) Stabilise the engine. Raise the engine speed to 3000 rpm for a minimum of 30 seconds, and then let the engine idle.*
- *b) If the cooling fan operates during adjustment, wait until it stops, re-stabilise the engine, and then restart the adjustment procedure.*
- *c) Allow the CO and idle speed to settle.*
- *d) Make all checks and adjustments within 30 seconds. If this time is exceeded, re-stabilise the engine and recheck.*

8 Throttle adjustments

Throttle valve position

1 Move the adjustment screw so that the throttle is fully closed.

2 Insert a feeler gauge, thickness 0.1 mm, between the throttle bore and the throttle valve **(see illustration 17.4)**.

3 Turn the adjustment screw so that the feeler gauge is a close sliding fit in the gap.

4 Remove the feeler gauge. The throttle should be open just enough to prevent the valve seizing or sticking in the throttle bore.

TPS (where used)

5 The TPS is not adjustable.

Throttle switches (where used)

Idle switch adjustment

6 Disconnect the throttle switch (TS) multi-plug.

7 Connect an ohmmeter between the earth terminal 1 and terminal 2.

8 With the TS closed, the ohmmeter should indicate very close to zero ohms.

9 Open the throttle and check that the meter indicates an open-circuit (infinity).

10 Whilst the throttle is open, insert a feeler gauge, thickness 0.4 mm, between the throttle lever and the throttle lever stop.

11 Close the throttle, and check that the ohmmeter indicates continuity. If the meter indicates an open-circuit, loosen the idle switch fixing screws and adjust as necessary. The lugs on the idle switch housing should just touch the stop.

12 Open and close the throttle, and recheck the correctness of the switching point after each adjustments of the TS.

Full-load switch adjustment

13 Leave the ohmmeter connected as for the idle switch adjustment.

14 Move the throttle about halfway towards the throttle closed position, when the ohmmeter should indicate infinity.

15 Slowly close the throttle until the full-load switch operates and the ohmmeter indicates continuity. The full-load switch should be around 10° from the fully-closed position.

16 If the meter indicates an open-circuit, loosen the full-load switch fixing screws and adjust as necessary. The sloping part of the switch lever should just touch the throttle valve lever roller.

17 Open and close the throttle, and recheck the correctness of the switching point after each adjustment of the TS.

18 Have an assistant fully depress the accelerator pedal, and check that full throttle is attained.

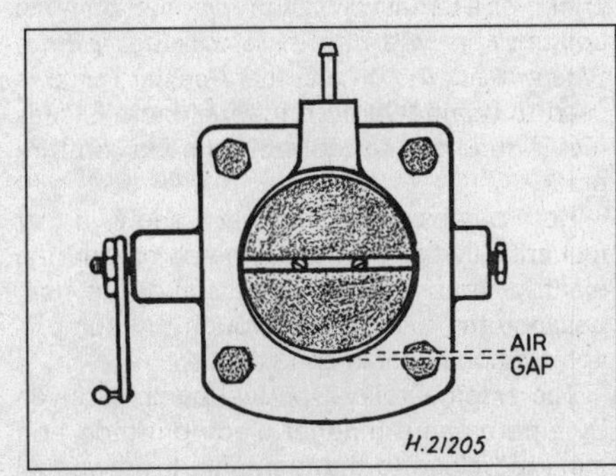

17.4 Throttle valve adjustment

9 Ignition timing checks

Base timing adjustment (typical 25 and 38-pin)

1 The base timing should only be checked and adjusted after the ECM has been placed into service-set mode. For 45 and 68-pin models, a fault code reader (FCR) is required for this function.

2 Refer to the adjustment pre-conditions in Section 7.

3 Start the engine, and allow it to idle until the cooling fan has switched on and off once.

4 Detach the multi-plug from the CTS. This places the ECM into service-set mode. The CTS multi-plug is coloured blue. **Note:** *If the engine stalls, it is essential that the CTS multi-plug is re-connected before the engine is restarted. Otherwise, the ECM will enter LOS, and CO/idle speed adjustment will be impossible.*

5 Set the engine speed to between 2000 and 2500 rpm, and check that the base timing is 4 to 8° at this engine speed **(see illustration 17.5)**.

6 If timing adjustment is required, slacken the distributor fixing bolts and rotate the distributor until the correct timing is obtained. Carefully tighten the distributor bolts and recheck the timing value.

7 Allow the engine speed to return to idle.

8 Reconnect the multi-plug to the CTS.

9 Blip the throttle three times (each blip must move the engine speed over 3000 rpm).

Timing advance

10 The CTS multi-plug must remain connected for this test. Set the engine speed to 2800 rpm. The timing advance at this speed should be 40° ± 5°.

Timing faults

11 If the total timing at 2800 rpm is substantially less than the specified value, check for a knock sensor circuit fault that has

17.5 Ignition timing marks

placed the ECM into 'limp-home' mode. **Note:** *If the knock sensor multi-plug is removed or the KS torque setting is changed, the engine must be stopped and restarted, and the timing values rechecked.*

10 Idle adjustments

1 Check the ignition timing.
2 Check the TS or TPS operation and adjustment.
3 Check that the ISCV operation is satisfactory.
4 Refer to the adjustment pre-conditions in Section 7.
5 Check the idle speed. The regulated idle speed is not adjustable. However, it is possible to check and adjust the base idle speed.
6 Check the CO value.

CO and idle speed adjustment (typical 25 and 38-pin)

Note: *For 45 and 68-pin cat models, the idle speed and CO are not adjustable.*

7 Connect the gas analyser to the tailpipe.
8 Remove the breather hose from the pressure-regulating valve on the rocker cover, and plug the hose.
9 Start the engine, and allow it to idle for approximately one minute.
10 Detach the multi-plug from the CTS. This places the ECM into service-set mode. The CTS multi-plug is coloured blue.
11 Blip the throttle three times (each blip must move the engine speed over 3000 rpm).
12 Allow the engine speed to return to idle.
13 Adjust the idle speed and the CO adjustment screws to set the idle speed and CO values to the specified levels **(see illustration 17.6)**.
14 Once both values are correctly adjusted, reconnect the CTS multi-plug.
15 Blip the throttle three times (each blip must move the engine speed over 3000 rpm).
16 Allow the engine speed to return to idle.
17 Recheck the adjustment values, and repeat the adjustments if necessary.
18 Unplug and reconnect the breather hose, and check that the CO value remains within the specified range.

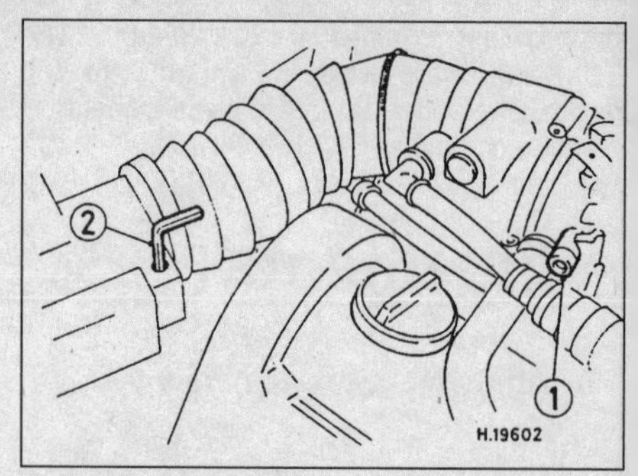

17.6 Idle adjustments (CTS disconnected)
1 Base idle speed 2 Mixture (CO)

Reasons for an increase in CO value

19 Contamination of the engine oil caused by stop-start driving condition. An oil change or a long fast drive may improve matters.
20 Excess blow-by caused by worn or sticking piston rings.
Note: *Vehicles with an OS should remain within the specification - even if the engine oil is contaminated.*

System sensor and actuator tests

Important note: *Please refer to Chapter 4, which describes common test procedures applicable to this system. The routines in Chapter 4 should be read in conjunction with the component notes and wiring diagrams presented in this Chapter. The wiring diagrams and other data presented in this Chapter are necessarily representative of the system depicted. Because of the variations in wiring and other data that often occurs, even between similar vehicles in any particular VM's range, the reader should take great care in identification of ECM pins, and satisfy himself that he has gathered the correct data before failing a particular component.*

11 Primary trigger - Hall-effect sensor (HES)

1 Refer to the note at the start of this Section, and refer to the relevant Section of Chapter 4 **(see illustrations 17.7 and 17.8)**.
2 Where the HES is mounted upon the flywheel, the test procedure is similar.

12 Primary ignition

1 Refer to the note at the start of Section 11, and refer to the relevant Section of Chapter 4.
2 Depending upon model, the primary ignition may be that of an ECM with internal or external amplifier.
3 Where the coil and amplifier are a combined unit, detach the amplifier from the coil, and check the connections between the coil unit and the amplifier unit. All other tests are broadly as described in Chapter 4 **(see illustrations 17.9 to 17.11)**.

Ignition coil resistances

System	Primary resistance	Secondary resistance
25-pin (Green Sticker)	*0.52 to 0.76*	*2400 to 3400*
25-pin (Grey Sticker)	*0.60 to 0.80*	*6900 to 8500*
38-pin (& 38-pin SD)	*0.50 to 0.70*	*3000 to 4000*
45 and 68-pin	*0.50 to 0.70*	*3000 to 4000*

13 Knock sensor (KS)

1 Refer to the note at the start of Section 11, and refer to the relevant Section of Chapter 4.
2 Two knock sensors are utilised in 68-pin models.

14 Fuel injector operation

1 Refer to the note at the start of Section 11, and refer to the relevant Section of Chapter 4 **(see illustrations 17.12 and 17.13)**.
2 Voltage to the injectors is provided from either the system main relay or the fuel pump relay. Where voltage is provided from the pump relay, a supply is only available whilst the engine is cranking or running. However, voltage could be applied for test purposes by by-passing the relay (see Chapter 4).
3 Injector operation is simultaneous, except for 68-pin models where it is sequential.
4 The injector resistance is normally 15.0 to 20.0 ohms.
5 Where the system is equipped with a cold start valve (CSV), testing follows similar lines to normal injector testing. However, the valve will only operate during a cold start.

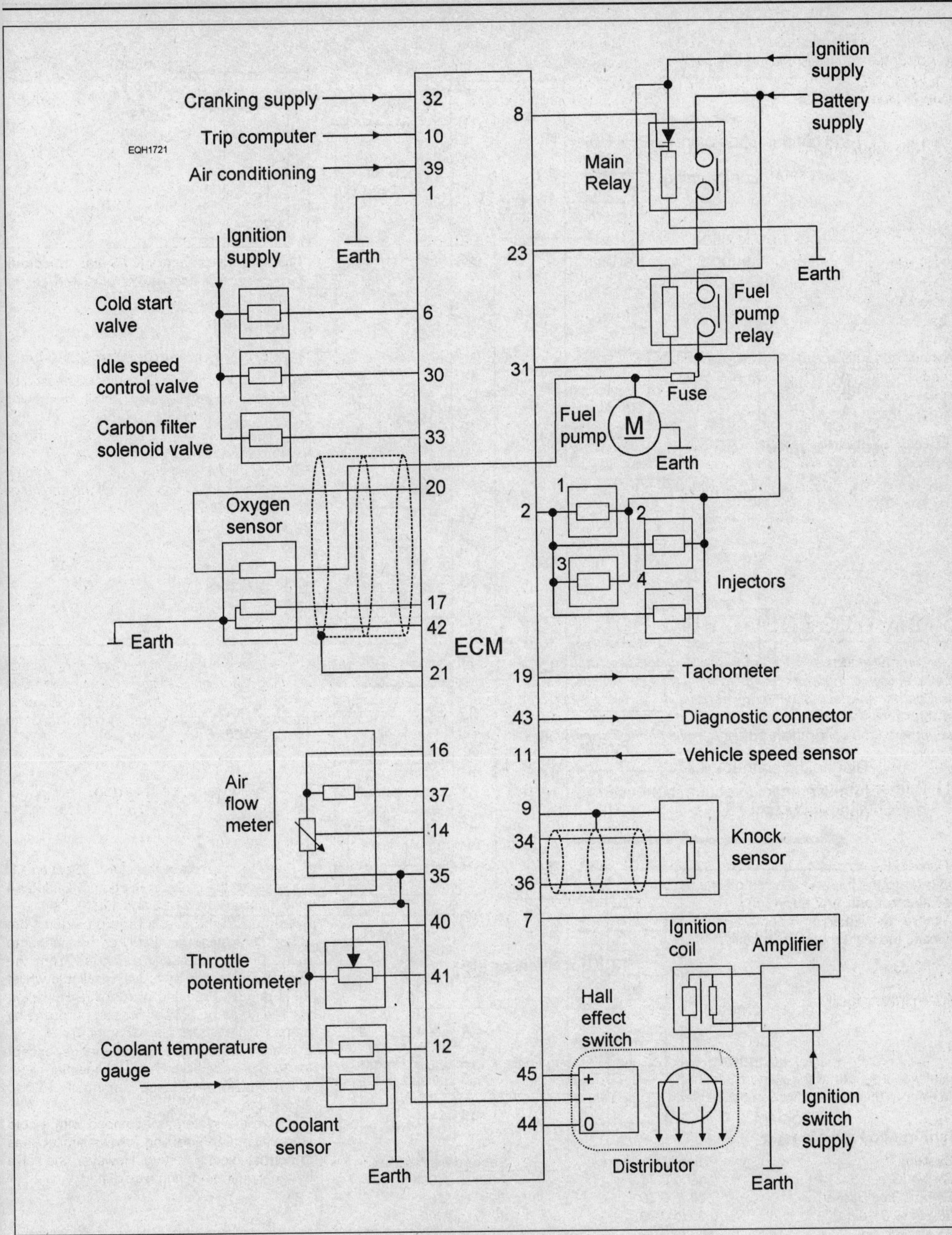

17.7 Typical 45-pin wiring

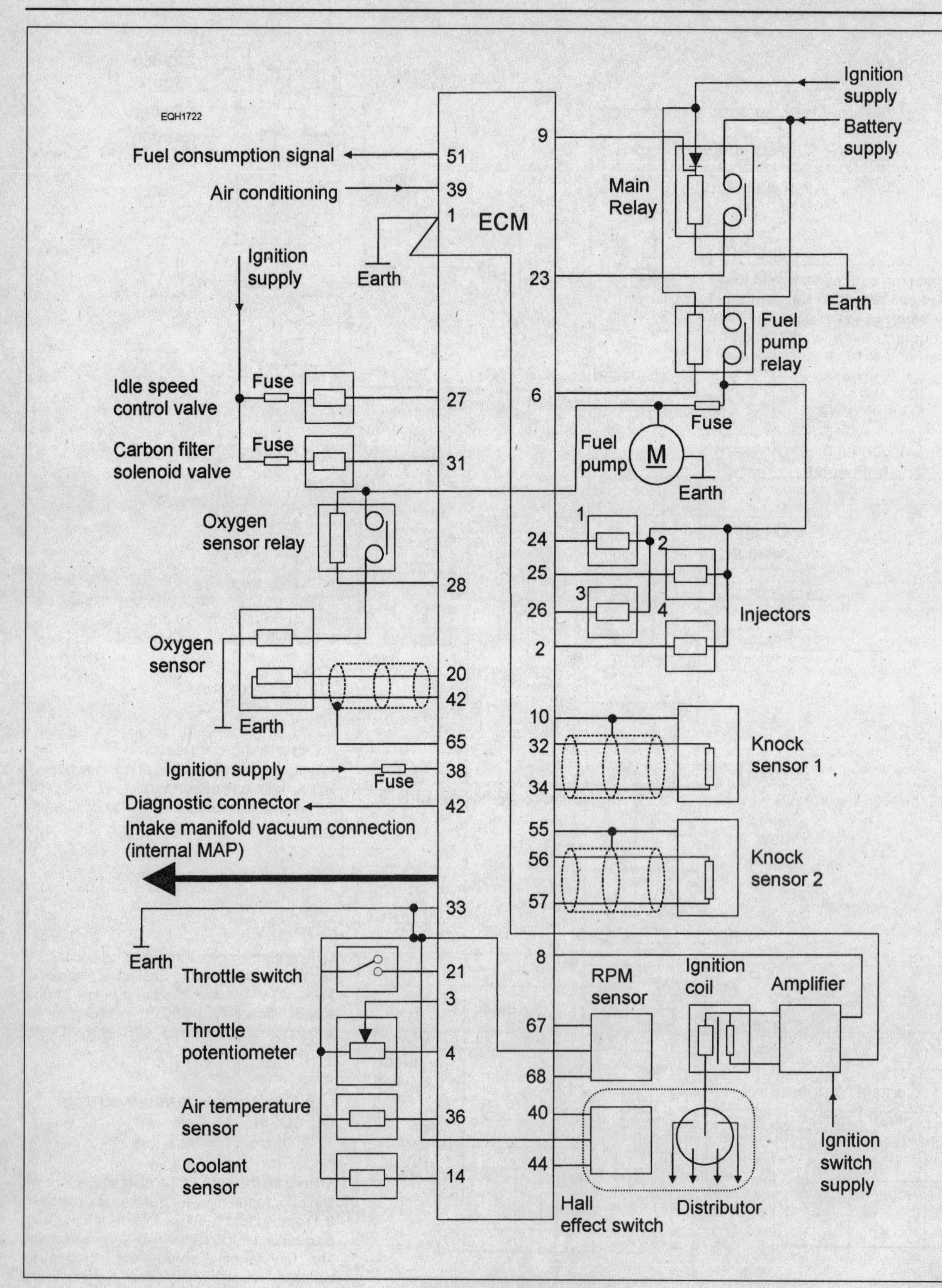

17.8 Typical 68-pin wiring

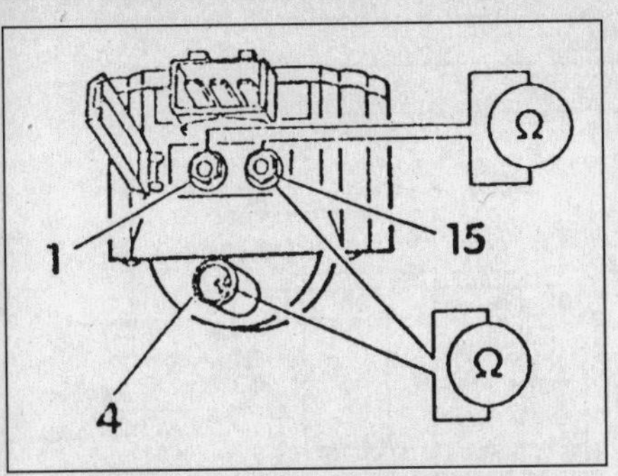

17.9 Checking coil resistance in the combined coil/amplifier. Connect the ohmmeter between terminals 1 and 15 to check primary resistance, or between terminals 4 and 15 to check secondary resistance

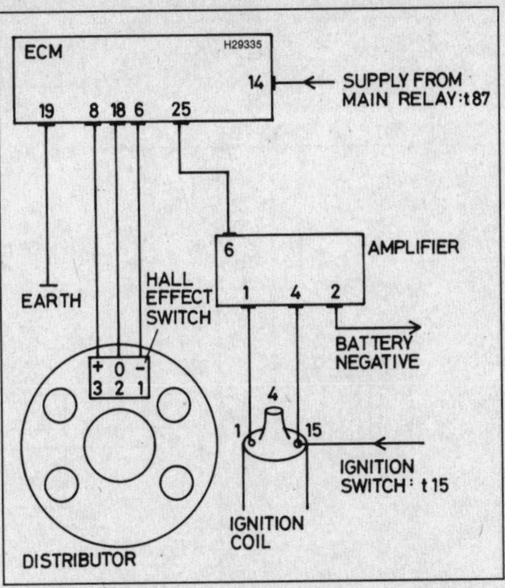

17.10 Typical 25-pin ignition wiring

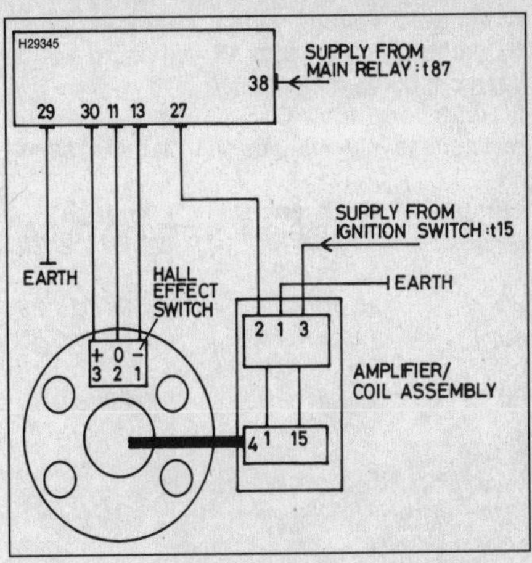

17.11 Typical 38-pin ignition wiring

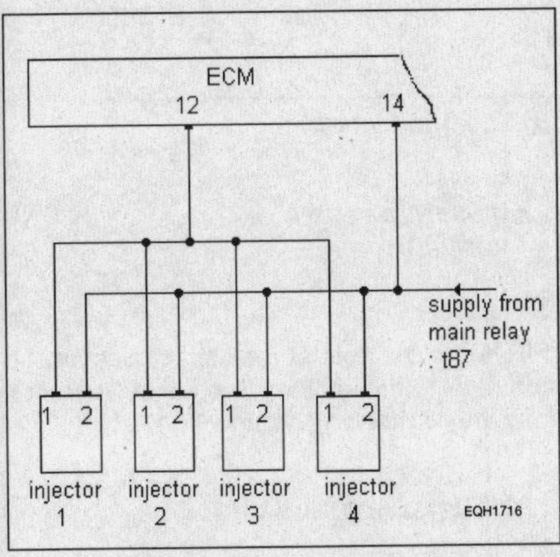

17.12 Typical 25-pin injector wiring

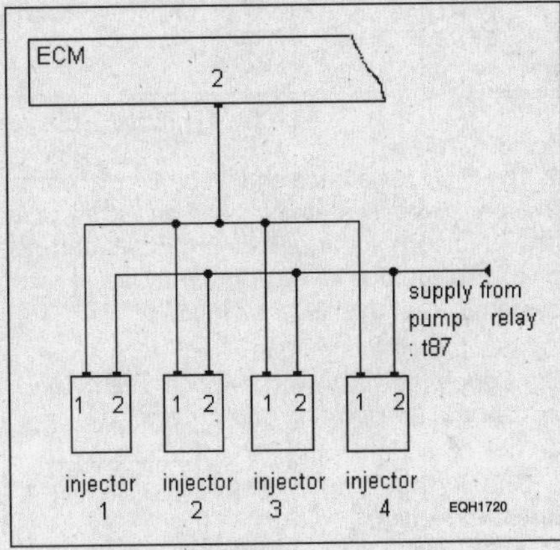

17.13 Typical 38-pin injector wiring

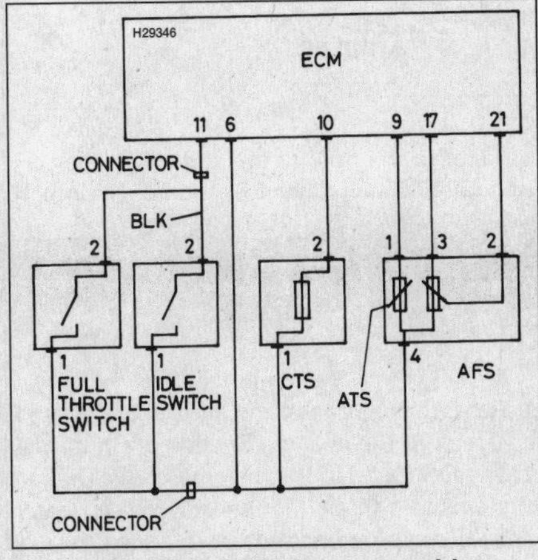

17.14 Typical 25-pin sensor wiring

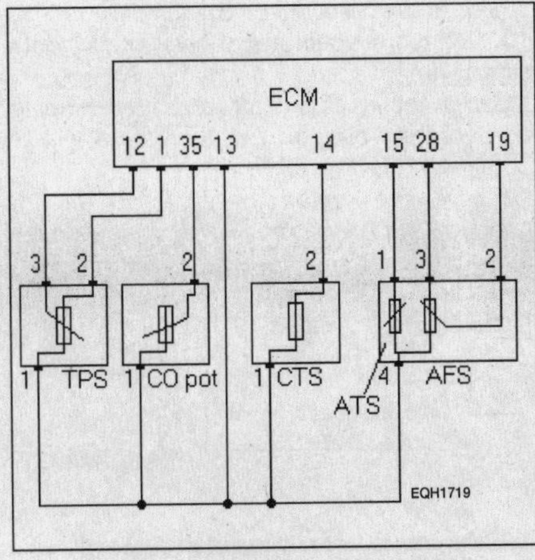

17.15 Typical 38-pin sensor wiring

15 Airflow sensor (AFS)

1 Refer to the note at the start of Section 11, and refer to the relevant Section of Chapter 4 **(see illustrations 17.14 and 17.15)**.

2 The AFS is of the vane type.

16 MAP sensor

1 Refer to the note at the start of Section 11, and refer to the relevant Section of Chapter 4.

2 The MAP sensor is usually located internally in the ECM.

17 Air temperature sensor (ATS)

1 Refer to the note at the start of Section 11, and refer to the relevant Section of Chapter 4.

2 The ATS is either mounted in the airflow sensor, or alternatively, the ATS may be located in a combined ATS and CO pot component.

18 Coolant temperature sensor (CTS)

1 Refer to the note at the start of Section 11, and refer to the relevant Section of Chapter 4.

2 From August 1991, a four-terminal multi-plug replaces the earlier two-terminal sensor. The four-terminal multi-plug includes an additional resistor which sends a signal to the temperature sender on the instrument panel.

A variable voltage signal between 4.0 to 6.0 volts hot and 10 to 12 volts cold will be seen on this wire.

3 Refer to the CTS table below for resistances and voltages seen in this system.

Temp	Resistance	Voltage
0	*5 to 6.5 k*	*1.80 to 2.25*
10	*3.2 to 4.2 k*	
20	*2.1 to 2.9 k*	*0.95 to 1.25*
40	*1.0 to 1.4 k*	*0.50 to 0.85*
60	*520 to 670*	
80	*280 to 370*	*0.20 to 0.40*

19 Throttle potentiometer sensor (TPS)

1 Refer to the note at the start of Section 11, and refer to the relevant Section of Chapter 4.

20 Throttle switch (TS) - where fitted

1 The TS multi-plug is connected to the upper TS (full load switch).

2 The two wires to the TS multi-plug connector are earth and a voltage supply.

3 Connect the voltmeter negative probe to an engine earth.

4 Roll back the rubber protection boot to the TS multi-plug.

5 With the engine stopped, and ignition on, connect the voltmeter positive probe to the wire attached to the TS supply terminal 2; the meter should indicate zero volts.

6 Crack open the throttle. The switch should 'click' and the voltage rise to 5.0 volts.

If the TS does not behave as described

a) Check the TS adjustment.

b) Check the throttle valve position.

c) Check the TS earth connection.

d) Disconnect the TS multi-plug and check for 5.0 volts at the multi-plug idle terminal. If no voltage, check for continuity of the wiring between the TS and the ECM.

e) Fully open the throttle. As the throttle angle moves within 10 ± 2° of full throttle, the voltage should drop to near zero volts.

f) If the voltage does not drop, check the TS adjustment.

g) If each TS does not behave as described, and are not prevented from opening or closing fully by the binding of the throttle linkage, the appropriate TS is suspect.

21 Idle speed control valve (ISCV)

1 Refer to the note at the start of Section 11, and refer to the relevant Section of Chapter 4.

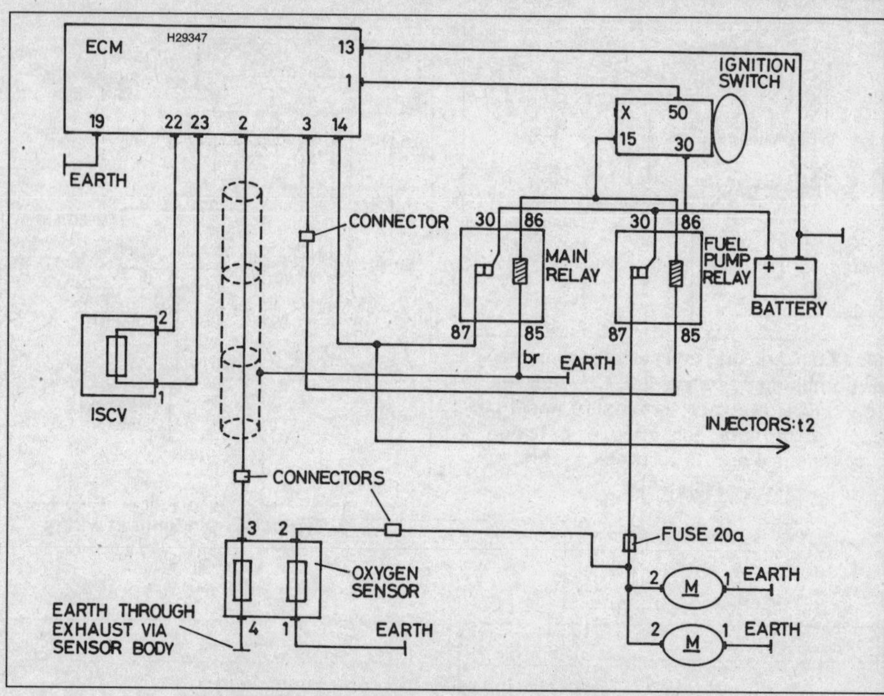

17.16 Typical 25-pin relay and components wiring

2 The ISCV resistance should be 2 to 10 ohms.

3 Early 25-pin systems utilised an ISCV that is provided with voltage from the ECM, and not from the ignition switch or relay as in later systems. Test this ISCV as follows:

a) Switch on the ignition.

b) Touch the ISCV with a finger. The ISCV should be vibrating and buzzing.

4 Start the engine and allow it to idle.

5 Check that the idle speed is within its operating limits.

6 If not, check the base idle adjustment.

7 Load the system by switching on the headlights, heated rear window and heater motor onto high. The idle speed should barely change.

8 Quickly squeeze one of the air hoses. The idle speed should surge and then return to normal.

9 If the idle condition meets the above criteria, it is unlikely to be at fault

10 Connect a voltmeter or dwell meter to the signal wire.

11 With the ignition on or the engine running, an average voltage or a duty cycle will be obtained

12 Load the system by switching on the headlights, heated rear window and heater motor onto high. The average voltage and duty cycle will change. The frequency of pulse should remain constant.

22 ECM voltage supplies and earths

1 Refer to the note at the start of Section 11, and refer to the relevant Section of Chapter 4.

23 System relays

1 Refer to the note at the start of Section 11, and refer to the relevant Section of Chapter 4 **(see illustrations 17.16 and 17.17)**.

24 Fuel pump and circuit

1 Refer to the note at the start of Section 11, and refer to the relevant Section of Chapter 4.

2 The fuel pump may be a single pump located externally, or may be part of a dual pump set-up located externally and internally.

25 Fuel pressure

1 Refer to the note at the start of Section 11, and refer to the relevant Section of Chapter 4.

26 Oxygen sensor (OS)

1 Refer to the note at the start of Section 11, and refer to the relevant Section of Chapter 4.

2 The OS found in the majority of VW Digifant systems is a three-wire sensor with a heater. The OS signal is earthed through the OS body and the exhaust pipe.

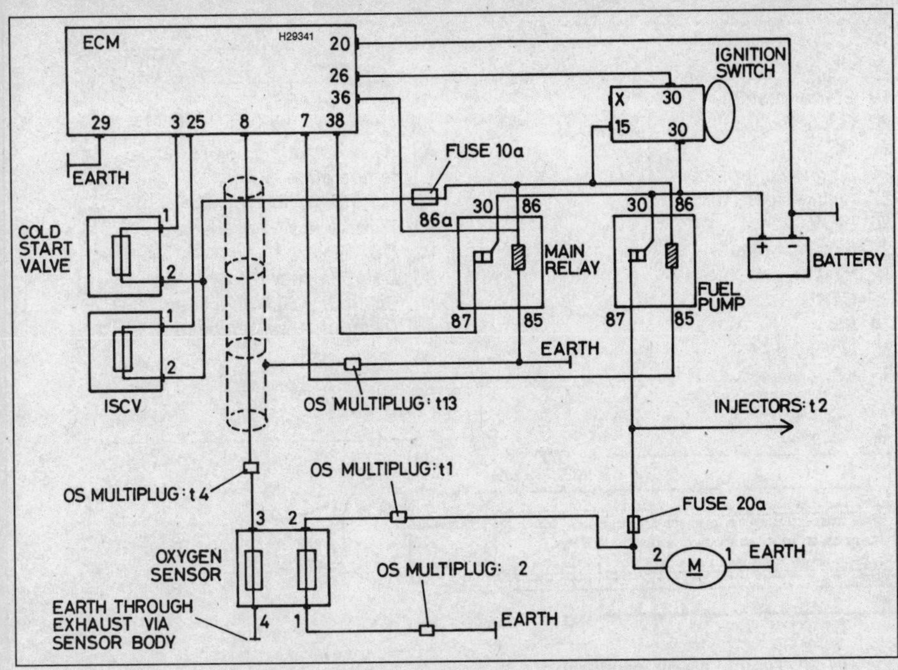

17.17 Typical 38-pin relay and components wiring

Pin table - typical 25-pin

Note: *Refer to* ***illustration 17.18.***

1 Cranking supply ign switch
2 OS
3 Fuel pump relay driver
4 KS signal
5 KS return
6 Sensor return (TS, CTS, AFS)
7 KS shield
8 HES
9 ATS signal
10 CTS signal
11 Full throttle switch
12 Injectors
13 Earth (battery negative)
14 Main relay output
15 -
16 Air conditioning
17 AFS supply
18 HES
19 Earth (inlet manifold)
20 -
21 AFS signal
22 ISCV signal
23 ISCV return
24 -
25 Amplifier

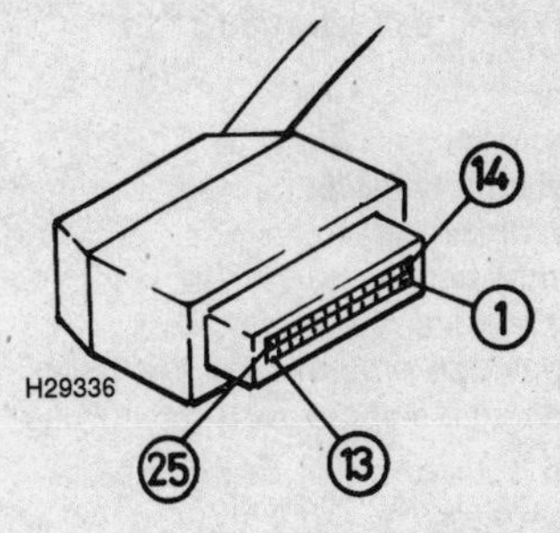

17.18 Typical 25-pin multi-plug

Pin table - typical 38-pin

Note: *Refer to* ***illustration 17.19.***

1 TPS supply
2 Injectors
3 Cold start valve
4 -
5 -
6 -
7 Fuel pump relay driver
8 OS signal
9 -
10 2-pin connector on bulkhead
11 HES signal
12 TPS signal
13 Sensor earth (HES, CO pot, TPS, CTS, AFS)
14 CTS signal
15 AFS (ATS)
16 KS return
17 KS signal
18 -
19 AFS signal
20 Battery negative
21 -
22 -
23 -
24 -
25 ISCV
26 Cranking supply ign switch
27 Ignition coil/amplifier signal
28 AFS supply
29 Earth
30 HES supply
31 2-pin connector on bulkhead
32 -
33 -
34 KS shield
35 CO pot signal
36 Ignition supply, main relay
37 A/C compressor
38 Main relay output

17.19 Typical 38-pin multi-plug

Pin table - typical 45-pin

Note: *Refer to **illustration 17.20**.*

1 Earth
2 Injector no. 1
4 Battery
6 Cold start injector
7 KS sensor
8 Engine control module relay
10 Engine loom connector
11 Trip computer
12 CTS
14 Hot-wire AFS
16 Hot-wire AFS
17 OS
19 Starter motor
20 OS
21 OS
23 Engine control module relay
27 Ignition amplifier
30 ISCV
31 Fuel pump relay
32 Ignition switch
33 CFSV
34 KS
35 Hot-wire AFS
36 KS
37 Hot-wire AFS
38 Ignition switch
39 Air conditioning engine coolant temperature switch
40 Throttle position sensor
41 Throttle position sensor
42 OS
43 Data link connector
44 Distributor Hall-effect sensor
45 Distributor Hall-effect sensor

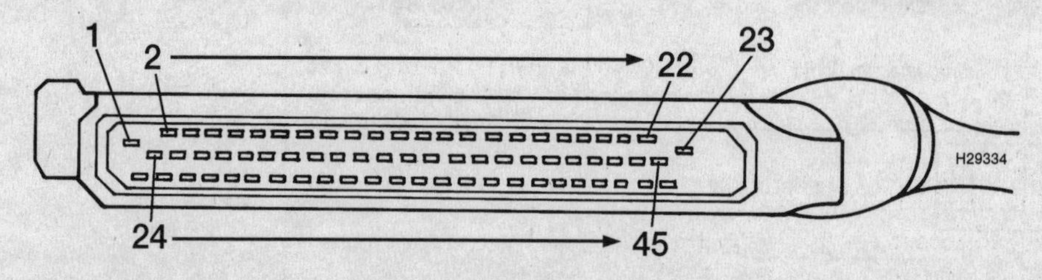

17.20 Typical 45-pin multi-plug

Pin table - typical 68-pin

Note: *Refer to **illustration 17.21**.*

1 Earth
2 Injector no. 4
6 Fuel pump relay
7 Ignition switch
8 Ignition amplifier
9 Engine control module relay
10 Engine oil pressure gauge sensor
11 Transmission connector
14 CTS
18 Transmission connector
20 OS
21 Throttle switch
22 Instrument panel
23 Engine control module relay
24 Injector no. 1
25 Injector no. 2
26 Injector no. 3
27 ISCV
28 OS control module
31 CFSV
32 KS
33 Earth
34 KS
36 Intake air temperature sensor
38 Ignition switch
39 Air conditioning data link connector
40 Throttle position sensor
41 Throttle position sensor
42 OS
43 Data link connector
44 Distributor hall-effect sensor
45 Distributor hall-effect sensor
51 Instrument panel
55 KS
56 KS
57 KS
65 Earth
67 CAS (Hall-effect) on crankshaft
68 CAS (Hall-effect) on crankshaft

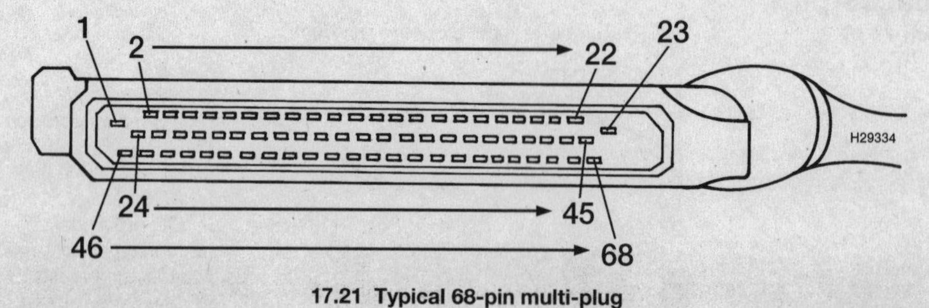

17.21 Typical 68-pin multi-plug

Fault codes

27 Obtaining fault codes

1 VW Digifant generates two kinds of fault codes. These are five-digit fault codes and four-digit flash codes.

2 Fault codes can only be output from the VW Digifant system with the aid of a dedicated fault code reader (FCR), but the four-digit flash codes can be output on the instrument panel warning lamp (if fitted) or via an LED lamp.

3 The dedicated FCR can be used for the following purposes:

a) Accessing and clearing fault codes.

b) Accessing Datastream.

c) Actuating components and making service adjustments. VW have assigned 5-digit code numbers for codes to be obtained through the use of a FCR.

d) Placing the ECM into a service-set mode for adjustment of the ignition timing and setting of the base idle speed. It is also possible to enter service-set mode without the FCR (see timing adjustments).

Note: *Oxygen sensor (OS) fault codes can only be retrieved after a road test of at least 10 minutes' duration.*

Obtaining codes without a FCR (flash codes)

4 The four-digit flash codes are indicated by the flashing of the diagnostic warning lamp on the instrument cluster (if fitted), or by connecting a suitable FCR or diode lamp to the SD plug **(see illustration 17.22)**.

5 The first series of flashes indicates the first digit, the second series of flashes indicates the second digit, and so on.

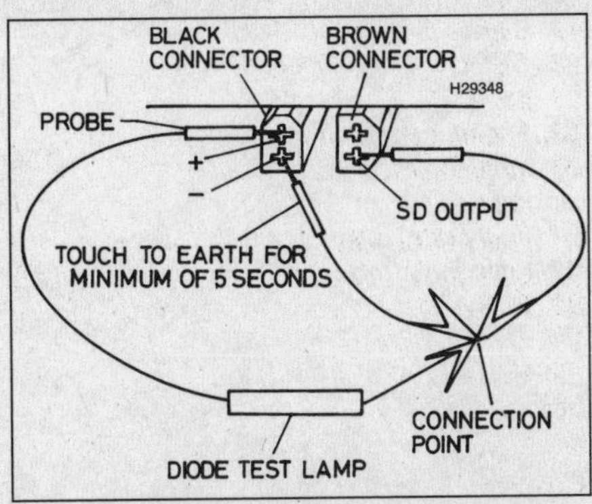

17.22 Obtaining flash codes (the diode lamp is only required if the vehicle is not equipped with a diagnostic warning lamp in the dash)

6 Locate the two-pin SD connection. Where the SD connection is in the footwell or near to the gear lever, the black connection to the left of the SD connector (white or brown) is a voltage supply and earth connector. **Note:** *It is not possible to obtain flash codes from the 68-pin Digifant system, nor when the SD connector is the 16-pin ISO connector.*

7 If no SD warning lamp is fitted on the dash, connect a diode test lamp between the battery (+) supply and the SD connector.

8 Start the engine.

9 Warm up the engine and allow it to idle. **Note:** *Oxygen sensor (OS) fault codes can only be retrieved after a road test of at least 10 minutes' duration.*

10 If the engine will not start, crank the engine for at least six seconds, and leave the ignition switch on.

11 Use a jumper lead to connect the SD connector to earth for at least five seconds. The warning lamp or LED will light, and will remain lit until the jumper lead is removed.

12 Remove the jumper lead, and the warning lamp or the diode test lamp will flash to indicate a four-digit code. **Note:** *There is a 2.5 second gap between each digit, and only one code can be output at a time.*

13 Count the flashes and record the code.

14 When the code 4444 is transmitted, no faults are stored (end of procedure).

15 If a code other than 4444 is transmitted, repeat the test by connecting the jumper lead to earth again for at least 5 seconds.

16 Record each code and continue extracting codes until code 0000 is transmitted. Code 0000 signifies that no more codes are stored.

17 Code 0000 is displayed when the lamp flashes off and on at 2.5 second intervals.

Cancelling a fault code

18 Carry out the above procedure to obtain the fault code.

19 Turn off the ignition.

20 Use a jumper lead to connect the SD connector to earth.

21 Switch the ignition on.

22 After 5 seconds, disconnect the SD connector from earth.

23 The fault codes should now be removed.

Cancelling codes 2341 or 2343 (OS)

24 Turn off the ignition. Remove the ECM multi-plug connector from the ECM (*refer to Warning No 3 in Reference)* for at least 30 seconds.

Flash code table appears overleaf

Flash code table

Note: *we have not listed the five-digit codes that can only be obtainable with the aid of a FCR.*

Code	Item
4444	No fault
1111	Internal ECM failure
1231	Vehicle speed sensor
1232	Throttle valve positioner
2112	Crankshaft position (CKP) sensor
2113	Hall-effect pick-up
2121	Idle switch/throttle position sensor
2123	Full throttle switch
2122	No engine speed signal
2212	TPS circuit or TPS fault
2222	MAP sensor
2232	Airflow sensor
2242	CO pot circuit or CO pot fault
2312	CTS circuit or CTS fault
2322	ATS circuit or ATS fault
2142	KS circuit or KS fault
2342	OS circuit or OS fault
2223	Barometric pressure sensor
2233	Airflow sensor
2234	Supply voltage incorrect
2231	Idle control
2114	Distributor
2141	Knock control 1 (ECM)
2143	Knock control 2 (ECM)
2341	Oxygen sensor control 1
2144	Knock sensor 2
2214	Max. engine speed exceeded
2224	Max. boost pressure exceeded
2142	AT signal missing
2314	Engine/gearbox electrical connection
2323	Airflow sensor
2324	Airflow sensor
2343	Mixture control adjustment - weak
2344	Mixture control adjustment - rich
2413	Mixture control 1
2221	Airflow sensor/MAP sensor
4332	ECM
4343	Evaporative canister purge valve
4411	Injector No. 1
4412	Injector No. 2
4413	Injector No. 3
4414	Injector No. 4
4421	Injector No. 5
4431	ISCV
4442	Boost pressure limiting solenoid valve
1111	ECM
0000	End of fault display sequence/no fault

Chapter 18
IAW Weber-Marelli MPi

Contents

Specifications

Vehicle	Idle speed	CO%
Fiat		
Croma 2000ie 834 B.000	800 ± 50	1.0 to 2.0
Croma 2000ie 8V 154 C.000	800 ± 40	1.5 ± 0.5
Croma 2.0ie 154 C3.000	850 ± 30	1.6 ± 0.5
Tempra 1.8ie SX 8V 159 A4.000	820 ± 50	1.5 ± 0.5
Tempra 1.8 76kW cat 835 C2.000	850 ± 50	0.5 max
Tempra 2.0ie SX/SLX 4x4 DOHC 8V 159 A4.046	850 ± 50	0.35 max
Tipo 1.8ie DOHC 8V 159 A.4000	820 ± 50	1.5 ± 0.5
Tipo 1.8ie DOHC 16V 160 A.5000	900 ± 30	1.5 ± 0.5
Tipo 2.0ie DOHC 8V cat 159 A5.046	820 ± 50	0.5 max
Tipo 2.0ie DOHC 8V cat 159 A6.046	820 ± 50	0.5 max
Tipo 2.0ie DOHC 16V cat 160 A8.046	900 ± 30	0.35 max
Lancia		
Dedra 1.8ie DOHC 835 A2.000	850 ± 50	1.5 ± 0.5
Dedra 1.8ie DOHC cat 835 A2.046	850 ± 50	0.5 max
Dedra 2.0ie DOHC 835 A5.000	820 ± 50	1.5 ± 0.5
Dedra 2.0ie 1991 onwards	850 ± 30	1.5 ± 0.5
Dedra 2.0ie AT cat 835 A5.045	820 ± 50	0.5 max
Dedra 2.0ie DOHC cat 835 A5 046	850 ± 30	0.5 max
Dedra 2.0ie Turbo 835 A8.000	850 ± 50	1.0 to 1.5
Dedra 2.0ie Turbo cat 835 A8.000	850 ± 30	0.5 to 0.9
Dedra 2.0ie Integrale Turbo 835 A7.000	850 ± 50	1.5 ± 0.5
Dedra 2.0ie Integrale Turbo & cat 835 A7.000	850 ± 30	0.5 to 0.9
Delta/Prisma 1600ie DOHC 831 B7.000	800 to 860	1.0 to 1.5
Delta/Prisma 1600ie DOHC 831 B7.000	800 to 860	1.5 ± 0.5
Delta/Prisma 1600ie DOHC Static 831 B7.000	800 to 860	1.5 ± 0.5
Delta HF Turbo & Martini 1600 DOHC 831 B3.000	800 to 860	1.0 ± 0.5
Delta HF Turbo cat 831 B7.046	800 to 860	0.5 max
Delta HF Integrale Turbo DOHC 831 B5.000	800 to 900	1.5 ± 0.5
Delta HF Integrale Turbo DOHC 831 C5.000	800 to 900	1.5 ± 0.5
Delta HF Integrale Turbo 16V DOHC 831 D5.000	850 to 950	1.5 ± 0.5
Delta HF Integrale Turbo 16V 831 E5.000	820 to 880	1.5 ± 0.5
Delta HF Integrale Turbo 16V cat 831 E5.000	820 to 880	0.5 max
Ford		
Escort Cosworth 4x4 non-cat	900	0.1 max
Sierra/Sapphire Cosworth 4x2 non-cat	850	1.5 ± 0.5
Sierra/Sapphire Cosworth 4x4 non-cat	850	0.1 max
Sierra/Sapphire Cosworth 4x4 cat	900	0.1 max

Overview of system operation

1 Introduction

The IAW Weber-Marelli system is a fully-integrated EMS that controls primary ignition, fuelling and idle speed from within the same ECM **(see illustration 18.1)**. Fuel system components and the ECM (which also controls the ignition timing) are generally of Weber origin, and the ignition components are supplied by Marelli. A distributor incorporating a phase sensor (CID sensor), is employed to control the sequential fuel injection.

The Weber-Marelli system has been fitted to a number of Fiat, Lancia, Ford and even some Aston-Martin vehicles. In some applications, the engine is turbocharged by a Garrett turbocharger.

The ignition point and injection duration are jointly processed by the ECM, so that the best moment for ignition and fuelling is determined for every operating condition. A 35-pin connector and multi-plug connects the ECM to the battery, sensors and actuators.

Although an ECM of similar appearance is used in all vehicles, there are a number of vital internal differences between applications. In addition, the types of sensors used to provide base information also differ. This Chapter attempts to deal with the majority of variations between the different years and vehicles.

The main differences between Ford and Fiat/Lancia applications concern the self-diagnostics. The differences are explained in the appropriate section.

2 Control functions

Signal processing

Basic ignition timing is stored in a three-dimensional map, and the engine load and speed signals determine the ignition timing. The main engine load sensor is the MAP sensor; engine speed is determined from the crank angle sensor (CAS) signal.

Correction factors are then applied for starting, idle, deceleration, and part- and full-load operation. The main correction factor is engine temperature (CTS). Minor corrections to timing and AFR are made with reference to the air temperature sensor (ATS) and throttle pot (TPS) signals.

The basic AFR is also stored in a three-dimensional map, and the engine load and speed signals determine the basic injection pulse value. Weber-Marelli calculates the AFR from the MAP signal and the speed of the engine (CAS).

The AFR and the pulse duration are then corrected on reference to ATS, CTS, battery voltage and position of the TPS. Other controlling factors are determined by operating conditions such as cold start and warm-up, idle condition, acceleration and deceleration.

The ECM fully controls the basic idle speed in some Fiat/Lancia 16-valve engines from 1993 (in earlier engines, normal idle rpm is set by adjusting an idle by-pass air screw). In all engines, the ECM raises the idle speed during engine warm-up and engine load conditions.

Basic ECM operation

A permanent voltage supply is not made from the vehicle battery to the ECM. When the ignition is switched on, a voltage supply is made to ECM pin 20 from terminal 87 of the main fuel injection relay. Terminal 87 also supplies voltage to the injectors, the idle speed control valve (ISCV), turbo wastegate control, and the fuel pump relay terminal 86. Voltage to the ignition coil is directly applied from the ignition switch.

The majority of sensors (other than those that generate a voltage such the CAS and OS), are now provided with a 5.0-volt reference supply from a relevant pin on the ECM. When the engine is cranked or run, a speed signal from the CAS causes the ECM to earth pin 28 so that the fuel pump will run. Ignition and injection functions are also activated. Actuators such as the injectors and ISCV are supplied with nbv from the main relay, and the ECM completes the circuit by

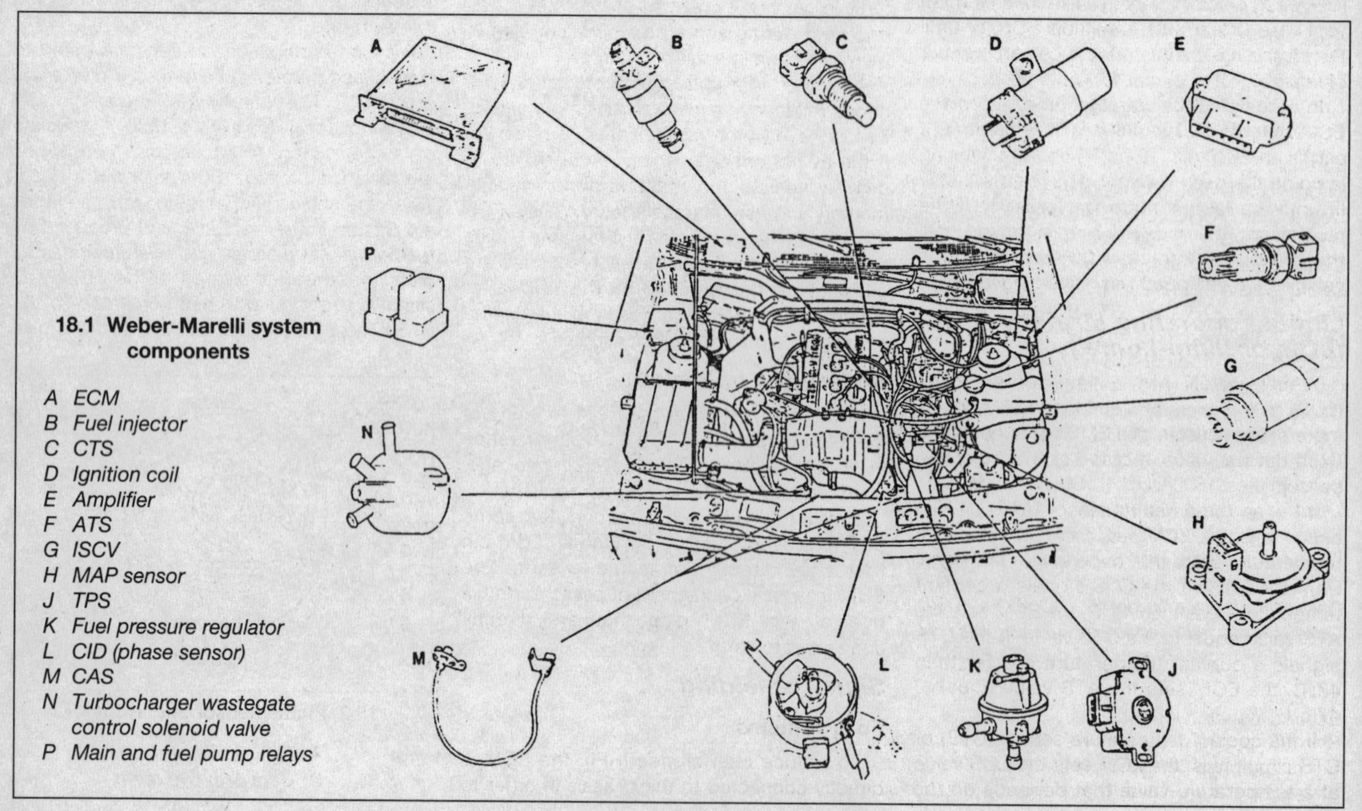

18.1 Weber-Marelli system components

A ECM
B Fuel injector
C CTS
D Ignition coil
E Amplifier
F ATS
G ISCV
H MAP sensor
J TPS
K Fuel pressure regulator
L CID (phase sensor)
M CAS
N Turbocharger wastegate control solenoid valve
P Main and fuel pump relays

pulsing the relevant actuator wire to earth. The various ignition switch and relay output connections vary according to whether a 15-pin relay or two separate relays are utilised (refer to the relay section for further details).

Self-diagnostic function

The Weber-Marelli system has a self-test capability that regularly examines the signals from engine sensors, and internally logs a code in the event of a fault being present. This code can be extracted from the Weber-Marelli serial port by a suitable fault code reader (FCR).

However, there are some differences in the self-diagnostic function between Fiat group (including Lancia) and Ford vehicles.

In the Ford version of the IAW Weber system, the codes are only available whilst the fault is present and when the ignition is switched on. If the fault is permanent (present all the time), then an appropriate code will be logged each time the ignition is switched on. However, if the fault is intermittent and the ignition is switched off, the fault code will be lost. The Escort and Sierra 4x4 models are capable of generating more codes than the earlier two-wheel-drive (4x2) model. The codes emitted by the ECM fitted to Ford vehicles are of the 'slow code' variety. This means that the codes can usually be extracted by a simple LED flashing tool.

In the Fiat/Lancia version, the memory is non-volatile, which means that codes are retained with the ignition off and even with the battery disconnected. However, slow (flash codes) cannot be extracted from this system. If the fault clears, the code will remain logged until wiped clean with a suitable FCR, or until the engine has been started a certain number of times.

In models with a warning lamp, when the ECM detects that a major fault is present, it earths an ECM pin (12 or 27) and the warning lamp on the dash will light. The lamp will stay lit until the fault is no longer present. If the fault clears, the code will remain logged until the ignition is switched off. However, not all vehicles are equipped with a warning lamp.

Limited operating strategy (LOS, or 'limp-home')

Weber-Marelli has a limp-home facility (LOS). In the event of a serious fault in one or more of the sensors, the EMS will substitute a fixed default value in place of the defective sensor.

If the air temperature sensor (ATS) or ATS circuit fails, the ECM sets the LOS value at a temperature value that depends on the signal from the CTS. If the CTS signals a coolant temperature less than 47°C, the ECM sets the ATS value equal to the CTS value. If the CTS signals a coolant temperature greater than 47°C, the ECM sets the ATS value equal to 47.5°C.

If the coolant temperature sensor (CTS) or CTS circuit fails, the ECM sets the LOS value at a temperature value that depends on the signal from the ATS. If the ATS signals an air temperature less than 30°C, the ECM sets the CTS value equal to the ATS value. If the ATS signals an air temperature greater than 30°C, the ECM sets the CTS value equal to 90°C.

If both ATS and CTS or their circuits fail at the same time, the LOS values are set to 47.5°C and 90°C respectively.

This means that the engine may actually run relatively well with failure of one or more minor sensors. However, cold starting and running during the warm-up period may be less than satisfactory. Also, failure of a major sensor may cause the ECM to restrict engine speed.

Adaptive and non-volatile memory (Fiat group only)

Over a period of time the ECM will learn the best injection duration for a particular engine - irrespective of age, engine condition and load, so that the correct duration is always maintained. The adaptive settings are stored in non-volatile memory. Consequently, a replacement ECM will need some time to re-learn the system parameters before proper control is restored.

Faults identified by the self-diagnostic function will also be stored in non-volatile memory, and will remain there until erased by a suitable FCR. This allows the self-diagnostic function to retain data of an intermittent nature. A second memory also retains sensor faults. However, this memory is of a volatile nature, and does not retain faults when they are no longer present. By scanning the ECM with a FCR, it is possible to determine if the fault is currently present, or whether it has occurred during some past occasion and is therefore of an intermittent nature.

Adaptive idle measurements and fault codes retained in non-volatile memory cannot be lost - even if the vehicle battery is removed. If the ECM from one vehicle is transferred to another vehicle, the contents of non-volatile memory will also be transferred, unless a FCR is used to erase the codes and tune the engine to the new set-up. However, the codes are automatically self-erased by the ECM after seven engine starts that result in the engine running for a minimum of 20 minutes.

Reference voltage

Voltage supply from the ECM to many of the engine sensors is at a 5.0-volt reference level. This ensures a stable working voltage, unaffected by variations in system voltage.

The earth return connection for some engine sensors is made through an ECM pin that is not directly connected to earth. The ECM internally connects that pin to earth via one of the ECM pins that are directly connected to earth.

Signal shielding

Ford vehicles

To reduce interference (RFI), the ECM is directly connected to the chassis in order to reduce interference to a minimum. In addition, the knock sensor (when fitted) and MAP sensor are equipped with shielded cables.

Fiat group

To reduce interference (RFI), the oxygen sensor (OS) and the ignition control signal are provided with shielded cables.

3 Primary trigger

Crank angle sensor (CAS)

The primary signal to initiate both ignition and fuelling emanates from a CAS mounted next to the front pulley. The CAS consists of an inductive magnet that radiates a magnetic field. Four teeth are set into the periphery of the pulley at 90° intervals. As the pulley spins, and the teeth are rotated in the magnetic field, an AC voltage signal is delivered to the ECM to indicate speed of rotation and the position of TDC. All four signals are used to indicate rpm, but only two of the signals (set 180° apart) are used by the ECM to indicate TDC.

The peak-to-peak voltage of the speed signal can vary from 5 volts at idle to over 100 volts at 6000 rpm. An analogue-to-digital converter (ADC) in the processor unit transforms the AC pulse into a digital signal.

Cylinder identification sensor (CID) - phase sensor

Because the engine utilises sequential injection, the system needs to know which cylinder is No 1.

A cylinder identification sensor is used to identify and correctly phase the cylinder firing sequence. The sensor is located in the distributor **(see illustration 18.2)**. It consists of a permanent magnet and two lobes (90° apart) attached to the distributor shaft. When the engine is cranked or run, the lobes are rotated in the magnetic field produced by the permanent magnet, and this generates an AC signal that is delivered to the ECM. The signal is very similar to that generated by the CAS. The ECM utilises an ADC to transform

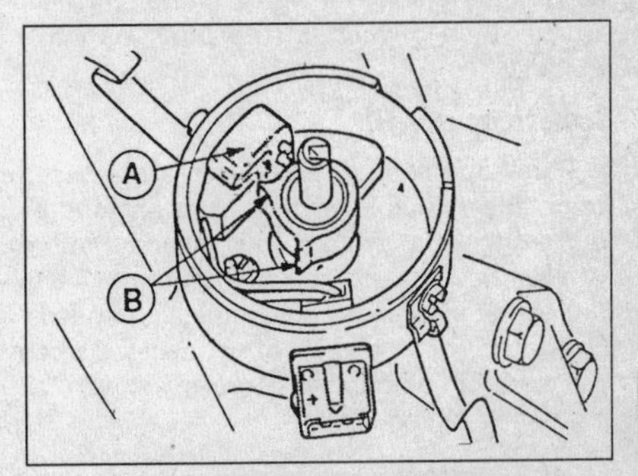

18.2 Phase sensor in distributor

A CID (Phase sensor)
B Cam with two teeth

the AC signal into a digital pulse, and the signal is used to correctly time the sequential injection pulses according to the firing order of the engine. The first lobe signals the start of the sequential pulse, and the second lobe signals the end of the sequence.

The ECM uses signals from both the CAS and the CID to determine the starting or trigger point of sequential injection. Depending on operating conditions, the ECM may vary the start time of the sequential injection pulses. This means that injection for any one or more cylinders may begin at some point during the exhaust stroke, right through to a point after the inlet valve has opened.

4 Ignition

Data on load (MAP), engine speed (CAS), engine temperature (CTS) and throttle position (TPS) are collected by the ECM, which then refers to the digital map stored within its microprocessor. This map contains an advance angle for each operating condition, and thus the best ignition advance angle for a particular operating condition can be determined. The ECM looks up the correct dwell duration and timing point, and signals the amplifier - which in turn switches the coil negative terminal to achieve ignition. During engine cranking the ignition timing is fixed at 10° until the engine has started, after which time the ECM regulates the timing according to its internal map.

Amplifier

The amplifier contains the circuitry for switching the coil negative terminal to instigate ignition. This version of Weber-Marelli utilises a separate amplifier mounted adjacent to the coil. The ECM timing signal is of an insufficient level to complete the necessary coil switching, and the signal is thus amplified to a level capable of switching the coil negative terminal. The ECM thus calculates the correct ignition dwell time and timing advance from data received from its sensors, and sends a signal to the amplifier, which then switches the coil negative terminal.

Ignition dwell

Dwell operation in Weber-Marelli is based upon the principle of the 'constant-energy current-limiting' system. This means that the dwell period remains constant at around 4.0 to 5.0 ms, at virtually all engine running speeds. However, the dwell duty cycle, when measured in percent or degrees, will vary as the engine speed varies.

Ignition coil

The ignition coil utilises low primary resistance in order to increase primary current and primary energy. The amplifier limits the primary current to around 8 amps, and this permits a reserve of energy to maintain the required spark burn time (duration).

Distributor

In the Weber-Marelli system, the distributor only serves to distribute the HT current from the coil secondary terminal to each spark plug in firing order. In addition, the distributor also contains the CID phase sensor.

Ignition timing

Essentially the base ignition timing is fixed on models equipped with Weber-Marelli. However, it is possible to physically move the distributor and therefore disturb the timing. If the distributor is turned to any position other than the datum position, the base timing (from which the ECM calculates the advance) will be incorrect, and the CID phasing will also be inaccurate. In Ford models, a service cable is provide to allow adjustment of the timing to suit various grades of petrol.

Service connections (Ford only)

The service connection cables are a method of informing the ECM of changed operating circumstances, so that the ECM can alter its internal program. When one or more of the cables are connected to earth and depending on the combination of cables used, the ECM will alter the timing advance map so that the engine will run on lower-octane fuel.

The ECM provides a 5.0-volt reference feed to each of the service cables. When this cable is connected to earth, the voltage drops to zero. Once the ECM sees zero volts upon a particular cable, appropriate adjustments are made to its internal program.

Knock sensor (some models)

The optimal ignition timing (at engine speeds greater than idle) for a given high-compression engine is quite close to the point of onset of knock. However, running so close to the point of knock occurrence means that knock will certainly occur on one or more cylinders at certain times during the engine operating cycle.

IAW Weber employs a knock control unit (KCU) in the ECM to determine the moment of knocking. The knock sensor is mounted on the engine block, and consists of a piezo-ceramic measuring element that responds to engine noise oscillations. This signal is converted to a voltage signal by the knock sensor and returned to the KCU for evaluation and action.

Initially, timing will occur at its optimal ignition point. Once knock is identified, the Knock Control microprocessor retards the ignition timing. After knocking ceases, the timing is advanced until the reference timing value is achieved or knock occurs once more, when the timing is again retarded. This procedure continually occurs so that the engine will consistently run at the optimum timing.

5 Fuel injection

Air intake system

The air intake system consists of the following components:

a) Air filter.
b) Inlet air trunking.
c) Throttle body
d) Throttle valve.
e) Inlet manifold.
f) Inlet valve.
g) Idle speed control valve (ISCV).
h) Throttle pot (TPS).
i) MAP sensor.
j) Air temperature sensor (ATS).

In addition, turbocharged engines utilise a number of extra components:

a) Turbocharger.
b) Intercooler.
c) Wastegate and wastegate control.
d) By-pass valve.

Air intake operation

Air is drawn through the induction system by the fall of a piston in the cylinder. When the piston falls in a sealed cylinder (sealed apart from an inlet leading in from the induction system) an area of low pressure forms above the piston. Atmospheric pressure, which is present in the engine compartment outside of the induction path, pushes the high-pressure air into the cylinder via the induction tract. A throttle valve regulates the flow of air through the system.

An ISCV, located in an air by-pass hose and controlled by the ECM, regulates the flow of air at idle speed so that a stable idle may be maintained under all conditions of temperature and idle load. An additional by-pass passage is provided in the throttle body, so that the base idle speed may be set. In early models, the base idle is set as part of the idle speed adjustment procedure. In later models, the base idle screw is pre-set and sealed during manufacture, and should not be moved during normal engine operation.

The MAP and TPS signals inform the ECM of various load conditions and throttle positions, and the ATS signals the temperature of the incoming air. From this data and also with reference to the CTS and rpm signals, the ECM is able to look up the injection duration to give the correct AFR for all operating conditions.

Fuel injection (general)

The Weber injection system is a multi-point system where the injectors are pulsed sequentially - ie in firing order and once per engine cycle. The timing of the pulse is determined from signals received by the ECM from the CAS and CID sensor. Each injector is connected to the ECM via a separate pin.

Please note that although the injectors are pulsed sequentially, the injector pulse is not necessarily synchronised to the ignition timing - the ECM may vary the timing of the pulse according to operating conditions. This means that injection for any one or more cylinders may begin at some point during the power stroke, right through to a point after the inlet valve has opened.

Data on engine load (MAP), engine speed (CAS), engine temperature (CTS) and throttle position (TPS) are collected by the ECM, which then refers to a digital map stored within its microprocessor. This map contains an injection duration for each operating condition, and thus the best pulse duration angle for a particular operating condition can be determined.

The injector is switched using two circuits. Operation depends on the principle that more current is required to open an injector than to keep it open. This kind of system is often termed 'current-controlled injection system'.

Once the injector is open, a second circuit holds the injector open to complete the required pulse duration. Advantages of this arrangement include a reduction in injector operating temperature, and immediate injector closure once the holding circuit is switched off. During engine start from cold, the pulse duration is increased to provide a richer air/fuel mixture.

Fuel injectors

The fuel injector is a magnetically-operated solenoid valve that is actuated by the ECM. Voltage to the injectors is applied from the main relay, and the earth path is completed by the ECM for a period of time (called pulse duration) of between 1.5 and 10 milliseconds. The pulse duration is very much dependent upon engine temperature, load, speed and operating conditions. When the magnetic solenoid closes, a back-EMF voltage of up to 60 volts is induced.

During engine deceleration above 1800 rpm with a closed throttle, the ECM cuts off injection. Fuel injection is re-instated as the rpm sinks below 1400 rpm or the throttle is re-opened. Fuel cut-off and re-instatement occurs at higher engine speeds when the engine is cold and during engine warm-up.

Above a certain engine rpm, the injectors operation is cut off to prevent engine damage.

MAP sensor

The main engine load sensor is the MAP sensor. A vacuum hose connects the MAP sensor and the inlet manifold. Manifold vacuum acts upon the MAP sensor diaphragm and the ECM internally converts the pressure into an electrical signal. MAP is calculated from the formula: Atmospheric Pressure less Manifold Pressure = Manifold Absolute Pressure.

Using the speed/density method, Weber-Marelli calculates the AFR from the MAP signal and the speed of the engine (CAS). This method relies on the theory that the engine will draw in a fixed volume of air per revolution.

When manifold vacuum is high (ie idle condition), MAP is moderately low and the ECM provides less fuel. When manifold vacuum is low (ie wide-open throttle), MAP is high and the ECM provides more fuel.

The inlet manifold on the MPi models is a 'dry' manifold. Since fuel does not enter the manifold - due to injection being directed into the passage leading to the inlet valve - there is no risk of fuel being drawn into the MAP sensor to contaminate the diaphragm, and a fuel trap is not used.

The MAP sensor will provide negative (or vacuum) measurements under naturally-aspirated (ie non-turbocharged) operating conditions. However, when the turbocharger is in operation, the inlet manifold is pressurised, and the signal returned to the ECM from the MAP sensor is a positive measurement of pressure.

A 5.0-volt reference voltage is applied to the sensor and connected to the sensor return circuit. A transducer converts the manifold pressure into a voltage signal that is returned to the ECM. The voltage signal reflects the fluctuating pressure in the inlet manifold according to engine load, and varies from about 1.0 volt at idle to around 4.5 volts at full load.

Air temperature sensor (ATS)

The ATS is mounted in the inlet manifold, where it measures the air temperature in the manifold. Because the density of air varies in inverse proportion to the temperature, the ATS signal allows more accurate assessment of the volume of air entering the engine.

The open-circuit supply to the sensor is at a 5.0-volt reference level, and the earth path is through the sensor return. The ATS operates on the NTC principle. A variable voltage signal is returned to the ECM based upon the air temperature. This signal is approximately 2.0 to 3.0 volts at an ambient temperature of 20°C, and reduces to about 1.5 volts as the temperature rises to around 40°C.

Because the density of air varies in inverse proportion to the temperature, the ATS signal allows more accurate assessment of the volume of air entering the engine. In turbocharger applications, the inlet air is pressurised, which raises its temperature. If the inlet air becomes too hot, the air density is reduced and the AFR will become leaner. A lean mixture could lead to detonation, and in turn this could cause engine damage. When the ECM senses an overheated air charge, it pulses the wastegate control solenoid (WCS) to relieve boost pressure. A lower boost pressure will reduce the air temperature, and the risk of detonation is averted or at least reduced.

CO potentiometer ('pot') - non-cat models only

The CO pot mixture adjuster is a potentiometer that is directly connected to the ECM. As the CO pot adjustment screw is turned, the change in resistance returns a voltage signal to the ECM that will result in a change in CO. The CO pot adjustment only affects idle CO, and the AFR at engine speeds above idle is not affected by changes made to the CO pot. Voltage and resistance measurements are not possible at this sensor. The CO pot is not fitted to catalyst-equipped vehicles, and the CO is thus non-adjustable.

When the CO pot is directly connected to the ECM, voltage and resistance measurements are not possible. However, measurements are possible for the component mounted in the engine compartment.

There are several variations to this range of vehicles. Very early vehicles (eg Fiat Croma and Lancia Dedra) are equipped with an ECM CO pot (otherwise known as a CO 'trimmer') alone. From about 1990, many models are equipped with an external CO pot in addition to the CO trimmer on the ECM. Vehicles with a catalytic converter and OS were not equipped with an external CO pot, but early versions retained the CO trimmer. A small amount of adjustment could be effected by virtue of the CO trimmer, or by using a FCR attached to the SD connector. The CO trimmer was then discontinued, and the FCR became the only means of making CO adjustments on catalyst engines. Finally, CO adjustment was discontinued altogether, and adjustments are not possible for all late vehicles. Replacement ECM units for cat vehicles may have the CO pot disabled, and no adjustments to CO are then possible.

Coolant temperature sensor (CTS)

The CTS is incorporated in the cooling system, and contains a variable resistance that operates on the NTC principle. When the engine is cold, the resistance is quite high. Once the engine is started and begins to warm-up, the coolant becomes hotter, and this causes a change in the CTS resistance. As the CTS becomes hotter, the resistance of the CTS reduces (NTC principle), and this returns a variable voltage signal to the ECM based upon the coolant temperature.

The open-circuit supply to the sensor is at a 5.0-volt reference level, and this voltage reduces to a value that depends upon the resistance of the CTS resistance. Normal operating temperature is usually from 80° to 100°C. The ECM uses the CTS signal as a main correction factor when calculating ignition timing and injection duration.

Throttle potentiometer sensor (TPS)

A TPS is provided to inform the ECM of throttle position and rate of acceleration. The TPS is a potentiometer with three wires. A 5.0-volt reference voltage is supplied to a resistance track, with the other end connected to earth. The third wire is connected to an arm which wipes along the resistance track, and so varies the resistance and voltage of the signal returned to the ECM.

There are two types of TPS fitted to this range of vehicles. Although the principle of operation remains similar for both types, the actual operation and measured signal is reversed. To some extent, this is accomplished by reversing the supply and earth connections at the TPS.

Early-type TPS: Ford two-wheel-drive models 1986 to 1990; Fiat Croma and some Lancia models

The wiper arm is not in contact with the track when the TPS is in the closed position. Five volts is measured on the signal wire in this position. Furthermore, the earth and supply connections are made so that the variable resistance between the signal and supply is at its lowest when the TPS is almost closed. As the throttle is initially opened, the wiper arm will engage the track and the voltage will jump to about 4.5 volts. As the throttle is further opened, the voltage will gradually decrease until a maximum of about 0.5 to 0.6 volts is measured. The variable resistance measured between the supply and signal terminals will be infinity when the throttle is closed, around 40 to 150 ohms when the throttle is just open, and increase to around 300 to 600 ohms as the throttle is opened.

Later-type TPS: Ford four-wheel-drive models; most Fiat and Lancia vehicles

The wiper arm is in contact with the track when the TPS is in the closed position. About 0.5 to 0.6 volts is be measured on the signal wire in this position. Furthermore, the earth and supply connections are made so that the variable resistance between the signal and earth is at its highest when the TPS is closed. As the throttle is opened, the voltage will gradually increase until a maximum of 4.5 volts is measured. The variable resistance measured between the supply and signal terminals will be around 300 to 600 ohms when the throttle is closed, and decrease to approximately 40 to 150 ohms as the throttle is opened.

Throttle body

In order to prevent condensation of fuel and ice formation under certain conditions of temperature and humidity, the throttle body is heated by a flow of coolant liquid that passes through the internal channels. Two different types of throttle body may be fitted to the Fiat and Lancia vehicles covered by this system. In one type, the base idle speed is adjustable and the engine is equipped with an base idle speed adjustment screw. In the second type, the base idle speed is factory-set and not adjustable, and the adjustment screw must not be tampered with.

Idle speed control valve (ISCV)

The ISCV is a solenoid-controlled actuator that is located in a hose by-passing the throttle body. In early versions of IAW Weber, the ECM controls the valve is to raise the idle speed during engine warm-up and when the engine is under load. Later versions of IAW control the valve similarly, with the addition that base idle speed is also controlled. Where the ECM does not control the base idle speed, normal idle rpm is set by adjusting an idle by-pass air screw in the throttle body. Where the ECM does control the base idle speed, the base idle rpm is non-adjustable.

A voltage supply is applied to the ISCV from the fuel pump relay, and the earth for the motor is made through a connection to ECM pin 34.

A duty cycle can be measured on the earth circuit, to determine the opening or closing time period as a percentage of the total time available. Total opening time is 11.0 ms or 100% duty cycle. The valve is pulsed at a frequency of 90 Hz, and the duty cycle will normally operate in a range of between 10 and 90%. This is equivalent to a timebase of between 1.1 and 9.9 ms. Events that influence the ECM in adjusting the ISCV opening time are: idle RPM, coolant temperature and manifold pressure.

When electrical loads such as the headlights or heater fan are switched on, the idle speed would tend to drop. The ECM will sense the load, and pulse the ISCV further open to increase the airflow through the valve and thus increase the idle speed. When the load is removed, the ECM will reduce the pulse width so that the airflow is reduced. Normal idle speed should be maintained under all cold and hot operating conditions.

The ECM fitted from about 1993 pulses the ISCV for a few seconds after the ignition is switched on. This action allows the ISCV an element of self-cleaning.

Turbocharger

Refer to Chapter 2 for a detailed description of turbocharger operation. The wastegate is controlled by the ECM according to engine load and speed, and an air by-pass valve is utilised to reduce the incidence of 'turbo lag'.

Voltage is applied to the WCS from either the main or fuel pump relay (depending on model) and the earth for the motor is made through a connection to ECM pin 16.

Wastegate control solenoid (WCS)

When the engine is stopped, the WCS is closed, and air is fully directed to the wastegate actuator. This is the fail-safe position; if the WCS fails, boost pressure will never reach its set limit and engine power will be reduced. Once the engine is running, the ECM pulses the WCS open so that around 50% of the turbo output is directed towards the wastegate. The ECM tends to pulse the valve with a fixed frequency, and the duration of the pulse is varied so that the valve is open for longer or shorter time periods as desired. This method allows the ECM to set the exact opening duration to achieve the correct boost pressure for all operating conditions.

Air temperature control

If the inlet air becomes too hot (above 70°C), the air density is reduced and the AFR will become leaner. A lean mixture could lead to detonation, and in turn this could cause engine damage. When the ECM senses an overheated air charge, it pulses the WCS towards the closed position to relieve boost pressure. A lower boost pressure will reduce the air temperature, and the risk of detonation is averted or at least reduced. In addition, when the ECM senses an overboost condition, engine rpm is limited as an additional precaution to prevent engine damage.

Relays

The Weber-Marelli electrical system is controlled by a main fuel injection relay and a fuel pump relay. In Ford and some Fiat group vehicles, these relays are separate components. However, a number of later Fiat group models employ the 15-pin dual contact relay. There are a number of variations in the wiring and actuation of both types of relay, and the following descriptions are typical.

Main and fuel pump relays (separate relays)

A permanent voltage supply is made to terminal 30 on both main and fuel pump relays from the battery positive terminal. When the ignition is first switched on, the ignition supplies voltage to terminal 86, and the ECM earths terminal 85 through ECM pin 10 which energises the first relay winding. **Note:** *In some models, the connections to terminals 30 and 87 on the main relay and terminal 85 and 86 on both main and fuel pump relays are reversed.* This causes the first relay contacts to close, and terminal 30 is connected to the output circuit at terminal 87. Terminal 87 supplies voltage to the injectors, ECM terminal 20, ISCV, WCS and the CFSV (when fitted). In addition voltage is supplied to the fuel pump relay terminal 86.

When the ignition is switched on. the ECM briefly earths fuel pump relay contact 85 at ECM terminal 28. This energises the relay winding, which closes the relay contact and connects voltage from terminal 30 to terminal 87, thereby providing voltage to the fuel pump circuit. After approximately one second, the ECM opens the circuit and the pump stops. This brief running of the fuel pump allows pressure to build within the fuel pressure lines, and provides for an easier start.

The fuel pump relay circuit will remain open until the engine is cranked or run. Once the ECM receives a speed signal from the CAS, the relay winding will again be energised by the ECM, and the fuel pump will run until the engine is stopped.

Main and fuel pump relays (single 'dual' relay)

A permanent voltage is applied to relay terminals 8 and 11 from the battery positive terminal. When the ignition is switched on, a voltage supply is applied to relay terminal 14, which connects to earth through terminal 7 thus energising the first relay winding.

When the relay winding is energised, this causes the relay contacts to close, and terminal 8 is connected to the output terminals. A voltage supply is thus output at terminal 4, 5, 6 and 13. Terminal 4 supplies voltage to terminal 3 of the 15 pin relay (some vehicles) and the other terminals supply voltage to ECM terminal 20, the ISCV, the injectors and the ignition coils and ignition amplifier.

When the ignition is switched on, a voltage supply is applied to terminal 2 from relay terminal 4 and the ECM briefly earths relay contact 10 at ECM pin 28. This energises the second relay winding, which closes the second relay contact and connects voltage from terminal 11 to output terminals 1and 9, thereby providing voltage to the fuel pump and OS heater circuits. After approximately one second, the ECM opens the circuit and the pump stops. This brief running of the fuel pump allows pressure to build within the fuel pressure lines, and provides for an easier start.

The second circuit will then remain open until the engine is cranked or run. Once the ECM receives a speed signal from the CAS, the second winding will again be energised by the ECM, and the fuel pump will run until the engine is stopped. In addition, the pump circuit usually supplies voltage to the ignition coil and throttle body heater from the second output terminal. However, these components are supplied from the first circuit in some vehicles.

Inertia switch (some later models only)

The inertia switch is a safety cut-out switch used to isolate the fuel pump in the event of a very sharp deceleration - ie a collision. Once the switch has been activated, the electrical supply to the fuel pump remain open-circuit until the inertia switch has been reset by raising the button.

Fuel pressure system

In the Ford Escort and most Fiat and Lancia vehicles, the fuel pump is mounted vertically in the fuel tank. The Ford Sierra and some early Lancia vehicles utilise an external roller type pump, mounted close to the fuel tank. Any internal pump may be of the roller type or the gerotor type.

Roller-type pump (internal or external)

A roller-type fuel pump, driven by a permanent magnet electric motor, draws fuel from the tank, and pumps it to the fuel rail via a fuel filter. The pump is of the 'wet' variety, in that fuel actually flows through the pump and the electric motor. There is no actual fire risk, because the fuel drawn through the pump is not in a combustible condition.

Mounted upon the armature shaft is an eccentric rotor, holding a number of pockets arranged around the circumference - each pocket containing a metal roller. As the pump is actuated, the rollers are flung outward by centrifugal force to act as seals. The fuel between the rollers is forced to the pump pressure outlet.

Internal pump

The fuel pump is mounted vertically in the fuel tank, and comprises an outer and inner gear assembly, termed a 'gerotor'. Once the pump motor becomes energised, the gerotor rotates and as the fuel passes through the individual teeth of the gerotor, a pressure differential is created. Fuel is drawn through the pump inlet, to be pressurised between the rotating gerotor teeth and discharged from the pump outlet into the fuel supply line.

Fuel pump (all)

The fuel pump normally provides much more fuel than is required, and surplus fuel is thus returned to the fuel tank via a return pipe. In fact, a maximum fuel pressure in excess of 5 bar is possible in this system. When the maximum pressure is exceeded, a pressure valve in the pump directs the fuel supply into the inlet, thereby preventing overheating of the fuel pump. To prevent pressure loss in the supply system, a non-return valve is provided in the fuel pump outlet. When the ignition is switched off, and the fuel pump ceases operation, pressure is thus maintained for some time.

Fuel pressure regulator

Fuel pressure in the fuel rail is maintained at a constant 2.5 to 3.5 bar (depending on model) by a fuel pressure regulator. The pressure regulator is fitted on the outlet side of the fuel rail, and consists of two chambers separated by a diaphragm. The upper chamber contains a spring, which exerts pressure upon the lower chamber and closes off the outlet diaphragm. Pressurised fuel flows into the lower chamber, and this exerts pressure upon the diaphragm. Once the pressure exceeds the system pressure, the outlet diaphragm is opened and excess fuel flows back to the fuel tank via a return line. In the Fiat Tipo 16-valve engine from 1993, the fuel flow to the return pipe is through an internal passage of the fuel rail, as opposed to the external flow of other engines.

A vacuum hose connects the upper chamber to the inlet manifold, so that variations in inlet manifold pressure will not affect the amount of fuel injected. This means that the pressure in the rail is always at a constant pressure above the pressure in the inlet manifold. The quantity of injected fuel thus depends solely on injector opening time, as determined by the ECM, and not on a variable fuel pressure.

At idle speed with the vacuum pipe disconnected, with the engine stopped and the pump running, or at full-throttle, the system fuel pressure will be around 2.5 to 3.5 bar (depending on model). At idle speed (vacuum pipe connected), the fuel pressure will be approximately 0.5 bar under the system pressure.

6 Catalytic converter and emission control

Some versions of the Weber-Marelli injection system are equipped with a catalytic converter, and implement a closed-loop control system so that exhaust emissions may be reduced. Closed-loop systems are equipped with an oxygen sensor (OS) which monitors the exhaust gas for oxygen content. A low oxygen level in the exhaust signifies a rich mixture. A high oxygen level in the exhaust signifies a weak mixture.

When the engine is operating in closed-loop control, the OS signal causes the ECM to modify the injector pulse so that the AFR is maintained close to the stoichiometric ratio. By controlling the injection pulse during most operating conditions, so that the air/fuel ratio is always in a small 'window' around the Lambda point (ie Lambda = 0.97 to 1.03), almost perfect combustion could be achieved. Thus, the catalyst has less work to do, and will last longer, with fewer emissions at the tail pipe.

The closed-loop control is implemented during engine operation at coolant temperatures above 45°C. When the coolant temperature is low, or the engine is at full-load or on the overrun, the ECM will operate in open-loop. When operating in open-loop, the ECM allows a richer or leaner AFR than the stoichiometric ratio. This prevents engine hesitation, for example, during acceleration with a wide-open throttle.

The OS only produces a signal when the exhaust gas has reached a minimum temperature of approximately 300°C. In order that the OS will reach optimum operating temperature as quickly as possible after the engine has started, the OS contains a heating element.

The OS heater supply is made from the fuel pump relay terminal number 87. This ensures that the heater will only operate whilst the engine is running.

Evaporative emission control (cat models)

An activated carbon canister is employed in catalyst-equipped vehicles, to aid evaporative emission control. However, different methods are used by Ford and the Fiat group in purging the canister and recycling the vapours.

Carbon filter solenoid valve (CFSV) - Sierra / Escort

The carbon canister stores fuel vapours until the CFSV is opened by the Weber-Marelli

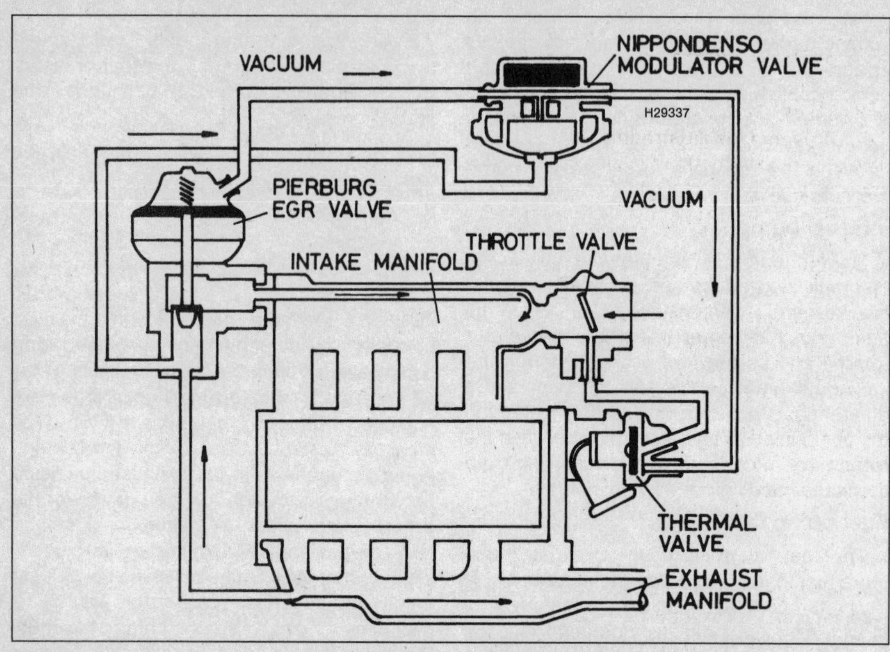

18.3 Typical Fiat EGR diagram

ECM under certain operating conditions. Once the CFSV is actuated by the ECM, fuel vapours are drawn into the inlet manifold to be burnt by the engine during normal combustion.

So that engine performance will not be affected, the CFSV remains closed during cold engine operation, and also during engine idle. Once the engine coolant temperature reaches normal operating temperature and the throttle position is in the mid-range, the CFSV will be modulated (pulsed) on and off by the ECM.

Carbon filter control valve - Fiat/Lancia

An mechanical control valve and activated carbon canister is employed in catalyst-equipped vehicles, to aid evaporative emission control and regulate the recycling of fuel vapours. The carbon canister stores fuel vapours until the control valve is opened during part-load operating conditions. The carbon filter control valve is not operated by the Weber-Marelli ECM in this system.

Two vacuum connections from the throttle body are connected to the control valve. The vacuum connection on the throttle body is ported; this ensures that when the engine is stopped or running at idle speed, no vacuum signal is present. When the throttle is opened, the vacuum connection is exposed to engine vacuum, which in turn acts on the diaphragm. The diaphragm moves against a spring, and uncovers a second vacuum channel. Vacuum acting upon the second connection is then allowed to draw the fuel vapours from the canister into the inlet manifold, to be burnt by the engine during normal combustion.

EGR system (Fiat/Lancia, where fitted)

Refer to Chapter 2 for a detailed description of EGR operation. The EGR system used in the Weber IAW equipped vehicles is a mechanical system that is controlled by engine vacuum and not by the ECM **(see illustration 18.3)**.

If the exhaust gas was recycled in a cold engine, performance and idle would be adversely affected. A thermal valve in the vacuum piping ensures that full EGR operation only occurs after the engine has attained a coolant temperature of 40 ± 3°C, although the EGR thermal valve actually begins to open at a coolant temperature of 30 ± 3°C.

The EGR system consists of a thermal valve, Nippondenso modulator valve and EGR valve. When the engine is cold, the thermal valve is closed, and the EGR system is inoperative. Once the coolant temperature rises above 30 ± 3°C, the thermal valve begins to open, and vacuum is piped to the EGR modulator valve.

The EGR modulator valve controls the vacuum supply to the EGR valve. A channel from the exhaust system pipes exhaust gases to the modulator. A combination of engine vacuum and exhaust gas pressure allows the modulator to control the opening of the EGR valve, which in turn opens to allow a finely-metered supply of exhaust gas to be introduced into the inlet manifold.

Engine at idle speed (coolant temperature above 30 ± 3°C)

The vacuum signal acting on the modulator is quite strong. However, the exhaust gases acting upon the modulator are relatively weak, and the vacuum signal is bled away through an internal channel to the incoming exhaust gases channel. The EGR valve remains closed.

Engine operating under part-load conditions

The throttle is partly open. The vacuum signal acting on the modulator is quite strong. The exhaust gases acting upon the modulator are also strong, which opens the modulator exhaust valve against a spring. In turn, this seals the vacuum channel, and allows the vacuum signal to be directed to the modulator outlet, where it actuates the EGR valve which opens in turn to allow a finely-metered supply of exhaust gas to be introduced into the inlet manifold.

Engine operating under full-load conditions

The throttle is fully open. The vacuum signal acting on the modulator is almost non-existent. The exhaust gases acting upon the modulator are strong, which opens the modulator exhaust valve against the spring. Since there is little vacuum, the EGR valve is not actuated and remains closed.

Adjustments

7 Adjustment pre-conditions

1 Ensure that all of these conditions are met before attempting to make adjustments:

a) *Engine at operating temperature. Engine oil at a minimum temperature of 80°C. A journey of at least 4 miles is recommended (particularly so if equipped with AT).*
b) *Ancillary equipment (all engine loads and accessories) switched off.*
c) *AT engines: Transmission in N or P.*
d) *Engine mechanically sound.*
e) *Engine breather hoses and breather system in satisfactory condition.*
f) *Induction system free from vacuum leaks.*
g) *Ignition system in satisfactory condition.*
h) *Air filter in satisfactory condition.*
i) *Exhaust system free from leaks.*
j) *Throttle cable correctly adjusted.*
k) *No fault codes logged by the ECM.*
l) *OS operating satisfactorily (catalyst vehicles with closed-loop control).*

2 In addition, before checking the idle speed and CO values, stabilise the engine as follows:

a) *Stabilise the engine. Raise the engine speed to 3000 rpm for a minimum of 30 seconds, and then allow the engine to idle.*
b) *If the cooling fan operates during adjustment, wait until it stops, re-stabilise the engine, and then restart the adjustment procedure.*
c) *Allow the CO and idle speed to settle.*
d) *Make all checks and adjustments within 30 seconds. If this time is exceeded, re-stabilise the engine and recheck.*

8 Crank angle sensor (CAS)

CAS clearance

1 Turn the engine so that the CAS is directly opposite one of the four teeth on the sensor.

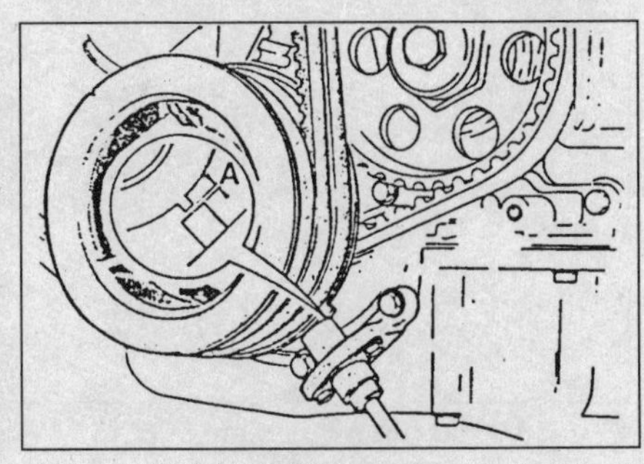

18.4 CAS clearance
A Clearance: 0.40 to 1.00 mm

2 Use a feeler gauge to check the clearance between the CAS and tooth. The clearance is 0.4 to 1.0 mm **(see illustration 18.4)**.
3 It is essential that the clearance is within specification. Adjustment is made by moving the CAS on its bracket, or by fitting and removing shims.
4 Repeat the check for each of the four teeth. The variation of clearance between neighbouring teeth must be no more than 0.2 mm; any irregularity will result in uneven running. An oscilloscope is ideal to check for an uneven waveform.

CAS position

Note: *This action is unnecessary unless the sensor has been moved or removed.*
5 Use a dial gauge to set piston Nos 1 and 4 at TDC.
6 On Fiat Croma 2.0 models, move the engine 1.06 mm anti-clockwise from TDC; this sets the piston at exactly 10° BTDC.
7 A Fiat special tool (part number 1895900000) is necessary to set the CAS position for maximum accuracy.
8 Remove the CAS, and replace with the Fiat tool.
9 Loosen the CAS carrier plate retaining bolts, and move the plate until the slot in the end of the tool fits snugly over the tooth on the pulley.
10 Tighten the CAS carrier plate bolts.
11 Remove the tool and refit the CAS.
12 Adjust the CAS as described above.

9 CID (phase sensor)

CID clearance

1 Rotate the distributor shaft until one of the two teeth on the cam is directly opposite the tooth on the sensor.
2 Insert a feeler gauge of 0.3 to 0.4 mm into the clearance between the teeth.
3 If the clearance is incorrect, loosen the two fixing screws on the distributor plate.
4 Move the plate until the correct clearance is attained.

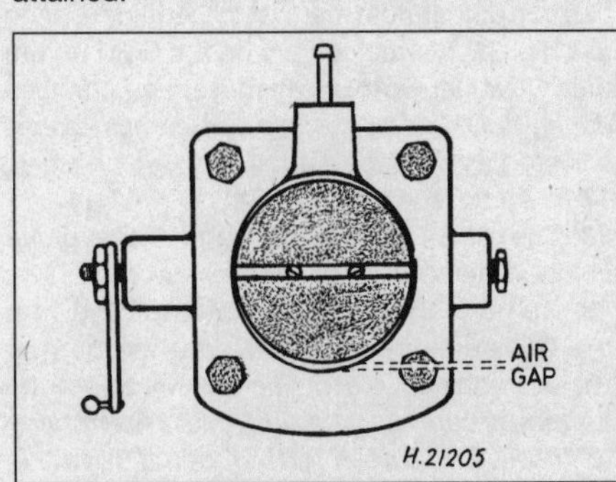

18.5 Throttle valve adjustment

5 Rotate the distributor shaft until the second of the two teeth on the cam is directly opposite the tooth on the sensor.
6 Insert a feeler gauge of 0.3 to 0.4 mm into the clearance between the teeth.
7 If the clearance is incorrect, loosen the two fixing screws on the distributor plate and move the plate until the correct clearance is attained.
8 Repeat the adjustments until both clearances are within the specification.

10 Throttle adjustments

Throttle valve position

1 The throttle valve position is critical, and should not normally be disturbed.
2 Carry out the following checks, and only make an adjustment where the throttle position has been disturbed or adjustment is deemed absolutely necessary.
3 Clean the throttle valve and surrounding areas with carburettor cleaner. Blow-by from the breather system could cause a sticky throttle action.
4 With the engine switched off, use the accelerator pedal to fully open and close the throttle. Check for a smooth progressive action that allows the throttle to fully open and then close against its stop.
5 If the throttle does not fully open, check for the following:

a) *Faulty or worn linkage or throttle body.*
b) *Faulty accelerator pedal action.*
c) *Displaced floor covering, or bent throttle pedal.*

6 If the throttle does not fully close, check for the following:

a) *Maladjusted throttle cable.*
b) *Maladjusted throttle valve position.*
c) *Carbon build-up around throttle valve.*

Adjustment

7 Move the adjustment screw so that the throttle is fully closed.
8 Insert a feeler gauge thickness 0.1 mm between the throttle bore and the throttle valve **(see illustration 18.5)**.
9 Turn the adjustment screw so that the feeler gauge is a close sliding fit in the gap.
10 Remove the feeler gauge. The throttle should be open just enough to prevent the valve seizing or sticking in the throttle bore.

Checking TPS adjustment

11 Connect a voltmeter between terminals 17 and 11.

a) *Pre-1990: Check for 5.0 volts. If the voltage is 4.5 or lower, the throttle is open.*
b) *Post-1990: Check for 0.6 volts or less.*

Adjustment of TPS

12 Loosen the two adjustment screws and move the TPS until the correct voltage is obtained. If the correct voltage cannot be obtained, renew the TPS assembly.

11 Ignition timing

1 Essentially, the base ignition timing is fixed on models equipped with Weber-Marelli. However, it is possible to physically move the distributor, and therefore disturb the timing. If the distributor is turned to any position other than the datum position, the base timing (from which the ECM calculates the advance) will be incorrect, and the CID phasing will also be inaccurate.

Adjusting the distributor

2 Set the engine to TDC, No 4 cylinder on the compression stroke.
3 Fit the distributor into its housing on the cylinder block. The distributor drive will only fit into one basic position.
4 Move the distributor casing until the mark on the top of the casing aligns with the mark in the centre of the rotor.
5 Tighten the distributor fixing screws, taking care that the distributor does not move out of alignment. **Note:** *A Fiat special tool, part number 1895896000, is available to ensure maximum accuracy in setting the distributor position. We cannot overstress the importance of correct distributor positioning. If the CID sensor and CAS are out of phase, the ECM will no longer be able to accurately time the injection pulse.*
6 In addition, timing marks are provided so that the dynamic timing can be checked.

Dynamic timing checks

7 Refer to the adjustment pre-conditions in Section 7.
8 Allow the engine to idle.
9 Check that the timing mark aligns with the mark on the timing case.
10 Ford models: The pulley marks indicate 16° BTDC and TDC. If the service-set cables are connected, the engine will be timed at a value corresponding to the degree of retard determined by which combination of cables are being used.
11 Fiat/Lancia models: The initial timing is between 9 and 15° depending upon model. **Note:** *Due to the ECM continually altering the timing, in order to make small changes to the idle speed, the pulley mark will be forever moving about the timing case mark.*
12 If the timing is incorrect, check the position of the CAS. Otherwise, the ECM is suspect.
13 Increase the engine speed. The timing should advance smoothly as the rpm increases.

12 Idle adjustments

1 Refer to the pre-conditions described in Section 7.
2 Check that the throttle plate and TPS are correctly adjusted.
3 Run the engine until it reaches normal operating temperature.
4 Stabilise the engine as before.
5 Check that the idle speed is within its normal operating parameters.

Idle speed adjustment

6 If the idle speed requires adjustment, disconnect the ISCV multi-plug.

All Ford engines, and Fiat/Lancia engines pre-1990

7 Turn the by-pass screw on the throttle body until the idle speed is 50 rpm lower than the specified value.

Fiat/Lancia engines post-1990

8 Turn the by-pass screw on the throttle body until the idle speed equals the specified value.

All engines

9 Reconnect the ISCV multi-plug. The engine speed should briefly rise and then settle down to idle at the correct rpm. **Note:** *If the idle speed remains high and cannot be set to the correct value, check for induction vacuum leaks.*

CO adjustment (non-cat models)

10 Refer again to the adjustment pre-conditions in Section 7.
11 Connect a gas analyser to the exhaust system.
12 Stabilise the engine as before.
13 Allow the CO value to settle and check the idle CO value. If the CO value is outside of its operating parameters, it will require adjustment.
14 Where an external CO pot is utilised, adjust this component first.
15 Remove the tamperproof cap, and turn the CO adjustment screw until the correct value is attained.
16 If an external CO pot is not fitted, or the correct adjustment cannot be attained, then use the CO trimmer screw on the ECM to trim the CO value. **Note:** *If the idle speed changes during adjustment, the idle speed must be re-adjusted as described above.*
17 Gain access to the ECM.
18 The ECM is located behind the glove compartment. Remove the glove box.
19 Remove the tamperproof cap, and turn the CO adjustment screw until the correct value is attained. **Note:** *The screw can only be turned through an angle of 270°. Attempting to force the screw further could result in destruction of the CO trimmer and damage to the ECM.*

CO adjustment (Fiat/Lancia cat models)

20 Refer again to the adjustment pre-conditions in Section 7.
21 Run the engine at normal operating temperature. Connect a gas analyser to the connection port that is located upstream of the catalyst.
22 Run the engine at normal operating temperature, and record the CO and HC values. If the CO value is outside of its operating parameters, it will require adjustment.
23 If possible, record the values of other gases, eg HC, CO_2 and O_2, and the Lambda value.
24 Adjustments can be effected with the aid of a FCR (preferred method) or by direct adjustment. Both methods are described. **Note:** *if the ECM is not equipped with a CO trimmer, the ECM is not adjustable. In this instance, a higher-than-normal CO value may be due to a component fault.*
25 Refer to the adjustment pre-conditions in Section 7, and ensure that all faults are corrected and all conditions met before proceeding.
26 Gain access to the ECM.

FCR adjustment method

27 Attach the FCR to the serial port. The oxygen sensor must remain connected for this method of adjustment.
28 Select Lambda adjustment on the FCR display. The display will indicate if the AFR is outside of its operating limits.
29 Remove the tamperproof cap from the ECM, and turn the CO adjustment screw until the correct Lambda value is attained **(see illustration 18.6)**. **Note:** *The screw can only be turned through an angle of 270°. Attempting to force the screw further could result in destruction of the CO trimmer and damage to the ECM.*

Direct adjustment method

30 Check that the idle speed is within its normal operating parameters.
31 Disconnect the oxygen sensor (OS) multi-plug. Arrange the OS cable (ECM side) so that it cannot touch to earth.

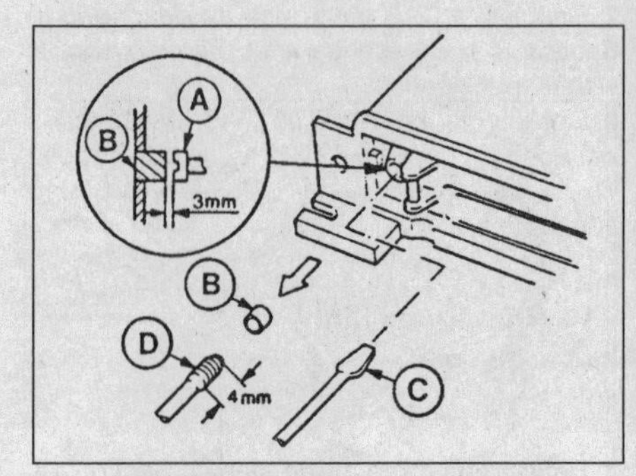

18.6 CO pot adjustment in ECM

A Adjustment screw *C Screwdriver*
B Tamperproof plug *D Extractor*

32 Remove the tamperproof cap from the ECM, and turn the CO adjustment screw until the correct CO value is attained as measured by the gas analyser. **Note:** *The screw can only be turned through an angle of 270°. Attempting to force the screw further could result in destruction of the CO trimmer and damage to the ECM.*
33 Reconnect the OS multi-plug.

Checking the CO at the exhaust tailpipe

34 Refer again to the adjustment pre-conditions in Section 7.
35 Reconnect the gas analyser to the exhaust pipe.
36 Run the engine at normal operating temperature, and record the CO and HC values. Normal CO & HC at the exhaust port, with high CO and HC at the exhaust pipe, indicate that the catalyst is suspect.

CO adjustment (Ford cat models)

37 Refer to the adjustment pre-conditions in Section 7. It is particularly important that the engine is at normal operating temperature before continuing.
38 Connect a gas analyser and check the idle CO value.
39 If the CO value is outside of its operating parameters, the CO value may require adjustment.
40 The following procedures are described using a FCR as test equipment. It is likely that the procedure can be modified for use with an LED or voltmeter, connecting or disconnecting the bridge between SD terminals 1 and 2 when the procedure calls for switching the FCR on or off. *See the section about obtaining fault codes for details on how to attach the LED or voltmeter.*
41 Gain access to the ECM, located behind the glove compartment.
42 Switch on the ignition.
43 Attach a FCR to the SD connector.
44 Switch the FCR away from obtaining codes.
45 Start the engine and allow it to idle. When the system is clear of faults, the FCR's lamp or LED will flash rapidly. If the lamp remains illuminated, check the ECM for fault codes. Do not proceed until all faults have been rectified.
46 Switch the FCR to obtain codes. The lamp should remain off. If the lamp flashes, check the ECM for fault codes. Do not proceed until all faults have been rectified.

Code 31 is displayed, or basic adjustment is lost:

a) Switch the FCR away from reading codes.
b) Switch the FCR to obtain codes again.
c) Wait for 10 seconds whilst the ECM checks and then displays the CO level.

Four possible conditions will be displayed:

a) If the engine coolant temperature is too low or the idle speed is judged incorrect, the LED will flash slowly.
b) If the CO level is judged correct, the LED will flash rapidly.
c) If the CO level is judged too rich, the LED will remain on.
d) If the CO level is judged too weak, the LED will remain off.

47 If the CO requires adjustment, carry out the following procedure.
48 Unclip the ECM from its retaining bracket.
49 Remove the tamperproof cap, and turn the CO adjustment screw until the correct value is attained; clockwise to enrich, anti-clockwise to weaken
50 Blip the throttle after adjustment, and then wait for the ECM to assess and display the new settings.
51 Continue with this procedure until the LED flashes rapidly.
52 Refit the ECM and the trim cover or glove box assembly.
53 Disconnect the ISCV multi-plug, and the engine should settle to an idle speed of about 850 rpm. If not, the idle speed and CO setting procedure must be restarted from the beginning until the two adjustments are correct.

System sensor and actuator tests

Important note: *Please refer to Chapter 4, which describes common test procedures applicable to this system. The routines in Chapter 4 should be read in conjunction with the component notes and wiring diagrams presented in this Chapter. The wiring diagrams and other data presented in this Chapter are necessarily representative of the system depicted. Because of the variations in wiring and other data that often occurs, even between similar vehicles in any particular VM's range, the reader should take great care in identification of ECM pins, and satisfy himself that he has gathered the correct data before failing a particular component.*

13 Primary trigger - crank angle sensor (CAS)

1 Refer to the note at the start of this Section, and refer to the relevant Section of Chapter 4 **(see illustration 18.7)**.
2 Check the CAS clearance as described in Section 8. It is essential that the clearance is within specification.
3 Fiat/Lancia models: The CAS resistance is between 578 and 782 ohms. Ford models: The CAS resistance is between 600 and 1000 ohms.

14 Primary ignition

1 Refer to the note at the start of Section 13, and refer to the relevant Section of Chapter 4.
2 The primary ignition is essentially that of an ECM with separate amplifier.
3 Fiat/Lancia models: Primary resistance is 0.405 to 0.495 ohms, secondary resistance is 4320 to 5280 ohms.
4 Ford models: Primary resistance is 0.72 to 0.88 ohms, secondary resistance is 4500 to 7000 ohms.

15 Knock sensor

1 Refer to the note at the start of Section 13, and refer to the relevant Section of Chapter 4.

16 Fuel injector operation

1 Refer to the note at the start of Section 13, and refer to the relevant Section of Chapter 4 **(see illustration 18.8)**.
2 The injector operation is sequential.
3 The injector resistance is 16.2 ohms.

17 Phase sensor (CID)

1 Refer to the note at the start of Section 13, and refer to the relevant Section of Chapter 4.
2 The CID phase sensor is located in the distributor.
3 The CID resistance should lie between 700 and 1200 ohms (Fiat/Lancia) or 758 and 872 ohms (Ford).
4 Check the sensor for damage, oil, or dirt, or a build-up of metal particles around the sensor.
5 Check the CID air gap (clearance) as described in Section 9.

18 MAP sensor

1 Refer to the note at the start of Section 13, and refer to the relevant Section of Chapter 4.

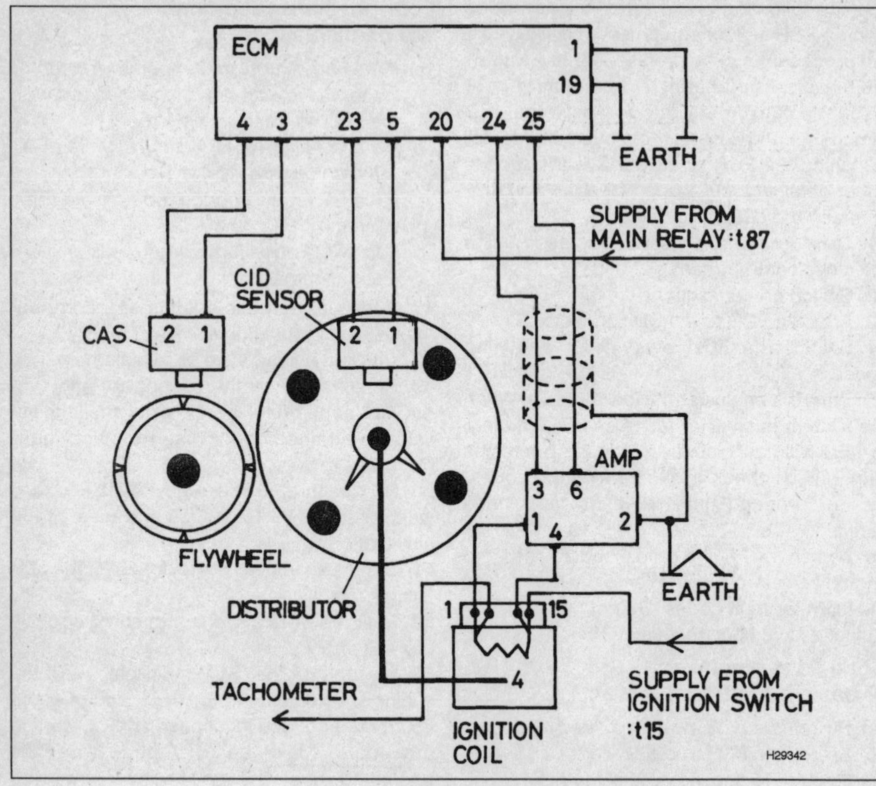

18.7 Typical ignition wiring

2 The MAP sensor is a separate sensor located in the engine compartment.

19 Air temperature sensor (ATS)

1 Refer to the note at the start of Section 13, and refer to the relevant Section of Chapter 4 **(see illustration 18.9)**.
2 The ATS is usually located in the inlet manifold.

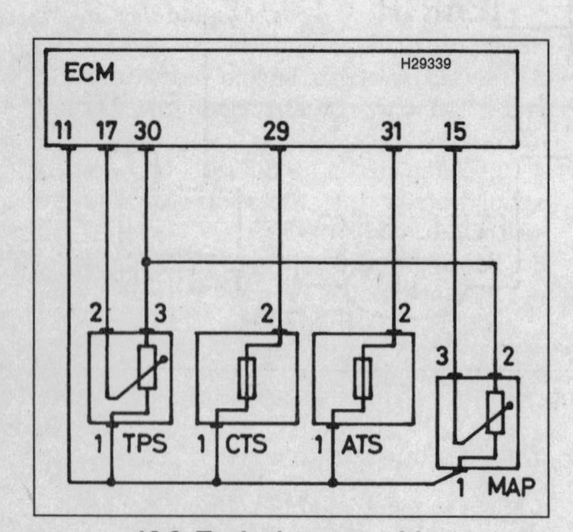

18.9 Typical sensor wiring

20 Coolant temperature sensor (CTS)

1 Refer to the note at the start of Section 13, and refer to the relevant Section of Chapter 4.

21 Throttle potentiometer sensor (TPS)

1 Refer to the note at the start of Section 13, and refer to the relevant Section of Chapter 4.
2 Testing of the TPS fitted to engines from about 1990 is similar to that described in Chapter 4.
3 The early type of TPS fitted to engines before approximately 1990 provides a reversed signal output. The voltages that should be obtained are as follows:

a) *Close the throttle: The voltage obtained should be 5.0 volts. This is the open-circuit voltage, and is obtained because the wiper arm does not engage with the track in the closed position.*
b) *Open the throttle slightly: The voltage should jump to 4.5 volts as the wiper arm engages with the track.*
c) *Open and close the throttle several times, and check for a smooth voltage decrease to a minimum of approximately 0.6 volts.*
d) *All other tests routines are similar to those described in Chapter 4.*

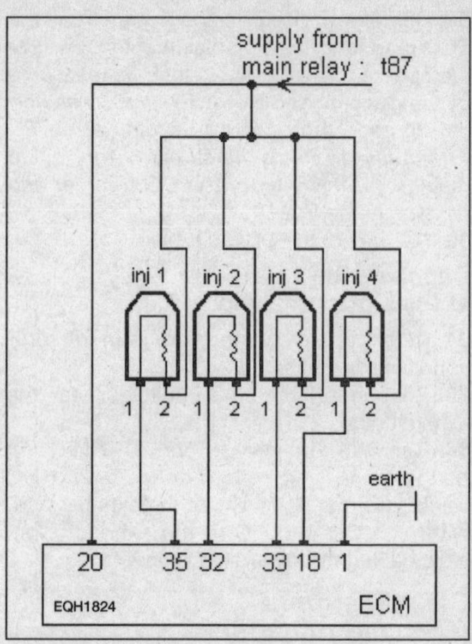

18.8 Typical injector wiring

22 Idle speed control valve (ISCV)

1 Refer to the note at the start of Section 13, and refer to the relevant Section of Chapter 4.
2 The ISCV resistance is 6.0 to 8.0 ohms.
3 The ISCV is an example of a two-wire ISCV.
4 Voltage to the ISCV is provided from either the main relay or the pump relay output. When voltage is supplied from the pump relay, a supply is only available whilst the engine is cranking or running. However, voltage could be applied for test purposes by by-passing the relay (see Chapter 4).

23 ECM voltage supplies and earths

1 Refer to the note at the start of Section 13, and refer to the relevant Section of Chapter 4.

24 System relays

1 Refer to the note at the start of Section 13, and refer to the relevant Section of Chapter 4 **(see illustrations 18.10 to 18.12)**.
2 Fiat/Lancia models utilise one of the following relay configurations:

a) *A main relay and a fuel pump relay, each with single contacts. Pin numbering is along the DIN lines.*
b) *A 15-pin single relay with dual contacts. Numbering is from 1 to 15.*

3 Ford vehicles utilise a main relay and a fuel pump relay, each with single contacts. Pin numbering is along the DIN lines.

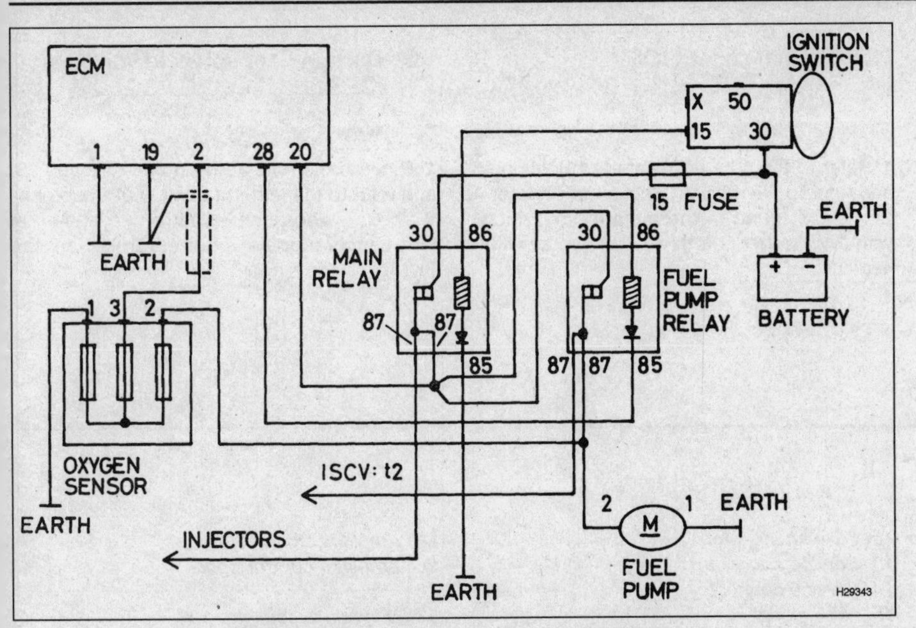

18.10 Typical relay and components wiring

18.11 Multi-plug for 15-pin relay
Pin numbers shown

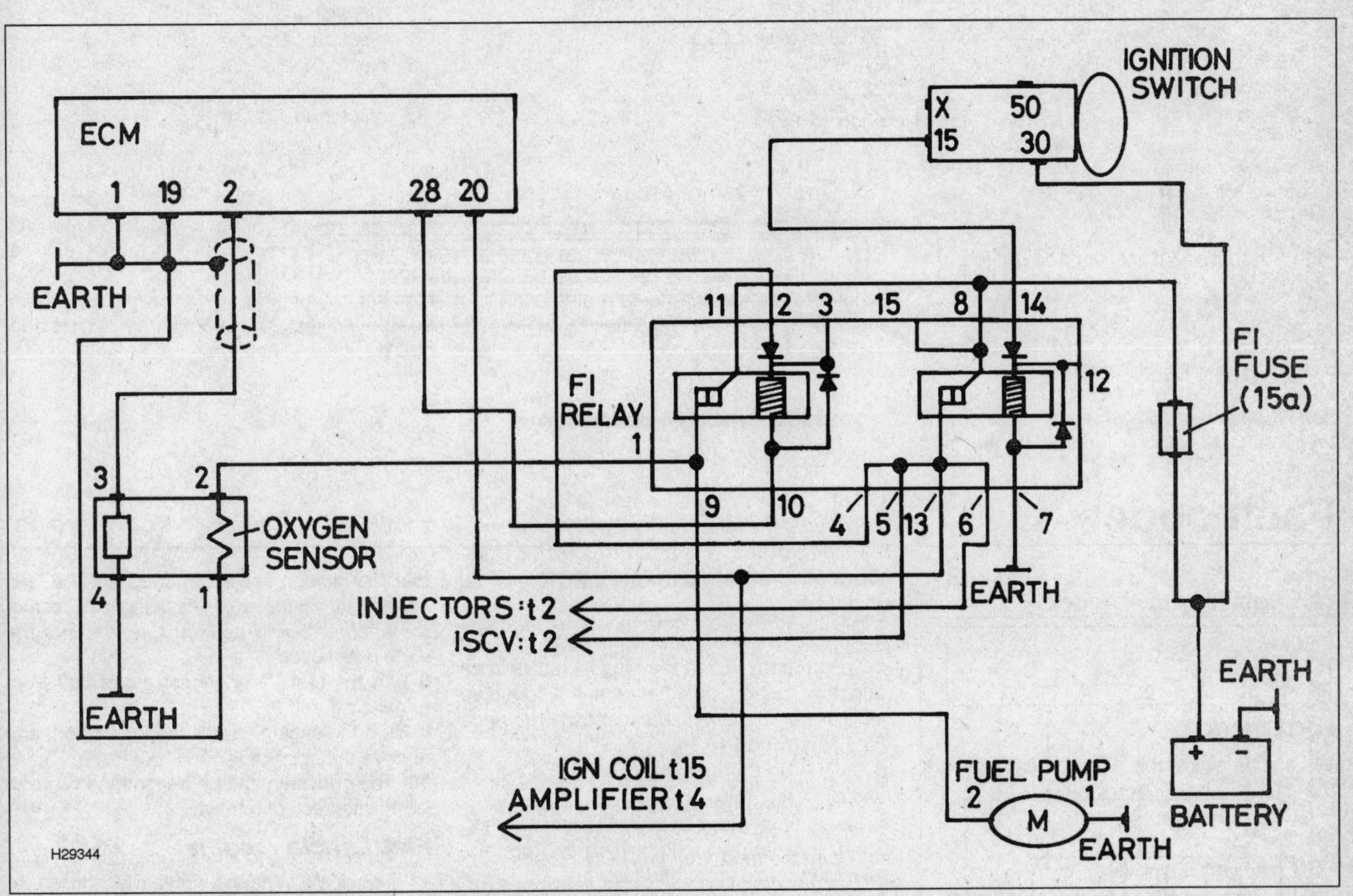

18.12 Typical 15-pin relay and components wiring

25 Fuel pump and circuit

1 Refer to the note at the start of Section 13, and refer to the relevant Section of Chapter 4.

26 Fuel pressure

1 Refer to the note at the start of Section 13, and refer to the relevant Section of Chapter 4.

27 Oxygen sensor (OS)

1 Refer to the note at the start of Section 13, and refer to the relevant Section of Chapter 4.
2 The OS found in the majority of vehicles with IAW Weber is a three-wire sensor with a heater.

28 Carbon filter solenoid valve (CFSV)

1 Refer to the note at the start of Section 13, and refer to the relevant Section of Chapter 4.
2 The evaporation control system in Fiat/Lancia models is not controlled by the ECM.

Pin table - typical 35-pin

Note: *Refer to **illustration 18.13**.*

1 Earth
2 OS signal
3 CAS return
4 CAS signal
5 CID return
6 KS return
7 CFSV
8 SD socket output
9 -
10 Main relay driver
11 Sensor return - ATS, CTS, MAP, SD socket, TPS
12 SD warning lamp
13 Service connector
14 Service connector
15 MAP signal
16 WCS
17 TPS signal
18 Injector no 4 pulse
19 Earth
20 Main relay supply
21 A/C
22 KS signal
23 CID signal
24 Amplifier signal return
25 Amplifier control signal
26 -
27 Diagnostic socket
28 FP relay driver
29 CTS signal
30 Sensor supply MAP, TPS
31 ATS signal
32 Injector no 2 pulse
33 Injector no 3 pulse
34 ISCV signal
35 Injector no 1 pulse

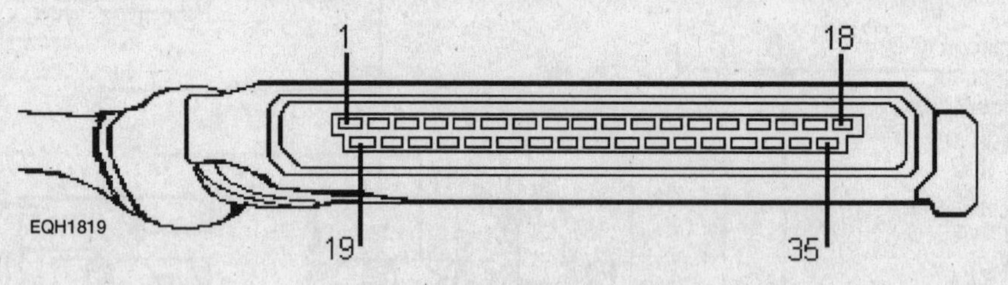

18.13 Typical 35-pin multi-plug

Fault codes

29 Obtaining fault codes

Ford models

1 If a FCR is available it could be attached to the SD serial connector, and used for the following purposes:

a) *Obtaining fault codes.*
b) *Checking that CO adjustment is within operating parameters (cat models only). Refer to Adjustments.*

2 If a FCR is not available, it is still possible to obtain fault codes as follows.

Obtaining codes without a FCR

3 Switch the ignition key off.
4 Attach an analogue voltmeter or LED between terminal 3 at the plug (negative lead) and the battery positive terminal (positive lead). *Refer to Warning number 5 in Reference* **(see illustration 18.14)**.
5 Switch on the ignition, or start the engine and allow it to idle.
6 Use a jumper lead to bridge terminals 1 and 2 in the serial port plug. Where appropriate, take the vehicle for a road test.
7 The codes are then output on the instrument as needle sweeps or flashes. By counting the sweeps or flashes and referring to the fault code table, faults can thus be determined. **Note:** *Codes are available only whilst the fault is present, and during the time that the ignition key is switched on. If a fault appears whilst the engine is being road tested, the engine should be kept running until the code is retrieved.*
8 End the test - disconnect the bridge from terminals 1 and 2.
9 Stop the engine (switch the ignition off) and remove the apparatus.
10 The codes should be transmitted twice to verify accuracy of retrieval.

Fiat/Lancia models

11 The IAW Weber-Marelli EMS fitted to Fiat/Lancia models requires a dedicated FCR to access fault codes **(see illustration 18.15)**. Flash codes are not available for output from this system. For the sake of completeness, we have provided list of components that will provide errors for readout upon a FCR.

Fault code table - Ford models

Code (4x2 models)	Code (4x4 models)	Item
11	11	CAS
12	12	Distributor phase sensor circuit (CID)
13	13	Mismatch between CAS signal and distributor phase sensor signal
	21	ATS
21		ATS, short in circuit
22		ATS, break in circuit
	22	Knock sensor
	23	CTS
23		CTS, short in circuit
31		CTS, break in circuit
	31	Oxygen sensor
	32	MAP sensor
32		MAP sensor, short in circuit
33		MAP sensor, break in circuit
	33	TPS
	43	ECM module - internal failure
	44	ECM module - internal failure

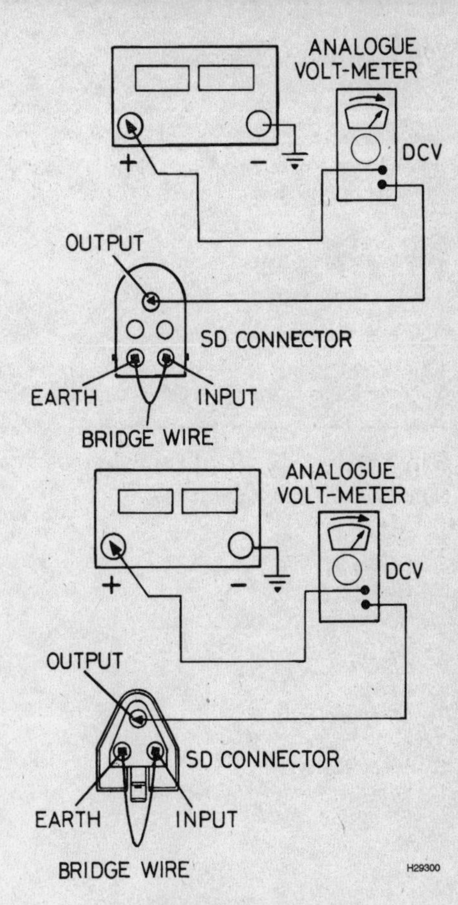

18.14 Obtaining codes (Ford)

Fault table - Fiat/Lancia models

Item
CAS
Distributor phase sensor circuit (CID)
Mismatch between CAS signal and distributor phase sensor signal
ATS, short in circuit
ATS, break in circuit
Knock sensor
CTS
CTS, short in circuit
CTS, break in circuit
Oxygen sensor
MAP sensor
MAP sensor, short in circuit
MAP sensor, break in circuit
TPS
ECM module - internal failure

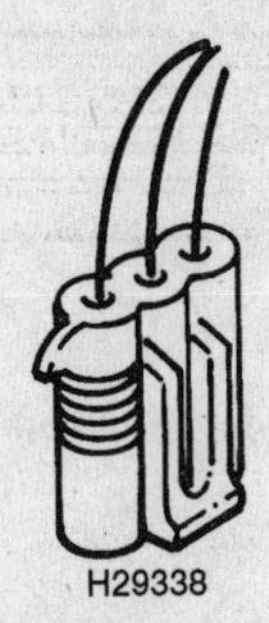

18.15 Obtaining codes (Fiat)

Chapter 19
Bosch Mono-Motronic

Contents

Specifications

Vehicle	Year	Idle speed	CO%
Citroën, Mono-Motronic MA3.0			
AX 1.0i cat CDZ(TU9M/L.Z)	1992 to 1996	850 ± 50	0.5 max
AX 1.1i cat HDY, HDZ (TU1M/Z)	1994 to 1996	850 ± 50	0.5 max
AX 1.4i cat KDX (TU3FM/L.Z)	1992 to 1995	850 ± 50	0.5 max
ZX 1.4i & Break cat KDX (TU3M)	1992 to 1996	850 ± 50	0.5 max
Fiat/Lancia, Mono-Motronic 1.7			
Tempra 1.6ie cat SOHC 159 A3.046	1993 to 1994	850 ± 50	0.35 max
Tipo 1.6ie SOHC cat 159 A3.046	1993 to 1995	800 to 850	0.4 to 1.0
Tipo 1.6ie SOHC 55kw 835 C1.000	1994 to 1996	850 ± 50	0.35 max
Y10 1108ie & 4x4 cat 156 C.046	1992 to 1995	800 ± 50	0.35 max
Peugeot, Mono-Motronic MA3.0			
106 1.0 cat TU9ML/Z (CDY, CDZ)	1993 to 1996	850 ± 50	0.3 max
106 1.4i cat TU3MCL/Z (KDX)	1993 to 1996	850 ± 50	0.3 max
205 1.4i TU3FM/L (KDY2)	1994 to 1996	850 ± 50	0.3 max
306 1.1i TU1ML/Z (HDY, HDZ)	1993 to 1996	850 ± 50	0.3 max
306 1.4i cat TU3MCL/Z (KDX)	1993 to 1995	850 ± 50	0.5 max
405 1.4i cat TU3MCL/Z (KDX)	1992 to 1994	850 ± 50	0.4 max
Peugeot, Mono-Motronic MA1.7			
Jumpy 1.6i 220 A2.000	1995 to 1996	800 to 850	0.5 max

Vehicle	Year	Idle speed	CO%
VAG (Audi/Volkswagen)			
Audi 80 1.8i cat PM	1990 to 1991	750 to 950	0.5 max
Audi 80 2.0i Quattro cat ABT	1991 to 1995	700 to 1000	0.5 max
Audi 100 2.0 cat AAE	1991 to 1994	750 to 950	0.5 max
Golf 1.3i cat AAV	1991 to 1992	-	-
Golf 1.4i cat ABD	1991 to 1995	750 to 850	0.5 max
Golf 1.4i AEX	1995 to 1996	650 to 750	0.5 max
Golf 1.6i cat ABU	1992 to 1995	800 ± 50	0.5 max
Golf 1.6i cat AEA	1994 to 1995	750 to 850	-
Golf 1.6i AEK	1994 to 1996	800 to 880	0.5 max
Golf 1.8i cat AAM	1992 to 1996	750 to 1000	0.5 max
Golf 1.8i cat ABS	1992 to 1994	750 to 1000	0.5 max
Golf 1.8i & 4x4 ADZ	1994 to 1996	700 to 900	0.5 max
Passat 1.8i RP	1990 to 1991	825 to 1025	0.2 to 1.2
Passat 1.8i & cat RP	1990 to 1991	825 to 1025	0.2 to 1.2
Passat 1.8i cat AAM	1990 to 1994	850 to 1025	0.5 max
Passat 1.8i cat AAM	1994 to 1995	825 to 1025	0.2 to 1.2
Passat 1.8i ABS	1991 to 1994	825 to 1025	0.2 to 1.2
Passat 1.8i AAM	1993 to 1996	825 to 1025	0.2 to 1.2
Passat 1.8i cat ABS	1992 to 1994	825 to 1025	0.5 max
Passat 1.8i cat ADZ	1994 to 1995	700 to 900	0.5 max
Polo 1.0i cat AEV	1994 to 1996	750 to 850	0.5 max
Polo 1.05i cat AAU	1990 to 1994	750 to 850	0.2 to 1.0
Polo 1.3i cat AAV	1993 to 1994	750 to 850	0.2 to 1.0
Polo 1.3i cat ADX	1994 to 1995	750 to 850	0.5 max
Polo 1.6i cat AEA	1994 to 1996	700 to 900	0.5 max
Sharan 2.0 ADY	1995 to 1996	770 to 870	0.5 max
Vento 1.4i cat ABD	1991 to 1995	750 to 850	0.5 max
Vento 1.4i AEX	1995 to 1996	650 to 750	0.5 max
Vento 1.6i cat ABU	1992 to 1995	800 ± 50	0.5 max
Vento 1.6i cat AEA	1994 to 1995	750 to 850	-
Vento 1.6i AEK	1994 to 1995	800 to 880	0.5 max
Vento 1.8i cat AAM	1992 to 1994	750 to 1000	0.5 max
Vento 1.8i cat ABS	1992 to 1994	750 to 1000	0.5 max
Vento 1.8i & 4x4 ADZ	1994 to 1996	700 to 900	0.5 max

Overview of system operation

1 Introduction

Please read this overview of Mono-Motronic operation in conjunction with Chapter 2, which describes some of the functions in more detail.

Bosch Mono-Motronic is a fully-integrated engine management system that controls primary ignition, single-point injection and idle speed from within the same ECM. Mono-Motronic has evolved from the Mono-Jetronic system - a single-point system which controls fuel injection alone. Many of the fuel injection sensors in both systems share a similar construction.

A 35, 45 or 55-pin connector and multi-plug connects the Mono-Motronic ECM to the battery, sensors and actuators. In VAG applications, the 35-pin ECM was used until about 1992, when it was generally replaced by the 45-pin ECM. Later versions from about late 1994 utilised a revised stepper motor, a new VSS and knock control. The early 35-pin system is labelled MA 1.2.1, and the first generation 45-pin MA 1.2.2 and 1.2.3. The later 45-pin is labelled MA 1.3. Fiat and Lancia applications utilise MA 1.7, and the ECM contains 35 pins. Citroën and Peugeot applications utilise MA 3.0, and the ECM contains 55 pins.

Ignition operation in Fiat, Lancia, Citroën and Peugeot vehicles is distributorless (DIS), whilst the VAG vehicles utilise a distributor. There are many differences between the various versions, and ECM pin numbers also differ widely.

2 Control functions

Signal processing

The Mono-Motronic ECM contains an ignition map and a fuel map. The maps contain tables of basic values for ignition timing and fuel injection duration.

When the ECM is supplied with data on engine speed and engine load from the engine sensors, the ECM looks up the correct values for dwell, timing and injector opening time. Correction factors are then applied for starting, deceleration, and part-and full-load operation.

The main engine load sensor is the dual throttle potentiometer sensor (TPS); engine speed is determined from the ignition signal (crank angle sensor - CAS or Hall-effect sensor - HES). The main correction factors are determined from the engine temperature (CTS), air temperature sensor (ATS) and oxygen sensor (OS) signals.

Basic ECM operation

A permanent voltage supply is made from the vehicle battery to the ECM. This allows the self-diagnostic function to retain data of an intermittent nature. Once the ignition is switched on, a voltage feed is supplied to the ECM and to pin 3 of the combined amplifier/ignition coil unit. When the ECM senses the ignition-on state, the pump relay driver pin is briefly connected to earth, so actuating the fuel pump relay and pressurising the fuel system.

The majority of sensors (other than those that generate a voltage such as the CAS or

HES, and OS), are now provided with a 5.0-volt reference supply from a relevant pin on the ECM. When the engine is cranked or run, a speed signal from the CAS or HES causes the ECM to earth the pump relay driver pin so that the fuel pump will run.

Ignition and injection functions are also activated. The actuators (injector, CFSV etc), are supplied with nbv from the fuel pump relay (injector, all but Citroën & Peugeot) or battery (CFSV), and the ECM completes the circuit by pulsing the relevant actuator wire to earth. The stepper motor regulates the idle speed under ECM control when the engine is at idle.

Over-speed fuel cut-off (rev limiter)

Mono-Motronic prevents engine speeds above 6300 rpm by inhibiting the injector earth path. As the engine speed drops below 6300 rpm, fuel injection is reinstated.

Reference voltage

Voltage supply from the ECM to the engine sensors (ATS, CTS and TPS) is made at a 5.0-volt reference level. This ensures a stable working voltage, unaffected by variations in system voltage.

The earth return connection for these engine sensors is made through an ECM pin which is not directly connected to earth. The ECM internally connects that pin to earth via one of the ECM pins that are directly connected to earth.

Signal shielding

To reduce interference (RFI), the oxygen sensor uses a shielded cable.

VSS (only fitted to some vehicles with 45-pin ECM)

The VSS is used to advise the ECM of vehicle speed. It operates upon the Hall-effect principle, and is usually mounted directly on the gearbox.

A voltage of approximately 10 volts is applied to the VSS from the ignition switch. As the speedometer cable turns, the Hall switch is alternately turned on and off, to return a square wave signal to the ECM. The frequency of the signal denotes the vehicle speed.

Self-diagnostic function

The Mono-Motronic system has a self-test capability that regularly examines the signals from engine sensors, and internally logs a code in the event of a fault being present. This code can be extracted from the serial port by a suitable fault code reader (FCR).

When the ECM detects that a fault is present, it earths an ECM pin. If the fault clears, the code will remain logged until wiped clean with a suitable FCR, or until the engine has been started for more than 10 times when the fault code is self-initialising. A self-diagnostic warning lamp is only fitted to Citroën and Peugeot models.

Limited operating strategy (LOS or 'limp-home')

Mono-Motronic has a limp-home facility. In the event of a serious fault in one or more of the sensors, the EMS will substitute a fixed default value in place of the defective sensor.

During LOS conditions when the CTS signal is open or short-circuited, the ECM will assign a CTS temperature of 90°C. The ATS signal will be used as a replacement value during engine start. If the ATS becomes faulty, the ECM will assign a ATS temperature of 20°C. This means that the engine may actually run quite well with failure of one or more minor sensors, but difficulties may be experienced in cold starting and running.

Adaptive memory

Over a period of time, the ECM will learn the best idle position for a particular engine - irrespective of age, engine condition and load, so that the correct idle speed is always maintained.

3 Primary trigger

General

The primary trigger to initiate both ignition and fuelling in the Mono-Motronic system is either a distributor-mounted Hall-effect sensor, or a flywheel-mounted crank angle sensor (CAS). Citroën, Peugeot, Fiat and Lancia use the CAS, and VAG use the HES.

Crank angle sensor (CAS)

The CAS is mounted next to the flywheel, and consists of an inductive magnet that radiates a magnetic field. The flywheel incorporates a reluctor disk containing steel pins set at intervals. As the flywheel spins, and the pins are rotated in the magnetic field, an AC voltage signal is generated to indicate speed of rotation. The two missing pins (set at 180° intervals) are a reference to TDC, and indicate crankshaft position by varying the signal as the flywheel spins. One missing pin indicates TDC for cylinders 1 and 4, and the other missing pin indicates TDC for cylinders 2 and 3.

The peak-to-peak voltage of the speed signal can vary from 5 volts at idle to over 100 volts at 6000 rpm. The ECM uses an analogue-to-digital converter (ADC) to transform the AC pulse into a digital signal.

Hall-effect sensor (HES)

The ECM supplies a voltage slightly under nbv to the Hall-effect switch in the distributor. The HES circuit is completed by a connection to earth **(see illustration 19.1)**.

Opposite the Hall switch is a magnet, whose field causes the switch to return a small voltage back to the ECM. Attached to the distributor shaft is a trigger vane with the

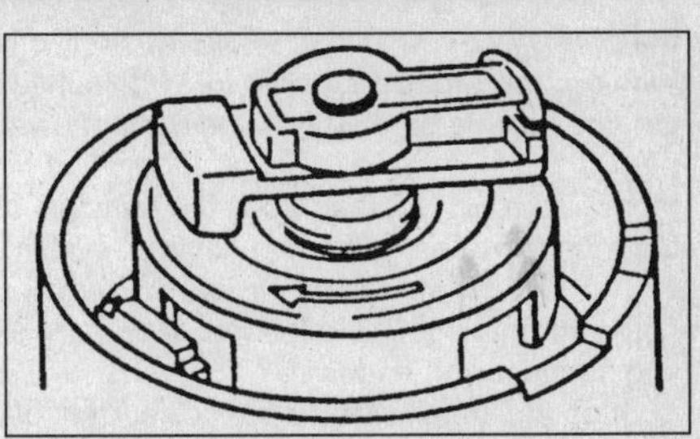

19.1 Hall-effect sensor (HES)

same number of cut-outs as cylinders. Passing the trigger vane between the switch and the magnet will cause the Hall switch to be turned off and on. As the cut-out space proceeds past the switch, a voltage is returned to the ECM via a third wire termed the output wire.

When the solid portion comes between the switch and magnet, the voltage is turned off as the magnetic field is diverted. Essentially, the voltage signal is returned as either voltage or no voltage, and the waveform produced is that of a square wave. The cut-out in the trigger vane is cut to provide a signal at 60° before TDC (leading edge) and 5° or 6° depending on vehicle (trailing edge). The HES signal is necessary for initiation of both ignition, injection and idle control. The engine will not run without the HES signal.

4 Primary and secondary ignition

Data on load (TPS), engine speed (CAS/HES), engine temperature (CTS) and throttle position (TPS) are collected by the ECM, which then refers to a three-dimensional digital map stored within its microprocessor. This map contains an advance angle for each operating condition, and thus the best ignition advance angle for a particular operating condition can be determined. VAG models are equipped with a distributor, whilst Fiat, Lancia, Citroën and Peugeot models utilise DIS ignition.

Ignition operation (distributor system)

When the ignition is switched on, voltage is applied to the ECM and to the combined amplifier/ignition coil unit. The circuit then lies dormant to await a cranking or running signal.

When the engine is cranked and run, the ECM receives a signal from the HES in the distributor, and in turn applies a control signal to the combined amplifier/coil unit so that ignition can be initiated. The amplifier controls the coil dwell circuit by turning the coil current on and off to initiate ignition.

The amplifier applies current to the coil primary windings by connecting coil terminal number one to earth for a period of time known as the dwell time. During the dwell period, the coil builds a magnetic field within the primary coil windings. While the engine is running, the Mono-Motronic ECM calculates the coil turn-on time so that the correct dwell period is maintained. Dwell operation in Mono-Motronic is based upon the principle of the 'constant-energy current-limiting' system. This means that the dwell period remains constant at about 3.0 to 3.5 ms, at virtually all engine running speeds.

Once the amplifier turns the coil current off, the magnetic field in the coil primary windings quickly collapses, and a high voltage is induced in the coil secondary windings. The secondary output travels to the distributor cap via the main HT lead through the medium of the rotor arm. From the distributor, the secondary output is distributed to the correct spark plug, in the firing order of the engine, via an HT lead.

Distributor

The Bosch distributor contains secondary HT components, and serves to distribute the HT current from the coil secondary terminal to each spark plug in firing order. The distributor is usually located on the camshaft at the cylinder No 4 end. The distributor also contains the HES and magnet.

Ignition coil

The ignition coil (which is part of the combined coil and amplifier unit) utilises low primary resistance in order to increase primary current and primary energy. The amplifier limits the primary current to around 8 amps, and this permits a reserve of energy to maintain the required spark burn time (duration).

Ignition timing

Basic timing is set a few degrees before TDC, and the value is calculated to provide efficient combustion and maximum power output at a particular speed.

The base ignition timing (VAG) is maintained under ECM control, and the distributor should only be moved once a suitable FCR has been attached to the serial port. The timing marks may be scribed upon the flywheel or on the front pulley, depending upon vehicle model. When the marks are aligned at idle speed, the base ignition timing is correct.

As the engine speed increases, combustion must occur earlier, and the ignition point is advanced by the ECM with reference to its own mapped ignition table. The load factor is calculated by the ECM with reference to the TPS setting, and the ignition timing is adjusted accordingly.

DIS ignition

Although the ignition system is termed DIS, the basic operation is much the same as on models with conventional ignition. In a DIS or so called 'wasted spark' system, a double-ended coil is used to fire two plugs at the same time. This means that the system can only be used where two cylinders rise and fall together.

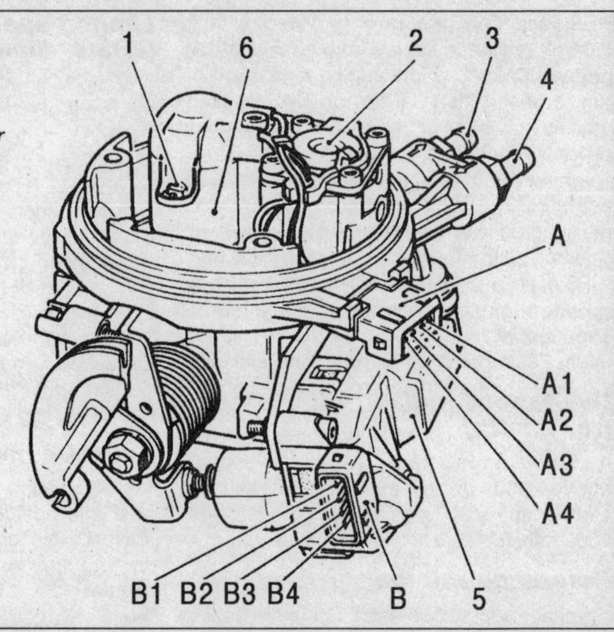

19.2 Mono-Motronic throttle body assembly

1 ATS
2 Fuel pressure regulator
3 Fuel return connection
4 Fuel feed connection
5 Stepper motor
6 Fuel injector
A ATS/Fuel injector wiring connector
A1 ATS
A2 Injector +
A3 Injector -
A4 ATS
B Stepper motor connector
B1 Winding connection
B2 Winding connection
B3 Idle switch
B4 Idle switch

One cylinder will fire on the compression stroke, and the companion cylinder will fire on the exhaust stroke, where the spark is 'wasted'. Two pairs of coils will therefore be required for a four-cylinder engine. About 3 kV is still needed to fire the 'wasted spark' plug, but this is far less than that required to bridge the rotor gap. Each ignition coil requires a voltage supply from the ignition switch, and a separate dwell connection to the ECM, so that the ECM can switch each coil individually.

Ignition timing

The ignition timing is not adjustable in DIS models.

Knock sensor (only fitted to some vehicles with 45-pin ECM)

The optimal ignition timing (at engine speeds greater than idle) for a given high-compression engine is quite close to the point of onset of knock. However, running so close to the point of knock occurrence, means that knock will certainly occur on one or more cylinders at certain times during the engine operating cycle.

Since knock may occur at a different moment in each individual cylinder, Mono-Motronic is able to pinpoint the actual cylinder or cylinders that are knocking from the distributor HES signal. The knock sensor normally begins to function once the coolant temperature has reached 40°C.

The knock sensor is mounted on the engine block, and consists of a piezo-ceramic measuring element that responds to engine noise oscillations. This signal is converted to a voltage signal by the knock sensor, and returned to the ECM for evaluation and action. Knocking frequency often occurs in the 15 kHz frequency band.

Initially, timing will occur at its optimal ignition point. Once knock is identified, the knock control microprocessor retards the ignition timing for that cylinder or cylinders in increments of 3°, up to a maximum of 12°. If no further knocking is detected, the timing is advanced back to the initial setting. This procedure continually occurs so that all cylinders will always run at their optimum timing.

If a fault exists in the knock sensor wiring circuit or no knocking is detected by the ECM, an appropriate fault code will be logged in the self-diagnostic unit, and the ignition timing for all cylinders is retarded by 12° by the LOS programme.

5 Fuel injection

The Mono-Motronic ECM contains a fuel map with an injector opening time for basic conditions of load and speed. Information is then gathered from engine sensors such as the CAS or HES, ATS, CTS, and TPS. As a result of this information, the ECM will look up the correct injector pulse duration right across the engine rpm, load and temperature range.

Single-point injection (SPi)

The Mono-Motronic system is a single-point injection (SPi) system. The SPi system consists of a single injector mounted in the throttle body **(see illustration 19.2)**. The amount of fuel delivered by the injector is determined by the fuel pressure and the injector opening time - otherwise known as the pulse duration. The ECM controls the period of time that the injector is held open, and this is determined by the signals from the various sensor inputs. During engine start-up from cold, the pulse duration is increased to provide a richer air/fuel mixture.

Fuel injector

The fuel injector is a magnetically-operated solenoid valve that is actuated by the ECM. Voltage to the injector is applied from the fuel pump relay (main relay on Citroën and Peugeot models), and the earth path is completed by the ECM for a period of time (called pulse duration) of between 1.5 and 10 milliseconds. The pulse duration is very much dependent upon engine temperature, load, speed and operating conditions. Injection frequency is two pulses per crankshaft revolution, or four pulses per four stroke cycle.

The injector is switched via a ballast resistor to reduce current flow through the injector. When the magnetic solenoid closes, a back-EMF voltage of up to 60 volts is induced.

Deceleration fuel cut-off

During engine over-run conditions (coolant temperature over 60°C), the ECM cuts off the injection pulse to improve economy and reduce emissions. The injector pulse is reinstated once the engine speed has reduced to between 1500 and 1900 rpm.

Air temperature control

The air filter casing contains a thermal valve system to regulate the temperature of the air supply to the throttle body. The supply functions very much like those fitted to carburettor models.

Manifold vacuum is piped via a small hose to the thermal valve in the air filter casing. Another hose is connected to a vacuum motor which controls a flap in the air filter nozzle. The flap opens or closes according to under-bonnet air temperature. The thermal valve is a bi-metal valve which contains a passage to allow the passing of vacuum. As the temperature rises, the valve opens to form an air bleed in the passage, and this causes the vacuum in the passage to collapse.

When the under-bonnet air temperature is low, the bi-metal valve is closed and vacuum acts to fully open the flap. Thus, heated air from the exhaust system enters the throttle body intake. As under-bonnet air temperature rises, the bi-metal air bleed begins to open, and the vacuum pull upon the flap is reduced. A mixture of heated and unheated air is thus fed to the throttle body. As the air temperature rises above 17°C, the air bleed becomes fully open. The flap, therefore, fully closes to shut off the exhaust heated air. Fully unheated air now enters the throttle body. Air is thus introduced to the throttle body at a fairly constant temperature, irrespective of ambient temperature.

Air temperature sensor (ATS)

The ATS is mounted in the single-point injector mouth, and measures the air temperature before it enters the inlet manifold. Because the density of air varies in inverse proportion to the temperature, the ATS signal allows more accurate assessment of the volume of air entering the engine.

The ATS operates on the NTC principle, and the open-circuit supply to the sensor is at a 5.0-volt reference level. A variable voltage signal is returned to the ECM based upon the air temperature. This signal is around 2.5 to 3.0 volts at an ambient temperature of 20°C. In fact, the voltage and resistance of the ATS and CTS sensors is very similar at similar temperatures. The ECM only uses the ATS signal to correct the injector pulse at an air temperature of less than 20°C. The pulse width is increased as the air temperature decreases until the pulse is 30% longer at -30°C.

Voltage is applied to the ATS resistance from the AFS voltage supply, and the signal returned to the ECM at pin number 27.

CO adjustment

There is no provision for CO adjustment on any of the models in this range.

Coolant temperature sensor (CTS)

The CTS is incorporated in the cooling system, and contains a variable resistance that operates on the NTC principle. When the engine is cold, the resistance is quite high. Once the engine is started and begins to warm up, the coolant becomes hotter and the resistance of the CTS becomes smaller (NTC principle); this returns a variable voltage signal to the ECM based upon the coolant temperature.

The signal is approximately 2.0 to 3.0 volts at an ambient temperature of 20°C, and reduces to between 0.5 to 1.0 volt at a normal operating temperature of 80 to 100°C.

The open-circuit supply to the sensor is at a 5.0-volt reference level. The ECM uses the CTS signal as a main correction factor when calculating ignition timing and injection duration.

Throttle potentiometer sensor (TPS)

A throttle potentiometer with dual resistance tracks is provided to inform the ECM of acceleration, throttle position, and full-load.

The TPS is a potentiometer with four wires. A common 5.0-volt reference voltage is applied to each resistance track, with the other end connected to a common earth. Each signal output wire is connected to an arm which wipes along the resistance track, and so varies the resistance and voltage of the signal returned to the ECM.

The more sensitive signals produced by two TPS signals enable the ECM to more accurately assess engine load. There is a strong correlation between throttle position, rpm and volume of air (load) entering the engine, and with reference to the mapped values, the ECM is able to calculate fuel injection duration. The first resistance covers the throttle angles from 0° to 24°, and the second resistance covers the angles from 18° to 90°. When the throttle position exceeds an angle of 70°, the ECM lengthens the injection pulse to provide an enriched full-load mixture.

Idle control

When electrical loads such as the headlights or heater fan are switched on or applied to the engine, the idle speed would tend to drop. The idle speed in Mono-Motronic equipped vehicles is not adjustable, and the ECM utilises a stepper motor to maintain a stable idle speed under all operating conditions.

The ECM constantly monitors the idle rpm, and compares the engine speed to a look-up map tabling rpm against temperature and load. If the difference between the actual engine rpm and the idle map are more than 25 rpm apart, the ECM indexes the stepper motor to bring the idle speed into alignment.

In addition, the ECM makes small adjustments to the idle speed by advancing or retarding the timing if the deviation between rpm and idle map is more than 10°. This results in a more stable idle speed and an ignition timing that is forever changing during engine idle. During periods of cold running, the stepper motor will set the throttle position so that the idle speed will be set to a suitable fast idle.

The stepper motor is a DC motor that operates a pushrod. The pushrod contacts the throttle lever which actuates the throttle plate and so maintains the correct idle speed. The stepper motor consists of a helical-toothed gear and pinion which is controlled by the ECM through a motor winding. The circuit for the winding originates and terminates at the ECM. Pulsing the winding causes the pushrod to move in one direction. The ECM moves the pushrod in the reverse direction by reversing the polarity of the winding, and the ECM is thus able to position the stepper motor pushrod exactly in its task to control the idle speed.

In addition, a set of contacts is used to signal idle position. When the throttle is closed, the contacts are closed and an ECM pin is connected to earth. When the throttle is opened, the contacts open, and the earth is removed from the ECM pin.

In later versions of the stepper motor (identified by a 6-pin multi-plug connector to the motor), the ECM also controls the stepper motor during engine deceleration, so that a controlled return to idle speed is maintained. When the throttle is opened and the idle contacts also become open, the ECM extends the stepper motor plunger to a distance determined by the signal from the TPS. Once the accelerator pedal is released and the throttle valve closes, the throttle lever touches the extended plunger, and the idle contacts close. The stepper motor then gradually retracts the plunger to secure a damped return to the correct idle speed. This reduces exhaust emissions, and prevents the dip in engine speed sometimes associated with a sudden closure of the throttle.

The placing of the plunger is controlled by a worm-drive and HES signal. The ECM recognises the exact plunger position by counting the Hall-effect pulses. Should the HES circuit fail, a fault code will be logged, and the stepper motor will no longer control the damped return to idle speed. This could result in a dip in engine speed sometimes after a sudden closure of the throttle. So long as the stepper motor idle contact and DC motor circuits are satisfactory, the idle speed will still be ECM-controlled as before.

Manifold heater (sometimes called a 'hedgehog')

This heater works on the PTC principle, and allows a greater current to quickly heat the inlet manifold during the warm-up period. This allows better driveability during engine warm-up. The manifold heater is controlled by a relay and a thermal switch. A permanent voltage supply is applied to terminal 30 of the relay by the battery.

When the engine is cold (below approximately 55°C) and the ignition switch is turned to the 'accessory' or 'run' positions, voltage is applied to terminal 86 and to earth through the thermal switch. This actuates the relay windings, the relay contacts close, and voltage to the manifold heater is output at terminal 87.

The manifold heater resistance is very small, which creates a high current level and rapid heating of the manifold heater element. The high current level increases the heater temperature and resistance, and this reduces the current level (PTC principle).

Once a preset temperature of approximately 65°C is reached, the thermal switch contacts open and the relay de-energises. This breaks the supply to the manifold heater, and it remains switched off during engine operation with a hot engine.

Fuel pump relay

The Mono-Motronic fuel pump is controlled by a single four-terminal relay (VAG), by two four-terminal relays (Fiat/Lancia), or a fifteen-terminal relay with dual contacts (Citroën and Peugeot models). Typical operation of the relays is as follows.

A permanent voltage supply is made to a terminal of the main and fuel pump relays from the battery positive terminal.

When the ignition is switched on, a voltage supply is made to fuel pump relay, and the ECM briefly earths the relay driver which energises the fuel pump relay winding. This causes the fuel pump relay contacts to close, and connects voltage to either the single or twin fuel pumps (as appropriate) and the fuel injector via a ballast resistor. After approximately one second, the ECM opens the circuit and the pump stops. This brief running of the fuel pump allows pressure to build within the fuel pressure lines, and provides for an easier start.

The fuel pump circuit will then remain open until the engine is cranked or run. Once the ECM receives a speed signal from the ignition, the fuel pump winding will again be energised by the ECM, and the fuel pump will run until the engine is stopped.

Fuel pressure system

The following description refers to VAG vehicles, but other models employ similar methods. In VAG vehicles, one of three different fuel supply strategies are used for providing fuel to the Mono-Motronic system.

Method one utilises an in-tank fuel pump in conjunction with an external fuel pump. Method two utilises an external fuel pump without the in-tank fuel pump. Method three utilises an in-tank fuel delivery unit, comprising a two-stage fuel pump, and without an external fuel pump. The components that make up the various fuel delivery systems are described below.

In-tank and external fuel pump

An in-tank fuel transfer pump is used to pump fuel from the fuel tank. The in-tank pump is part of a combined pump and fuel level sender unit. Operating performance is 65 litres of fuel per hour at a pressure of 0.25 bar with a 12-volt electrical supply. Pump operating noise is much reduced by a rubber mounting inserted between the pump and fuel sender.

The transfer pump provides fuel to the main external pump through a fuel filter (filter number one). The number one fuel filter has a fuel capacity of 200 cc, and this reserve of fuel prevents fuel starvation during high cornering speeds with a low fuel level in the fuel tank. Excess fuel is returned to fuel filter number one via a return pipe.

The transfer fuel pump enjoys a much easier life when fuel is returned to the filter, rather than the more common method of returning the fuel directly to the fuel tank. Both pumps are of the 'wet' variety, in that fuel actually flows through the pump and the electric motor. An external fuel pump, mounted close to the fuel tank, draws fuel from the tank, and pumps it to the fuel injector assembly via a second fuel filter (filter number two).

The pump design is of the internal gearwheel type, driven by a permanent magnet electric motor. Operating performance is 80 litres of fuel per hour at a pressure of 1.2 bar with a 12-volt electrical supply. Current draw is approximately 5 amps.

To prevent pressure loss in the supply system, a non-return valve is provided in the fuel pump outlet. When the ignition is switched off, and the fuel pump ceases operation, pressure is thus maintained for some time.

Once the engine is running, fuel is fed through a non-return valve and fuel filter to the single throttle body injector.

Fuel delivery unit (eg VW Golf and Passat)

The two stage fuel pump assembly (including the fuel level sender) is accommodated in a housing which also serves as a fuel accumulator, containing a reserve capacity of 600 cc of fuel.

The housing is mounted on the floor of the fuel tank, with a quick-release bayonet fastener. Turning the housing 1/8th of a turn anti-clockwise will release the housing from the its mounting. Most of the component parts are available as separate replacement parts.

Stage one of the fuel pump replaces the fuel transfer pump used in earlier models. Stage two of the fuel pump replaces the external fuel pump used in earlier models. The two pumps operate independently, and are simultaneously driven by the shaft of a single electric motor.

The Stage one pump is a side-channel vane-type pump, and draws fuel from the fuel tank bottom through an initial fuel filter into the fuel accumulator. Operating performance is 65 litres of fuel per hour at a pressure of 0.25 bar with a 12-volt electrical supply. Excess fuel, and also fuel delivered from the return pipe, are returned to the fuel tank via a fuel outlet.

The Stage two pump is of the internal gearwheel type, and delivers fuel to the single-point injector. Operating performance is 80 litres of fuel per hour at a pressure of 1.2 bar with a 12-volt electrical supply. Current draw is approximately 5 amps.

Fuel pressure regulator

Fuel pressure of approximately one bar is controlled by the pressure regulator, which is located within the throttle body next to the injector. As the pressure rises over the pre-determined level, excess fuel is returned to either the fuel tank or to the fuel filter number one according to system.

Fuel pressure regulation according to manifold vacuum is unnecessary in SPi vehicles. This is because injection is made into the airstream above the throttle plate, and injection is therefore unaffected by changes in manifold vacuum.

6 Catalytic converter and emission control

All UK models with the Mono-Motronic EMS are fitted with a catalyst as standard equipment.

The Mono-Motronic injection system fitted to catalyst vehicles implements a closed-loop control system, so that exhaust emissions may be reduced. Closed-loop systems are fitted with an oxygen sensor (OS) which monitors the exhaust gas for its oxygen content. The OS signal oscillates between 100 and 1000 mV. A low oxygen level in the exhaust signifies a rich mixture. A high oxygen level in the exhaust signifies a weak mixture. The ECM will then drive the mixture to the opposite extreme so that a weak signal may create a rich mixture, and vice versa.

The OS only produces a signal when the exhaust gas has reached a minimum temperature of approximately 300°C. An OS heater is fitted to the Mono-Motronic system, so that the OS reaches its operating temperature every quickly (within 20 to 30 seconds) after the engine is started.

Evaporative emission control

A carbon filter solenoid valve (CFSV) and activated carbon canister are employed to prevent petrol (hydrocarbon) fumes from escaping to atmosphere.

The carbon canister is connected to the fuel tank, and stores fuel vapours until the CFSV is opened by the ECM under certain operating conditions. Once the CFSV is actuated by the ECM, fuel vapours are drawn into the inlet manifold, to be burnt by the engine during normal combustion.

Fumes from the fuel tank are routed to the carbon canister via the fuel tank ventilation line. When the engine is stopped or is at idle, the fumes are trapped in the canister and cannot escape. A one-way valve (CFSV) that is actuated by the ECM is used to purge the canister.

The CFSV is open when the engine is at rest. A voltage supply is permanently supplied to the valve from the battery terminal 30. Earth to the valve is provided by the ECM, and only completed under certain operating conditions.

Once the engine is started, the CFSV is actuated (closed) by the ECM until engine temperature exceeds 60°C. This prevents an excessively-rich mixture due to the stored vapours being released into the inlet manifold.

Once the operating temperature of 60°C has been reached, the ECM completes a cycle of 90 seconds open and 60 seconds closed. During the opening phase, the ECM pulses the CFSV so that the carbon canister is purged. The duration of the pulses is determined by the ECM, according to signals received from the TPS and the OS.

When the engine is stopped, the CFSV is pulsed closed for approximately 4 seconds after the ignition is switched off. This prevents any tendency by the engine to run-on.

Adjustments

7 Adjustment pre-conditions

1 Ensure that all of these conditions are met before attempting to make adjustments:

a) *Engine at operating temperature. Engine oil at a minimum temperature of 80°C. A journey of at least 4 miles is recommended (particularly so if equipped with AT).*
b) *Ancillary equipment (all engine loads and accessories) switched off.*
c) *AT engines: Transmission in N or P.*
d) *Engine mechanically sound.*
e) *Engine breather hoses and breather system in satisfactory condition.*
f) *Induction system free from vacuum leaks.*
g) *Ignition system in satisfactory condition.*
h) *Air filter in satisfactory condition.*
i) *Exhaust system free from leaks.*
j) *Throttle cable correctly adjusted.*
k) *No fault codes logged by the ECM.*
l) *OS operating satisfactorily (catalyst vehicles with closed-loop control).*

2 In addition, before checking the idle speed and CO values, stabilise the engine as follows:

a) *Stabilise the engine. Raise the engine speed to 3000 rpm for a minimum of 30 seconds, and then allow the engine to idle.*
b) *If the cooling fan operates during adjustment, wait until it stops, re-stabilise the engine, and then restart the adjustment procedure.*
c) *Allow the CO and idle speed to settle.*
d) *Make all checks and adjustments within 30 seconds. If this time is exceeded, re-stabilise the engine and recheck.*

8 Throttle adjustments

TPS adjustment

1 Adjustment of the TPS is not possible.
2 If the TPS is judged defective, the lower part of the throttle body must be replaced.

9 Ignition timing checks (VAG models only)

General

1 The base timing should only be checked and adjusted after a suitable fault code reader (FCR) has placed the ECM into service-set mode.
2 For 35-pin models, it is also possible to place the ECM into service-set mode by using a jumper wire to connect the SD connector to earth. The distributor must not be turned or moved until the service-set mode is induced. During service-set mode, the ECM no longer automatically controls the idle speed. If the distributor were to be turned whilst the idle speed is under ECM control, the ignition timing could not be set correctly. **Note:** *On 45-pin models, timing can only be adjusted by use of a FCR.*

Base timing adjustment

3 Run the engine until it has reached normal operating temperature.
4 Connect a suitable FCR to the serial port and initiate the timing adjustment program, or on 35-pin models only, use a jumper wire to connect the SD connector to earth (brown/white connector with yellow/white wire that connects to ECM pin 22).
5 Start the engine and allow it to idle.
6 Check the base timing (5 ± 1° BTDC).
7 If timing adjustment is required, slacken the distributor fixing bolts and rotate the distributor until the correct timing is obtained. Carefully tighten the distributor bolts and recheck the timing value.
8 Stop the engine and terminate the FCR timing program, or remove the jumper lead from the SD connector.

Timing advance

9 The timing advance is controlled by the Mono-Motronic ECM according to engine load and speed, and is non-adjustable. However, the advance can be checked with a standard stroboscopic timing light, and this check should not be made under FCR control.
10 Allow the engine to idle, and record the position of the timing marks. Increase the engine speed; the timing mark on the pulley should move smoothly to an advanced position.
11 Reduce the engine speed; the timing mark should return to the base position.

10 Idle adjustments

1 Check the ignition timing. The ignition timing must be correctly set before making the idle and CO checks.
2 Refer to the adjustment pre-conditions in Section 7. It is particularly important that that the OS is functioning correctly.
3 Conduct a 10-minute road test, and then interrogate the ECM serial port with a suitable FCR.

4 If any one of the OS fault codes is present, the faults should be diagnosed and repaired before any idle adjustments are attempted.
5 Check the stepper motor idle switch operation.
6 Check the idle speed. **Note:** *the regulated idle speed is not adjustable. However, it is possible to check and adjust the base idle speed using the methods described below.*
7 Check the CO value.

Base idle speed

8 Warm up the engine to normal operating temperature, then switch off.
9 Place a 10mm spacer between the throttle lever and the base idle adjuster.
10 Turn the ignition on, and the stepper motor should retract.
11 Disconnect the stepper motor.
12 Start the engine, and allow the idle speed to stabilise for approximately 1 minute. The idle speed should stabilise at approximately 700 ± 50 rpm.
13 Adjust the base idle screw as necessary. **Note:** *The throttle plate stop screw must NOT be moved under any circumstances.*
14 Check the TPS adjustment.
15 Switch the engine off and reconnect the stepper motor.
16 Start the engine; the idle speed should stabilise to that specified.

Idle switch clearance

Note: *This adjustment procedure is only necessary if the above procedure was unsuccessful.*

17 Set the stepper motor to its base position
18 Use a finger to check that the plunger is fully withdrawn, and push it further into the stepper motor body if required.
19 Use a feeler gauge to check the clearance between the tip of the plunger and the plunger stop. The clearance should be within the range 0.4 mm to 0.6 mm.
20 Reconnect the stepper motor multi-plug.

CO value

21 Check and record the CO value at the exhaust tailpipe. The CO value is not adjustable. Compare with the specification; a value outside of the specification would be due to a mechanical, ignition, catalyst or sensor fault.

System sensor and actuator tests

Important note: *Please refer to Chapter 4, which describes common test procedures applicable to this system. The routines in Chapter 4 should be read in conjunction with the component notes and wiring diagrams presented in this Chapter. The wiring diagrams and other data presented in this Chapter are necessarily representative of the system depicted. Because of the variations in wiring and other data that often occurs, even between similar vehicles in any particular VM's range, the reader should take great care in identification of ECM pins, and satisfy himself that he has gathered the correct data before failing a particular component* **(see illustrations 19.4 to 19.6)**.

11 Crank angle sensor (CAS) - Fiat/Lancia, Citroën/Peugeot models

1 Refer to the note at the start of this Section, and refer to the relevant Section of Chapter 4.
2 Citroën/Peugeot: The CAS resistance is between 300 and 500 ohms. Fiat/Lancia: The CAS resistance is between 486 and 594 ohms.

12 Hall-effect sensor (HES) - VAG models

1 Refer to the note at the start of Section 11, and refer to the relevant Section of Chapter 4.

13 Primary ignition

1 Refer to the note at the start of Section 11, and refer to the relevant Section of Chapter 4 **(see illustration 19.3)**.
2 The primary ignition is essentially that of an ECM with an external amplifier. However, the amplifier is combined with the coil and the following additional test should be made.
3 Remove the two fixing screws and disconnect the amplifier unit.

a) Check the connection between the coil terminal 15 and the amplifier unit number 3.
b) Check the connection between the coil terminal 1 and the amplifier unit number 1.

4 When testing the ignition circuit (with distributor) for a primary signal, the routines described in 'Primary signal not available (external amplifier)' are generally the most suitable.
5 When testing the ignition circuit for a primary signal (DIS), the routines described in 'Primary signal not available (amplifier inside the ECM)' are generally the most suitable. Test both coils in a similar fashion.
6 ECM and component pin numbers may vary depending upon the Mono-Motronic system under test.
7 A supply to the ignition coil(s) is applied from the fuel pump relay (Citroën and Peugeot models), and voltage is only available with the engine cranking or running. However, voltage could be applied for test purposes by by-passing the relay (see Chapter 4).

19.3 Checking coil resistance in the combined coil/amplifier. Connect the ohmmeter between terminals 1 and 15 to check primary resistance, or between terminals 4 and 15 to check secondary resistance

8 Citroën/Peugeot: Primary resistance is 0.80 ohms, secondary resistance is 8600 ohms (Sagem coil) or 14 600 ohms (Bosch coil).
9 Fiat/Lancia: Primary resistance is 0.45 to 0.55 ohms, secondary resistance is 12 000 to 14 600 ohms.
10 VAG: Primary resistance is 0.50 to 1.20 ohms, secondary resistance is 2400 to 4000 ohms.

14 Knock sensor (KS)

1 Refer to the note at the start of Section 11, and refer to the relevant Section of Chapter 4.
2 A knock sensor is only used in 2.0 litre engines.

15 Fuel injector operation

1 Refer to the note at the start of Section 11, and refer to the relevant Section of Chapter 4.
2 Voltage to the injectors is provided from the system relay.
3 The injector resistance is normally 1.2 to 1.6 ohms. The ballast resister resistance is normally 4.0 to 8.0 ohms.
4 In-line ballast resistor: Remove the injector multi-plug, and measure the resistance of the ballast resistor between the injector multi-plug and terminal 87 of the fuel pump relay.

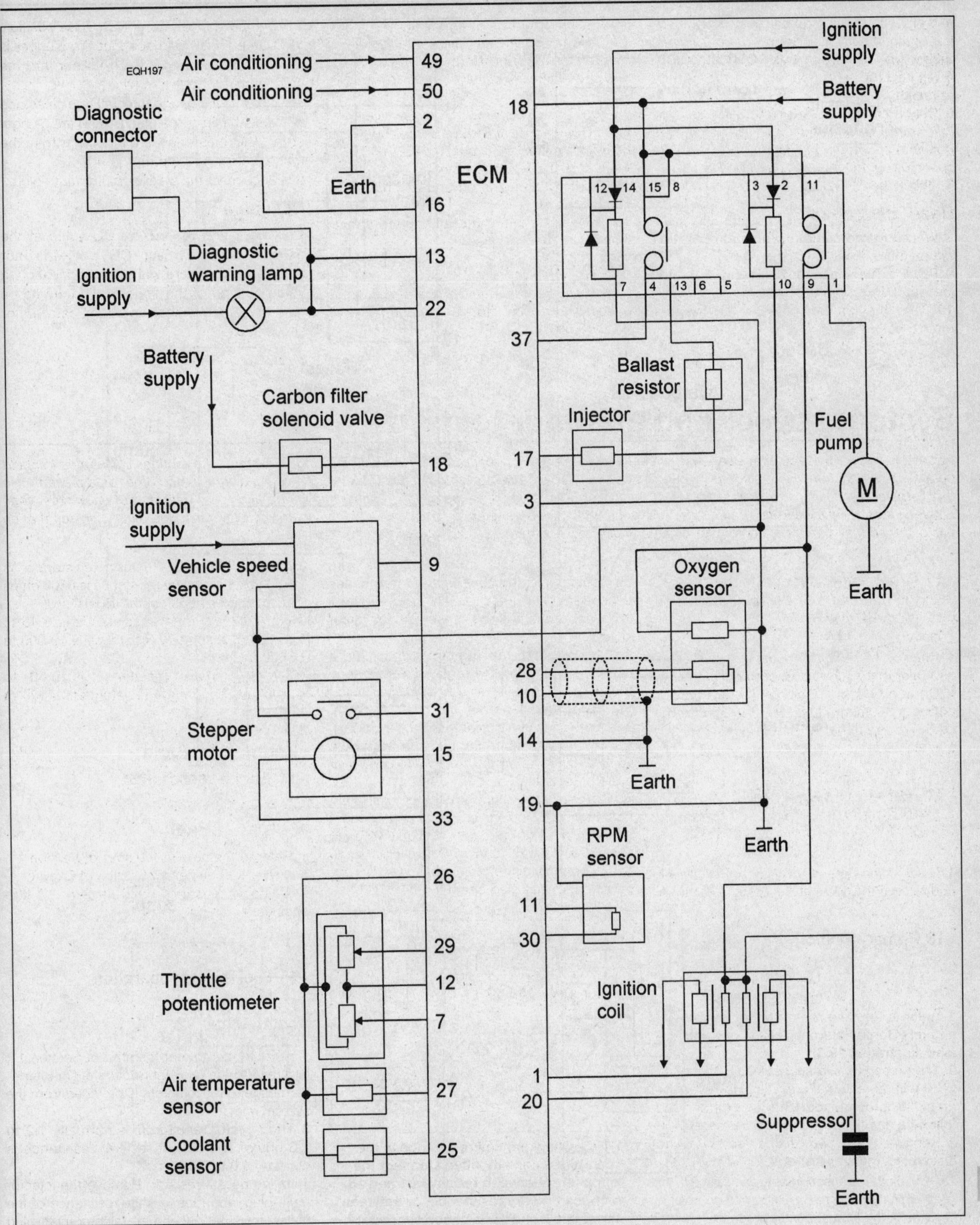

19.4 Typical system wiring - Citroën and Peugeot

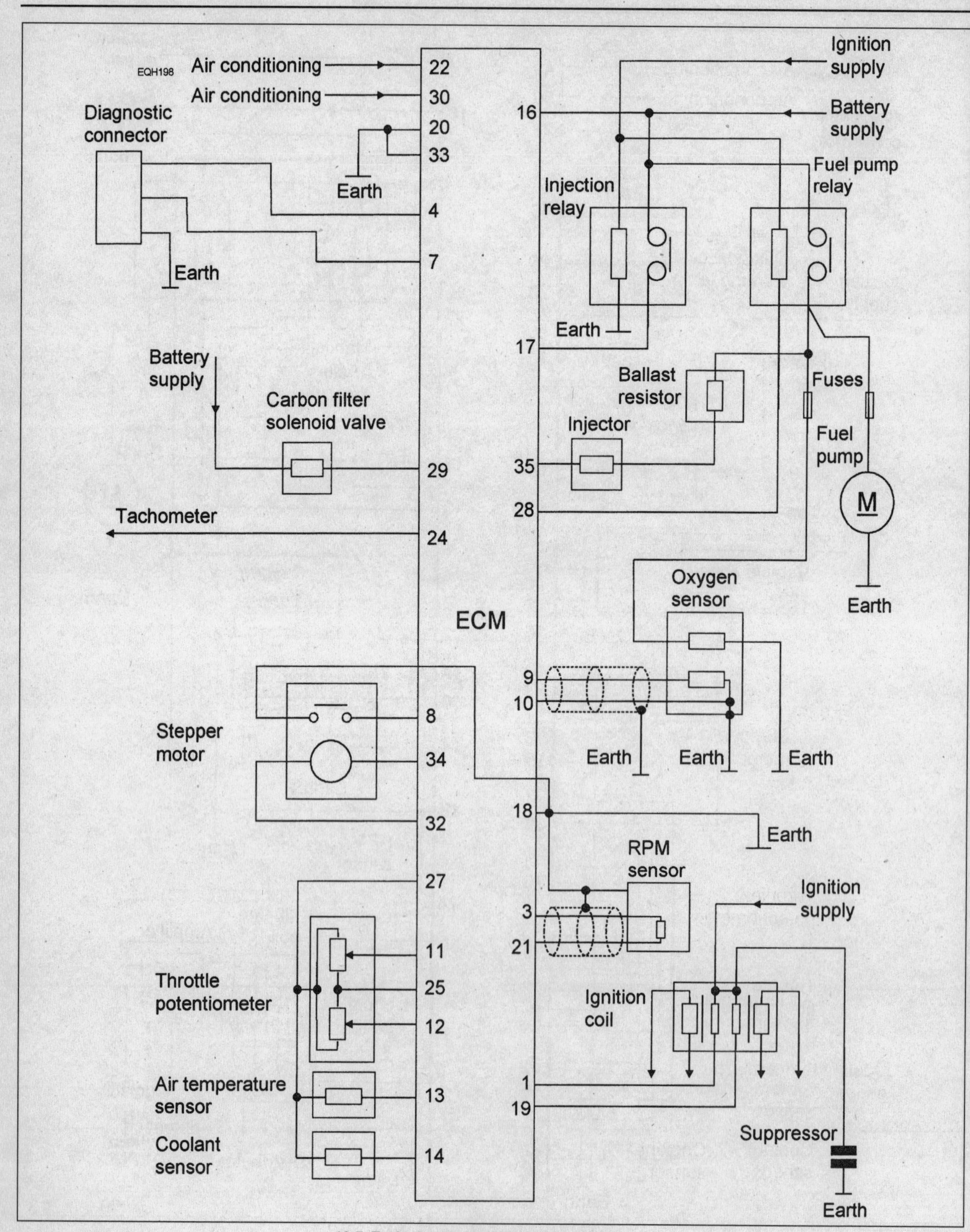

19.5 Typical system wiring - Fiat and Lancia

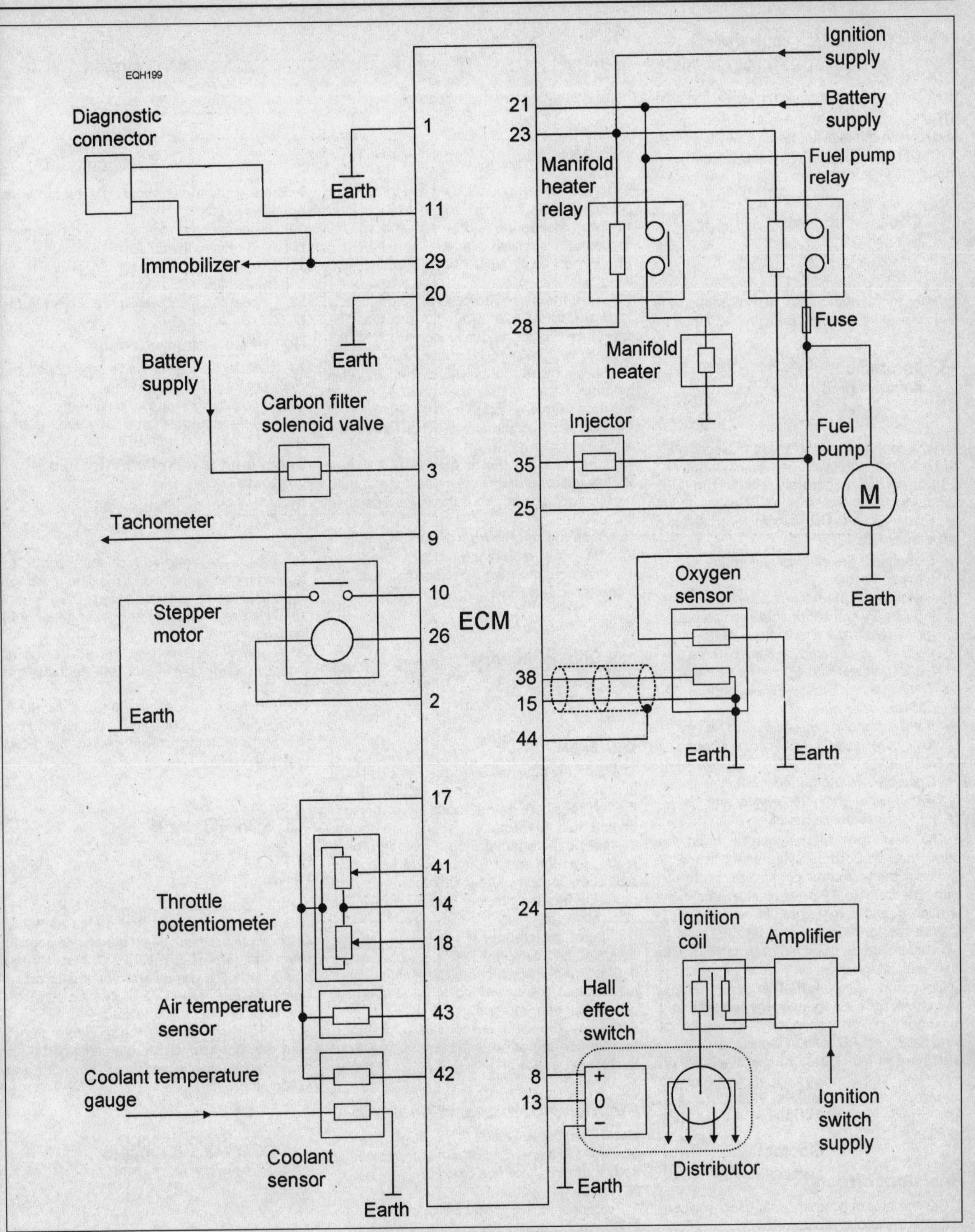

19.6 Typical system wiring - VAG

16 Air temperature sensor (ATS)

1 Refer to the note at the start of Section 11, and refer to the relevant Section of Chapter 4.
2 The ATS is mounted in the throttle body, on top of the injector.

17 Coolant temperature sensor (CTS)

1 Refer to the note at the start of Section 11, and refer to the relevant Section of Chapter 4.

18 Throttle potentiometer sensor (TPS)

1 Refer to the note at the start of Section 11, and refer to the relevant Section of Chapter 4.
2 In order to accurately check the TPS voltages with the throttle closed, it is necessary to set the stepper motor to its base position as follows:

a) Disconnect the multi-plug from the stepper motor.
b) Use a pair of jumper leads to connect a 4.5 volt dry cell battery between stepper motor terminal 1 and 2. **Note:** *The stepper motor could be damaged If a higher voltage than 6.0 volts is applied.*
c) The actuator pin should move either outward or inward.
d) If the actuator plunger does not move fully in, reverse the battery connections and retry.
e) Once the actuator plunger is fully withdrawn, remove the battery and jumper lead connections.

3 The test for voltage output must be performed at both TPS terminals 2 and 4. Connect the voltmeter positive probe to the wire attached to TPS terminal 2, and then terminal 4, and carry out the following tests.
4 With the ignition on, and throttle closed, 1.0 volt should be obtained at terminal 2, with zero volts at terminal 4.
5 Open and close the throttle several times, and check for a smooth voltage increase to a maximum of approximately 4.5 volts at terminal 2, and 4.0 volts at terminal 4.
6 If there is no signal voltage available on either terminal 2 or terminal 4, check for the reference voltage supply at TPS terminal 5, and check the earth connection at TPS terminal 1.

Resistance tests

7 Set the stepper motor to its base position. Refer to the above procedure.
8 Disconnect the TPS multi-plug.

TPS resistance table

Terminals	TPS position	Resistance (ohms)
1 and 2	Closed	600
1 and 2	Closed to 1/4-throttle	600 to 3500
1 and 2	1/4-throttle to full throttle	3500 constant
1 and 4	Closed up to 1/4-throttle	600 constant
1 and 4	1/4-throttle to full throttle	600 to 6600

9 Connect an ohmmeter between terminals 1 and 5.
10 The resistance obtained should fall between the specified figures.
11 Connect an ohmmeter between terminals 1 and 2.
12 From the closed throttle position, slowly open the throttle to about 1/4-throttle. The resistance should gradually increase from the lower to the higher specified figure (see table).
13 Slowly move the throttle to the fully open position. The resistance should remain constant from 1/4- to full-throttle.
14 Connect an ohmmeter between terminals 1 and 4.
15 Open the throttle to about 1/4-throttle. During this operation, the resistance should remain constant at about the lower specified figure.
16 Open the throttle from 1/4-throttle to full-throttle. The resistance should gradually increase from the lower specified figure, to the higher specified figure.

19 Stepper motor

General

1 Switch the ignition key to the 'on' position
2 After 5 seconds, switch the ignition key to the 'off' position. The stepper motor plunger should fully retract, and then step to the correct position (according to temperature), ready for the next engine start. If this operation is completed satisfactorily, it is probable that the stepper motor condition is also satisfactory.
3 Inspect the stepper motor multi-plug for corrosion and damage.
4 Check that the connector terminal pins are fully pushed home, and making good contact with the stepper motor multi-plug.
5 Any of the above faults are common reasons for an poor or inaccurate signal from the stepper motor.

Stepper motor operational test

Note: *This test will result in the ECM storing a fault code. After testing is completed, the fault code memory should be cleared.*
6 Turn on the ignition.
7 Disconnect the CTS multi-plug.
8 Connect a resistance of 15 k-ohms across the two terminals in the CTS multi-plug.
9 The stepper motor should extend to further open the throttle.
10 Disconnect the resistance, and reconnect the multi-plug to the CTS.
11 The stepper motor should return to its original position.
12 Cancel the CTS fault code stored in the ECM.

No stepper motor operation

13 Backprobe terminals 1 and 2 at the stepper motor with a voltmeter.
14 Switch the ignition key on and off.
15 A voltage should be briefly seen as the stepper motor is actuated.

Checking the stepper motor idle contacts

16 Ignition on, throttle closed.
17 Attach the voltmeter negative probe to an earth.
18 Attach the voltmeter positive probe to stepper motor terminal 3. A maximum voltage of 0.25 volts should be obtained.
19 Open the throttle; the voltage should increase to nbv.
20 If the voltage is nbv, throttle open or closed, the stepper motor idle contacts are suspect.
21 If there is no voltage when the throttle is open, check the continuity of the wiring from the stepper motor terminals to the ECM terminals.

20 Manifold heater

1 Refer to the note at the start of Section 11, and refer to the relevant Section of Chapter 4.
2 Carry out the tests when the engine coolant temperature is less than 55°C. **Note:** *If the engine is hot, a variable potentiometer could be connected to the CTS multi-plug so that a cold engine could be simulated.*
3 If a FCR is available, the manifold heater relay can be actuated via the serial port. This would prove the integrity of the relay and associated wiring.

21 ECM voltage supplies and earths

1 Refer to the note at the start of Section 11, and refer to the relevant Section of Chapter 4.

2 In addition to relay drivers for the main relay and pump relay, a relay driver may be available for the manifold heater relay. The relay will only actuate to feed the manifold heater with voltage when the temperature is below 55°C.

22 System relays

1 Refer to the note at the start of Section 11, and also refer to the relevant Section of Chapter 4.
2 In the Mono-Motronic system, the manifold heater is also supplied from a relay.

23 Fuel pump and circuit

1 Refer to the note at the start of Section 11, and also refer to the relevant Section of Chapter 4.

24 Fuel pressure

1 Refer to the note at the start of Section 11, and also refer to the relevant Section of Chapter 4.

25 Oxygen sensor (OS)

1 Refer to the note at the start of Section 11, and refer to the relevant Section of Chapter 4.
2 The OS found in the majority of Mono-Motronic systems is a three-wire sensor (OS earth through the exhaust pipe) with a heater.

26 Carbon filter solenoid valve (CFSV)

1 Refer to the note at the start of Section 11, and refer to the relevant Section of Chapter 4.

Pin table - typical 35-pin (VAG)

Note: *Refer to* ***illustration 19.7****.*

1 Main ECM earth
2 Battery positive
3 -
4 -
5 HES
6 HES
7 -
8 Sensor return (CTS, ATS,TPS)
9 -
10 CTS
11 Earth
12 Fuel pump relay driver
13 Ignition amplifier/coil
14 -
15 Manifold heater relay driver
16 Stepper motor
17 CFSV
18 Earth, final stage drivers
19 Ignition switch supply
20 -
21 -
22 SD connector
23 SD connector
24 TPS
25 TPS
26 TPS
27 ATS
28 OS
29 -
30 Stepper motor
31 Warning lamp controller
32 -
33 -
34 Stepper motor
35 Injector

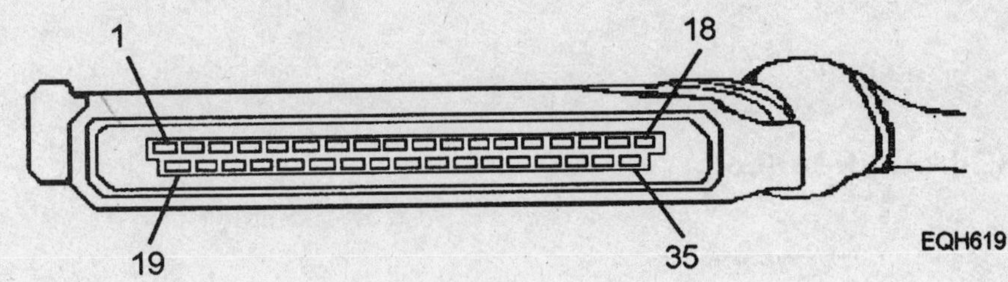

19.7 Typical 35-pin multi-plug (VAG)

Pin table - typical 35-pin (Fiat and Lancia)

Note: *Refer to* ***illustration 19.8****.*

1 Ignition coil
2 -
3 RPM sensor
4 SD connector
5 -
6 -
7 SD connector
8 ISCV
9 OS
10 OS
11 TPS
12 TPS
13 Injector
14 CTS
15 -
16 Battery
17 Injection relay
18 Earth
19 Ignition coil
20 Earth
21 RPM sensor
22 -
23 -
24 Tachometer
25 TPS
26 -
27 CTS, TPS, Injector
28 Fuel pump relay
29 CFSV
30 -
31 Instrument panel
32 ISCV
33 Earth
34 ISCV
35 Injector

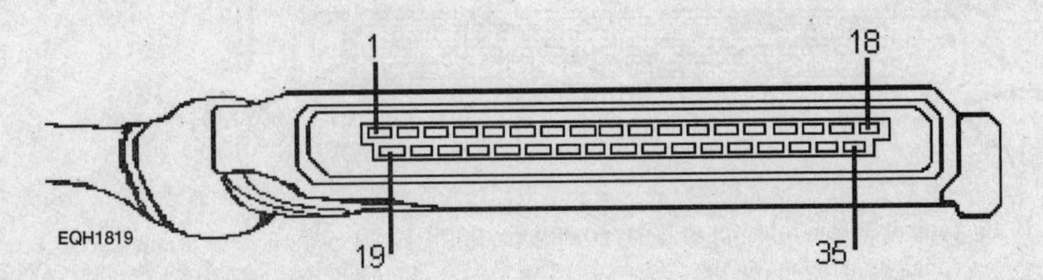

19.8 Typical 35-pin multi-plug (Fiat and Lancia)

Pin table - typical 45-pin (VAG)

Note: *Refer to **illustration 19.9**.*

1 Earth
2 Stepper motor
3 CFSV
4 -
5 -
6 -
7 Injector
8 HES
9 Tachometer
10 Stepper motor
11 -
12 -
13 HES
14 TPS
15 Earth
16 -
17 Sensor return(CTS, ATS, TPS)
18 TPS
19 -
20 Earth
21 Battery positive
22 -
23 Ignition supply
24 Ignition coil/amplifier
25 Fuel pump relay driver
26 Stepper motor
27 -
28 Manifold heater relay driver
29 SD connector
30 -
31 -
32 -
33 -
34 -
35 -
36 -
37 -
38 OS
39 -
40 -
41 TPS
42 CTS
43 ATS
44 -
45 -

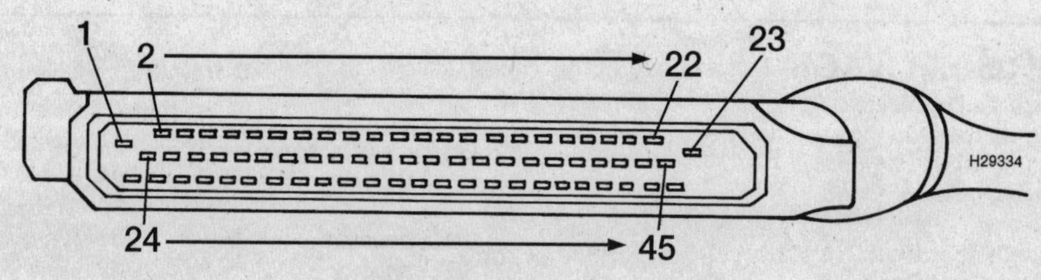

19.9 Typical 45-pin multi-plug (VAG)

Pin table - typical 55-pin (Citroën/Peugeot)

Note: *Refer to **illustration 19.10**.*

1 Ignition coil
2 Earth
3 Engine control module relay
4 -
5 CFSV
6 Tachometer
7 TPS
8 -
9 VSS
10 OS
11 RPM sensor
12 TPS
13 SD connector
14 Earth
15 ISCV
16 SD connector
17 Injector
18 Battery supply
19 Earth
20 Ignition coil
21 -
22 SD warning lamp
25 CTS
26 Sensor return (CTS, ATS, TPS)
27 ATS
28 OS
29 TPS
30 RPM sensor
31 ISCV
32 -
33 ISCV
34 -
35 -
36 -
37 Engine control module relay

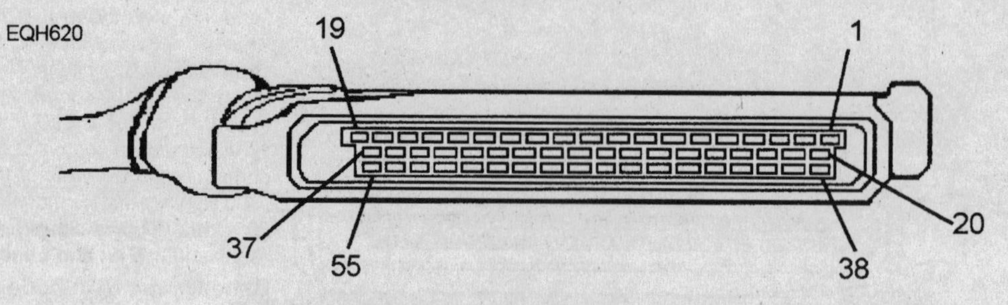

19.10 Typical 55-pin multi-plug (Citroën and Peugeot)

Fault codes

27 Obtaining fault codes

Citroën and Peugeot models

1 If a FCR is available, it could be attached to the SD serial connector and used for the following purposes:
- *a) Obtaining fault codes.*
- *b) Clearing fault codes.*
- *c) Obtaining Datastream information.*
- *d) Actuating the system actuators - this may include one or more of the following:*
  Fuel injectors
  ISCV
  CFSV (where fitted)

2 If a FCR is not available, it is still possible to obtain fault codes, so long as the SD plug is of the two-pin type **(see illustration 19.11)**. A FCR is required for those systems equipped with the 16-pin SD plug.

3 When the ECM determines that a fault is present, it internally logs a fault code, and will also turn on the diagnostic warning lamp if the fault is regarded by the system as major. Faults regarded as minor will light the warning lamp, although a code will still be logged. All of the various two-digit fault codes in Citroën and Peugeot vehicles equipped with a Mono-Motronic system are of the 'slow' variety, and can be output as flash codes on the dash-mounted warning lamp. The first series of flashes indicates the number of tens, the second series of flashes indicates the single units.

Obtaining codes without a FCR

- *a) Attach an on/off accessory switch between the FCR green multi-plug terminal 2 and earth.*
- *b) Switch on the ignition.*
- *c) Close the switch for three seconds (the dash warning lamp will remain off).*

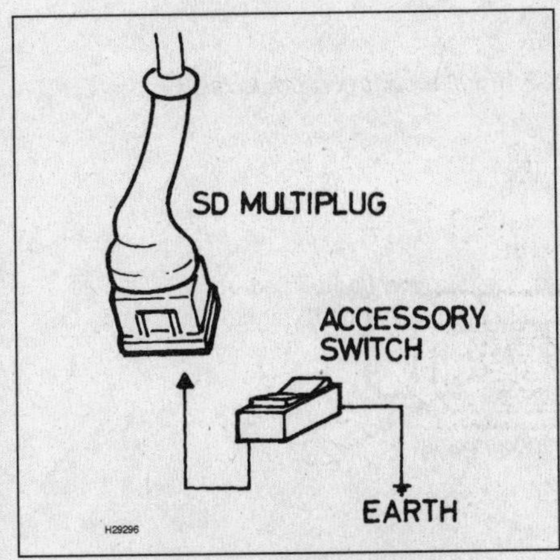

19.11 Obtaining flash codes (Citroën and Peugeot)

- *d) Open the switch; the warning lamp will:*
  Flash once (indicating 10).
  Pause for 1.5 seconds.
  Flash twice (indicating 2).
  This indicates the code of twelve (12), which is the test start code.
  The warning lamp will extinguish.
- *e) Close the switch for three seconds (the dash warning lamp will remain off).*
- *f) Open the switch, and the warning lamp will flash to indicate a code.*
- *g) Once the lamp has extinguished, wait for three seconds before continuing.*
- *h) Close the switch for three seconds, and repeat the test to obtain further codes. When code 11 is obtained, this indicates End of Test.*
- *i) After code 11 is obtained, the complete test may be repeated.*
- *j) If code 11 is the first code obtained after code 12, no faults are logged by the ECM.*

Clearing fault codes from the memory of the ECM

- *a) Repair all circuits indicated by the fault codes.*
- *b) Switch on the ignition.*
- *c) Perform the test as detailed above to reveal code 11 with no fault codes (optional).*
- *d) Close the accessory switch for more than ten seconds.*
- *e) The warning lamp will remain extinguished.*

VAG models

4 VAG Mono-Motronic system generates two kinds of fault codes - five-digit fault codes and four-digit flash codes.

5 Fault codes can only be output with the aid of a dedicated FCR.

6 Four-digit flash codes can only be output from Mono-Motronic MA1.2.1 (35-pin) and MA1.2.2 (45-pin) via an LED lamp. An instrument panel warning lamp is not fitted. Flash codes cannot be output from later versions of Mono-Motronic.

7 The dedicated FCR can be used for the following purposes:
- *a) Accessing and clearing fault codes.*
- *b) Accessing Datastream.*
- *c) Actuating components and making service adjustments. VAG have assigned 5-digit code numbers for codes to be obtained through the use of a FCR.*
- *d) Placing the ECM into a service-set mode for adjustment of the ignition timing, and setting of the base idle speed. It is also possible to enter service-set mode without the FCR (see timing adjustments).*

Note: *Oxygen sensor fault codes can only be retrieved after a road test of at least 10 minutes' duration.*

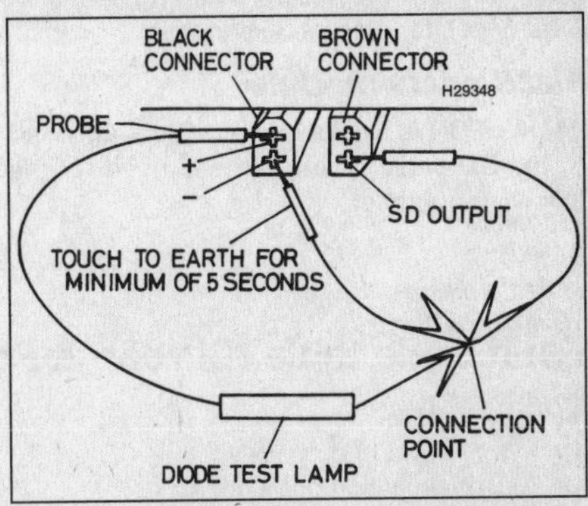

19.12 Obtaining flash codes (VAG)

Obtaining codes without a FCR

8 The four-digit fault codes are obtained by connecting a suitable FCR or a diode lamp to the SD plug **(see illustration 19.12)**.

9 The first series of flashes indicates the first digit, the second series of flashes indicates the second digit, and so on.

10 Locate the two-pin SD connection. Where the SD connection is in the footwell or near to the gear lever, the black connection to the left of the SD connector (white or brown) is a voltage supply and earth connector. **Note:** *It is not possible to obtain flash codes from 55-pin Mono-Motronic systems, nor when the SD connector is the 16-pin ISO connector.*

11 Start the engine.

12 Warm up the engine and allow it to idle. **Note:** *Oxygen sensor fault codes can only be retrieved after a road test of at least 10 minutes' duration.*

13 If the engine will not start, crank the engine for at least six seconds, and leave the ignition switch on.

14 Use a jumper lead to connect the SD connector to earth for at least five seconds. The warning lamp or LED will light, and will remain lit until the jumper lead is removed.

15 Remove the jumper lead, and the warning lamp or the diode test lamp will flash to indicate a four-digit code. **Note:** *There is a 2.5 second gap between each digit, and only one code can be output at a time.*

16 Count the flashes, and record the code.

17 When the code 4444 is transmitted, no faults are stored and the procedure is at an end.

18 If a code other than 4444 is transmitted, repeat the test by connecting the jumper lead to earth again for at least 5 seconds.

19 Record each code, and continue extracting codes until code 0000 is transmitted. Code 0000 signifies that no more codes are stored.

20 Code 0000 is displayed when the lamp flashes off and on at 2.5 second intervals.

Cancelling a fault code

21 Carry out the above procedure to obtain the fault code.

22 Turn off the ignition,

23 Remove the ECM multi-plug connector from the ECM *(refer to Warning No 3 in Reference)*, for at least 30 seconds.

Fiat/Lancia models

24 If a FCR is available, it could be attached to the SD serial connector and used for the following purposes:

a) Obtaining fault codes.
b) Clearing fault codes.
c) Obtaining Datastream information.
d) Actuating the system actuators - this may include one or more items from the following list:
Fuel injectors
ISCV
CFSV (where fitted)

25 Fiat/Lancia models require a dedicated FCR to access fault codes. Flash codes are not available for output from this system. For the sake of completeness, we have provided a list of components that will provide errors for readout upon a FCR.

Fault code table (Citroën & Peugeot)

Code	Item
11	End of diagnosis
12	Initiation of diagnosis
13x	ATS
14x	CTS
21x	TPS
22	Stepper motor
27x	VSS
31x	Lambda control
41	CAS
42	Injector or fuel pump control
51	OS
52	Lambda control
53x	Battery voltage
54	ECM

Actuator selection code	
81	Fuel pump relay
82	Injector
83	Stepper motor
84	CFSV
85	A/C compressor supply relay

x *Faults that typically will cause the ECM to enter LOS and use a default value in place of the sensor.*

Some faults are designated as major faults, and will light the warning lamp. However, major faults vary from system to system, and it is best to interrogate the ECM for codes if a fault is suspected.

Flash code table (VAG)

Code	Item	Fault
4444	Initiation of diagnosis	No faults
1111	Internal ECM failure	Check earth and voltage to ECM
1231	Vehicle speed sensor	
1232	Stepper motor circuit	Stepper motor or ECM fault
2113	HES circuit or HES fault	Open-circuit (see note below)
2114	Distributor	
2121	Stepper motor idle contacts or ignition control valve circuit fault	
2122	No engine speed signal	
2123	Full-throttle switch	
2141	Knock control 1 (ECM)	
2142	KS circuit or KS fault	
2143	Knock control 2 (ECM)	
2212	TPS circuit or TPS fault	Open-circuit or short to earth
2214	Max. engine speed exceeded	
2231	Idle control	
2234	Supply voltage incorrect	Battery voltage too low/high
2242	CO pot circuit or CO pot fault	Open-circuit or short to earth
2312	CTS circuit or CTS fault	Open-circuit or short to earth
2314	Engine/gearbox electrical connection	
2322	ATS circuit or ATS fault	open-circuit or short to earth
2341	OS control inoperative	Vacuum leak, ignition fault, fuel supply, faulty injector, poor engine compression, short to earth in OS signal wire, faulty OS
2342	OS circuit or OS fault	Faulty OS or signal wiring
2343	Mixture control adjustment - weak	
2344	Mixture control adjustment - rich	
2413	Mixture limits	Misfire/fuel pressure/leaking exhaust
4332	ECM	
4343	Evaporative canister purge valve	
0000	End of output - flashing at 2.5 second intervals	

Note: *Fault code number 2113 (no Hall signal) will always be present when the ignition is switched on and the engine is stopped.*

Fault condition table (Fiat & Lancia)

Item	Fault
CAS	Loss of signal
TPS	
MAP	No correlation between MAP signal and TPS & CAS signals
ATS	
CTS voltage	Voltage less than 6.2 volts or greater than 15.5 volts
Lambda control	
Injector control	
Ignition coils control	
Stepper motor	
CFSV	
Relay control	
ECM memories	Limits of adaptive control. When the limits are reached, this suggests a serious engine (mechanical) condition

Note: *Fault conditions and not fault codes are logged in the Fiat/Lancia Mono-Motronic system, and a FCR is required to read the fault conditions.*

Reference

Abbreviations and glossary of technical terms

A

A/C (Air Conditioning)

AATS (Ambient Air Temperature Sensor)

AAV (Auxiliary Air valve)

AC (Alternating Current) An electric current that first flows in one direction and then the opposite. AC voltage is produced by an alternator or by a pulse generator. AC voltage must be rectified to DC before it can be used in the vehicle charging system. AC voltage from a pulse generator is converted to DC by an analogue to Digital converter.

ACAV (Variable Acoustic Characteristic Induction - Citroen/Peugeot term)

ACC (Air Conditioning compressor Clutch - Ford term)

ACS (Air Conditioning Switch - Ford term)

ACT (Air Charge Temperature - Ford term - see ATS) Usually refers to a totally separate sensor, as distinct to one that is integrated into the AFS.

Actuator A device controlled by the ECM. Examples would be injectors, ISCV etc.

Actuator driver Refer also to driver (actuator), relay driver, control signal and final stage.

ACW (Anti Clock Wise) Direction of rotation.

Adaptive system An EMS that is able to learn or relearn the best setting for each application is said to be adaptive.

ADC (Analogue to Digital Converter)

Advance curve Progressive increase in ignition timing advance as rpm increases. The curve is determined by the manufacturer, and may be mechanical or electronic in operation. It can be checked with a stroboscopic light over the rpm range. An accurate advance curve, matched to the engine, will give economical and powerful running.

AEI (see Renix)

AFM (Air Flow Meter - see AFS)

AFR (Air Fuel Ratio) Ratio of air to fuel by weight in a vaporised charge: ie 14.7 kilos of air to 1.0 kilo of fuel. The ideal AFR for complete combustion is 14.7: 1, and the EMS (via the Lambda sensor) will be set up to maintain this ratio as closely as possible (the Lambda "window") - see AFR / Lambda chart. The AFR in carburettor systems varies according to intake air temperature and density. This makes accurate control of the correct mixture strength virtually impossible. In contrast, the electronic fuel injection system uses a number of sensors to monitor all conditions that will affect the AFR. This means that very accurate control of the mixture is possible.

AFR/ Lambda Chart
AFR: = 14.7: 1 by weight

AFR	Lambda
0.7	10.29
0.8	11.76
0.9	13.23
0.97	14.26) Lambda
1.0	14.70) "window"
1.03	15.14)
1.1	16.17
1.2	17.64
1.3	19.11

AFS (Air Flow Sensor) A sensor that measures the volume of air being drawn into the engine and passes this information to the ECM as an electrical signal. The AFS signal determines the load factor from which the ECM looks up the appropriate injection duration. Common types of AFS would include the hot-wire or hot-film types and the mechanical vane type.

ALDL (Assembly Line Diagnostic Link) The name given to the serial data port used mainly on GM vehicles.

Air Air is a mixture of nitrogen (79%), oxygen (20%), carbon dioxide (0.04%) and inert gases (0.06%).

ALT (alternator - Ford term)

Alternator A current generating device used in a vehicle charging system.

Ammeter An instrument for measuring current in amperes.

Amp (abbreviation for ampere) A unit measurement of current flow.

Amp (abbreviation for amplifier)

Amplifier operation
In a conventional ignition, the CB switches the negative side of the coil on and off to produce a spark. The electronic system is very similar in operation but uses (typically) a pulse generator and amplifier to achieve the same result.

A pulse generator provides the amplifier with correctly timed electrical pulses to trigger the ignition. The generated pulse is too weak to operate the switching transistor and must be amplified. The amplifier senses the trigger pulse and amplifies the voltage to the correct level to operate the switching transistor. The coil negative (-) terminal is thus switched on by the amplifier circuitry to build the magnetic field, and switched off by the switching transistor to collapse the magnetic field and induce the secondary spark. In an EMS, the amplifier may be an integral part of the ECM, or may be a separate amplifier that is switched by the ECM.

When located within the ECM, no separate wiring is required. However, if the amplifier fails, the only course of action is to renew the ECM.

A safety circuit is used to prevent coil overheating. The primary current is switched off after (typically) one second if the ignition is switched on and the engine not started. The amplifier also contains the constant energy limiting circuitry.

Amplitude

Square waveform: Difference between the maximum and minimum voltage.

AC waveform: Difference between zero and either the maximum or minimum peak. The positive amplitude is likely to be slightly greater than the negative amplitude in CAS waveforms.

Analogue signal An analogue signal is defined as a continuous signal that can change by an infinitely small amount. Any sensor that meets these conditions can also be called an analogue sensor. Typically, an analogue signal is measured by an instrument that uses a needle to progressively sweep across a fixed scale. Any change in the signal will cause the needle to move by a similar amount. One example would be the throttle pot. As the throttle is opened and closed, the voltage output signal from the throttle pot increases and decreases and an analogue signal is passed to the ECM.

Annular coil A type of signal generator that utilises a coiled wire magnet attached to a stator plate. The plate contains a number of magnetised upright arms equal to the number of cylinders and also equal to the number of arms on the reluctor.

API (American Petroleum Institute) Refers to body who sets a worldwide standard for motor lubrication.

APS (Absolute Pressure Sensor - see MAP sensor)

Arcing Unwanted electrical bridging in a circuit.

ASV (Air Switching Valve) A vacuum switching valve - often found on Japanese vehicles.

Asynchronous Refers usually to an injection system that is not synchronised to the ignition. Asynchronous pulses may occur at a set time interval or be intermittent in operation.

AT (Automatic Transmission)

ATA (Automatic Transmission Actuator - Ford term)

ATDC (After Top Dead Centre.) After the piston has reached TDC and is descending. Refers to retarded ignition timing OR measurement of valve timing.

ATF (Automatic Transmission Fluid)

Atmospheric pressure The weight of atmosphere per unit area. At sea level the atmospheric pressure is 14.7 psi absolute or 102 KPa. See pressure conversion table under Pressure.

ATR (Automatic Transmission Relay - Ford term)

ATS (Air Temperature Sensor) A thermistor that changes in resistance according to temperature. Most ATS usually work on the NTC principle. However, ATS fitted to Renix equipped EMS may be NTC or PTC. As the temperature changes, the thermistor resistance changes, and thus the ECM is able to calculate the air temperature from the level of voltage (or current) that is registered on the sensor signal wire.

Available HT voltage The maximum secondary voltage that an ignition system is capable of producing.

B

Backprobe A method of obtaining a voltage measurement from the multiplug pin of an electronic component or sensor. The multiplug must remain connected to the component. The multiplug insulating boot should be peeled back and the voltmeter positive probe attached to the relevant pin - ignition key on. Note: In in this book, the multiplug diagram shows the terminals of the harness connector. When back-probing the multiplug (or viewing the sensor connector terminals), the terminal positions will be reversed.

Backcycling Reversal of crankcase fumes due to a blocked PCV system.

Backfire Noise of exploding air/ fuel charge in the intake or exhaust system. Usually occurs during cranking or deceleration. Often due to leaking exhaust, weak air/ fuel mixture, retarded timing, other ignition fault or valve related compression fault.

Back pressure Unwanted additional pressure in the exhaust system of a running engine. Caused by a plugged exhaust and results in loss of power and efficiency.

Ballast resistor

A current compensating device that alters current flow in direct proportion to the temperature of the resistor. When used in the primary ignition circuit It serves two purposes.

(1) By providing the proper current level to a low primary resistance coil, it promotes cool coil running under all operating conditions.

(2) When a full 12 volt by-pass supply is introduced to the coil under cranking, the coil output will be greater and starting will therefore be aided.

The ballast resistor was mainly use in conventional CB ignition systems to compensate in part for some of the deficiencies of that system. A number of the early electronic ignition systems, that were not of the constant energy type, also utilised a ballast resistor for current control purposes. The ballast resistor can also be found in other circuits where current compensation is necessary. An example would be the fuel pump circuit on the Lucas LH system fitted to some Rover fuel injected systems and in the voltage supply to the fuel injector solenoid on some early systems.

Banked or simultaneous injection Injectors connected in parallel circuits. In some four cylinder engines the four injectors may be connected together so that they all open at the same moment. In other four cylinder systems, the four injectors are connected in two banks of two cylinders. However, all injectors may still be actuated simultaneously. In a six cylinder engine the six injectors may be connected in two banks of three cylinders, In an eight cylinder engine the eight injectors may be connected in two banks of four cylinders, In a twelve cylinder engine the twelve injectors may be connected in four banks of three cylinders.

Bar A unit of pressure. One bar is almost equal to atmospheric pressure. See pressure conversion table under Pressure.

Barometric pressure Equal to atmospheric pressure. At sea-level, atmospheric pressure is 100 Kpa. See pressure conversion table under MAP.

Battery

A storage device for electrical energy in chemical form. The primary function of the battery is to provide ignition current during the starting period and power to operate the starter motor. This must be accomplished irrespective of adverse temperature conditions. The battery also serves, for a limited time, as a current source to satisfy the electrical demands of the vehicle which are in excess of the generator output. A battery is now rated in terms of its CSP or CCA. There are three Internationally known standards and virtually all batteries in Europe, the Far East and the Americas are marked in accordance with these standards.

The three standards are:-

BS / IEC:

The current in amperes that can be drawn from the battery for one minute at -18°C before cell voltage drops below 1.4 volts per cell. (BS3911 1982).

SAE / BCI:

The current in amperes that can be drawn from the battery for thirty seconds at -18°C before cell voltage drops below 1.2 volts per cell. (SAE J537 June 1982).

DIN:

The current in amperes that can be drawn from the battery for thirty seconds at -18°C before cell voltage drops below 1.5 volts per cell. (DIN 425-39 PT2 1983).

BBDC (Before Bottom Dead Centre)

BCI See battery. An SAE standard for measuring battery performance.

BDC (Bottom Dead Centre) Piston at exact bottom of stroke.

BHP (Brake Horse Power) Measurement of engine power.

Bimetallic Two strips of different metals bonded together. When heated or cooled the different expansion rates of the metals cause the strips to bend. Often used to operate a carburettor automatic choke.

Blowby Combustion fumes that are blown past the piston rings during the power stroke. Worn or gummed pistons and rings will admit excessive blowby.

BOB (Break Out Box)

BOO (Brake On / Off switch - Ford term)

BPC (Boost Pressure Control solenoid (turbo) - Ford term)

Breather As the pistons ascend and descend the crankcase air is displaced and proper ventilation via a breather is required if a pressurised crankcase is to be avoided.

BS / IEC See battery. A standard for measuring battery performance.

BTDC (Before Top Dead Centre.) Ascending piston before top of stroke. Refers to advanced ignition timing OR measurement of valve timing.

Burn time See spark duration.

C

°C (Celsius or Centigrade) Measurement of temperature. Temperature conversion scale.

Cable Heavy electrical wire used to conduct high voltage or high current. ie spark plug cables or battery cables.

Calibrate The setting of an instrument to a base zero for greatest accuracy.

CANP (CANister Purge solenoid valve)

Capacitor A device that absorbs electricity by offering an alternative path.

Carbon brush A brush centred in the distributor cap. It contacts the rotor and passes secondary voltage for distribution to the correct cylinder.

Carburettor A device that atomises air and fuel in the correct proportion over the engine operating range.

CAS (Crank Angle Sensor)

The CAS works on the same principle as the inductive permanent magnet pick-up. A number of steel pegs or pins are set at regular intervals around the circumference of the flywheel or crankshaft. Typically, a peg may be set at every 10° - 36 in all. One or more of the pegs may be removed at TDC, BDC or a known distance from these points. The flywheel thus becomes a reluctor.

A permanent magnet inductive signal generator is mounted in close proximity to the flywheel. As the flywheel spins, an alternating (AC) waveform is produced which signals RPM and flywheel position to the ECM. Although most modern systems utilise a single CAS, some of the older systems use two CAS - one for RPM and one for position. The waveform produced by a each type of CAS will be slightly different.

Cat (catalytic converter) Since January 1993, all new UK vehicles are required to be fitted with a catalytic converter. A catalyst is something which promotes a reaction, but itself remains unaffected by the reaction. The catalytic converter consists of a stainless steel housing containing a ceramic monolith with a honeycomb of passages called cells.

CB Contact Breaker (points) A switch which turns the flow of primary current on and off to induce ignition. Used in vehicles that utilise conventional ignition systems.

CCA (Cold Cranking Amps - see battery) A standard for measuring battery performance.

CCMC The EC standard for lubricating oil, it is the European equivalent to API.

CCO (Clutch Converter lock-up solenoid - Ford term)

CD (Constant Depression) A type of carburettor that uses a piston to vary the choke area according to speed and load. This results in a constant air velocity and depression over the jet at all engine speeds and does away with the need for separate compensating and idle jets.

Cell A single battery unit consisting of positive and negative plates covered by Electrolyte. A twelve volt battery consists of six cells connected in series and measuring approximately 2.1 volts each.

CEL (Check Engine Light - diagnostic warning lamp)

Celsius See °C

Centrifugal advance See mechanical advance.

Ceramic block Insulating block used in construction of a certain type of ballast resistor.

CFI (Central Fuel Injection - Ford/ Vauxhall term - see SPi)

CFCV (Carbon Filter Control Valve) Mechanically operated valve used in the evaporation control system to control recycling of vapours from the carbon canister.

CFSV (Carbon Filter Solenoid Valve) Electrically operated solenoid valve used in the evaporation control system to control recycling of vapours from the carbon canister. Sometimes termed a purge valve.

CFCOSV (Carbon Filter Cut-off Solenoid Valve) This valve is often fitted to Peugeot and Citroen vehicles. The CFCOSV is actuated by the ignition key and is used in conjunction with the CFSV. When the ignition is switched off, the valve closes and fumes are retained in the system.

CID (Cylinder IDentification (camshaft sensor) - Ford term)

CIH (Cam In Head) A camshaft located in the cylinder head. Differs from the OHC design in that the camshaft uses short pushrods to open the valves.

Circuit An electrical path through which current can flow and that begins and ends at the current source. A circuit is NOT complete unless the current can return to the source. In modern systems the current flows from the positive terminal of the battery, through wires or cables and switches to the load (ie a starter motor). The return is through earth to the negative terminal of the battery.

CIS (Continuous Injection System.) A Bosch fuel injection system where the injectors spray fuel continuously during running. Another name for Bosch K-Jetronic.

Clear flood Usually, if a fuel injected vehicle fails to start, continued cranking will result in excessive fuel being injected into the cylinders. Where the fuel injection system has a 'clear flood' facility, fully opening the throttle will result in a reduced volume of fuel being injected whilst the engine is cranked.

Closed loop control An engine with a Lambda sensor is known as a closed loop engine. This is because of the measure of tight engine control about the stoichiometric point.

CLT (Cylinder Leakage Tester) A gauge for measuring compression loss. Compressed air is pumped into the cylinder under test with the piston at TDC on the compression stroke. The rate of loss is recorded upon the CLT gauge. The higher the rate of loss, the less efficient is the cylinder. By listening at the carburettor intake, exhaust pipe, oil filler cap and radiator cap - the reason for the high loss can usually be determined.

CMH (Cold Mixture Heater Plate see manifold heater)

CO (Carbon Monoxide)

Carbon Monoxide is formed by the partial burning of the fuel due to a lack of oxygen. A low proportion of CO indicates how well the air/fuel ratio is maintained. A high proportion of CO in the exhaust indicates a rich fuel mixture, choked air filter, choked PCV valve or low idle speed. Low CO would indicate a lean fuel mixture or a vacuum leak or even an exhaust leak. CO (and HC) emissions decrease as load (heat and temperature) rises to give a more efficient engine.

The CO content in the exhaust is an indicator of the AFR, but only when the engine is functioning normally. Any engine condition that causes a misfire will reduce the amount of CO that is burnt. CO is produced from the partial burning of fuel and if you don't burn the fuel you wont produce the CO.

It is therefore obvious that an engine with a burnt valve or a dead spark plug would produce less CO. In this instance, any attempt to adjust the fuel mixture would result in an over-rich mixture even though the Gas Analyser indicated a lean mixture.

Only a Gas Analysers that could calculate a 'corrected' CO reading would provide the complete picture. It is essential therefore that all mechanical and ignition faults are corrected before making fuel adjustments.

CO is a very poisonous, tasteless, colourless and odourless gas. It is a serious health hazard in dense traffic in cities and semi-enclosed areas. A concentration of 0.3% can be fatal if breathed in continually for 30 minutes. CO combines with red blood cells at the expense of oxygen and causes suffocation. By weight CO accounts for about 47% of air pollution but is thought to have little effect on the environment.

One molecule of CO contains one atom of carbon and one of oxygen and it is measured in % volume. CO is inversely proportional to the AFR, the less fuel the lower the CO.

CO_2 (Carbon Dioxide)

CO_2 is the product of an efficient engine. With low CO and HC levels, the percentage of CO_2 in the exhaust is likely to be 13 to 15%. Less than 8% CO_2 indicates an incorrect AFR, or a misfire or a leaky exhaust. CO_2 is directly proportional to the AFR, but inversely proportional to CO. The less fuel, the higher the CO_2. At speeds over 2000 rpm, the level will be 1-2% higher than at idle due to an increase in engine efficiency.

One molecule of CO_2 contains one atom of carbon and two of oxygen. CO_2 is chemically stable and does not easily react with other substances. Not poisonous it is produced by all breathing animals including fish. Oxygen is inhaled and CO_2 exhaled at a concentration of about 5%. CO_2 is absorbed by all green plants by a process called "photo-synthesis", which only happens in daylight and which also releases oxygen (O_2) into the atmosphere.

Any burning process produces CO_2 and the contribution from automotive sources is said to be less than half that of industrial and domestic sources. The contribution from people and animals is insignificant. A heavy concentration of CO_2 is like placing a blanket over the atmosphere and this prevents heat loss by radiation. At present, more CO_2 is being produced than is being consumed and the disappearance of the rain forests is another significant factor. As the forests fade away, less CO_2 is absorbed and the increase in atmospheric concentration is said to contribute towards global warming and the so-called 'greenhouse effect'.

In the automobile, the only way to produce less CO_2 is to burn less petrol or even none at all. This means an efficient engine with good economy (a lean-burn engine), or a diesel engine with high economy or even a car with no engine - ie an electric motor. But electric cars need electricity, and electricity is produced by power stations, and power stations also produce CO_2. . .

Coil A device that transforms low (battery) voltage into the high voltage required to bridge the rotor and spark plug gaps.

Cold start device A choke or a starting device to enrich the air/fuel ratio during cold starting and during the warm-up period.

Combustion

During the combustion process, oxygen combines with carbon to form carbon dioxide (CO_2), and with hydrogen to form water (H_2O). If the air and fuel were homogenised prior to combustion and all the petrol was completely burnt then the ideal engine would inhale a perfect mixture of fuel and air and exhale Carbon Dioxide (CO_2) and water (H_2O). For every gallon of petrol that an engine consumes, a gallon of water is produced. When the engine is at normal operating temperature, this water is exhausted as steam.

Unfortunately, this ideal engine does not exist and for a number of reasons incomplete combustion occurs in all engines to a degree in even the most efficient engine. In addition to CO_2 and H_2O the exhaust thus contains varying quantities of CO, HC, O_2 and NOx. Some of these gases are harmless such as CO_2, H_2O and O_2, whilst others ie HC, CO and NOx are atmospheric pollutants. A less efficient engine will exhaust a greater volume of the more harmful pollutants. A regular tune-up and gas analysis should reduce pollution to acceptable levels. However, the more efficient the engine, the more CO_2 will be exhausted.

Compression The charging of a maximum volume of air and fuel into a minimum volume.

Compression tester A gauge to measure the compression pressure of an engine and usually graduated in bars or psi.

Conductor A material that will pass electrical current efficiently. A good conductor depends on material used, length, cross sectional area and temperature.

Constant energy The use of high primary current limited, to a pre-set figure, for efficient electronic ignition operation.

Constant energy operation (electronic ignition) Electronic ignition, used with a coil of lower primary resistance, produces increased primary current resulting in increased coil output. Coupled with higher coil energy, this will produce an arc of longer duration at the spark plug, and enable a weaker mixture to be ignited with a corresponding improvement in economy and exhaust emissions. Improved reliability, better control of timing and longer periods between 'tune-ups' are other benefits over the conventional CB system. Virtually all modern types of electronic ignition use the variable dwell current limiting constant energy system.

Control signal See also relay driver, driver, final stage.

Conventional ignition system A system that uses CB and a condenser to induce ignition. Replaced generally by electronic ignition in recent years.

Conversion tables See Pressure conversion table, Vacuum conversion table, Temperature conversion table.

Coolant A mixture of water, anti-freeze and corrosion inhibitor to allow efficient cooling system operation.

Cooling system

The energy produced by combustion generates tremendous amounts of heat. About 25% of this heat energy is turned into the power that drives the road wheels. A further 50% is expelled with the exhaust gases which leaves approximately 25%. It is the function of the cooling system to dissipate this excess heat.

All water cooled engines should use a mixture of anti-freeze and water known as a coolant. The coolant mixture is usually 40-50% by volume and this will give protection down to about -40°C. Water alone will affect the temperature rating of all thermal engine temperature sensors and can cause incorrect metering of fuel in electronic carburettor and electronic fuel injection systems.

Corrected CO reading A calculation that takes improper combustion into consideration. If the corrected CO and CO readings are dramatically different, then the engine has a combustion problem.

Corrosion Deterioration and crumbling of a component by chemical action. Sensor terminals and multiplugs are particularly susceptible to this complaint.

Corrosion inhibitor A preparation to prevent corrosion. Often used to prevent corrosion of the radiator internal channels by water action.

CPS (Crankshaft Position Sensor See CAS) Ford term corresponding to CAS.

CPU (Central processing unit)

Cranking Rotating the engine by use of the starter motor.

CSP (Cold Start Performance.) A standard for measuring battery performance.

CSI (cold start injector see Cold Start Valve)

CSV (Cold Start Valve) An injector mounted in the inlet manifold that is only actuated during cold starts when the engine temperature is below a certain threshold. Usually earthed through a TTS that completes the CSV earth path. The CSV is not fitted to modern EMS's.

CTS (Coolant Temperature Sensor) A thermistor that changes in resistance according to temperature. Most CTS usually work on the NTC principle. However, CTS fitted to Renix equipped EMS may be NTC or PTC. As the temperature changes, the thermistor resistance changes, and thus the ECM is able to calculate the engine coolant temperature from the level of voltage (or current) that is registered on the sensor signal wire.

Current The flow of electrons through a conductor and measured in amps.

Current controlled or pulse modulation injection See EFi systems.

CVH (Compound Valve angle Head - Ford term) Cylinder head with valves arranged in two planes in a V configuration.

CW (clockwise) Direction of rotation.

Cylinder balance See power balance.

Cylinder contribution A method of comparing the relative power output of each cylinder without removing the spark as in conventional power balance operation. The acceleration time between each pair of ignition sparks is compared. A cylinder that is less efficient will have a lower acceleration time compared with the other cylinders. This method is much safer on catalyst equipped vehicles.

Dashpot A device that enables the throttle to close slowly rather than suddenly, thus preventing the removal of droplets of fuel from the inlet manifold walls due to the high vacuum present during deceleration. These droplets are emitted as excess HC during this operation.

Datastream

Once the FCR has decoded a fault, a Datastream enquiry (some systems only) is a quick method of determining where the fault might lie. This data may take various forms but is essentially electrical data on voltage, frequency, dwell or pulse duration, temperature etc, provided by the various sensors and actuators. Unfortunately, such data is not available from all vehicle systems.

Since the data is in real time, various tests can be made and the response of the sensor or actuator evaluated.
Actuating the idle control valve, relays and injectors through the ECM is an excellent method of testing effectiveness of the actuator and associated wiring circuit.

DC (Direct Current) An electrical current source which flows in only one direction.

DC - ISC (Throttle plate control motor - Ford term)

Decarbonisation Removing the cylinder head and scraping away the accumulated levels of carbon build-up from the head, valves and tops of pistons.

Deceleration Closing the throttle and allowing the engine speed to reduce to idle.

Decoke Abbreviated term for Decarbonisation.

Degree 1/360 part of a circle.

DEI (De-ice switch) Ford term

Detonation Refer to knock

Diaphragm A thin sheet of rubber that is moved by vacuum to actuate a mechanical device.

Digital signal A digital signal is represented by a code that has two states, on and off. In simple terms, the signal consists of a series of digital pulses when the frequency, pulse width or number of pulses is used to indicate a specific value.

Because the ECM works in a digital fashion, all analogue signals must pass through an analogue to digital converter when the signal will be stored by the ECM in digital format. A digital signal from a digital sensor does not need converting, and processing by the ECM is therefore much faster.

DIN International standard used in the automotive industry.

Diesel A fuel injected engine that uses the high temperature generated in compression to ignite the charge.

Dieseling A fault condition where a petrol engine continues running after the ignition has been switched off. Often caused by cylinder hot spots or carbon deposits that continue to glow and which are hot enough to explode the air/fuel charge. May be cured by a decoke.

Differential pressure The method by which air is drawn through a carburettor and into an engine. By the rules of physics, air will flow from high (atmospheric) pressure to low pressure (depression caused by fall of piston).

Diode A transistor that allows current flow in one direction alone.

DIS (Direct Ignition System) sometimes termed DIStributorless An ignition system where a distributor is not used.

DIS (alternate) Digital Idle Stabiliser

Distributor A component that distributes the secondary voltage to the correct spark plug in firing order. It is also used to house and operate the CB mechanism in conventional ignition and the reluctor and stator in some electronic ignition systems. The distributor turns at the same speed as the camshaft and at half the speed of the flywheel.

Distributor cam Located in the distributor, it is mounted upon the distributor shaft and contains a number of peaks (equivalent to the number of cylinders). The distributor can often be adjusted to time the ignition and distributes the HT spark to the correct spark plug in firing order.

Distributor cap An insulated cap with a centre tower and a circular series of terminals, one for each cylinder. The secondary HT pulses travel from the coil to the centre tower and are delivered, in firing order, to each terminal by the rotor.

DME Digital Motor Electronics Generic term often used to describe the Bosch Motronic EMS. The term is used in particular by BMW.

DMM (Digital Multi-Meter) An instrument designed for automotive use that can measure voltage, current, resistance and sometimes covers other functions such as dwell, duty cycle, frequency, rpm and amperage etc.

DOHC (Double Over Head Camshaft) A set of two camshafts mounted in the cylinder head. Operation is similar to the SOHC type except that one of the camshafts opens the inlet valves, and the other one opens the exhaust valves. This leads to more efficient valve operation and improved engine efficiency.

DPFE (Delta Pressure Feedback Electronic system - Ford term) An ECM controlled valve that regulates the flow of exhaust gas to the EGR valve.

Driver (actuator) - refer also to relay driver, control signal and final stage

The system actuators are supplied with a voltage feed from either the ignition switch or from one of the EFi system relays. The earth connection is then connected to an ECM earth pin. When the ECM actuates the component, it drives the appropriate ECM pin to earth by completing the circuit internally for as long as the actuation is required. In general, the earth connection will only be completed after the ECM has received one or more signals from relevant sensors and either looked up the associated maps or calculated the correct actuator 'on' time.

This signal could be termed a 'driver' or a 'final stage' or a 'control' signal. In the this book we have settled for the 'driver' term. Examples of an actuator driver are: injector, relay, ISCV, CFSV, EGR solenoid etc.

DTR (Distributor - Ford term)

Duty cycle The period of time in % or ms, during which a component is switched on or energised. By connecting the dwell meter between the pulse terminal and earth on actuators such as the coil, ignition module, hall-effect switch, injector, ISCV or in fact any other switchable device, a duty cycle may be obtained. By comparing this dwell with known operating parameters, correct operation of the device can be determined. Refer to dwell below for more information.

DVM (Digital VoltMeter)

Dwell

Traditionally, a dwell angle is defined as being the number of degrees through which a distributor rotates when the CB points are closed. However, in modern times we should consider the wider context of the meaning of 'dwell'. A good definition of a dwell angle would be the time or rotational period through which a device passes when it is energised.

Dwell could thus be measured in terms of degrees of rotation, time 'on' - (or off) in percentage (%) compared with the total time for one occurrence, or time on or off in milliseconds (ms). All we need is the appropriate meter. Usually, dwell is measured in degrees, but if we use either (%) or (ms), it is more common to refer to duty cycle.

To convert dwell degrees to dwell percent and vice versa, use the following formulae:

Dwell° x (CYLS/360) x 100 = Dwell% ie 45° x (4/360) x 100 = 50%

(Dwell% / 100) x (360/CYLS) = Dwell° ie (50% /100) x (360/6) = 30°

Dwell angle Number of rotational degrees during which a device is switched 'on'. Normally used in reference to CB points. and refers to the degrees of rotation of the distributor cam whilst the points are closed. See also Duty Cycle.

Dwell meter An instrument used to measure dwell angle.

Dwell variation The difference in dwell reading taken at any two different engine speeds. Normally refers to CB equipped distributors.

Dynamic testing The testing of a device whilst it is running under load as opposed to static testing.

Dynamic volt drop In vehicles with electronic ignition, the dynamic volt drop refers to the volt drop over the primary circuit from the coil negative terminal to earth through the amplifier final driver stage. Equivalent to the so-called distributor resistance or distributor volt drop in CB systems. This measurement is only available with the engine cranking or running, because current must be flowing in the circuit before a measurement can be taken. Not all DMM 's are capable of measuring this circuit.

E

Earth A path for current to return to the power source.

Earthing probe A tool used to test for current leaks. Often used to test for secondary voltage insulation faults.

EACV (Electronic Air Control Valve Honda, Rover Term)

EAI (Electronic Advance Ignition GM term)

EBCV (Electronic Air Bleed Control Valve)

EC (European Community)

ECM (Electronic control module) A computer control unit that assimilates information from various sensors and computes an output. Can be used to control the engine ignition timing, injection duration, opening of the ISCV, ABS brakes, air bag etc etc.

ECR (Electric Choke Resistor - Ford term)

ECT (Engine Coolant Temperature) Refer to CTS. Ford term corresponding to CTS.

ECOTEC (Emission Consumption Optimised TECnology) GM term Applied to the late series of engines.

ECU (Electronic Control Unit) Refer to ECM

EDIS (Electronic Distributorless Ignition System) Ford term

EDIS-4 applied to EDIS - 4 cylinder engines.

EDF (Electro Drive Fan - Ford term)

EDM (EDIS Diagnostics Monitor Signal - Ford term)

EEC (Electronic Engine Control - Ford term)

EEC IV (Electronic Engine Control 4th generation - Ford term)

EFi Electronic Fuel injection

A fuel injection system where the injectors are opened (pulsed) by an ECM. There are a several different kinds of injection system in current use and a description of each type now follows.

EFi systems: Current controlled or pulse modulation injection

Some systems rely on the principle that more current is required to open the injector than to actually keep it open. The injector solenoid circuit is also earthed - but for only about one millisecond, which is just long enough to open the injector. The opening circuit is then switched off, and another circuit rapidly closed and opened, to apply a small holding current to the injector so that it remains open for the correct time duration. The pulsing is so blindingly fast that the injector does not have time to close, and current flow is therefore much reduced. This type of system is known as current controlled or pulse modulated. A variation of this method is termed 'Peak and hold'. After the initial pulse, the second circuit holds the injector open without rapid pulse modulation.

EFi systems: Standard injection

In the standard EFi system, the injector is simply earthed by the ECM for a calculated period of time. During this time, known as the pulse duration or the injector 'on' time, the injector solenoid operates and fuel is injected.

EFi pulse duration The period of time that the injector is held open. Can be measured in ms or by a dwell meter as a duty cycle.

EGOS (Exhaust Gas Oxygen Sensor) See Oxygen Sensor

EGR (Exhaust Gas Re-circulation) A method of recycling a small amount of exhaust gas into the intake system. This leads to lower peak combustion temperature with a reduction in NOx emissions.

EHPR (Electro-Hydraulic Pressure Regulator - Ford term)

Electrode An electrical conductor.

Electrolyte A sulphuric acid and water solution used in a lead / acid batteries. Chemical reaction between the acid and battery plates produce voltage and current.

Electro-magnet A magnet that requires electrical energy to create an electrical field.

Electronic 'MAP' See mapped timing / injection advance.

EI (Electronic Ignition) An ignition system that uses a magnetic sensor and transistors to switch the coil negative terminal on and off.

Emissions Pollution of the atmosphere by fumes from the exhaust, breather vent or fuel tank.

Emission standards

US 79: This standard was set in the USA in 1979 and has been superseded by the US83 standard. The vehicle must be equipped with a regulated three way catalyst with OS.

US 83: This is the most stringent of the current European emission levels and the standard was set in the USA in 1983. The vehicle must be equipped with a regulated three way catalyst with OS and evaporative emission control.

US 88 LDT (Light Duty Truck): This standard sets the same requirements as the US83 standard. However, commercial vehicles over a certain weight will fall into this category.

NEEC 5th amendment: This is an European standard for emission control and vehicles equipped with at least one of the following systems will meet the standard.

15.04: This is not a standard and is a category applied to vehicles that do not meet a particular emission standard. Vehicles without a catalytic converter, EGR, pulse air system or evaporative emission control will fall into this category.

Emission control Devices used to control and minimise poisonous fume emissions.

EMR (Engine Management Relay - Ford term)

EMS (Engine Management System) An EMS is essentially an electronic system whereby the engine ignition and fuelling functions are controlled by one or more ECM. The distributor, when used, is provided purely to distribute the HT spark to the correct cylinder in firing order. When separate ECM's are provided for ignition and fuelling, the two units do not operate independently and connections are made so that they can communicate with each other. An Ignition ECM would signal the Injection ECM to initiate injection. In some EMS's, a separate amplifier is pulsed by the ECM, which in turn switches the coil negative to initiate ignition.

Energised The period during which an electrical device is switched on.

Engine sensor see sensors.

ENR (ENgine run Relay - Ford term)

EPT (Electronic Pressure Transducer - Ford term)

ERIC (Electronically Regulated Ignition & Carburettor - Rover term)

ESA (Electronic Spark Advance - Toyota term)

ESC (Electronic Spark Control - Ford term)

ESC II (Electronic Spark Control 2nd generation (module) - Ford term)

EVAP (EVAPorative emission control systems - Ford term)

EVR Electronic Vacuum Regulator - Ford term)

Exhaust gas Burned and unburned gases that are exhausted after combustion.

External influences An influence that is not directly attributable to a particular component but could affect the operation of that component.

F

Fahrenheit Temperature scale.

Fast codes Digital fault codes emitted by an EMS that are too fast to be displayed on an LED lamp or on a dash mounted warning lamp. A digital FCR instrument is required for capturing fast codes.

Fault codes

Electronics are now extensively used throughout the modern vehicle and may control functions such as the transmission, suspension, automatic gearbox, air conditioning and myriad others.

Most modern vehicle EMS or ECM have the facility of making self-diagnostic checks upon the sensors and actuators that interface with the vehicle computer or computers. A fault in one of the component circuits causes a flag or code to be set in the ECM memory.

If a suitable code reading device is attached to the serial port on the vehicle harness, these faults can then be read out from the vehicle computer and displayed in the form of a two or three digit output code.

FCR (Fault Code Reader)

A device that can be connected to the vehicle serial (diagnostic port) to interrogate the vehicle ECM. Fault codes and Datastream information can then be read from the ECM. In some instances, vehicle actuators can be actuated from the controls on the FCR. A FCR is sometimes termed a scanner.

Where adjustments to the ignition timing or fuel system are possible, for example on some Ford or Rover systems, then these adjustments must be made through an FCR.

The codes may be described as slow or fast and some ECM's are capable of emitting both types. Slow codes can be captured by an LED tool, whereas fast codes must be captured by a digital FCR. Future EMS's are more likely to utilise fast codes.

FI (fuel injection)

Final stage See driver, relay driver and control signal.

FIR (Fuel Injection Relay - Ford term)

Firing line The actual firing voltage as represented on an oscilloscope.

Firing order The order in which the cylinders are fired.

Firing voltage The secondary voltage required to overcome the rotor and spark plug gaps.

Fixed jet A type of carburettor that uses fixed and calibrated fuel, air and compensating jets to ensure correct air / fuel mixture over the engine operating range.

Flash codes Fault codes of the slow variety that are output on a dash mounted warning lamp or via an LED lamp.

Flashshield A cover used in the distributor to prevent secondary arcing interfering with primary operation.

Flat spots Hesitation of the engine under acceleration.

Flow rate Describes the volume of fuel pumped during a pre-determined period of time in order to test fuel system output.

Flywheel sensor See CAS.

FLW (Fuse Link Wire - Ford term)

FO (Fuel Octane - Ford term)

Fouled spark plug Formation of deposits on the electrodes. This often cause a short to earth of the secondary voltage and the charge is not correctly fired.

FP (Fuel Pump)

FPR (Fuel Pump Relay - Ford term)

Frequency Pulse Frequency. Usually measured in Hz.

FRS (Fuel Restrictor Solenoid - Rover term)

FRTS (Fuel Rail Temperature Sensor)

FSOR (Fuel Shut-Off Relay - Ford term) A sensor to measure the temperature of fuel in the fuel rail.

FSOS (Fuel shut off solenoid - Ford term)

FT (Fuel Temperature sensor)

FTS (Fuel Temperature Switch)

FTVV (Fuel Tank Vent Valve) A solenoid valve used to control evaporation emissions in GM vehicles.

Fuel atomisation Proper mixing of air and fuel to ensure good combustion.

Fuel injector (EFi systems) The injector is a solenoid operated valve that delivers an exact amount of fuel according to an opening duration signal from the ECM. A fine filter is used to prevent debris damaging the precision action. However, gums and lacquers can build-up on this filter and on the injection pintle eventually reducing fuel flow. Injection fouling is a serious problem on many injection systems.

Fuse A small component containing a sliver of metal that is inserted into a circuit. The fuse will blow at a specified current rating, in order to protect the circuit from voltage overload.

Fuselink (also known as fusible link). A heavy duty circuit protection component that can burnout if the circuit becomes overloaded.

G

Gas analyser A device used to sample gases at the exhaust pipe, so that an analysis may be made of the exhaust constituents.

Generator An alternator or dynamo that produces voltage and current. See also alternator.

GM (General Motors) Manufacturer of Opel and Vauxhall in Europe. The parent company is based in the USA.

GND (ground) USA term for earth. See also earth.

H

Hall-Effect generator A type of pulse generator which returns a small digital voltage to trigger the coil negative.

Hall-Effect Switch operation A constant 12 volt supply is passed through the Hall Effect switch in the distributor. Opposite the Hall switch is a magnet whose field causes the Hall switch to return a small voltage back to the amplifier. Attached to the distributor shaft is a rotor vane with the same number of cut-outs as cylinders. Passing the rotor between the switch and the magnet will cause the switch to be turned off and on. As the cut-out space proceeds past the switch then a voltage is returned to the amplifier. When the solid portion comes between the switch and magnet then the voltage is turned off as the magnetic field is diverted. The number of voltages returned per four-stroke engine cycle will equal the number of cut-outs.

Hard faults Generally refers to faults logged by an ECM self-diagnosis routine. The faults are usually present at the moment of testing,

HC (High compression (engine)

HC (Hydrocarbons)

Typically 15% Hydrogen and 85% carbon (petrol is almost pure hydrocarbons). HC is a generic term and refers to unburnt fuel and partially burnt fuel; it is measured in PPM - parts per million).

There are many different kinds of HC in the exhaust, and HC is generally capable of serious damage to eyes, nose and lungs. When mixed with NOx and in the presence of bright sunshine, photochemical smog is formed. HC emissions are also said to be a reason for the death of the rainforests.

During combustion, the Hydrogen atoms combine with the O_2 atoms to produce H_2O. The Carbon atoms combine with O_2 atoms to produce CO_2. High levels of HC in the exhaust signifies ignition problems such as defective plugs or HT leads, incorrect timing, vacuum leaks, incorrect air/fuel ratio or engine mechanical faults. In fact, anything that causes inefficient engine operation will increase the level of unburnt HC in the exhaust.

As the AFR weakens, the HC emissions increase due to a lean misfire. This is why a black exhaust is often the result of a too-lean idle mixture. Careful design of the combustion chamber can overcome this problem.

HCS (High Compression Swirl - Ford term) Refers to a Ford design of piston/combustion chamber, intended to promote efficient combustion.

Heat range With reference to a spark plug, the operating range in which the plug will safely and effectively operate.

Heat sink A component to dissipate high operating temperatures.

HEDF (High speed Electro Drive Fan - Ford term)

HEGOG (see HEGOS) Heated Exhaust Gas Oxygen sensor Ground - Ford term

HEGOS (HEGO) Heated Exhaust Gas Oxygen Sensor The oxygen sensor will not operate under 250° C, and so it may be equipped with a heater to provide a faster warm-up. Heated oxygen sensors are often called HEGOS. The heater element is a resistance within the oxygen sensor, with a battery voltage supply from the fuel system relay and a connection to earth. See also oxygen sensor.

HES Hall Effect Switch (or Sensor).

HG Chemical symbol for measurement of mercury.

HLG Hall effect generator.

Hot-film AFS Very similar in operation to the hot-wire sensor.

Hot-wire AFS operation The hot-wire AFS is mounted in the air flow trunking between the air filter and the engine. A box containing the electronics for hot-wire operation sits over the AFS body. A voltage of either 5 or 12 volts, according to system, is applied to the AFS unit.

Hot-wire sensor

A type of AFS in which the resistance of an electrically heated wire is measured. The hot-wire AFS is becoming increasingly popular as an alternative to the Vane and MAP sensor types. This is because the volume, temperature and density of air, at all altitudes can be more accurately measured than by the Vane or MAP sensor systems.

Air passes through the AFS body into the engine. A small quantity of air is drawn into a by-pass channel containing two wires. These wires are known as the sensing wire and the compensating wire. A small current is applied to the compensating wire which remains unheated. As air passes over the wire, its resistance and current change and the AFS is able to determine the temperature of the incoming air. The sensing wire is heated to a temperature of 100° C above that of the compensating wire. Air passing over the sensing wire causes it to become cooler and its current and resistance value change. More current is passed through the sensing wire so that it remains 100° C above that of the compensating wire. An output (signal) voltage, proportional to the current applied to the sensing wire, is returned to the ECM.

The value of this voltage is directly related to the volume, temperature and density of air introduced into the engine. The hot-wire system thus allows automatic compensation for altitudes from sea-level to mountain top, and the ECM will accurately calculate the AFR under virtually all conditions.

HT High tension. High voltage induced in the secondary windings of the ignition coil.

HT lead (High Tension lead) Cable used to distribute secondary ignition to the distributor cap and to the spark plugs.

Hydrogen Odourless highly-explosive gas. Forms two-thirds of the chemical make-up of water.

Hz (Hertz) Frequency in cycles per second.

I

IA (Idle Adjust - Ford term)

IBR (Injector Ballast Resistor - Ford term)

ID (Identification)

Idle speed adjustment (EFi systems)

Most modern vehicles have fully automatic idle control with no means of adjustment. Where adjustment is possible, this is usually effected by a by-pass idle speed air screw. Turning the screw one way will reduce the air flow and therefore the idle speed. Turning the screw the other way will increase the air flow and therefore the idle speed.

Although most later systems use an ECM controlled ISCV or stepper motor to maintain idle speed under engine load, some versions of the ISCV or stepper motor may be adjustable. Generally, this only possible with early units.

Idle speed control Idle speed control devices are actuated by the ECM and are therefore known as actuators - as distinct to sensors. On most modern engines, speed at idle is maintained at a constant speed irrespective of engine load or temperature. As idle conditions alter, or a temperature or an electrical load condition occurs, the ECM actuates either a solenoid controlled ISCV or a stepper motor to maintain the correct idle position - no matter the speed or load. This prevents poor idle and stalling with heavy electrical loads and a lean mixture. Some versions of the ISCV or stepper motor may be adjustable, although generally this only possible with early units.

Idle-up (Far Eastern term) Any mechanical or electronic system that is used to increase the idle speed according to temperature or engine load could be termed an idle-up system.

IDM (Ignition Diagnostics Monitor signal - Ford term)

IGC (Ignition coil Ford term)

IGf (Ignition confirmation signal - Toyota term)

IGN (Ignition switch - Ford term)

Igniter (Ignition module (amplifier)) Term used by Far Eastern vehicle manufacturers to describe the ignition amplifier.

Ignition module Term used to describe the ignition amplifier.

Ignition switch An on-off switch that provides current to the primary ignition circuit. When the switch is closed and the module is switched on (or the CB is closed), then current will flow through the primary circuit and return to the battery via the engine and body earths.

Ignition timing The correct moment to ignite the compressed air/fuel charge for maximum downforce to be exerted upon the piston.

IGt (Ignition trigger signal from the ECM - Toyota term)

IIA (Integrated Ignition Assembly - Toyota term) Ignition module integral with the distributor.

IMA (Idle Mixture adjuster Honda, Rover term)

Impedance Resistance to the flow of current and often used to describe the resistance of a voltmeter. A minimum 10 megohm impedance is recommended for instruments used to measure values in electronic circuits.

IMPH (Inlet Manifold Pre-Heater) See manifold heater.

Inductive trigger

Intake system The components responsible for the intake of the air/fuel mixture. ie air filter, carburettor (where used), manifold and inlet valve.

Inductive (permanent magnet) pick-up

The pick-up is a permanent magnet and inductive coil wound around a pole piece. It is usually fixed securely in the distributor and radiates a magnetic field. The two most common types in current service are the pick-up limb or the annular coil.

The reluctor or trigger wheel is mounted on the rotating distributor shaft with a number of triggering lugs equal to the number of engine cylinders. As the rotating lug passes the pick-up a small alternating voltage is generated that is strongest as the pick-up and lug are exactly opposite. This voltage is the ignition trigger and is sent to the amplifier for amplification.

Injection system See MPi & SPi systems.

Injector fouling Build-up of deposits on the injector internal filter, or on the injector head, so that flow is reduced or disturbed - resulting in improper injector operation.

Insulator A material that will not pass current readily, and therefore used to prevent electrical leakage.

Inst. panel Instrument panel on the vehicle dashboard.

Intercooler A device for cooling the air charge supplied to the engine from the TurboCharger. Cooler air is denser than hot air and so a greater volume of air is inducted into the engine. The greater the volume of air inducted, the greater will be the horsepower produced by the engine.

IS (Inertia switch)

ISC (Idle speed control) See ISCV - Ford term.

ISC - BPA (Idle Speed Control - By-Pass Air solenoid - Ford term)

ISCV (Idle Speed Control Valve)

A gate or rotary valve that is actuated by the ECM to maintain the correct idle speed, no matter the load or temperature. The ISCV is also used to provide a higher idle during engine warm-up. Early versions of engines fitted with an ISCV may be adjustable, although generally this is not the case with later units.

The ISCV contains an electro-magnet to open a by-pass port, thus allowing a small volume of air to by-pass the throttle plate. This air may pass through a hose, or through a port in the inlet manifold. The ISCV is mounted in situ, thus allowing the by-pass air to pass through the body of the valve. As the temperature decreases, or the load increases, the ECM pulses the valve for longer intervals (the pulse width increases) and the valve is further opened to allow more air to by-pass the throttle.

This results in a higher idle speed when the engine is cold, or no drop in idle speed when the engine is hot.

Early Bosch systems used an ISCV attached to an electric motor that can be rotated clockwise or anti-clockwise by virtue of two opposing circuits. The motor is supplied with a voltage supply and two earth paths that are made through the ECM. When one path is earthed, the motor will attempt to rotate in one direction. When the other path is earthed, the motor will attempt to rotate in the opposite direction. By varying the time that each circuit is energised, the ECM will place the ISCV in the exact position required. A duty cycle for the time energised can be obtained on each of the ISCV earth terminals, or at the corresponding ECM terminal. The waveform viewed at each terminal on an oscilloscope is that of a square waveform. This type is characterised by three wires at the electrical multi-plug (a battery voltage supply and the two earth wires).

Later Bosch systems use a solenoid that is opposed by a strong spring. The solenoid is supplied with a voltage supply and one earth path, made through the ECM. When the ISCV is earthed by the ECM, the solenoid will overcome the spring force and open the ISCV. If the solenoid fails, it will normally fail-safe closed. However, even when closed, a small amount of air will travel through the valve to give a basic (but low) idle speed. The waveform viewed on an oscilloscope is that of a square waveform.

The longer the time that the ECM pulses (holds open) the ISCV, the further open it will become. Pulsing occurs many times a second (the frequency is about 110), and by varying the time that the circuit is energised, the ECM will place the ISCV in the exact position required. A duty cycle for the time energised can be obtained on the ISCV earth terminal, or at the corresponding ECM terminal.

Ford use an ISCV which is very similar in operation to the later Bosch type. However, the waveform viewed on an oscilloscope is that of a sawtooth waveform.

ISO International Standards Organisation.

ITS (Idle Tracking Switch - Ford term)

IV PWR (Ignition voltage power - Ford term)

J

Jumper lead A small electrical cable that is used to bridge a component or wire on a temporary basis.

J1930 SAE standard for acronyms describing electrical and electronic components. Adopted by Ford and Mazda in 1994, other VM's may soon follow.

K

KA PWR (Keep Alive PoWeR - Ford term)

KAM (Keep Alive Memory - Ford term) Ford term for a dynamic memory in the EEC IV ECM. This memory retains soft faults and also the vehicle idle speed settings.

KCM (Knock Control Module - Ford term)

KDS (Kick-Down Switch - Ford term)

KEM (KE Module - Ford term)

KEMKE (fuelling module - Ford term)

King HT lead The cable that carries secondary voltage from the coil to the distributor cap. "King lead" is the term in common use.

KNK (Knock signal (from knock sensor) - Ford term)

Knock The spontaneous explosion of the remaining air/fuel charge in the combustion chamber when only a portion of it has burnt progressively. A direct result of excessive combustion chamber temperature. Known also as detonation.

Knock threshold The moment during engine operation when the onset of knocking is imminent.

KOHMS (Kilohms) A resistance measurement equal to 1000 ohms. Many DMM's and engine analysers give a measurement in k.OHMS.

Kpa (KiloPascals) International standard for the measurement of pressure and vacuum. See pressure conversion table and vacuum conversion table.

KS Knock Sensor A sensor that outputs a small electrical signal on detecting 'engine knock'. On receiving a knock signal, the ECM will temporarily adjust (retard) the ignition timing to prevent the condition. Some engine systems with KS can detect engine knock in an individual cylinder. Timing for that cylinder alone will be retarded by the ECM until knock ceases.

KV KiloVolt A unit of secondary voltage measurement equal to 1000 volts.

L

LAF (Linear Air Flow sensor (Honda)) Digital OS.

Lambda - Greek word for the 'stoichiometric symbol'

As the engine operates, fuel and air are mixed together and drawn into each cylinder. The AFR at which fuel burns most efficiently is called the Stoichiometric point, and this is where HC and CO are lowest and CO_2 is highest. This ratio is 14.7:1 by weight, and it is also called Lambda = 1 which is the Greek word for correct.

A catalyst equipped engine will attempt to maintain the AFR between a Lambda factor of 0.97 and 1.03.

Although Lambda = 1 is not the best point for best fuel consumption, we have already established that it is the best compromise ratio for using a catalytic converter to oxidise CO, HC and NOx. Therefore, if the engine's AFR can be contained within the 'window' of 0.97 to 1.03, the resultant engine emissions will raise the efficiency of the catalytic converter to about 95 %. The lower the emissions from the engine, the less work the cat has to do, and the more efficient it will become. Moreover, by reducing the engine emissions, the cat will also last much longer.

Lambda sensor See Oxygen Sensor. A sensor that monitors the amount of oxygen in the exhaust stream, and passes a voltage signal back to the ECM. The ECM then alters the amount of fuel passed to the engine. An attempt is therefore made to keep the AFR at the most suitable ratio for perfect combustion.

Lb/in^2 (Pounds per Square Inch) An Imperial measurement of pressure. See pressure conversion table under Pressure.

LDT (Light Duty Truck) See emission standards. Refers to the US88 LDT emission standards for commercial vehicles.

Lead

A substance (tetra-ethyl or TEL) that is added to petrol to assist the fuel's ability to resist knocking and pre-ignition. Lead also lubricates the valves and seats in the engine. Lead levels in petrol have gradually been reduced in recent years and even leaded petrol contains a far smaller concentration than at one time.

Lead is a poisonous substance, and progressively and irreversibly reduces the efficiency of the blood to transport oxygen. It functions as cellular poison for blood, bone marrow and nerve cells. Lead also poisons the catalytic converter and clogs the cells thus quickly reducing efficiency.

LED (Light Emitting Diode)

LHS (Left Hand Side) Viewed from the driver's seat.

Limp home See LOS.

LOS (Limited Operating Strategy)

Often called LIMP HOME, this is a safety system that allows the vehicle to be driven to a service area if a fault occurs. Some LOS systems are so smart that the driver may be unaware from the way that the vehicle operates, that a fault has occurred.

When the system perceives that a sensor is operating outside of its design parameters, a substitute value is used which allows the engine to operate. However, this value is usually that for a hot or warm engine, and this means that the engine may be difficult to start, and run badly, when it is cold.

The instrument panel warning light (where fitted) may illuminate to indicate that a fault has occurred.

Some systems (for example Ford) may also lock the timing to a set figure (with no timing advance) and allow the fuel pump to run continuously.

LT (low tension) Primary ignition circuit.

LUS (Lock-up Solenoid (clutch of automatic transmission) - Ford term)

Ma (milli-amperes)

MAF (Mass Air Flow sensor - term for hot-wire AFS)

Magnet A substance that has the ability to attract iron.

Magnetic field The space around a magnet that is filled by invisible lines of magnetic force.

Manifold heater

The inlet manifold heater is sometimes termed a 'hedgehog' because of its distinctive shape. The MH may be found in many single point injection engines or some carburettor equipped engines and usually functions on the PTC principle.

The voltage supply to the MH is often made through a thermal switch or a relay when the engine coolant is cold. As the engine coolant rises above a pre-determined temperature, the thermal switch or relay opens and the voltage supply is to the MH is cut. The switch is usually placed in a coolant hose, or located in the coolant passage of the inlet manifold.

MAP (Manifold Absolute Pressure sensor)

This is an inexpensive and less accurate alternative to the AFS. The MAP sensor measures the manifold vacuum or pressure, and uses a transducer to pass an electrical signal back to the ECM. The unit may be located in the engine compartment or in the ECM. Used in both simultaneous MPi and SPi systems, the MAP sensor is particularly popular in SPi systems. MAP is calculated from the formula: Atmospheric pressure - vacuum = MAP. Refer to the MAP table.

Where the manifold is of the 'wet' type (ie SPi), the changing pressures in the manifold will cause fuel to enter the vacuum hose where it may eventually reach the MAP sensor. Installation of a fuel trap and careful routing of the vacuum hose may slow down the ingress of fuel. However, once fuel reaches the MAP sensor, its diaphragm may be adversely affected. If the MAP sensor is a separate unit, renewal is comparatively inexpensive.

MAP sensors may take one of two forms. Older generation vehicle use an analogue sensor where the voltage signal output is proportional to the load. A newer system that is fast gaining popularity is the digital type. Digital MAP sensors send a square waveform in the form of a frequency. As the load increases, the frequency also increases and the time in ms between pulses becomes shorter. An ECM will respond much faster to a digital signal, because an analogue to digital converter is unnecessary in this system.

MAP table

Atmospheric condition	Pressure	Vacuum	MAP
Engine off/ ign on	*1.0 ± 0.1*	*Zero*	*1.0 ± 0.1*
Idle speed	*1.0 ± 0.1*	*0.72 to 0.45*	*0.28 to 0.55*
High load (wide-open throttle)	*1.0 ± 0.1*	*Zero*	*1.0 ± 0.1*
Deceleration	*1.0 ± 0.1*	*0.80 to 0.75*	*0.20 to 0.25*

All units are in bars and typical rather than definitive. Refer to the Vacuum conversion table and the Pressure conversion table for conversion to/from other units.

Note: *Atmospheric pressure - vacuum = MAP.*

Mapped ignition timing or injection Electronic timing advance or injection pulse that is controlled by the ECM from a 'map' located within the ECM. A two dimensional map contains settings for a number of engine load and speed variations. A three dimensional map contains settings for a number of engine load, speed and temperature variations. The timing and injection settings are usually contained in separate maps within the ECM.

Max. Abbreviation for maximum.

Mechanical advance A unit that uses centrifugal action to advance and retard the ignition timing. Usually mounted in a distributor in conventional engines.

MEMS (Modular Engine Management System) A type of EMS manufactured by Rover.

MH (Manifold Heator) See manifold heater above.

MHR (Manifold Heater Relay)

Mixture adjustment

This is a trimming device and only a small change in CO at the idle condition is generally possible. Once the throttle is opened from its idle stop, the quantity of injected fuel depends upon the pulse duration. Where CO adjustment is possible, there are two methods of CO adjustment in current use. Catalyst equipped vehicles often have no form of CO adjustment.

1) *An air screw that varies the air flow through an idle passage in the AFS. As the screw position is varied, the airflow acting upon the metering flap varies, causing the flap to change its idle position. The changed position results in an altered voltage signal to the ECM, and the idle mixture will either change appropriately. This type is usually fitted to older type vehicles.*
2) *A potentiometer with a variable resistance. As the adjustment screw is turned, the resistance varies, causing a change in the voltage signal being returned to the ECM. This sensor may be mounted upon the ECM, on the airflow meter, or even upon the inner engine compartment wing.*

Mixture screw See volume screw.

Molecule The smallest particle into which a chemical compound may be divided.

Motronic A type of EMS manufactured by Bosch.

MPi (Multi-Point Injection)

One injector per cylinder. May be triggered in banks (simultaneous) or sequentially.

MPi (Multi-Point Injection - simultaneous)

This is the most common type of EFi system in current use. A number of injectors are looped together in a parallel 'bank' with a single connection to the ECM. Where an engine has more than one bank, each bank has its own ECM connection.

In a 4-cylinder engine, one bank connects all of the injectors. In a 6-cylinder engine the injectors are placed in two groups of three, and in an 8-cylinder engine the injectors are placed in two groups of four termed left and right bank. In a 12-cylinder engine the injectors are placed into four groups of three cylinders. Two power resistors control two groups each.

The injectors are triggered from a reference signal which may originate from the ignition system, or from a timing pulse at the CAS. Normally, the injectors operate twice per complete engine cycle. Half of the fuel required is injected onto the back of a closed inlet valve, waiting for it to open, and the other half is injected as the valve opens for the intake stroke. Once the valve has opened, the fuel enters the cylinder in the normal way.

This system is fairly effective and usually works quite well. It is also cheaper to develop than a full-blown sequential system, which makes it very popular amongst vehicle manufacturers.

MPi (Multi-Point Injection - sequential)

Eventually, both SPi and simultaneous MPi systems are likely to succumb to the sequential MPi system, where the injectors open in cylinder sequence. Emissions can be significantly reduced with this type - particularly if the engine suffers a mechanical or ignition problem. The sequential MPi system uses the same sensors as other injection systems. However, an additional sensor pinpoints the correct cylinder for the sequential system. In some instances this is a Hall-effect trigger located in the distributor.

ms (millisecond) 1/1000 second (0.001 s).

MSTS-h (Microprocessor Spark Timing System - HES ignition - GM term)

MSTS-i (Microprocessor Spark Timing System - inductive ignition - GM term)

MT (Manual Transmission)

Multimeter see DMM

Multiplug A connecting plug in the wiring harness. Often used to connect the harness to a sensor or actuator. In this book, the multiplug diagram shows the terminals of the harness connector. When back-probing the multiplug (or viewing the sensor connector terminals), the terminal positions will be reversed.

mV (millivolt) one millivolt = 1/1000 of a volt (0.001 V)

MY Model Year Most VM's start manufacturing their models for the new year in the months leading up to the end of the preceding year. The actual date when manufacturing commences is usually termed the 'model year' date, and the year used is usually that of the following year. In the UK, the new model year starts soon after the registration letter changes on August 1st; many VM's would for example call a vehicle manufactured in August or September 1996 a '1997 model'.

N

nbv (nominal battery voltage)

Nominally 12 volt, the voltage will vary under engine operating conditions:

Engine stopped: 12 - 13 volts.
Engine cranking: 9.0 to 12.0 volts.
Engine running: 13.8 to 14.8 volts.

NDS (Neutral Drive Switch - Ford term

Ne RPM signal from the PU coil Toyota term

Nearside Side nearest to the kerb on any vehicle - irrespective of whether LH or RH drive.

NEEC (New European Economic Community)

Newton (N) An international unit of force that is independent of gravity. This unit was introduced because gravity varies in different parts of the world. The Newton is defined as the force required to accelerate a mass of 1kg at 1 metre per second per second. Newton units of force are measured as N/m^2 and called Pascal units. This unit is very small, and is measured in MPa (1,000.000 Pascals) or KPa (1,000 Pascals). See also Pascal.

Nitrogen An atmospheric gas.

Non-cat Non catalyst. Vehicles without a catalytic converter.

Non-sinusoidal Waveforms such as sawtooth (ie Ford ISCV), square, ripple etc.

Non-volatile memory ECM memory that is able to retain information - even when the vehicle battery is disconnected.

NOx (Oxides of Nitrogen)

NOx is a poisonous gas formed due to high temperatures (exceeding 1300° C - 2500° F). and high compression. There are many different kinds of NOx (ie NO, NO_2, NO_3 etc) and they are all lumped together under the term 'NOx'. The N representing one Nitrogen atom, and Ox representing any number of Oxygen atoms.

The Nitrogen (N_2 content of air (an inert gas) passes through the combustion process unchanged until high temperature (over 1370° C) and pressures are reached. Under these conditions, Nitrogen and oxygen react to form Nitrogen Monoxide - sometimes called Nitric oxide - (NO). The breeding conditions for NOx are wide-open throttle, acceleration and high-speed cruising. When NO is combined with HC in the presence of strong sunshine, NO_2 (Nitrogen Dioxide), Ozone (O_3) and NO_3 (nitrogen nitrate) are the result. NO_2 is a light brown gas commonly called 'SMOG'. Unfortunately, NOx emissions reach their peak at Lambda = 1, the so-called perfect combustion point.

The Diesel engine, whilst producing low levels of CO and HC, has a poor record where NOx is concerned. NOx is a particular problem due to the high temperature and high pressures present in a Diesel engine combustion chamber.

NOx causes irritation of eyes and respiratory organs and symptoms of poisoning. Inhalation over a long period leads to destruction of lung tissues.

One method of controlling NOx is to recycle a small amount of exhaust gas into the combustion chamber (EGR, or Exhaust Gas Recirculation.) This reduces combustion temperature (and power) by recycling the inert exhaust gas.

NTC (Negative Temperature Co-efficient) A thermistor in which the resistance falls as the temperature rises. An NTC resistor decreases in resistance as the temperature (ie coolant temperature) rises.

O

O_2 (Oxygen)

A harmless gas that is present in about 21% of air and is necessary for proper combustion.

O_2 consists of two oxygen atoms and is measured in % volume. A small proportion of oxygen (1 - 2%) will be left after proper combustion. Too much or too little would indicate an incorrect air / fuel ratio, ignition or mechanical problems or an exhaust leak.

The amount of O_2 that is expelled into the exhaust is that which is left over after combustion, and is a good indicator of the AFR - so long as the engine is operating correctly.

OA (Octane Adjuster) A device to finely tune the engine timing for fuels of differing octane levels.

OAI (Octane Adjust Input - Ford term)

Octane level The level of fuel resistance to knock. The higher the octane level the more resistance to knock.

OHC (Over Head Camshaft)

Ohm A unit of resistance that opposes the flow of current in a circuit.

Ohmmeter An instrument that is used to measure resistance in ohms.

Ohms Law
Volts = Amps X Ohms (V = I X R)
Amps = Volts/Ohms (I = V / R)
Ohms = Volts/Amps (R = V / I)
Also:
Power (Watts) = Volts x Amps

Open circuit A break in an electrical circuit which prevents the flow of current.

Open loop control When an engine with Lambda control is operating outside of that control, it is in 'open loop'. This may occur during acceleration, wide-open throttle, or during the warm-up period, and when in LOS. some system may go into open loop at idle. When the system is under 'open loop' control, a richer mixture is allowed to prevent hesitation or poor driveability.

Optical distributor Alternative CAS that utilises LED's. Mainly used on some Japanese and other Far Eastern vehicles. Refer to Nissan for a detailed description of operation.

OS (Oxygen Sensor) Also refer to Lambda.

An oxygen Sensor is a ceramic device placed in the exhaust manifold on the engine side of the catalytic converter for measuring the amount of oxygen that is left in the exhaust after combustion.

Essentially, the OS contains two porous platinum electrodes. The outer surface electrode is exposed to exhaust air and coated in porous ceramic. The inner surface electrode is exposed to ambient atmospheric air.

The difference in oxygen at the two electrodes generates a voltage signal which is transmitted to the ECM. This voltage is inversely proportional to the amount of oxygen The quantity of oxygen remaining after combustion is an excellent indicator of a deficit or surplus of air (rich or weak mixture). The oxygen sensor measures the surplus or deficit of air and sends a signal back to the ECM, which almost instantaneously adjusts the injection duration (within 50 milliseconds). By controlling the engine electronically so that the air/ fuel ratio is always in a small window around the Lambda point (ie Lambda = 0.97 to 1.03), during most operating conditions, almost perfect combustion could be achieved. Thus the catalyst has less work to do and it will last longer with fewer emissions at the tail pipe.

The oxygen sensor closed loop voltage is quite low and switches between 100 mVolts (weak) to 1.0 volt (rich). The signal actually takes the form of a switch and switches from weak to rich at the rate of approximately 1 Hz.

Various names have been given to this sensor, and it could equally be called a lambda sensor, oxygen sensor or even an EGOS.

OS heater Because the sensor does not operate efficiently below about 300° C, many Oxygen sensors incorporate a heater element for rapid warm-up. Such sensors may also be termed HEGOS.

Oscilloscope A high speed voltmeter that visually displays a change in voltage against time. Used to display ignition, alternator and engine sensor or actuator waveforms.

OTS (Oil Temperature Sensor)

Overrun See deceleration.

OVP (Over Voltage Protection - Ford term)

Oxidation A chemical change in a lubricating oil caused by combustion, heat and oxygen.

Oxides of nitrogen refer to NOx.

P

Parade An oscilloscope pattern where all cylinders are displayed in line.

Pascal International standard for the measurement of pressure and vacuum. See pressure conversion table and vacuum conversion table. Refer also to Newton.

PA (Pressure atmospheric Honda, Rover term)

PAS (Power Assisted Steering)

PCS (Pressure Control Switch - Ford term)

PCV (Positive Crankcase Ventilation) A control system to recycle crankcase fumes into the intake system for burning in the combustion chamber.

Percent Parts of a hundred.

Permanent magnet A magnet that has a magnetic field at all times. Compare 'Electro-magnet'.

Petrol A hydrocarbon based fuel composed of a mixture of hydrogen and carbons.

Pick-up See also inductive. Used as a trigger in an electronic system. The pick-up generates a small voltage which signals the amplifier or ECM to switch off and thus instigate ignition. The pick-up is usually some form of permanent magnet fixed in the distributor or on the flywheel. When a reluctor is rotated in the magnetic field, the signal to switch occurs when the signal is at its strongest.

Pick-up air gap A clearance between the reluctor and pick-up, which is often adjustable.

PIM (MAP sensor signal - Honda/Toyota term)

Pinging The audible sound produced by pre-ignition/detonation.

Pinking A commonly used aberration of pinging.

P / N (Park Neutral switch) A switch to cut the electrical supply to the starter motor and so prevent the engine from being started in gear, most often found on vehicles with automatic transmission. Sometimes called a 'Starter Inhibitor' switch.

PIP (Profile Ignition Pick-up - Ford term) Ford term for the basic timing signal.

Plugged exhaust An exhaust blockage causing back pressure and lack of performance. Can occur in catalyst equipped vehicles when the catalyst exceeds its normal operating temperature and melts thus obstructing the exhaust system.

Polarity A positive or negative state with reference to two electrical poles.

Pollutants See emissions.

Ported vacuum A vacuum source located in front of the throttle valve. The valve must be opened before a vacuum signal is produced.

Pot (potentiometer) A variable resistance.

Power balance For an engine to give maximum power then each cylinder must contribute an equal share to the workload. By cutting the spark to each cylinder in turn, and noting the rpm drop, it is possible to measure the amount of work, or balance, that each cylinder is contributing to the overall power. A weak cylinder will drop less in rpm than a strong one.

PPM (Parts Per Million) A measurement value of unburned HC.

Pre-emission Engines that do not have emission control devices.

Pre-ignition The premature explosion of the compressed air/fuel charge before proper ignition by the spark plug. Usually caused by excessive combustion temperature.

Pressure conversion table

bar	*lb/in²*	*KPa*
0.1	*1.45*	*10*
0.2	*2.90*	*20*
0.3	*4.35*	*30*
0.4	*5.80*	*40*
0.5	*7.25*	*50*
1.0	*14.50*	*100*
1.02	*14.75*	*102 **
1.1	*15.95*	*110*
1.2	*17.40*	*120*
1.3	*18.85*	*130*
1.4	*20.30*	*140*
1.5	*21.75*	*150*
1.6	*23.20*	*160*
1.7	*24.65*	*170*
1.8	*26.10*	*180*
1.9	*27.55*	*190*
2.0	*29.00*	*200*
3.0	*43.50*	*300*
4.0	*58.00*	*400*
5.0	*72.50*	*500*

** Approximate atmospheric pressure at sea level.*

Pressure regulator The fuel pump supplies fuel at a pressure that exceeds the required system pressure. A spring-loaded diaphragm relieves this pressure by allowing excess fuel to flow back to the tank via the fuel return line.

Primary ignition circuit The low-voltage circuit required to begin the ignition process. Components are the ignition switch, ballast resistor (if fitted), ignition coil, distributor (if fitted), amplifier (if fitted), CB points & condenser (if fitted), distributor cap & rotor (if fitted) and the wiring cables between these components.

Primary switching Primary windings. The outer windings of relatively heavy wire in an ignition coil in which the primary current flows.

Probe A method of obtaining voltage from the multiplug pin of an electronic component or sensor. The multiplug should be disconnected from the component and the voltmeter positive test lead used to probe the relevant pin.

Primary trigger This is the speed and position sensor that signals the ECM to begin actuating ignition, injection and relay control. The ECM will not function without the primary trigger. Examples of primary triggers include the CAS, inductive trigger or the Hall Effect sensor.

PROM (programmable read only memory)

PS (Phase Sensor - Ford term)

PSA (Citroen and Peugeot group)

PSI (Pounds per Square Inch) An Imperial measurement of pressure. See pressure conversion table under Pressure.

PSPS (Power Steering Pressure Switch - Ford term)

PU (inductive pick-up coil)

PUA (Pulse Air solenoid - Ford term)

PTC (Positive Temperature Co-efficient) A thermistor in which the resistance rises as the temperature rises. A PTC resistor increases (positively) in resistance as the temperature (ie coolant temperature) rises.

Pulse A digital signal actuated by the ECM.

Pulse generator

The pulse generator is a trigger used to initiate ignition. It sends a correctly timed signal to the amplifier, which then amplifies the signal to switch the coil negative terminal. Examples of pulse generators are:

1) *An inductive permanent magnet pick-up located inside the distributor.*
2) *An inductive permanent magnet located adjacent to the flywheel (CAS).*
3) *Hall Effect trigger located inside the distributor.*

Pulse width The time period during which electronic components (especially fuel injectors) are energised. It is usually measured in milliseconds.

Purge valve Refer to CFSV.

PVS (Ported Vacuum Switch (valve))

R

RAM (Random Access Memory - computer term)

Raster Display of all cylinders on an oscilloscope, one below the other in firing order beginning with number one. The order may be from the top down or bottom up, depending on the 'scope.

Reference voltage During normal engine operation, battery voltage could vary between 9.5 (cranking) and 14.5 (running). To minimise the effect on engine sensors (for which the ECM would need to compensate), many ECM voltage supplies to the sensors are made at a constant value (known as a reference voltage) of 5.0 volts.

REG (Regulator)

Relay

An electro-magnetic switching solenoid controlled by a fine shunt coil. A small current activates the shunt winding, which then exerts magnetic force to close the relay switching contacts. The relay is often used when a low current circuit is required to connect one or more circuits that operate at high current levels. The relay terminal numbers are usually annotated to the DIN standard, to which most (but not all) European VM's subscribe.

Relays - EFi system

One system relay may be used to control the whole fuel injection system. In that instance the relay will have double contacts. Alternatively, two or more relays may be used to control the system.

Relay typical annotation to DIN standard

30 Supply voltage direct from the battery positive terminal.
31 Earth return direct to battery.
85 Relay earth for energising system. May be connected direct to earth, or 'driven' to earth through the ECM.

85b Relay earth for output. May be connected direct to earth, or 'driven' to earth through the ECM.
86 Energising system supply. May arrive from battery positive or through the ignition switch.
87 Output from first relay or first relay winding. This terminal will often provide power to the second relay terminal 86 and provide voltage to the ECM, injectors, ISCV etc.
87b Output from second relay or second relay winding. Often provides power to the fuel pump and OS.

Relay control/relay driver

The system relays are supplied with a voltage feed from either the battery, ignition switch or from another of the EFI system relays. The earth connection is then connected to an ECM earth pin. When the ECM actuates the relay, it drives the appropriate ECM pin to earth by completing the circuit internally for as long as the actuation is required. In general, the relay earth connection will only be completed once the ECM receives a pre-determined sensor input signal.

Depending upon the relay, the input signal may be instigated by switching on the ignition or cranking the engine (ie CAS signal). Once the ECM has received the signal, the ECM will 'drive' the relay to earth by completing the circuit internally. The signal could be termed a 'driver' or a 'final stage' or a 'control' signal. In the this book we have settled for the 'driver' term. Examples of other actuator drivers are: injector, ISCV, CFSV etc.

Reluctor A metal rotor with a series of tips equal to the number of cylinders.

REMCO (Remote adjustment for CO pot - Ford term)

Remote start A device to operate the starter solenoid directly from under the bonnet and which enables more efficient turning or inching over of the engine.

Renix A type of EMS used mainly on Renault and Volvo vehicles.

Required voltage The minimum amount of secondary voltage that must be produced to bridge the rotor and spark plug gaps.

Res. Abbreviation for resistance

Resistance Opposition to the flow of current.

Retarded timing Opposite to advance. When the ignition timing fires AFTER the correct moment. Can also be used to describe ignition timing that occurs ATDC.

Return Term used to describe the earth return path to an ECM or module of typically a sensor, CAS or relay when the return is not directly connected to earth. The ECM or module will internally connect the return to one of its own earth connections. By this method the number of earth connections is much reduced.

RFI (Radio Frequency Interference) The EMS is susceptible to outside interference. Radiated RFI can be a problem if the levels are high enough and this can emanate from items such as a faulty secondary HT circuit or a faulty alternator. Excess RFI can disrupt and affect ECM and EMS operation - particularly where both ignition and fuelling are located in the same ECM.

RHS (Right Hand Side) Viewed from the driver's seat.

RMS (Root mean square) AC equivalent to DC voltage. Can be calculated from AC amplitude by the formula:
AC amplitude x 0.707.

ROM (Read Only Memory - computer term)

Rotor Rotating part of a component such as a rotor arm or an electro-magnet used in an alternator.

Rotor air gap The space between the rotor tip and the distributor cap terminal.

Rotor arm The rotor is an electrical contact, keyed to the distributor shaft so that it points directly at the correct distributor cap terminal when a plug is fired.

Rotor register The alignment of the rotor tip to the distributor cap terminal. Where the register is misaligned, the resulting large air gap will cause high firing voltages.

RPM (revolutions per minute) A measure of engine speed.

RSS (remote starter switch)

Rubbing block The part of the CB that rubs against the distributor cam. When the cam peak touches the rubbing block the points will open to instigate ignition.

S

SAE (Society of Automotive Engineers) The Society sets standards for automotive engineering. See also BCI and J1930.

SAW (Spark Advance Word) A Ford term for the modified timing signal passed from the EEC IV ECM to the EDIS module.

Scanner See FCR US term for a FCR.

Scope See oscilloscope. Abbreviation for an oscilloscope.

SD (Self Diagnostics)

Secondary ignition circuit The high voltage circuit used to distribute secondary voltage to the spark plug.

Secondary voltage Output from ignition coil.

Secondary windings Ignition coil HT windings.

SEFI (Sequential Electronic Fuel Injection - Ford term)

Self-diagnosis of serial data See fault codes.

Sensor A device that can measure one or more of the following parameters: temperature, position, airflow, pressure etc. and returns this information to the ECM, in the form of a voltage or current signal, for processing by the ECM.

Sequential injection See MPi systems.

Serial data port The serial port is an output terminal from the ECM. Signals have therefore been processed and faults or values are output to the terminal as a coded digital signal.

SG (Signal Generator) Distributor pick-up coil.

Short Short to earth, or short circuit. When electricity goes to earth and takes a shorter path back to the power source. Because extremely high current values are present, the condition can cause an electrical fire.

Signal generator See pulse generator.

Signal voltage A varying voltage returned to the ECM by a sensor so that the ECM can detect load, or temperature.

Simultaneous injection Refer to MPi systems. An injection system in which all the injectors are pulsed simultaneously (all fire at the same time).

Sinusoidal A sine wave, ie a CAS or inductive pick-up waveform where the amplitude of the positive part of the waveform is roughly equal to the amplitude of the negative part of the waveform.

Slow codes Fault codes emitted by an EMS that are slow enough to be displayed on an LED lamp or on a dash mounted warning lamp.

Smog So-called 'photo-chemical smog'. Formed by combining HC and NOx in the presence of strong sunshine. A particular problem in car-dense, sunny climates such as California in the USA.

Soft faults Generally refers to intermittent faults logged by an ECM self-diagnosis routine. The faults are often not present at the moment of testing, but have been logged at some period in the past.

SOHC (Single Over Head Camshaft) A single rotating camshaft that controls the opening and closing of both inlet and exhaust valves. The camshaft is mounted above the valves in the cylinder head and acts directly upon them.

Solenoid An electrical device that produces a mechanical effort when energised.

SP (Sensor phase - Ford term)

Spark advance See timing advance.

Spark control Spark advance control by electronic or thermostatic means.

Spark duration The time taken for a spark to bridge the spark plug electrodes. Shown as a spark line on an oscilloscope.

Spark line See spark duration. Also known as burn time.

Spark plug A device screwed into the cylinder head for igniting the compressed air / fuel charge.

Spark plug electrodes
1) *The centre rod passing through the spark plug insulator.*
2) *The 'earth' rod welded to the outer shell.*

Spark plug gap The spark plug electrodes can be adjusted to an exact gap for the spark to jump across.

SPi (Single Point injection)
Sometimes known as throttle body injection (TBI), the SPi system has gained much popularity over recent years. Essentially less costly, SPi uses the same sensors as the MPi systems. A single injector (normally of the current controlled type) injects fuel into a distributing manifold in much the same fashion as a carburettor.

Although the injection of fuel is much more precise, the problems of manifold heating becomes critical and the warm-up period must be carefully controlled if driveability is not to be impaired. Furthermore, the manifold is said to be of the 'wet' type. This term means that fuel is present in the manifold. An MPi system is said to be of the 'dry' type because fuel is injected into the inlet stub to the valve, and thus only air is present in the manifold.

SPOUT Spark Out. A Ford term for the modified timing signal passed from the EEC IV ECM to the TFI module.

Square waveform A waveform that illustrates the switching on and off of a particular circuit. The higher voltage line at supply voltage & the lower voltage at earth potential. The transitions is straight and the distance between the transitions defines the time of 'switch on' and 'switch off'.

STA (Starter motor signal - Toyota term)

STAR (Self Test Automatic Readout (electronic FCR test) - Ford term) Ford scanner or FCR.

Starter motor An electrical motor that rotates the engine to starting speed.

Static ignition This term is often used by European VM's to describe a Direct Ignition System.

Stator Used in electronic ignition or an alternator. As the rotating reluctor and stationery stator become opposite then AC voltage is induced.

STC (Self-Test Connector Ford term) Refer to Self Diagnosis.

Stepper motor
The stepper motor may take several forms and here are described the two most common systems.
1) *A motor is used to drive a valve which opens or closes an air by-pass passage in the inlet manifold.*
2) *A motor is used to increment the throttle plate by so many steps, thereby allowing more or less air through the opening.*
Usually the motor is supplied with nbv from the fuel system relay. The windings of the motor are then connected to four earth paths. By pulsing the motor using a combination of the earth paths, the ECM can step the motor to the correct position.

STI (Self-test Input - Ford term)

STO (Self-test Output - Ford term)

Stoichiometric ratio The point at which fuel burns most efficiently is called the Stoichiometric ratio and this is where HC and CO are lowest and CO_2 is highest. The air / fuel ratio by weight at this point is approximately 14.7:1. ie 14.7 kilograms of air to 1 kilogram of fuel.

Strobe Abbreviation for stroboscope.

Stroboscopic A light that flashes in unison with the number one spark plug, giving the impression of a 'frozen' rotating timing mark.

Sulphation Slow formation of a hard insoluble compound upon the lead battery plates during discharge. Can be reduced by long slow charge. A heavily sulphated battery will reject a charge.

Superimposed An oscilloscope display pattern where all cylinder traces are placed on top of each other. Differences between the various cylinders will tend to 'stick out'.

Suppression Reduction of radio or television interference generated by the high voltage ignition system. Typical means used are radio capacitors or resistive components in the secondary ignition circuit.

Suppresser Used to prevent radio interference. See capacitor.

SVC Service Connector (octane/ idle adjustment) - Ford term

Synchronised Usually refers to an injection pulse that is synchronised with the ignition system. The injector will be pulsed at a pre-determined time interval before ignition occurs.

System overview A term to describe the technical description of how the system operates.

T

Tacho (tachometer) A device used to indicate engine speed in RPM.

Tachometric relay A relay that requires a speed signal from the ignition to function.

TAD (Thermactor Air Diverter vacuum solenoid valve - Ford term)

TBH (Throttle Body Heater) An PTC device that quickly warms-up the throttle area; thereby preventing ice from forming during engine operation at low and moist temperatures.

TBI (Throttle Body Injection) see SPi

TBV (Turbo Boost Valve)

TCATS (Turbo Charge Air Temperature Sensor)

TDC (Top Dead Centre) Position of the piston at the top of its stroke.

TDCL (Total Diagnostic Communication Link) Used for extraction of fault codes on some Toyota vehicles.

Temp Abbreviation for temperature.

Temperature conversion table

° C	value	°F
-17.8	*zero*	*32*
-17.2	*1*	*33.8*
-15	*5*	*41.0*
-12.2	*10*	*50.0*
-9.4	*15*	*59.0*
-6.7	*20*	*68.0*
-3.9	*25*	*77.0*
-1.1	*30*	*86.0*
zero	*32*	*89.6*
4.4	*40*	*104.4*
7.2	*45*	*113.0*
10.0	*50*	*122.0*
12.8	*55*	*131.0*
15.6	*60*	*140.0*
18.3	*65*	*149.0*
21.1	*70*	*158.0*
23.8	*75*	*166.6*
26.7	*80*	*176.0*
29.4	*85*	*185.0*
32.2	*90*	*194.0*
35.0	*95*	*203.0*
37.8	*100*	*212.0*
40	*105*	*221*
43	*110*	*230*
46	*115*	*239*
49	*120*	*248*
52	*125*	*257*
54	*130*	*266*
57	*135*	*275*
60	*140*	*284*
63	*145*	*293*
66	*150*	*302*
68	*155*	*311*
71	*160*	*320*
74	*165*	*329*
77	*170*	*338*
79	*175*	*347*
82	*180*	*356*
85	*185*	*365*
88	*190*	*374*
91	*195*	*383*
93	*200*	*392*
96	*205*	*401*
99	*210*	*410*
102	*215*	*419*
149	*300*	*572*
204	*400*	*752*
260	*500*	*932*
316	*600*	*1112*
371	*700*	*1292*
427	*800*	*1472*
482	*900*	*1652*
538	*1000*	*1832*
743	*1370*	*2500*
1206	*2202*	*4000*

Conversion formula:
°C x 1.8 + 32 = °F
°F - 32 x 0.56 = °C

Terminal An electrical connecting point.

TFI (Thick Film Ignition) Ford term for ignition module.

THA (Air Temperature Sensor - Toyota term, see ATS)

Thermistor A potentiometer controlled by temperature.

Three wire sensor The three wire sensor has a voltage supply of 5 volts, an earth connection (often made through the ECM) and an output (signal) wire. The output wire returns a variable voltage signal to the ECM. The two most common forms of output are by resistance track and wiper arm, or via a transducer. Examples would include the AFS and TPS (wiper arm) and MAP (transducer).

Throttle valve A valve that controls the volume of airflow into the engine. Sometimes known as throttle plate or throttle disc.

Throttle valve positioner VAG term - see stepper motor.

THS 3/4 (Transmission Hydraulic Switch (3rd/4th gear solenoid) - Ford term)

THW (Coolant Temperature Sensor - Toyota term, see CTS)

Timing advance As engine speed increase, combustion must occur earlier so that a correctly timed maximum force is exerted upon the piston.

Timing belt or chain A belt or chain that connects crankshaft and camshaft.

Timing light A stroboscopic light used to check and set ignition timing.

Timing marks Two marks, or a scale and a mark, to indicate TDC or the timing point when aligned. These marks may be on the timing case and front pulley, or on the flywheel and viewed through an inspection hatch.

TP (Throttle plate)

TPS (Throttle Potentiometer Sensor) The throttle pot is a potentiometer that sends a variable voltage signal to the ECM to indicate (depending on system), throttle position, idle mode, WOT and rate of throttle opening. It is adjustable on some models. Additionally, the TPS may be used in conjunction with a TS. If so, the TS will indicate idle position and a non-adjustable Throttle pot will only be used to indicate rate of opening.

Transducer A device that converts pressure or vacuum etc into an electrical signal. ie Manifold vacuum may be taken to a transducer which turns it into an electrical load signal.

Transistor An electronic switching component.

Trigger See pulse generator.

Trigger wheel See reluctor.

Trouble codes US term for fault codes.

TS (Throttle Switch) The throttle switch informs the ECM when the engine is in idle mode. An additional contact may indicate wide-open throttle. Additional enrichment may be provided at idle and during full throttle running. The TPS is adjustable on some models. Some systems may support both a TS and a TPS, although most systems support only one of either type.

TSS (throttle stop screw)

TSS (Turbo Speed Sensor)

TTS (Thermo Time Switch) A switch dependant on time and temperature.

Turbocharger An exhaust gas driven compressor that compresses the air inducted by the engine to increase the horsepower for any given engine capacity.

TVS (Thermal Vacuum Switch) Used to control vacuum according to engine temperature. Mainly used in carburettor systems.

TVSV (Thermostatic Vacuum Switching Valve, see VSV)

Two wire sensor The two wire sensor utilise an earth wire and a 5 volt supply wire in a circuit that begins and ends at the ECM. The supply wire also doubles as the output wire in the following manner. Once the supply and earth wires are connected to the sensor, the resistance value of the sensor causes the voltage value of the supply to vary. Thus, if we take an example of a two wire CTS, the supply value of 5 volts will reduce (typically) to between two and three volts if the engine is cold (20° C), and to between 0.6 and 0.8 volts once the engine has become warm (80° C). Examples of two wire sensors would include the ATS and CTS.

UCL (Upper Cylinder Lubricant.)

UESC (Universal Electronic Spark Control (module) - Ford term)

Unleaded petrol A hydrocarbon fuel that is blended without the addition of lead. Even unleaded petrol contains a very small amount of natural lead that is not usually removed during refining. This amount is insignificant from an emissions viewpoint, and has no adverse effect upon the catalytic converter.

Unported vacuum A vacuum source located on the manifold side of the throttle plate. A vacuum signal is produced irrespective of throttle valve position.

Vacuum

A negative pressure or a pressure less than atmospheric. Measured in millibars or inches of mercury. A perfect vacuum exists in a space which is totally empty. It contains no atoms or molecules and therefore has no pressure. In practice a perfect vacuum cannot be achieved.

A vacuum occurs in the inlet manifold of a petrol engine because the fall of the piston continually attempts to draw air into each cylinder at a greater speed than the partially closed throttle disc will allow air to flow past it. The level of vacuum will depend on engine speed and throttle opening. The lowest reading will occur with the engine on full load (wide open throttle), and the highest reading when the throttle is closed with the engine running at high rpm's ie. when the engine is descending a hill.

Vacuum gauge A gauge used to measure the amount of vacuum in the engine intake system.

Vacuum conversion table

in.Hg	mm.Hg	KPa	millibar
0.5	12.75	1.7	17
1.0	25.395	3.386	33.86
1.003	25.50	3.4	34
2.0	51.00	6.8	68
3.0	76.50	10.2	102
4.0	102.00	13.6	136
5.0	127.50	17.0	170
6.0	153.00	20.4	204
7.0	178.50	23.8	238
8.0	204.00	27.2	272
9.0	229.50	30.5	305
10.0	255.00	34.0	340
11.0	280.50	37.3	370
12.0	306.00	40.8	408
13.0	331.50	44.2	442
14.0	357.00	47.6	476
15.0	382.50	51.0	510
16.0	408.00	54.0	544
17.0	433.50	57.8	578) normal
18.0	459.00	61.2	612) engine
19.0	484.50	64.6	646) operating
20.0	510.00	68.0	680) range
21.0	535.50	71.4	714) at idle
22.0	561.00	74.8	748
23.0	586.50	78.2	782
24.0	612.00	81.6	816
25.0	637.50	85.0	850
26.0	663.00	88.4	884
27.0	688.50	91.8	918
28.0	714.00	95.2	952
29.0	739.50	98.6	986
29.53	750.00	100.0	1000
30.0	765.00	102.0	1020

Note: *in.Hg figures rounded to nearest whole number.*

Valve timing The timing of valve opening and closing in relation to the piston and crankshaft position.

VAF (Vane Air Flow - Ford term) Refers to a particular type of AFS. See vane type AFS below.

VAT (Vane air temperature sensor - Ford term)

Vane type AFS As air is drawn through the sensor, the Vane or AFS door is pushed open. The vane is attached to a potentiometer that varies as the door position varies. A voltage signal that varies according to the position of the sensor door is thus returned to the ECM. The ECM is therefore able to compute an injection duration that relates to the actual volume of air being drawn into the engine. No recognition is made of density and this AFS is less accurate than the hot-wire / hot-film types. This sensor is an example of a three wire sensor.

Vb batt (+) (Voltage supplied from the ECM - Toyota term)

Vc (AFM reference voltage - Toyota term)

Vcc (PIM (MAP sensor) reference voltage - Toyota term)

Venturi A restriction in the carburettor throat which results in a speeding up of the air flow.

Vf (feedback voltage)

VIN (Vehicle Identification Number) A serial number to identify the vehicle, The number often contains coded letters to identify model and year.

VM (Vehicle Manufacturer)

Volt A unit of electrical pressure.

Voltage Electrical pressure.

Voltage drop Voltage drop is voltage expended when a current flows through a resistance. The greater the resistance then the higher the voltage drop. The total voltage drop in any automotive circuit should be no more than 10%.

Voltage regulator A device use to limit the voltage output of a generator such as an alternator or dynamo.

Voltage reserve The ignition system must provide sufficient secondary HT voltage to bridge the rotor and sparkplug gaps under normal operating conditions. In addition, an adequate reserve of coil voltage must be maintained to meet the greater demands made by the ignition system during conditions such as hard acceleration or high engine rpm's. If at some point during engine operation the coil reserve becomes lower than the voltage demanded by the ignition, misfiring and loss of power will be the result. A low voltage reserve can be caused by poor ignition components (ie plugs, HT leads etc) or poor primary ignition connections.

Voltmeter An instrument used to measure voltage in a circuit in volts.

Volume screw A screw that regulates fuel in the idle circuit of a carburettor by gradually restricting the idle mixture channel.

VRS (Variable Reluctance Sensor - Ford term)

Vs (Variable signal from the AFM to the ECM -Toyota term)

VSS (Vehicle Speed Sensor) A sensor to measure the road speed of the vehicle.

VSTP (Vacuum Solenoid Throttle Plate - Ford term)

VSV (Vacuum Switching Valve) Japanese vehicle manufacturer term

VTEC (Variable Valve Timing and Electronic Control - Honda Term)

WAC (Wide-open throttle A/C cut-off)

WCS (Wastegate Control Solenoid - Ford term)

Watt A unit of electrical power. 746 watts are equal to one mechanical horsepower.

Wiggle test With the engine running, a suspect connection is wiggled, or gently tapped, or gentle heated or cooled. If the engine misfires or otherwise misbehaves, that connection may be suspect.

WOT (Wide Open Throttle) Throttle position when fully open. Many EFi systems provide more fuel when this condition is met.

Warnings: Precautions to be taken with automotive electronic circuits

1

The electronic ignition high tension (HT) system generates a high secondary voltage. Care must be taken that no parts of the body contact HT components. Shock or injury may be caused by allowing the HT to pass to earth through the human body. DO NOT work on electronic vehicle systems if you have a heart condition or any form of heart pacemaker. Pacemaker operation can also be disrupted by radiated RFI (eg the alternator).

2

The ECM and other electronic components can easily be damaged by an open HT circuit. When HT is faced with an impossible gap to jump, it will look for an alternative path. This path may be via the ECM, and sensitive components such as transistors may be damaged. In addition, spurious electrical signals from the HT circuit or from other sources of RFI (eg the alternator) may disrupt ECM operation.

3

VERY IMPORTANT: Avoid severe damage to the ECM, or amplifier by switching the ignition OFF before disconnecting the multiplug to these components. It is generally safe to disconnect the multiplug to other sensors, actuators and components with the ignition switched on, or even with the engine running.

4

Many modern radios are coded as a security measure, and the radio will lose its coding and its pre-selected stations when the battery is disconnected. The code should be obtained from the vehicle owner before disconnecting the battery for renewal or to make other repairs.

5

When taking voltage readings at a multiplug or terminal block, the use of meter leads with thin probes is strongly recommended. However, it is useful to attach a paper clip or split pin to the terminal and attach the voltmeter to the clip. Be very careful not to short out these clips. A number of ECM's employ gold plated pins at the ECM multiplug. Particular care should be taken that this plating is not removed by insensitive probing.

6

DO NOT use an analogue voltmeter, or a digital voltmeter with an electrical impedance of less than 10 megohms, to take voltage readings at an ECM or AFS with the ECM in circuit.

7

To prevent damage to a DMM or to the vehicle electronic system, the appropriate measuring range should be selected before the instrument probes are connected to the vehicle.

8

During resistance tests with an ohmmeter, always ensure that the ignition is OFF and that the circuit is isolated from a voltage supply. Resistance tests should NOT be made at the ECM pins. Damage could be caused to sensitive components, and in any case results would be meaningless.

9

When removing battery cables, good electrical procedure dictates that the earth (negative) cable is disconnected before the live (positive) cable. This will prevent spurious voltage spikes that can cause damage to electronic components.

10

Use protected jumper cables when jump starting a vehicle equipped with an ECM. If unprotected cables are used, and the vehicle earth cables are in poor condition, a voltage spike may destroy the ECM.

11

When a battery is discharged, by far the best course of action is to recharge the battery (or renew the battery if it is faulty), before attempting to start the vehicle. The ECM is put at risk from defective components such as battery, starter, battery cables and earth cables.

12

Do not use a boost charger, nor allow a voltage higher than 16.0 volts, when attempting to start an engine. The battery leads should be disconnected before a boost charger is used to quick charge the battery.

13

All fuel injection systems operate at high pressure. Keep a fire extinguisher handy, and observe all safety precautions. Before loosening fuel banjos or fuel hoses, it is a good idea to de-pressurise the system.

14

A number of diagnostic procedures - such as engine cranking and power balance - may result in unburnt fuel passing into the exhaust, and this is potentially harmful to catalyst-equipped vehicles. Each test must be completed quickly, and back-to-back tests must not be attempted if damage to the catalytic converter is to be avoided. Do not therefore, make repeated cranking or power balance tests with catalyst equipped vehicles. Always run the engine at a fast idle for at least 30 seconds between such tests to clear the exhaust of the fuel residue. Where the engine is a non-runner, the catalyst may need to be disconnected to allow cranking to continue. If this advice is not followed the petrol in the catalyst may explode once the temperature in the exhaust reaches a certain temperature.

15

Catalyst damage can be caused when the catalyst temperature exceeds 900° C. When unburnt fuel passes into the catalyst, as the result of any engine malfunction or misfire, the catalyst temperature could easily pass the 900° C mark causing the catalyst to melt. Apart from catalyst destruction, the melted catalyst will often cause an exhaust blockage with loss of engine power.

16

Disconnect all ECM's when welding repairs are to be made upon a vehicle.

17

The ECM must not be exposed to a temperature exceeding 80° C. If the vehicle is to be placed in a vehicle spray booth, or if welding is to be carried out near the ECM, the ECM must be disconnected and removed from the car to a place of safety.

18

Compression test: Where possible, disable both ignition and injection systems before attempting a compression test. The above advice about avoiding catalyst damage should also be heeded.

19

The following precautions must be taken with vehicles that utilise Hall-Effect electronic ignition:

a) Do not connect a suppresser or condenser to the negative coil terminal.
b) If the electronic ignition is suspect, the HES connection to the distributor and to the amplifier should be disconnected before the vehicle is towed.
c) During engine cranking tests - compression test or otherwise - remove the HES connection to the distributor.
d) All other precautions, as detailed above, should also be taken.

20

Do not run the fuel pump or by-pass the relay when the fuel tank is empty; the pump or pumps will overheat and may be damaged.

21

Some modern vehicles are now equipped with SRS (Supplemental Restraint System) which is an airbag assembly installed in the steering column or passenger compartment. Extreme caution must be exercised when repairing components situated close to the wiring or components of the SRS. In some vehicles, the SRS wiring runs under the dash, and related SRS components are situated in the steering wheel, in and around the under-dash area, and adjacent to some components used in the vehicle EMS. Any damage to the SRS wiring must be repaired by renewing the whole harness. Improper removal or disturbance of SRS components or wiring could lead to SRS failure or accidental deployment. Failure to observe these precautions can lead to unexpected deployment of the SRS and severe personal injury. In addition, the SRS must be repaired and serviced according to the procedures laid down by the manufacturer. Any impairment of the SRS could lead to its failure to deploy in an emergency, leaving the vehicle occupants unprotected.

Haynes Manuals – The Complete List

Title	Book No.
ALFA ROMEO	
Alfa Romeo Alfasud/Sprint (74 - 88) up to F	0292
Alfa Romeo Alfetta (73 - 87) up to E	0531
AUDI	
Audi 80 (72 - Feb 79) up to T	0207
Audi 80, 90 (79 - Oct 86) up to D & Coupe (81 - Nov 88) up to F	0605
Audi 80, 90 (Oct 86 - 90) D to H & Coupe (Nov 88 - 90) F to H	1491
Audi 100 (Oct 82 - 90) up to H & 200 (Feb 84 - Oct 89) A to G	0907
Audi 100 & A6 Petrol & Diesel (May 91 - May 97) H to P	3504
Audi A4 (95 - Feb 00) M to V	3575
AUSTIN	
Austin A35 & A40 (56 - 67) *	0118
Austin Allegro 1100, 1300, 1.0, 1.1 & 1.3 (73 - 82)*	0164
Austin Healey 100/6 & 3000 (56 - 68) *	0049
Austin/MG/Rover Maestro 1.3 & 1.6 (83 - May 95) up to M	0922
Austin/MG Metro (80 - May 90) up to G	0718
Austin/Rover Montego 1.3 & 1.6 (84 - 94) A to L	1066
Austin/MG/Rover Montego 2.0 (84 - 95) A to M	1067
Mini (59 - 69) up to H	0527
Mini (69 - Oct 96) up to P	0646
Austin/Rover 2.0 litre Diesel Engine (86 - 93) C to L	1857
BEDFORD	
Bedford CF (69 - 87) up to E	0163
Bedford/Vauxhall Rascal & Suzuki Supercarry (86 - Oct 94) C to M	3015
BMW	
BMW 1500, 1502, 1600, 1602, 2000 & 2002 (59 - 77)*	0240
BMW 316, 320 & 320i (4-cyl) (75 - Feb 83) up to Y	0276
BMW 320, 320i, 323i & 325i (6-cyl) (Oct 77 - Sept 87) up to E	0815
BMW 3-Series (Apr 91 - 96) H to N	3210
BMW 3- & 5-Series (sohc) (81 - 91) up to J	1948
BMW 520i & 525e (Oct 81 - June 88) up to E	1560
BMW 525, 528 & 528i (73 - Sept 81) up to X	0632
CITROËN	
Citroën 2CV, Ami & Dyane (67 - 90) up to H	0196
Citroën AX Petrol & Diesel (87 - 97) D to P	3014
Citroën BX (83 - 94) A to L	0908
Citroën C15 Van Petrol & Diesel (89 - Oct 98) F to S	3509
Citroën CX (75 - 88) up to F	0528
Citroën Saxo Petrol & Diesel (96 - 01) N to X	3506
Citroën Visa (79 - 88) up to F	0620
Citroën Xantia Petrol & Diesel (93 - 98) K to S	3082
Citroën XM Petrol & Diesel (89 - 00) G to X	3451
Citroën Xsara Petrol & Diesel (97 - Sept 00) R to W	3751
Citroën ZX Diesel (91 - 98) J to S	1922
Citroën ZX Petrol (91 - 98) H to S	1881
Citroën 1.7 & 1.9 litre Diesel Engine (84 - 96) A to N	1379
FIAT	
Fiat 126 (73 - 87) *	0305
Fiat 500 (57 - 73) up to M	0090
Fiat Bravo & Brava (95 - 00) N to W	3572
Fiat Cinquecento (93 - 98) K to R	3501
Fiat Panda (81 - 95) up to M	0793
Fiat Punto Petrol & Diesel (94 - Oct 99) L to V	3251
Fiat Regata (84 - 88) A to F	1167
Fiat Tipo (88 - 91) E to J	1625
Fiat Uno (83 - 95) up to M	0923
Fiat X1/9 (74 - 89) up to G	0273
FORD	
Ford Anglia (59 - 68) *	0001
Ford Capri II (& III) 1.6 & 2.0 (74 - 87) up to E	0283
Ford Capri II (& III) 2.8 & 3.0 (74 - 87) up to E	1309
Ford Cortina Mk III 1300 & 1600 (70 - 76) *	0070
Ford Cortina Mk IV (& V) 1.6 & 2.0 (76 - 83) *	0343
Ford Cortina Mk IV (& V) 2.3 V6 (77 - 83) *	0426
Ford Escort Mk I 1100 & 1300 (68 - 74) *	0171
Ford Escort Mk I Mexico, RS 1600 & RS 2000 (70 - 74)*	0139
Ford Escort Mk II Mexico, RS 1800 & RS 2000 (75 - 80)*	0735
Ford Escort (75 - Aug 80) *	0280
Ford Escort (Sept 80 - Sept 90) up to H	0686
Ford Escort & Orion (Sept 90 - 00) H to X	1737
Ford Fiesta (76 - Aug 83) up to Y	0334
Ford Fiesta (Aug 83 - Feb 89) A to F	1030
Ford Fiesta (Feb 89 - Oct 95) F to N	1595
Ford Fiesta (Oct 95 - 01) N-reg. onwards	3397
Ford Focus (98 - 01) S to Y	3759
Ford Granada (Sept 77 - Feb 85) up to B	0481
Ford Granada & Scorpio (Mar 85 - 94) B to M	1245
Ford Ka (96 - 02) P-reg. onwards	3570
Ford Mondeo Petrol (93 - 99) K to T	1923
Ford Mondeo Diesel (93 - 96) L to N	3465
Ford Orion (83 - Sept 90) up to H	1009
Ford Sierra 4 cyl. (82 - 93) up to K	0903
Ford Sierra V6 (82 - 91) up to J	0904
Ford Transit Petrol (Mk 2) (78 - Jan 86) up to C	0719
Ford Transit Petrol (Mk 3) (Feb 86 - 89) C to G	1468
Ford Transit Diesel (Feb 86 - 99) C to T	3019
Ford 1.6 & 1.8 litre Diesel Engine (84 - 96) A to N	1172
Ford 2.1, 2.3 & 2.5 litre Diesel Engine (77 - 90) up to H	1606
FREIGHT ROVER	
Freight Rover Sherpa (74 - 87) up to E	0463
HILLMAN	
Hillman Avenger (70 - 82) up to Y	0037
Hillman Imp (63 - 76) *	0022
HONDA	
Honda Accord (76 - Feb 84) up to A	0351
Honda Civic (Feb 84 - Oct 87) A to E	1226
Honda Civic (Nov 91 - 96) J to N	3199
HYUNDAI	
Hyundai Pony (85 - 94) C to M	3398
JAGUAR	
Jaguar E Type (61 - 72) up to L	0140
Jaguar MkI & II, 240 & 340 (55 - 69) *	0098
Jaguar XJ6, XJ & Sovereign; Daimler Sovereign (68 - Oct 86) up to D	0242
Jaguar XJ6 & Sovereign (Oct 86 - Sept 94) D to M	3261
Jaguar XJ12, XJS & Sovereign; Daimler Double Six (72 - 88) up to F	0478
JEEP	
Jeep Cherokee Petrol (93 - 96) K to N	1943
LADA	
Lada 1200, 1300, 1500 & 1600 (74 - 91) up to J	0413
Lada Samara (87 - 91) D to J	1610
LAND ROVER	
Land Rover 90, 110 & Defender Diesel (83 - 95) up to N	3017
Land Rover Discovery Petrol & Diesel (89 - 98) G to S	3016
Land Rover Series IIA & III Diesel (58 - 85) up to C	0529
Land Rover Series II, IIA & III Petrol (58 - 85) up to C	0314
MAZDA	
Mazda 323 (Mar 81 - Oct 89) up to G	1608
Mazda 323 (Oct 89 - 98) G to R	3455
Mazda 626 (May 83 - Sept 87) up to E	0929
Mazda B-1600, B-1800 & B-2000 Pick-up (72 - 88) up to F	0267
Mazda RX-7 (79 - 85) *	0460
MERCEDES-BENZ	
Mercedes-Benz 190, 190E & 190D Petrol & Diesel (83 - 93) A to L	3450
Mercedes-Benz 200, 240, 300 Diesel (Oct 76 - 85) up to C	1114
Mercedes-Benz 250 & 280 (68 - 72) up to L	0346
Mercedes-Benz 250 & 280 (123 Series) (Oct 76 - 84) up to B	0677
Mercedes-Benz 124 Series (85 - Aug 93) C to K	3253
Mercedes-Benz C-Class Petrol & Diesel (93 - Aug 00) L to W	3511
MG	
MGA (55 - 62) *	0475
MGB (62 - 80) up to W	0111
MG Midget & AH Sprite (58 - 80) up to W	0265
MITSUBISHI	
Mitsubishi Shogun & L200 Pick-Ups (83 - 94) up to M	1944
MORRIS	
Morris Ital 1.3 (80 - 84) up to B	0705
Morris Minor 1000 (56 - 71) up to K	0024
NISSAN	
Nissan Bluebird (May 84 - Mar 86) A to C	1223
Nissan Bluebird (Mar 86 - 90) C to H	1473
Nissan Cherry (Sept 82 - 86) up to D	1031
Nissan Micra (83 - Jan 93) up to K	0931
Nissan Micra (93 - 99) K to T	3254
Nissan Primera (90 - Aug 99) H to T	1851
Nissan Stanza (82 - 86) up to D	0824
Nissan Sunny (May 82 - Oct 86) up to D	0895
Nissan Sunny (Oct 86 - Mar 91) D to H	1378
Nissan Sunny (Apr 91 - 95) H to N	3219
OPEL	
Opel Ascona & Manta (B Series) (Sept 75 - 88) up to F	0316
Opel Ascona (81 - 88) *(Not available in UK see Vauxhall Cavalier 0812)*	3215
Opel Astra (Oct 91 - Feb 98) *(Not available in UK see Vauxhall Astra 1832)*	3156
Opel Astra & Zafira Diesel (Feb 98 - Sept 00) *(See Astra & Zafira Diesel Book No. 3797)*	
Opel Astra & Zafira Petrol (Feb 98 - Sept 00) *(See Vauxhall/Opel Astra & Zafira Petrol Book No. 3758)*	
Opel Calibra (90 - 98) *(See Vauxhall/Opel Calibra Book No. 3502)*	
Opel Corsa (83 - Mar 93) *(Not available in UK see Vauxhall Nova 0909)*	3160
Opel Corsa (Mar 93 - 97) *(Not available in UK see Vauxhall Corsa 1985)*	3159
Opel Frontera Petrol & Diesel (91 - 98) *(See Vauxhall/Opel Frontera Book No. 3454)*	
Opel Kadett (Nov 79 - Oct 84) up to B	0634
Opel Kadett (Oct 84 - Oct 91) *(Not available in UK see Vauxhall Astra & Belmont 1136)*	3196
Opel Omega & Senator (86 - 94) *(Not available in UK see Vauxhall Carlton & Senator 1469)*	3157
Opel Omega (94 - 99) *(See Vauxhall/Opel Omega Book No. 3510)*	
Opel Rekord (Feb 78 - Oct 86) up to D	0543
Opel Vectra (Oct 88 - Oct 95) *(Not available in UK see Vauxhall Cavalier 1570)*	3158
Opel Vectra Petrol & Diesel (95 - 98) *(Not available in UK see Vauxhall Vectra 3396)*	3523
PEUGEOT	
Peugeot 106 Petrol & Diesel (91 - 01) J to X	1882
Peugeot 205 Petrol (83 - 97) A to P	0932
Peugeot 206 Petrol and Diesel (98 - 01) S to X	3757
Peugeot 305 (78 - 89) up to G	0538

* Classic reprint

Title	Book No.
Peugeot 306 Petrol & Diesel (93 - 99) K to T	3073
Peugeot 309 (86 - 93) C to K	1266
Peugeot 405 Petrol (88 - 97) E to P	1559
Peugeot 405 Diesel (88 - 97) E to P	3198
Peugeot 406 Petrol & Diesel (96 - 97) N to R	3394
Peugeot 505 (79 - 89) up to G	0762
Peugeot 1.7/1.8 & 1.9 litre Diesel Engine (82 - 96) up to N	0950
Peugeot 2.0, 2.1, 2.3 & 2.5 litre Diesel Engines (74 - 90) up to H	1607
PORSCHE	
Porsche 911 (65 - 85) up to C	0264
Porsche 924 & 924 Turbo (76 - 85) up to C	0397
PROTON	
Proton (89 - 97) F to P	3255
RANGE ROVER	
Range Rover V8 (70 - Oct 92) up to K	0606
RELIANT	
Reliant Robin & Kitten (73 - 83) up to A	0436
RENAULT	
Renault 4 (61 - 86) *	0072
Renault 5 (Feb 85 - 96) B to N	1219
Renault 9 & 11 (82 - 89) up to F	0822
Renault 18 (79 - 86) up to D	0598
Renault 19 Petrol (89 - 94) F to M	1646
Renault 19 Diesel (89 - 96) F to N	1946
Renault 21 (86 - 94) C to M	1397
Renault 25 (84 - 92) B to K	1228
Renault Clio Petrol (91 - May 98) H to R	1853
Renault Clio Diesel (91 - June 96) H to N	3031
Renault Clio Petrol & Diesel (May 98 - May 01) R to Y	3906
Renault Espace Petrol & Diesel (85 - 96) C to N	3197
Renault Fuego (80 - 86) *	0764
Renault Laguna Petrol & Diesel (94 - 00) L to W	3252
Renault Mégane & Scénic Petrol & Diesel (96 - 98) N to R	3395
Renault Mégane & Scénic (Apr 99 - 02) T-reg onwards	3916
ROVER	
Rover 213 & 216 (84 - 89) A to G	1116
Rover 214 & 414 (89 - 96) G to N	1689
Rover 216 & 416 (89 - 96) G to N	1830
Rover 211, 214, 216, 218 & 220 Petrol & Diesel (Dec 95 - 98) N to R	3399
Rover 414, 416 & 420 Petrol & Diesel (May 95 - 98) M to R	3453
Rover 618, 620 & 623 (93 - 97) K to P	3257
Rover 820, 825 & 827 (86 - 95) D to N	1380
Rover 3500 (76 - 87) up to E	0365
Rover Metro, 111 & 114 (May 90 - 98) G to S	1711
SAAB	
Saab 90, 99 & 900 (79 - Oct 93) up to L	0765
Saab 95 & 96 (66 - 76) *	0198
Saab 99 (69 - 79) *	0247
Saab 900 (Oct 93 - 98) L to R	3512
Saab 9000 (4-cyl) (85 - 98) C to S	1686
SEAT	
Seat Ibiza & Cordoba Petrol & Diesel (Oct 93 - Oct 99) L to V	3571
Seat Ibiza & Malaga (85 - 92) B to K	1609
SKODA	
Skoda Estelle (77 - 89) up to G	0604
Skoda Favorit (89 - 96) F to N	1801
Skoda Felicia Petrol & Diesel (95 - 01) M to X	3505

Title	Book No.
SUBARU	
Subaru 1600 & 1800 (Nov 79 - 90) up to H	0995
SUNBEAM	
Sunbeam Alpine, Rapier & H120 (67 - 76) *	0051
SUZUKI	
Suzuki SJ Series, Samurai & Vitara (4-cyl) (82 - 97) up to P	1942
Suzuki Supercarry & Bedford/Vauxhall Rascal (86 - Oct 94) C to M	3015
TALBOT	
Talbot Alpine, Solara, Minx & Rapier (75 - 86) up to D	0337
Talbot Horizon (78 - 86) up to D	0473
Talbot Samba (82 - 86) up to D	0823
TOYOTA	
Toyota Carina E (May 92 - 97) J to P	3256
Toyota Corolla (Sept 83 - Sept 87) A to E	1024
Toyota Corolla (80 - 85) up to C	0683
Toyota Corolla (Sept 87 - Aug 92) E to K	1683
Toyota Corolla (Aug 92 - 97) K to P	3259
Toyota Hi-Ace & Hi-Lux (69 - Oct 83) up to A	0304
TRIUMPH	
Triumph Acclaim (81 - 84) *	0792
Triumph GT6 & Vitesse (62 - 74) *	0112
Triumph Herald (59 - 71) *	0010
Triumph Spitfire (62 - 81) up to X	0113
Triumph Stag (70 - 78) up to T	0441
Triumph TR2, TR3, TR3A, TR4 & TR4A (52 - 67)*	0028
Triumph TR5 & 6 (67 - 75) *	0031
Triumph TR7 (75 - 82) *	0322
VAUXHALL	
Vauxhall Astra (80 - Oct 84) up to B	0635
Vauxhall Astra & Belmont (Oct 84 - Oct 91) B to J	1136
Vauxhall Astra (Oct 91 - Feb 98) J to R	1832
Vauxhall/Opel Astra & Zafira Diesel (Feb 98 - Sept 00) R to W	3797
Vauxhall/Opel Astra & Zafira Petrol (Feb 98 - Sept 00) R to W	3758
Vauxhall/Opel Calibra (90 - 98) G to S	3502
Vauxhall Carlton (Oct 78 - Oct 86) up to D	0480
Vauxhall Carlton & Senator (Nov 86 - 94) D to L	1469
Vauxhall Cavalier 1300 (77 - July 81) *	0461
Vauxhall Cavalier 1600, 1900 & 2000 (75 - July 81) up to W	0315
Vauxhall Cavalier (81 - Oct 88) up to F	0812
Vauxhall Cavalier (Oct 88 - 95) F to N	1570
Vauxhall Chevette (75 - 84) up to B	0285
Vauxhall Corsa (Mar 93 - 97) K to R	1985
Vauxhall/Opel Corsa (Apr 97 - Oct 00) P to X	3921
Vauxhall/Opel Frontera Petrol & Diesel (91 - Sept 98) J to S	3454
Vauxhall Nova (83 - 93) up to K	0909
Vauxhall/Opel Omega (94 - 99) L to T	3510
Vauxhall Vectra Petrol & Diesel (95 - 98) N to R	3396
Vauxhall/Opel 1.5, 1.6 & 1.7 litre Diesel Engine (82 - 96) up to N	1222
VOLKSWAGEN	
Volkswagen 411 & 412 (68 - 75) *	0091
Volkswagen Beetle 1200 (54 - 77) up to S	0036
Volkswagen Beetle 1300 & 1500 (65 - 75) up to P	0039
Volkswagen Beetle 1302 & 1302S (70 - 72) up to L	0110
Volkswagen Beetle 1303, 1303S & GT (72 - 75) up to P	0159
Volkswagen Beetle Petrol & Diesel (Apr 99 - 01) T reg onwards	3798
Volkswagen Golf & Bora Petrol & Diesel (April 98 - 00) R to X	3727

Title	Book No.
Volkswagen Golf & Jetta Mk 1 1.1 & 1.3 (74 - 84) up to A	0716
Volkswagen Golf, Jetta & Scirocco Mk 1 1.5, 1.6 & 1.8 (74 - 84) up to A	0726
Volkswagen Golf & Jetta Mk 1 Diesel (78 - 84) up to A	0451
Volkswagen Golf & Jetta Mk 2 (Mar 84 - Feb 92) A to J	1081
Volkswagen Golf & Vento Petrol & Diesel (Feb 92 - 96) J to N	3097
Volkswagen LT vans & light trucks (76 - 87) up to E	0637
Volkswagen Passat & Santana (Sept 81 - May 88) up to E	0814
Volkswagen Passat Petrol & Diesel (May 88 - 96) E to P	3498
Volkswagen Passat 4-cyl Petrol & Diesel (Dec 96 - Nov 00) P to X	3917
Volkswagen Polo & Derby (76 - Jan 82) up to X	0335
Volkswagen Polo (82 - Oct 90) up to H	0813
Volkswagen Polo (Nov 90 - Aug 94) H to L	3245
Volkswagen Polo Hatchback Petrol & Diesel (94 - 99) M to S	3500
Volkswagen Scirocco (82 - 90) up to H	1224
Volkswagen Transporter 1600 (68 - 79) up to V	0082
Volkswagen Transporter 1700, 1800 & 2000 (72 - 79) up to V	0226
Volkswagen Transporter (air-cooled) (79 - 82) up to Y	0638
Volkswagen Transporter (water-cooled) (82 - 90) up to H	3452
Volkswagen Type 3 (63 - 73) *	0084
VOLVO	
Volvo 120 & 130 Series (& P1800) (61 - 73) *	0203
Volvo 142, 144 & 145 (66 - 74) up to N	0129
Volvo 240 Series (74 - 93) up to K	0270
Volvo 262, 264 & 260/265 (75 - 85) *	0400
Volvo 340, 343, 345 & 360 (76 - 91) up to J	0715
Volvo 440, 460 & 480 (87 - 97) D to P	1691
Volvo 740 & 760 (82 - 91) up to J	1258
Volvo 850 (92 - 96) J to P	3260
Volvo 940 (90 - 96) H to N	3249
Volvo S40 & V40 (96 - 99) N to V	3569
Volvo S70, V70 & C70 (96 - 99) P to V	3573
AUTOMOTIVE TECHBOOKS	
Automotive Air Conditioning Systems	3740
Automotive Brake Manual	3050
Automotive Carburettor Manual	3288
Automotive Diagnostic Fault Codes Manual	3472
Automotive Diesel Engine Service Guide	3286
Automotive Electrical and Electronic Systems Manual	3049
Automotive Engine Management and Fuel Injection Systems Manual	3344
Automotive Gearbox Overhaul Manual	3473
Automotive Service Summaries Manual	3475
Automotive Timing Belts Manual – Austin/Rover	3549
Automotive Timing Belts Manual – Ford	3474
Automotive Timing Belts Manual – Peugeot/Citroën	3568
Automotive Timing Belts Manual – Vauxhall/Opel	3577
Automotive Welding Manual	3053
In-Car Entertainment Manual (3rd Edition)	3363

* Classic reprint

CL13.4/02